The Atomic Nucleus

INTERNATIONAL SERIES IN PURE AND APPLIED PHYSICS

LEONARD I. SCHIFF, *Consulting Editor*

The late F. K. Richtmyer was Consulting Editor of the series from its inception in 1929 to his death in 1939. Lee A. DuBridge was Consulting Editor from 1939 to 1946; and G. P. Harnwell from 1947 to 1954.

THE ATOMIC NUCLEUS

Robley D. Evans, Ph.D.

PROFESSOR OF PHYSICS
MASSACHUSETTS INSTITUTE OF TECHNOLOGY

New York   Toronto   London

McGRAW-HILL BOOK COMPANY, INC.

1955

THE ATOMIC NUCLEUS

Library of Congress Catalog Card Number 55-7275

V

THE MAPLE PRESS COMPANY, YORK, PA.

Preface

This book represents the present content of a two-semester course in nuclear physics which the author has taught at the Massachusetts Institute of Technology for the past twenty years. During this time nuclear physics has expanded greatly in depth and breadth. Nuclear physics was originally a subject which represented the research interests of a small number of academic scientists, and whose modest size permitted easy coverage in a one-year graduate course. Now pure and applied nuclear physics is a gigantic area of research and engineering. Numerous subtopics have grown rapidly into large and separate fields of professional competence, but each of these derives its strength and nourishment from fundamental experimental and theoretical principles. It is this fundamental core material which is discussed here. Even this central body of empirical knowledge and of theoretical interpretation has grown to be very large. This book embraces more material than my students and I are now able to cover, with adequate regard for depth of understanding, in a one-year course of ninety class hours. Those topics which seem most lively and timely are selected from it by each year's group of students. Material which has to be excluded from the course is thus fully available for reference purposes.

This text is an experimentalist's approach to the understanding of nuclear phenomena. It deals primarily with the area in which theory and experiment meet and is intermediate between the limiting cases of a theoretical treatise and of a detailed handbook of experimental techniques. It undertakes to strike that compromise in viewpoint which has been adopted by the majority of working physicists.

Detailed attention is given in the early chapters to several fundamental concepts, so that the student may learn to think in center-of-mass coordinates and may visualize clearly the phenomena of barrier transmission, particle interactions during collisions, and collision cross sections. The physical aspects receive emphasis in the main text, while the corresponding mathematical details are treated more fully in appendixes. This reiteration, with varied emphasis and viewpoint, has been preserved because of the experiences of students and colleagues.

As to prerequisites, it is expected that the reader has had at least an introductory course in atomic physics and that his mathematical equipment is in working order through the calculus and differential equations. Prior experience in wave mechanics is not assumed, and the necessary mathematical and conceptual portions of this subject are developed from first principles as the need and application arise.

I have been repeatedly impressed by the varied preparation and by the nonuniform backgrounds of seniors and first-year graduate students as they enter this course. Each student is well prepared in some areas but is blank in others. In an average class of fifty students there is a nearly random distribution of areas of competence and areas of no previous experience. These observations have dictated the level of approach. It must be assumed that each subfield is a new area to the majority. With this experience in mind, the discussion of each topic usually begins at an introductory level. Within each subfield, the discussion extends through the intermediate level and into the area of the most recent advances in current research. The aim is to bring the student to a level of competence from which he can understand the current research literature, can profitably read advanced treatises and the many excellent monographs which are now appearing, and can undertake creative personal research. To help encourage early familiarity with the original papers, numerous references to the pertinent periodical literature appear throughout.

Nuclear physics today embraces many topics which are strongly interdependent, such as nuclear moments and β decay, and some topics which are nearly independent fields, such as some aspects of mass spectroscopy. An optimum sequential arrangement of these topics is a difficult, if not insolvable, problem. The collection of indisputably nuclear topics definitely does not form a linear array, in which one may start at A and proceed to B, C, D, . . . , without having to know about Q in the meantime. The order of topics which is used here is that which has developed in the classroom as an empirical solution involving "minimum regret."

I begin as Bethe and Bacher have done, with the fundamental properties of nuclei. These are the characteristics which are measurable for any particular nuclide and which comprise the entries in any complete table of the ground-level nuclear properties: charge, size, mass, angular momentum, magnetic dipole moment, electric quadrupole moment, isobaric spin, parity, and statistics. In order to evaluate even these "static" properties of nuclei, it is necessary to invoke many types of experimental and theoretical studies of the "dynamic" behavior of nuclei, including α decay, β decay, and nuclear reactions. The result is that those aspects of nuclear dynamics which enlighten the static properties are referred to early. This might have been done by saying, "It can be shown . . . " or "We shall see later that . . . ," but it has proved more satisfactory to give a reasonable account of the pertinent dynamic aspect at the place where it is first needed. This has been found to lead to better understanding, although it does give rise to occasional duplication, or "varied reiteration," and, in some instances, to division of dynamic topics, such as α decay and β decay, into two parts.

Cross references appear throughout these topics, in order to reinforce the integration of the dynamic subjects.

The middle of the book deals with the systematics of nuclei, with binding energy and separation energy, with internucleon forces and illustrative nuclear models, and with the dynamics of nuclear reactions, α-ray spectra, β decay, and radioactive-series transformations. Chapters 18 through 25 treat the behavior of charged particles and of photons while passing through matter, concluding with a chapter containing basic material on a group of "practical" scientific, military, and industrial problems on the physical evaluation of penetrating radiation fields. The final three chapters deal with the statistical theory of fluctuations and uncertainties due to the randomicity of nuclear events, which is so often a governing factor in the design of nuclear experiments. Practical topics given detailed treatment include the effects of resolving time, random coincidences, scaler and counting-rate-meter fluctuations, and the statistics of rapidly decaying sources.

Reference tables of many of the reasonably well-established nuclear properties accompany the corresponding text. For more comprehensive tables, explicit references are made to the voluminous and valuable standard compilations. For the latest data, these compilations must be augmented by the summaries of new nuclear data published quarterly in *Nuclear Science Abstracts*.

Every worker in nuclear physics faces the opportunity of making a significant new discovery. It is useful to know how discoveries have been made by those who have preceded us. Most of the history of nuclear physics is very recent and has occurred within the memory of people still working in the field. In order to illuminate the "anatomy of discovery" and at the same time to focus on fundamental physical principles, some chapters, such as Chap. 13, Nuclear Reactions, Illustrated by $B^{10}(\alpha,p)$ and Its Associates, have been arranged with due regard to the history of nuclear physics and to the pitfalls and accidental triumphs of research. This was done to encourage the student to develop a feeling for the stages through which nuclear science has progressed and a sense of the conditions under which new discoveries are made.

Problems are offered for solution at the end of many sections. These have been selected from homework and quizzes and are the type which one likes to work through in order to see that the principles of the subject are understood. Many problems supplement the text by containing their own answers, in the well-known "show that" style of Miles S. Sherrill and the late Arthur A. Noyes.

Much help, both explicit and general, has been received from professional colleagues, especially Profs. V. F. Weisskopf, H. Feshbach, and W. A. Fowler, and from the hundreds of students who have taken the course over the many years during which this book has been in preparation. The students' experiences have determined the content, the order of presentation, the amount of detail needed on particular topics, the nature and number of problems, and the topics which should be transferred to other new courses in specialized aspects of pure or applied nuclear physics. Some former students may find that their favorite topic has been deleted altogether, in order to make space for the remainder in an already vast field.

Each year one or more graduate students have collaborated closely in developing and presenting certain sections of the course, and to these men I welcome this opportunity of recalling our joint experiences of the past two decades and of recording my thanks, especially to Alfredo Banos, Keith Boyer, Sanborn Brown, Gordon Brownell, Randall Caswell, Eric Clarke, Franklin Cooper, Martin Deutsch, Robert Dudley, Lloyd Elliott, Wilfred Good, Clark Goodman, Arthur Kip, Alexander Langsdorf, Melvin Lax, John Marshall, Otto Morningstar, Robert Osborne, Wendell Peacock, Norman Rasmussen, Norman Rudnick, Leonard Schiff, and Marvin Van Dilla. Special thanks go to Norman Rasmussen for extensive work on semifinal revisions of the chapters dealing with the interaction of radiation and matter.

Miss Mary Margaret Shanahan has been tireless, accurate, and patient in editing and typing a series of hectographed partial editions for student use and in preparing the entire final manuscript. The assistance of Miss Betsy Short, Mrs. Elizabeth Backofen, Mrs. Grace Rowe, Joel Bulkley, and Harry Watters has been invaluable. Transcending all this, the unbounded patience, insight, and encouragement of my wife, Gwendolyn Aldrich Evans, have made it possible to put this volume together.

ROBLEY D. EVANS

Contents

Contents

CHAPTER 9
BINDING ENERGY OF NUCLEI

CHAPTER 10
FORCES BETWEEN NUCLEONS

CHAPTER 11
MODELS OF NUCLEI

CHAPTER 12
CONSERVATION LAWS FOR NUCLEAR REACTIONS

CHAPTER 13
NUCLEAR REACTIONS, ILLUSTRATED BY $B^{10}(\alpha,p)$
AND ITS ASSOCIATES

CHAPTER 14
ENERGY DEPENDENCE OF NUCLEAR-REACTION CROSS SECTIONS

Contents

Contents

CHAPTER 21
STOPPING OF ELECTRONS BY THICK ABSORBERS

CHAPTER 22
PASSAGE OF HEAVY CHARGED PARTICLES THROUGH MATTER

CHAPTER 23
THE INTERACTION OF ELECTROMAGNETIC
RADIATIONS WITH MATTER.
COMPTON SCATTERING AND ABSORPTION

CHAPTER 24
PHOTOELECTRIC EFFECT AND PAIR PRODUCTION

CHAPTER 25
ATTENUATION AND ABSORPTION OF ELECTROMAGNETIC RADIATION

CHAPTER 26
STATISTICAL FLUCTUATIONS IN NUCLEAR PROCESSES

CHAPTER 27
STATISTICAL TESTS FOR GOODNESS OF FIT

INTRODUCTION

Historical Sketch of the Development of the Concept of the Atomic Nucleus

The earliest speculations on the atomic hypothesis of the ultimate structure of matter are ascribed to the Ionian philosophers of the fifth century B.C. Anaxagoras, Leucippus, and Democritus postulated that all matter is made up of a set of particles which were called *atoms* to denote their presumed indivisibility. Their concept of a world made up of invisible, incompressible, eternal atoms in motion is best known now through the writings of the Latin poet Lucretius (98 to 55 B.C.), especially through his six-book scientific poem "Concerning the Nature of Things" (*De Rerum Natura*) (D1).†

> Bodies of things are safe 'till they receive
> A force which may their proper thread unweave,
> Nought then returns to nought, but parted falls
> To *Bodies* of their prime *Originals*.
> . . . Then nothing sure its being quite forsakes,
> Since *Nature* one thing, from another makes;
> . . .   LUCRETIUS

Through the subsequent centuries many philosophers speculated on the ultimate structure of matter. Because nearly every possible guess was made by one person or another, it is no surprise that some of them were close to the truth, but all these theories lacked any experimental foundation.

At the beginning of the nineteenth century the researches on chemical combining weights by John Dalton and his contemporaries (C54) led to his enunciation, *on experimental grounds*, of the atomic theory of matter in his great book "A New System of Chemical Philosophy" (1808). Three years later, Avogadro, professor of physics at Turin. distinguished clearly between atoms and molecules and filled the only gap in Dalton's logic when he pointed out that equal volumes of different gases contain equal numbers of molecules when the temperatures and pressures are equal. Then followed the first hypothesis concerning the structure of the atoms themselves. Prout, an Englishman, as was

† For references in parentheses, see the Bibliography at the end of the book, which is arranged alphabetically and by number.

1

Dalton, suggested in 1815 that the atoms of all elements were made up of atoms of hydrogen. Prout's hypothesis was soon discredited by the more accurate atomic-weight measurements of the later nineteenth century, only to be reestablished, in modified form, after the discovery of isotopes during the early part of the present century. This discovery required the introduction of the concept of *mass number*.

Modern atomic physics had its inception in the discovery of X rays by Röntgen (R26) in 1895, of radioactivity by Becquerel (B25) in 1896, and of the electron by J. J. Thomson (T22) in 1897. J. J. Thomson's measurement of e/m for the electron and H. A. Wilson's determination (W64, M46) of the electronic charge e by the cloud method showed the mass of the electron to be about 10^{-27} g. The value of e, combined with Faraday's electrolysis laws, showed that the hydrogen atom was of the order of 1,800 times as heavy as the electron. Thomson's studies had shown that all atoms contained electrons, and Barkla's (B12) experiments on X-ray scattering showed that the number of electrons in each atom (except hydrogen) is approximately equal to half the atomic weight.

It was then evident that the mass of the atom is principally associated with the *positive* charge which it contains. Nagaoka's (N1) nuclear atom model, with rings of rotating electrons, had attracted few endorsements because, from considerations of classical electromagnetic theory, the revolving electrons should continually radiate, because of their centripetal acceleration, and should eventually fall into the central nucleus. J. J. Thomson circumvented this difficulty with his "charged-cloud" atom model, consisting of "a case in which the positive electricity is distributed in the way most amenable to mathematical calculation; i.e., when it occurs as a sphere of uniform density, throughout which the corpuscles (*electrons*) are distributed" (T23).

By this time α rays from radioactive substances were under intensive study. Following Rutherford's (R42) semiquantitative observation of the scattering of α rays by air or by a thin foil of mica, Geiger (G10) found the most probable angular deflection suffered by α rays in passing through 0.0005-mm gold foils to be of the order of 1°. Geiger and Marsden (G13) had shown that 1 α ray in 8,000 is deflected *more than* 90° by a thin platinum film. The Thomson model had predicted only small deflections for single scattering and an extremely minute probability for large deflections resulting from multiple scattering. The predictions of the Thomson model fell short of these experimental results by at least a factor of 10^{10}. Accordingly, Rutherford proposed (R43) that the charge of the atom (aside from the electrons) was concentrated into a very small central body, and he showed that such a model could explain the large deflections of α rays observed by Geiger and Marsden. Whereas Thomson's positive cloud has atomic dimensions ($\sim 10^{-8}$ cm), Rutherford's atomic nucleus has a diameter of less than 10^{-12} cm. Rutherford's theory did not predict the sign of the nuclear charge, but the electronic mass and the X-ray and spectral data indicated that it must be positive, with the negative electrons distributed about it to form the neutral atom.

The quantitative dependence of the intensity of α-ray scattering on the angular deflection, foil thickness, nuclear charge, and α-ray energy was predicted by Rutherford's theory—a prediction completely confirmed by Geiger and Marsden's (G14) later experiments. In agreement with Barkla's experiments on X-ray scattering, and with Moseley's (M60) brilliant pioneer work on X-ray spectra, Geiger and Marsden's experiments showed that *"the number of elementary charges composing the center of the atom is* (approximately) *equal to half the atomic weight."* Thus the concept of *atomic number Z* became recognized as the charge on the nucleus; with its aid the few *irregularities in Mendeleev's periodic table* (M42) *were resolved.*

Once the existence of a small, massive, positive nucleus and an array of external electrons had been established, it became obligatory to abandon classical electromagnetic theory and to postulate nonradiating electronic orbits. Bohr (B92) took the step and, by combining Planck's quantum postulate with Nicholson's (B27) suggestion of the constancy of angular momentum, succeeded in describing the then observed hydrogen spectra in detail, as well as in deriving the numerical value of Rydberg's constant entirely theoretically. These striking successes established the Rutherford-Bohr atom model and the existence of the small, massive, positively charged atomic nucleus.

Soddy, Fajans, and others established the so-called displacement law (S58), according to which the emission of an α ray is accompanied by a change in the chemical properties of an atom by an amount corresponding to a leftward displacement of two columns in the Mendeleev periodic table of the elements (Appendix F). Similarly, a β-ray transformation corresponds to a displacement of one column in the opposite direction. Since the omitted α ray carries a double positive charge, whereas the β ray carries a single negative charge, it was evident that radioactive emission was a spontaneous nuclear disintegration process. Moreover, two elements differing from each other by one α-ray and two β-ray emissions would have the same nuclear charge, hence the same chemical properties, but would exhibit a mass difference due to the loss of the heavy α particle. Thus the existence of isotopes was postulated by Soddy as early as 1910 from chemical and physical studies (A36) of the heavy radioactive elements. J. J. Thomson (T24) had succeeded in obtaining positive-ion beams of several of the light elements, and their deflection in magnetic and electrostatic fields proved that all atoms of a given type have the same mass. In 1912 Thomson, by his "parabola method," discovered the existence of two isotopes of neon, later shown by Aston (A36) to have masses of 20 and 22.

Chadwick's (C12) proof of the existence of neutrons now permits us to contemplate the α particle as a close combination of two protons and two neutrons, and the nuclei of all elements as composed basically of protons and neutrons. Spectroscopy has dealt with the structure of the extranuclear swarm of electrons and, in so doing, has found it necessary to make at least two refinements in the Rutherford-Bohr atom model. The wave-mechanical treatment of the electrons has removed the definiteness of planetlike electronic orbits, substituting a cloudlike distribution

CHRONOLOGICAL REVIEW OF SOME MAJOR STEPS IN THE ACCRETION OF
EXPERIMENTAL KNOWLEDGE CONCERNING THE ATOMIC NUCLEUS

Advance	Date	By whom	Where
First experimental basis for the atomic hypothesis. Chemical combining weights	1808	Dalton	England
Atoms and molecules distinguished. Gas laws unified................................	1811	Avogadro	Italy
Precursor of mass number. Hydrogen as a basic unit in structure of heavy atoms.....	1815	Prout	England
Periodic chemical classification of the elements	1868	Mendeleev	Russia
Discovery of continuous X rays..............	1895	Röntgen	Germany
Discovery of radioactivity of uranium.......	1896	Becquerel	France
Discovery of electron as constituent of all atoms.................................	1897	J. J. Thomson	England
Charge of electron measured by cloud method. Avogadro's number estimated............	1903	H. A. Wilson	England
Identification of α particle as a helium nucleus	1903	Rutherford	England
Equivalence of mass and energy............	1905	Einstein	Switzerland
Number of electrons per atom estimated from X-ray scattering	1904–1911	Barkla	England
Isotopes, isobars identified................	1911	Soddy	England
Discovery of stable isotopes of $Ne^{20,22}$.......	1912	Thomson	England
Atomic nucleus discovered by interpretation of α-ray-scattering results	1911–1913	Rutherford, Geiger, and Marsden	England
Nuclear atom model "completed" by explanation of origin of spectra. Quantization of atomic states........................	1913	Bohr	Denmark
Assignment of atomic numbers, from X-ray spectra.................................	1913	Moseley	England
Nuclear transmutation induced; proton identified..................................	1919	Rutherford	England
Wavelength proposed for corpuscles.........	1924	de Broglie	France
The wave equation........................	1926	Schrödinger	Germany
Uncertainty principle.....................	1927	Heisenberg	Germany
De Broglie wavelength observed when electrons diffracted by crystals	1927	Davisson and Germer	U.S.A.
α-ray decay explained as wave penetration of a nuclear barrier	1928	Gamow, Condon, and Gurney	Germany, U.S.A.
Discovery of deuterium....................	1932	Urey	U.S.A.
Discovery of the neutron..................	1932	Chadwick	England
Nuclear transmutation by artificially accelerated particles	1932	Cockroft and Walton	England
Positron discovered.......................	1932	Anderson	U.S.A.
Anomalous magnetic dipole moment of proton discovered	1933	R. Frisch and O. Stern	Germany
{ Neutrino hypothesis.....................	1933	Pauli	Switzerland
{ Theory of β decay.....................	1934	Fermi	Italy

CHRONOLOGICAL REVIEW OF SOME MAJOR STEPS IN THE ACCRETION OF
EXPERIMENTAL KNOWLEDGE CONCERNING THE ATOMIC NUCLEUS
(Continued)

Advance	Date	By whom	Where
Radioactive light nuclides discovered.......	1934	I. Curie and F. Joliot	France
Radioactive nuclides produced by accelerated particles	1934	Lawrence et al., Lauritsen et al.	U.S.A.
Transformation of nuclei by neutron capture	1934	Fermi	Italy
Anomalous proton-proton scattering.........	1936	White, Tuve, Hafstad, Herb, Breit, etc.	U.S.A.
$\pm\mu$ meson discovered....................	1936	Anderson and Neddermeyer	U.S.A.
Precise measurements of nuclear moments by molecular-beam magnetic-resonance methods..............................	1938	Rabi	U.S.A.
Nuclear fission discovered.................	1939	O. Hahn and F. Strassmann	Germany
Measurement of magnetic moment of the neutron	1940	Alvarez and Bloch	U.S.A.
$\pm\pi$ meson discovered.....................	1946	Powell	England
Artificial production of π mesons...........	1948	Gardner and Lattes	U.S.A.

of position probabilities for the extranuclear electrons. Secondly, detailed examination (hyperfine structure) of line spectra has shown that at least three more properties must be assigned to nuclei. These are the mechanical moment of momentum, the magnetic dipole moment, and an electric quadrupole moment.

The nuclear transmutation experiments of Rutherford (R46), of Cockroft and Walton (C27), of I. Curie and Joliot (C62), and of Fermi (F33) opened up a vast field of investigation and suggested new experimental attacks on the basic problems of nuclear structure—the identification of the component particles within nuclei and of the forces which bind these particles together, the determination of the energy states of nuclei and their transition probabilities, and the investigation of the nature and uses of the radiations associated with these transitions. These are the problems with which we shall deal in the following chapters.

CHAPTER 1

Charge of Atomic Nuclei

The number Z of positive elementary charges ($e = 4.8 \times 10^{-10}$ esu, or 1.6×10^{-19} coulomb) carried by the nuclei of all isotopes of an element is called the *atomic number* of that element. At least five different experimental approaches have been needed for the ultimate assignment of atomic numbers to all the chemical elements.

Originally, the atomic number was simply a serial number which was assigned to the known elements when arranged in a sequence of increasing atomic weight. The connection between these serial numbers and the quantitative structural properties of the atoms remained undiscovered for half a century. At present, Z is probably the only nuclear quantity which is known "without error" for all nuclei. Of course, the actual *charge* Ze contains the experimental uncertainty of the best determinations of the elementary charge e. Thus the absolute nuclear charge, like everything else in physics, is known only within experimental accuracy.

1. Chemical Origin of Atomic Number

About the time of the American Civil War the Russian chemist D. I. Mendeleev proposed his now well-known periodic table† of the elements. Mendeleev's successful classification of all elements into columns exhibiting similar chemical properties, and into rows with progressively increasing atomic weights, dictated several revisions in the previously accepted atomic weights. The chemical atomic weight of multivalent elements is determined by multiplying the observed chemical combining weight by the smallest integer which is compatible with other known evidence. For example, indium has a chemical combining weight of 38.3 and had been incorrectly assigned an atomic weight of twice this figure; the progressions of chemical properties in the periodic system showed that the atomic weight of indium must be three times the combining weight, or 114.8. After minor readjustments of this type, and the

† The American physician James Blake, by observing the effects of all available chemical elements on the circulation, respiration, and central nervous system of dogs, arranged the elements in chemical *groups* [*Am. J. Med. Sci.*, **15**: 63 (1848)] but the *periodicities* were first shown two decades later by Mendeleev (B64).

subsequent discovery of helium and argon, which required the addition of the eighth and final column to the original table, the periodic table became a systematic pattern of the elements in which successive whole numbers, known as the *atomic number, could be assigned confidently to all the light elements,* on a basis of increasing atomic weight. Because the total number of rare-earth elements was unestablished, it was impossible to be certain of the atomic numbers of elements heavier than these, though tentative assignments could be made. Outside the rare-earth group, the periodic system successfully predicted the existence and properties of several undiscovered elements and properly reserved atomic numbers for these.

Three inversions were noted in the uniform increase of atomic number with atomic weight. Because of their chemical properties, it was necessary to assume that the three pairs K (39.1) and A (39.9), Co (58.9) and Ni (58.7), Te (127.6) and I (126.9) were exceptions in which the element with lower atomic weight has the higher atomic number. These inversions are now fully explained by the relative abundance of the isotopes of these particular elements. For example, Table 1.1 shows that while argon contains some atoms which are lighter than any of those of potassium, the heaviest argon isotope is the most abundant. Also, while potassium contains some atoms which are heavier than any of argon, the lightest potassium isotope happens to be most abundant.

TABLE 1.1. THE RELATIVE ABUNDANCE OF THE ISOTOPES OF ARGON AND OF POTASSIUM

Element	Atomic number	Mass numbers and their relative abundance						Average atomic weight
		36	37	38	39	40	41	
A	18	0.3	..	0.06	....	99.6	...	39.9
K	19	...	..	....	93.4	0.01	6.6	39.1

There seems little room to doubt the completeness of the chemical evidence of the light elements, and on this basis the first 13 atomic numbers were assigned to the elements from hydrogen to aluminum. From aluminum upward, the atomic numbers have been assigned on a basis of a variety of mutually consistent physical methods. Final confirmation of even the lowest atomic numbers has been obtained from observations of the scattering of X rays and of α rays and from spectroscopic evidence. The atomic numbers for the 101 elements which are now well established will be found in the periodic table of Appendix F.

2. *Number of Electrons per Atom. X-ray Scattering*

a. Scattering of X Rays by Atomic Electrons. One of the earliest experiments undertaken with X rays was the unsuccessful effort to reflect them from the surface of a mirror. It was found instead that the X rays were diffusely scattered, more or less in all directions, by the mirror or, indeed, by a slab of paraffin or any other object on which the X rays impinged.   J. J. Thomson interpreted this simple observation as probably due to the interaction of the X rays with the electrons which he had only recently shown to be present in all atoms.   Treating the X ray as a classical electromagnetic wave, Thomson derived an expression for the scattering which should be produced by each electron.   In this classical theory, each atomic electron is regarded as free to respond to the force produced on it by the electric vector of the electromagnetic wave.   Then each electron oscillates with a frequency which is the same as that of the incident X ray.   This oscillating charge radiates as an oscillating dipole, and its radiation is the scattered X radiation.

From classical electromagnetic theory, Thomson showed that each electron should radiate, or "scatter," a definite fraction of the energy flux which is incident on the electron.   In Thomson's theory, the fraction of the incident radiation scattered by each electron is independent of the wavelength of the X ray.   It is now known that this is true only for electromagnetic radiation whose quantum energy $h\nu$ is large compared with the binding energy of the atomic electrons, yet small compared with the rest energy, $m_0c^2 = 0.51$ Mev,† of an electron.

b. Cross Section for Thomson Scattering.   A derivation which follows in principle that performed by J. J. Thomson is given in Appendix A. It is found that each electron scatters an energy $_eQ$ ergs when it is traversed for a time t sec by a plane wave of X rays whose intensity is I ergs/(cm²)(sec).   The scattered radiation has the same frequency as the incident radiation.   The rate at which energy is scattered by each electron, i.e., the scattered power $_eQ/t$ ergs/sec, is found to be

$$\frac{_eQ}{t} = \left[\frac{8\pi}{3} \left(\frac{e^2}{m_0c^2} \right)^2 \right] I \equiv {}_e\sigma I \tag{2.1}$$

where e = electronic charge
$\quad m_0$ = rest mass of electron
$\quad c$ = velocity of light
e^2/m_0c^2 = "classical radius" of electron = 2.818×10^{-13} cm
The proportionality constant between the incident *intensity* (or power per unit area) and the *power* scattered by each electron appears in the square bracket of Eq. (2.1) and is represented by the symbol $_e\sigma$.   It will be noted that $_e\sigma$ has the dimensions of an area, i.e.,

$$\frac{\text{ergs/sec}}{\text{ergs/(cm}^2)(\text{sec})} = \text{cm}^2$$

It is the area on which enough energy falls from the plane wave to equal the energy scattered by one electron.   Each electron in the absorber scatters independently of the other electrons.   Therefore $_e\sigma$ is called the *Thomson electronic cross section*.   When the most probable values of the fundamental physical constants (see Appendix E) e, m_0, and c are sub-

† For definitions of abbreviations and mathematical symbols, see Glossary of Principal Symbols at the end of the book.

stituted, the Thomson cross section has the numerical value

$$_e\sigma = \frac{8\pi}{3}\left(\frac{e^2}{m_0c^2}\right)^2 = 0.6652 \times 10^{-24} \text{ cm}^2/\text{electron} \qquad (2.2)$$

The popular and now officially recognized international unit of cross section is the *barn*,† which is defined as

$$1 \text{ barn} \equiv 10^{-24} \text{ cm}^2$$

Then the Thomson cross section is very close to

$$_e\sigma = \tfrac{2}{3} \text{ barn/electron}$$

c. Linear and Mass Attenuation Coefficients. In a thin absorbing foil of thickness Δx, containing N atoms/cm³, there are (NZ) electrons/cm³ and $(NZ\,\Delta x)$ electrons/cm² of absorber area as seen by an incident beam of X rays. If each electron has an effective cross section of $_e\sigma$ cm²/electron, then the total effective scattering area in 1 cm² of area of absorbing foil is $(NZ\,\Delta x)\,_e\sigma$ "cm² of electrons"/cm² of foil. Thus $(NZ\,\Delta x)\,_e\sigma$ is the *fraction* of the superficial area of the foil which appears to be "opaque" to the incident X rays.

Then if an X-ray intensity I is incident normally on the foil, ΔI is the fraction of this intensity which will not be present in the transmitted beam, the corresponding energy having been scattered more or less in all directions by the electrons in the foil. This decrease in the intensity of the collimated beam is therefore

$$\Delta I = -INZ\,_e\sigma\,\Delta x$$

The quantity $(NZ\,_e\sigma)$ has dimensions of cm⁻¹ and is often called the *linear attenuation coefficient* σ. Then we may write

$$\frac{dI}{I} = -\sigma\,dx \qquad (2.3)$$

Integrating this equation, we find that, if an intensity I_0 is incident on a scattering foil of thickness x cm, the transmitted unscattered intensity I is given by the usual exponential expression

$$\frac{I}{I_0} = e^{-\sigma x} = e^{-(\sigma/\rho)(x\rho)} \qquad (2.4)$$

In practice, the thickness of absorbing foils is often expressed in terms of mass per unit area. Then if ρ g/cm³ is the density of the foil material,

† The origin of the barn unit is said to lie in the American colloquialism "big as a barn," which was first applied to the cross sections for the interaction of slow neutrons with certain atomic nuclei during the Manhattan District project of World War II. The international Joint Commission on Standards, Units, and Constants of Radioactivity recommended in 1950 the international acceptance of the term "barn" for 10^{-24} cm² because of its common usage in the United States [F. A. Paneth, *Nature*, **166**: 931 (1950); *Nucleonics*, **8** (5): 38 (1951)].

the "thickness" is $(x\rho)$ g/cm², and the *mass attenuation coefficient* is (σ/ρ) cm²/g.

d. Number of Electrons per Atom. Barkla first carried out quantitative experiments on the attenuation suffered by a beam of X rays in passing through absorbing layers of various light materials, especially carbon. The number of atoms of carbon per gram N/ρ is simply Avogadro's number divided by the atomic weight of carbon. Hence the number of electrons Z per atom can be computed from the measured X-ray transmission I/I_0, assuming only the validity of Thomson's theory of X-ray scattering.

Actually, at least two other phenomena contribute significantly to the attenuation of low-energy X rays in carbon. These are the excitation of fluorescence radiation following photoelectric absorption of the X rays by K and L electrons, and the coherent and diffuse scattering from the crystal planes in graphite. The crystal effects were unknown at the time of Barkla's work, but they appear to have been fortuitously averaged out by the combined effects of wavelength inhomogeneity in the incident X rays and wide-angle geometry in the detection system. Barkla recognized the influence of photoelectric absorption, which is strongly dependent on wavelength, and undertook to extrapolate this effect out by comparing σ/ρ for carbon at several different wavelengths. Finally, the theoretical value of the Thomson cross section depends on

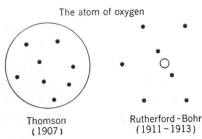

The atom of oxygen

Thomson (1907) Rutherford-Bohr (1911–1913)

Fig. 2.1 The atom model of J. J. Thomson (T23) distributed the electrons, shown as black dots, inside a large sphere of uniform positive electrification. The Rutherford-Bohr model compressed all the positive charge, and its associated large mass, into a small central nucleus, with the electrons performing Copernicanlike orbits at distances of the order of 10^3 to 10^4 times the nuclear radius.

e^2/m_0c^2 and hence on measured values of both e and e/m_0. The numerical values of e and e/m_0 were known only approximately in Barkla's time. They were sufficiently accurate to show unambiguously that the X-ray scattering would be produced by the atomic electrons, because of their small mass, and not by the positively charged parts of the atom.

In fact, *the X-ray scattering does not depend on the disposition of the positive charges in the atom, as long as these are associated with the massive parts of the atom*, as can be seen from the $1/m_0^2$ factor in Eq. (2.2). Barkla's experiments were done while Thomson's atom model, Fig. 2.1, was in vogue, but the results are equally valid on the Rutherford-Bohr nuclear model. In the nuclear model, it is obvious that an electrically neutral atom must contain the same number of electrons as there are elementary charges Z in the nucleus.

It is interesting to note that Barkla's first values, obtained in 1904, ran to 100 to 200 electrons per molecule of air; by 1907 (T23) his results were down to 16 electrons per molecule of air. Improvements in technique, and better values of e and e/m_0, led Barkla in 1911 (B12) to conclude that the mass attenuation coefficient σ/ρ for Thomson scattering by carbon is about 0.2 cm²/g, which corresponds to the currently acceptable value of six electrons per atom of carbon. For other light elements, Barkla concluded correctly that "the number of scattering electrons per atom is about half the atomic weight of the element."

It should be remarked that Barkla's results would have been incorrect if he had applied the Thomson theory to atoms of such large Z that the (then unknown) electron binding energies were comparable with the relatively small quantum energy [~40 kev (kiloelectron volts)] of his X rays. Secondly, if Barkla's X-ray quantum energy had been sufficiently large so that it was comparable with $m_0c^2 = 0.51$ Mev, the Thomson formula would also have been invalid because it omits consideration of the recoil of the electron, which was discovered much later by Compton. At the time of Barkla's work, many phenomena now regarded as fundamental in atomic physics were unknown. The atomic nucleus had not yet been discovered, and Thomson's model of the atom was still fashionable. Bohr's explanation of atomic spectra and of the binding energy of atomic electrons and Compton's explanation of the interaction of higher-energy photons with electrons were yet unborn. The principles of Bragg diffraction of X rays by crystal planes were unknown.

With all these factors in view, Hewlett, in 1922 (H49), found $\sigma/\rho = 0.2$ cm²/g for 17.5-kev X rays in carbon, and consequently six electrons per atom of carbon, and this result is acceptable from all viewpoints.

In 1928 Klein and Nishina applied the Dirac relativistic electron theory to the problem of the scattering of high-energy photons by atomic electrons. The details of this work are discussed later, in Chap. 23. Here we may note that the excellent agreement between this theory and the experimental observations on the scattering of photons up to as much as 100 Mev constitutes a fairly direct modern measurement of the number of electrons per atom for a wide variety of elements. In all cases, of course, Z is found to agree with the atomic numbers which have been assigned in the meantime on a basis of other types of evidence.

Problems

1. Assuming only Thomson scattering, calculate the fractional transmission of low-energy X rays through 5 mm of graphite, assuming that carbon has six electrons per atom.

2. What transmission would be expected if carbon had 12 electrons per atom?

3. About what photon energy should be used in the measurement of Z, if deviations from Thomson scattering, due to both photoelectric absorption and Compton losses, are to be minimized?

4. What is the fractional transmission if the graphite slab in Prob. 1 is tilted so that the X-ray beam strikes the slab at 30° with the normal?

3. *Charge on the Atomic Nucleus. α-Ray Scattering*

a. Qualitative Character of the Rutherford-Bohr Atom Model. Rutherford, in 1906, first noticed that the deflections experienced by α rays while passing through air, mica, and gold were occasionally much greater than could be accounted for by the Thomson model of the atom. Rutherford's first mathematical paper on the α-ray scattering appeared in 1911. This is a classic (R43, B53) which should be read in its original form by every serious student.

He assumed that each atom contains a small central nucleus, whose radius is less than 10^{-12} cm, whereas the radius of the entire atom was known to be of the order of 10^{-8} cm. Although it is now evident that the nucleus is positively charged, Rutherford left the sign of the charge on the nucleus as an open question in 1911 and pointed out that the angular distribution of scattered α rays is independent of the sign of the nuclear charge. If the nucleus be regarded as having a positive charge Ze and if an equal amount of negative charge be distributed throughout the volume of the entire atom, all α-ray deflections greater than about 1° were shown to be attributable to nuclear scattering and to have an intensity proportional to Z^2.

The mass of the atom is now known to be found primarily in the nucleus, but this fact was not needed in order to explain the early α-ray-scattering results and was not used in Rutherford's original theory. It was only necessary to make the tacit assumption that the atom was not disrupted by the collision; thus the nucleus was simply the center of mass of the atom. The essentially new feature in Rutherford's model of the atom was the concentration of all the positive charge Ze into a nucleus, or central region, smaller than 10^{-12} cm in radius, with an equal amount of charge of the opposite sign distributed throughout the entire atom in a sphere whose radius is much greater than that of the nucleus. He simply deprived Thomson's atom model of its uniform sphere of positive electricity and concentrated all this charge at the center of his new atom model.

Two years later Bohr (B92) put the atom's mass into the nucleus, gave quantized energy states to the atomic electrons, produced his successful theory of the origin of spectra, and essentially completed the Rutherford-Bohr nuclear model for the atom. Darwin (D5) later generalized Rutherford's theory of scattering by giving the solutions on classical theory for collisions in which the mass of the struck atom is comparable with that of the incident ray, and for collisions in which the force varies as the inverse nth power of the separation. In 1920 Chadwick (C11) showed experimentally that $n = 2.00 \pm 0.03$ for the scattering of α rays by heavy nuclei and therefore that Coulomb's law is valid for these collisions.

b. Scattering in Center-of-mass Coordinates and in Laboratory Coordinates. All collision problems between free particles are greatly simplified through the use of a coordinate system whose origin is at the center of mass of the colliding particles. This coordinate system is known as the "particle coordinates," the "zero-momentum coordinates," the "center-of-mass coordinates," or most simply the "C coordinates." Physically, it is usually more realistic to visualize the collision in the C coordinates than in the laboratory, or "L coordinates." The words "projectile" and "target" particle have a meaning only in the L coordinates. In the C coordinates neither particle is the aggressor; both particles approach their common center of mass with equal and opposite momenta, interact with each other, and depart from the scene of the "collision." *The total linear momentum of the colliding particles is always zero in the C coordinates.* We shall discuss here only nonrelativistic collisions. The corresponding transformation equations for the relativistic case have been given by Bergmann (B35), Blaton (B65), Morrison (M57), and others.

The use of C coordinates has a profound mathematical advantage. In both classical mechanics and wave mechanics, the use of C coordinates reduces any two-body collision problem to a one-body problem, namely, the interaction of one particle having the reduced mass M_0 and velocity V with a potential field which can always be considered as centered at the origin of the C coordinates. The *reduced mass M_0* of a system of two particles having masses M_1 and M_2 is

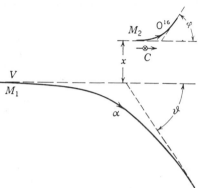

Fig. 3.1 Coulomb elastic scattering of an α ray (M_1) by an oxygen nucleus (M_2), seen in the laboratory coordinates. The center of mass, marked C, moves through the laboratory with a constant velocity V_c which is one-fifth the initial velocity of the α ray. The impact parameter x is the separation at which the particles would pass if there were no interaction between them. Note that the initial direction of M_2 is *away* from M_1. The trajectories are not simple hyperbolas in the L coordinates.

$$\frac{1}{M_0} = \frac{1}{M_1} + \frac{1}{M_2}$$

or

$$M_0 = \frac{M_1 M_2}{M_1 + M_2} \qquad (3.1)$$

Therefore the reduced mass always lies between 0.5 and 1.0 times the mass of the lighter particle.

The analytical relationships between various collision parameters in the C and L coordinates are derived in Appendix B. Here we quote only some of the principal results. In the L coordinates, a typical collision is the encounter of a projectile particle having mass M_1 and initial velocity V with a target particle having mass M_2 and being initially at rest. This pair of particles must always share the initial momentum $M_1 V$; therefore their center of mass moves through the laboratory at a constant velocity $V_c = M_1 V / (M_1 + M_2)$ which is always parallel to the initial direction of V. This state of affairs is illustrated in Fig. 3.1, where for definiteness we have shown an elastic collision between an α ray ($M_1 = 4$) and an oxygen nucleus ($M_2 = 16$). As a result of the collision, the α ray is deflected through an angle ϑ, while the oxygen nucleus is projected at an angle φ with the original direction of the incident α ray. In the L coordinates, the analytical relationships which connect the scattering angles ϑ and φ with the impact parameter x

and with the charges, masses, and velocities of M_1 and M_2 are unduly complicated and are too cumbersome for use in the general case. Indeed, the relationships are derived by solving the problem first in the C coordinates and then transforming the motion to the L coordinates.

In the C coordinates, all parameters are measured with respect to an origin at the center of mass. The motion of the particles in the C coordinates can always be transformed to motion in the L coordinates by noting that the C-coordinate system moves through the laboratory with the same uniform velocity V_c which the center of mass possesses in the L coordinates.

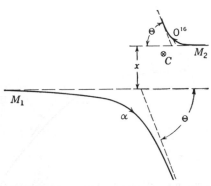

In the C coordinates, both particles initially approach each other, as shown in Fig. 3.2. They move in such a way that their total linear momentum is always zero. Their total angular momentum about the origin at their center of mass is always $M_0 V x$, where x is the impact parameter. The initial velocity of M_1 in the C coordinates is

$$V - V_c = V \frac{M_0}{M_1} \qquad (3.2)$$

Fig. 3.2 The same collision as Fig. 3.1 but now seen as the particles actually experience it, in the center-of-mass coordinates. The center of mass, marked C, is now at rest. The total linear momentum is zero. Each particle traverses a true hyperbolic orbit about C as its external focus. The deflection angle Θ is the same for both particles. Note that the initial direction of M_2 is *toward* M_1, or opposite to the motion of M_2 in the L coordinates of Fig. 3.1.

to the right, while the initial velocity of M_2 is

$$V_c = V \frac{M_0}{M_2} \qquad (3.3)$$

to the left in Fig. 3.2. The mutual velocity with which M_1 and M_2 approach each other initially is therefore V, which is the same as in the L coordinates.

In the C coordinates, *both* particles are scattered through the *same* angle Θ, and their final velocities are equal to their initial velocities. Neither of these simple relationships holds in the L coordinates. The angular deflection ϑ of M_1 in the L coordinates turns out to be given by

$$\cot \vartheta = \frac{M_1}{M_2} \csc \Theta + \cot \Theta \qquad (3.4)$$

Then in general $\vartheta \leq \Theta$. The relationship between ϑ and Θ is simple only in two special cases, which are

for $M_1 \ll M_2$, $\qquad\qquad \vartheta \simeq \Theta$

for $M_1 = M_2$, $\qquad\qquad \vartheta = \dfrac{\Theta}{2}$

The laboratory angle φ through which M_2 is projected in the L coordinates is given by

$$\varphi = \frac{\pi}{2} - \frac{\Theta}{2} \tag{3.5}$$

Finally, the angle between the final directions of M_1 and M_2 is always 180° in the C coordinates but in the L coordinates has the values

for $M_1 = M_2,$ $\varphi + \vartheta = \dfrac{\pi}{2}$

for $M_1 < M_2,$ $\varphi + \vartheta < \dfrac{\pi}{2} + \dfrac{\Theta}{2}$

for $M_1 \ll M_2,$ $\varphi + \vartheta \simeq \dfrac{\pi}{2} + \dfrac{\Theta}{2}$

All these angular relationships are consequences of the conservation of momentum and energy and are independent of the force laws which may govern the scattering for the particular type of collision involved. The nature of the interaction between the particles determines the cross section for the collision in the C coordinates.

   c. Elastic Scattering by Coulomb Forces. It can be shown quite generally (see Appendix B) that, when any incident nonrelativistic particle interacts with a target particle according to an inverse-square law of force (either attractive or repulsive), both particles must, in order to conserve angular momentum, traverse hyperbolic orbits in a coordinate system whose origin is at the center of mass of the colliding particles. (Note that the incident particle's path in the laboratory-coordinate system is not necessarily hyperbolic.) When the restriction is added that the sum of the kinetic energy and potential energy of the two particles is constant, it is found that the angle of deflection Θ in the center-of-mass coordinates is given by

$$x = \frac{b}{2} \cot \frac{\Theta}{2} \tag{3.6}$$

where the "*impact parameter*" x is the distance at which the two particles would pass each other if there were no interaction between them, and where b is the *collision diameter* defined by

$$b \equiv \frac{2|Zz|e^2}{M_0 V^2} \tag{3.7}$$

where ze = charge on incident particle
   Ze = charge on target particle
   V = mutual velocity of approach
   M_0 = reduced mass of colliding particles, Eq. (3.1)
The absolute value of Zz is to be taken, without regard to sign. The collision radius $b/2$ is the value of the impact parameter for which the scattering angle is just 90° in the center-of-mass coordinates, both for

attractive and for repulsive forces. For the special case of repulsive forces, as in the nuclear scattering of α rays, the collision diameter b is also equal to the *closest possible distance of approach*, i.e., to the minimum separation between the particles during a head-on collision. At this minimum separation the particles are stationary with respect to one another, and therefore their initial kinetic energy $\frac{1}{2}M_0V^2$ is just equal to their mutual electrostatic potential energy Zze^2/b.

d. Cross Section for Rutherford Scattering. In all collisions for which the minimum distance of approach b is significantly greater than the radius of the nucleus, the only force acting will be the inverse-square coulomb force, and Eq. (3.6) will be valid. All collisions for which the impact parameter lies between 0 and x will result in scattering of the incident particle through an angle between 180° and Θ. Then the cross section, $\sigma(\geq \Theta)$, for scattering through an angle equal to or greater than Θ is the area of a disk of radius x, or

$$\sigma(\geq \Theta) = \pi x^2 = \frac{\pi}{4}\, b^2 \cot^2 \frac{\Theta}{2} \tag{3.8}$$

Thus the cross section for backscattering ($\Theta \geq 90°$) is simply $\pi b^2/4$, which is the area of a disk whose radius equals the collision radius $b/2$.

For $\Theta = 0$, σ and x are both infinite; thus every α ray appears to suffer some slight deflection. Physically, this situation does not occur, because for very large impact parameters the nuclear coulomb field is neutralized, or "screened," by the field of the atomic electrons.

The differential cross section $d\sigma$ for nuclear scattering between angles Θ and $\Theta + d\Theta$ is the area of a ring of radius x and width dx, or

$$d\sigma = 2\pi x\, dx = \frac{\pi}{4}\, b^2 \cot \frac{\Theta}{2} \csc^2 \frac{\Theta}{2}\, d\Theta \tag{3.9}$$

The solid angle $d\Omega$, into which particles scattered between Θ and $\Theta + d\Theta$ are deflected, is

$$d\Omega = 2\pi \sin \Theta\, d\Theta$$
$$= 4\pi \sin \frac{\Theta}{2} \cos \frac{\Theta}{2}\, d\Theta$$

Therefore the differential cross section for scattering into the solid angle $d\Omega$ at mean angle Θ is

$$d\sigma = \frac{b^2}{16}\left[\frac{1}{\sin^4 (\Theta/2)}\right] d\Omega \tag{3.10}$$

Equations (3.8) to (3.10) are various equivalent forms which all represent Rutherford (i.e., classical) scattering. Each is best suited to particular types of experiments. Each exhibits the marked predominance of forward scattering which is generally characteristic of long-range forces, such as the inverse-square interaction.

e. Single Scattering by a Foil. A scattering foil of thickness Δs cm, containing N atoms/cm³, will present $N\, \Delta s$ scattering centers per square centimeter to normally incident α rays. If the cross section of each scattering center is σ cm^2/atom, then the scattering centers comprise the fraction $\sigma N \Delta s$ of the total area of the foil. Then if n_0 α rays are incident normally on the foil, n α rays will be scattered in the directions represented by the particular value of the cross section σ being used. The fraction so scattered is simply

$$\frac{n}{n_0} = \sigma(N \Delta s) \qquad \text{or} \qquad \frac{dn}{n_0} = d\sigma \, (N \Delta s) \qquad (3.11)$$

It is understood that the foil is sufficiently thin so that $(\sigma N \Delta s) \ll 1$. Therefore the number of α rays which are scattered twice is negligible in comparison with the number scattered only once. More briefly, only *single scattering* is considered here, not *plural scattering* (a few collisions per particle) nor *multiple scattering* (many collisions per particle).

When the mass of the incident particle can be neglected in comparison with the mass of the target particle, then the reduced mass M_0 becomes substantially equal to the mass of the (lighter) incident particle. Also, the deflection angle Θ in the center-of-mass coordinates becomes substantially equal to the deflection angle ϑ in the laboratory coordinates. These simplified conditions do apply to the scattering of α particles by heavy nuclei such as gold. In these collisions the heavy target nucleus remains essentially stationary, or "clamped," during the collision.

f. Experimental Verification of Rutherford's Nuclear Atom Model. In proposing that all the (positive) charge in the atom should be regarded as concentrated in a small central nucleus, Rutherford made use of experimental results which had been obtained by Geiger on the angular distribution of the α rays scattered by a thin gold foil. These results were in sharp contrast with the predictions of the Thomson model of the atom, but they were in substantial agreement with the $1/\sin^4 (\Theta/2)$ distribution of Eq. (3.10) predicted by the nuclear model in which the central positive charge has such small dimensions that it is not reached by swift α rays even in head-on collisions (R43).

Geiger and Marsden subsequently completed a beautiful series of experiments which completely verified Eqs. (3.10) and (3.11) point by point. Their original paper (G14) warrants reading by every serious student. The angle of deflection ϑ in the laboratory coordinates was varied in small steps from 5 to 150°; this brings about a variation in $\sin^4 (\Theta/2)$ of more than 250,000 to 1. Figure 3.3 shows the results for a particular gold foil. The collision diameter b was varied in two independent ways. First, the velocity V of the incident α rays was varied by interposing absorbers between the RaB + RaC source and the scattering foils; in this way the $1/V^4$ term which enters all the cross sections through b^2 was varied in seven steps over a factor of about 9 to 1. Secondly, the nuclear charge Ze was varied by studying the scattering from gold, silver, copper, and aluminum foils. It was found that the intensity of the scattering per atom was approximately proportional to the square of the atomic weight.

This showed experimentally for the first time that the nuclear charge is approximately proportional to the atomic weight. The actual value of the nuclear charge was found to be about one-half the atomic weight, with an experimental uncertainty of about 20 per cent. These experiments by Geiger and Marsden completely verified Rutherford's concept of the atom as containing a small central nucleus in which all the charge of one sign is located.

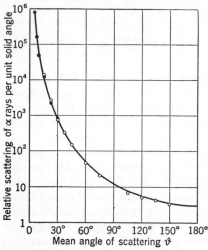

Fig. 3.3 Differential cross section for the single scattering of α rays by a thin foil of gold. The vertical scale represents the relative number of α rays scattered into a constant element of solid angle at the mean scattering angles ϑ which are shown on the horizontal scale. The curve is proportional to $1/\sin^4 (\vartheta/2)$, as predicted by the classical theory, and is fitted to the arbitrary vertical scale at $\vartheta = 135°$. The closed and open circles are the experimental data of Geiger and Marsden (G14) in two overlapping series of observations, one at small and one at large scattering angles. The agreement at all angles shows that, under the conditions of these experiments, the only force acting between the incident α rays and the gold nuclei is the inverse-square coulomb repulsion. The closest distance of approach in these experiments was 30×10^{-13} cm (for 150° scattering of the 7.68-Mev α rays from RaC'), and so the positive charge in the gold atom is confined to a small central region which is definitely smaller than this, or about 10^{-4} of the atomic radius.

g. The Equivalence of Nuclear Charge and Atomic Number. It fell to van den Broek (B125) in 1913 to collect the various types of evidence then available and to make the fertile suggestion that the *charge on the atomic nucleus is actually equal to the atomic number.* Bohr adopted this suggestion and developed his quantum theory of the structure of atoms and the origin of spectra. This theory predicted that the frequency of the X-ray lines in the K series should increase with the square of the charge on the atomic nucleus, i.e., with Z^2. Moseley's observations of these X-ray lines showed instead that the frequency ν is substantially proportional to $(Z - 1)^2$, if it be assumed that the charge Z on the nucleus equals the atomic number and that the atomic number of aluminum is 13. Moseley suggested correctly that the effective charge on the atomic nucleus, for K-series X rays, is about one unit less than the actual charge Z on the nucleus because of *screening* of the nuclear charge, especially by the one K-shell electron which is present in the initial atomic state of any K-series transition. Any doubt which may have persisted about this interpretation was later removed by Chadwick's direct measurement of the nuclear charge of Cu, Ag, and Pt by the α-ray-scattering method.

h. Absolute Determination of Nuclear Charge. Chadwick introduced an ingenious experimental arrangement which greatly increases the observable scattered intensity for any given angle, source, and thickness of scattering foil. The foil is arranged, as shown in Fig. 3.4, as an annular ring around an axis between the source of α rays and the scintillation-screen detector. Precision α-ray-scattering experiments with this arrangement gave the absolute value of the nuclear charge of Cu, Ag, and Pt as $29.3e$, $46.3e$, and $77.4e$, with an estimated uncertainty of 1 to 2 per cent (C11). This is final confirmation of the atomic numbers 29, 47, and 78 which had been assigned to these elements by Moseley.

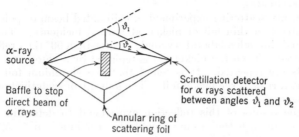

Fig. 3.4 Chadwick's arrangement of source, scatterer, and detector for increasing the intensity of α rays scattered between angles ϑ_1 and ϑ_2, as used for his direct measurement of the nuclear charge on Cu, Ag, and Pt. This annular geometry for the scattering body has subsequently been widely adapted to a variety of other scattering problems, e.g., the shadow scattering of fast neutrons by lead (Chap. 14).

i. Limitations of the Classical Theory. It should be noted that the general wave-mechanical theory of the elastic scattering of charged particles adds a number of terms to the simple cross sections given in Eqs. (3.8) to (3.10), which are based only on classical mechanics. However, the wave mechanics (M63) and the classical mechanics give identical solutions for the limiting cases in which a heavy nucleus scatters an α ray of moderate energy. In general, the classical theory is valid when the rationalized de Broglie wavelength, $\lambda/2\pi \equiv \lambda = \hbar/M_0V$, for the collision in the C coordinates is small compared with the collision diameter b. These conditions are equivalent to $b/\lambda = 2Zz/137\beta \gg 1$, where $\beta = V/c$, and are derived in Eqs. (83) and (100) of Appendix C. For the special case of the scattering of identical particles (such as α rays by He nuclei, protons by H nuclei, and electrons by electrons), the wave-mechanical results [Chap. 10, Eq. (5.1); Chap. 19, Eq. (2.4)] are markedly different from those of the classical mechanics. The wave-mechanical theory is well supported by experiments.

Problems

1. A thin gold foil of thickness Δs cm has N atoms of gold per cubic centimeter. Each atom has a nuclear cross section σ cm^2 for scattering of incident α rays through more than some arbitrary angle Θ. The fraction of normally incident α rays scattered through more than Θ is $n/n_0 = \sigma N \Delta s$. Show clearly what fraction of the incident α rays is scattered through more than Θ if the α rays are incident at an angle ψ with the normal to the foil.

2. Starting with any of the general equations for Rutherford scattering, derive an expression for the cross section for backscattering in the laboratory coordinates (that is, $\vartheta \geq 90°$), and show that your equation will reduce to

$$\sigma(\text{backscatter}) = \pi \left(\frac{Zze^2}{M_1 V^2} \right)^2 \left[1 - \left(\frac{M_1}{M_2} \right)^2 \right]$$

where, as usual, the incident particle has charge ze, mass M_1, and velocity V, and the target particle has charge Ze and mass M_2 and is initially stationary in the laboratory coordinates.

3. In an α-ray-scattering experiment, a collimated beam of polonium α rays (5.30 Mev) strikes a thin foil of nickel, at normal incidence. The number of α rays scattered through a laboratory angle greater than 90° (i.e., reflected by the foil) is measured. Then the nickel foil is replaced by a chromium foil, and the measurements are repeated. It is found that the chromium foil reflects 0.83 times as many α rays as the nickel foil. The foils are of such thickness that each weighs 0.4 mg/cm².

(a) Use the results of this reflection experiment to determine the nuclear charge for chromium, if the atomic weight of chromium is $W = 52.0$, while for nickel $Z = 28$ and $W = 58.7$.

(b) Show whether classical theory should be valid for these collisions between 5.30-Mev α rays and chromium nuclei.

4. Consider the classical (Rutherford) scattering of 1.02-Mev α rays by aluminum nuclei. For the particular collisions in which the impact parameter is just equal to the collision diameter, determine the following details:

(a) Velocity of the center of mass in the L coordinates.

(b) Reduced mass of the system, in amu (atomic mass units).

(c) Kinetic energy in the C coordinates, in Mev.

(d) Collision diameter, in 10^{-13} cm.

(e) Scattering angle in C coordinates.

(f) Deflection angle of the α ray in L coordinates.

(g) Deflection angle of the Al nucleus in L coordinates.

(h) Minimum distance of approach between the α ray and the Al nucleus during the collision, in 10^{-13} cm.

(i) Minimum distance of approach of the α ray to the center of mass during the collision.

(j) Approximate nuclear radius of Al, if $R = 1.5 \times 10^{-13} A^{\frac{1}{3}}$ cm.

(k) The angular momentum of the colliding system, about the center of mass, in units of $h/2\pi$.

(l) The nuclear cross section for deflections larger than those found in (e) or (f) above, in barns per nucleus.

(m) The fraction of 1.02-Mev α rays, incident normally on an Al foil 0.01 mg/cm² thick, which are deflected through more than the angles found in (e) or (f).

(n) From the same foil, the fraction of the normally incident α rays which would strike a 1-mm-square screen placed 3 cm away from the scattering foil and normal to the mean scattering angle found in (f).

(o) Sketch the trajectories of both particles during the collision, in C coordinates and also in L coordinates. Are the paths hyperbolas in L coordinates?

(p) De Broglie wavelength for the collision in the C coordinates, in 10^{-13} cm.

(q) Same as (p) but for an incident α-ray energy of 10.2 Mev. Would classical theory be valid for such a collision? Why?

4. *Frequency of K- and L-series X Rays*

a. Bohr Theory. Following the proof of the existence of atomic nuclei by the α-ray-scattering experiments, Bohr (B92) assigned the principal part of the atomic mass to nuclei and introduced his quantum theory of the origin of atomic spectra. To the extent that the simple theory is valid, the energy $h\nu$ of characteristic X-ray quanta would be expected to be given by

$$h\nu = Z^2 \frac{2\pi^2 m_0 e^4}{h^2} \left(\frac{1}{n_1^2} - \frac{1}{n_2^2} \right) \qquad (4.1)$$

$$h\nu = (\alpha Z)^2 \frac{m_0 c^2}{2} \left(\frac{1}{n_1^2} - \frac{1}{n_2^2} \right) \qquad (4.2)$$

where n_1 and n_2 are the principal quantum numbers for the initial and final electron vacancies ($n_1 = 1$, $n_2 = 2$, for the K_α series; $n_1 = 2$, $n_2 = 3$, for the L_α series), α is the fine-structure constant ($\alpha \simeq \frac{1}{137}$; $\alpha^2 m_0 c^2/2 = 13.6$ ev), and all other symbols have their customary meaning and the numerical values given in Appendix E.

b. Screening of Nuclear Charge by Atomic Electrons. However, the effective nuclear charge is actually somewhat less than Ze because of *screening* of the nuclear field by the potential due to the other K, L, . . . electrons present in the ionized atom. The screening in the initial state will be less than the screening in the final state of an X-ray transition, and separate screening corrections can be introduced for each electron level in the atom if desired (C37).

Moseley applied the then new principles of Bragg reflection to the study of X-ray lines and thereby introduced a new era of X-ray spectroscopy. In two monumental papers (M60) he showed the existence of a linear relationship between the atomic numbers of the light elements, as previously assigned from chemical data, and $\nu^{\frac{1}{2}}$ for the characteristic K_α and L_α X-ray lines.

Moseley's data are shown in Fig. 4.1. The plot of atomic number against $\nu^{\frac{1}{2}}$ for the K_α series does not pass through the origin but has an intercept of about unity on the atomic number axis. If the nuclear charge Z is assumed to be the same as the atomic number, then Moseley's data on the K_α series have the form

$$\nu^{\frac{1}{2}} = \text{const} \times (Z - 1) \qquad (4.3)$$

and an effective value of the screening constant for the over-all transition can be taken as about unity. Similarly, Moseley's data on the L_α series exhibit a substantially linear relationship given by

$$\nu^{\frac{1}{2}} = \text{const} \times (Z - 7.4) \qquad (4.4)$$

Under the same interpretation, this would suggest an over-all or effective screening constant of about 7.4, as seen from the L shell. Both these effective screening constants are physically reasonable.

It is concluded that the atomic number is equal to the charge on the atomic nucleus and hence also to the number of atomic electrons in the neutral atom.

c. Atomic Numbers for Heavy Elements. The original method of assigning atomic numbers on a basis of increasing atomic weight and the periodicity of chemical properties was applicable only up to $Z = 57$. Beginning at $Z = 57$, the group of 15 rare-earth elements all exhibit similar chemical properties and stand in the same column of a Mendeleev periodic table. The total number of rare-earth elements was unknown

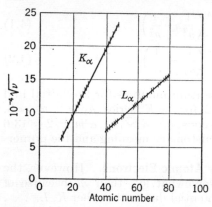

Fig. 4.1 Moseley's original data (1914) showing the frequency ν of the K_α and L_α X-ray lines of all available elements and the uniform variation of $\nu^{\frac{1}{2}}$ with integers Z assignable as atomic numbers to the 38 elements tested. Each K_α and L_α line is actually a close doublet; none of these had been resolved at Moseley's time.

in 1912. Therefore it was impossible to assign correct atomic numbers to the elements which are heavier than the rare earths. For example, it was conventional to assume the value $Z = 100$ for uranium, which is now known to be $Z = 92$. Moseley's work was the first to show that a total of 15 places ($Z = 57$ to 71) had to be reserved for the rare earths.

Moseley examined the K_α X rays of 21 elements from $_{13}$Al to $_{47}$Ag, and also the L_α X rays of 24 elements from $_{40}$Zr to $_{79}$Au. The overlap, between $_{40}$Zr and $_{47}$Ag, oriented the L series and permitted its use for *bridging over the rare-earth group of elements* in order to establish for the first time the atomic numbers in the *upper* part of the periodic table.

The fundamental significance of atomic number was firmly established by Moseley's data. Cobalt was shown to be atomic number 27 and Ni to be 28, as had been suspected from their chemical properties. It may be noted that the ratio of atomic weight, or more accurately the mass number A, to the atomic number Z is nearly constant and has the value

$$2.0 \leq \frac{A}{Z} \leq 2.6$$

for all stable nuclei, except H^1 and He^3.

d. The Identification of New Elements. There have been a number of new elements produced by transmutation processes in recent years. These elements ($Z = 43, 61, 85, 87, 93, 94, 95, \ldots$) have no stable isotopes, but each does have at least one isotope whose radioactive half-period is sufficiently long to permit the accumulation of milligram quantities of the isotope. In every case, the atomic number has been assigned first by combining chemical evidence and transmutation data, at a time when the total available amount of the isotope was perhaps of the order of 10^{-10} g. Confirmation of most of these assignments of atomic number has been made by measurement of the K- and L-series X rays, excited in the conventional way by electron bombardment of milligram amounts of the isotope. [See (B143) for $Z = 43$, (B144) and (P13) for $Z = 61$.] Such measurements are regarded as conclusive in the identification of any new element.

e. Characteristic X Rays from Radioactive Substances. Whenever any process results in the production of a vacancy in the K or L shell of atomic electrons, the ensuing rearrangement of the remaining electrons is accompanied by the emission of one or more X-ray quanta of the K or L series, or by Auger electrons, or both. There are two general types of radioactive transformation in which vacancies are produced in the inner electron shells of atomic electrons. Any radioactive substance whose decay involves either electron capture or internal conversion is found to be a source of an entire line spectrum of X rays. Full discussions of internal conversion will be found in Chap. 6, Sec. 5, and of electron capture in Chap. 17, Sec. 3. Here we focus our attention only on the determination of atomic number by means of the X rays which are invariably associated with these transitions.

Electron Capture. The capture of an atomic electron by a nucleus is an important mode of radioactive decay, which generally competes with all cases of positron β-ray decay. Several radioactive substances are known in which the transition energy is insufficient to allow positron β-ray emission, and in which all radioactive transitions proceed by electron capture (for example, $_4Be^7$, $_{24}Cr^{51}$, $_{31}Ga^{67}$, $_{49}In^{111}$). It is generally more probable that a K electron will be in the vicinity of the nucleus and will be captured than that an $L, M, \ldots$ electron will be captured. The majority of the vacancies are therefore produced in the K shell. If Z is the atomic number of the parent radioactive substance, then $(Z - 1)$ is the atomic number of the daughter substance in which the electron vacancy exists and from which the X rays are emitted. The existence of the electron-capture mode of radioactive decay was first established by Alvarez's observation (A22) of relatively intense K_α X rays of titanium ($Z = 22$) among the radiations emitted in the radioactive decay of the 16-day isotope of vanadium, $_{23}V^{48}$. More rigorous experimental proof was subsequently obtained from absorption curves (A23) and from Abelson's bent-crystal spectrometer studies (A1) of the X rays of zinc ($Z = 30$) which are emitted in the pure electron-capture decay of $_{31}Ga^{67}$. Several isotopes of technetium ($Z = 43$) decay predominantly by electron capture, and the early identification of element 43 was aided by the observation of the molybdenum ($Z = 42$) X rays which are emitted in the decay of these technetium isotopes.

Internal Conversion. The second general class of nuclear transitions which invariably result in X-ray-emission spectra is the internal-conversion transitions. There are numerous methods for producing nuclei in excited energy levels. Perhaps half the daughter nuclei which are produced by α decay or β decay are formed in excited levels rather than in their ground levels. Generally the deexcitation of these nuclei proceeds by the emission of γ rays. Internal conversion is an alternative mode of deexcitation which always competes with γ-ray emission and which often predominates over γ-ray emission if the nuclear excitation energy is small and the angular-momentum change is large (Chap. 6, Sec. 5). The nuclear excitation energy is transferred directly to a penetrating atomic electron, and this additional energy allows the electron to overcome its atomic binding energy and to escape, or indeed to be expelled, from the atom. In the most common cases, internal conversion is more likely to expel a K electron than an $L, M, \ldots$ electron from the atom. Thus the majority of the vacancies are produced in the K shell of atomic electrons.

Internal-conversion transitions are therefore accompanied by X-ray-emission spectra. Neither internal conversion nor γ-ray emission involves any change in the nuclear charge, so that the X-ray spectra are characteristic of the element in which the actual nuclear transition took place. For example, the β-ray decay of $_{79}\text{Au}^{198}$ results in the production of the daughter nucleus $_{80}\text{Hg}^{198}$ in an excited level which is 0.41 Mev above the ground level of Hg^{198}. About 95 per cent of these excited nuclei go to ground level by emitting a 0.41-Mev γ ray. The others go to ground level by internal conversion, 3 per cent in the K shell, 1 per cent in the L shell, and 0.3 per cent in the M shell. The X-ray-emission spectra are characteristic of mercury ($Z = 80$), not gold.

The chemical identification of a number of radioactive nuclides among the transuranium elements has been made or confirmed by observations of the L-series X rays of $_{90}\text{Th}, _{91}\text{Pa}, _{92}\text{U}, _{93}\text{Np}, _{94}\text{Pu}, _{95}\text{Am}$, and $_{96}\text{Cm}$ (B18).

Nuclear Isomers. Nuclear isomers are long-lived excited levels of nuclei, in which the decay by internal conversion and γ-ray emission to the ground level is measurably delayed (Chap. 6, Sec. 6). Many nuclear isomers are sufficiently long-lived to permit them to be isolated chemically and to be dealt with as a parent radioactive substance. The isomeric transition to the ground level involves no change in Z. Consequently, the X rays which are associated with the isomeric transition by internal conversion will be characteristic of the Z of the parent radioactive element, even if its ground level is a β-ray emitter (for example, $_{51}\text{Sb}^{122}$). This X-ray-emission property is useful in identifying nuclear isomers, especially in those cases in which isomeric transitions are in competition with β-ray emission from the excited level (for example, $_{49}\text{In}^{115}$).

Problems

1. The wavelengths of the $K_{\alpha1}$ line and of the K edge (for ionization of the K shell) are given below, in angstrom units (A), for a number of elements.

Element	$_6$C	$_{13}$Al	$_{29}$Cu	$_{42}$Mo	$_{73}$Ta	$_{92}$U
$K_{\alpha1}$, A......	44.54	8.3205	1.5374	0.7078	0.2149	0.12640
K_{edge}, A.....	43.5	7.9356	1.3774	0.6197	0.1836	0.10658

(a) Make a new table, expressing $K_{\alpha1}$ and K_{edge} energy in kev.
(b) Test the simple Bohr theory: $(h\nu)_{K_{\text{edge}}} = m_0c^2(\alpha^2/2)Z^2 = 0.0136Z^2$ kev,

and $(h\nu)_{K_{\alpha 1}} = 0.0136Z^2 \tfrac{3}{4}$ kev, for these elements. Do the experimental values approach the theoretical values for large Z or for small Z? What is the physical reason for this?

(c) Does the ratio of K_{edge} to $K_{\alpha 1}$ energy approach the theoretical value of $\tfrac{4}{3}$ for small Z or for large Z? What physical reason is there for this behavior?

2. The wavelength of the L_α X rays of Ag, I, and Pt are 4.1456, 3.1417, and 1.3103 A. Taking the atomic numbers of Ag and I as known (47 and 53), determine the atomic number of Pt.

3. A source of $_{30}Zn^{69}$ emits a continuous negatron β-ray spectrum, a single γ ray of about 0.44 Mev, and a line spectrum of conversion electrons as shown at the left. The decay scheme is one of the two shown below.

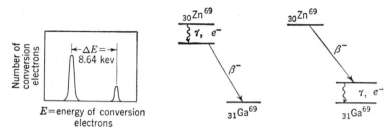

E=energy of conversion electrons

The X-ray energies for various lines of $_{29}Cu$ and $_{32}Ge$ are

Element	Z	K_α, kev	L_α, kev
Cu	29	8.06	0.93
Ge	32	9.89	1.19

Determine, with the aid of Moseley's law, which of the two possible decay schemes is actually followed.

5. *The Displacement Law*

Comparative studies of the chemical properties of the radioactive decay products of uranium and thorium first led Soddy (S58) to enunciate his so-called displacement law in 1914. In its original form the displacement law simply stated that any element which is the product of an α-ray disintegration is found in the Mendeleev periodic table two columns to the left of the parent radioactive element, while the product of a β-ray disintegration is found one column to the right of its parent. For example, thorium is found in group IV of the periodic table (Appendix F), while the product of its α-ray decay has chemical properties which are indistinguishable from those of radium, in group II. This product, mesothorium-1, happens to be a β-ray emitter, and so is its daughter product, mesothorium-2. The product of these two successive β transformations is radiothorium, which has chemical properties which put it again in group IV. In series-decay notation, we have simply:†

$$_{90}Th^{232} \xrightarrow{\alpha} {}_{88}MsTh_1^{228} \xrightarrow{\beta} {}_{89}MsTh_2^{228} \xrightarrow{\beta} {}_{90}RdTh^{228} \xrightarrow{\alpha}$$

† It was, of course, the fact that Th and RdTh differ in atomic weight by four

Since Soddy's day several other types of radioactive decay have been discovered. These are summarized in Table 5.1, with their characteristic shifts in atomic number.

TABLE 5.1. THE SHIFT IN ATOMIC NUMBER ASSOCIATED WITH VARIOUS TYPES OF SPONTANEOUS NUCLEAR TRANSFORMATIONS

Type of radioactive transformation	Usual symbol	Atomic number of initial state, or parent	Atomic number of final state, or daughter
Alpha decay.................	α	Z	$Z - 2$
Positron beta decay..........	β^+	Z	$Z - 1$
Electron capture.............	EC	Z	$Z - 1$
Gamma ray..................	γ	Z	Z
Internal conversion..........	e^-	Z	Z
Isomeric transition...........	IT	Z	Z
Neutron emission............	n	Z	Z
Negatron beta decay.........	β^-	Z	$Z + 1$

A self-evident extension of Soddy's displacement law applies to all types of nuclear reactions. Thus if boron ($Z = 5$) captures an α ray and emits a neutron, the product of the reaction has to have a nuclear charge of $Z + 2 = 7$, and it therefore must be an isotope of nitrogen. This reaction is written more compactly as $B(\alpha,n)N$. A few of the best-known nuclear type reactions, such as the (α,n) reaction, are listed in Table 5.2 with the change in atomic number which they produce.

TABLE 5.2. THE SHIFT IN ATOMIC NUMBER ASSOCIATED WITH SOME COMMON NUCLEAR TYPE REACTIONS
(α = alpha, n = neutron, p = proton, d = deuteron, γ = gamma ray)

Type of nuclear reaction			Atomic number of target	Atomic number of product
(α,n)			Z	$Z + 2$
(α,p)	(d,n)		Z	$Z + 1$
	(d,p)	(n,γ)	Z	Z
	(d,α)	(n,p)	Z	$Z - 1$
		(n,α)	Z	$Z - 2$

The atomic number Z for many artificially produced radioactive substances has been determined by applications of the displacement law. For example, neptunium ($_{93}Np$) and plutonium ($_{94}Pu$) were first assigned their atomic numbers from studies of the negatron β decay of $_{92}U^{239}$ which was formed in the reaction $U^{238}(n,\gamma)U^{239}$. A part of this series is

units (because of the one α decay in the chain), but have identical chemical properties, which formed the type of evidence on which Soddy based his suggestion of the existence of isotopes.

$$_{92}U^{238} + _{0}n^{1} \rightarrow _{92}U^{239} \xrightarrow[23 \text{ min}]{\beta} _{93}Np^{239} \xrightarrow[2.3 \text{ d}]{\beta}$$

$$_{94}Pu^{239} \xrightarrow[24,400 \text{ yr}]{\alpha} _{92}U^{235} \xrightarrow{\alpha} \cdots$$

Similarly, atomic-number assignments were first made for americium ($_{95}$Am), curium ($_{96}$Cm), berkelium ($_{97}$Bk), and californium ($_{98}$Cf) from applications of the displacement law. All these have been confirmed subsequently by observations of their L-series X-ray spectra as excited by internal conversion or by electron-capture transitions.

Problems

1. A uranium target is bombarded with high-energy α rays, and then at some later time the following three chemically distinct radioactive elements are separated from the target.

Element	Principal radiations	Half-period
1	α, γ, X ray	490 yr
2	β^-, γ, X ray	6.6 d
3	X ray (no β^-, β^+, or γ ray)	40 d

Each of these three elements emits the *same* line spectrum of X rays, which is characteristic of a certain atomic number Z. The $L_{\alpha 2}$ line of this spectrum has a quantum energy of 13.79 kev. It is known that the $L_{\alpha 2}$ line of $_{96}$Cm (curium) has a quantum energy of 14.78 kev, while the $L_{\alpha 2}$ line of $_{90}$Th (thorium) has an energy of 12.84 kev.

(*a*) From the X-ray data, determine the atomic number Z of the atoms which emit the 13.79-kev $L_{\alpha 2}$ line.

(*b*) Determine the atomic number of element 1, and state what physical process gives rise to the X rays accompanying its radioactive decay.

(*c*) Same as (*b*) for element 2.

(*d*) Same as (*b*) for element 3.

2. In the series decay of $_{92}U^{235}$ to its final stable product, seven α particles and four negatron β rays are emitted.

(*a*) Deduce the nuclear charge and mass number of the final product of this decay series.

(*b*) If the wavelength of the $K_{\alpha 1}$ line of $_{92}U^{235}$ is 0.1267 A, calculate the wavelength to be expected for the $K_{\alpha 1}$ line of the stable atoms formed in (*a*).

(*c*) The observed value for the $K_{\alpha 1}$ line of Pb is 0.165 A. Assuming the discrepancy to be due to the assignment of a value of unity to the screening constant, what value of the screening constant would be required to make Moseley's law check with experiment? Is this value reasonable? If not, are there any other factors which would cause a departure from Moseley's law?

(*d*) Give an approximate expression for the ratio of the volume of the nucleus of $_{92}U^{235}$ to that of the nucleus of the nuclide formed in (*a*).

3. Mention several types of experimental evidence which show that the atomic numbers of H, He, and Li are 1, 2, and 3 and are not, for example, 2, 3, and 4. How many of these observations depend, for their interpretation, on theories which have been convincingly verified by independent experiments?

CHAPTER 2

Radius of Nuclei

We now turn our attention to the experimental and theoretical evidence concerning the *size* and the *shape* of atomic nuclei.

The α-ray-scattering experiments, which we have reviewed in Chap. 1, first showed that the positive charge in each atom is confined to a very small region within the atom. On grounds of symmetry, this positive region was thought of as being spherical in shape and as being located in the center of the atom. It was therefore called the *nucleus*. The original observations on α-ray scattering showed only that the nucleus was not reached by α rays whose closest distance of approach to the center of the atom is about 30×10^{-13} cm for the case of gold (Chap. 1, Fig. 3.3) and several other heavy elements.

Bohr's theory of the origin of atomic spectra met with sufficient initial success in 1913 to constitute an acceptable confirmation of his assumption that the principal part of the atomic mass is also located within this small, positively charged, central nucleus.

Experimental studies of the spatial distribution of nuclear charge and mass involve a wide variety of nuclear and atomic phenomena. The finite size of the nucleus acts only as a minor perturbation in some phenomena, e.g., in the fine-structure splitting of X-ray levels in heavy atoms. At the opposite extreme, there are phenomena in which the nuclear radius plays the predominant role, such as in the elastic scattering of fast neutrons. In this chapter we shall review and correlate a number of different types of evidence which have been brought to bear upon the question of nuclear radius.

1. *The Growth of Concepts Concerning the Size of Nuclei*

By 1919, Rutherford (R45) himself had shown that deviations from the scattering which would be produced by a pure coulomb field are experimentally evident when α rays are scattered by the lightest elements. In these light elements, the closest distance of approach, for the energy of α ray used, was of the order of 5×10^{-13} cm. The noncoulomb scattering observed at these close distances became known as *anomalous scattering*. The distance of closest approach at which anomalous scattering begins was identified as the first measure of the nuclear radius.

We shall discuss the contemporary interpretation of the experiments on anomalous scattering later, in Sec. 7. Here it is worth noting that the early efforts to interpret these results, in terms of collisions which could be described by classical mechanics, led to the introduction of a number of *ad hoc*, if not bizarre, models of the inner structure of atomic nuclei. Some of these models had to stay in vogue for over a decade because no more acceptable model could then be found. These included Chadwick's (C13) "platelike α particle" and Rutherford's (R49) "core-and-neutral-satellite" nucleus which contained a small positively charged core, surrounded by other nuclear matter in the form of heavy but uncharged satellites moving in quantized orbits, under a central $1/r^5$ law of attraction which was attributed to polarization of the neutral satellites. The early speculations on the idea of neutrons are visible in this model.

The gradual development of the wave mechanics, in the latter 1920s, provided the first basis for scrapping many of these classical *ad hoc* models of the structure of nuclei. A wide variety of nuclear phenomena can now be interpreted on a basic of wave mechanics, as it is applied to a few newer nuclear models which are reasonably self-consistent. Much progress has been made, but much remains to be done.

A variety of experimental evidence (Chap. 8) *now is consistent with the concept that nuclei are composed of only protons and neutrons* and that these two forms of the *"nucleon,"* or heavy nuclear particle, are bound together by very strong short-range forces. The shape of the nucleus is taken as being substantially *spherical*, because for a given volume this shape possesses the least surface area and will therefore provide maximum effectiveness for the short-range binding forces between the nucleons in the nucleus.

The existing experimental evidence also supports the view that within the nucleus the spatial distribution of positive charge tends to be substantially uniform; thus the protons are not appreciably concentrated at the center, the surface, the poles, or the equator of the nucleus. Small asymmetries of the distribution of positive charge are present in some nuclei, as is known from the fact that many nuclei have measurable electric quadrupole moments. These charge asymmetries are discussed in Chap. 4; here we note that, if the positive charge in a nucleus is regarded as uniformly distributed within an ellipsoid of revolution, then the largest known nuclear quadrupole moment (of Lu^{176}) corresponds to a major axis which is only 20 per cent greater than the minor axis of the assumed ellipsoid. In most nuclei the corresponding ellipticity is only of the order of 1 per cent. Therefore we may regard most nuclei as having nearly uniform and spherical internal distributions of positive charge.

In the succeeding sections of this chapter we shall discuss nine varied types of experimental evidence, which lead to the conclusion that *the nuclear volume is substantially proportional to the number of nucleons in a given nucleus.* This means that nuclear matter is essentially incompressible and has a constant density for all nuclei. The variations from constant density, due to nuclear compressibility, appear to be only of the order of 10 per cent (P30, F17).

The number of nucleons in a nucleus is equal to the *mass number A;* hence in the constant-density model, the nuclear radius R is given by

$$R = R_0 A^{\frac{1}{3}} \qquad (1.1)$$

where the nuclear unit radius R_0 probably varies slightly from one nucleus to another but is roughly constant for A greater than about 10 or 20.

There is no single, precise definition of nuclear radius which can be applied conveniently to all nuclear situations. The nuclear surface cannot be defined accurately but is always a surface outside of which there is a negligible probability of finding any of the nuclear constituents. In the following sections, we shall see that there are several specific definitions of nuclear radius, each applying to the particular experimental situation used for evaluating the radius. Even with this vagueness, the nuclear radius can usually be specified within 1×10^{-13} cm or less, or the order of 10 or 20 per cent. Thus nuclear radii are actually known with much greater accuracy than the radii of the corresponding whole atoms.

The trend of present experimental results is toward a nuclear unit radius in the domain of

$$R_0 = (1.5 \pm 0.1) \times 10^{-13} \text{ cm} \qquad (1.2)$$

for phenomena which depend primarily on the "specifically nuclear" forces between nucleons. Such radii are called *nuclear-force radii,* and they serve to describe phenomena in which coulomb effects are minor or absent, such as the cross section for elastic scattering of fast neutrons by nuclei.

All other common experimental methods involve the use of some charged particle as a probe of the nuclear interior. These phenomena therefore depend partly upon coulomb effects and also on any non-coulomb interactions which may exist between the probing particle (proton, electron, μ meson, etc.) and nuclear matter. For phenomena which depend primarily upon the spatial distribution of the nuclear charge, the trend of present experimental results is toward a different and smaller nuclear unit radius, in the domain of

$$R_0 = (1.2 \pm 0.1) \times 10^{-13} \text{ cm} \qquad (1.3)$$

This smaller radius is closely related to the radius of the "proton-occupied volume," and it is now commonly called the *electromagnetic radius* of the nucleus.

As the mass numbers of all nuclei run from $A = 1$ to about 240, we see from Eq. (1.1) that nuclear radii can be expected to extend from about 2×10^{-13} to 10×10^{-13} cm. Aluminum, for which $A = 27$, has a nuclear radius of about $1.4 \times 27^{\frac{1}{3}} \times 10^{-13} = 4.2 \times 10^{-13}$ cm, and a nuclear volume of $\frac{4}{3}\pi(4.2 \times 10^{-13})^3$ cm^3 = 3.1×10^{-37} cm^3. In aluminum there are

$$\frac{(2.7 \text{ g/cm}^3)(6 \times 10^{23} \text{ atoms/mole})}{27 \text{ g/mole}} = 6 \times 10^{22} \text{ atoms/cm}^3$$

and the total volume of their nuclei is 2×10^{-14} cm^3. Thus the nuclei occupy only about 2 parts in 10^{14} of the volume of the solid material. *The density of nuclear matter is then of the order of* 10^{14} g/cm^3.

It is useful to classify the types of nuclear experiments through which nuclear radii are measured, according to the physical principles involved in each method. This is done in Table 1.1. It will be noted that only one of the methods can be interpreted clearly by classical electrodynamics. The other types of experiments give results which are sometimes in direct violation of the predictions of classical mechanics. Many of

TABLE 1.1. CLASSIFICATION OF NINE PRINCIPAL METHODS FOR MEASURING
THE RADII OF NUCLEI

Experimental phenomenon which depends on nuclear radius	Basic physical principles on which the method rests	Type of mechanics which can provide an interpretation of the observations
1. Energy of radioactive β-ray decay (coulomb-energy difference between isobars)	Coulomb energy of a sphere of charge	Classical
2. Isotope shift in line spectra 3. Elastic scattering of fast electrons by nuclei 4. Characteristic electromagnetic radiations from μ-mesonic atoms 5. Fine-structure splitting of ordinary electronic X-ray levels in heavy atoms	Coulomb potential inside a sphere of charge	Wave
6. Lifetime of α-ray emitters 7. Anomalous scattering of α rays 8. Cross section for nuclear reactions produced by charged particles, such as (α,n), (α,2n), (p,n), etc.	Penetration of nuclear potential barriers by charged particles	Wave
9. Elastic scattering of fast neutrons by nuclei	Diffraction of uncharged matter waves	Wave

these are historically important experiments which first showed the limitations of classical mechanics. In each case, the wave mechanics has provided an acceptable interpretation of the observations.

It should be pointed out that only the ninth method (scattering of fast neutrons) gives experimental results which are independent of nuclear charge. The other eight methods all involve the combined effects of nuclear charge and nuclear size.

2. *Coulomb-energy Difference between Isobars*

The electrostatic energy of a charge q which is uniformly distributed throughout a sphere of radius R is

$$W_{coul} = \frac{3}{5}\frac{q^2}{R} \tag{2.1}$$

If the nuclear charge Ze is considered as smeared out throughout the nuclear volume, then the coulomb energy W_{coul} of a nucleus is

$$W_{coul} = \frac{3}{5}\frac{e^2}{R} Z^2 \tag{2.2}$$

If, on the other hand, each proton remains an aloof and discrete entity inside the nucleus and interacts electrostatically with all other protons, but not with itself, then the coulomb energy would be

$$W_{coul} = \frac{3}{5}\frac{e^2}{R} Z(Z - 1) \tag{2.3}$$

The difference between Eqs. (2.2) and (2.3) depends simply on the model chosen and becomes smaller as Z increases.

a. Classical Theory of the Coulomb-energy Radius. The coulomb energy is a measurable quantity in some nuclei which undergo radioactive β decay. For such nuclei Eq. (2.2) constitutes one of our definitions of nuclear radius. This particular radius is often called the *coulomb-energy radius* R_{coul} whenever it is necessary to distinguish it from other definitions of the size of the same nucleus.

In β decay, the mass number A does not change, and therefore R does not change, at least not within the domain of validity of the constant-density model $R = R_0 A^{\frac{1}{3}}$. In positron β decay, the nuclear charge Z of the parent decreases to $Z - 1$ for the decay product. Therefore, in positron β decay, a decrease in nuclear coulomb energy occurs, and this energy is a part of the total disintegration energy. Conversely, in negatron β decay, in which Z changes to $Z + 1$, the corresponding increase in coulomb energy detracts from the transition energy which would be available otherwise. For positron β decay the decrease in coulomb energy is, using Eq. (2.2),

$$\Delta W_{coul} = \frac{3}{5}\frac{e^2}{R} [Z^2 - (Z - 1)^2] = \frac{3}{5}\frac{e^2}{R} (2Z - 1) \tag{2.4}$$

where Z is the atomic number of the *parent* nucleus.

In positron β decay, one proton in the parent nucleus changes into a neutron in the product nucleus. Simultaneously a neutrino and a positron (the β ray) are expelled from the nucleus. The total energy of the nuclear transition [Chap. 3, Eq. (4.23)] is seen as the total kinetic energy of the neutrino and positron (equal to the maximum kinetic energy E_{max} of the positron β-ray spectrum) plus the rest energy of the positron $(m_0 c^2)$ and of the neutrino (zero) plus the recoil energy of the residual nucleus (negligible for β decay). Thus the total *nuclear* disintegration energy can be written as

$$E_{max} + m_0 c^2 \tag{2.5}$$

This energy is supplied by and is equal to the change of total mass energy between the parent and the product nucleus. In the particular positron β decay transitions which we shall consider here, the dominant contribution to the transition energy comes from the change in nuclear coulomb energy. The remaining contributions include any difference in the nucleon binding energies but come almost entirely from the difference between the rest mass of the parent proton M_p and the product neutron M_n. We shall derive general expressions for all these contributions in Chap. 11, but we need not await those generalizations in order to establish the one special case with which we are concerned here.

Fowler et al. (F61, B130) first drew attention to a group of nuclei, which undergo β decay, in which the binding energy due to short-range nuclear forces between the nucleons is substantially the same in both parent and product. These nuclei constitute a series of so-called *mirror nuclei*, one example of which is the isobaric pair, O^{15} and N^{15}, in which O^{15} undergoes positron β decay to stable N^{15}, according to

$$_8O^{15} \rightarrow {}_7N^{15} + \beta^+ \text{ (positron)} + \nu \text{ (neutrino)}$$

Any pair of nuclei which can be made from each other by interchanging all protons and neutrons are called mirror nuclei. A number of known positron emitters from $_6C^{11}$ to $_{21}Sc^{41}$ have just one more proton than the number of neutrons. Their stable decay products each contain just one more neutron than the number of protons; hence each of these particular pairs of parent and product are mirror nuclei. In each of these nuclei, the mass number A is

$$A = 2Z - 1 \tag{2.6}$$

where Z is the atomic number of the parent positron β-decaying nucleus.

With respect to the specifically nuclear attractive binding forces between nucleons, there is good experimental evidence that the nuclear binding between two neutrons is the same as that between two protons, if the classical coulomb repulsion between the protons is not included as a "specifically nuclear force." The analysis of the mirror nuclei, carried out below, supports other evidence (Chap. 10) that the nuclear forces are symmetrical in neutrons and protons.

As an example, consider the isobaric pair $_8O^{15}$ and $_7N^{15}$ as composed of some kind of core or central nuclear structure containing seven neutrons and seven protons and thus corresponding in this case to $_7N^{14}$. Adding one proton to this structure gives us O^{15}, whereas adding one neutron gives us N^{15}. We can express the mass of the O^{15} and N^{15} nuclei as the mass of their constituent protons and neutrons, diminished by the net binding energy resulting from the short-range attractive nucleon forces and from repulsive coulomb forces. Then the mass of the nuclei of O^{15} and of N^{15} can be expressed as

$$M(O^{15})$$
$$= [(7M_p + 7M_n) + M_p] - [\text{(nucleon binding energy)} - W_{coul}] \tag{2.7}$$
$$M(N^{15})$$
$$= [(7M_p + 7M_n) + M_n] - [\text{(nucleon binding energy)} - W_{coul}] \tag{2.8}$$

With respect to the total binding energy given in the second square brackets, note that, because the coulomb force is a repulsive one, the coulomb energy is a negative term and is deducted from the binding energy term which describes the attractive nuclear forces between the nucleons. The difference between the nuclear mass of parent and product is then the difference between Eqs. (2.7) and (2.8) and can be written

$$M_p - M_n - \Delta W_{\text{nuc}} + \Delta W_{\text{coul}} \qquad (2.9)$$

in which ΔW_{coul} has been defined and evaluated in Eq. (2.4), while ΔW_{nuc} is the difference between the nucleon binding energies in the pair of mirror nuclei.

We now equate the two expressions (2.5) and (2.9) for the nuclear disintegration energy, obtaining

$$E_{\text{max}} = \Delta W_{\text{coul}} - m_0 c^2 - (M_n - M_p) - \Delta W_{\text{nuc}} \qquad (2.10)$$

which, on substitution of the measured values, $m_0 c^2 = 0.51$ Mev and $(M_n - M_p) = 1.29$ Mev, becomes

$$E_{\text{max}} = \Delta W_{\text{coul}} - 1.80 \text{ Mev} - \Delta W_{\text{nuc}} \qquad (2.11)$$

We wish to compare this equation with the experimental data on the β decay energy of the mirror nuclei for which $A = 2Z - 1$, to see whether their radii R are consistent with the constant-density model $R = R_0 A^{\frac{1}{3}}$. Then Eq. (2.4) becomes

$$\Delta W_{\text{coul}} = \frac{3}{5} \frac{e^2}{R} (2Z - 1) = \frac{3}{5} \frac{e^2}{R} A$$

$$= \frac{3}{5} \frac{e^2}{R_0} A^{\frac{2}{3}} \qquad (2.12)$$

Substituting this into Eq. (2.11), we have as the theoretical connection between E_{max}, A, and R_0

$$E_{\text{max}} = \frac{3}{5} \frac{e^2}{R_0} A^{\frac{2}{3}} - 1.80 \text{ Mev} - \Delta W_{\text{nuc}} \qquad (2.13)$$

Table 2.1 lists the current (H61) experimental values of the maximum positron energy E_{max} for this series of mirror nuclei. None of these emits any γ rays; hence the total kinetic energy of the decay process is simply E_{max}. These values of E_{max} are plotted in Fig. 2.1 against $A^{\frac{2}{3}}$.

It will be noted that the best straight line through the data intersects the $A = 0$ axis at -1.80 Mev. Thus in Eq. (2.13) we find $\Delta W_{\text{nuc}} = 0$, providing independent evidence for the general symmetry of nuclear forces in protons and neutrons. The slope of the best straight line is a measure of the nuclear unit radius R_0 and corresponds in Fig. 2.1 to about

$$R_0 \simeq 1.45 \times 10^{-13} \text{ cm} \qquad (2.14)$$

Dotted lines for $R_0 = 1.4$ and 1.6×10^{-13} cm are shown; they clearly bracket the probable value of R_0 for the coulomb-energy unit radius.

TABLE 2.1. MEASURED VALUES (H61, R24) OF THE MAXIMUM KINETIC
ENERGY E_{max} OF THE POSITRON β DECAY SPECTRA IN THE MIRROR NUCLEI
FOR WHICH $A = 2Z - 1$

Z Element A	E_{max}, Mev	Z Element A	E_{max}, Mev
5 B 9		14 Si 27	3.48
6 C 11	0.99	15 P 29	3.94
7 N 13	1.24	16 S 31	3.9
8 O 15	1.68	17 Cl 33	4.1
9 F 17	1.72	18 A 35	4.4
10 Ne 19	2.18	19 K 37	4.6
11 Na 21	2.50	20 Ca 39	5.1
12 Mg 23	2.99	21 Sc 41	4.94
13 Al 25		22 Ti 43	

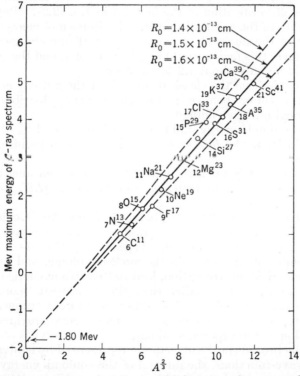

Fig. 2.1 Positron β-ray energy vs. the two-thirds power of mass number A for the mirror nuclei $A = 2Z - 1$.   The intercept of -1.80 Mev on the energy axis shows that the nuclear forces in these nuclei are essentially symmetric in neutrons and protons.   The fact that the experimental values tend to lie on a straight line indicates that these nuclei have *coulomb-energy radii* which correspond to a constant-density model $R_{coul} = R_0 A^{\frac{1}{3}}$, with the slope of the data giving the particular value $R_0 \simeq 1.45 \times 10^{-13}$ cm for the nuclear unit radius.

If we had used the discrete-proton model, Eq. (2.3), then we would have had

$$\Delta E_{\text{coul}} = \frac{3}{5} \frac{e^2}{R} (2Z - 2) \tag{2.15}$$

$$E_{\text{max}} = \frac{3}{5} \frac{e^2}{R_0} (A^{\frac{2}{3}} - A^{-\frac{1}{3}}) - 1.80 \text{ Mev} - \Delta W_{\text{nuc}} \tag{2.16}$$

When the experimental data on E_{max} are plotted against the quantity $(A^{\frac{2}{3}} - A^{-\frac{1}{3}})$, the fit is about the same as that in Fig. 2.1, and the nuclear unit radius is again about $R_0 \simeq 1.45 \times 10^{-13}$ cm. Future improvements of the data in Table 2.1 should be watched. In the meantime, the data fit the smeared-proton model of Eqs. (2.2) and (2.13) and the discrete-proton model of Eqs. (2.3) and (2.16) about equally well.

The coulomb-energy unit radius $R_0 \simeq 1.45 \times 10^{-13}$ cm obtained from Fig. 2.1 is in good agreement with the nuclear radii obtained for these same nuclei by other methods. We may note that this constitutes some degree of verification of the factor $\frac{3}{5}$ in Eq. (2.2). Physically, the factor $\frac{3}{5}$ is due to the assumed uniform distribution of charge throughout the volume of the nucleus. For example, if all the charge were on the nuclear surface, this factor would be $\frac{1}{2}$ instead of $\frac{3}{5}$, and the coulomb unit radius would be only about 1.2×10^{-13} cm.

We conclude from the classical analysis of the β decay energies that

1. Nuclear charge behaves as though uniformly distributed throughout a spherical nuclear volume.

2. The coulomb-energy radii of nuclei having $A \leq 41$ follow the constant-density model $R_{\text{coul}} = R_0 A^{\frac{1}{3}}$ and have a unit radius of $R_0 \simeq 1.45 \times 10^{-13}$ cm.

3. The specifically nuclear binding forces between nucleons are substantially symmetrical in neutrons and protons. [$\Delta W_{\text{nuc}} = 0$, in Eq. (2.13).]

b. Electromagnetic Radius Deduced from the Coulomb-energy Radius. The coulomb-energy unit radius is a purely classical quantity, defined by Eq. (2.12). Some other types of experiments, which depend upon coulomb potentials within the nuclear volume, and which require a wave-mechanical interpretation, lead to "electromagnetic radii" which are about 20 per cent smaller than these classical "coulomb-energy radii," for the same nuclei. These differences can be reconciled, at least qualitatively, when wave-mechanical refinements are invoked in the interpretation of the experimental data.

When the protons in the nucleus are represented by equivalent central potential wave functions, the integral of the coulomb energy throughout the nuclear volume reduces, in the case of $A = 2Z$, to (B48, C42)

$$W_{\text{coul}} \simeq \frac{3}{5} \frac{e^2}{R} [Z(Z - 1) - 0.77Z^{\frac{4}{3}}] \tag{2.17}$$

instead of the classical expression of Eq. (2.2). The correction term $-0.77Z^{\frac{4}{3}}(3e^2/5R)$ arises from the antisymmetry of the proton wave functions and is called the *coulomb exchange energy*. For $Z \sim 15$, the square bracket in Eq. (2.17) is roughly 10 per cent smaller than the corresponding classical expression. Consequently, the experimental values of W_{coul} lead, on this model, to nuclear radii R which are roughly 10 per cent smaller than the classical coulomb-energy radii.

A second wave-mechanical correction arises when a more detailed model is assumed for the interior of the nucleus. When individual quantum numbers are assigned to each of the nucleons in the nucleus, in accord with the shell model of nuclei (Chap. 11), it can be presumed that in many of the mirror nuclei the transforming nucleon is initially in a state of greater orbital angular momentum than most of the other protons. As a consequence of its greater angular momentum, the individual β transforming proton would not correspond to a uniformly distributed charge, but its radial distribution would tend to be concentrated near the nuclear surface. If this is so, then the β transforming proton is one whose contribution to the total coulomb energy is less than that for a uniformly distributed proton, because its charge distribution is concentrated near the surface of the nucleus, where the coulomb potential due to the rest of the nucleus is smallest. The over-all distribution of charge within the nucleus is still regarded as uniform. When this concept is quantified, the presumed reduction in coulomb effectiveness of the individual β transforming proton requires a corresponding decrease in the effective radius of the nuclear charge distribution, in order to match the experimental values of W_{coul}. In this way, the observed coulomb-energy differences for mirror isobars (Fig. 2.1) can be reconciled with an effective, or *electromagnetic, radius*, whose unit value is as small as (C42)

$$R_0 \simeq 1.2 \times 10^{-13} \text{ cm} \qquad (2.18)$$

The distinction between this wave-mechanical "electromagnetic unit radius" and the classical "coulomb-energy unit radius" ($R_0 \simeq 1.45 \times 10^{-13}$ cm) lies entirely in the nuclear models which are used for the theoretical interpretation of the experimental data. If the transforming proton is thought of as a probe for studying the coulomb potential in the interior of the nucleus, then the wave-mechanical interpretation represents a means of correcting the observed coulomb energies for the specifically nuclear (noncoulomb) effects between the transforming proton and the other nucleons in the nucleus.

Problems

1. Calculate the total coulomb energy of a homogeneous distribution of charge Ze occupying a sphere of radius R.

2. Calculate a predicted value for the maximum kinetic energy of the positron β rays emitted by (a) $_{12}Mg^{23} \rightarrow \beta^+ + _{11}Na^{23}$ and (b) $_{13}Al^{25} \rightarrow \beta^+ + _{12}Mg^{25}$, using the constant-density nuclear model, with $R = 1.45 \times 10^{-13}A^{\frac{1}{3}}$.

(c) Compare with observed values found in tables.

3. Prepare a graph similar to Fig. 2.1 but based on the classical discrete-proton model, and compare the correlation between E_{max} and A for the discrete-proton model and the uniformly distributed proton (classical) model.

3. *Coulomb Potential inside a Nucleus*

a. Isotope Shift in Line Spectra. The size of nuclei and the distribution of the charge within nuclei produce small but observable effects, known as *isotope shift*, in certain atomic spectra. The origin of these effects can be understood on classical grounds, but their quantitative interpretation requires evaluation of the wave functions for atomic electrons near, and indeed inside, the nucleus. To the extent that these electron wave functions are known, the observations on the isotope shift in the line spectra of heavy elements can be interpreted in terms of the classical size and charge density of the "proton-occupied volume" within the atomic nucleus. In the present section we shall examine only those aspects of the isotope-shift phenomena which shed light on the questions of nuclear size and charge distribution. Chapter 7 contains a discussion of isotope shift and its implications with respect to nuclear mass and nuclear moments.

Most of the quantitative aspects of atomic spectroscopy are determined in one way or another by the total charge Ze of the atomic nucleus. Thus the energy of an electronic state depends upon the energy of the atomic electron in the central coulomb potential $U(r)$ provided by the nucleus. The s electrons have a finite probability of being at and near the origin $(r = 0)$ of this central field and hence of being actually inside the nuclear radius $(r = R)$. If $\psi^2(r)$ represents the probability density of the electron being at distance r from the center of the nucleus, then the potential energy of this electron e in the central field $U(r)$ could be written as

$$e \int_0^\infty \psi^2(r)U(r)4\pi r^2\,dr \tag{3.1}$$

If the nucleus had no finite size, then the potential $U(r)$ would have its simple coulomb value

$$U(r) = \frac{Ze}{r} \tag{3.2}$$

for all values of r. For a nucleus of finite size, Eq. (3.2) is valid only outside the nucleus, i.e., for $r > R$, where R is the nuclear radius. If the nuclear charge Ze is spread in a uniform layer on the outer surface only of the nucleus, then the potential $U_s(r)$ everywhere inside this simple shell of charge would be the same as the value at the surface, which is the constant value

$$U_s(r) = \frac{Ze}{R} \tag{3.3}$$

On the other hand, if the nuclear charge is distributed uniformly throughout the nuclear volume, then the internal potential $U_v(r)$ at distance r from the center can be shown to be

$$U_v(r) = \frac{Ze}{R}\left[\frac{3}{2} - \frac{1}{2}\left(\frac{r}{R}\right)^2\right] \quad \text{for } r \leq R \tag{3.4}$$

The decrease of the atomic binding energy of an s electron, because of the finite size of the nuclear charge, can then be calculated (B123, B83), using the potential $U_s(r)$ for the surface-charged nucleus, or $U_v(r)$ for the volume-charged nucleus. The decrease ΔW in electron binding energy can then be represented, for the volume-charged nuclear model, as

$$\Delta W = e \int_0^R \psi^2(r)(U_v - U)4\pi r^2 \, dr \qquad (3.5)$$

where $U = Ze/r$ for the point nucleus and the integration extends only throughout the nuclear volume $0 \le r \le R$.

The three potentials, $U(r)$ for a point nucleus, $U_s(r)$ for a surface-charged nucleus, and $U_v(r)$ for a uniform volume-charged nucleus, are compared graphically in Fig. 3.1, from which a qualitative idea of the

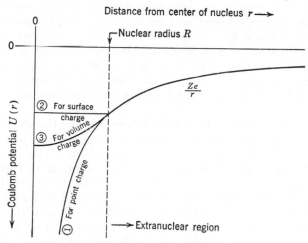

Fig. 3.1 Comparison of the electrostatic potential inside nuclei, on three models. Curve 1 is for a point nucleus of zero radius, Eq. (3.2). Curve 2 is for a nucleus having all its charge on its surface, Eq. (3.3). Curve 3 is for a nucleus in which the charge is uniformly distributed throughout the nuclear volume, Eq. (3.4).

direction and relative magnitude of the resulting energy changes ΔW can be obtained.

It is found experimentally that there are a number of elements having two or more stable isotopes which differ in mass number by two units. Examples include $_{82}Pb^{204}$, Pb^{206}, Pb^{208}; $_{80}Hg^{196}$, Hg^{198}, Hg^{200}, Hg^{202}, Hg^{204}, etc. Under high resolution, certain lines in the emission spectra of these elements will be found to consist of a number of closely spaced components, one for each isotope of even mass number. These are the isotope-shifted components in which we are interested here. Each of these components is itself single, i.e., it is not further split into a group of hyperfine-structure components, because the nuclear moments are zero-valued. [The actual spectral "line" will generally contain other components which arise from one or more stable isotopes whose mass numbers are odd, for example, Pb^{207}, Hg^{201}, etc. These components from odd isotopes will be further split by hyperfine structure (Chap. 5) because of their finite nuclear moments.]

The largest isotope shifts are usually found in transitions between atomic configurations containing different numbers of s electrons, especially the deeply penetrating $6s$ electrons, as, for example, in the transition $5d^n6p \rightarrow 5d^n6s$. The isotope shift is seen to represent the energy difference $\Delta W_1 - \Delta W_2$ between two evaluations of Eq. (3.5), once for each of the two isotopes concerned. That these differences are finite shows at once that the nuclear radii R_1 and R_2 are different for the two isotopes. More exactly, the "electromagnetic radius," which is the true meaning of R in Eq. (3.5), is found to be larger in the heavier isotope. Of course, the nuclei of both isotopes contain the same number of protons and have the same total charge Ze. If the heavier isotope were formed from the lighter isotope by merely adding two extra neutrons to the outside of the lighter nucleus, and not also increasing the proton-occupied volume, there would be no isotope shift. Thus the very existence of *the isotope shift shows that the protons in the nuclei of both isotopes move in regions of different size.* The penetrating s electron serves as a useful probe because it spends a part of its time actually within the nuclear volume, and its noncoulomb interactions with protons and neutrons are negligible.

In principle, we should be able to determine how the nuclear charge is distributed inside the nucleus by appropriate application of Eq. (3.5), and its corollaries, to suitable spectroscopic data. This cannot yet be done with high accuracy because of both theoretical and experimental inadequacies. The existing status has been ably summarized, especially by Brix and Kopfermann (B123), Foster (F59), and Bitter and Feshbach (B61). In general, it is found that the data are in better agreement with theory when the nuclear charge is assumed to be *uniformly* distributed throughout the nucleus than when the charge is assumed to lie only on the nuclear surface. This same conclusion was reached as early as 1932 by Breit (B111) in his excellent pioneer work on the theoretical explanation of isotope shift in heavy elements as an effect due to the finite extension of the nuclear volume.

Figure 3.2 summarizes (B123, F59, B61) the present experimental data on 19 elements in a form which allows comparison with the predictions of existing theory. It will be noted that the observed isotope shifts are about one-half as large as the calculated shifts if the nuclear unit radius is taken as $R_0 = 1.5 \times 10^{-13}$ cm. Although the variations are large, the data are not in disagreement with an electromagnetic nuclear unit radius as small as $R_0 = 1.1 \times 10^{-13}$ cm. Important improvements in the use of isotope shift as a means of studying the inner structure of nuclei (C52) can be expected as spectroscopic investigations are extended to enriched or separated isotopes and as advances are made in the theory (B83), especially with regard to the evaluation of the electronic wave functions.

b. Elastic Scattering of Fast Electrons by Nuclei. Nuclei are essentially transparent to electrons, and their mutual interactions are confined to the long-range coulomb force.   Bombardment of nuclei by high-energy electrons (say, > 10 Mev) therefore provides an opportunity for probing the coulomb field in the interior of the nucleus, with a minimum of interference from noncoulomb effects.   Classically, the collision diameter between an incident 10-Mev electron and a Cu nucleus ($Z = 29$) is $b \simeq 4 \times 10^{-13}$ cm.   The rationalized de Broglie wavelength for the same

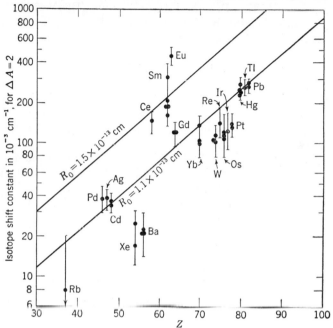

Fig. 3.2   Comparison of observed and theoretical values of the isotope shift in 19 elements, in the form developed by Brix and Kopfermann (B123, F59).   The "isotope-shift constant," shown on the vertical scale, is proportional to the absolute term difference, which contains several other parameters of the optical transition.   The isotope-shift constant depends strongly on Z and only weakly on the mass number A; hence the data for each element are plotted against Z, using an average value of the mass.   The solid lines are the predicted values for nuclei containing a uniform distribution of charge within a sphere whose *electromagnetic radius* is $R = 1.5 \times 10^{-13} A^{\frac{1}{3}}$ cm, or $R = 1.1 \times 10^{-13} A^{\frac{1}{3}}$ cm.   All theoretical and experimental values correspond to the shifts when ΔR corresponds to $\Delta A = 2$.   [*From Bitter and Feshbach* (B61).]

electron is $\lambda \simeq 20 \times 10^{-13}$ cm.   Therefore, by the criteria noted in Chap. 1, classical collision theory is invalid because $b/\lambda < 1$.   For incident electron energies below about 2 Mev the nucleus can be considered as a point charge.   Then the relativistic wave-mechanical theory of electron scattering developed by Mott gives good agreement with experiments (Chap. 19).   At higher energies, and for nuclei of finite size, the incident electron may be considered as penetrating into the nucleus and thereby experiencing a smaller coulomb potential (Fig. 3.1).   The cross sections for elastic scattering of swift electrons are therefore diminished, especially at large scattering angles.

Physically, high-energy electron scattering is closely related to isotope shift, and both can be shown to depend primarily upon the volume integral of the potential taken throughout the nucleus (F43, B61, B83). Experimentally, marked deviations from the scattering which would be expected from a point nucleus have already been observed for a variety of elements, with electrons of 15.7 Mev (L37), 30 to 45 Mev (P22), and 125 to 150 Mev (H58). Present interpretations (B61) of these experiments give reasonable agreement with a uniformly charged nucleus having an electromagnetic unit radius in the domain of

$$R_0 \simeq (1.1 \pm 0.1) \times 10^{-13} \text{ cm} \qquad (3.6)$$

Both the theory and the experiments are difficult, but the importance of the results suggests that marked improvements can be forecast.

c. Characteristic Electromagnetic Radiations from μ-Mesonic Atoms.
The properties and behavior of π mesons and μ mesons are now rather well understood (M14, M15, P29, B63, T25). Bombardment of nuclei by high-energy particles or photons (≥ 150 Mev) (B11) can evoke the emission of positive or negative π mesons from the target nuclei. Because of their positive charge, the π^+ mesons are repelled by nuclei. They decay with a mean life of about 0.02 μsec into μ^+ mesons, which in turn decay into positive electrons, according to

$$\pi^+ \rightarrow \mu^+ + \nu \qquad \tau \simeq 0.02 \ \mu\text{sec} \qquad (3.7)$$
$$\mu^+ \rightarrow e^+ + 2\nu \qquad \tau \simeq 2.15 \ \mu\text{sec} \qquad (3.8)$$

where ν represents a neutrino. In terms of the rest mass m_0 of the electron or positron, the rest masses of the π meson and μ meson are close to $M_\pi \simeq 276 m_0$, $M_\mu \simeq 212 m_0$, for both the positive and negative varieties.

The negative π mesons are especially interesting. If they are not captured by a nucleus, they decay into a μ^- meson in a manner analogous to Eq. (3.7). The resulting μ^- meson has the opportunity of being slowed down by ionizing collisions to a substantially thermal velocity and then of being captured by a nucleus. This capture process is thought to proceed somewhat as follows: A μ^- meson, having the same spin and charge as an atomic electron, may be expected to fall into a hydrogenlike "Bohr orbit" around the nucleus. This atomic energy level should be similar to an energy level for an atomic electron, except that the "Bohr radius" around a point nucleus, $(n\hbar)^2/Ze^2m_0$, will be about 200 times smaller than the corresponding radius for an electron, because of the larger rest mass of the μ^- meson. As all the mesonic "atomic states" are unoccupied, the μ^- meson will fall to states of lower energy, the transitions being accompanied by the emission of characteristic electromagnetic radiation, or of Auger electrons, and taking place within a time of the order of 10^{-13} sec. In the "K shell," the μ^- meson will be some 200 times nearer the nucleus than is a K-shell electron, and the μ^- meson will therefore spend an appreciable fraction of the time within the nucleus itself. The life of the individual μ^- meson may terminate by a charge-exchange reaction with a proton in the nucleus

$$\mu^- + p \rightarrow n + \nu \qquad \tau \sim 10^{-7} \left(\frac{82}{Z}\right)^4 \qquad \text{sec} \tag{3.9}$$

or by radioactive decay into an energetic electron and two neutrinos

$$\mu^- \rightarrow e^- + 2\nu \qquad \tau \simeq 2.15 \ \mu\text{sec} \tag{3.10}$$

In Pb, the radius of the μ-mesonic K shell for a point nucleus ($R_0 = 0$) would be only about 3×10^{-13} cm, while the L shell would have a radius of about 12×10^{-13} cm. Transitions between the $2p_{\frac{3}{2}}$ and $1s$ states, which correspond to the $K_{\alpha 1}$ X ray in the ordinary electronic case, would be expected to have an energy release of 16.4 Mev. When μ mesons are captured into Pb atoms, the $2p_{\frac{3}{2}} \rightarrow 1s$ electromagnetic radiation is observed, but it has a quantum energy of only 6.02 Mev (F52).

This enormous shift from the transition energy expected for a point nucleus is identical in principle with the isotope shift in ordinary electronic line spectra, but it is greatly exaggerated by the smallness of the μ^--mesonic Bohr radii. For light elements the theoretical shift in the energy of the $1s$ level (K shell) is approximately proportional to $R^2 Z^4$, where $R = R_0 A^{\frac{1}{3}}$ is the radius of an assumed uniform distribution of charge within the finite volume of the nucleus (F52, C42, W33). The shift is greatest for the $1s$ level, much less for the $2p_{\frac{1}{2}}$ level (L_{II} level in X-ray notation), and still smaller for the $2p_{\frac{3}{2}}$ level (L_{III} level). Figure 3.3 summarizes the experimental measurements by Fitch and Rainwater (F52) of the quantum energies for the characteristic μ^--mesonic "X rays" arising from the $2p_{\frac{3}{2}} \rightarrow 1s$ transition in nine elements. Comparison with the calculated values for a point nucleus ($R_0 = 0$) and for a homogeneously charged nucleus having a unit radius of $R_0 = 1.3 \times 10^{-13}$ cm is shown by the two curves in Fig. 3.3. Clearly, the measured transition energies in μ^--mesonic atoms correspond to a unit radius which is slightly smaller than 1.3×10^{-13} cm. When computed numerically, the data for Ti, Cu, Sb, and Pb give nuclear *electromagnetic unit radii*, $R_0 = R/A^{\frac{1}{3}}$, which fall in the domain

$$R_0 = (1.20 \pm 0.03) \times 10^{-13} \text{ cm} \tag{3.11}$$

if the distribution of charge is assumed to be homogeneous within the nucleus.

The nearly ideal character of the μ^- meson (or the electron) as a probe for the distribution of nuclear charge arises from its exceedingly weak interaction with nucleons, as well as from its large mass, as was first pointed out by Wheeler (W32, W33). The role of the μ^- meson has been beautifully pictorialized by Wheeler (W33):

To it (the μ^- meson), the nucleus appears as a transparent cloud of electricity. The degree of transparency is remarkable, in view of the density of nuclear matter, 1 or 2 $\times 10^5$ tons/mm³. Thus a meson moving in the K orbit of lead spends roughly half of its time within the nucleus, and in this period of $\sim 4 \times 10^{-8}$ sec traverses about 5 meters of nuclear matter, or $\sim 10^{17}$ g/cm². This circumstance means that the major features of the nuclear electric field uniquely determine the mesonic energy level diagram. Conversely, these features can be determined by the position of the mesonic states.

The fine-structure splitting of the μ-mesonic "X-ray" spectra appears to have been resolved in the experiments by Fitch and Rainwater (F52). In electronic X-ray spectra, the electron spin of $\frac{1}{2}$ gives rise to the two fine-structure levels $2p_{\frac{1}{2}}$ (or L_{II}) and $2p_{\frac{3}{2}}$ (or L_{III}). Transitions from these to the $1s_{\frac{1}{2}}$ (or K) level constitute the $K_{\alpha 2}$ and $K_{\alpha 1}$ lines, respectively, and the $K_{\alpha 1}$ energy slightly exceeds the $K_{\alpha 2}$ energy. For the μ-mesonic levels in Pb, a fine-structure splitting of about 0.2 Mev is observed for the

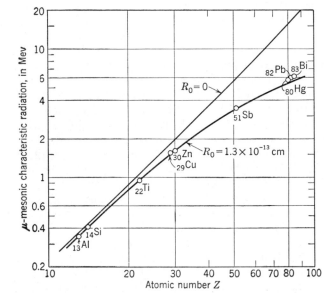

Fig. 3.3 Energies of the μ-mesonic transition $2p_{\frac{3}{2}} \rightarrow 1s$, which corresponds to the $K_{\alpha 1}$ line in electronic X-ray spectra. Calculated values for point nuclei ($R_0 = 0$) and for homogeneously charged nuclei with $R_0 = 1.3 \times 10^{-13}$ cm are shown by the two curves. The experimental values obtained by Fitch and Rainwater (F52) are shown as open circles.

corresponding fine-structure doublet. When higher accuracy becomes available, observations of this type may be useful for measuring the magnetic moment of the μ meson, as well as verifying the values of nuclear electromagnetic radius.

In marked contrast with μ mesons, π mesons have a very strong interaction with nucleons. Hence π^--mesonic atoms are not useful for studying nuclear radii. In elements of low Z (Be, C, O), the π-mesonic K-shell radius lies outside the nuclear volume, and for these cases the $2p \rightarrow 1s$ transition in π^--mesonic atoms has been observed also (C4, S68).

d. Fine-structure Splitting of Electronic X-ray Levels in Heavy Atoms. Each ordinary electronic X-ray level is also reduced slightly in energy because of the finite size of the nucleus, but of course the effect is minute when compared with the shifts in μ^--mesonic atoms. Schawlow and Townes (S7) have summarized the pertinent theoretical and experimental material, showing that a homogeneously charged nucleus, whose electromagnetic unit radius is $R_0 \simeq 1.5 \times 10^{-13}$ cm, should produce a change of only 0.3 per cent in the fine-structure separation of the $2p_{\frac{3}{2}}$ and the $2p_{\frac{1}{2}}$ levels for $Z = 90$. The effect diminishes rapidly for smaller Z. Schawlow and Townes found that the existing data on the $K_{\alpha 1}$-$K_{\alpha 2}$ X-ray fine-structure separations for $Z = 70$ to 90 appear to be in agreement with an electromagnetic unit radius of $R_0 \simeq 1.5 \times 10^{-13}$ cm. Further improvements in X-ray energy measurements and in the theory of X-ray fine structure would be required in order to improve the accuracy of this estimate of R_0.

Problems

1. Show that the electrostatic potential $U(r)$ at distance r from the center of a sphere containing a uniform density of positive charge is

$$U(r) = \frac{q}{R}\left[\frac{3}{2} - \frac{1}{2}\left(\frac{r}{R}\right)^2\right] \qquad \text{for } r \leq R$$

if q is the total charge in a sphere whose radius is R.

2. In the sphere containing a uniform density of positive charge, evaluate the electric field strength for all values of r and show that the field strength is continuous at the boundary $r = R$.

4. *The Nuclear Potential Barrier*

a. Coulomb Barrier with Rectangular Well. Imagine that originally we have a mercury nucleus, whose charge is $Ze = 80e$, fixed with its center at the origin of coordinates in Fig. 4.1, and let r be the distance between this center and the center of a stationary α particle whose charge is $ze = 2e$. We will call the potential energy zero when the separation between these two nuclei is very large. Imagine that we can, by some means, push on the α particle and force it closer to the mercury nucleus. Then for any large separation distance r, the work done will equal the electrostatic potential energy $(Ze)(ze)/r$ between the charges.

As we decrease r, we finally come to some small distance which is of the order of the nuclear radius of mercury. Here the short-range attractive nuclear force begins to be felt, and as we continue to decrease r this attractive force increases until it just equals the coulomb repulsive force, leaving zero net force between the two particles. On decreasing r still further, the attractive force dominates, and the two nuclei coalesce. If the original nucleus was $_{80}Hg^{204}$, then the addition of an α particle ($_2He^4$) forms $_{82}Pb^{208}$. Now $_{82}Pb^{208}$ is a stable nucleus. It does not spontaneously emit α rays. Therefore its total energy may be taken tentatively as less than that of the original system of widely separated Hg^{204} and He^4 nuclei.

Figure 4.1 is the usual schematic illustration of the potential energy

U as a function of distance r for such a system. The simplest model is the so-called *square-well model*, in which the potential energy of the bound system is taken as constant and equal to $-U_0$ for $r = 0$ to $r = R$, while at $r = R$ the potential energy increases discontinuously to the coulomb value $(Ze)(ze)/R$. For $r > R$ the potential energy consists only of the coulomb energy $(Ze)(ze)/r$. In the square-well model, R is called the *nuclear radius*.

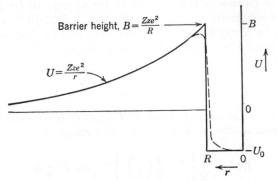

Fig. 4.1 Schematic diagram of the nuclear potential barrier between a nucleus of charge Ze and a particle of charge ze at a center-to-center distance r.

The coulomb region from $r = R$ to $r = \infty$ is called the *coulomb potential barrier*, while the entire curve of U against r is called the *nuclear potential barrier*. The so-called *height B* of the barrier is its maximum value, which occurs at the nuclear radius, and is

$$B = \frac{(Ze)(ze)}{R} \tag{4.1}$$

Note that the height of the barrier depends on the incident particle's charge ze.

b. Modifications Due to Short-range Forces. Clearly the discontinuities in this square-well model are unrealistic. The simplest refinement is to replace the infinite potential slope at $r = R$ by a finite but very steep slope and to round off the bottom and top of the potential well, as indicated by the dotted potential curve in Fig. 4.1. When this is done, the definition of nuclear radius requires reconsideration; it will generally be some parameter entering the analytical functions which are chosen to describe the new potential well. In some such models the nuclear radius remains defined as the position of the top of the rounded-off barrier, i.e., the distance for zero force. In other models the nuclear radius may signify the point of maximum slope within the potential well. Moreover, the distance r signifies only the separation between the centers of the two particles, Ze and ze. Each particle has an assignable radius of its own, and the radius of the ze particle will obviously depend on whether ze is a proton, an α particle, or even some larger nucleus such as, say, O^{16}. If Ze and ze are regarded as uniformly charged spheres, it is well known that their external electrostatic fields are the same as though their entire charges were located at their geometrical centers.   There is, therefore, no ambiguity in the coulomb potential $(Ze)(ze)/r$, as long as r is larger than the sum of the radii of the two particles.

In contrast to coulomb forces, the attractive nuclear forces between nucleons are short-range forces and are significant only when the distance between two nucleons is of the order of 2×10^{-13} cm or less, or pictorially when the two nucleons are practically in contact with each other.   Then, when r is essentially equal to the sum of the radii of Ze and ze, the nuclear attractive forces depend on the separation between the *surfaces* of the two particles, while the coulomb forces are still dependent on the separation of the *centers* of the two particles.

This marked difference in behavior between short-range and long-range forces has to be recognized in those models in which nuclear radius signifies some particular point along the mutual potential energy curves of Fig. 4.1, such as the top of the barrier.   For example, if Ze and ze are spheres having radii R_Z and R_z, then their surfaces first make contact when the centers are separated by $r = R_Z + R_z$.   For smaller values of r the two nuclei begin to merge, and the attractive nuclear forces become stronger because of the overlap.   At some separation $r < (R_Z + R_z)$ the nuclear attractive forces will just balance the coulomb repulsion.   This is the "top of the barrier," and it corresponds to some separation r lying between the radius of the larger nucleus and the sum of the radii.   When the joint action of long-range and short-range forces is included in the model, a more realistic definition of barrier height B, in terms of nuclear radii R_Z and R_z, would be

$$B = \frac{Zze^2}{r} \tag{4.2}$$

where $$R_Z < r < (R_Z + R_z) \tag{4.3}$$

Although there are many alternative choices for the parameter called the nuclear radius, the actual absolute difference between them is usually less than about 10 to 20 per cent.   In nonspecialized discussions, the terms nuclear radius and coulomb barrier height generally connote the simpler and approximate relationships of Eq. (4.1), that is, $B = Zze^2/R$, with $R = R_0 A^{\frac{1}{3}}$.

c. **Inability of Classical Mechanics to Reconcile α-Ray Scattering and Radioactive α Decay.**   According to classical electrodynamics, an α particle which is released with no initial velocity from the surface of a radioactive nucleus, such as uranium, will be accelerated away from the residual nucleus whose charge is Ze.   When the α particle and residual nucleus have become widely separated, the total kinetic energy gained must be just equal to their initial electrostatic potential energy $(Ze)(ze)/r$, where r was their initial separation when the α particle was released. Classically, we would require that r be substantially equal to the nuclear radius.

In the particular case of the radioactive decay of $_{92}U^{238}$, α rays are spontaneously emitted for which the kinetic energy of disintegration is 4.2 Mev.   Equating this to an initial potential energy between the α

particle ($z = 2$) and the residual nucleus ($Z = 90$) gives $r = 61 \times 10^{-13}$ cm as the apparent initial separation and hence as a classical measure of the radius of the decay product $_{90}Th^{234}$.

We have noted in Chap. 1 that the α-ray-scattering experiments had shown the presence of only a pure coulomb field down to much smaller distances than this, at least for the case of gold. Rutherford first overcame the technical difficulties of preparing and studying thin scattering foils of uranium and showed (R49) that the 8.57-Mev α rays which are emitted by a source of ThC' are scattered classically by uranium nuclei. In central collisions, these 8.57-Mev α rays can approach to within 30×10^{-13} cm of the center of the uranium nucleus. Therefore the potential is surely purely coulomb down to this distance, as shown in Fig. 4.2.

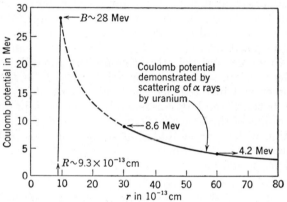

Fig. 4.2 The coulomb barrier to α particles ($z = 2$) for Z about 90 or 92. The region of the solid curve beyond $r = 30 \times 10^{-13}$ cm is verified by direct α-ray-scattering experiments. If the 4.2-Mev α rays of U^{238} were emitted classically, i.e., over the top of the barrier, the coulomb potential would have to stop at about $r = 60 \times 10^{-13}$ cm. Classical mechanics is therefore unable to provide a simple, single model which can account for both observations.

This observation marked the complete breakdown of classical mechanics in dealing with nuclear interactions. The α rays from uranium could not have been emitted from the top of a potential barrier of 4.2-Mev height at a distance of 61×10^{-13} cm if the coulomb potential actually extends in to 30×10^{-13} cm or less.

The subsequent development of the wave-mechanical treatment of the interaction of charged particles with potential barriers provided a satisfactory description of a wave mechanism whereby particles can penetrate through potential barriers, instead of being required to surmount them as they must in classical mechanics. In the case of the uranium decay, the evidence is now that the radius of the residual nucleus is about 9.3×10^{-13} cm and the barrier height about 28 Mev. The 4.2-Mev uranium α ray has a probability of only 10^{-39} of penetrating this barrier in a single collision, either from outside or inside the nucleus, but this is sufficient to account for the known radioactive half-period of U^{238}. We shall review the wave-mechanical principles of the transmission of material particles through potential barriers in the next section.

Problems

1. Consider the details of the collision of a 5.3-Mev α particle with a nucleus of chromium ($_{24}Cr^{52}$). Calculate the following parameters, and locate them on a plot of the coulomb barrier.

(a) The approximate radius R of the chromium nucleus.

(b) The barrier height to α rays.

(c) The initial kinetic energy in C coordinates.

(d) The de Broglie wavelength of the relative motion in C coordinates.

(e) The collision diameter b, or distance of closest approach, for a head-on collision.

2. Show that an approximate expression for the height of any nuclear coulomb barrier is

$$B = 0.76zZ^{\frac{2}{3}} \quad \text{Mev}$$

if $R_0 = 1.5 \times 10^{-13}$ cm.

3. The α rays emitted by U^{238} have a kinetic energy of 4.180 Mev.

(a) Compute the total kinetic energy of the disintegration by evaluating and adding in the kinetic energy of the residual recoil nucleus.

(b) At what distance from the center of a U^{238} nucleus would this α ray have been released with zero velocity, if it acquires its final velocity by classical coulomb repulsion from the residual nucleus?

4. What is the distance of closest approach between a U^{238} nucleus and an incident 8.57-Mev α ray for the case of 160° scattering in the laboratory coordinates?

5. *Wave Mechanics and the Penetration of Potential Barriers*

The introduction of wave mechanics brought tremendous improvements in the theoretical description of the interaction of atomic particles. Classical mechanics was then recognized as a special case of the more general wave mechanics. Classical mechanics is the limit approached by the wave mechanics when very large quantum numbers are involved. In describing atomic interactions the quantum numbers are commonly small; therefore classical mechanics can usually give only approximate solutions, and wave mechanics is required for the more accurate solutions.

The inherent stability and reproducibility of atomic and nuclear systems are to be attributed to the existence of discrete quantized states of internal motion, which are the only states in which the system can exist.

a. **Particles and Waves.** The original quantum concepts of Planck (1901) introduced the quantum of action h into the theory of electromagnetic waves. Thus the frequency of oscillation ν when multiplied by h was recognized as representing the quantum of energy $h\nu$ in electromagnetic radiation. A number of physical phenomena involving light were soon found to be best understood by descriptions in terms of these photons. The simplest classical properties of electromagnetic waves in free space are the frequency ν, wavelength λ, and the phase, or wave, velocity c, connected by the relationship $\lambda\nu = c$. The introduction of

Planck's constant h has the effect of introducing the characteristic corpuscular properties of energy, $W = h\nu$; of momentum, $p = W/c = h\nu/c$; and of relativistic mass, $M = W/c^2 = h\nu/c^2$, into the description of the physical behavior of these waves. This "dual" approach has been fruitful in the theoretical description of black-body radiation, of the photoelectric effect, of the Compton effect, and of many other phenomena. *Corpuscular properties are conferred on waves by the introduction of h.*

The "new quantum theory," or "quantum mechanics," or "wave mechanics," confers wave properties on corpuscles, also by the introduction of h. The wavelength of a photon can be expressed in terms of its momentum and Planck's constant as $\lambda = c/\nu = h/(h\nu/c) = h/p$. De Broglie (1924) first proposed the extension of this "definition" of wavelength to a description of corpuscles. Thus an electron, proton, neutron, or any other material particle whose momentum is p is said to have a *de Broglie wavelength* of

$$\lambda = \frac{h}{p} \tag{5.1}$$

Due to the smallness of h, these wavelengths of material particles are usually of the order of atomic or of nuclear dimensions. As in the case of visible light or any other wave motion, phenomena in which the wavelength plays a role are confined to interactions involving obstacles whose linear dimensions are at least roughly comparable with the wavelength. In such interactions, *wave properties are conferred on corpuscles by the introduction of h.*

In response to the question "Is an electron a wave or a particle?" the late E. J. Williams said, "It is, of course, a particle. The wave properties are not properties of the electron but properties of quantum mechanics."

Experimentally, there is abundant evidence that electrons, protons, neutrons, and other particles exhibit diffraction phenomena (and hence can be described by waves) in their collisions with atoms and nuclei. Thus, as was first shown by Davisson and Germer (1927), the regularly arranged atoms in a crystal of zinc act as a diffraction grating for incident monoenergetic electrons whose energy is of the order of 100 ev and whose corresponding de Broglie wavelength is comparable with the distance between successive planes of zinc atoms in the crystal. In addition to exhibiting *diffraction* maxima and minima in the reflected beam, the electrons could be shown to suffer *refraction* on entering the zinc crystal at an angle with the normal.† Similarly G. P. Thomson (1928) first obtained electron diffraction patterns by passing an electron beam through a thin film of metal composed of randomly oriented crystals. These diffraction patterns are similar in appearance to the powder diffraction patterns obtained with X rays.

b. Refractive Index. The experimental evidence by Davisson and Germer that a beam of electrons suffers refraction when entering a metal-

† An excellent summary of these and related experiments has been given, for example, by Richtmyer and Kennard (pp. 248–259 of R18).

lic single crystal at an angle with the normal suggests that a *refractive index* μ can be formulated for matter waves. An impinging free electron is attracted by the surface of a metal and, in the case of nickel, experiences a drop of about 18 volts in potential energy, and a corresponding increase of about 18 ev in its kinetic energy, as it passes through the surface into the metal. We note that the electron has a different velocity, momentum, and de Broglie wavelength outside and inside the metal. We want to express these as an equivalent index of refraction for matter waves.

In optics, the refractive index μ of a medium is defined (S76) in terms of the wave velocity as

$$\mu = \frac{\text{wave velocity in free space}}{\text{wave velocity in medium}} \tag{5.2}$$

Because the frequency remains constant, the refractive index is also given by

$$\mu = \frac{\text{wavelength in free space}}{\text{wavelength in medium}} \tag{5.3}$$

The *wave velocity* w (or "phase velocity") is a concept which applies strictly only to periodic fields which represent wave trains of infinite duration. For such fields the wave velocity is the product of the frequency ν and the wavelength λ, or

$$w = \lambda \nu \tag{5.4}$$

However, a wave train of finite extent, such as that representing a moving particle, cannot be represented in simple harmonic form by a single frequency. It must contain a mixture of frequencies in order that the wave train, under Fourier analysis, may have a beginning and an end. When two wave trains, having slightly different frequencies, are combined, their net amplitude as a function of both time and distance contains "beats," or "groups." These beats are propagated at a different velocity, known as the *group velocity* g, which can be shown (p. 331 of S76) to be given quite generally by

$$g = w - \lambda \frac{dw}{d\lambda} = \frac{d\nu}{d(1/\lambda)} \tag{5.5}$$

Turning to the wave-mechanical description of a moving particle, we write

$$\lambda = \frac{h}{p} \qquad \text{de Broglie} \tag{5.6}$$

$$\nu = \frac{W}{h} \qquad \text{Schrödinger} \tag{5.7}$$

in which the momentum p and total energy W have their usual classical values

$$W = \tfrac{1}{2}MV^2 + U \tag{5.8}$$

$$p = MV = \sqrt{2M(W - U)} \tag{5.9}$$

where M = mass of particle
V = velocity of particle (nonrelativistic)
U = potential energy of particle
Then the phase, or wave, velocity of the particle is

$$w = \lambda\nu = \frac{h}{p}\frac{W}{h} = \frac{W}{p} = \frac{V}{2} + \frac{U}{MV} = \frac{W}{\sqrt{2M(W-U)}} \tag{5.10}$$

On the other hand, the group velocity g, which can be obtained with the help of Eq. (5.5), is given by

$$\frac{1}{g} = \frac{d}{d\nu}\left(\frac{p}{h}\right) = \frac{d}{d\nu}\left(\frac{\sqrt{2M(W-U)}}{h}\right) = \frac{d}{d\nu}\left(\frac{\sqrt{2M(h\nu-U)}}{h}\right)$$

$$= \frac{M}{p} = \frac{1}{V} \tag{5.11}$$

or

$$g = V \tag{5.12}$$

Thus we have the important result that the group velocity g does in fact correspond, under Eqs. (5.6) and (5.7), to the classical velocity V of the moving particle. The phase, or wave, velocity w corresponds only to the velocity of propagation of the individual waves comprising the wave train, whereas the group velocity g is the velocity V at which the energy or the particle actually travels.

We may note in passing that the product of the wave velocity and the group velocity is a constant of the motion of the particle. Thus from Eqs. (5.10) and (5.11) we obtain the relationship

$$wg = \frac{W}{p}\frac{p}{M} = \frac{W}{M} \qquad \text{or} \qquad \frac{wg}{c^2} = \frac{W}{Mc^2} \tag{5.13}$$

We can now utilize some of these relationships to express in a variety of ways the effective refractive index μ for matter waves passing from one region (analogous to free space in the optical case and denoted by subscripts zero) to a second region (denoted without subscripts). From optics we have

$$\mu = \frac{w_0}{w} \tag{5.14}$$

and because wg = constant (c^2 for electromagnetic waves and W/M for nonrelativistic matter waves)

$$\mu = \frac{g}{g_0} \tag{5.15}$$

For matter waves, utilizing Eqs. (5.6) and (5.12), we have

$$\mu = \frac{V}{V_0} = \frac{p}{p_0} = \frac{\lambda_0}{\lambda} \tag{5.16}$$

Then particles which are represented as matter waves, upon passing from a region in which $U = U_0$ into a region in which the potential energy is U, experience a change of wavelength and momentum which corresponds to their having entered a medium whose refractive index is

$$\mu = \sqrt{\frac{W - U}{W - U_0}} \qquad (5.17)$$

If U varies with position, as it does in the potential field of a nucleus, we see that refraction phenomena analogous to those encountered in classical physical optics are to be expected. Indeed, if $U > W$, the equivalent index of refraction becomes an imaginary number, and we may expect phenomena which are analogous to the interaction of electromagnetic waves with conducting media, such as the reflection of light from metallic surfaces. Also, the wave interaction of a charged particle incident on a pure coulomb potential barrier $U(r) = Zze^2/r$ does yield refraction which is equal to the Rutherford scattering, and when the wave is incident on a barrier $U > W$, for which the kinetic energy is negative and the refractive index is imaginary, the incident wave does penetrate exponentially into the barrier and has a finite probability of penetrating through the barrier. The quantitative evaluations of these interactions are carried through as special solutions of the Schrödinger wave equation.

c. The Nonrelativistic Schrödinger Equation. The simplest differential equation which represents a traveling wave in a homogeneous medium is

$$\frac{\partial^2 \Psi}{\partial z^2} = \frac{1}{w^2} \frac{\partial^2 \Psi}{\partial t^2} \qquad (5.18)$$

where Ψ = amplitude of wave motion
  w = wave velocity
  z = distance in direction of propagation
  t = time

It is well known that this wave equation gives a correct description of elastic waves in a string or in a membrane, of sound waves, and of electromagnetic waves in nonconductors. This equation has a large number of solutions, which are applicable to a variety of particular physical situations.

For a plane wave in an isotropic, homogeneous medium we could use as solutions of this wave equation

$$\Psi = A \, \frac{\sin}{\cos} \, 2\pi(\nu t \pm z/\lambda) \qquad (5.19)$$

or

$$\Psi = A e^{\pm 2\pi i (\nu t \pm z/\lambda)} \qquad (5.20)$$

where $i = \sqrt{-1}$ and A is the amplitude of the wave. In all these solutions, $(\nu t - z/\lambda)$ represents travel in the $+z$ direction and $(\nu t + z/\lambda)$ represents travel in the $-z$ direction. This follows at once from the fact that

$$\left(\nu t - \frac{z}{\lambda} \right) = \text{const} \qquad (5.21)$$

represents a surface of constant phase. Differentiation gives

$$\frac{dz}{dt} = \nu\lambda = w \qquad (5.22)$$

so that $\nu\lambda = w$ is the velocity of propagation of any particular feature of the wave, i.e., the "phase velocity," or "wave velocity."

The periodic character of exponential solutions such as Eq. (5.20) is best seen from the conventional complex-plane presentation of complex numbers (p. 255 of S45) with the real parts plotted as abscissas and the imaginary parts plotted as ordinates. Then each complex quantity, such as $e^{-i\varphi}$, is represented by a point in the complex plane. Expansion in power series shows directly that

$$e^{i\varphi} = \cos\varphi + i\sin\varphi \qquad (5.23)$$
$$e^{-i\varphi} = \cos\varphi - i\sin\varphi \qquad (5.24)$$

Hence $e^{\pm i\varphi}$ returns to the same value when the argument φ changes by $2\pi, 4\pi, \ldots$, etc. Therefore $e^{\pm i2\pi\nu t}$ is periodic in time, with frequency ν.

In the general wave equation of Eq. (5.18) we can separate the variables if we elect to use only solutions of the form

$$\Psi = \psi(z)\vartheta(t) \qquad (5.25)$$

in which $\psi(z)$ is some function of position only and $\vartheta(t)$ is some function of time only. Then

$$\frac{\partial^2\Psi}{\partial z^2} = \frac{\partial^2\psi}{\partial z^2}\vartheta(t)$$

$$\frac{\partial^2\Psi}{\partial t^2} = \psi(z)\frac{\partial^2\vartheta}{\partial t^2}$$

and Eq. (5.18) becomes

$$\frac{\partial^2\psi}{\partial z^2}\vartheta(t) = \frac{1}{w^2}\psi(z)\frac{\partial^2\vartheta}{\partial t^2}$$

Separating the variables, we have two differential functions which must be equal to each other for all values of z and t and which therefore must be equal to some constant. We will call this separation constant $-k^2$. Then Eq. (5.18) can be written

$$\frac{1}{\psi(z)}\frac{\partial^2\psi}{\partial z^2} = \frac{1}{w^2}\frac{1}{\vartheta(t)}\frac{\partial^2\vartheta}{\partial t^2} = -k^2 \qquad (5.26)$$

Solutions of these two separated differential equations include

$$\psi(z) = \frac{\sin}{\cos}(kz) \qquad \text{and} \qquad \psi(z) = e^{\pm ikz} \qquad (5.27)$$

$$\vartheta(t) = \frac{\sin}{\cos}(wkt) \qquad \text{and} \qquad \vartheta(t) = e^{\pm iwkt} \qquad (5.28)$$

In any of these forms, there is spatial periodicity when kz changes by 2π. Hence the corresponding motion has the wavelength λ, where

$$k = \frac{2\pi}{\lambda} \qquad (5.29)$$

The reciprocal length k, defined by Eq. (5.29), is of broad general usefulness and is called the *wave number*, or the *propagation number*.

Among the periodic solutions of the wave equation, we then arbitrarily choose the particular time-dependent function $\vartheta(t) = e^{-iwkt}$, and we write the *wave function* Ψ from Eqs. (5.25) and (5.28) as

$$\Psi = \psi(z)e^{-2\pi i\nu t} \qquad (5.30)$$

in which $\psi(z)$ is any function of position only. When Eq. (5.30) is substituted into the general wave equation, Eq. (5.18), we obtain at once

$$\frac{\partial^2\psi}{\partial z^2} + \left(\frac{2\pi}{\lambda}\right)^2 \psi = 0 \qquad (5.31)$$

In a conservative system, the total energy W of a particle remains constant and equal to the sum of the kinetic energy $p^2/2M$ and the potential energy U. Then

$$W = \frac{p^2}{2M} + U \qquad (5.32)$$

or

$$p^2 = 2M(W - U)$$

and substitution of the de Broglie wavelength $\lambda = h/p$ gives

$$k^2 = \left(\frac{2\pi}{\lambda}\right)^2 = \left(2\pi\frac{p}{h}\right)^2 = \frac{8\pi^2 M(W - U)}{h^2} \qquad (5.33)$$

Then Eq. (5.31) can be written

$$\frac{\partial^2\psi}{\partial z^2} + \frac{8\pi^2 M(W - U)}{h^2} \psi = 0 \qquad (5.34)$$

which is known as "Schrödinger's amplitude equation," or simply as *Schrödinger's equation.* In three dimensions, Schrödinger's equation becomes

$$\nabla^2\psi + \frac{8\pi^2 M(W - U)}{h^2} \psi = 0 \qquad (5.35)$$

where ∇^2 is the Laplacian operator and, in the cartesian coordinates x, y, z, has the value

$$\nabla^2 \equiv \frac{\partial^2}{\partial x^2} + \frac{\partial^2}{\partial y^2} + \frac{\partial^2}{\partial z^2}$$

Equation (5.31) is a completely classical wave equation and is valid whenever the spatial wave function ψ oscillates with a *constant* spatial periodicity λ. The transition to wave mechanics begins with the identification of λ as the de Broglie wavelength of matter waves, Eq. (5.33). The de Broglie relationship $\lambda = h/p$ can be regarded as an empirical relationship given by the experiments of Davisson and Germer and of others. Schrödinger's amplitude equation, Eq. (5.34) or (5.35), is therefore semiclassical, provided that λ, and consequently U, is constant. The transition to wave mechanics is completed when we postulate that Schrödinger's amplitude equation may be valid even when λ, and therefore U, is not a constant but varies from point to point. The validity and usefulness of Schrödinger's amplitude equation, when λ and therefore U and p are functions of the spatial coordinates, rest solely on the considerable success which this equation has experienced in matching experimental results.

The Schrödinger Equation Containing Time. Schrödinger's more general wave equation containing time makes use of the total wave function Ψ of Eq. (5.25) rather than just the spatial portion ψ.

Using Eqs. (5.6), (5.7), and (5.19), we could represent a plane wave moving in the $+z$ direction by

$$\Psi = A \sin \frac{2\pi}{h} (Wt - pz) + B \cos \frac{2\pi}{h} (Wt - pz) \qquad (5.36)$$

A differential equation which satisfies Eq. (5.32) could then be constructed (R18) by utilizing: (1) the time derivative $\partial\Psi/\partial t$ in order to obtain a term proportional to W, (2) the derivative $\partial^2\Psi/\partial z^2$ to obtain a term proportional to p^2, and (3) the product $U\Psi$ to obtain a term proportional to U. Such a differential equation could have the form

$$\frac{\partial\Psi}{\partial t} = a \frac{\partial^2\Psi}{\partial z^2} + bU\Psi \qquad (5.37)$$

If we substitute Eq. (5.36) into Eq. (5.37) and equate coefficients of sine terms, and separately of cosine terms, so that Eq. (5.37) is valid for all t and z, then Eq. (5.32) is satisfied only if $A^2 = -B^2$, or $A = \pm iB$. The choice of sign here is arbitrary, and most commonly the minus sign is chosen, so that $A = -iB$. Then the wave function of Eq. (5.36) becomes

$$\Psi = A e^{-(2\pi i/h)(Wt-pz)}$$
$$= e^{-(2\pi i/h)Wt}\psi \qquad (5.38)$$

where ψ contains the spatial parameters and the amplitude but is independent of time. With this choice of sign, the conservation-of-energy law, Eq. (5.32), is satisfied by Eq. (5.37) if its coefficients are chosen as

$$\frac{4\pi M}{ih} \frac{\partial\Psi}{\partial t} = \frac{\partial^2\Psi}{\partial z^2} - \frac{8\pi^2 M}{h^2} U\Psi \qquad (5.39)$$

which is *Schrödinger's wave equation containing time.* If the opposite choice of sign were made, that is, $A = iB$, then the signs of the time-dependent factor in Eq. (5.38) and of the left side of Eq. (5.39) would both change.

Equation (5.38) is equivalent to Eq. (5.30) and, when substituted into Eq. (5.39), leads at once to Eq. (5.31) and hence to Schrödinger's amplitude equation, Eq. (5.34), with which the great majority of our considerations will be concerned.

d. Physical Significance of the Wave Function. Equations (5.34) and (5.35) have the form of "amplitude equations" representing the maximum value of Ψ at x, y, z, as t takes on all possible values. In Eq. (5.25) we defined Ψ as a wave function in which time can be expressed as a separate factor. Therefore the phase of Ψ at any instant is the same throughout the entire wave. Such waves are called *standing waves*, in contrast with traveling waves in which there is at any instant a progression of phase along the wave train. For bound states, the solutions ψ of Schrödinger's equation therefore represent the maximum values, or amplitudes of the standing wave Ψ as functions of position.

The amplitude ψ is generally complex for the de Broglie waves which describe unbound material particles. This is in contrast to the analogous amplitude equations of acoustics and of electromagnetic theory, where the amplitudes are real quantities. However, in those theories, the state of the wave is described by *two* quantities, for example, ε and H in the electromagnetic wave. As N. F. Mott (M68) has clearly pointed out, the de Broglie wave can also be thought of as defined by two quantities, say, f and g, but for convenience these are combined to form a complex wave function, $\Psi = f + ig$.

It is necessary that, at each point in space, the de Broglie wave associated with a particle must be described by some parameter which does not oscillate with time. The absolute value $|\Psi|$ of the wave function is such a quantity, if we regard the real and imaginary parts, f and g, of the wave function as 90° out of phase. For example, if A is some slowly varying real function of z, we could regard a particular wave as made up of a real component

$$f = A \cos 2\pi \left(\nu t - \frac{z}{\lambda} \right)$$

and an imaginary component, 90° out of phase, given by

$$g = A \sin 2\pi \left(\nu t - \frac{z}{\lambda} \right)$$

Then if $\Psi = f + ig$

we form the complex conjugate of Ψ, represented by the symbol Ψ^*, by changing the sign of i wherever i occurs in Ψ, obtaining

$$\Psi^* = f - ig$$

Then the product of Ψ and its complex conjugate Ψ^* is

$$|\Psi|^2 \equiv \Psi\Psi^* = f^2 + g^2 = A^2 \tag{5.40}$$

which is a real quantity equal to the square of the absolute value of Ψ and written $|\Psi|^2$.

It will be noted that, when time is expressed as a separate factor, as in Eqs. (5.25) and (5.38), the absolute values of the total wave function Ψ and of the spatial wave function ψ are equal. Thus

$$|\Psi|^2 = \Psi\Psi^* = \psi\psi^* e^{-2\pi i\nu t} e^{+2\pi i\nu t} = \psi\psi^* = |\psi|^2 \qquad (5.41)$$

The solutions ψ of the wave equation which can correspond to physical reality must be everywhere *single-valued*, *finite*, and *continuous*, and they must *vanish at infinity*.

In optics, the intensity of light is proportional to the square of the amplitude of the electromagnetic wave. In wave mechanics, the square of the amplitude is analogously related to the density of particles at a given position in space. When ψ is normalized so that

$$\int |\psi|^2 \, dx \, dy \, dz = 1 \qquad (5.42)$$

then

$$|\psi|^2 \, dx \, dy \, dz \qquad (5.43)$$

corresponds physically to the probability of finding the particle described by ψ in the volume element, $dx \, dy \, dz$, if an experiment could be performed to look for it. Thus the physical interpretation of $|\psi|^2$ is that it is a probability density, with *dimensions of cm^{-3}*. Therefore $|\psi|^2$ is large in those regions of space where the particle is likely to be and is small elsewhere.

In the physical interpretation of solutions of the wave equation, the wave function Ψ is taken as describing the behavior of a *single particle* and not merely the statistical distribution of the behavior of a large group of particles. This means that the wave can interfere with itself, in order that Ψ may describe the motion of a single particle as a diffraction phenomenon.

Because of its close parallelism with other wave problems in physics, Schrödinger's equation is bound to work in those cases where λ does not change much in a distance of one wavelength. But in the region of strong fields around nuclei and in atoms, the de Broglie wavelength can change a great deal in a distance of one wavelength; consequently it had to be shown that Schrödinger's equation would describe the experimental findings in such cases. It is found that Eq. (5.35) does successfully describe many atomic and nuclear phenomena. In a number of important cases, however, the wave functions are still inaccurately known. In all but the simplest physical cases, an assortment of special mathematical methods may be needed in order to obtain the actual solutions of the Schrödinger equation for any particular problem.

e. The Uncertainty Principle and the Complementarity Principle. Heisenberg (1927) has shown quite generally that the order of magnitude of the product of the uncertainties in the values of pairs of certain canonically conjugate variables is always at least as large as $h/2\pi$. Thus the uncertainty in momentum Δp, and the uncertainty in position Δx

in the direction of Δp, of a particle are related by

$$\Delta p \, \Delta x \geq \frac{h}{2\pi} \equiv \hbar \qquad (5.44)$$

Equation (5.44) can be expressed in an equivalent form which is convenient for numerical applications. For a particle having mass M, velocity $V = \beta c$, momentum $p = \beta M c$, and rest energy Mc^2

$$\Delta(pc) \, \Delta x \simeq \hbar c$$
$$\Delta(\beta M c^2) \, \Delta x \simeq \hbar c = 1.97 \times 10^{-11} \text{ Mev-cm} \qquad (5.44a)$$

The uncertainties in angular momentum ΔJ, and in angular position $\Delta \varphi$, of a system are related by

$$\Delta J \, \Delta \varphi \geq \frac{h}{2\pi} \equiv \hbar \qquad (5.45)$$

If J is expressed in natural units, $J = l\hbar$, then Eq. (5.45) becomes

$$\Delta l \, \Delta \varphi \simeq \frac{\hbar}{\hbar} = 1 \text{ radian} \qquad (5.45a)$$

The uncertainty in kinetic energy ΔT, and in the time Δt during which the energy is measured, are related by

$$\Delta T \, \Delta t \geq \frac{h}{2\pi} \equiv \hbar = 0.66 \times 10^{-21} \text{ Mev-sec} \qquad (5.46)$$

The *Heisenberg uncertainty principle*, or the "principle of indeterminacy," is expressed by these three quantitative relationships. Because of the smallness of h, these uncertainties are significant primarily in atomic or nuclear systems.

Bohr has made the physical implications of the uncertainty principle especially clear and useful through his *complementarity principle* (1928). It can be shown, quite generally, that measuring instruments always interfere with and modify the system which they are intended to measure. In the domain of classical physics, it is usually possible to calculate the disturbance produced by the instrument and to correct for it exactly. But in the domain of small quantum numbers, as in observations on a single elementary particle, the exact magnitude of the influence of the measuring instruments cannot be determined precisely. The magnitudes of the minimum attainable uncertainties are just those specified by the uncertainty principle. This is often illustrated by the hypothetical observation of an electron with a light microscope, in which the scattering of the light quantum into the microscope's optical system by the electron introduces just these same minimum uncertainties in the attainable simultaneous knowledge of position and momentum (see, for example, p. 11 of S11 or p. 169 of S29). *These effects are produced by even perfectly ideal instruments, and they preclude our observation of too small momentum changes in small regions of space.* For example, in an elastic collision between two particles we cannot actually hope to observe (and therefore verify as true) a small momentum change Δp at an impact parameter x, if Δp is only of the order of $\hbar/x$.

Within this domain we must therefore *forgo the possibility of experimental knowledge of the intimate details of the interaction.* If two theories of the interaction specify two different models or mechanisms for the interaction within this domain, we have no way of experimentally determining which, if either, actually occurs. This is a domain of "blackout" which prevents our observing the mechanism of the collision too intimately. Within this domain, whose boundaries are set quantitatively by the uncertainty principle, we cannot reject a particular model merely because it differs from the only model which we can set up on a basis of classical mechanics. The test of validity of the new theory cannot be at the level of the details of the interaction but is rather in the over-all success which the model may have in describing the things which can be observed, such as the final angular distribution of scattered particles. The wave mechanics, or any other subsequent theory, is therefore permitted to differ from the classical within just the domains specified by the uncertainty principle.

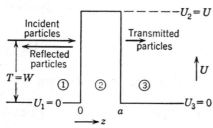

Fig. 5.1 A one-dimensional rectangular potential barrier of height $U_2 - U_1 = U$ and thickness a. Particles incident from the left (region 1), whose kinetic energy is less than the barrier height, have a finite probability of being transmitted through the barrier and into region 3.

f. Transmission of Particles through a Rectangular Barrier. One of the fruitful general results of the wave mechanics is its quantitative description of the probability that a charged particle can pass through a potential barrier, even if the particle has insufficient energy to surmount the barrier.

In Fig. 5.1, a particle which has mass M, velocity V, and kinetic energy $T = \frac{1}{2}MV^2$ is moving from left to right in a region of space where the potential U_1 is taken as zero. At $z = 0$, we imagine that an abrupt increase of the potential energy to the value $U_2 = U$ occurs and that this continues for a distance $z = a$, where the potential again drops to zero. In classical mechanics, all particles whose incident kinetic energy is smaller than U would be thrown back by the barrier, while all particles of greater energy would pass the barrier. In the wave mechanics neither of these statements is exactly true. A fraction of the incident particles, when represented as waves, will be reflected, and the remainder will pass the barrier when $T = U$. The fraction transmitted will increase when $T > U$, and it will decrease when $T < U$. The classical values will be approached most closely when the thickness of the barrier is large compared with the de Broglie wavelength of the incident particles.

Localization of a Particle. Let us first apply the uncertainty principle, in order to develop a plausibility argument concerning the transparency of this barrier. If we are seeking only to locate the particle, we can accept an uncertainty Δp in its momentum which equals the full value p of the momentum. To this maximum possible uncertainty in momentum there corresponds a minimum possible uncertainty of position, which is

$$(\Delta z)_{\min} \simeq \frac{\hbar}{p} = \frac{\lambda}{2\pi} \equiv \lambdabar \tag{5.47}$$

This is a very general result: *A particle cannot be localized more closely than its de Broglie wavelength divided by* 2π. In the present case, if the barrier width a is comparable with or less than $\lambda/2\pi$, we cannot say whether a particle whose momentum is $p = h/\lambda$ will be found on the left side of the barrier or on the right side. But if the particle is found on the right side of the barrier we should have to regard it as having successfully passed through the barrier.

We can make this qualitative argument semiquantitative. In asking whether the particle is on the left side or the right side of the barrier, we accept an uncertainty of $\Delta z = a$ in the position of the particle. To this uncertainty in position, there corresponds an uncertainty in momentum, which is

$$\Delta p \simeq \frac{\hbar}{a} \tag{5.48}$$

Instead of p, we now represent the momentum by $(p \pm \Delta p)$. We will first examine the case of $(p + \Delta p)$ which is of special interest when $T < U$. Then the energy of the particle will not be represented by $T = p^2/2M$ but may be as much as

$$\begin{aligned}
T' &= \frac{(p + \Delta p)^2}{2M} \\
&= \frac{p^2}{2M} + \frac{p\,\Delta p}{M} + \frac{(\Delta p)^2}{2M} \\
&= T + \frac{p}{M}\,\Delta p \qquad \text{whenever } \Delta p \ll p \\
&= T + \frac{MV}{M}\frac{\hbar}{a} \\
&= T + \frac{\hbar}{a/V} \tag{5.49}
\end{aligned}$$

This can be written as

$$\Delta T \equiv T' - T = \frac{\hbar}{a/V} \tag{5.50}$$

Here (a/V) is the time Δt required for the particle to travel a distance equal to the thickness of the barrier. Equation (5.50) is seen to be equivalent to $\Delta T\,\Delta t \simeq \hbar$, that is, to Eq. (5.46). Suppose that the barrier is $a = 10^{-12}$ cm thick (about the radius of a heavy nucleus) and that the particle is traveling at one-tenth the velocity of light (about the velocity of a 4-Mev proton). Then

$$\Delta T = \frac{h}{2\pi}\frac{V}{a} = \frac{1}{2\pi}\frac{(h/m_0c)}{a}\left(\frac{V}{c}\right)(m_0c^2)$$

$$= \frac{1}{2\pi}\frac{2.43 \times 10^{-10} \text{ cm}}{1 \times 10^{-12} \text{ cm}}(0.1)(0.51 \text{ Mev})$$

$$\simeq 2 \text{ Mev} \tag{5.51}$$

This particle might therefore succeed in passing a barrier which is of the order of 2 Mev higher than its own kinetic energy.

Conversely, we may consider the case of $(p - \Delta p)$. Here we have only to change the sign of the second term in Eq. (5.49). We obtain $(T - T') = \hbar/(a/V)$. The same particle therefore might fail to pass the barrier even if its own kinetic energy were of the order of 2 Mev greater than the barrier energy U.

With the help of the Schrödinger equation, we can treat the problem quantitatively and can determine the actual reflection coefficient and transmission coefficient of the barrier. In the remainder of this section we emphasize the physical principles and the physical interpretation of the mathematical results. The corresponding algebraic details are carried out fully in a parallel treatment given in Sec. 1 of Appendix C.

Wave Representation. The incident particles in region 1 are represented by a plane wave moving in the direction of increasing z. The time-dependent factor in Eqs. (5.20) and (5.30) can be omitted, because $\nu = W/h$ is a constant of the motion and therefore has the same value in regions 1, 2, and 3 of Fig. 5.1. Accordingly, the wave function for the incident particles can be written as

$$\psi_{\text{incident}} = A_1 e^{ik_1 z} \tag{5.52}$$

where the subscripts 1 refer to region 1. The propagation number for the incident wave is

$$k_1 = \frac{2\pi}{\lambda_1} = \frac{MV_1}{\hbar} = \frac{\sqrt{2MT}}{\hbar} \tag{5.53}$$

The amplitude A_1 of the incident wave could be taken as unity without loss of generality. However, A_1 will be retained in order to facilitate identification of the incident amplitude in subsequent equations. Equation (5.52) is a solution of the wave equation, Eq. (5.31), in region 1, when k_1 has the value given by Eq. (5.53).

The incident flux of particles is the probability density $|\psi_{\text{incident}}|^2$ multiplied by the group velocity V_1 of the particles in region 1; thus

$$\text{Incident flux} = |\psi_{\text{incident}}|^2 V_1 = |A_1|^2 V_1 \tag{5.54}$$

Some particles will be turned back by the potential barrier. These reflected particles move toward the left in region 1 and can be represented by a wave of amplitude B_1, propagated in the $-z$ direction, or

$$\psi_{\text{reflected}} = B_1 e^{-ik_1 z} \tag{5.55}$$

The total disturbance in region 1 is then represented by the wave function ψ_1, which has the value

$$\psi_1 = A_1 e^{ik_1 z} + B_1 e^{-ik_1 z} \tag{5.56}$$

This total wave function also is a solution of Schrödinger's equation for region 1, where $U = 0$.

In region 2, under the barrier, we can expect a disturbance moving toward $+z$ and also one reflected from the potential discontinuity at $z = a$ and therefore moving toward $-z$. The total disturbance could be written

$$\psi_2 = A_2 e^{ik_2' z} + B_2 e^{-ik_2' z} \tag{5.57}$$

where

$$k_2' = \frac{\sqrt{2M(T - U)}}{\hbar} \tag{5.58}$$

In region 2, the potential energy exceeds the incident energy T. Hence the kinetic energy $(T - U)$ is negative in region 2, and the propagation number k_2' is imaginary. It is mathematically convenient, but not mathematically necessary, to use in region 2 a real propagation number k_2 defined as

$$k_2 \equiv \frac{\sqrt{2M(U - T)}}{\hbar} = -ik_2' \tag{5.59}$$

Then k_2 is the wave number which would be associated with a hypothetical particle whose kinetic energy is positive and equal to the energy difference between the top of the barrier and the incident kinetic energy T.

The disturbance under the barrier is then represented by

$$\psi_2 = A_2 e^{-k_2 z} + B_2 e^{k_2 z} \tag{5.60}$$

Because k_2 is a real number, Eq. (5.60) shows that the disturbance under the barrier is nonoscillatory.

In region 3, we can have a transmitted wave moving toward $+z$. There is no wave moving toward $-z$ because there is no potential change beyond $z = a$ from which a reflected component could be produced. In other words, region 3 is a domain of constant refractive index from $z = a$ to $z = \infty$. The total wave function in region 3 therefore consists of a plane wave moving toward $+z$, with a propagation number $k_3 = k_1$, because U is zero in both regions. This gives for region 3

$$\psi_3 = A_3 e^{ik_1 z} \tag{5.61}$$

Boundary Conditions. The wave functions ψ_1, ψ_2, and ψ_3 are the solutions of Schrödinger's equation in the three regions. Across the boundaries between these regions ψ and $\partial\psi/\partial z$ must be continuous. Only in this way can $\partial^2\psi/\partial z^2$ remain finite across the boundaries and hence conform with noninfinite values of the total and potential energy W and

U in Schrödinger's equation. Therefore the boundary conditions are

$$\psi_1 = \psi_2 \qquad \frac{\partial \psi_1}{\partial z} = \frac{\partial \psi_2}{\partial z} \qquad \text{at } z = 0$$

$$\psi_2 = \psi_3 \qquad \frac{\partial \psi_2}{\partial z} = \frac{\partial \psi_3}{\partial z} \qquad \text{at } z = a \tag{5.62}$$

These boundary conditions give us four linear equations, from which the amplitudes A_2, A_3, B_1, B_2 can be obtained in terms of the incident amplitude A_1.

Transmission. The flux of transmitted particles, by analogy with Eq. (5.54), is for region 3

$$|A_3|^2 V_3 \tag{5.63}$$

where V_3 is the group or particle velocity in region 3.

The fractional transmission, or the probability for the transmission of a single particle through the barrier, is given by

$$\mathsf{T}_l = \frac{|A_3|^2}{|A_1|^2} \frac{V_3}{V_1} \tag{5.64}$$

where we will call T_l the *transmission coefficient*, or, synonymously, the "transparency," of the barrier (B68, F41). This is to be distinguished physically from a closely related quantity, the so-called *penetration factor* P, which is merely the ratio of the probability densities on the two sides of the barrier, i.e.,

$$P = \frac{|A_3|^2}{|A_1|^2} \tag{5.65}$$

This systematic distinction between "transmission" and "penetration" follows the nomenclature adopted by Blatt and Weisskopf (B68) and is seldom found in the earlier literature, where "transmission" was often synonymous with "penetration," and usually (but not always) denoted T_l.

The penetration factor will arise later in connection with our discussions of nuclear barriers and nuclear reactions [e.g., Eq. (8.6a)]. In general, $\mathsf{T}_l = P(V_3/V_1)$. It happens in the present problem that $V_3 = V_1$, because $U = 0$ for regions 1 and 3. In such special cases the transmission coefficient and the penetration factor are equal.

In order to evaluate the transmission coefficient, we must determine A_3/A_1, the ratio of the transmitted amplitude to the incident amplitude. In general, A_3 will be complex, as will all other amplitudes except that of the incident plane wave A_1.

A more detailed discussion of the wave-mechanical treatment of this and other related barrier problems is given in Appendix C. It is shown that, when $T < U$, the exact solution of Eqs. (5.62) gives for the transmission coefficient of the rectangular barrier of Fig. 5.1

$$\mathsf{T}_l = \frac{|A_3|^2}{|A_1|^2} \frac{V_3}{V_1} = \left[1 + \frac{U^2}{4T(U - T)} \sinh^2 k_2 a \right]^{-1} \tag{5.66}$$

The transmission coefficient T_l for the case in which the incident kinetic energy is $T = 0.8U$ is illustrated in Fig. 5.2.   The barrier thickness a is plotted in terms of the de Broglie wavelength λ_1 of the incident particles.   Then

$$\left(\frac{a}{\lambda_1}\right) = \left(\frac{a}{h}\right)\sqrt{2MT}$$

while

$$k_2 a = \left(\frac{a}{h}\right) 2\pi \sqrt{2M(U - T)}$$

$$= \left(\frac{a}{h}\right) 2\pi \sqrt{\frac{2MT}{4}}$$

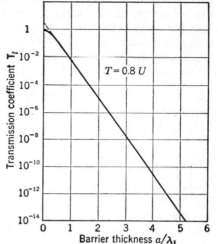

Hence $k_2 a = \pi(a/\lambda_1)$.   It should be noted that the transmission coefficient decreases slowly for barriers up to the order of $a \simeq \lambda_1/4$ (or $k_2 a \simeq 1$) in thickness.   For barriers which are thicker than about $a \simeq \lambda_1/2$ (or $k_2 a \simeq 2$), $\log T_l$ is seen to decrease substantially linearly as a increases. In this region, therefore, the transmission coefficient decreases exponentially with increasing barrier thickness.

Fig. 5.2   The probability of transmission T_l of a rectangular barrier by particles whose kinetic energy is 0.8 of the barrier height.   The thickness a of the barrier is given in terms of the de Broglie wavelength λ_1 of the incident particles.   The solid curve represents the exact expression, Eq. (5.66).   The dotted line represents the approximation for thick barriers, as given by Eq. (5.70).

Reflection.   There are no sinks or sources of particles under the barrier of Fig. 5.1.   Consequently those incident particles which are not transmitted must be reflected by the barrier.   The probability of reflection, therefore, is

$$\text{Reflectance} = 1 - T_l \tag{5.67}$$

This relationship can be verified in detail by computing the amplitude B_1 of the reflected wave.   The result of the computation turns out to be, as expected,

$$\frac{|B_1|^2}{|A_1|^2} = 1 - \frac{|A_3|^2}{|A_1|^2} = 1 - T_l \quad \text{or} \quad T_l = \frac{|A_1|^2 - |B_1|^2}{|A_1|^2} \tag{5.68}$$

We see that the probability of reflection is generally less than unity and increases toward unity as the barrier becomes thicker.   This is in sharp contrast with the classical model.   In classical mechanics, the incident particles would all be turned back, or reflected, if $T < U$.   Moreover, this reflection would occur sharply at the incident surface, $z = 0$, of the barrier.   In contrast, the wave mechanics predicts a reflectance which depends on the barrier thickness.   This means that the reflection process occurs not just at the incident surface, but *within* the barrier as well, and also from the back, or emergent, surface. An analogous conclusion regarding the reflection and transmission of visible light by a metallic film or mirror is a well-known result in physical optics. In the limiting case of a very thick barrier, the classical and wave theories both predict 100 per cent reflection. But the reflection is from the front surface alone in classical theory, whereas it occurs throughout a finite depth of the barrier in the wave-mechanical theory.

Graphical Representation. It is helpful to visualize the boundary conditions and the general character of the wave functions ψ_1, ψ_2, and ψ_3 in the three regions of Fig. 5.1.

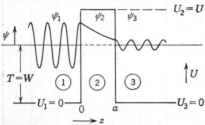

To do so, we first note some general characteristics of any solution ψ of Schrödinger's equation

$$\frac{\partial^2 \psi}{\partial z^2} + \frac{8\pi^2 M}{h^2}(W - U)\psi = 0$$

(5.69)

Fig. **5.3** Graphical representation of the total wave functions ψ_1, ψ_2, and ψ_3 in the three regions of Fig. 5.1. There are two vertical scales. One is an energy scale, with respect to which the horizontal lines show the total energy W (equal in this case to the initial kinetic energy T) and the potential energies. The second vertical scale is the real part (or, alternatively, the imaginary part) of the wave functions, which are plotted with respect to the energy line W as a horizontal axis. This schematic representation of ψ can be regarded as applying to some arbitrary value of time t, because the time factor $e^{-2\pi \nu t}$ is common to all three regions. The boundary conditions are satisfied by making ψ go straight across the discontinuities of potential at $z = 0$ and $z = a$.

In any region of positive kinetic energy $(W - U)$, it is necessary that $\partial^2\psi/\partial z^2$ be of opposite sign to ψ. This condition requires that, if ψ is positive, its slope must decrease as z increases. Similarly, if ψ is negative, $\partial\psi/\partial z$ must increase as z increases. This requires at once that ψ be an oscillatory function of z. In Fig. 5.3, we therefore portray ψ_1 to the left of the barrier as an oscillatory function. Because the reflected component has a complex amplitude B_1, we can regard Fig. 5.3 as a representation of the real part (or, alternatively, the imaginary part) of ψ_1.

Inspection of the Schrödinger equation also shows that, in any region of negative kinetic energy $U > W$, it is necessary that $\partial^2\psi/\partial z^2$ and ψ be of the same sign. Then, if ψ is positive, its slope will increase as z increases; that is, ψ must always be convex toward the origin of coordinates. Then ψ is not oscillatory but will have general features similar to those of an exponentially decreasing function. In Fig. 5.3, the wave function ψ_2 in the region under the barrier is shown as such a function.

At $z = 0$, the boundary conditions require that ψ and its slope $\partial\psi/\partial z$ have the same values in regions 1 and 2. Therefore the curves representing ψ in the two regions must be joined at $z = 0$ in such a way that they pass *straight across the potential boundary*. Thus the boundary conditions are easily visualized graphically, as shown in Fig. 5.3.

At $z = a$, ψ must again pass straight across the potential boundary. In region 3, the kinetic energy again becomes positive. Therefore ψ_3 is an oscillatory function but of smaller amplitude than ψ_1, as shown in Fig. 5.3.

It is to be emphasized that ψ_1 is not the incident wave but is the sum of the incident and reflected waves. Hence the real part of ψ_1 is not necessarily a pure sinusoidal curve, but it does have to be oscillatory.

Thick Barriers. In many of the cases which are of practical interest in nuclear physics, the barrier thickness a is large compared with the de Broglie wavelength $\lambda_2 = 2\pi/k_2$ of a particle whose energy is $(U - T)$. This condition corresponds to $k_2 a \gg 1$ in Eq. (5.66). Such barriers could be described as either "thick" (large a) or as "high" (large k_2). For $k_2 a \gg 1$, the exact relationship Eq. (5.66) can be represented with good approximation by

$$T_l = 16 \frac{T}{U}\left(1 - \frac{T}{U}\right) e^{-2k_2 a} \quad (5.70)$$

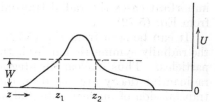

For T/U not too close to 0 or 1, the coefficient of the exponential term is of the order of unity. The dominant term is the exponential. A plot of Eq. (5.70) for $T = 0.8U$ is

Fig. 5.4 Generalized potential barrier $U(z)$ for a particle whose total energy is W.

shown as the dotted line in Fig. 5.2, where the domain of validity of the approximation can be seen clearly.

The exponential term in Eq. (5.70) can be derived by an entirely different method. Approximate solutions of the wave equation can be determined by the so-called Wentzel-Kramers-Brillouin (W.K.B.) method, if the potential $U(z)$ does not vary too rapidly with z. Then an approximate solution of the wave equation can be obtained for barriers of arbitrary shape, such as the barrier shown in Fig. 5.4. The transmission coefficient for such barriers can be written as

$$T_l \simeq e^{-\gamma} \quad (5.71)$$

where the dimensionless exponent γ is known as the barrier transmission exponent. Then the W.K.B. method leads to the following approximate general solution for γ

$$\gamma = \frac{4\pi}{h} \sqrt{2M} \int_{z_1}^{z_2} [U(z) - W]^{\frac{1}{2}} \, dz$$

$$\gamma \equiv 2 \int_{z_1}^{z_2} k_2(z) \, dz \quad (5.72)$$

Here z_1 and z_2 are the distances between which the barrier height $U(z)$ is greater than the total energy W of the incident particle.

For the special case of the rectangular barrier, $\sqrt{U(z) - W}$ is constant and equal to $\sqrt{U - T}$. Then Eq. (5.72) integrates directly to give

$$\gamma = 2a \frac{2\pi}{h} \sqrt{2M(U - T)} = 2k_2 a \qquad (5.73)$$

which is in agreement with Eqs. (5.70) and (5.71).

The integration of Eq. (5.72) can be carried out analytically for certain simple potentials, such as the coulomb barrier combined with a rectangular well. For more complicated potential barriers, Eq. (5.72) is evaluated by numerical integration.

g. Transmission of Particles through a Nuclear Coulomb Barrier. The approximate expression for barrier penetration, as given by Eq. (5.72), is in one dimension. We must now go over to three dimensions, in order to evaluate the radial transparency of a nuclear coulomb barrier for a charged particle. We shall find that for certain restricted but very important cases the radial transmission coefficient can also be obtained from Eq. (5.72).

It can be seen from Eq. (5.72) that the transmission exponent γ for the radially symmetric barrier is the same for incoming and for outgoing particles. Thus nuclear disintegrations by charged particles and α-ray radioactive decay are based on the same general theory concerning the transmission of nuclear potential barriers.

Wave Equation in Spherical Polar Coordinates. For the three-dimensional coordinate system, it is most convenient to choose spherical polar coordinates, r, ϑ, φ. If the potential U depends only on r, and not on ϑ and φ, then it is possible to find wave functions ψ in which the variables r, ϑ, φ appear only in separate functions. Thus

$$\psi = R(r)\Theta(\vartheta)\Phi(\varphi) \qquad (5.74)$$

where the "radial wave function" $R(r)$ depends only on r, the polar function $\Theta(\vartheta)$ depends only on ϑ, and the azimuthal function $\Phi(\varphi)$ depends only on φ. For such a wave function, Schrödinger's equation can then be separated into three differential equations, one in r and $R(r)$, one in ϑ and $\Theta(\vartheta)$, and one in φ and $\Phi(\varphi)$.

Modified Radial Wave Equation. Of these three differential equations, the radial equation is of direct interest here. The separation of the three-dimensional wave equation is carried out in Appendix C, Sec. 2, where it is shown that the radial wave equation is

$$\frac{1}{r^2} \frac{d}{dr} \left[r^2 \frac{dR(r)}{dr} \right] + \frac{8\pi^2 M}{h^2} \left[W - U(r) - \frac{l(l + 1)}{2Mr^2} \left(\frac{h}{2\pi} \right)^2 \right] R(r) = 0$$

$$(5.75)$$

This equation does not involve ϑ or φ, and the two companion differential equations, one in ϑ and one in φ, do not involve r.

It is mathematically convenient to use a *modified radial wave function* χ defined as r times the radial wave function, or

$$\chi \equiv r R(r) \qquad (5.76)$$

Upon substituting $R(r) \equiv \chi/r$ into Eq. (5.75), algebraic simplifications occur, and we obtain the simpler and more useful *modified radial wave equation*, which is

$$\frac{d^2\chi}{dr^2} + \frac{8\pi^2 M}{h^2}\left[W - U(r) - \frac{l(l+1)}{2Mr^2}\left(\frac{h}{2\pi}\right)^2\right]\chi = 0 \qquad (5.77)$$

In Eqs. (5.75) and (5.77), r is the radial distance measured from the origin of the potential $U(r)$, such as the center of a nucleus, and M is the reduced mass of the colliding particles, or of the disintegration products, whose separation is r. The quantity $l(l+1)$ in Eqs. (5.75) and (5.77) arises purely from the mathematical operation of separating the wave equation into radial and angular equations. In this operation it is found that the separation constant can have only the values 0, 2, 6, 12, 20, 30, . . . in order that the solution $\Theta(\vartheta)$ of the polar equation (Legendre's equation) be finite. These numbers are conveniently represented by the quantity

$$l(l+1)$$

where the index l is zero or a positive integer, $l = 0, 1, 2, 3, \ldots$. The modified radial wave equation has a separate solution χ_l for each value of the index l, and there are corresponding solutions Θ_l for the polar equation. The mathematical details are given in Appendix C, Sec. 2.

Centrifugal Barrier. Comparison of Eq. (5.77) with Eq. (5.69) shows that the modified radial wave equation is markedly similar to the one-dimensional wave equation. However, in the three-dimensional case the potential is replaced by the quantity

$$U(r) + \frac{l(l+1)}{2Mr^2}\left(\frac{h}{2\pi}\right)^2 \qquad (5.78)$$

The second term, therefore, has the dimensions of energy. In its denominator, the quantity Mr^2 will be recognized as the classical moment of inertia for two particles whose reduced mass is M and whose separation is r. In classical mechanics, rotational kinetic energy can be written as $J^2/2I$, where J is angular momentum and I is moment of inertia. Then by dimensional reasoning we can identify the second term in Eq. (5.78) as associated with the rotational kinetic energy of the two particles about their center of mass. Because this term has the same sign as the potential energy $U(r)$ and thus physically augments the potential barrier, the quantity

$$\frac{l(l+1)}{2Mr^2}\left(\frac{h}{2\pi}\right)^2 \qquad (5.79)$$

is known as the *centrifugal barrier* in collision problems and in disintegration problems. A schematic diagram of the centrifugal barrier will be found in Fig. 10 of Appendix C.

Angular Momentum. Comparison of Eq. (5.79) with the classical expression for rotational kinetic energy $J^2/2I$ shows that a portion of Eq. (5.79) can be identified as the angular momentum J. Thus the magnitude of the angular momentum of the wave-mechanical system of two particles is taken as

$$J_l = \sqrt{l(l + 1)}\, \hbar \qquad (5.80)$$

In contrast with the classical angular momenta MVx as used in collision theory, the angular momentum of the quantum-mechanical system can have only the discrete quantized values given by Eq. (5.80) with $l = 0, 1, 2, 3, \ldots$. In both theories, of course, the angular momentum is a constant of the motion.

Because the index l physically determines the angular momentum of the system, we call l hereafter the *angular-momentum quantum number*. Note that the magnitude of the angular momentum is not $l\hbar$, as in the older quantum theory, but is $\sqrt{l(l + 1)}\, \hbar$.

Plane Wave in Polar Coordinates. In collision problems, we express a collimated beam of monoenergetic particles as the usual plane wave e^{ikz}. Such a plane wave represents a mixture of particles which have *all possible values of angular momentum* with respect to any scattering center being traversed by the wave. We need to locate the origin of spherical polar coordinates at some position to be occupied later by a scattering center and then find an expression for the plane wave in these coordinates. In this way we express the plane wave as the sum of a number of "partial waves." Each partial wave must be a solution of the wave equation when the scattering potential $U(r)$ is zero, i.e., for uniform motion. Each partial wave will be characterized by a particular value of l and will therefore correspond physically to those particles in the incident beam for which the angular momentum about the scattering center is $\sqrt{l(l + 1)}\, \hbar$. The sum of all the partial waves, for $l = 0$ to $l = \infty$, must equal the plane wave $e^{ikz} = e^{ikr \cos \vartheta}$.

It is shown in Appendix C, Eq. (75), that the representation of the plane wave which satisfies these conditions is

$$e^{ikz} = \sum_{l=0}^{l=\infty} (2l + 1) i^l\, j_l(kr)\, P_l(\cos \vartheta) \qquad (5.81)$$

Here $j_l(kr)$ are the spherical Bessel functions of order l, and $P_l(\cos \vartheta)$ are the Legendre polynomials of order l.

A correlation between the l values of the partial waves and the angular momentum associated with classical impact parameters x can be made with the help of the uncertainty principle. It is shown in Appendix C, Sec. 4, that in a classical coulomb collision it would be impossible to obtain a precise experimental verification of the relationship between the classical impact parameter x and the deflection in an individual coulomb collision. The minimum uncertainty in the impact parameter $(\Delta x)_{min}$ for a particular observed deflection would be

$$(\Delta x)_{min} \geq \lambda = \frac{h}{2\pi MV} \qquad (5.81a)$$

Then central collisions could be regarded as extending from $x = 0$ to at least $x \simeq \lambda$ and thus including classical angular momenta between 0 and at least $J = MVx \simeq \hbar$. These correspond to the "*central collisions*" $l = 0$ of the wave theory. Similarly, collisions whose classical angular momentum lies between $MVx \simeq l\hbar$ and $MVx \simeq (l + 1)\hbar$ correspond to the l-wave collisions of the wave theory, for which the quantized value of the angular momentum is the geometric mean between $l\hbar$ and $(l + 1)\hbar$, that is, $\sqrt{l(l + 1)}\,\hbar$. These values can be visualized from Fig. 8 of Appendix C.

The individual spherical partial waves are designated by their numerical l values, or more commonly by borrowing the Rydberg letter notation from atomic spectroscopy. This is

l...................	0	1	2	3	4	5	. . .
Letter designation.........	s	p	d	f	g	h	. . .

The s Wave. Transmission through a barrier is, of course, most probable for those particles which have central collisions. In these cases no energy is "wasted" as rotational energy, and all the initial kinetic energy is available for attacking the potential barrier. The collisions which have no angular momentum are the $l = 0$ or s-wave collisions. The s wave from Eq. (5.81) has the simple form

$$\psi_0 = R_0(r)\Theta_0(\vartheta)\Phi_0(\varphi) = R_0(r) = \frac{\sin kr}{kr} \tag{5.82}$$

The s wave is the only partial wave which has no dependence on ϑ, and it is therefore spherically symmetric. The modified radial wave function, for the s wave, is then

$$\chi_0 = r\,R_0(r) = \frac{\sin kr}{k} \tag{5.83}$$

Transmission through a Nuclear Coulomb Barrier by s Wave. For the $l = 0$ partial wave, the modified radial wave equation becomes

$$\frac{d^2\chi_0}{dr^2} + \frac{8\pi^2 M}{h^2}[W - U(r)]\chi_0 = 0 \tag{5.84}$$

This is identical with the one-dimensional wave equation. The probability that a particle will be found in a volume element between r and $r + dr$ is

$$|R_0(r)|^2 4\pi r^2\,dr = 4\pi|\chi_0|^2\,dr$$

We can therefore use the one-dimensional integral in Eq. (5.72) to calculate the radial transparency for s waves.

Let the nuclear potential barrier be a coulomb barrier, cut off at the edge of an inner rectangular well, and given by

$$\begin{aligned} U(r) &= 0 & r &< R \\ U(r) &= \frac{Zze^2}{r} & r &> R \end{aligned} \tag{5.85}$$

where R is the nuclear radius. The integration of Eq. (5.72) can be carried out explicitly for this potential. The general result is developed in Appendix C, Eq. (95), and is

$$\gamma = \frac{8\pi Zze^2}{hV}\left[\cos^{-1}\left(\frac{T}{B}\right)^{\frac{1}{2}} - \left(\frac{T}{B}\right)^{\frac{1}{2}}\left(1 - \frac{T}{B}\right)^{\frac{1}{2}}\right] \tag{5.86}$$

where $B = Zze^2/R$ = coulomb barrier height
$T = \frac{1}{2}MV^2$ = total kinetic energy of particles in C coordinates when widely separated
M = reduced mass
V = mutual velocity of approach or recession

Figure 5.5 shows the behavior of the $l = 0$ transmission coefficient $T_0 = e^{-\gamma}$ as given by Eq. (5.86) for three representative elements of low, medium, and large nuclear charge (Al, Sn, and U), using protons and α rays as the incident particles. In each case the effective radius has been taken as

$$R = 1.5 \times 10^{-13}A^{\frac{1}{3}} \quad \text{cm}$$

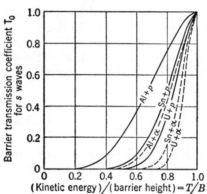

Fig. 5.5 Approximate barrier transparency T_0 for s waves as given by Eq. (5.86). Curves are for protons and α rays passing through the coulomb barriers of aluminum ($_{13}\mathrm{Al}^{27}$), tin ($_{50}\mathrm{Sn}^{118}$), and uranium ($_{92}\mathrm{U}^{238}$), on the assumption that these nuclei have radii $R = 1.5 \times 10^{-13}A^{\frac{1}{3}}$ cm.

The transmission exponent γ takes on a simpler form for the physically important case of a "high" barrier. When the kinetic energy T is small compared with the barrier height B, the transmission coefficient $T_0 = e^{-\gamma}$ is given to a good approximation by

$$\gamma = \frac{4\pi^2 Zze^2}{hV} - \frac{8\pi}{h}(2Zze^2MR)^{\frac{1}{2}} \tag{5.87}$$

This expression can be used as a reasonable approximation for the treatment of α decay in the heavy elements, where $B \simeq 25$ Mev and $T \simeq 5$ Mev $\simeq B/5$. The physics of Eq. (5.87) is portrayed more clearly by rearranging the variables, so that the barrier transmission exponent is given by

$$\gamma = \pi\left(\frac{2Zz}{137\beta}\right) - \frac{4}{137}\left(2Zz\frac{M}{m_0}\frac{R}{r_0}\right)^{\frac{1}{2}} \tag{5.88}$$

where $\frac{1}{137} = 2\pi e^2/hc$ = fine-structure constant
$\beta = V/c$ = relative velocity of particles Ze and ze, in terms of velocity of light
M/m_0 = reduced mass in terms of rest mass m_0 of electron
R/r_0 = nuclear radius in terms of classical electron radius $r_0 = e^2/m_0c^2 = 2.818 \times 10^{-13}$ cm

In many practical cases, the first term in Eq. (5.88) predominates. We see that when the charge parameter $2Zz/137\beta$ is large, the transmission is small, and the classical limit of no barrier transmission is approached.

When the first term is used alone, the approximate barrier transparency, for s waves through a very high or thick barrier, is called the *Gamow factor G* which is

$$\mathsf{T}_0(R \to 0) \equiv G \simeq e^{-4\pi^2 Zze^2/hV} = e^{-\pi(2Zz/137\beta)} \qquad (5.89)$$

The Gamow factor corresponds to the transparency of a coulomb barrier which has zero internal radius. This can be seen by setting

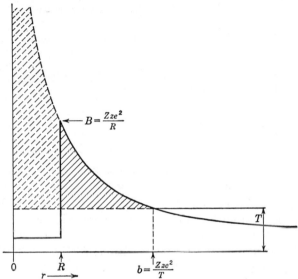

Fig. 5.6 Approximate physical interpretation of the coulomb-barrier transmission exponent γ. The *Gamow factor* corresponds to the integration of Eq. (5.72) all the way to the origin $r = 0$. This is the entire shaded region, above T, and extending from $r = 0$ to b. The region shown with dotted shading corresponds to the deduction to be made because of the presence of the inner potential well between $r = 0$ and R. This dotted part corresponds to the second term in Eq. (5.88) and portrays the reduction of γ as produced by R. The difference between the two terms corresponds to the integral through the region shown by the unbroken shading from $r = R$ to b. Note that the integral in Eq. (5.72) involves the square root of elements of area in this figure, rather than simply the area itself.

$R = 0$, hence $B = \infty$ in Eq. (5.86), or by setting $R = 0$ in Eq. (5.87). With this in mind, the two terms in Eqs. (5.87) and (5.88) for the barrier-penetration exponent can be given an approximate physical interpretation which can be visualized as in Fig. 5.6. The first term corresponds to the integration of Eq. (5.72) from $r = 0$ to $r = b = Zze^2/T$, that is, over the entire shaded region in Fig. 5.6. The second term corresponds to the integration from $r = 0$ to R, which is shown as dotted shading in Fig. 5.6. This term is of opposite sign to the first term and corresponds to the reduction in γ on account of the presence of the inner potential well. All the dependence of γ on the well radius R is seen to be contained both mathematically and physically in this second term.

Figure 5.7 makes use of the net shaded area of Fig. 5.6, in order to provide a visualization of the physical effect of changes in the parameters Z, z, R, V, M, and T.

Penetration When $l \neq 0$. When the angular momentum is not zero, the penetrability of a nuclear coulomb barrier is much more complicated than it is for s waves. If Z is large, the effects due to l are small in

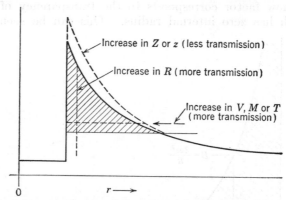

Fig. 5.7 Pictorial representation of the effects of Z, z, R, V, M, and T on the net shaded area of Fig. 5.6 and hence on the barrier transmission.

comparison with the profound dependence of γ on V and on R. In general, the penetrability decreases as l increases. Some approximate analytical expressions have been deduced, and tables which are more accurate than these have been prepared by numerical integration. These expressions and comments on the tables are given in Appendix C, Sec. 5.

Problem

Compute from the approximate formula Eq. (5.87) the transmission coefficient for at least one of the barriers in Fig. 5.5 and compare with the values plotted. For about what values of T/B is the approximate formula acceptable?

6. *Lifetime of α-Ray Emitters*

We return now to reconsider the impasse which classical nuclear theory faced in 1928. It was shown experimentally that 8-Mev α rays are elastically scattered by a pure coulomb field surrounding the uranium nucleus but that the same nucleus emits only 4-Mev α rays in radioactive decay. The experimental situation was summarized in Fig. 4.2.

In 1928 Gamow and, independently, Gurney and Condon first applied the wave mechanics to the problem of α decay (G2, G50). It was shown that the wave model does not oblige the α ray to go over the top of the barrier but allows the α ray to tunnel through the barrier instead.

As we have just seen, the qualitative model of wave penetration can be quantified if certain simple potential shapes are assumed. Equation (5.86) gives us the basis for a quantitative theory of some aspects of α decay, if we are willing to represent the potential energy between a nucleus and an α ray by a coulomb potential which is cut off at a radius R by a rectangular potential well of poorly defined depth. Actually, we shall find that the experimental data agree so well with this simple model that we must accept it as a reasonable approximation to the ultimate truth.

We have noted that Eq. (5.86) is valid only for the transmission of s waves through the barrier. Happily, the largest and most important class of α-ray emitters does correspond to $l = 0$. These are the nuclei which have even atomic number Z and even mass number A. There are an even number of protons and an even number of neutrons in such nuclei and also in their decay products after the emission of an α ray (helium nucleus, $_2He^4$). Such "even-Z even-A" nuclei are found quite universally to have zero total nuclear angular momentum (Chap. 4). Because angular momentum is conserved in all types of nuclear reactions, the α rays emitted in transitions between the ground levels of even-Z even-A nuclei must be emitted with $l = 0$, that is, as s waves.

When the experimentally known values of α decay energy, $T \sim 5$ to 8 Mev, are substituted in Eq. (5.86), with $R \sim 10^{-12}$ cm, the transmission coefficient $T_0 = e^{-\gamma}$ is found to extend over a domain of about 10^{-20} to 10^{-40}. This range is just what is needed to relate T and R to the broad domain of known α decay half-periods. These extend from 1.39×10^{10} yr for thorium, down to 0.3 μsec for ThC', or a spread of about 10^{23}.

a. Radioactive Decay Constant. The half-period for radioactive decay $T_{\frac{1}{2}}$ is given by

$$T_{\frac{1}{2}} = \frac{\ln 2}{\lambda} = \frac{0.693}{\lambda} \tag{6.1}$$

where the so-called *radioactive decay constant* λ is the probability of decay per unit time for one nucleus. It is known experimentally (Chap. 15) that λ is a constant for any particular type of nucleus and especially that λ is independent of the age of the nucleus.

For a particular type of radioactive atom, say radium, we can express λ as

$$\lambda = \lambda_0 e^{-\gamma} \tag{6.2}$$

where $e^{-\gamma}$ is the barrier transmission coefficient and λ_0 is the decay constant without barrier. Both λ and λ_0 have dimensions of sec^{-1}.

Decay Constant without Barrier. Many investigators have developed theoretical estimates of λ_0. These differ from one another because of the variety of nuclear models which have been assumed and because the calculations for any particular model have been done with varying degrees of approximation. In many models, λ_0 is related to the average spacing between energy levels in the nucleus (p. 573 of B68). The various models give different results for λ_0 which are usually in agreement with experiment only within a factor of about 10^3. At present an empirical value for λ_0 is usually the best choice for quantitative work. Then the variation of $T_{\frac{1}{2}}$ with the kinetic energy T and with R is given very accurately by the $e^{-\gamma}$ term.

A useful rough estimate of λ_0 can be obtained in the following way: The α particle within the parent nucleus is regarded as a standing wave corresponding to a particle having some velocity V_{inside}. This particle would then hit the barrier about V_{inside}/R times per second, which is a crude estimate of λ_0.

In addition, we must include some factor which represents the probability that the α particle exists as a preformed particle in the nucleus. This probability is currently estimated (C28) as lying in the domain between 0.1 and 1 for nuclides which have even-Z and even-A. Then we can express λ_0 roughly as

$\lambda_0 \simeq$ (probability that preformed α particle exists in nucleus)

$$\times \text{(rate of hitting barrier)}$$

$$\simeq (0.1 \text{ to } 1) \times \left(\frac{V_{\text{inside}}}{R} \right) \tag{6.3}$$

The equivalent velocity inside the parent nucleus can be estimated in various ways. One simple method is to associate V_{inside} with the velocity of a nucleon which is confined to a region of space whose dimensions are comparable with the average spacing between nucleons. Then the uncertainty principle gives

$$\Delta p = \frac{\hbar}{\Delta x} \sim M V_{\text{inside}} \tag{6.4}$$

On this basis V_{inside} is of the order of 3×10^9 cm/sec if Δx is of the order of 2×10^{-13} cm and M is a proton or neutron. Then, roughly,

$$\lambda_0 \simeq (0.1 \text{ to } 1) \times \left(\frac{V}{R} \right) \tag{6.5}$$

$$\simeq \frac{10^9 \text{ cm/sec}}{10^{-12} \text{ cm}}$$

$$\simeq 10^{21} \text{ sec}^{-1} \tag{6.6}$$

Figure 6.1 illustrates the strong dependence of the half-period for α decay on nuclear radius. It will be noted that a 10 per cent change in R produces about a 40-fold change in the decay constant and half-period. Because of this very strong exponential dependence of λ on R, it is possible to obtain very close estimates of the effective nuclear radius R even though λ_0 is known only approximately.

b. Empirical Evaluation of Nuclear Unit Radius. We may now represent the decay constant of Eq. (6.2) in the form

$$\lambda = \lambda_0 e^{-\gamma} = \lambda_0 e^{-(a - bR_0^{\frac{1}{2}})} \tag{6.7}$$

where a and b are known functions of Z, z, V, M, and A given by Eq. (5.86) or (5.88). Then each measured case of α decay provides experimental data which make Eq. (6.7) an equation in two unknowns, the empirical constant λ_0 and the nuclear unit radius R_0. Consequently, data on any two suitable cases of α decay permit an empirical evaluation of the nuclear unit radius. When such calculations are carried through, values in the neighborhood of $R_0 = 1.5 \times 10^{-13}$ cm and $\lambda_0 \sim 1 \times 10^{21}$ sec^{-1} are obtained. In Fig. 6.1, the empirical value $\lambda_0 = 1.2 \times 10^{21}$ sec^{-1} was used.

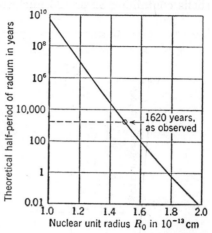

A systematic study of the data on all known cases of α decay in even-Z even-A nuclides has been made by Perlman and Ypsilantis (P16). They calculated the nuclear radius R which would correspond to the observed value of half-period and α decay energy for these nuclei. The exact integral for γ as given by Eq. (5.86) was used, and λ_0 was taken as simply V/R, where V is the velocity of the emitted α ray, with respect to the residual nucleus. The calculated radii show close agreement with the constant-density model $R = R_0 A^{\frac{1}{3}}$. For all *parent* nuclei with $Z \geq 86$, the unweighted average value of R_0 for the daughter nucleus is 1.55×10^{-13} cm. Considering the direction and magnitude of the most common experimental errors in the measurement of α decay energies, Perlman and Ypsilantis

Fig. 6.1 Illustration of the strong dependence of the theoretical half-period for α decay upon small changes in the nuclear radius. The curve shows how rapidly the predicted half-period for radium varies with one's choice of the nuclear unit radius R_0 in the constant-density model $R = R_0 A^{\frac{1}{3}}$. Note that the half-period $T_{\frac{1}{2}}$ varies by 10^{12} when R_0 varies by a factor of 2.

gave greater weight to the relatively few energy determinations which have been made by magnetic analysis and thereby selected as the best value

$$R = 1.48 \times 10^{-13} A^{\frac{1}{3}} \quad \text{cm} \tag{6.8}$$

The radius R and mass number A refer to the *decay product*.

Figure 6.2 presents their results. The points are experimental; the curves are theoretical. General agreement is evident. Those points which are below the curves, especially U^{238} and Th^{232}, may be due to small negative experimental errors in the values of the α decay energy. If the measured values are correct, then these two nuclei have radii which are about 4 per cent greater than Eq. (6.8).

In Fig. 6.2, only the α-ray transitions between nuclear ground levels are plotted. However, the transitions to excited levels in the product nucleus also show excellent agreement with Eq. (6.8) among the even-Z even-A α emitters. The systematics of α decay in odd-A nuclides shows a marked dependence on several factors besides R and T and is discussed in connection with Fig. 4.3 of Chap. 16.

Shell Structure. The polonium isotopes ($Z = 84$) and $_{86}\text{Rn}^{212}$ are not plotted in Fig. 6.2. These nuclei show abnormally small radii, with deviations from Eq. (6.8) amounting to between 1 and 9 per cent. These deviations are probably real. In Chap. 11 we will discuss the abundant evidence for the existence of a shell structure in nuclei and for closed shells containing 82 or 126 nucleons. Nuclei containing 82 protons are

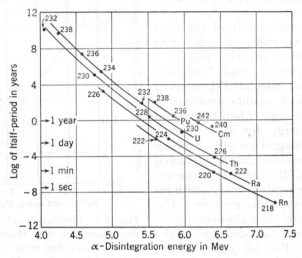

Fig. 6.2 Consistency of the radii of even-Z even-A nuclei with the constant-density model $R = R_0 A^{\frac{1}{3}}$. The experimental points show the observed values of the half-period and total α decay energy for each nuclide. The mass number of the radioactive parent nuclide is given for each point. The curves represent the theoretical values for radioactive parents having the same atomic number (isotopes) and are drawn (P16) from α decay theory, using γ as given by Eq. (5.86) when $R = 1.48 \times 10^{-13} A^{\frac{1}{3}}$ cm, and with λ_0 taken as simply V/R. These effective radii R refer to the daughter nuclides. Note that the values of Z and A given in the figure are for the *parent* nuclides.

found to be especially tightly bound, and they are expected to have radii which are slightly smaller than the "standard" radii. The polonium isotopes decay by α-ray emission to lead ($Z = 82$). Therefore the effective radii for these transitions are small.

The nuclide $_{86}\text{Rn}^{212}$ is an isotope of radon which is produced in the spallation reaction of 340-Mev protons on thorium. In $_{86}\text{Rn}^{212}$, the neutron number is 126, which corresponds to a closed neutron shell in the parent nuclide. The calculated radius for α decay of this nuclide is about 5 per cent less than the "standard" radius. Thus closed shells in either the parent or daughter nucleus do affect R measurably, but only by a few per cent.

c. Effect of Finite Radius of the α Particle. The effective radius R of the inner rectangular potential well is a fictitious radius which was introduced in order to make Eq. (5.72) integrable, so that Eq. (5.86) could be obtained. We have seen that, when λ_0 is taken as V/R, this "well" radius is about $R = 1.48 \times 10^{-13}A^{\frac{1}{3}}$ cm. Other values of R_0 correspond to other models for λ_0. Thus Preston (P31) finds $R_0 \simeq 1.52 \pm 0.02 \times 10^{-13}$ cm when R and the inner potential well depth U_0 are determined from the decay energy T and the half-period. A more clab-

orate analysis by Devaney (D33, B68) leads to $R_0 = 1.57 \times 10^{-13}$ cm when λ_0 is determined by the level spacing in the parent nucleus.

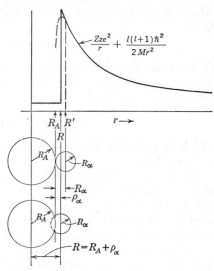

Blatt and Weisskopf (p. 574 of B68) have pointed out that the corrected radius R_A of the daughter product will be a little smaller than R. This is because of the finite effective radius R_α of the α particle. Neutron scattering experiments (D14) have indicated that the radius of the helium nucleus is about $R_\alpha \simeq 2.5 \times 10^{-13}$ cm. The short-range attractive nuclear forces will be felt when the effective separation of centers between the daughter nucleus and the α particle is anything less than

$$R' = R_\alpha + R_A \qquad (6.9)$$

This distance R' is the radius at which the corrected potential barrier begins to be lower than the assumed barrier, as indicated by the dotted potential curve in Fig. 6.3.

The effective well radius R lies somewhere between R' and R_A. It can be expressed analytically as

$$R = R_A + \rho_\alpha \qquad (6.10)$$

Fig. 6.3 Schematic representation of the relationship between the corrected nuclear radius R_A, the effective radius R of the rectangular potential well, and the effective radius R_α of the α particle. The corrected potential (dotted) breaks away from the assumed potential at $r = R_A + R_\alpha \equiv R'$. The α particle and the daughter nucleus are still partially immersed in each other when the separation of their centers is R. The potential well radius can be expressed as $R = R_A + \rho_\alpha$, with $\rho_\alpha \simeq 1.2 \times 10^{-13}$ cm.

where ρ_α is a semiempirical radius correction for the α particle. We can eliminate R_A between the last two equations to obtain

$$R_\alpha - \rho_\alpha = R' - R \qquad (6.11)$$

The choice of ρ_α is somewhat arbitrary. The value

$$\rho_\alpha = 1.2 \times 10^{-13} \text{ cm} \qquad (6.12)$$

has been picked by Weisskopf (W21, B68) as being reasonable. This quantity also enters the interpretation of nuclear barrier transparency to bombarding α particles, as in (α,n) reactions, where $\rho_\alpha = 1.2 \times 10^{-13}$ cm gives reasonable agreement with observations (Chap. 14, Fig. 2.9).

We can relate the corrected radii R_A to the effective well radius R by means of Eqs. (6.10) and (6.12).   Then

$$R = R_A + \rho_\alpha = R_{0A}A^{\frac{1}{3}} + \rho_\alpha$$

$$= \left(R_{0A} + \frac{\rho_\alpha}{A^{\frac{1}{3}}}\right) A^{\frac{1}{3}} \tag{6.13}$$

where R_{0A} is the unit corrected radius.   For the heavy nuclei, $A^{\frac{1}{3}} \simeq 6$; hence

$$R \simeq (R_{0A} + 0.2 \times 10^{-13})A^{\frac{1}{3}} \qquad \text{cm} \tag{6.14}$$

If we take the α-decay data as corresponding to $R \simeq (1.5 \pm 0.1) \times 10^{-13}A^{\frac{1}{3}}$ cm, then the unit corrected radius R_{0A} of the daughter product whose mass number is A becomes

$$R_{0A} \simeq (1.3 \pm 0.1) \times 10^{-13} \text{ cm} \tag{6.15}$$

which is probably the best value now available from the appraisal of α-decay data.

d. Electromagnetic Radius in α Decay.   We note from Eq. (6.15) that the effective radii R_A for α decay have a somewhat larger unit radius than would be expected from the electromagnetic unit radii determined, for example, from μ-mesonic atoms, Eq. (3.11).   A possible reconciliation of the two results has been discussed by Hill and Wheeler (H53) in terms of the so-called *collective model* of nuclei.   The finite electric quadrupole moment found for many nuclides (Chap. 4) suggests that truly spherical nuclei are rare, and that most nuclei are slightly ellipsoidal, including many which have even-Z and even-A.   From an ellipsoidal nucleus the α decay probability would be slightly greater than from a spherical nucleus of equal volume, because the α decay rate is really a function of both the average nuclear radius and the ellipticity.

Hill and Wheeler have estimated that an ellipsoidal deformation which stretches the nuclear axis by 10 per cent would result in about a 16-fold increase in the α decay rate, as compared with a spherical nucleus of the same volume.   Thus if the electromagnetic radius means the radius of a sphere whose volume equals that of the ellipsoidal nucleus, the ellipsoidal shape enhancement of the α decay rate would emerge from conventional α decay theory in the form of an apparent nuclear radius R_A which is larger than the corresponding electromagnetic radius.   Measurements of the quadrupole moments, and of the μ-mesonic "X rays," for nuclides heavier than Bi^{209} are clearly needed for the future quantitative clarification of this topic.

Problems

1. Use the uncertainty principle to show that a nucleon which is confined to a region of the order of $\Delta x \sim 1 \times 10^{-13}$ cm must have a velocity of the order of 6×10^9 cm/sec and a kinetic energy of the order of 20 Mev.

2. Calculate empirical values of λ_0 and R_0, as indicated by Eq. (6.7), using the data for any pair of the following carefully measured cases of α decay.

Parent	Daughter	T_α, Mev	T, Mev	Half-period	λ, sec^{-1}
$_{88}Ra^{226}$	$_{86}Rn^{222}$	4.777	4.863	1620 yr	1.27×10^{-11}
$_{86}Rn^{222}$	$_{84}RaA^{218}$	5.486	5.587	3.825 d	2.097×10^{-6}
$_{84}RaA^{218}$	$_{82}RaB^{214}$	5.998	6.110	3.05 min	3.78×10^{-3}

NOTE: The tabulated λ for Ra corresponds to the approximately 94 per cent of the disintegrations which go to the ground level of Rn. These correspond to a "*partial half-period*" of about 1,740 yr, if the *total* half-period is 1,620 yr.

3. Radium has been found to emit a small percentage of 4.593-Mev α rays in addition to the main group whose energy is 4.777 Mev. This weak group of α rays corresponds to transitions to a 0.187-Mev excited level in radon. Estimate from α decay theory what fraction of the transitions should go to the excited level, if $l = 2$ for this transition and $l = 0$ for transitions to the ground level.

4. Justify the extremely strong dependence of λ on T and R by showing that the *fractional* change in λ equals the *absolute* change in γ, that is,

$$\frac{\Delta\lambda}{\lambda} = -\Delta\gamma$$

if $\Delta\gamma$ is small.

7. *Anomalous Scattering of* α *Particles*

We have seen that the elastic scattering of 4- to 8-Mev α rays by heavy nuclei follows the Rutherford scattering law (Chap. 1, Fig. 3.3). This scattering is therefore due to a simple inverse-square coulomb force between the scattering particles. In these classical experiments the numerical value of the parameter $2Zz/137\beta$ was of the order of 50. Therefore the transparency of the nuclear barrier was negligible (Eq. 5.88).

In experiments conducted at small values of $2Zz/137\beta$ some barrier transmission will occur. Then mechanisms other than the coulomb interaction will also become effective, and the observed scattering will become more complicated. The name *anomalous scattering* applies to all instances of elastic nuclear scattering in which any type of deviations from pure coulomb scattering is observable. Several separate nuclear mechanisms often conspire to produce these deviations.

a. Classical Model of Anomalous Scattering. Rutherford was among the first to recognize that an estimate of the size of nuclei could be obtained by determining the smallest α-ray energy which would produce anomalous scattering. Classically, anomalous scattering should set in at an α-ray energy which is just large enough to bring the incident α ray to the edge of the scattering nucleus. In a strictly head-on collision, this would occur when the initial kinetic energy $\frac{1}{2}MV^2$ in the center-of-mass system is just equal to the barrier height $B = Zze^2/R$. Then the classical collision diameter $b = 2Zze^2/MV^2$ would be a rough measure of the nuclear radius R.

For scattering angles which are less than 180°, the minimum separation ρ_{min}, or *closest distance of approach*, between the particles is greater than the collision diameter b and is given classically by [see Appendix B, Eq. (82)]

$$\rho_{min} = \frac{b}{2}\left(\csc\frac{\Theta}{2} + 1\right) \qquad (7.1)$$

where Θ is the deflection in the center-of-mass coordinates. Then for $\Theta = 180°$, $\rho_{min} = b$; but $\rho_{min} = 2b$ when Θ is about $39°$, and $\rho_{min} = 4b$ when Θ is about $16.5°$.

Classically, anomalous scattering should set in at an α-ray energy which depends on the angle of scattering Θ and which has a minimum value just equal to the barrier height if $\Theta = 180°$. We shall see that the experiments contradict both these classical predictions. As the energy of the incident particles is increased, anomalous scattering actually makes its appearance almost simultaneously at all angles of scattering. Moreover, the onset occurs at α-ray energies which are well below the barrier height.

In his observations of the scattering of α rays by hydrogen, Rutherford (R45) first studied anomalous scattering as early as 1919. Throughout the subsequent decade Rutherford inspired a number of workers who collected fundamental but puzzling data on the anomalous scattering of α rays by a number of low-Z elements. These data were admirably compiled by Rutherford, Chadwick, and Ellis (R50) in 1930. Subsequently, Mott and others applied the wave mechanics to the interpretation of scattering in terms of a phase-shift analysis (Appendix C) and thus resolved many of the accumulated conflicts between theory and experiment.

b. Wave Model of Anomalous Scattering. We can expect a measurable amount of barrier transmission for bombarding energies which are distinctly below the barrier height (Fig. 5.5). Those particles which penetrate the coulomb barrier and reach the nuclear surface will experience nuclear forces in addition to the coulomb forces and will be anomalously scattered. Anomalous scattering is thus intimately related to barrier transparency.

Some of the particles which reach the nuclear surface may be able to penetrate it and thereby form a compound nucleus. For example, an α ray transmitted through the surface of an $_8O^{16}$ nucleus forms the compound nucleus $_{10}Ne^{20}$. Such a compound nucleus will not be in its ground level but will be highly excited because it comprises the rest masses of the interacting particles plus their mutual kinetic energy. Each such compound nucleus possesses a number of quantized excited levels, which are the quasi-stationary energy levels, or "virtual levels," of the nucleus. If the kinetic energy of the bombarding particle happens to be near or equal to that required for the formation of one of these excited levels, then penetration of the nuclear surface is facilitated. This *resonance* formation of the compound nucleus occurs when the magnitude and slope of the wave functions inside and outside the nuclear surface can be matched at substantially full amplitude (compare Appendix C, Fig. 11; also Chap. 14, Figs. 1.1 and 1.2).

Once the excited compound nucleus has been formed, it will experience one of a number of possible competing transitions (Chap. 14). One possibility is the reemission of the incident particle, or one identical with it, without loss of total kinetic energy in the system. The directional distribution of reemission will depend on many factors, especially those involving angular momenta (Chap. 6). The total process of resonance formation of the compound nucleus and its subsequent dissociation by emission of a similar particle, without loss of kinetic energy in the system, is called elastic *resonance scattering*.

In principle, the total elastic scattering can now be divided, somewhat arbitrarily, into three cooperating phenomena.

1. *Coulomb Potential Scattering.* This is the classical Rutherford scattering. In the wave model its predominantly forward distribution is due to interference between partial waves of all angular momenta *l*. Large values of *l* are effective here because of the long-range character of the coulomb force.

2. *Nuclear Potential Scattering.* This is the reflection from the abrupt change in potential at the surface of the nucleus, combined with "shadow" diffraction around the nucleus. Its existence presupposes the penetration of the coulomb barrier, which is greatest for partial waves of small angular momentum. For this reason, and because it depends on short-range forces, its principal contribution at low bombarding energies is to *s*-wave scattering. The *s* wave is spherically symmetric. Therefore the nuclear potential scattering can give rise to anomalous scattering at all angles at the smallest bombarding energies which permit significant barrier penetration. As the Rutherford scattering is smallest in the backward direction ($\Theta = 180°$), the ratio of anomalous to classical scattering is generally greatest in the backward direction. Theoretical estimates of the pure nuclear potential scattering are obtained by presuming that penetration of the nuclear surface is negligible if the energy is not near a resonance. The corresponding scattering can then be evaluated as that due to an impenetrable sphere.

3. *Nuclear Resonance Scattering.* This occurs only at energies near a resonance level, where the incident particle can easily form a compound nucleus and a similar particle may be emitted before any other competing emission or radiative process takes place in the compound nucleus. In the incident plane wave, only that partial wave will be involved whose angular momentum *l* will permit formation of the particular excited level involved.

Coherence. These three processes must be regarded in the wave theory as taking place simultaneously. Each can, in principle, be described by an appropriate phase shift for each partial wave. The net result is very complicated analytically (B41, F45, M69) because *all three effects add coherently*. There are, therefore, opportunities for the occurrence of many interference minima and maxima in the net angular distribution. In a few cases involving resonance scattering it is now possible to deduce the angular momentum of the excited compound level from the angular distribution of the scattering intensity (K29, L13).

The three processes may be better visualized by a grouping into the "external scattering" or "total potential scattering" of a perfectly reflecting sphere surrounded by a coulomb field and the "internal scattering" due to resonance formation of a compound nucleus. These processes are indicated schematically in Fig. 7.1.

c. General Characteristics of the Experimental Results on Anomalous Scattering. The simplest cases of elastic scattering of charged particles are those in which the incident and target particles both have zero spin.

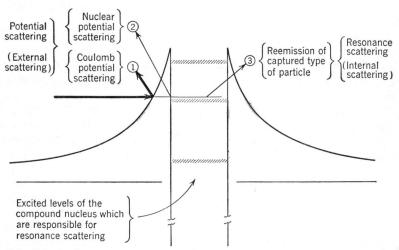

Fig. 7.1 Schematic representation of the three coherent elastic-scattering processes whose cooperative effect is the total anomalous scattering.

Then an analytical representation which is not too formidable can be obtained (p. 319 of M69) for the scattering amplitude $f(\vartheta)$ and for the differential cross section $|f(\vartheta)|^2 \, d\Omega$, as defined by Eq. (107) of Appendix C. Among the light particles which are available as projectiles, only the α particle has zero spin. These particular theoretical restrictions are satisfied, then, in collisions between α rays and target nuclei which have even-Z and even-A and, hence, zero spin. The corresponding experimental work is meager, and most of it has been done only with sources of natural α rays, such as RaC'. There results an inevitable lack of high resolution in energy and angle, which usually makes precise analysis difficult. Nevertheless, the over-all features of elastic scattering of charged particles are well portrayed in these experiments.

Figures 7.2 and 7.3 show the experimental results for the scattering of α rays by oxygen nuclei. Bearing in mind the experimental uncertainties, which are suggested in part by the vertical and horizontal lines through the points, the following general characteristics may be seen.

1. *Onset below Barrier Energy.* The coulomb barrier height, between $_8O^{16}$ and $_2He^4$, is about 6.1 Mev if $R \simeq 1.5 \times 10^{-13}A^{\frac{1}{3}}$ cm. An α-ray

kinetic energy $T_\alpha = 7.6$ Mev (laboratory system) would be required to produce $T = 6.1$ Mev in the center-of-mass coordinates. Deviations from classical scattering are clearly evident at $T_\alpha \le 5$ Mev, which is only about two-thirds of the barrier height. From Fig. 5.5, we could

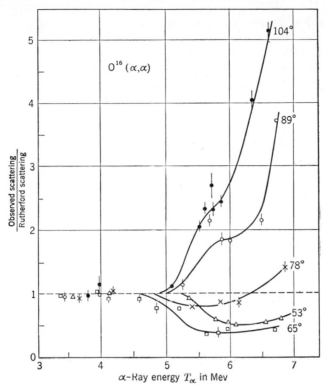

Fig. 7.2 Elastic scattering of α rays by O^{16}. The ratio of the observed scattering to that expected classically is plotted against the energy in the laboratory coordinates of the incident α rays. The mean scattering angle in laboratory coordinates is shown for each of the five curves, but the angular widths were actually quite large and somewhat overlapping. The α rays were from RaC' (7.68 Mev) and, in some cases, ThC' (8.77 Mev) and were slowed down to the smaller energies by absorbing foils. This absorption introduces an inhomogeneity of incident energy, because of straggling. Below about $T_\alpha \simeq 4.5$ Mev, the observed scattering was indistinguishable from classical. At the higher energies, all the principal features of nuclear potential scattering and resonance scattering are seen. [*Brubaker* (B136).]

estimate that the barrier penetration may be of the order of 10 to 20 per cent for this α-ray energy.

2. *Simultaneous Onset at All Angles.* At the lowest energies, the anomalous scattering is seen to vary smoothly with energy. This monotonic deviation, at any particular scattering angle, is characteristic of the potential scattering. Its shape is due to the coherent combination of the potential scattering amplitudes from the nuclear surface and from the coulomb barrier. From classical theory, Eq. (7.1), one would expect

the anomalies to appear at the smallest energies for the largest scattering angles. This is clearly not the case. Within the accuracy of measurement, Fig. 7.2 shows that at all directions the anomalies begin at the same energy. This occurs at the smallest energy for which s-wave penetration of the coulomb barrier is sufficient to produce a detectable amplitude of nuclear potential scattering.

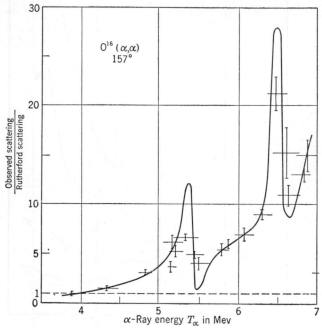

Fig. 7.3   Elastic scattering of α rays by O^{16} at a mean angle of 157° in the laboratory coordinates.   Sources and techniques are somewhat similar to Fig. 7.2, but the angular spread is confined to about 15°.   The curve drawn represents the theoretical variation of p-wave resonance scattering, from two levels at about 5.5 Mev and 6.5 Mev, superimposed on the monotonic deviation due to nuclear potential scattering.   As in Fig. 7.2, detectable deviations from classical scattering occur at all energies above about 4.5 Mev, which is only about two-thirds the barrier height. [*Ferguson and Walker* (F30).]

3. *Resonances.*   At $T_\alpha \simeq 5.5$ Mev the two upper curves of Fig. 7.2 are clearly not monotonic.   The irregularity is more apparent in Fig. 7.3, where the effects of two discrete resonance levels can be seen.   In Fig. 7.3 the curve has been drawn with a general shape and amplitude which correspond to the theoretical resonance scattering for p waves, superimposed on a monotonic increase in potential scattering.   The fit is distinctly better than could be obtained by assuming s-wave or d-wave resonance scattering (F30, R28).   This implies that both the corresponding excited levels in the compound nucleus Ne^{20} have an angular momentum of unity, because they are formed from spinless particles by capture

in the $l = 1$ wave. These two isolated resonance levels occur at bombarding energies of $T_\alpha \simeq 5.5$ and 6.5 Mev. It can be shown from mass-energy relationships that they therefore correspond to excited levels at about 10.1 and 9.0 Mev about the ground level of $_{10}Ne^{20}$. Five additional scattering anomalies, corresponding to excited levels between 6.738 Mev and 7.854 Mev in Ne^{20}, have been found by Cameron (C5), who made precision measurements of the $O^{16}(\alpha,\alpha)$ elastic scattering, using electrostatically accelerated helium nuclei over the energy range from 0.94 Mev to 4.0 Mev.

4. *Angular Distribution.* The angular distribution is nonuniform. Note from Fig. 7.2 that the sign of the initial potential scattering anomaly can be either positive or negative, depending on the angle of observation. The potential scattering anomaly is most apparent in the backward direction, where the classical scattering is smallest. The over-all angular distribution contains maxima and minima which are due to constructive and destructive interference between the three components of scattering intensity. In any particular direction, such as the 157° observations of Fig. 7.3, the peak and valley due to resonance scattering may dominate the monotonic background of potential scattering. The angular distribution of resonance scattering is determined primarily by the Legendre polynomials $P_l(\cos \vartheta)$ which characterize the partial waves of angular-momentum quantum number l [see, for example, Appendix C, Eq. (118)]. In particular, nodes can occur at angles which are determined by the condition $P_l(\cos \vartheta) = 0$. For example, $P_1(90°) = 0$, $P_2(125°) = 0$. Thus the angular distribution of maxima and minima of resonance scattering can be used to determine the angular momentum of the resonance level in the case of a collision between two spinless particles (R28, C5).

d. **Nuclear Radii.** The smallest bombarding energy at which nuclear potential scattering is detectable depends upon the experimental resolution and upon the shape and position of peaks due to resonance scattering, which may mask the onset of potential scattering. As a means of measuring nuclear radii, anomalous scattering therefore is usually less accurate than several other contemporary methods. Such results as

TABLE 7.1. NUCLEAR BARRIER HEIGHT B, EFFECTIVE RADIUS R, AND
EFFECTIVE UNIT RADIUS $R_0 = R/A^{\frac{1}{3}}$

Based on Pollard's (P25) summary of the minimum energy T (center of mass) for anomalous scattering of α rays.

Element	Z	T, Mev	B, Mev	R, 10^{-13} cm	R_0, 10^{-13} cm
He	2	1.4	2.4	2.4	1.5
Li	3	2.0	3.3	2.6	1.4
Be	4	2.4	4.0	2.9	1.4
B	5	2.8	4.5	3.2	1.5
C	6	3.1	5.1	3.4	1.5
N	7	3.5	5.6	3.6	1.5
Mg	12	5.4	8.5	4.0	1.4
Al	13	5.8	9.0	4.1	1.4

have been obtained are in acceptable agreement with the values obtained by all other methods.

Pollard (P25), in 1935, correlated the data then available on the energy of onset of anomalies in the scattering of α rays by eight light elements. Pollard's interpretation of the data accumulated by various investigators was based on the reasonable assumption that nuclear potential scattering would become experimentally detectable when the barrier transmission is about 10 per cent for s waves. With this assumption, a recalculation of all the data led to the values of nuclear radii which are summarized in Table 7.1 and in Fig. 7.4. It will be seen that these data are in accord with the constant-density nuclear model

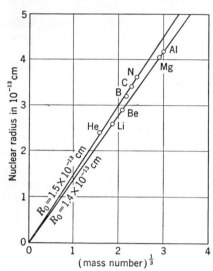

$$R = R_0 A^{\frac{1}{3}} \qquad (7.2)$$

with an effective nuclear unit radius in the domain of $R_0 = 1.4$ to 1.5×10^{-13} cm. When the effective radii are corrected for the finite size of the α ray, in the manner of Eq. (6.15), the unit corrected radii

Fig. 7.4   Effective nuclear radius R, from Table 7.1, vs. $A^{\frac{1}{3}}$.

for the target nuclei are again in the domain of $R_{0A} \simeq (1.3 \pm 0.1) \times 10^{-13}$ cm.

Problems

1. The scattering of α rays by hydrogen was found by Chadwick and Bieler (C13) to be in accord with the Rutherford scattering law for 1.9-, 2.8-, and 3.3-Mev α rays but to be markedly anomalous for 4.4-, 5.7-, 7.5-, and 8.6-Mev α rays (laboratory coordinates).

(a) Show that the numerical value of the parameter $2Zz/137\beta$ is about 0.6 for the 4.4-Mev α rays.

(b) Comment on the degree of validity which you would expect for classical theory in such a collision.

(c) Calculate $2Zz/137\beta$ for some of the other α-ray energies used. How can such small variations in $2Zz/137\beta$ be expected to spell the difference between classical and anomalous scattering?

2. (a) When α rays are scattered by hydrogen, show that the kinetic energy in the center-of-mass coordinates is only one-fifth of the laboratory kinetic energy of the incident α ray.

(b) Could the same nuclear interaction be studied by bombarding helium with accelerated protons?

(c) Determine what fraction of the proton energy would then be available in the C coordinates.

(d) If anomalous scattering is observed with 4.4-Mev α rays on hydrogen, what energy protons should be used to produce the same nuclear effects when helium is bombarded by protons?

(*e*) Does $2Zz/137\beta$ have a different value for the 4.4-Mev α rays and for the proton energy determined in (*d*)?

(*f*) Show that, in general, the parameter $2Zz/137\beta$ is not dependent upon which of the interacting particles is the target in the laboratory, so long as the kinetic energy in the center-of-mass coordinates is kept constant.

3. The elastic scattering observed when helium is bombarded by 1-Mev to 4-Mev protons has been shown (C55) to be largely due to resonance scattering, involving the formation and prompt dissociation of excited levels of the compound nucleus Li^5, which is formed by the coalescence of He^4 and H^1. The mirror nucleus of Li^5 is He^5, which should have an analogous internal structure and could be studied by scattering fast neutrons in helium (A3). Would you anticipate that the neutron energy required to excite these levels in He^5 would be about the same as the proton energy required to excite the analogous levels in Li^5, or would you think that the coulomb barrier in the (p-α) interaction would require that greater energies be used in this case? Why?

8. *Cross Sections for Nuclear Reactions Produced by Charged Particles*

Classically, nuclear reactions initiated by charged particles should begin to take place when the bombarding energy T in center-of-mass coordinates is just equal to the coulomb barrier height $B = Zze^2/R$, because then the classical closest possible distance of approach is just equal to the nuclear radius R. Actually, of course, these reactions take place abundantly at T considerably less than B. This fundamental fact was dramatically proved in the pioneer experiments by Cockroft and Walton (C27) in 1932.

Using high-voltage transformers and rectifiers in voltage doubling circuits, and a suitable ion source and discharge tube, Cockroft and Walton produced a beam of protons which had been accelerated to about 0.6 Mev. This energy is far below the barrier height, even for the lightest elements ($B \simeq 1.5$ Mev for $Li + p$). But the success of Gamow's barrier-transmission concepts as applied to α decay stimulated Cockroft and Walton to believe that these low-energy protons could penetrate into nuclei and possibly produce observable disintegrations. A proton beam current of up to 5 μa provided enough incident particles to compensate for their very small individual probability of penetrating the nuclear barrier. At proton energies as small as 0.12 Mev, the (p,α) reaction was observed in lithium targets, Fig. 8.1, and the (p,α) reaction was reported for a number of heavier target elements as well (B, C, F, Al, . . .). The daring and brilliant success of these experiments should be kept in view today, when the work has long since taken its place in the archives of physics.

a. Bohr's Compound-nucleus Model of Nuclear Reactions. The experimental and theoretical aspects of nuclear reactions are discussed in more detail in several later chapters. Here we shall note some of the fundamental physical concepts which underlie our current views about nuclear reactions, especially with regard to the influence of nuclear radius.

Bohr, in 1936, first clearly emphasized the so-called compound-nucleus model of nuclear reactions, which has since been well verified in a large class of nuclear reactions. It is assumed that when some target nucleus A is bombarded by an incident nuclear particle a, the two may coalesce to form a compound nucleus $(A + a)$, where the parentheses denote (F62) that the compound nucleus is produced at an excitation energy which is dictated by the bombarding energy. In the compound nucleus $(A + a)$, there are assumed to be strong interactions between all the nucleons. The incident nuclear particle a loses its independent identity, and the total energy of the excited compound nucleus is shared in a complicated manner by all the nucleons present. The compound nucleus $(A + a)$ is thought of as being in a quasi-stationary quantum state, whose mean life is long ($\sim 10^{-16 \pm 3}$ sec) compared with the time for a proton to cross the nucleus ($\sim 10^{-22}$ sec). Identically the same compound nucleus, and in the same level of excitation, can be produced by the collision (usually at a different bombarding energy) of other nuclei, say, B and b, so that it is possible to have

$$(A + a) = (B + b)$$

(See, for example, Figs. 1.4 and 2.8 of Chap. 14.) In the Bohr postulates, the properties of the compound nucleus $(A + a)$ are independent of its mode of formation, i.e., the compound nucleus "forgets" how it was formed.

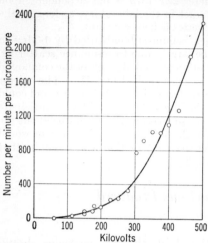

Fig. 8.1 The first "excitation function" for artificially accelerated particles, as obtained by Cockroft and Walton (C27). The yield of α particles, from a thick target of lithium, is plotted as a function of the energy of the incident protons. The absolute yield was estimated to be about one α particle per 10^8 protons at 0.5 Mev. Note that the (p,α) reaction is detectable here at an incident energy which is only about one-tenth the estimated coulomb-barrier height ($B \simeq 1.5$ Mev), and note that the yield increases rapidly (roughly exponentially) with bombarding energy. The reaction has since been observed at proton energies as small as 10 kev. This excitation function for Li(p,α) was promptly confirmed, and was extended to 700-kev protons from a small cyclotron, by Lawrence, Livingston, and White (L14). [*From Cockroft and Walton* (C27).]

The second step in the nuclear reaction is the dissociation of the compound nucleus. This dissociation can generally take place in a large number of ways, sometimes called "exit channels," subject to the conservation laws for mass-energy, charge, angular momentum, etc. The competition among various alternative modes of dissociation does not depend on the manner in which the compound nucleus was formed, i.e., on the "entrance channel." Schematically, any nuclear reaction in which a compound nucleus is formed can be represented as

Entrance	Compound	Exit
channel	nucleus	channels

$$A + a \longrightarrow (A+a) \begin{cases} A + a & \text{(elastic scattering)} \\ A^* + a & \text{(inelastic scattering)} \\ B + b & \text{(nuclear transformation)} \\ C + b + c & \text{(nuclear transformation)} \\ D + d & \text{(nuclear transformation)} \\ \text{etc.} & \text{(nuclear transformation)} \end{cases} \tag{8.1}$$

The asterisk, as in A^*, denotes an excited level of a nucleus. As an explicit example, the reaction on F^{19} in which a proton is captured and an α particle is emitted would be written

$$_9F^{19} + {}_1H^1 \rightarrow ({}_{10}Ne^{20}) \rightarrow {}_2He^4 + {}_8O^{16} \tag{8.2}$$

The same compound nucleus might instead emit a neutron, leaving $_{10}Ne^{19}$ as the residual nucleus, according to

$$_9F^{19} + {}_1H^1 \rightarrow ({}_{10}Ne^{20}) \rightarrow {}_0n^1 + {}_{10}Ne^{19} \tag{8.3}$$

In the more compact notation which is usually used for nuclear reactions, these two competing reactions would be written $F^{19}(p,\alpha)O^{16}$ and $F^{19}(p,n)Ne^{19}$, without explicit designation of the compound nucleus.

The cross section for any nuclear reaction which involves a compound nucleus can then be written as

$$\sigma(a,b) = [\sigma_{\text{com}}(a)]\left(\frac{\Gamma_b}{\Gamma}\right) \qquad \text{all } b \neq a \tag{8.4}$$

where $\sigma_{\text{com}}(a)$ is the cross section for formation of the compound nucleus. The partial level width Γ_b is proportional to the probability that the compound nucleus will dissociate by the emission of the particle b, and the total level width $\Gamma = \Sigma\Gamma_i$ is the sum of the partial widths for all possible modes of dissociation. Thus Γ_b/Γ is simply the fraction of the compound nuclei which dissociates by emission of b. Equation (8.4) is applicable to all cases of reactions ($b \neq a$) and to inelastic scattering. It is not applicable to elastic scattering, $\sigma(a,a) = \sigma_{sc}$, because of interference effects [Chap. 14, Eq. (1.16)].

b. **Cross Section for Formation of the Compound Nucleus.** One major objective of the theoretical treatment of nuclear reactions (Chap. 14) is the prediction of σ_{com} as a function of the incident energy and other parameters of the colliding particles. The incident particles are represented as a plane wave, whose rationalized de Broglie wavelength of relative motion is

$$\lambdabar = \frac{\hbar}{MV} = \frac{\hbar}{\sqrt{2MT}} \tag{8.5}$$

where M = reduced mass

V = velocity of relative motion

$T = \frac{1}{2}MV^2$ = kinetic energy in center-of-mass coordinates

This plane wave is the sum of partial waves, corresponding to particles whose angular-momentum quantum numbers are l. For each partial wave, the maximum possible reaction cross section is $(2l + 1)\pi\lambda^2$ [Appendix C, Eq. (85)]. Then the actual cross section, for each partial wave l, can be represented as

$$\sigma_{\text{com},l} = (2l + 1)\pi\lambda^2 \mathsf{T}_l \tag{8.6}$$

in which T_l is the over-all barrier-transmission coefficient. For purposes of visualization, we may write

$$\mathsf{T}_l = P_l(T)\xi_l(T) \tag{8.6a}$$

in which $P_l(T)$ is a Gamow-type coulomb-penetration factor representing the chance that the incident particle, with kinetic energy T, can penetrate the coulomb and centrifugal barrier and thus reach the nuclear surface, while $\xi_l(T)$ is called the "sticking probability" and represents the chance that the particle can pass through the potential discontinuity at the nuclear surface and be absorbed to form the compound nucleus. When all values of l are considered, we can write the cross section for formation of the compound nucleus as

$$\sigma_{\text{com}} = \sum_{l=0}^{l=\infty} (2l + 1)\pi\lambda^2 P_l(T)\xi_l(T) \tag{8.7}$$

In the actual calculation of σ_{com} along the lines represented schematically by Eq. (8.7), the over-all transmission probability $P_l\xi_l$ cannot in fact be treated purely as two sequential probabilities, but this simplified viewpoint is convenient for giving a physical picture of the absorption process. The theoretical values of σ_{com} for charged particles depend in a complicated way on Z, z, T, R, and on assumed properties of the interior of the nucleus, and they cannot be expressed in any simple analytical form. In the continuum theory of nuclear reactions, which is most applicable for reasonably large T and Z, σ_{com} is averaged over any individual resonances which may be present. The theoretical results for σ_{com} are given in the form of tables and graphs, such as Fig. 2.10 of Chap. 14. Some simple and important qualitative generalizations should be noted at this time:

1. σ_{com} is small but finite for bombarding energies T which are far below the coulomb barrier height $B = Zze^2/R$.

2. σ_{com} increases very rapidly with T, when $T < B$, behaving roughly like a Gamow-type barrier penetration.

3. σ_{com} definitely does not reach its maximum value at $T = B$. The barrier height is B only for s waves. For $l > 0$ the centrifugal barrier must be added.

4. σ_{com} approaches asymptotically a maximum value which is simply the geometrical area of the target nucleus, πR^2, when $T \gg B$.

Semiclassical Approximation for σ_{com}. An instructive approximation for the cross section σ_{com} for large bombarding energies can be obtained easily and is found to be in surprisingly good agreement with the results obtained by the detailed wave-mechanical calculation.

In the classical collision between two charged particles Ze and ze, the closest distance of approach ρ_{min} is given by Eq. (7.1), which can be written

$$\rho_{min} = \frac{Zze^2}{2T}\left[\frac{1}{\sin{(\Theta/2)}} + 1\right] \tag{8.8}$$

where the incident energy T and the scattering angle Θ are both in center-of-mass coordinates, and where the impact parameter is

$$x = \frac{Zze^2}{2T}\cot\frac{\Theta}{2}$$

The classical cross section for forming the compound nucleus, by collision of the charged particles, is simply $\sigma_{com} = \pi x^2$, where x is the largest value of the impact parameter for which the charged particles come in contact, that is, $\rho_{min} \leq R'$, if R' is the effective nuclear radius. If we set $R' = (R + \lambda)$, where R is the radius of the target nucleus and λ represents the "size" of the projectile, or the lack of definition of its impact parameter, as in Eq. (5.81a), then we find at once that

$$\sigma_{com} = \pi x^2 = \pi(R + \lambda)^2\left(1 - \frac{U}{T}\right) \tag{8.9}$$

where

$$U \equiv \frac{Zze^2}{R + \lambda} = B\frac{R}{R + \lambda}$$

is the coulomb potential at a separation $R + \lambda$, and $T = \hbar^2/2M\lambda^2$ is the incident kinetic energy in C coordinates. Equation (8.9) gives meaningful results obviously only if $T > B > U$, that is, for incident energies which are well above the barrier height for s waves. The detailed wave-mechanical calculations give values of σ_{com} which are only 15 per cent lower than Eq. (8.9) when $T/B = 1.2$ and which are essentially equivalent when $T/B > 2$. As T increases, λ decreases and $\sigma_{com} \to \pi R^2$ in the limit of $T \gg B$.

Effects of Nuclear Radius on σ_{com}. In the higher-energy domain, the effects of the nuclear radius R on the cross section σ_{com} for formation of the compound nucleus are evident from Eq. (8.9). For fixed values of Z, z, M, and T, an increase in R increases σ_{com}, both by increasing the asymptotic limit πR^2 and by lowering the coulomb barrier height B. Also, at small bombarding energies, an increase in R increases σ_{com}.

When $T < B$, an increase in R makes the coulomb barrier lower and thinner (Fig. 5.7) and also reduces the centrifugal barrier, all these effects tending to increase σ_{com}. The magnitude of these changes is shown in Figs. 2.9 and 2.10 of Chap. 14, for two representative values of the nuclear unit radius $R_0 = 1.3 \times 10^{-13}$ cm and $R_0 = 1.5 \times 10^{-13}$ cm.

The presently available experimental data on the cross section for formation of the compound nucleus, when interpreted in terms of the theory (S30) of charged-particle reactions as available at the beginning of 1954, correspond to nuclear unit radii near the domain of

$$R_0 = (1.4 \pm 0.1) \times 10^{-13} \text{ cm} \qquad (8.10)$$

on the constant-density model $R = R_0 A^{\frac{1}{3}}$. This radius is a "nuclear-force radius," and because of the assumptions which enter the theory of nuclear reactions, R may be expected to differ by the order of 1×10^{-13} cm from the radii deduced from other types of experiments.

9. *Nuclear Cross Sections for the Attenuation of Fast Neutrons*

The attenuation of a collimated monoenergetic beam of fast neutrons, by a wide selection of absorbing materials, has been measured in a number of experiments. In this way the total nuclear cross section, for absorption plus scattering, can be determined as a function of mass number A. Some of the conclusions, which bear on the question of nuclear radii, will be summarized here, but we defer the details for discussion in Chap. 14.

Because it possesses no charge, a fast neutron passes easily through bulk matter. In a close collision with a nucleus, there is no coulomb deflection, and so the target cross section might be expected to be simply the geometrical cross section πR^2. Ascribing, as in Eq. (8.9), a "size" λ to the neutron, a better estimate of the cross section for a direct encounter is

$$\sigma_{\text{abs}} \simeq \pi (R + \lambda)^2 \qquad (9.1)$$

where $\sigma_{\text{abs}} = \sigma_{\text{com}}$ when there is no elastic reemission of neutrons after formation of the compound nucleus. This simple relationship corresponds to $z = 0$ in Eq. (8.9), and it is found to be a good representation of the detailed wave-mechanical theory (F49) whenever $R \gg \lambda$. Equation (9.1) has been thought of as valid for neutrons of greater than about 10 Mev, for which $\lambda = 1.44 \times 10^{-13}$ cm. Equation (9.1) represents the actual absorption cross section only to the extent that all neutrons which strike the target sphere are actually absorbed by the nucleus. Recent evidence has shown clearly that swift incident neutrons have a small but finite probability of passing through nuclear matter without being absorbed (see Fig. 2.3 of Chap. 14). Thus nuclei can be described as slightly "translucent," rather than completely "opaque," to incident fast neutrons.

Considering the neutron beam as a plane wave, we note that each nucleus should cast a shadow, just as would be the case for an opaque disk intercepting a beam of light. This shadow, in the wave-optical model, is the result of interference from waves scattered from near the edge of the opaque sphere. It can be shown easily that exactly the same amount of incident energy is diffracted as is absorbed by the opaque sphere (see Fig. 2.5 of Chap. 14). In the case of fast neutrons, with

$\lambda \ll R$, this diffraction, or "shadow scattering," corresponds to a small-angle elastic scattering, for which the cross section σ_{sc} is the same as σ_{abs}, or

$$\sigma_{sc} \simeq \pi(R + \lambda)^2 \tag{9.2}$$

Then the total nuclear cross section σ_t is

$$\sigma_t = \sigma_{abs} + \sigma_{sc} \simeq 2\pi(R + \lambda)^2 \tag{9.3}$$

or just twice the effective geometrical area of the nucleus.

When the measured values of the total attenuation cross section σ_t are interpreted in terms of Eq. (9.3), the data are fairly consistent (see Fig. 2.2 of Chap. 14) with nuclear unit radii in the domain of

$$R_0 \simeq (1.4 \pm 0.1) \times 10^{-13} \text{ cm} \tag{9.4}$$

on the constant-density model $R = R_0 A^{\frac{1}{3}}$. Again, as in the case of charged-particle interactions, this is a "nuclear-force radius." Refinements of the theory, and some reinterpretation of the experimental data, can be expected when the degree of "transparency" of nuclei to fast neutrons becomes more precisely evaluated.

CHAPTER 3

Mass of Nuclei and of Neutral Atoms

Much of our present knowledge about the structure of nuclei and the forces between nucleons is derived from carefully measured values of the mass of nuclei. These measurements present a variety of special experimental problems. Most of the accurate mass values now available have been obtained either by mass spectroscopy or by measurements of the energy released or absorbed in various nuclear reactions. We shall survey these two principal methods, and some fundamental results obtained from them, in this chapter. The measurement of atomic mass by microwave spectroscopy is discussed in Chap. 5, Sec. 3.

1. *The Discovery of Isotopes and Isobars*

In Dalton's atomic theory (1808) each chemical element consisted of an assembly of identical atoms. Prout's hypothesis (1815) visualized each such atom as a close aggregate of hydrogen atoms. These two concepts maintained their simple attractiveness until the middle of the nineteenth century.

a. The Discovery of Nonintegral Values of Chemical Atomic Weight. By the latter half of the nineteenth century, chemical-atomic-weight determinations had disclosed several elements which definitely do not have integral whole-number atomic weights on the oxygen-equals-16 (chemical) scale. Although the atomic weight of carbon is 12.00; fluorine, 19.00; and sodium, 23.00, that of neon is 20.2, chlorine is 35.46, and magnesium is 24.32. These fractional atomic weights were incompatible with continued acceptance of both Dalton's and Prout's hypotheses, and in due course Prout's theory was discarded, only to be reestablished in a modified form after the discovery of isotopes and of the neutron.

With the atomic-weight data before him, Sir William Crookes combined clear thinking and happy guesswork, reminiscent of the Greek atomists, to prophesy correctly the now basic concept of isotopes when he said in his 1886 address before the British Association (C56): "I conceive, therefore, that when we say the atomic weight of, for instance, calcium is 40, we really express the fact that, while the majority of calcium atoms have an actual atomic weight of 40, there are not a few represented by 39 or 41, a less number of 38 or 42, and so on." Except that calcium later turned out to be a mixture of isotopes having mass numbers of 40, 42, 43, 44, 46, and 48, Crookes's hypothesis states our contemporary beliefs quite perfectly.   Before these ideas could become tenable, it was necessary to show experimentally that *atoms of different weights can have the same chemical properties*.   This was accomplished by two widely different techniques just before the outbreak of World War I.

   b. Radiochemical Discovery of Isotopes, Isobars, and Isomers. Experimental proof of the chemical identity of atoms of different weight was first definitely established in 1911 by Soddy, who proposed the name *isotopes* for such atomic species (S58, S57).   In the first 15 years following the discovery of natural radioactivity in 1896, chemists and physicists had separated many of the 40 radioactive species found in uranium and thorium minerals.   Although the available quantities of many of these species are very small, the chemical behavior of any of them can be observed accurately by detecting the presence of the element in chemical precipitates, filtrates, etc., through its α or β radiations.   Each of the natural radioactive species has its own characteristic radiations and decay constant which identify it uniquely.   Thus it was possible for Soddy to establish the chemical identity of two new trios of radioactive substances: thorium ($_{90}\text{Th}^{232}$), radiothorium ($_{90}\text{RdTh}^{228}$, or, in the newer simplified radiochemical notation, $_{90}\text{Th}^{228}$), and ionium ($_{90}\text{Io}^{230}$, or $_{90}\text{Th}^{230}$); also mesothorium-1 ($_{88}\text{MsTh}_1^{288}$, or $_{88}\text{Ra}^{228}$), thorium X ($_{88}\text{ThX}^{224}$, or $_{88}\text{Ra}^{224}$), and radium ($_{88}\text{Ra}^{226}$).

   At this time the mass and charge of the α and β rays had been determined, and the existence of atomic nuclei was just being established by Rutherford's interpretation of the α-ray-scattering experiments of Geiger and Marsden.   Radiothorium is a decay product of thorium, corresponding to the loss of one α particle and two β particles from the parent Th^{232} nucleus.   According to the displacement law, RdTh^{228} and Th^{232} should have the same atomic number.   Therefore the two species have the same nuclear charge but differ in mass by four units, corresponding to the emitted α particle.   Somewhat similar considerations established the masses of the four other species involved.

   While thus demonstrating the existence of isotopes among the radioactive substances, Soddy correctly inferred that some of the common elements are also mixtures of chemically nonseparable species which differ by whole units in atomic weight.   Consequently, the average atomic weight might be nonintegral, as in neon, chlorine, and others.

   In addition to pointing out the existence of isotopes among the radioactive elements, Soddy called attention to the substances $_{90}\text{RdTh}^{228}$ (or $_{90}\text{Th}^{228}$) and $_{88}\text{MsTh}_1^{288}$ (or $_{88}\text{Ra}^{228}$).   These two have the same mass number but different chemical properties, due to the difference in their nuclear charges.   Such species are called *isobars*.

   Later Soddy suggested (S59) a further basis of classification of nuclei to meet the possibility that nuclei which have the same mass number and atomic number might still exhibit distinct radioactive properties, or they might differ in "any new property concerned with the nucleus of the atom."   Such isobaric isotopes with distinguishable nuclear properties are called *isomers*. The first case of nuclear isomerism was observed in 1921 by Hahn for the isomeric pair uranium X_2 ($_{91}UX_2^{234}$, or $_{91}Pa^{234}$) and uranium Z ($_{91}UZ^{234}$, or $_{91}Pa^{234}$), both of which have atomic number 91 and mass number 234 but whose radioactive properties are widely different. Feather and Bretscher first showed in 1938 that UX_2 is only a long-lived excited nuclear level of UZ. Numerous other isomeric pairs have been discovered among the artificially radioactive substances.

c. Discovery of Stable Isotopes by Positive-ray Analysis. While using a new parabola positive-ray apparatus (H19) in the fall of 1912, Sir J. J. Thomson discovered in neon samples a faint line of unknown origin having a probable mass value of 22 in addition to a strong line at about mass 20. Neon is the lightest element having a definitely non-integral atomic weight (20.20). F. W. Aston immediately undertook a new precision measurement of the density and atomic weight of neon and endeavored unsuccessfully to concentrate appreciably the mass 22 material by some 3,000 fractionations of neon over charcoal cooled by liquid air, and by repeated diffusion experiments (A37). The mass 22 persisted with the mass-20 neon parabola, and while it seemed that the mass-20 parabola corresponded to slightly less than an atomic weight of 20.2, the experimental precision of 10 per cent was inadequate to clinch the matter. The existence of two isotopes of neon was strongly indicated by all these experiments, but none of them was absolutely convincing when World War I interrupted the work.

By the close of the war in 1919 the existence of stable isotopes had been put beyond doubt by further work on the radioactive elements and by the accurate measurement of the atomic weight of ordinary lead (207.22), thorium lead (207.77), and uranium lead (206.05), and by the observations of Paneth and Hevesy (P4) on the inseparability of lead from radium D ($_{82}RaD^{210}$, or $_{82}Pb^{210}$).

2. *Nomenclature of Nuclei*

a. Nomenclature of Individual Nuclei

Atomic Number. The atomic number, or "proton number," equals the number of protons in a nucleus (Chap. 1) and is always denoted by the symbol Z. Atoms having the same Z are *isotopes* and in chemistry are usually studied as an unseparated group because they have similar configurations of valence electrons and substantially identical *chemical* properties.

In sharp contrast, the *nuclear* properties of isotopes are generally highly dissimilar. For example, $_{11}Na^{22}$ is a positron β-ray emitter, $_{11}Na^{23}$ is the stable sodium isotope, and $_{11}Na^{24}$ is a negatron β-ray emitter. In nuclear physics each isotope of an element needs to be studied as an individual nuclear species. The successful separation of stable isotopes, for independent study, is therefore of special importance to progress in nuclear physics (Chap. 7).

Mass Number. The mass number A is the integer nearest to the exact atomic isotopic weight. In all cases, the mass number is equal to the total number of protons and neutrons in a nucleus. It is therefore also called the "nucleon number." Atoms having the same mass number are *isobars*. The chemical properties of isobars are generally dissimilar, but their nuclear properties tend to present many parallel features, especially with regard to radius, binding energy, and spacing of excited levels.

Neutron Number. With good experimental justification (Chap. 8), the number of neutrons in any nucleus is taken as $(A - Z)$. The neutron number $(A - Z)$ can be represented by the single symbol N whenever confusion with other definitions of this much-overworked letter can be excluded. Nuclei having the same neutron number are *isotones*. Because of the symmetry of nuclear forces in protons and neutrons, isotones and isotopes play very similar roles in nuclear physics.

Unpaired Neutron Number. The number of neutrons which are in excess of the number of protons in a nucleus is $(A - 2Z) = (N - Z)$. This quantity reflects the asymmetry of a nucleus in neutrons and protons. It is of importance in considerations of the binding energy of nuclei, especially in the liquid-drop model (Chap. 11). The name "isotopic number" for the quantity $(A - 2Z)$ was used in 1921 by Harkins in his discussions of the relative natural abundance of isotopes, light elements having $A - 2Z = 0$ being by far the most abundant. The discovery of the neutron in 1932 endowed the quantity $(A - 2Z) = (N - Z)$ with basic physical significance as an index of asymmetry. The name "isotopic number" is seldom used because it does not connote this asymmetry. Instead, $(N - Z)$ is called the number of "unpaired neutrons," or the number of "binding neutrons," or the *"neutron excess."* Nuclei having the same value of $N - Z$ are called *isodiapheres*.

Atomic Mass. The exact value of the mass of a neutral atom, relative to the mass of a neutral atom of the oxygen isotope of mass number 16, is the "atomic mass," or *"isotopic mass,"* M. Note that even for a single isotope this is not equivalent to the chemical atomic weight, which is based on a different mass scale (Chap. 7).

Nuclear Mass. In nuclear physics it is the mass of the nucleus itself which is usually of primary interest. This value is seldom, if ever, tabulated because all the necessary calculations usually can be carried out using only the neutral atomic masses. Moreover, it is the neutral atomic masses which are usually measured. When needed, the nuclear mass M' is given by

$$M' = M - [Zm_0 - B_e(Z)] \qquad (2.1)$$

where m_0 is the rest mass of one electron and the total binding energy $B_e(Z)$ of all the electrons in an atom is given approximately by the Thomas-Fermi model, with an empirical proportionality constant, as (F57)

$$B_e(Z) = 15.73Z^{\frac{7}{3}} \qquad \text{ev} \qquad (2.2)$$

Illustrative values of $B_e(Z)$ are given in Table 2.1. For the heaviest elements, the total electron binding energy approaches 1 Mev. But even this value is negligible compared with the binding energy of the nucleus (Chap. 9), which is of the order of 8 Mev per nucleon. It is customary to neglect the electron binding energy in all but the most precise nuclear calculations.

TABLE 2.1. APPROXIMATE TOTAL BINDING ENERGY OF ALL THE ATOMIC
ELECTRONS IN ATOMS OF ATOMIC NUMBER Z
[According to the Thomas-Fermi model, Eq. (2.2)]

Element.............	Ne	Ca	Zn	Sn	Yb	Th
Z..................	10	20	30	50	70	90
$B_e(Z)$, kev..........	3.4	17	44	145	318	570

b. Nomenclature of Nuclear Species. Kohman (K32) first proposed that any individual atomic species be called a *nuclide,* rather than an "isotope" as had been conventional for some time, because the word "isotopes" literally connotes different nuclear species which have the same chemical properties. Kohman suggested a set of self-consistent definitions, which have been generally adopted.

These definitions may be visualized and compared in Table 2.2. All have proved useful, especially in systematic presentations of the known nuclei, such as Sullivan's "Trilinear Chart of Nuclear Species" (S80).

TABLE 2.2. SUMMARY OF CURRENT NOMENCLATURE OF NUCLEAR SPECIES
(When the neutron number $N = A - Z$ is pertinent, it is written as a subscript beneath the mass number.)

Term	Characterized by	Examples	Remarks
Nuclides......	Z, A	$_1H^1$, $_{50}Sn^{120}$, $_{92}U^{238}$	>700 known
Isotopes......	Constant Z	$_7N^{13}$, $_7N^{14}$, $_7N^{15}$	3 to 19 known per element
Isotones......	Constant $A - Z = N$	$_6C_8^{14}$, $_7N_8^{15}$, $_8O_8^{16}$	The neutron analogue of isotopes
Isobars.......	Constant A	$_6C^{14}$, $_7N^{14}$	In β decay the parent and product are isobars
Isodiapheres..	Constant $A - 2Z = N - Z$	$[_6C_6^{12}$, $_7N_7^{14}$, $_8O_8^{16}]$, $[_{88}Ra_{138}^{226}$, $_{86}Rn_{136}^{222}]$	In α decay the parent and product are isodiapheres
Isomers.......	Constant Z and A	$_{35}Br^{80m}$ (4.4 hr), $_{35}Br^{80}$ (18 min)	Metastable excited level, ~100 known

Problems

1. Explain qualitatively why the total binding energy of atomic electrons should vary faster than Z^2.

2. Derive an approximate expression for the change in the total binding energy of atomic electrons (*a*) following α decay and (*b*) following β decay. Evaluate in kev for $Z \sim 50$.

Ans.: (*a*) -13.5 kev; (*b*) ± 6.7 kev.

3. *Mass Spectroscopy*

F. W. Aston returned to the new but broad problem of isotopes as soon as World War I was concluded. He developed the first mass spectrograph for the accurate determination of atomic weights by the analysis of positive rays. Aston's brilliant work soon established the existence of many stable isotopes among the nonradioactive elements and brought him the Nobel Prize (for chemistry) in 1922. The data and techniques which had been developed up to 1941 are ably drawn together in Professor Aston's book "Mass Spectra and Isotopes" (A37).

Mass spectroscopy has matured into a basic field in nuclear physics. Various workers have developed mass spectroscopes of many varieties, each designed for a particular type of duty. These include the accurate determination of atomic masses, the measurement of isotopic abundance ratios, the identification of the stable and radioactive nuclides found in nature, and the identification of products of nuclear reactions. Mass spectroscopes have also been developed for a variety of service uses. These include the chemical analysis of complicated vapor mixtures such as the products of human respiration; the measurement of isotopic dilution in tracer studies with stable isotopes; the bulk separation of isotopes, as in the "calutron"; and the routine testing for gas leaks of a variety of enclosures ranging from basketball bladders to naval gun turrets.

Although very different in detail, all these instruments embody merely a varying combination of a few fundamental components. We shall examine these basic principles in the following subsection.

a. Basic Components of Mass Spectroscopes. In an ion source the substance to be examined is obtained in the form of free atomic or molecular ions carrying single or multiple positive charges.

Regardless of the type of source used, its exit slits provide the remainder of the apparatus with a diverging bundle of positive ions containing a continuous distribution of velocities V and a discrete set of ne/M values, corresponding to the charge ne and mass M of the various atomic and molecular ions emitted by the source. Because the ionic charge ne can only be an integral multiple of the electronic charge e, and is usually e or $2e$, it is always possible to determine ne by inspection of the final record. Aside from the directional distribution of the ion beam which then enters the mass spectroscope's focusing and analyzing portions, *there are two parameters, M and V, in the properties of the individual ions.*

It is therefore evident from the simple theory of equations that two independent operations must be performed on the beam in order to eliminate the parameter V and obtain the desired mass M. Fortunately, the properties of kinetic energy $\frac{1}{2}MV^2$ and momentum MV of each ion are combinations of these independent parameters which may be independently and consecutively determined by the action on the ion of known electrostatic and magnetic fields. Thus, if both the energy and momentum of an ion are determined, its mass is uniquely specified.

Most mass spectroscopes therefore consist essentially of a combination of an energy (electrostatic) and a momentum (magnetic) filter. Alternatively, a velocity filter (crossed electrostatic and magnetic fields) may be combined with either a momentum or an energy filter. Different types of mass spectroscopes result from combinations and permutations of the options available among these filter systems.

Positive-ion Source. The selection of a source depends somewhat on the element or compounds whose mass spectrum is sought.

Positive ions of the alkali metals (Li, Na, K, Cs) may be obtained readily by heating certain of their minerals (K48). Particularly with this type of source, and to a lesser degree with other types, the true isotopic abundance ratios of the solid material may not be faithfully reproduced in the positive ions resulting from evaporation. Where accurate isotopic abundance ratios are to be determined, great care is necessary in the selection and operation of the ion source.

Ions of very refractory materials, such as gold, uranium, and others, may often be obtained from an oscillating spark discharge (D21) between electrodes containing the materials to be examined.

Positive ions of many elements and molecules may be obtained from near the cathode of a high-voltage discharge tube containing the appropriate gas at a low pressure. A small amount of neon in the tube will stabilize the high-voltage discharge and produce controlled evaporation of metals, halides, and some other compounds which may be packed into small depressions prepared in the cathode (B5). The dense stream of high-velocity electrons along the axis of the discharge tube serves to dissociate and ionize the heterogeneous vapors of the substances evaporated. The positive ions are drawn out of this versatile source through an axial opening in the cathode.

When the material to be examined can be put in gaseous or vapor form, it can be allowed to leak into a low-pressure ion source in which the ions are produced by bombardment with low-voltage electrons (≤ 100 ev) from an electron gun (N16). The ionized atoms and molecular fragments so formed are then drawn off through accelerator slits into the analyzing portion of the apparatus.

Energy Filters. Since the force on a charge ne (esu) due to an electrostatic field ε is simply $ne\varepsilon$, electrodes can be arranged in an arc (Fig. 3.1a) so that ions originally directed along their central tangent may be deflected to follow a circular path with a radius of curvature ρ. The centripetal force MV^2/ρ is then provided by the electrostatic force $ne\varepsilon$ due to the radial field ε, which is of constant magnitude along the arc of radius ρ. Since $MV^2/\rho = ne\varepsilon$, it immediately follows that ions having any M and V, but possessing a nonrelativistic kinetic energy $\frac{1}{2}MV^2$, and entering the field while directed exactly along this arc, will follow the arc of radius ρ, where

$$\tfrac{1}{2}MV^2 = \tfrac{1}{2}ne\varepsilon\rho \tag{3.1}$$

The ions are not changed in energy by passing through this cylindrical-condenser filter, because they enter and leave at the same potential. For the central ray, whose radius is exactly ρ, the electrostatic force is always normal to the motion.

The ion optics of cylindrical-condenser filters (H45, W8) and of sector magnets has been reviewed and extended by Bainbridge (B4), by Johnson and Nier (J16), and others. Cylindrical-condenser sectors possess optimum direction-focusing properties, which are analogous to the well-known 180° magnetic focusing, when the sector angle is $\pi/\sqrt{2}$ radians, or about 127°. Under these conditions all ions having the same kinetic energy but diverging in direction by the order of 1° as they enter the filter are brought to a focus at the exit slit. This focusing action greatly increases the intensity of the beam, without impairing the energy resolution of the filter, by permitting the use of wider entrance and exit slits. Its use is illustrated in the mass spectrograph shown in Fig. 3.3, where the ions enter the energy filter with a large kinetic energy and a moderate uniformity of direction as they emerge from the axis of the 20,000-volt, low-pressure discharge-tube ion source.

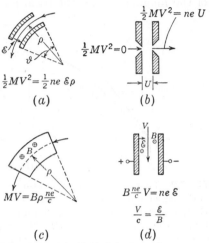

Fig. 3.1 (*a*) Cylindrical-condenser energy filter, (*b*) accelerator energy filter, (*c*) magnetic momentum filter, and (*d*) velocity filter. Mass spectroscopes are combinations of fundamental elements, arranged to focus ions having identical values of ne/M. For example, the mass spectroscope of Fig. 3.3 combines the elements (*a*) and (*c*).

An alternative, but less exact, energy filter is obtained by accelerating low-velocity ions obtained from a low-voltage ion source. If the original velocity of the positive ions is low enough to be neglected, they may be accelerated by passing from entrance to exit slits between which is a potential difference of U electrostatic volts (Fig. 3.1*b*).

They then emerge with a uniform kinetic energy of

$$\tfrac{1}{2}MV^2 = neU \qquad (3.2)$$

on which is superposed the original low-voltage energy distribution with which they entered the accelerator filter.

Momentum Filters. The force on a particle of charge ne (esu, or ne/c emu) moving with velocity V in a magnetic field of B gauss is simply $BneV/c$ and is directed at right angles to the field. Therefore, a moving ion is deflected in a circular path by a uniform magnetic field directed normal to its plane of motion. Equating the centrifugal force to the magnetic centripetal force, we have $MV^2/\rho = BneV/c$, from which it immediately follows that the momentum MV of the ion determines its radius of curvature ρ, as

$$MV = B\rho \frac{ne}{c} \qquad (3.3)$$

The uniform magnetic field therefore acts as a momentum filter (Fig.

3.1c). The deflecting force on the moving ion is always normal to the path; hence the initial momentum is unaltered by the filter.

The *direction-focusing properties of a uniform magnetic field* are of special importance in mass spectroscopy [as they are also in β-ray spectroscopy (P18)] because they permit greatly increased beam intensities without serious loss of resolution. The well-known 180° focusing property of a uniform magnetic field is a special case of a more general theorem. In Fig. 3.2 a slightly diverging beam of charged particles is deflected by a wedge-shaped sector magnet and is "focused" at B. The nature of this focusing action is such that the entrance slit A, the apex of the magnet O, and the focal position B all lie on a straight line.

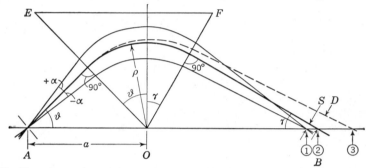

Fig. 3.2 Focusing action of a sector magnet OEF, whose field is normal to the plane of the paper and is uniform within OEF and zero outside OEF. [*From Stephens* (S70).] (1) Crossing for rays whose initial direction is $\pm\alpha$ but which have the same momentum as those which cross at B. (2) Crossing for the "central" ray which enters and emerges from the magnet faces at 90°. (3) Crossing for central rays whose momentum is larger than those crossing at B.

Actually, only the central ray from A, which enters the edge OE of the magnetic field at normal incidence, passes exactly through the "focus" at B. Those initial rays which diverge from the central ray by a small angle $\pm\alpha$ (such that $\alpha^2 \ll 1$) cross the base line AOB inside the focus at B. The so-called lateral *spread*, or aberration, marked S in Fig. 3.2, can be shown to be (M28, S70)

$$S = a\,\frac{\alpha^2}{2}\left(\frac{\sin^2\vartheta}{\sin\gamma} + \frac{\sin^2\gamma}{\sin\vartheta}\right) \tag{3.4}$$

for rays having the same momentum. Note that the spread is proportional to the line width at the focus B and increases as the square of the acceptance angle α. For a symmetrical sector-type magnet, with the half angle of the wedge equal to $\vartheta = \gamma$, the lateral spread becomes simply

$$S = (a\,\sin\vartheta)\alpha^2 = \rho\alpha^2 \tag{3.5}$$

where ρ is the radius of curvature of the central ion path in the magnetic field. Note that this result is independent of the angle of the magnetic sector. The classical "semicircular focusing" is simply the special case $2\vartheta = 180°$.

It is helpful to develop from Fig. 3.2 a qualitative explanation of the focusing action of sector magnets. The initial ray which diverges by $+\alpha$ must traverse a longer path than the central ray in the magnetic field. It is therefore acted on longer and is deflected more than the central ray. Conversely, an initial ray which diverges by $-\alpha$ traverses a shorter path in the magnetic field and is deflected less than the central ray. The three rays therefore have the opportunity of approaching or crossing each other and thus of forming a focus. The mathematical analysis shows that, in fact, the outer ray $(+\alpha)$ is always overcorrected and crosses the base line and the inner ray $(-\alpha)$ slightly on the near side, or magnet side, of B, as shown in Fig. 3.2. The "line shape" at B is therefore asymmetric, with the central ray at its outer edge.

So far, we have considered only rays which all have the same momentum. Now let the initial central ray be made up of one group whose momentum is MV and another whose momentum is $MV + \Delta MV$. Where will the outer edge of the higher-momentum group fall? It can be shown that the lateral *velocity dispersion*, as measured by the separation D in Fig. 3.2, is given by (S70)

$$D = a \left(\frac{\Delta MV}{MV}\right) \left(\frac{\sin \vartheta}{\sin \gamma}\right) (\sin \vartheta + \sin \gamma) \qquad (3.6)$$

In a symmetrical sector, of half angle $\vartheta = \gamma$, the velocity dispersion is therefore given by

$$D = 2(a \sin \vartheta) \frac{\Delta MV}{MV} = 2\rho \frac{\Delta MV}{MV} \qquad (3.7)$$

which is independent of magnet angle and proportional to the path radius ρ.

Velocity Filter. The electrostatic and magnetic forces on a charged particle, moving through electric and magnetic fields which are directed at right angles to one another, may be balanced so that particles of velocity V and any charge experience no sideward force. The electrostatic force is εne, while the magnetic force is $BVne/c$. Equating these, and eliminating ne, we have

$$V = c \frac{\varepsilon}{B} \qquad (3.8)$$

Figure 3.1d illustrates the arrangement of electrostatic and magnetic fields, at right angles to each other, which deflects all particles except those having the velocity V.

Trochoidal Filter. Crossed electric and magnetic fields deflect any moving charged particle whose velocity differs from Eq. (3.8) into a path which is trochoidal when projected onto a plane normal to the magnetic field. The trochoids for particles having the same specific charge ne/M have a common crossing, or focus, whose position is independent of the velocity of the particles. This property has been utilized in a mass spectrometer which involves only a single filter (B69, M51).

The mass scale in the trochoidal mass spectrometer is rigorously linear, since the focal distance from the source is proportional to $(\mathcal{E}/B^2)/(ne/M)$.

Angular Velocity Filters. The angular velocity ω of a charged particle, about an axis parallel to a uniform magnetic field B, is given at once by rearrangement of Eq. (3.3) and is

$$\omega = \frac{V}{\rho} = B \frac{ne/c}{M} \tag{3.9}$$

Therefore particles which have the same specific charge ne/M will traverse circular paths in the same period of time, regardless of their speed V and their path radius ρ. This is the well-known *cyclotron resonance frequency* condition. The conventional cyclotron has, in fact, been used as a mass spectrometer in first proving the existence of the stable isotope He³ in atmospheric and commercial helium (A25).

A magnetic *time-of-flight* mass spectrometer has been developed which utilizes Eq. (3.9). Low-velocity positive ions (~ 10 ev) from a pulsed ion source traverse about 10 revolutions of a helical path ($\rho \sim 12$ cm) about the axis of a uniform field of 450 gauss. Their travel time is then of the order of 10 μsec/amu. With the aid of timing equipment based on the principle of Loran navigation receivers, the time of flight can be measured with an accuracy corresponding to about 0.001 amu (H26, R17).

b. Mass Spectroscopes. Any source and filter combination which provides a means of forming and observing mass spectra is called a mass spectroscope. Although there are innumerable individual forms, most of them fall into two broad general classes:

1. The *mass spectrographs* are, in Aston's definition, "those forms of apparatus capable of producing a focused mass spectrum of lines on a photographic plate."

2. The *mass spectrometers* are forms "in which the focused beam of rays is brought up to a fixed slit, and there detected and measured electrically" (A37).

Aston built the first mass spectrograph; Dempster devised the earliest mass spectrometer. The term *mass spectroscopes* connotes collectively the *mass spectrographs* and the *mass spectrometers*.

Mass spectroscopes which achieve both direction focusing and velocity focusing, usually by employing two direction-focusing elements (Fig. 3.1a and 3.1c), are known as *double-focusing* instruments. Those which have direction-focusing action in only one element (usually because the electrostatic filter is of the accelerator type, Fig. 3.1b) are called *single-focusing*.

Double-focusing Mass Spectrograph. When the 127° electrostatic analyzer is employed, the resulting velocity dispersion can be just annulled by a momentum filter if the total magnetic sector angle is 60°. The stray field at the edge of the magnet can be corrected for by cutting back the edges of the poles by about 1.6 gap widths. This combination of energy and momentum filters, with good direction-focusing values, has been so arranged by Bainbridge that it possesses the further advantage of a linear mass scale. The resulting mass spectrograph of Bainbridge and Jordan, in which ρ is about 25 cm for both filters, will separate ions having a mass difference of 1 per cent by about 5 mm on the photographic plate. This permits a resolving power $M/\Delta M$ of about 10,000 and makes this instrument valuable particularly for the accurate determination of nuclear masses. A schematic diagram of this mass spectrograph is seen in Fig. 3.3, where the components described earlier can be identified. The photographic registration is well suited to the accurate measurement of mass differences, as in the doublet method. It is less desirable for the measurement of isotopic abundance ratios, because of the limited and nonlinear contrast scale of a photographic emulsion.

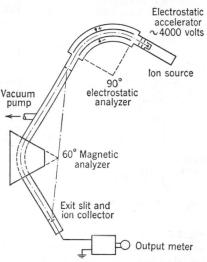

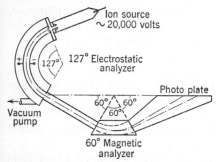

Fig. 3.3 Simplified schematic diagram of the *mass spectrograph* of Bainbridge and Jordan (B5). The mean radius of the ion path in both the electrostatic analyzer and the magnetic analyzer is about 25 cm. The mass scale is linear at the photographic plate, where ions of discrete ne/M values are separately focused. Note that the exit slit of the energy analyzer, the apex of the magnet, and the photographic plate are collinear.

Fig. 3.4 Simplified schematic drawing of the *mass spectrometer* of Nier and Roberts (N21, J16). The mean radius of the electrostatic analyzer is about 19 cm and of the magnetic analyzer, about 15 cm. The entrance slit, apex of the magnet, and the exit slit of the magnetic analyzer are collinear.

Double-focusing Mass Spectrometer. In a mass spectrometer, final focusing need be achieved at only one point. The ion current which passes through this point can then emerge through a slit and can be measured with the high precision which is characteristic of electrical null methods.

Let ions having a discrete set of values of the specific charge ne/M, and a continuous distribution of velocities V, pass successively through a cylindrical-condenser energy filter and a momentum filter. Let ρ_e be the radius of the ion path in the energy filter. Arrange entrance and exit slits in the momentum filter such that only those ions whose radius of curvature is ρ_m will be transmitted. Then elimination of V between

Eqs. (3.1) and (3.3) shows that the only ions which can be transmitted successively through both filters must have the specific charge

$$\frac{ne}{M} = \frac{\rho_e}{\rho_m^2} c^2 \frac{\varepsilon}{B^2} = K \frac{\varepsilon}{B^2} \qquad (3.10)$$

where K is a constant for any particular slit arrangement.

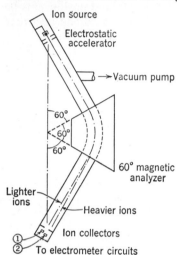

Fig. 3.5 Schematic diagram of a single-focusing mass spectrometer, developed by Nier (N17) especially for the routine measurement of relative isotopic abundances. This instrument incorporates two fixed ion collectors. By comparing the simultaneous ion currents to the two collectors, the ratio of ions of two nearby mass numbers can be determined. For example, the relative abundance of C^{13} to C^{12} in carbon dioxide is obtained from the relative ion currents of masses 45 and 44, $(C^{13}O_2^{16})^+$ and $(C^{12}O_2^{16})^+$, with correction, if needed, for $(C^{12}O^{16}O^{17})^+$. As a single-collector instrument, the resolution can be pushed to allow accurate mass measurements on atomic or molecular ions.

The mass spectrum of discrete ne/M values can therefore be scanned by changing ε, or B, or both. In order to avoid uncertainties due to hysteresis in the magnet, it is generally preferable to hold B constant and to sweep through the mass spectrum by varying the potential applied to the electrostatic filter. The ion path through the mass spectrometer can therefore be thought of as a paved highway, along which ions of various mass can be sent by adjusting ε to a value appropriate for the particular ion.

The transmitted ion current will generally be in the domain of 10^{-12} amp or less and can be measured accurately with a vibrating-reed electrometer, a vacuum-tube electrometer, or an electron multiplier tube.

Figure 3.4 shows schematically a double-focusing mass spectrometer developed by Nier and Roberts (N21, J16). The ions are produced by electron impact or thermionic emission and then accelerated through a potential difference of about 4,000 volts as they leave the ion source. This acceleration is equivalent to an energy filter of the type shown in Fig. 3.1b, so that most of the ion current leaving the ion source is reasonably homogeneous in energy. The ions then pass through a 90° cylindrical-condenser electrostatic analyzer followed by a 60° magnetic analyzer. The mass spectrum is scanned by varying the field ε in the electrostatic analyzer. Simultaneously, the accelerating potential at the ion-source exit is varied proportionately, both potentials being obtained from a common potential divider. The resolving power $M/\Delta M$ is comparable with the mass spectrograph shown in Fig. 3.3.

Single-focusing Mass Spectrometer. Many varieties of single-focusing mass spectrometers have been developed. Usually, these are similar to the double-focusing mass spectrometer, but the electrostatic analyzer is omitted.   Where only moderate resolution is required, as in the measurement of isotopic abundance ratios and for gas analyses in general, high ion intensities can be obtained by the use of relatively wide slits.   A typical instrument (N17) is illustrated in Fig. 3.5.

Sufficiently high resolution can be obtained from such instruments for accurate mass measurements on atomic or molecular ions (N10). However, molecular ion fragments cannot be used because these fragments acquire a sufficient initial kinetic energy during the dissociation process in the ion source to spoil the resolution (N21).   Accurate mass measurements are therefore usually carried out on double-focusing instruments.

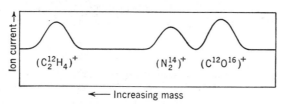

Fig. 3.6   Mass triplet for singly ionized molecular ions each having mass 28.   The resolving power is such that the peaks have a width ΔM at half height of $\Delta M \simeq M/$ 4,600.   The doublet separation $(N_2^{14})^+ - (C^{12}O^{16})^+$ is about 0.01 amu.   [*From a record taken on the mass spectrometer shown in Fig. 3.4, by Collins, Nier, and Johnson* (C35).]

c. The Doublet Method in Mass Spectroscopy.   The high dispersion available in mass spectroscopes of the type illustrated by Figs. 3.3 and 3.4 permits the complete resolution of ions having the same integral value of ne/M but slightly different exact numerical values.   Thus the high accuracy always associated with measurements based on null methods becomes available in these determinations, because *differences* in mass can be determined with high precision.   By adjustment of the ion source or the exposure time, *mass doublets* may be obtained in which both components have about the same intensity and the same integral value of ne/M.   The doublet separation is then a measure of the fractional difference in mass.   The doublet method is illustrated by Fig. 3.6, which shows a doublet (actually a triplet) of singly ionized molecular ions, each of which has a total mass number of 28.

The Fundamental O, C, D, H Doublets.   Following an original experiment by Aston, many mass spectroscopists have measured a group of so-called "fundamental doublets" from which the masses of C^{12}, H^2, and H^1 can be obtained relative to O^{16}.   These three doublets are: $(C^{12}H_4^1)^+$ $- (O^{16})^+$, $(H_3^2)^+ - (C^{12})^{++}$, and $(H_2^1)^+ - (H^2)^+$.   For simplicity in notation, we shall write

$$O^{16} \equiv O \qquad C^{12} \equiv C \qquad H^2 \equiv D \qquad H^1 \equiv H$$

Then the three fundamental doublets can be written as three simultaneous equations in O, C, D, and H, with the observed doublet separations of a, b, and c.

$$M/ne \simeq 2: \quad (H_2^1)^+ - (H^2)^+ = 2H - D = a$$
$$M/ne \simeq 6: \quad (H_3^2)^+ - (C^{12})^{++} = 3D - \tfrac{1}{2}C = b \qquad (3.11)$$
$$M/ne \simeq 16: \quad (C^{12}H_4^1)^+ - (O^{16})^+ = C + 4H - O = c$$

Simultaneous solution of these three relationships, using $O = 16$, gives

$$H^1 \equiv H = 1 + \tfrac{1}{16}(6a + 2b + c)$$
$$H^2 \equiv D = 2 + \tfrac{1}{8}(-2a + 2b + c) \qquad (3.12)$$
$$C^{12} \equiv C = 12 + \tfrac{1}{4}(-6a - 2b + 3c)$$

All masses and mass differences are in *atomic mass units* (abbreviated amu) defined by O^{16} equals exactly 16 amu.

The mass-spectroscopic literature has been summarized from time to time, with a view to deducing by least-squares analysis the "best values" of the three fundamental doublets and the corresponding masses of C^{12},

TABLE 3.1. DOUBLET SEPARATION AND DERIVED MASSES

Summary, for the three fundamental doublets, of illustrative pre-1950 "best values" of doublet separation and derived masses, with probable errors, from least-squares analysis of available mass-spectroscopic results. The last line gives the results for the same quantities as obtained purely from nuclear-reaction data.

	Doublet separation ΔM, 10^{-3} amu			Mass excess $(M - A)$, 10^{-3} amu		
	$H_2 - D$	$D_3 - \tfrac{1}{2}C$	$CH_4 - O$	H^1	D^2	C^{12}
Mattauch (1940)				8.130 ±0.003	14.722 ±0.006	3.861 ±0.024
Cohen and Hornyak (1947)	1.539 ±0.002	42.230 ±0.019	36.369 ±0.021	8.1284 ±0.0027	14.718 ±0.005	3.847 ±0.016
Bainbridge (1948)	1.5380 ±0.0021	42.228 ±0.019	36.369 ±0.021	8.1283 ±0.0028	14.7186 ±0.0055	3.856 ±0.019
Li et al. (1951) (L27)	1.5494 ±0.0024	42.302 ±0.016	36.372 ±0.019	8.142 ±0.003	14.735 ±0.006	3.804 ±0.017

J. Mattauch, *Phys. Rev.*, **57**: 1155 (1940).

E. R. Cohen and W. F. Hornyak, *Phys. Rev.*, **72**: 1127L (1947).

K. T. Bainbridge, Isotopic Weights of the Fundamental Isotopes, *Natl. Research Council Nuclear Science Rept.* 1, 1948.

H^2, and H^1. The final results of three illustrative compilations are compared in Table 3.1. There are also given in Table 3.1 the entirely independent numerical values for the same doublets and atoms, derived from observations of the energy evolved in nuclear reactions. The basis of these data will be discussed in Sec. 4 of this chapter. Here we must note that the "best data" are often mutually inconsistent, and by many times the probable errors assigned.

As orientation, we see in Fig. 3.7 a graphical comparison of measurements on the important, and troublesome, methane-oxygen doublet. The direct mass-spectroscopic measurements of this doublet vary by about $\pm 10^{-4}$ amu. As can be seen from Eqs. (3.12), this uncertainty in the quantity c has only a small absolute effect on the derived mass of H^1 and D^2 but affects the derived mass of C^{12} by nearly $\pm 10^{-4}$ amu.

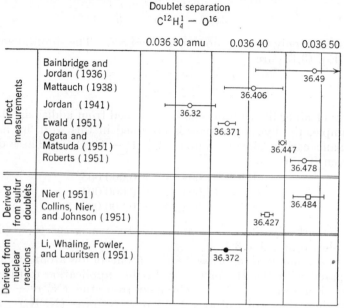

Fig. 3.7 Graphical comparison of some evaluations of the mass doublet $CH_4 - O$. The reported numerical values are given in 10^{-3} amu. Each author's declared probable error is shown graphically. Six observations which are representative of the direct mass-spectroscopic results are given at the top. Below these are shown two evaluations calculated from differences between doublets containing sulfur compounds and measured with the mass spectrometer shown in Fig. 3.4. The solid point at the bottom is the calculated value which would agree with the energy liberation in a cycle of nuclear reactions. [*References: K. T. Bainbridge and E. B. Jordan, Phys. Rev.*, **50**: 282 (1936); *J. Mattauch, Physik. Z.*, **39**: 892 (1938); *E. B. Jordan, Phys. Rev.*, **60**: 710 (1941); *H. Ewald, Z. Naturforsch.*, **6a**: 293 (1951); *K. Ogata and H. Matsuda, Phys. Rev.*, **83**: 180 (1951); *T. R. Roberts, Phys. Rev.*, **81**: 624L (1951); *A. O. Nier, Phys. Rev.*, **81**: 624L (1951); *T. L. Collins, A. O. Nier, and W. H. Johnson, Jr., Phys. Rev.*, **84**: 717 (1951); *C. W. Li, W. Whaling, W. A. Fowler, and C. C. Lauritsen, Phys. Rev.*, **83**: 512 (1951).]

Even so, the doublet method forms the basis for tables in which the uncertainties in atomic mass are only a few parts per million.

These uncertainties lie far outside the probable errors assigned on a basis of the statistical reproducibility of the results. They are therefore due to unknown systematic errors in the particular techniques used. These systematic errors can presumably be isolated and reduced by extending the work to a number of other doublets.

The S, O, C, H *Doublets.* Nier has utilized sulfur in order to evaluate the C^{12} mass through a shorter cycle of doublets (N19, C35), using the mass spectrometer shown in Fig. 3.4. By introducing a mixture of O_2 and H_2S into the ion source, the doublet $(O_2)^+ - (S^{32})^+$ is obtained in the ion beam. A mixture of C_4H_6 and SO_2 in the ion source gives the doublet $(C_4)^+ - (S^{32}O^{16})^+$. These doublet separations can be written

$$2O^{16} - S^{32} = a$$
$$4C^{12} - S^{32}O^{16} = b \tag{3.13}$$

There are now only two unknowns, C^{12} and S^{32}. The simultaneous solutions of Eq. (3.13) are

$$C^{12} = 12 + \tfrac{1}{4}(b - a) \tag{3.14}$$
$$S^{32} = 32 - a$$

The mass of other light atoms can be obtained from additional doublets. For example, the hydrogen mass is obtained in this work by including the propane–carbon dioxide doublet $(C_3^{12}H_8^1 - C^{12}O_2^{16})$. These doublets have given (C35)

$$H^1 = \ \ 1.008\ 146 \pm 0.000\ 003$$
$$C^{12} = 12.003\ 842 \pm 0.000\ 004 \tag{3.15}$$
$$S^{32} = 31.982\ 236 \pm 0.000\ 007$$

which are markedly different from the pre-1950 mass-spectroscopic "best values" shown in Table 3.1.

Secondary Standards of Mass. Other atoms of low atomic weight may be compared with H^1, H^2, or C^{12} by further application of the doublet method. For example, N^{14} is obtained from the $(N_2^{14})^+ - (C^{12}O^{16})^+$ doublet, then the rare isotopes N^{15} from $(N^{15})^+ - (N^{14}H^1)^+$, and O^{18} from $(O^{18})^+ - (O^{16}H_2^1)^+$. In this way, accurate masses of many of the principal stable isotopes of the lighter elements have been determined.

Agreement on a few secondary standards of mass is an important prerequisite to the gradual completion of self-consistent mass tables, from which accurate calculations of nuclear binding energy can be made. Representative pre-1950 and post-1950 mass values for the original secondary standards H^1, H^2, and C^{12} are compared graphically in Figs. 3.8, 3.9, and 3.10. Even the more recent mass-spectroscopic values (except those of Ewald) tend to exceed the values derived from nuclear reactions, and by several times the probable error of measurement. In 1954, general agreement on mass substandards was still to be achieved. In the meantime, *all new mass values must be given relative to an arbitrary choice of reference substandard.*

The masses of the secondary standards H^1, H^2, and C^{12} appear to be known only to about $\pm 20 \times 10^{-6}$ amu at present, although each individual evaluation is always reported to the nearest 10^{-6} amu.

Masses of Heavy Nuclei. Knowledge of the masses of middleweight and heavy nuclei is particularly important for the evaluation of nuclear forces and nuclear shell structure. Many of the mass values now available were obtained by using the mass spectroscope as an absolute instru-

Atomic mass of H¹
1.008 120
140
160 1.008 180 amu
From fundamental OCDH doublets
Mattauch (1940)
8.130
Cohen et al (1947)
8.128
Bainbridge (1948)
8.128
Roberts (1951)
8.169
Ewald (1951)
8.141
From SOCH doublets
Nier (1951)
8.159
Collins et al (1951)
8.146
From nuclear reactions
Li et al (1951)
8.142

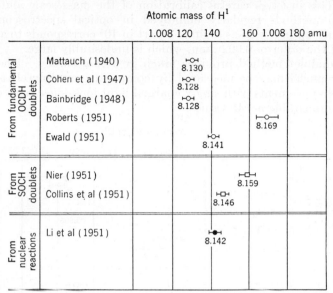

Fig. 3.8 Graphical comparison of values recommended for the mass of hydrogen. The first three entries are from the compilations reported in Table 3.1. Roberts's value uses the first two doublets of Eq. (3.11) combined with the doublet difference $2(D_2O^{16} - \frac{1}{2}A^{40}) - (C_3H_4 - A^{40})$. The numerical value shown under each point is the mass excess $(M - A)$ in millimass units (10^{-3} amu). Space has been left for the reader to add later "best values" as they develop in the literature.

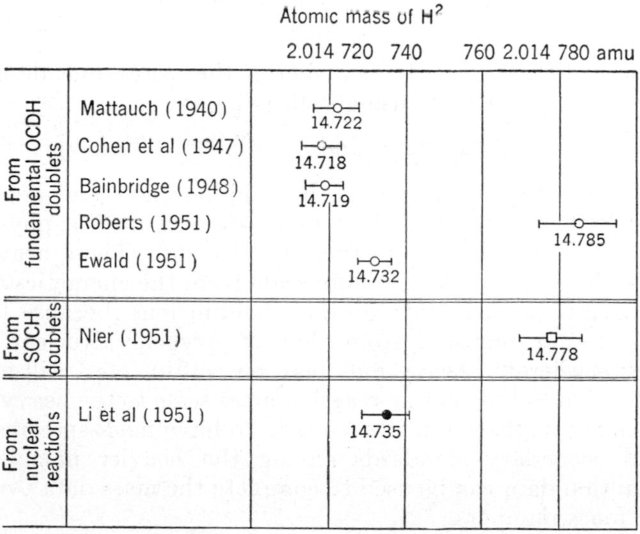

Atomic mass of H²
2.014 720
740
760 2.014 780 amu
From fundamental OCDH doublets
Mattauch (1940)
14.722
Cohen et al (1947)
14.718
Bainbridge (1948)
14.719
Roberts (1951)
14.785
Ewald (1951)
14.732
From SOCH doublets
Nier (1951)
14.778
From nuclear reactions
Li et al (1951)
14.735

Fig. 3.9 Graphical comparison of values for the mass of deuterium. Units and notation are similar to Fig. 3.8.

ment. This involves careful calibration of the mass scale and is analogous to methods regularly employed in optical spectroscopy. For heavy nuclei a precision as high as 1 part in 10^5 corresponds to an uncertainty of the order of 0.002 amu, which is undesirably large.

The doublet method provides much greater accuracy. The masses of heavy nuclei may be measured by comparing multiply charged ions of the heavy elements with singly charged light ions, since both can then possess comparable ne/M values.

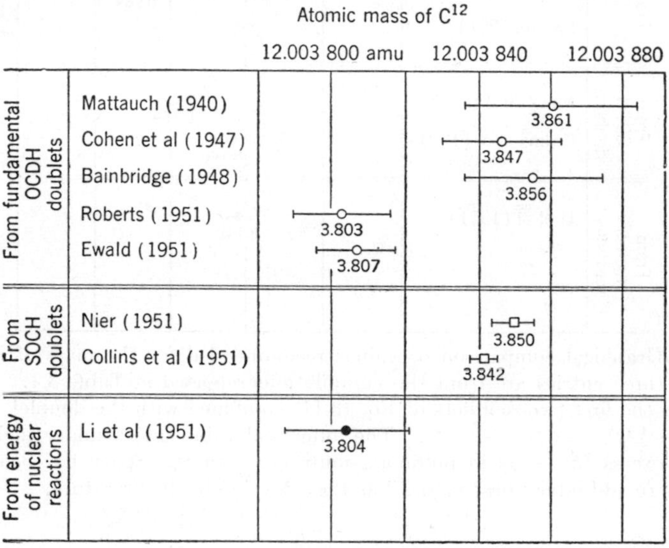

Fig. 3.10 Graphical comparison of values for the mass of C^{12}. Units and notation are similar to Fig. 3.8.

Dempster (D21) began the invasion of the heavy nuclide masses by the doublet method in 1938, using such pairs as

$$(O^{16})^+ - (Ti^{48})^{+++} \quad \text{and} \quad (Ti^{50})^+ - (Au^{197})^{++++}$$

Doublet measurements among the middleweight and heavy nuclei will be one of the most important contributions to nuclear physics which mass spectroscopy will make in the next decade. These heavy masses cannot be determined on an absolute scale from the energetics of nuclear reactions involving only hydrogen and helium ions, because the heavy masses are so far removed from that of oxygen. Nuclear reactions induced by accelerated heavy ions (carbon, sulfur, etc.) will eventually permit extension of the nuclear-reaction mass scale to the heavy nuclides. Until this is accomplished, it is necessary to have mass-spectroscopically determined secondary standards among the heavier nuclides. Then nuclear-reaction data can be used to complete the mass data over a wider domain of mass numbers.

Examples of systematic studies of this type are beginning to appear. In the mass region from $A = 31$ to 93, Collins, Nier, and Johnson (C35,

C36, C34) have reported about 70 atomic masses, from S^{32} to Nb^{93} (Table 5.2), relative to their own substandards of H^1, C^{12}, and S^{32}. These new masses, when combined with data on nuclear-reaction energies, give mass values for many of the unstable nuclides in this mass domain (C36, C34).

Problems

1. In a radial electrostatic filter, find the field strength in volts per centimeter necessary to bend singly ionized atomic oxygen ions in an arc having a 25-cm radius, if the ions have fallen through a potential difference of 20,000 volts before entering the filter. *Ans.:* 1,600 volts/cm.

2. For the same oxygen ions, find the magnetic field necessary to bend them in an arc having a 25-cm radius. *Ans.:* 3,260 gauss.

3. What is the optimum relationship between the angles ϑ and γ of the magnet faces in Fig. 3.2 for minimum line width, or "spread," in a homogeneous magnetic field, Eq. (3.4), if $(\vartheta + \gamma)$ is held constant?

4. Derive from first principles the expressions for the lateral spread and velocity dispersion in the focus produced by a homogeneous magnetic field, for the particular case of a symmetrical sector magnet, and $(\alpha^2 \ll 1)$.

5. How would you modify the sector magnet of Fig. 3.2 to obtain an instrument which would (*a*) accept a bundle of rays diverging by $\pm\alpha$ and produce a substantially parallel, or "collimated," beam and (*b*) accept a parallel beam of rays and produce a beam converging to a focal region?

6. In a crossed magnetic and electric field velocity filter, find the magnetic field necessary to filter 20,000-ev singly charged argon ions (A^{40}) if the electric field is 2,000 volts/cm. *Ans.:* 6,430 gauss.

7. The two stable isotopes of silver Ag^{107} and Ag^{109} are to be separated, using electromagnetic means. The singly charged ions are first accelerated through

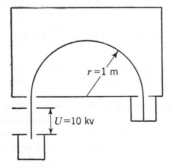

an electrostatic potential of 10 kv and then deflected in a uniform magnetic field through a semicircular path of radius 1 m.

(*a*) What magnetic field intensity is required?

(*b*) Assuming that the entrance and exit slits are the same size, and that the entrance slit is imaged perfectly on the exit slit, calculate the maximum slit width for which the two isotopes will be completely separated.

Ans.: (*a*) 1,490 gauss; (*b*) 1.87 cm.

8. A uniform magnetic field is to be used as a momentum filter for high-energy particles. A slit system is adjusted to allow the passage only of particles having a radius of curvature ρ. With a magnetic field of B gauss, it is found that the filter transmits polonium α rays, whose energy is 5.30 Mev.   The magnetic field is now raised to 2.3B and deuterons are passed into the filter.   What is the energy of the deuterons transmitted by the filter?   *Ans.:* 14.0 Mev.

9. Protons are accelerated through a potential difference of 2.50 million volts in a certain discharge tube and are then deflected into a circular orbit of radius ρ in a uniform magnetic field of 8,000 gauss.   Without altering the slit system, what magnetic field would be required to deflect through the same path in the magnetic field a beam of doubly ionized helium (artificial α rays) which had been accelerated through a potential difference of 2.00 million volts?   *Ans.:* 10.1 kilogauss.

10. The following is a diagrammatic representation of a mass spectrograph used by A. J. Dempster.   Ionized particles from the source are accelerated through the slits by the potential U into a region where they are deflected by a uniform magnetic field B and recorded on the photographic plate.

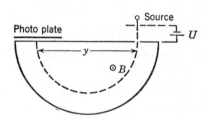

(*a*) Derive an expression for y in terms of the charge on the particle ne, its mass M, and the fields of U and B.

(*b*) The apparatus can be used to determine mass differences in the following way: With U and B held constant, a line is recorded at y_1 for singly charged light hydrogen molecules $(H_2^1)^+$ and then a line at y_2 for singly charged atomic deuterium $(H^2)^+$.   Call the absolute separation between these lines $|y_1 - y_2| \equiv \Delta y$, and their average value $(y_1 + y_2)/2 \equiv \bar{y}$.   Show that the absolute value of the mass difference is

$$2(H^1) - (H^2) = \frac{eB^2}{4c^2U} \, \bar{y} \, \Delta y$$

where H^1 and H^2 represent the *neutral* atomic masses of hydrogen and deuterium, and the binding energy of the atomic electrons has been neglected in comparison with their mass.

(*c*) In order to eliminate errors in B, U, and $\bar{y}$ from the determinations, it is customary to hold B and U constant and then compare the separations for several mass doublets.   Under these conditions, $\bar{y}$ remains essentially constant.   In the apparatus described, the absolute values of two doublet separations are

$$\Delta y_H = 0.097 \text{ mm} \quad \text{for } (H_2^1)^+ \text{ and } (H^2)^+$$
$$\Delta y_{He} = 0.897 \text{ mm} \quad \text{for } (H_2^1)^+ \text{ and } (He^4)^{++}$$

In both these doublets, y is larger for $(H_2^1)^+$ than for the other member of the doublet.   From these data, find the mass of the neutral H^2 atom if the neutral atomic masses for hydrogen and helium are $H^1 = 1.008\ 14$ amu and

$$He^4 = 4.003\ 87$$

Include the effects, if any, of the electron masses, as in $(He)^{++}$, but neglect the atomic binding energy of these electrons.   *Ans.:* 2.014 73 amu.

11. Show that the mass correction for electron deficiencies is the same in both ions of a doublet. Thus the mass difference for the corresponding neutral molecules is the same as the observed doublet separation for the ions, and no net correction is needed for electron masses. For example,

$$(D_3)^+ - (C^{12})^{++} = 3D - \tfrac{1}{2}C$$

Is this relationship also true when the ratios of charge to mass number are unequal, as in $(Ti^{50})^+ - (Au^{197})^{++++} = Ti^{50} - \tfrac{1}{4}Au^{197}$?

12. From the mass-spectroscopic doublets (N19)

$$CO_2 - CS = b = 17.78 \times 10^{-3} \text{ amu}$$
$$C_3H_8 - CO_2 = c = 72.97 \times 10^{-3} \text{ amu}$$
$$C_6H_4 - CS_2 = d = 87.33 \times 10^{-3} \text{ amu}$$

(where $S \equiv S^{32}$, $O \equiv O^{16}$, $C \equiv C^{12}$, and $H \equiv H^1$), show that

$$H = 1 + \tfrac{1}{32}(4b + 5c - 2d)$$

and determine the mass of hydrogen which is obtained from this group of doublets. *Ans.:* 1.008 166 amu.

13. If the nitrogen–carbon monoxide doublet separation

$$(N^{14})_2 - (C^{12}O^{16}) = 11.28 \text{ millimass units}$$

what would you cite as the atomic mass of N^{14}? [Data from Nier, *Phys. Rev.*, **81**: 624L (1951).]

14. From the doublets (C36):

$$(S^{32}O_2^{16})^+ - (Zn^{64})^+ = (326.82 \pm 0.20) \times 10^{-4} \text{ amu}$$
$$(O_2^{16})^+ - (Zn^{64})^{++} = (252.46 \pm 0.22) \times 10^{-4} \text{ amu}$$

determine the atomic mass of S^{32} and Zn^{64}. *Ans.:* 31.982 190 $\pm$ 0.000 049 amu; 63.949 508 $\pm$ 0.000 014 amu

4. *Atomic Mass from Nuclear Disintegration Energies*

Einstein's special theory of relativity requires that the inertial mass m of any body moving at velocity V with respect to the observer be given by

$$m = \frac{m_0}{\sqrt{1 - (V/c)^2}} \qquad (4.1)$$

where c is the velocity of light and m_0 is the rest mass of the body. The relativistic momentum is mV. Direct experimental verification of this dependence of mass on velocity is obtained from observations of the magnetic deflection of the high-speed electrons emitted by radioactive substances (Z1).

The kinetic energy T is given by

$$T = m_0c^2 \left[\frac{1}{\sqrt{1 - (V/c)^2}} - 1 \right]$$
$$= mc^2 - m_0c^2 = (m - m_0)c^2 = \Delta mc^2 \qquad (4.2)$$

where m_0c^2 is the rest energy and mc^2 is called the total energy. The kinetic energy therefore is equivalent to an increase of mass

$$(m - m_0) = \frac{T}{c^2}$$

The principle of conservation of energy includes mass as a form of energy, on a par with chemical, electrical, mechanical, and other common forms. The well-known chemical law relating to the conservation of mass in all chemical reactions is not rigorously true. The actual deviations from strict mass conservation are simply too small to be detected in the case of chemical reactions. Nevertheless, the release of energy T in a chemical reaction must be accompanied by a slight reduction Δm_0 in the total rest mass of the reacting components, in accord with

$$\frac{T}{c^2} = \Delta m_0 \tag{4.3}$$

The energy per atom involved in nuclear processes is vastly greater than in chemical processes and thus constitutes the best test and an everyday application of the so-called Einstein law, Eq. (4.3).

a. The Mass Equivalent of Energy. We need to evaluate the numerical factors connecting mass and energy. The unit of energy used most commonly in nuclear physics is 1 million electron-volts, abbreviated Mev. This is the kinetic energy acquired by an individual particle carrying a single electronic charge and falling through a potential difference of 10^6 volts. By definition, 1 statvolt $= (c/10^8)$ volts; hence

$$1 \text{ Mev} = 10^6 \text{ volts} \left[\frac{1 \text{ statvolt}}{(c/10^8) \text{ volts}} \right] e \text{ esu}$$

$$= \frac{e}{c} 10^{14} \text{ ergs} \tag{4.4}$$

For a single particle, the numerical equivalence between atomic mass units and energy is

$$1 \text{ amu} = \frac{1}{N} \text{ g} = \frac{c^2}{N} \text{ ergs} \tag{4.5}$$

in which N is the number of atoms in 1 mole on the *physical scale*, e.g., in 16 g of O^{16}.

If F is the faraday constant, in coulombs per mole on the physical scale, then

$$1 \text{ faraday} \equiv Ne = \left(F \frac{\text{coulombs}}{\text{mole}} \right) \left[\frac{(c/10) \text{ esu}}{1 \text{ coulomb}} \right] = F \frac{c}{10} \quad \frac{\text{esu}}{\text{mole}} \tag{4.6}$$

Eliminating Avogadro's number (N) between Eqs. (4.5) and (4.6), then using the conversion factor of Eq. (4.4), we have

$$1 \text{ amu} = \frac{10ce}{F} \text{ ergs} \left[\frac{1 \text{ Mev}}{(10^{14} e/c) \text{ ergs}} \right]$$

$$= \frac{c^2}{F} 10^{-13} \text{ Mev} \tag{4.7}$$

It should be noted that the relationship between Mev and ergs, Eq. (4.4), depends on the numerical value adopted for the charge on the electron, whereas the relationship between Mev and amu, Eq. (4.7), is independent of e. Using the 1952 values (D44) of

$$e = (4.8029 \pm 0.0002) \times 10^{-10} \text{ esu}$$
$$c = (2.997\ 929 \pm 0.000\ 008) \times 10^{10} \text{ cm/sec}$$

and $F = 96{,}520.1 \pm 2.5$ coulombs/mole   physical scale

gives the currently adopted relationships

$$1 \text{ Mev} = (1.602\ 07 \pm 0.000\ 07) \times 10^{-6} \text{ erg} \tag{4.8}$$
$$1 \text{ amu} = 931.162 \pm 0.024 \text{ Mev} \tag{4.9}$$

The reciprocal value is often useful and is

$$1 \text{ Mev} = 0.001\ 073\ 93 \pm 0.000\ 000\ 03 \text{ amu} \tag{4.10}$$

or, in round numbers, 1 Mev $\simeq$ 1 millimass unit.

The rest mass of one electron m_0 is $1/1{,}836.13$ times the proton mass, or $0.000\ 548\ 76$ amu, and corresponds to an energy

$$m_0 c^2 = 0.510\ 98 \pm 0.000\ 02 \text{ Mev} \tag{4.11}$$

This "rest energy" $m_0 c^2$ of an electron is used commonly as a natural basic unit of atomic and nuclear energy.

b. Experimental Verification of the Equivalence of Mass and Energy. The first direct experimental comparison of the energy liberated in a nuclear reaction and the accompanying change in total rest mass was made in 1933 by Bainbridge (B3), using the reaction $\text{Li}^7 + \text{H}^1 \rightarrow \text{He}^4 + \text{He}^4$. A more accurate comparison is obtained from nuclear reactions in which the masses are known from mass-spectroscopic doublet data (J19).

Q Values of Reactions Compared with Mass-spectroscopic Doublets. When nitrogen is bombarded by high-speed deuterons a nuclear reaction takes place in which energetic protons are produced. The nuclear reaction is

$$\text{N}^{14} + \text{H}^2 \rightarrow \text{N}^{15} + \text{H}^1 + Q \tag{4.12}$$

where Q is the kinetic energy released in the reaction when N^{15} is formed in its ground level. A discussion of the methods of measuring Q values will be found in Chap. 12. Here it is sufficient to recognize Q as the difference between the kinetic energy of the products and the kinetic energy of the original particles in any nuclear reaction. When the products have greater kinetic energy than the original particles, Q is positive, and the reaction is said to be *exoergic* since it releases kinetic energy by the conversion of a portion of the rest mass into kinetic energy. Conversely, when the products have less kinetic energy than the original particles, the reaction is called *endoergic*, and Q is negative and numerically equal to the kinetic energy converted into rest mass in the reaction.

The reaction Eq. (4.12) is strongly exoergic; energy measurements on the ejected protons give $Q = 8.615 \pm 0.009$ Mev. Equation (4.12) can be rewritten to represent the difference between two mass doublets. Solving for Q, after adding H^1 to both sides, we obtain

$$Q = (N^{14}H^1 - N^{15}) - (2H^1 - H^2) \tag{4.13}$$

Substituting the mass differences observed for these doublets (J19), we find

$$\begin{aligned}
Q &= (0.010\ 74 \pm 0.0002) - (0.001\ 53 \pm 0.000\ 04)\ \text{amu} \\
&= 0.009\ 21 \pm 0.0002\ \text{amu} \\
&= 8.57 \pm 0.2\ \text{Mev}
\end{aligned} \tag{4.14}$$

Thus the combined rest mass of N^{14} and H^2 is 0.009 21 amu greater than the total rest mass of the products N^{15} and H^1, and the mass decrease in the reaction appears quantitatively as kinetic energy of the reaction products.

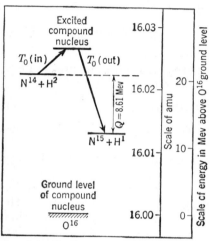

Fig. 4.1 Typical graphical representation of the energetics of a nuclear reaction. The numerical equivalence of changes in rest mass and kinetic energy is shown on the matched energy and mass scales.

This mass-energy balance, and many others like it, shows also that *the stable atoms produced by nuclear disintegration are indistinguishable from their sister atoms* found in nature. Regardless of their mode of origin, the ground levels of all nuclei of any given nuclide appear to be completely identical.

The exact equivalence of mass and energy is one of the most firmly established principles of modern physics. By means of this principle and the large number of available nuclear reactions, relative masses of the atoms can be established independently of mass-spectroscopic data. There are many cases, particularly the neutron and a number of rare or radioactive nuclides, where the mass spectrograph cannot be used, and so disintegration masses are used to complement the mass-spectroscopic data in compiling our mass tables.

Energy Diagram for Nuclear Reactions. It is useful to visualize the energetics of nuclear reactions by means of energy diagrams. Figure 4.1 portrays the energetics of the reaction of Eq. (4.12). The total rest mass of the original particles is shown in the left-hand scale of the diagram and has the numerical value

$$\begin{aligned}
N^{14} &= 14.007\ 515 \\
H^2 &= \underline{\ \ 2.014\ 735} \\
N^{14} + H^2 &= 16.022\ 250 = 16\ \text{amu} + 20.71\ \text{Mev} \tag{4.15}
\end{aligned}$$

The total rest mass of the reaction products, when N^{15} is formed in its ground level, is shown at the right and is

$$N^{15} = 15.004\ 863$$
$$H^1 = \ \ 1.008\ 142$$
$$N^{15} + H^1 = 16.013\ 005 = 16\ \text{amu} + 12.10\ \text{Mev} \qquad (4.16)$$

The reaction takes place when N^{14} and H^2 approach each other with a kinetic energy in center-of-mass coordinates which is adequate for transmission through the potential barrier. The colliding particles form a compound nucleus, which in this case is $N^{14} + H^2 \to (O^{16})$. This compound nucleus has an internal excitation energy which is generally so high that it lies in the region of broad overlapping excited levels which act like a continuum. Thus the compound nucleus can be formed over a broad and continuous domain of incident kinetic energy T_0 (in). The mass of the excited compound nucleus is shown in the center of Fig. 4.1.

Generally, the compound nucleus can disintegrate in any one of a number of competing modes, or "exit channels." If a proton is emitted, and the residual N^{15} is left in its lowest possible level of internal energy, then the mutual kinetic energy of the reaction products will be T_0 (out) in center-of-mass coordinates, as shown in Fig. 4.1. The Q value of the reaction is

$$Q = T_0\ (\text{out}) - T_0\ (\text{in}) \qquad (4.17)$$

and this is equal to the mass difference between the original particles and the reaction products, Eqs. (4.15) and (4.16), as can be seen graphically in Fig. 4.1.

Atomic masses, rather than nuclear masses, usually are used throughout. At each stage of the reaction the atomic masses exceed the nuclear masses by the same number of atomic electrons. If the small differences in the binding energies of the atomic electrons are neglected, then all mass differences in Eqs. (4.12) to (4.16) and in Fig. 4.1 are the same for atomic masses as they would be for nuclear masses.

c. The Energetics of Radioactive Decay. Quite accurate determinations of atomic-mass differences can be obtained from measurements of the energy of α, β, and γ rays, provided that the radioactive-decay scheme of the parent nuclide is known.

Negatron β Decay. In that class of β decay which involves the emission of a negative electron, a nucleus of charge Z and *nuclear mass* $_ZM'$ transforms spontaneously into a nucleus of charge $(Z + 1)$ and mass $_{Z+1}M'$. Mass-energetically, this can be written

$$_ZM' = {}_{Z+1}M' + m_0 + \nu + T_\beta + T_\nu + T_{M'} + T_\gamma \qquad (4.18)$$

where $m_0 =$ rest mass of β ray
$\quad \nu =$ rest mass of accompanying neutrino
$\quad T_\beta =$ kinetic energy of β ray
$\quad T_\nu =$ kinetic energy of neutrino
$\quad T_{M'} =$ kinetic energy of recoil nucleus $_{Z+1}M'$
$\quad T_\gamma =$ total γ-ray energy emitted after β ray

Experimentally, $\nu = 0$; $T_\beta + T_\nu = T_{max}$ is the measured maximum kinetic energy or "end point" of the continuous β-ray spectrum, and $T_{M'} \ll T_{max}$. Then we can call the observed decay energy T_0, where to a good approximation

$$T_0 = T_{max} + T_\gamma \qquad (4.19)$$

Then the relationship between the nuclear masses, Eq. (4.18), becomes

$$_z M' = _{z+1}M' + m_0 + T_0 \qquad (4.20)$$

If we now add the mass of Z atomic electrons to both sides, we have

$$(_z M' + Z m_0) = [_{z+1}M' + (Z+1)m_0] + T_0 \qquad (4.21)$$

which, if the small difference in the binding energy of the atomic electrons be neglected, is

$$_z M = _{z+1}M + T_0 \quad \text{ for } \beta^- \text{ decay} \qquad (4.21a)$$

where $_z M$ and $_{z+1}M$ are the neutral *atomic* masses of the parent and product of *negatron* β decay. Utilizing the letter Q, with appropriate subscripts, to denote the differences in atomic mass which occur in radioactive decay, we write for β^- decay

$$Q_{\beta^-} \equiv {}_z M - {}_{z+1}M = T_0 = T_{max} + T_\gamma \qquad (4.22)$$

Thus, to a good approximation, the total kinetic energy of decay T_0 equals the difference in neutral atomic mass Q_{β^-} between the isobaric parent and decay-product atoms.

Energy-level Diagrams for Negatron β Decay. Many types of energy-level diagram have been proposed for displaying the decay schemes of radioactive substances. The two most fundamental varieties are shown in Fig. 4.2, where the energetics of the negatron β decay of Al^{28} are plotted. This nuclide decays by emitting a simple continuous spectrum of negatron β rays whose maximum kinetic energy is 2.865 ± 0.010 Mev (M71). After the emission of the β ray, each residual nucleus of Si^{28} is left in an excited level at about 1.78 Mev above its ground level. The prompt emission by Si^{28} of a single γ ray, whose measured quantum energy is 1.782 ± 0.010 Mev (M71), puts this decay product into its ground level.

The measured decay energy T_0 of Al^{28} is, from Eq. (4.19), $2.865 + 1.782 \simeq 4.65$ Mev, or 4.99×10^{-3} amu. The change in *nuclear* mass, Eq. (4.20), equals this sum of the β-ray and γ-ray energies plus the rest mass m_0 of the emitted β ray.

The right-hand side of Fig. 4.2 is the Al^{28} decay scheme on the *nuclear* mass-energy scale. The ground level of Al^{28} is

$$T_0 + m_0 = 4.65 + 0.51 = 5.16 \text{ Mev} = 5.54 \times 10^{-3} \text{ amu}$$

above the ground level of Si^{28}. The diagonal line represents the rest energy $m_0 c^2 = 0.51$ Mev of the β ray and also the increase of one unit in nuclear charge when the β-ray negatron is emitted. The vertical line represents the kinetic energy 2.865 Mev of the electron-neutrino pair, as measured by the maximum energy of the β-ray spectrum. The wavy line shows the final γ-ray transition in Si^{28}.

The left-hand side of Fig. 4.2 shows the same transitions but drawn on the more common *atomic* mass-energy scale. The atomic mass of Al^{28} includes the mass of its 13 atomic electrons. One more atomic electron is required in the product atom Si^{28} than in the parent Al^{28}. From the standpoint of over-all mass balance, we can imagine that the emitted β-ray electron eventually joins the product atom as this additional atomic electron. Hence no mass correction m_0 is needed, and the

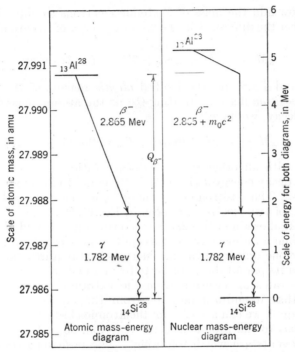

Fig. 4.2 Negatron β decay scheme for Al^{28}. At left, the conventional diagram in which nuclear energy levels and transitions are plotted against a scale of atomic mass. At right, the nuclear energy-level and mass diagram. An absolute mass scale for the nuclear mass-energy diagram would equal the atomic-mass scale diminished by about the mass of 14 atomic electrons, Eq. (2.1).

difference in atomic mass $Q_{\beta-}$ is given by T_0. Thus, using atomic masses, we find from Eq. (4.22) that

$$_{13}Al^{28} = {}_{14}Si^{28} + Q_{\beta-}$$

where
$$Q_{\beta-} = 4.65 \text{ Mev} = 0.004\ 99 \text{ amu}$$

Taking (L26) Si^{28} as 27.985 77 amu, we find

$$Al^{28} = 27.990\ 76 \text{ amu}$$

These atomic-mass values, as well as the corresponding $Q_{\beta-}$ and m_0 values, are shown in the dual scales of mass and of energy in Fig. 4.2.

Positron β Decay. In the class of β decay which involves the emission of a positive electron, a nucleus of charge Z and nuclear mass $_zM'$ transforms into a nucleus of charge $(Z - 1)$ and mass $_{z-1}M'$. In a manner which is completely analogous to that of Eqs. (4.18) to (4.20), we conclude that for positron β decay the change in *nuclear* mass is the same as for negatron β decay, that is, $(T_0 + m_0)$, where m_0 is the positron mass. Thus for positron decay, Eq. (4.20) becomes

$$_zM' = _{z-1}M' + m_0 + T_0 \tag{4.23}$$

When we now add the mass of Z atomic electrons to both sides and, as before, neglect the difference in the binding energy of the atomic electrons, we find

$$_zM = _{z-1}M + 2m_0 + T_0 \qquad \text{for } \beta^+ \text{ decay} \tag{4.23a}$$

where $_zM$ and $_{z-1}M$ are the neutral *atomic* masses of the parent and product of *positron* decay. Writing Q_{β^+} as the atomic mass difference in positron β decay, we have

$$Q_{\beta^+} \equiv _zM - _{z-1}M = 2m_0c^2 + T_0 = 2m_0c^2 + T_{\max} + T_\gamma \tag{4.24}$$

In contrast with all other types of disintegration and decay reactions, the positron decay energy T_0 is not directly equal to the change in neutral atomic mass. The positron decay energy must be increased by the rest energy $2m_0c^2$ of two electrons, as seen in Eq. (4.24).

The physical origin of this $2m_0c^2$ correction term should be understood clearly. When a radioactive nucleus emits a positron, its nuclear charge decreases by one unit, and the product nucleus requires one less atomic electron than its parent did in order to form a neutral atom. The decay therefore liberates an electron from the extranuclear structure at the same time that it emits a positron from the nucleus. Because their masses are equal, we can account for the atomic electron and the positron by adding $2m_0$ to the products of the reaction, as in Eq. (4.23a). The subsequent events are worth following. The positron lives only about 10^{-10} sec and then combines with some atomic electron. Both are annihilated, and the mass energy $2m_0c^2$ appears ordinarily as two photons each having a quantum energy of $m_0c^2 = 0.511$ Mev. Thus in Eq. (4.24) we may regard the annihilation quanta as an additional energy of $2m_0c^2 = 1.022$ Mev which is always emitted as an ultimate consequence of positron β decay.

Energy-level Diagrams for Positron β Decay. Diagrams for positron decay schemes require a slightly special treatment in order to present the $2m_0c^2$ term. In Fig. 4.3, the nuclear mass-energy diagram on the right is completely analogous to the negatron β decay situation in Fig. 4.2. This identity arises from Eqs. (4.20) and (4.23). From a nuclear standpoint, either type of β decay requires an expenditure of m_0 for the production of the rest mass of the negatron or the positron β ray.

The atomic-mass diagrams differ. One common method of representing the $2m_0c^2$ term is shown on the left of Fig. 4.3. Here the two electron masses are regarded as subtracted from the mass of the parent Na^{22}; then the diagonal line represents only the kinetic energy of the positron-neutrino pair, as evaluated by the maximum energy of the positron β-ray spectrum.

The atomic mass of Na^{22}, from Eq. (4.24) or Fig. 4.3, is given by

$$Na^{22} = Ne^{22} + 2m_0 + T_{max} + T_\gamma$$
$$= 21.998\ 36\ \text{amu} + 2 \times (0.000\ 549)\ \text{amu} + 0.542\ \text{Mev}$$
$$+ 1.277\ \text{Mev}$$

$$= 22.001\ 41\ \text{amu}$$

Electron-capture Transitions. Radioactive decay by electron capture competes with all cases of positron β decay. The parent nucleus $_zM'$ captures one of its own atomic electrons and emits a neutrino. The final decay product nucleus has charge $(Z - 1)$ and mass $_{z-1}M'$ after the

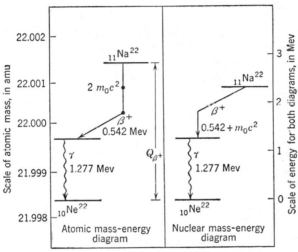

Fig. 4.3 Positron β decay scheme of Na^{22} (competing modes < 1 per cent not shown). Scales analogous to Fig. 4.2. Note in the atomic-mass diagram that among the products of the decay process the total mass $2m_0$ of the positron and one atomic electron can be regarded physically as either a mass product (before annihilation) or an energy product (after annihilation). Compare Eq. (4.24).

emission of any γ rays which accompany the over-all transition. Mass-energetically, the transition corresponds to

$$_zM' + m_0 = _{z-1}M' + \nu + T_\nu + T_{M'} + T_\gamma \qquad (4.25)$$

Experimentally, the total γ-ray energy T_γ is relatively easy to measure, the recoil energy $T_{M'}$ has been measured in a few cases (Chap. 17, Sec. 2), the neutrino energy T_ν cannot be measured directly, and the rest mass ν of the neutrino is zero. In general, $T_\nu \gg T_{M'}$. The decay energy

$$T_0 = T_\nu + T_{M'} + T_\gamma \simeq T_\nu + T_\gamma \qquad (4.26)$$

is therefore not directly measurable for electron-capture (EC) transitions.

Now we can add $(Z - 1)$ electrons to both sides of Eq. (4.25) and, if differences in atomic binding energy are neglected, we obtain

$$zM = {}_{z-1}M + T_0$$

or
$$Q_{EC} \equiv zM - {}_{z-1}M = T_0 = T_\nu + T_\gamma \qquad (4.27)$$

Thus, to a good approximation, the electron-capture decay energy T_0 is equal to the difference in *atomic* mass Q_{EC} between the isobaric parent and product.

Energy-level Diagrams for Electron Capture. Figure 4.4 illustrates a case of electron capture for which the competing positron β decay is excluded energetically. The difference in atomic mass ${}_4Be^7 - {}_3Li^7$ is known from nuclear disintegration data to be only about 0.93×10^{-3}

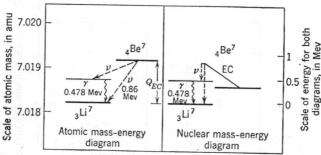

Fig. 4.4 Electron-capture decay scheme of Be^7. Scales analogous to Fig. 4.2. The neutrino energies T_ν are shown dotted. About 11 per cent of the transitions involve a low-energy neutrino group followed by a 0.478-Mev γ ray. The remaining transitions go directly to the ground level of Li^7 and involve neutrinos whose kinetic energy equals, to a good approximation, the difference in *atomic* mass Q_{EC} between the isobaric parent and product atoms.

amu, or 0.86 Mev. Because the Be atom contains one more atomic electron than the Li atom, the difference in nuclear mass is only

$$(0.93 \times 10^{-3}) - (0.55 \times 10^{-3}) = (0.38 \times 10^{-3}) \text{ amu} = 0.35 \text{ Mev}$$

The minimum mass difference required for positron β decay [Eqs. (4.23) and (4.23a)] is therefore not available.

In the *nuclear* mass-energy diagram, on the right-hand side of Fig. 4.4, the diagonal line shows the Be^7 nucleus gaining the mass m_0 of the captured electron and, at the same time, decreasing its charge to that of Li. Simultaneously, the neutrino is emitted. Its energy is represented by the vertical line, which is dotted as an indication that this kinetic energy cannot be measured directly. In about 11 per cent of the Be^7 → Li^7 transitions a low-energy neutrino is emitted, and the Li^7 nucleus is left in an excited level at 0.478 Mev. A γ-ray transition to the ground level of Li^7 follows promptly.

Note that in an electron-capture transition the neutrinos are emitted in one or more *monoenergetic* groups, in contrast with the continuous distributions of neutrino energy found in β decay. Each neutrino in the transition to the ground level of Li^7 has a kinetic energy of 0.86 Mev. The neutrinos in the transition to the excited level of Li^7 each have $T_\nu = 0.86 - 0.478 = 0.38$ Mev.

Competition between Electron Capture and Positron β-Ray Emission. Equation (4.27) shows that the electron-capture transition, which is permitted energetically whenever $Q_{EC} > 0$, can occur whenever $_zM > _{z-1}M$. Comparison with Eq. (4.24) shows that the competing positron β decay is possible energetically only if $_zM > 2m_0 + _{z-1}M$. Transitions between isobars whose mass is nearly the same may therefore take

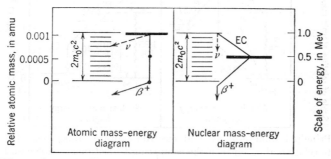

Fig. 4.5 These schematic diagrams emphasize the difference between the energetics of electron capture and positron β decay. Electron-capture transitions can take place to any level in the domain shown ($2m_0c^2$ wide) but positron β transitions are excluded. Compare Eqs. (4.24) and (4.27). The nuclear diagram shows more clearly that the origin of this $2m_0c^2$ band is the difference between the capture of m_0 and the emission of m_0 by a nucleus. Note from the nuclear diagram that the electron-capture transitions can "climb," i.e., the final nucleus can be even heavier than the initial nucleus.

place by electron capture even when positron β decay is excluded energetically. In the domain of mass differences

$$0 \leq (_zM - _{z-1}M) \leq 2m_0 \tag{4.28}$$

only electron-capture transitions can take place between isobars, as can be visualized from Fig. 4.5.

Dual β Decay. There is a large class of radioactive nuclei which have odd Z and even A. Many of these have stable neighboring isobars at both $Z - 1$ and $Z + 1$. These radioactive nuclei may therefore transform by negatron β decay, by electron capture, and by positron β decay. A familiar example is Cu^{64}, which is illustrated in the decay schemes and energy-level diagrams of Fig. 4.6. Such cases of dual β decay provide a means of determining mass differences between pairs of stable isobars which differ in atomic number by two units.

In the case of Cu^{64}

$$_{29}Cu^{64} = _{30}Zn^{64} + T_{max}(\beta-) \tag{4.29}$$
$$_{29}Cu^{64} = _{28}Ni^{64} + 2m_0c^2 + T_{max}(\beta+) \tag{4.30}$$

Eliminating the radioactive nuclide by subtraction, we obtain

$$_{30}\text{Zn}^{64} - {}_{28}\text{Ni}^{64} = 2m_0c^2 + T_{\max}(\beta^+) - T_{\max}(\beta^-)$$
$$= 1.02 + 0.66 - 0.57 \text{ Mev}$$
$$= 1.11 \text{ Mev} = 0.001\ 19 \text{ amu} \qquad (4.31)$$

Note that systematic errors in the measurement of the end points of the two β spectra tend to cancel in the determination of the mass difference.

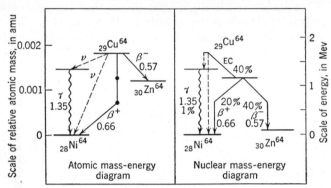

Fig. 4.6 Principal dual β-decay and electron-capture transitions of Cu^{64}. The approximate relative abundance of the competing transitions is shown on the nuclear mass-energy diagram. Note that the difference in *nuclear* mass between Ni^{64} and Zn^{64} is very small, and also that the excited level at 1.35 Mev in Ni^{64} lies *above* the nuclear mass of the ground level of Cu^{64} and can only be reached by the electron-capture transition.

α *Decay.* In α decay, the parent nucleus $_zM'$ emits a helium nucleus α. Mass-energetically, the transition can be written

$$_zM' = {}_{z-2}M' + \alpha + T_\alpha + T_{M'} + T_\gamma \qquad (4.32)$$

The kinetic energy $T_{M'}$ of the residual recoil nucleus is of the order of 2 per cent of the laboratory kinetic energy T_α of the α ray and cannot be neglected in a mass-energy balance. The total kinetic energy T_0 of the heavy particles, which is often called the "disintegration energy," is

$$T_0 = T_\alpha + T_{M'} = T_\alpha \left(\frac{M_\alpha}{M_0}\right) \qquad (4.33)$$

where M_0 is the reduced mass of the α ray M_α and of the recoil nucleus.

Equation (4.32) can be put in terms of neutral atomic masses by adding Zm_0 to both sides and neglecting differences in the binding energy of the atomic electrons. This gives

$$_zM = {}_{z-2}M + \text{He}^4 + T_0 + T_\gamma$$

or
$$Q_\alpha \equiv {}_zM - {}_{z-2}M - \text{He}^4 = T_\alpha \left(\frac{M_\alpha}{M_0}\right) + T_\gamma \qquad (4.34)$$

where He^4 is the neutral atomic mass of the helium atom. The decay scheme of Ra^{226} is represented in the atomic mass-energy diagram of Fig. 4.7.

Effects of Electron Binding Energy. Equation (4.34) represents the usual experimental situation. Measurements of $T_\alpha = T_0(M_0/M_\alpha)$ and T_γ lead to experimental values of the mass difference $(_z M - _{z-2} M)$ between the parent and product neutral atoms. If $Z \sim 90$, Eq. (2.2) will show that the difference in electron binding energy between $_z M$ and $_{z-2} M$ is ~ 0.03 Mev, which is in fact much greater than the error of measurement of T_α. This just means that in Eq. (4.32), for bare nuclei,

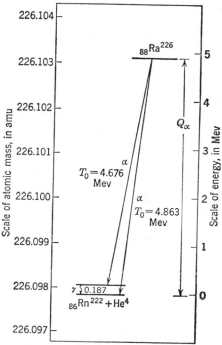

Fig. 4.7 The decay scheme of Ra²²⁶, on a scale of neutral atomic mass. Note that the rest mass of a neutral He⁴ atom is added in with the atomic mass of the decay product Rn²²². This is done to hold the mass scale in the domain of 226 amu and still allow the energy scale to show the total "disintegration energies" of the α ray and recoil atom T_0 in center-of-mass coordinates. The lower-energy α transition and its 0.187-Mev γ ray occur in only about 6 per cent of the transitions of Ra²²⁶. The atomic-mass scale is the tentative one proposed by Stern (S71), based on the assumption that Pb²⁰⁶ = 206.045 19 amu.

the actual kinetic energy of the emitted α ray is, in fact, *greater* than the observed T_α in the laboratory, by ~ 0.03 Mev for $Z \sim 90$. As the emitted α ray emerges through the negatively charged cloud of atomic electrons, it is decelerated to the energy T_α as observed in the laboratory. Thus, if electron binding energy is not neglected, Eq. (4.34) remains valid, but T_α in Eq. (4.32) would be changed to a larger value, say, T'_α. This legitimate correction is usually ignored.

Analogous considerations apply also to β decay, except that the effects of electron binding are smaller and are usually comparable with present experimental uncertainties. For β decay, Eqs. (4.19), (4.22), (4.24), and (4.27) represent correctly the usual experimental situation.

d. The Neutron-Hydrogen Mass Difference. Accurate knowledge of the mass of the neutron is of fundamental importance in evaluating the binding energy of nuclei and the nature of the forces between nucleons. The neutron, being uncharged, cannot be studied directly with a mass spectroscope. Its mass must be determined from the energetics of nuclear reactions.

The quantity which is actually determined from the nuclear-reaction data is the neutron-hydrogen mass difference $(n - \mathrm{H}^1)$. C. W. Li et al. (L27) have evaluated $(n - \mathrm{H}^1)$ from eight independent cycles of nuclear reactions. The weighted mean value is

$$n - \mathrm{H}^1 = 0.7823 \pm 0.001 \text{ Mev} \tag{4.35}$$

Threshold for Reactions with Tritium. The most direct and accurate determination of $(n - \mathrm{H}^1)$ is obtained by measuring the Q value of the reaction

$$\mathrm{H}^3 + \mathrm{H}^1 \rightarrow n + \mathrm{He}^3 + Q \tag{4.36}$$

In contrast with the reactions discussed in the previous section, this reaction has a negative Q value. Then Eq. (4.17) shows that the reaction cannot take place if the incident kinetic energy in the center-of-mass coordinates T_0 (in) is less than a definite minimum value given by

$$[T_0 \text{ (in)}]_{\min} = -Q \tag{4.37}$$

At this minimum incident energy the products of the reaction are stationary in the center-of-mass coordinates. But the reaction is detectable at this incident energy because the velocity of the products in the laboratory is finite and equal to the velocity of center of mass.

The minimum kinetic energy of the bombarding particle, in the *laboratory coordinates*, which is just sufficient to produce a reaction is called the *threshold energy*. If M_1 is the mass of the bombarding particle and M_0 is the reduced mass of the system, then

$$T_1 = \frac{M_1}{M_0} T_0 \text{ (in)} \tag{4.38}$$

where T_1 is the laboratory kinetic energy of M_1. The threshold energy $(T_1)_{\min}$ is therefore given by

$$(T_1)_{\min} = -\frac{M_1}{M_0} Q \tag{4.39}$$

for all reactions which have negative Q values.

The threshold proton energy for the reaction $\mathrm{H}^3(p,n)\mathrm{He}^3$ of Eq. (4.36) has been measured relative to an $\mathrm{Al}^{27}(p,\gamma)\mathrm{Si}^{28}$ resonance whose value is taken as a substandard of proton energy at 0.9933 Mev. When H^3 is bombarded, neutrons first appear at 0° from the direction of the bombarding protons when the proton energy is 26 ± 1 kev above the reference energy, or at an absolute energy of 1.019 ± 0.001 Mev (T7).

Then, from Eq. (4.39), $Q = -0.764 \pm 0.001$ Mev for the $H^3(p,n)He^3$ reaction.

The negatron β-ray spectrum of H^3 has an end point of only 0.0185 ± 0.0002 Mev. By combining the two reactions

$$H^3 + H^1 = n + He^3 - 0.764 \text{ Mev} \tag{4.40}$$
$$H^3 = He^3 + 0.018 \text{ Mev} \tag{4.41}$$

we obtain the present "best value" for the neutron-hydrogen mass

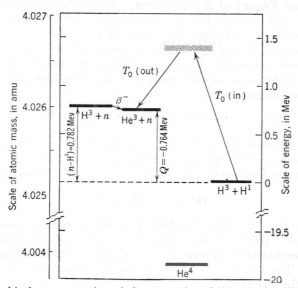

Fig. 4.8 Graphical representation of the energetics of the reaction $H^3(p,n)He^3$ and of the negatron β decay $H^3(\beta^-)He^3$, from which $(n - H^1)$ is determined. This diagram combines the principles of Fig. 4.1 for plotting reaction energetics with the methods of Fig. 4.2 for plotting radioactive decay, by adding in the mass of one neutron on the β decay scheme. In this way, all masses are in the domain of 4 amu and can be plotted together. Then both the Q value of the reaction $H^3(p,n)He^3$ and the $(n - H^1)$ mass difference appear as energy-level separations on the diagram. Note that the ground level of the compound nucleus He^4 is really far off scale, at about -20 Mev. The compound nucleus in the $H^3(p,n)He^3$ reaction is a highly excited level in the continuum of overlapping excited levels of He^4.

difference.

$$n - H^1 = 0.782 \pm 0.001 \text{ Mev}$$
$$= (0.840 \pm 0.001) \times 10^{-3} \text{ amu} \tag{4.42}$$

The energetics of the nuclear reactions of Eqs. (4.40) and (4.41) can be visualized in Fig. 4.8.

Radioactive Decay of the Free Neutron. The neutron is about 2.5 electron masses heavier than a proton. A neutron which evades capture by some nucleus should therefore undergo ordinary negatron β decay.

$$n \xrightarrow{\beta^-} H^1 + Q_{\beta^-} \tag{4.43}$$

The radioactive decay of free neutrons has been observed directly by passing a collimated beam of slow neutrons between two magnetic-lens spectrometers arranged end to end. The β-ray spectrum has been measured, using coincidences between protons focused in one spectrometer and β rays focused in the other (R22, S54). In this way, the end point of the β-ray spectrum of the free neutron is found to be 0.782 $\pm$ 0.013 Mev. This result confirms the more accurate but less direct value of $(n - \text{H}^1)$ obtained in Eq. (4.42).

e. Binding Energy of the Deuteron. In the deuteron, the nature of the fundamental nuclear forces between nucleons is approachable as a two-body problem. The binding energy of the deuteron is therefore an experimental quantity of special importance. The *binding energy* of any system of particles is the difference between the mass of the free constituents and the mass of the bound system. Then the binding energy $B(\text{H}^2)$ of the deuteron is

$$B(\text{H}^2) = n + \text{H}^1 - \text{H}^2 \tag{4.44}$$

The most direct determination of $B(\text{H}^2)$ is the measurement of the quantum energy of the photons which are emitted when slow neutrons are captured by hydrogen. These "capture γ rays" from the reaction

$$\text{H}^1 + n - \text{H}^2 + T_\gamma$$

have an energy of 2.229 $\pm$ 0.005 Mev, as measured relative to the standard ThC'' γ ray taken as 2.615 Mev. Adding 1.3 kev for the recoil energy of the deuterium nucleus, and including a probable error of 0.004 Mev in the ThC'' standard γ ray, Bell and Elliott (B29) obtain for the Q value of the reaction

$$\text{H}^1 + n = \text{H}^2 + Q$$
$$Q = B(\text{H}^2) = 2.230 \pm 0.007 \text{ Mev} \tag{4.45}$$

The binding energy of the deuteron has been computed by Li et al. (L27) from the energetics of six independent cycles of nuclear reactions. Their weighted mean value is

$$B(\text{H}^2) \equiv n + \text{H}^1 - \text{H}^2 = 2.225 \pm 0.002 \text{ Mev} \tag{4.46}$$

f. Mass of Rare Nuclides. Mass-spectroscopic determinations of the mass of stable nuclides whose natural abundance is small, such as O^{17}, are often difficult or impossible. Many of these masses can be obtained from nuclear-reaction data, for example, O^{17} from the reaction $\text{O}^{16}(d,p)\text{O}^{17}$. In this way complete mass tables will become available eventually.

g. Reaction Cycles. The atomic masses of all known nuclides, up to at least $A = 33$, have now been obtained relative to O^{16} entirely from nuclear-reaction data. The work of C. W. Li et al. (L27, L26) is the first example of such a compilation.

The O^{16} mass can be related to that of lighter nuclides in a reaction such as $O^{16}(d,\alpha)N^{14}$. Then

$$O^{16} = N^{14} + He^4 - H^2 + Q$$

Other reactions can be obtained relating these products to the other light nuclei.   Simultaneous equations can then be set up relating a number of independent reactions, called a *nuclear cycle*, to obtain the mass of any required nuclide.

As an illustration, the mass of H^1 is given in terms of O^{16} by (L27)

$$H^1 = \tfrac{1}{16}O^{16} + \tfrac{1}{16}[-9Q_a + 10Q_b + 5Q_c$$
$$- (Q_1 - Q_2 - Q_3 + Q_4 + Q_5 + Q_6 + Q_7 - Q_8)] \quad (4.47)$$

where

$Q_a = n - H^1$	$Q_b = n + H^1 - H^2$	$Q_c = 2H^2 - He^4$
$Q_1 = O^{16}(d,\alpha)N^{14}$	$Q_2 = C^{14}(\beta^-)N^{14}$	$Q_3 = C^{13}(d,p)C^{14}$
$Q_4 = C^{13}(d,\alpha)B^{11}$	$Q_5 = B^{11}(d,\alpha)Be^9$	$Q_6 = Be^9(p,\alpha)Li^6$
$Q_7 = Li^6(p,\alpha)He^3$	$Q_8 = H^2(d,n)He^3$	

It is evident that many more terms are involved here than in the analogous derivation of H^1 from a small number of mass-spectroscopic doublets, as in Eq. (3.12).   However, the accuracy of the Q-value determinations is now sufficiently high so that good atomic-mass values can be obtained for the light nuclides.   In general, the mass-spectroscopic masses are consistently larger than the nuclear-reaction cycle masses and by more than the probable error of measurement.

Problems

1. The kinetic energy of the two nuclei produced in the fission of U^{235} is about 170 Mev.   Approximately what fraction of the original mass of $(U^{235} + n)$ appears as kinetic energy?

2. In any nuclear reaction at nonrelativistic energies, develop a simple argument based on the mass definition of the Q value which will show that the difference in kinetic energy of the incident and residual particles is the same in laboratory coordinates as it is in center-of-mass coordinates.

3. From the following nuclear-reaction data (L26), calculate the atomic-mass difference $(Al^{28} - Si^{28})$.   Compare with the β decay energetics of Fig. 4.2.

Reaction	Q value, Mev	Doublet	Mass difference, amu
$Al^{27}(d,p)Al^{28}$	5.494	$(2H^1 - H^2)$	1.549×10^{-3}
$Si^{28}(d,p)Si^{29}$	6.246	$(2H^2 - He^4)$	25.596×10^{-3}
$Si^{29}(d,\alpha)Al^{27}$	5.994		

4. Show that in β decay the maximum value of the ratio of the recoil energy T_M to the maximum β-ray energy T_{max} depends on the mass of the nuclide and is given by

$$\frac{T_M}{T_{max}} = \frac{T_{max}}{2Mc^2} + \frac{m_0}{M} \quad (4.48)$$

Derive analogous expressions for the recoil energy resulting from the emission of a neutrino whose energy is T_ν and from the emission of a γ ray whose energy is T_γ. Evaluate the recoil energy for $M \sim 50$ amu if $T_{max} \sim 1$ Mev; $T_\gamma \sim 1$ Mev; $T_\nu \sim 1$ Mev.

5. Estimate the difference between the binding energy of the atomic electrons in Al^{28} and Si^{28}. Compare with the combined experimental uncertainty of the β-ray and γ-ray energy in the $Al^{28}(\beta^-)Si^{28}$ transition.

6. In the decay of I^{131}, as given in Fig. 4.9,

(a) Show that the total disintegration energy Q is independent of which competing mode of decay a particular nucleus follows.

(b) Compute the atomic-mass difference in amu between the ground levels of I^{131} and Xe^{131}.

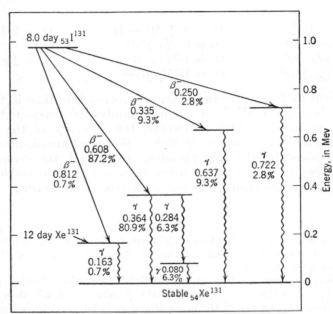

Fig. 4.9 The decay scheme proposed by Bell and Graham (B30) for the principal transitions in the complicated β decay of I^{131}. Note that one of the competitive β-ray transitions leads to the 12-day isomer of Xe^{131}. The percentages shown for each γ ray include the competing internal-conversion transitions.

7. Nier and Roberts [*Phys. Rev.*, **81**: 507 (1951)] find that the mass doublet separation $Ca^{40} - A^{40} = 0.32 \pm 0.08 \times 10^{-3}$ amu.

(a) If the β rays of K^{40} have a maximum energy of 1.36 Mev, and no γ rays accompany the negatron β rays, what is the neutral atomic-mass difference between K^{40} and Ca^{40}, in amu?

(b) What would be the maximum possible γ-ray energy following an electron-capture transition in K^{40}?

(c) What is the actual kinetic energy of the neutrinos if the observed γ-ray energy following electron capture is 1.46 Mev?

(d) Draw to scale a decay scheme for these observed transitions of K^{40}. What would be the maximum energy expected for a positron β-ray spectrum of K^{40} (none is observed)?

8. Determine an experimental value for the mass of the neutrino by comparing the energetics of the positron β decay of N^{13} ($T_{max} = 1.200 \pm 0.004$ Mev; no γ rays) with the reaction $C^{13}(p,n)N^{13}$ for which $Q = -3.003 \pm 0.003$ Mev. Use $(n - H^1) = 0.782 \pm 0.001$ Mev. Plot the $N^{13}(\beta^+)C^{13}$ and $C^{13}(p,n)N^{13}$ reactions on a single mass-energy diagram in the vicinity of 14 amu.

9. What error, in kev, is introduced in the determination of Q from the threshold proton energy of the reaction $H^3(p,n)He^3$ if one assumes that M_1/M_0 can be represented by (a) neutral atomic masses and (b) mass numbers, instead of by nuclear masses? Compare with the estimated experimental uncertainty in the threshold proton energy.

10. If H^3 nuclei are used to bombard hydrogen, what is the threshold energy for the reaction $H^1(t,n)He^3$ ($t \equiv$ tritium $\equiv H^3$)? Explain physically why this is so vastly different from the proton threshold for $H^3(p,n)He^3$, which involves the same actual nuclear interaction. What is the kinetic energy, in the laboratory coordinates, of the neutrons which are produced just at the threshold in the reactions (a) $H^1(t,n)He^3$ and (b) $H^3(p,n)He^3$?

11. Evaluate the $(n - H^1)$ mass difference from the energetics of the two fundamental d-d reactions (L27)

$$H^2(d,p)H^3; \quad Q_1 = 4.036 \text{ Mev}$$
$$H^2(d,n)He^3; \quad Q_2 = 3.265 \text{ Mev}$$

combined with the β decay energy of tritium. Plot the energetics of all these reactions on an atomic mass-energy diagram and show graphically the values of Q_1, Q_2, T_{max}, and $(n - H^1)$.

12. Determine the atomic-mass difference $Be^7 - Li^7$ from the energetics of the reactions

$$B^{10}(p,\alpha)Be^7; \quad Q_1 = 1.150 \pm 0.003 \text{ Mev}$$
$$B^{10}(n,\alpha)Li^7; \quad Q_2 = 2.789 \pm 0.009 \text{ Mev}$$

Plot the energetics on a mass-energy diagram, showing graphically the values of Q_1, Q_2, and $Be^7 - Li^7$. Use $(n - H^1) = 0.782$ Mev. From energetic considerations alone, what would be the maximum possible neutrino energy in the electron-capture decay of Be^7?

13. Determine the binding energy of the deuteron from the energy released in the nuclear reactions

$$H^2(d,p)H^3; \quad Q_1 = 4.036 \pm 0.012 \text{ Mev}$$
$$H^2(n,\gamma)H^3; \quad Q_2 = 6.251 \pm 0.008 \text{ Mev}$$

Does the value obtained conflict with the direct measurement obtained from $H^1(n,\gamma)H^2$? Plot the energetics of these reactions, showing graphically the values of Q_1, Q_2, and $B(H^2)$.

5. *Tables of Atomic Mass*

The atomic mass of a large number of the known nuclides has not yet been measured. All tables are fragmentary. Compilations of the material available are made from time to time by various authors. In each instance the mass recommended for an individual nuclide depends upon the values adopted at the time for the substandards of atomic mass. Caution must be exercised in using any particular table.

Four of the recently most used compilations of atomic masses are those of Mattauch (M21, M22), Bethe (B43), Sullivan (S80), and Wapstra (R36).   These are all pre-1950 tables and are therefore subject to some revisions because of changes in the mass substandards.

Data on mass doublet separations, nuclear-reaction energies, and derived atomic masses, up to December 31, 1951, will be found in the valuable compilations by Bainbridge (B4).

The October, 1954, issue of the *Reviews of Modern Physics* combined five excellent compilations of data up to early 1954, including mass doublet separations (D40a), nuclear-reaction Q values (V3a), β decay energies (K18a), α decay energies (A34a), and mass ratios from microwave spectroscopy (G18a).

In Table 5.1 we give for future reference the self-consistent set of atomic-mass values derived entirely from nuclear-reaction data by Li et al. in 1951 and 1952 (L27, L26).   A comparison with recent mass-spectroscopic values for those nuclides which are stable has been given by Li (L26).

Table 5.2 gives post-1951 mass-spectroscopic values determined by Collins, Nier, and Johnson (C35, C36, C34) for most of the stable nuclides between S^{32} and Nb^{93} and by Halsted (H11) in the same laboratory for many nuclides between Pd^{102} and Xe^{136}.   By combining these masses with nuclear-reaction data, tables of atomic masses (in terms of $A - M$) for many of the unstable nuclides from S^{31} to Sr^{90} (C36, C34) and from Rh^{105} to I^{131} (H11) have been compiled.

TABLE 5.1. TABLE OF ATOMIC MASSES FOR STABLE AND RADIOACTIVE NUCLIDES DERIVED ENTIRELY FROM NUCLEAR-REACTION DATA (L27, L26)

Probable errors are given in 10^{-6} amu. The reference substandard used for **many** of the reactions is $Q = -1.6457 \pm 0.002$ Mev for $Li^7(p,n)Be^7$, corresponding to a threshold energy of 1.882 ± 0.002 Mev.

Mass number	Atomic mass	Mass number	Atomic mass
n 1	1.008 982 (± 3)	F 17	17.007 505 (± 5)
		F 18	18.006 651 (± 22)
H 1	1.008 142 (± 3)	F 19	19.004 456 (± 15)
H 2	2.014 735 (± 6)	F 20	20.006 350 (± 17)
H 3	3.016 997 (± 11)		
		Ne 19	19.007 952 (± 15)
He 3	3.016 977 (± 11)	Ne 20	19.998 777 (± 21)
He 4	4.003 873 (± 15)	Ne 21	21.000 504 (± 22)
He 6	6.020 833 (± 39)	Ne 22	21.998 358 (± 25)
		Ne 23	23.001 768 (± 26)
Li 6	6.017 021 (± 22)		
Li 7	7.018 223 (± 26)	Na 21	21.004 286 (± 39)
Li 8	8.025 018 (± 30)	Na 22	22.001 409 (± 25)
		Na 23	22.997 055 (± 25)
Be 7	7.019 150 (± 26)	Na 24	23.998 568 (± 26)
Be 8	8.007 850 (± 29)		
Be 9	9.015 043 (± 30)	Mg 23	23.001 453 (± 26)
Be 10	10.016 711 (± 28)	Mg 24	23.992 628 (± 26)
		Mg 25	24.993 745 (± 27)
B 9	9.016 190 (± 31)	Mg 26	25.990 802 (± 29)
B 10	10.016 114 (± 28)	Mg 27	26.992 876 (± 30)
B 11	11.012 789 (± 23)		
B 12	12.018 162 (± 22)	Al 27	26.000 071 (± 30)
		Al 28	27.990 760 (± 32)
C 11	11.014 916 (± 24)		
C 12	12.003 804 (± 17)	Si 28	27.985 767 (± 32)
C 13	13.007 473 (± 14)	Si 29	28.985 650 (± 34)
C 14	14.007 682 (± 11)	Si 30	29.983 237 (± 36)
		Si 31	30.985 140 (± 39)
N 13	13.009 858 (± 14)		
N 14	14.007 515 (± 11)	P 31	30.983 550 (± 39)
N 15	15.004 863 (± 12)	P 32	31.984 016 (± 41)
		P 33	32.982 166 (± 44)
O 15	15.007 768 (± 13)		
O 16	16.000 000 (std.)		
O 17	17.004 533 (± 7)	S 32	31.982 183 (± 42)
O 18	18.004 857 (± 23)	S 33	32.981 881 (± 44)

TABLE 5.2. TABLE OF ATOMIC MASSES OF STABLE NUCLIDES DETERMINED
BY MASS-SPECTROSCOPIC DOUBLETS (C35, C36, C34, H11)

The substandards used are $H^1 = 1.008\ 146\ (\pm 0.3)$ and $C^{12} = 12.003\ 842\ (\pm 0.4)$, as given in Eq. (3.15). The probable errors are in 10^{-5} amu.

Mass number		Atomic mass	Mass number		Atomic mass
S	32	31.982 236 (± 0.7)	Fe	57	56.953 59 (± 10)
S	33	32.982 13 (± 5)	Fe	58	57.952 0 (± 40)
S	34	33.978 76 (± 5)			
			Co	59	[58.951 3 (± 30)]†
Cl	35	34.980 04 (± 5)			
Cl	37	36.977 66 (± 5)	Ni	58	57.953 45 (± 10)
			Ni	60	59.949 01 (± 29)
A	36	35.979 00 (± 3)	Ni	61	60.949 07 (± 23)
A	38	37.974 91 (± 4)	Ni	62	61.946 81 (± 9)
A	40	39.975 13 (± 3)	Ni	64	63.947 55 (± 7)
K	39	38.976 06 (± 3)	Cu	63	62.949 26 (± 6)
K	41	40.974 90 (± 4)	Cu	65	64.948 35 (± 6)
Ca	40	39.975 45 (± 9)	Zn	64	63.949 55 (± 2)
Ca	42	41.972 16 (± 4)	Zn	66	65.947 22 (± 6)
Ca	43	42.972 51 (± 6)	Zn	67	66.948 15 (± 6)
Ca	44	43.969 24 (± 6)	Zn	68	67.946 86 (± 7)
Ca	48	47.967 78 (± 10)	Zn	70	69.947 79 (± 6)
Sc	45	44.970 10 (± 5)	Ga	69	68.947 78 (± 6)
			Ga	71	70.947 52 (± 9)
Ti	46	45.966 97 (± 5)			
Ti	47	46.966 68 (± 10)	Ge	70	69.946 37 (± 7)
Ti	48	47.963 17 (± 6)	Ge	72	71.944 62 (± 7)
Ti	49	48.963 58 (± 5)	Ge	73	72.946 69 (± 4)
Ti	50	49.960 77 (± 4)	Ge	74	73.944 66 (± 6)
			Ge	76	75.945 59 (± 5)
V	51	50.960 52 (± 5)			
			As	75	74.945 70 (± 5)
Cr	50	49.962 10 (± 7)			
Cr	52	51.957 07 (± 9)	Se	74	73.946 20 (± 8)
Cr	53	52.957 72 (± 8)	Se	76	75.943 57 (± 5)
Cr	54	53.956 3 (± 20)	Se	77	[76.944 59 (± 5)]
			Se	78	[77.942 32 (± 5)]
Mn	55	54.955 81 (± 10)	Se	80	79.942 05 (± 5)
			Se	82	81.942 85 (± 6)
Fe	54	53.957 04 (± 5)	Br	79	78.943 65 (± 6)
Fe	56	55.952 72 (± 10)	Br	81	80.942 32 (± 6)

† Brackets designate masses of stable nuclides determined from mass-spectroscopic values for adjacent nuclides, combined with disintegration data.

TABLE 5.2. *(Continued)*

Mass number	Atomic mass	Mass number	Atomic mass
Kr 78	77.945 13 (±9)	Cd 114	113.939 97 (±9)
Kr 80	[79.941 94 (±7)]	Cd 116	115.942 02 (±12)
Kr 82	81.939 67 (±7)		
Kr 83	82.940 59 (±7)	In 113	112.940 45 (±12)
Kr 84	83.938 36 (±7)	In 115	114.940 40 (±11)
Kr 86	85.938 28 (±8)		
		Sn 115	114.940 14 (±25)
Rb 85	84.939 20 (±8)	Sn 116	115.939 27 (±11)
Rb 87	86.937 09 (±17)	Sn 117	116.940 52 (±10)
		Sn 118	117.939 78 (±16)
Sr 84	83.940 11 (±15)	Sn 119	118.941 22 (±12)
Sr 86	85.936 84 (±11)	Sn 120	119.940 59 (±14)
Sr 87	86.936 77 (±8)	Sn 122	121.942 49 (±15)
Sr 88	87.934 08 (±11)	Sn 124	123.944 90 (±11)
Y 89	88.934 21 (±11)	Te 120	119.942 88 (±16)
		Te 122	121.941 93 (±8)
Zr 90	89.933 11 (±25)	Te 123	122.943 68 (±39)
		Te 124	123.942 78 (±11)
Nb 93	92.935 40 (±9)	Te 125	124.944 60 (±31)
		Te 126	125.944 20 (±7)
Pd 102	101.937 50 (±9)	Te 128	127.946 49 (±13)
Pd 104	103.936 55 (±11)	Te 130	129.948 53 (±10)
Pd 105	104.938 40 (±15)		
Pd 106	105.936 80 (±19)	I 127	126.945 28 (±13)
Pd 108	107.938 01 (±11)		
Pd 110	109.939 65 (±13)	Xe 124	123.945 78 (±7)
		Xe 126	125.944 76 (±14)
Cd 106	105.939 84 (±14)	Xe 128	127.944 46 (±9)
Cd 108	107.938 60 (±11)	Xe 129	128.946 01 (±15)
Cd 110	109.938 57 (±13)	Xe 130	129.945 01 (±10)
Cd 111	110.939 78 (±10)	Xe 131	130.946 73 (±42)
Cd 112	111.938 85 (±17)	Xe 132	131.946 15 (±10)
Cd 113	112.940 61 (±11)	Xe 134	133.948 03 (±12)
		Xe 136	135.950 46 (±11)

CHAPTER 4

Nuclear Moments, Parity, and Statistics

The concept of a nuclear magnetic moment associated with an angular momentum axis in nuclei was introduced in 1924 by Pauli, as a means of explaining the hyperfine structure which had been disclosed in atomic optical spectra by spectrographs of very high resolving power. At that time the neutron had not been discovered, and very little was known about the inner constitution of nuclei. It was then impossible to postulate how the angular momenta of the unknown individual constituents of a given nucleus might combine in order to produce the intrinsic total angular momentum, or spin, apparently exhibited by the nucleus as a whole.

In the following year, 1925, Uhlenbeck and Goudsmit extended the concept to atomic electrons. By assuming that each electron "spins" about its own axis and hence contributes to both the angular momentum and the magnetic dipole moment of its atom, they derived a satisfactory explanation of the anomalous Zeeman effect. The concept of electron spin was soon found necessary in the theoretical description of the fine structure of optical spectra, of the scattering of β rays by electrons, and of many other phenomena. Empirically, it was necessary to assume that each electron possesses an intrinsic angular momentum, in addition to its usual orbital angular momentum, as though it were a spinning rigid body. The observable magnitude of this spin angular momentum is $\hbar/2$. Because this is of the order of $\hbar$ we can infer that spin is essentially a quantum-mechanical property. No satisfactory theoretical basis was forthcoming until Dirac showed that the existence of electron spin is a necessary consequence of his relativistic wave-mechanical theory of the electron. In the nonrelativistic limit, the electron behaves as if it had a real intrinsic angular momentum of $\hbar/2$.

Analogously, the nuclear angular momentum was found empirically to play an important role in a variety of molecular, atomic, and nuclear phenomena. Chadwick's discovery of the neutron in 1932 opened a new era in the study of nuclear structure. The proton and neutron were each shown to have the same spin as an electron and to obey the Pauli exclusion principle. A variety of nuclear models could then be visualized. Each proton and neutron in the nucleus can be assigned values of orbital angular momentum and of spin angular momentum, and these can be combined by some kind of suitable coupling scheme to give the observed total nuclear angular momentum. Nuclear models of this type will be discussed in Chap. 11.

The quantum numbers for individual particles (Appendix C, Sec. 2) and their addition, or coupling, rules can be shown to emerge in a natural way from the quantum-mechanical description of systems of particles. Similarly, the quantum mechanics leads to expectation values for the magnetic moments which are associated with spin and orbital angular momenta (B68).   The results of these derivations can be visualized best in terms of a so-called *vector model*, which has long been used in optical spectroscopy to translate the quantum-mechanical results into a visualizable system (W39).   In this chapter we shall review the concepts of angular momentum and magnetic dipole moment in terms of the vector model, and also the closely associated nuclear electric moments, parity, and statistics.   In Chaps. 5 and 6 we shall discuss a number of molecular, atomic, and nuclear phenomena which are affected by these nuclear properties and which provide the means of measuring the various nuclear moments.

1. *Nuclear Angular Momentum*

The total angular momentum of a nucleus, taken about its own internal axis, is readily measurable.   The complex motions of the individual protons and neutrons within this nucleus cannot be measured directly.   Nevertheless, it is convenient to visualize a vector model of the individual nuclear particles which represents the quantum-mechanical results and is analogous to the existing vector model for atomic electrons in the central field of the nucleus.

a. **Quantum Numbers for Individual Nucleons.**   The "state" of a particular nucleon is characterized by quantum numbers which arise in solutions of the wave equation for an individual nucleon bound in a nuclear potential well.   The notation and nomenclature for these quantum numbers parallel the conventions adopted previously for atomic electrons bound in the coulomb field of a nucleus.

Principal Quantum Number (n).   Each bound individual particle has associated with it a principal quantum number n which can take on only positive integer values greater than zero.   Thus $n = 1, 2, 3, \ldots$. In a coulomb field, the first-order term for the total energy of the state is determined by n.   This is not true for the noncoulomb fields in which nuclear particles are bound.   The principal quantum number is the sum of the radial quantum number ν and the orbital quantum number l; thus $n = \nu + l$.

Orbital Quantum Number (l).   The orbital-angular-momentum quantum number l is restricted to zero or positive integers up to $(n - 1)$. Thus, $l = 0, 1, 2, \ldots, (n - 1)$.   The magnitude of angular momentum of the corresponding motion is $\hbar \sqrt{l(l + 1)}$.   Individual values of l are commonly designated by the following letter symbols as previously adopted in atomic spectroscopy.

l...........	0	1	2	3	4	5	6	. . .
Symbol.........	s	p	d	f	g	h	i	. . .

Magnetic Orbital Quantum Number (m_l). The orbital magnetic quantum number m_l is the component of l in a specified direction, such as that of an applied magnetic field. It can take on any of the $(2l + 1)$ possible positive or negative integer values, or zero, which lie between l and $-l$. Thus, $l \geq m_l \geq -l$. More explicitly, $m_l = l, (l - 1), \ldots, 1, 0, -1, \ldots, (-l + 1), -l$.

Spin Quantum Number (s). The spin quantum number s has the value $\frac{1}{2}$ for all elementary particles which follow Fermi-Dirac statistics and which obey the Pauli exclusion principle. In particular, $s = \frac{1}{2}$ for the proton, neutron, and electron. The magnitude of angular momentum of the corresponding spin is $\hbar \sqrt{s(s + 1)}$.

Magnetic Spin Quantum Number (m_s). The spin magnetic quantum number m_s is the component of s in an arbitrary direction, such as that of an applied magnetic field. It is restricted, for elementary particles with $s = \frac{1}{2}$, to the two integer-spaced values $m_s = \frac{1}{2}, -\frac{1}{2}$.

Total Angular-momentum Quantum Number for a Single Particle (j). The total angular momentum of a single particle is the summation of its orbital and its spin angular momenta and is represented by the intrinsically positive quantum number j. The magnitude of angular momentum of the corresponding motion is $\hbar \sqrt{j(j + 1)}$. For particles with $s = \frac{1}{2}$, there are, at most, just two permitted, positive, integer-spaced values of j. These are $j = (l + s)$ and $(l - s)$, or $j = (l + \frac{1}{2})$ and $(l - \frac{1}{2})$. If $l = 0$, then j has only the value $j = s = \frac{1}{2}$. Thus j is restricted to the odd half-integer values $j = \frac{1}{2}, \frac{3}{2}, \frac{5}{2}, \ldots$.

Magnetic Total Angular-momentum Quantum Number for a Single Particle (m_j). The component of j in any arbitrary direction, such as that of an applied magnetic field, is the total magnetic quantum number m_j. Like the other magnetic quantum numbers, positive and negative values, with integer spacing, are permitted. Thus, for $s = \frac{1}{2}$ particles, m_j can have any of the $(2j + 1)$ possible values given by $m_j = j, (j - 1), \ldots, \frac{1}{2}, -\frac{1}{2}, \ldots, -j$.

Radial Quantum Number (ν). In a noncoulomb field, such as a rectangular potential well, the principal quantum number is not a good index of the energy of the state. In the solution of the radial wave equation for the rectangular potential well, there arises the so-called radial quantum number ν which represents the number of radial nodes in the wave function and can have only nonzero positive integer values $\nu = 1, 2, 3, \ldots$.

Isobaric-spin Quantum Number (T_ζ). Neutrons and protons are so similar in all respects except charge that much progress has been made through Heisenberg's concept that the proton and neutron can be represented as the two possible quantum states of one heavy particle, the nucleon. This has given rise to a charge quantum number, originally called the "isotopic-spin" and more recently the "*isobaric-spin*" quantum number (W47, I4). A common but arbitrary assignment for the total isobaric-spin quantum number T is based on a mathematical analogy with the two intrinsic spin states $m_s = \pm\frac{1}{2}$. According to this convention, the component T_ζ in a hypothetical "isobaric-spin space" has the value $+\frac{1}{2}$ for the neutron state and $-\frac{1}{2}$ for the proton state of a nucleon.   Then for any nucleus, $T_\zeta = \frac{1}{2}(N - Z)$, where $(N - Z)$ is the neutron excess, and T_ζ must be a component of the total isobaric spin T associated with any quantized level of this nucleus.   For example, in the isobaric triad $_6C^{14}$, $_7N^{14}$, $_8O^{14}$, the respective values of T_ζ are 1, 0, -1. Present evidence suggests that the ground levels of the outer members C^{14} and O^{14} of this triad have total isobaric spin $T = 1$, while the ground level of N^{14} is $T = 0$.   An excited level at 2.3 Mev in N^{14} appears to be the $T = 1$ level which forms a set, having multiplicity $2T + 1$, with the ground levels of C^{14} and O^{14}.   There is increasing evidence that total isobaric spin is conserved in nuclear interactions, in a manner analogous to the conservation of total nuclear angular momentum.

b. Nomenclature of Nucleon States.   When the character of the force between individual particles is known, a solution of the appropriate wave equation gives the energy of an individual bound particle in terms of four quantum numbers, such as n, l, m_l, m_s.   According to the Pauli exclusion principle, which has been shown experimentally to apply to nucleons, *no two protons can have in one nucleus the same set of values for their orbital and spin quantum numbers*, e.g., for the four quantum numbers

$$n, \; l, \; m_l, \; m_s$$

or, alternatively, for the four quantum numbers

$$n, \; l, \; j, \; m_j$$

or for
$$\nu, \; l, \; j, \; m_j$$

The same condition applies to any two *neutrons* in one nucleus.   However, one neutron and one proton can each have the same set of values of these four quantum numbers because they still will differ in one property, namely, *charge*.

Atomic Shells, Subshells, and States.   We review here the notation of atomic states from which some main features of the nomenclature for nuclear states have been borrowed.

Because of the characteristics of a coulomb field, only the principal quantum number n enters the first-order term for the energy of an atomic state.   In optical spectroscopy, a *shell* generally includes all electrons which have the same value of n.   Each completed shell then contains a total of

$$\sum_{l=0}^{l=n-1} 2(2l + 1) = 2n^2 = 2, 8, 18, 32, \ldots \tag{1.1}$$

electrons.   These correspond to the $(2l + 1)$ values of m_l for each l and to the 2 values of m_s for each m_l.

A *subshell* of atomic electrons includes all electrons having the same n and l.   Thus a completed subshell contains $2(2l + 1)$ electrons.   The *occupation number*, or total number of electrons permitted in the $l = 2$ subshell, is $2(2l + 1) = 10$.   These are made up of $(2j + 1)$ electrons from each of the $j = l \pm s$ states.   Thus for $j = l - s = \frac{3}{2}$ there are four electrons, and for $j = l + s = \frac{5}{2}$ there are six electrons, making the permitted total of 10 for the $l = 2$ subshell.

The notation of an *electronic state*, then, includes the value of n, along with the values of l and of j. Thus an electron state having $n = 3$, $l = 2, j = l - s = 2 - \frac{1}{2} = \frac{3}{2}$, would be designated

$$3d_{\frac{3}{2}}$$

Nucleon States and Shells. In a nuclear potential well, the energy of a nucleon state does not depend primarily on the principal quantum number n, but rather on l and ν. Many, but not all, authors now write the *radial quantum number*, $\nu = (n - l)$, in the position formerly occupied by n, in accord with a convention introduced in 1949 by Maria Mayer (M24). Thus a nucleon having $n = 3$, $l = 2$, $\nu = 1$, $j = l - s$, would, in this notation, be designated

$$1d_{\frac{3}{2}} \tag{1.2}$$

instead of $3d_{\frac{3}{2}}$, as in the notation of atomic spectroscopy. This newer notation is attractive mnemonically because the $1d$ state (old $3d$) can be read "the first d state," the $2d$ state (old $4d$) can be read "the second d state," etc. We shall use this newer notation hereafter for nuclear states.

In nuclei, the word *shell* does not connote constant values of n, as it does in optical spectroscopy. When a variety of nuclear properties (mass, binding energy, angular momentum, magnetic dipole moment, neutron-capture cross section, etc.) are plotted as a function of either the number of protons Z or the number of neutrons $N = (A - Z)$ in the nucleus, discontinuities are apparent when either Z or N has the value 2, 8, 20, 50, 82, or 126. These and possibly other so-called *magic numbers* are currently considered as representing "closed-shell" configurations in nuclei. As will be seen in Chap. 11, the sequence of levels by which such shells can be filled does not represent a simple progression in n, l, or ν.

c. Coupling of Nucleon States. Nuclear Levels. When two or more nucleons aggregate to form a nucleus, the quantum state of the system as a whole is called† a *nuclear level*. This level may be the ground level or any one of a number of excited levels of the particular nucleus. Among other properties, each nuclear level is characterized by a particular value of the total nuclear angular momentum.

The manner in which the values of l and s for the individual nucleons are added in order to form the total nuclear-angular-momentum quantum number I depends on the type of interaction, or "coupling," assumed between the particles. The actual individual motions of the nuclear

---

† We follow in this chapter the nomenclature used by Blatt and Weisskopf (p. 644 of B68), in which "state" refers to a single nucleon and "level" refers to the quantum condition of the entire nucleus. The literature and current usage do not always draw this distinction. Often "level" and "state" are used interchangeably, as in "excited level" or "excited state," and "ground level" or "ground state." Common usage favors "level width" and "level spacing," but "triplet state" and "singlet state." We shall adhere usually to "nucleon state" and "nuclear level."

particles must be strongly interdependent because of the small distances and large forces between neighboring particles. It is undoubtedly incorrect to imagine that the coupling scheme can be simple.

In atomic spectroscopy, the analogous problem has been dealt with by defining two limiting ideal types of coupling, near or between which lie all actual cases. These limiting types are the Russell-Saunders, or LS, coupling and the spin-orbit, or jj, coupling. In the absence of precise information about nuclei, and to provide convenient and familiar notations, these two coupling forms are also assumed for nuclei. Then we can use the addition rules of the usual vector models of optical spectroscopy (p. 191 of W39, or p. 175 of H44).

Russell-Saunders Coupling (LS). In this coupling scheme it is assumed that there is a negligibly weak coupling between the orbital (l) and the spin (s) angular-momentum vectors of an individual nucleon. Instead, the individual orbital vectors l are assumed to be strongly coupled to one another, and to form, by vector addition, a total orbital-angular-momentum quantum number L for all the nucleons in the system. Levels of different L are presumed to have quite different energies. Similarly, it is assumed that the individual spin vectors s are strongly coupled together to form, by vector addition, a resultant total spin quantum number S for the system. For the same value of L, it is assumed that different values of S correspond to clearly separated energy levels, the so-called *spin multiplets*. Finally, the resultant L and S couple together to form the total angular-momentum quantum number I for the nuclear level.

The nomenclature of nuclear levels in LS coupling then follows the usual nomenclature of optical spectroscopy. For $L = 0, 1, 2, 3, \ldots$, the levels are designated $S, P, D, F, \ldots$. For each value of L there are $(2S + 1)$ possible integer-spaced values of I, provided that $S \leq L$. Regardless of the relative values of L and S, the *multiplicity* is taken as $(2S + 1)$ by definition and is written as a superscript before the letter designating the L value. The particular I value appears as a subscript. For example, if $L = 1$ and $S = \frac{1}{2}$, the possible "levels," or "configurations," or "terms" are written

$$^2P_{\frac{1}{2}} \quad \text{and} \quad ^2P_{\frac{3}{2}}$$

Here one level might be the ground level of a nucleus, while the other is a low-lying excited level. The two levels taken together are a "spin doublet" in Russell-Saunders coupling.

jj Coupling. This coupling scheme is the extreme opposite of LS coupling. It is assumed in jj coupling that the predominant interaction is between the orbital (l) and spin (s) vectors of the *same* individual nucleon. These combine to form the total angular-momentum quantum number j for the individual nucleon, where $j = l \pm s$. In turn, the total nuclear-angular-momentum quantum number I is a vector sum of the individual j values. Hence jj coupling is also called strong spin-orbit coupling.

In jj coupling, the individual l values for *different* nucleons do not couple together; neither do the individual s values. Therefore there is neither an L nor an S quantum number for the level. The Russell-Saunders notation of term values for levels does not apply. The only "good" quantum number in jj coupling is the total nuclear-angular-momentum quantum number I.

When it is necessary to designate the separate energy levels which arise from the jj coupling of individual nucleon states, we may use a modified form of the notation adopted by White (p. 196 of W39) for jj coupling in atomic spectroscopy. Suppose an s nucleon ($l = 0$) is to be coupled with a p nucleon ($l = 1$). For the s nucleon $j = \frac{1}{2}$, while for the p nucleon $j = \frac{1}{2}, \frac{3}{2}$. These individual j values can be combined vectorially in four ways, to produce $I = 0, 1, 1,$ or 2. These four levels can be represented by the notation

$$(s_{\frac{1}{2}}p_{\frac{1}{2}})_0 \qquad (s_{\frac{1}{2}}p_{\frac{3}{2}})_1$$
$$(s_{\frac{1}{2}}p_{\frac{1}{2}})_1 \qquad (s_{\frac{1}{2}}p_{\frac{3}{2}})_2 \tag{1.3}$$

in which the resultant I value is shown as a subscript.

In Russell-Saunders coupling, the (s,p) configuration could result only in P levels ($L = 0 + 1 = 1$), but these could be either singlet ($S = \frac{1}{2} - \frac{1}{2} = 0$) or triplet ($S = \frac{1}{2} + \frac{1}{2} = 1$) levels. The L and S values can be combined vectorially in four ways, to produce four levels, $I = 0, 1, 1, 2$. The LS coupling levels for an (s,p) configuration would then be

$$^1P_1 \qquad \text{and} \qquad ^3P_0, \ ^3P_1, \ ^3P_2 \tag{1.4}$$

This example illustrates the generalization that *the type of coupling which is assumed for the configuration does not affect the total number of levels produced nor the angular momenta of these levels.* However, the coupling scheme does profoundly affect the relative and absolute *energy separation* of these separate levels.

Intermediate Coupling. In optical spectroscopy, jj coupling is recognized as originating physically in an interaction energy between the spin magnetic moment of an electron and the magnetic field due to its own orbital motion. It therefore becomes most important for large l values. Light elements with two valence electrons tend to exhibit nearly pure LS coupling, while heavy elements with two valence electrons having larger l values exhibit nearly pure jj coupling. White (p. 200 of W39) has illustrated well the gradual progression from LS to jj coupling for the fine structure of optical levels in the group of elements $_6$C, $_{14}$Si, $_{32}$Ge, $_{50}$Sn, $_{82}$Pb, each of which consists of completed subshells of electrons, with two valence electrons outside. The elements Si, Ge, Sn exhibit an energy separation of the fine-structure levels which is intermediate between LS and jj coupling.

In nuclei, it was believed until 1949 that jj coupling would not be exhibited, because of the very small absolute value of the magnetic dipole moment of the proton and the neutron. This has proved a false clue. Empirically, the evidence since 1949 indicates that heavy nuclei exhibit nearly pure jj coupling (Chap. 11). The energy-level spacing in some of the lightest nuclei ($A \sim 10$) is appropriate for intermediate coupling (I4). Pure *LS* coupling is seldom seen. A physical origin for strong spin-orbit interactions in nuclei has been sought but as yet without compelling success.

d. Total Nuclear Angular Momentum. The total nuclear-angular-momentum quantum number I represents a rotational motion whose absolute angular momentum has the value

$$\hbar \sqrt{I(I + 1)}$$

The quantum mechanics shows that in any given direction, such as that of an applied magnetic field, the observable values of the time average of a component of this angular momentum are given by

$$m_I \hbar \qquad (1.5)$$

where the *magnetic quantum number* m_I can take on a series of $(2I + 1)$ integrally spaced values from I to $-I$. Thus the permitted values are

$$m_I = I, (I - 1), (I - 2), \ldots, -(I - 2), -(I - 1), -I \quad (1.6)$$

The largest value of m_I is I, and the *largest observable component of the total nuclear angular momentum is $I\hbar$.*

These relationships can be represented conveniently in the usual type of vector diagram, Fig. 1.1. It is seen that the angular-momentum vector, whose magnitude we denote (W39, F41) for typographical convenience as I^*, where

$$I^* \equiv \sqrt{I(I + 1)} = I \sqrt{1 + \frac{1}{I}} \qquad (1.7)$$

can take up any of $(2I + 1)$ orientations, at various angles β with respect to the applied field H, and subject to the restriction that

$$m_I \hbar = (I^* \cos \beta)\hbar$$

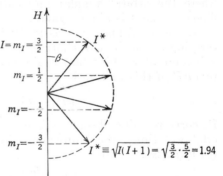

Fig. 1.1 Vector model of the relationship between m_I, I, and I^*, for $I = \frac{3}{2}$. The observable components of the angular momentum are $m_I \hbar = \hbar I^* \cos \beta$.

The quantity which is colloquially called the "*nuclear angular momentum*," or sometimes less aptly the "nuclear spin," is just the maximum value of m_I, that is, I.

Problems

1. Assuming an "outer" proton or neutron to be in a circular orbit with $l = 1$ and a radius $r = 4 \times 10^{-13}$ cm, compute its velocity. Does the result suggest that nonrelativistic theory will be satisfactory for descriptions of the heavy particles in nuclei? *Ans.: v $= 0.22 \times 10^{10}$ cm/sec.*

2. Assuming a proton to be a sphere of radius of 1.5×10^{-13} cm and of uniform density and to have an actual angular momentum of $(h/2\pi) \sqrt{s(s + 1)}$, where $s = \frac{1}{2}$, compute the angular velocity in revolutions per second and the peripheral speed at the equator of the proton. *Ans.:* $\omega = 0.96 \times 10^{22}$ revolutions/sec, 0.91×10^{10} cm/sec.

2. *Nuclear Magnetic Dipole Moment*

Any charged particle moving in a closed path produces a magnetic field which can be described, at large distances, as due to a magnetic dipole located at the current loop. Therefore the spin angular momentum of a proton, and the orbital angular momentum of protons within nuclei, should produce extranuclear magnetic fields which can be described in terms of a resultant magnetic dipole moment located at the center of the nucleus.

a. Absolute Gyromagnetic Ratio. When a particle of mass M and charge q moves in a circular path, the motion possesses both angular momentum and a magnetic dipole moment. Using primed symbols to denote moments in absolute units, the classical absolute *gyromagnetic ratio* γ is defined as

$$\gamma \equiv \frac{\mu'}{I'} \text{ gauss}^{-1} \text{ sec}^{-1} \tag{2.1}$$

where the orbital angular momentum is I' erg-sec and the magnetic dipole moment is μ' ergs/gauss.

We can evaluate γ classically for an element of mass dM grams, carrying an element of charge dq esu, and moving with angular velocity ω, in a circular orbit whose radius is r cm. The absolute angular momentum dI' of this motion is

$$dI' = dM \omega r^2 \qquad \text{erg-sec} \tag{2.2}$$

Its corresponding absolute magnetic dipole moment $d\mu'$ is the area of the orbit πr^2 times the equivalent circulating current in emu, which is $(dq/c)(\omega/2\pi)$. Thus

$$d\mu' = \frac{dq}{2c} \omega r^2 \qquad \text{ergs/gauss} \tag{2.3}$$

The absolute gyromagnetic ratio for this element of mass and charge is

$$\gamma \equiv \frac{d\mu'}{dI'} = \frac{1}{2c} \frac{dq}{dM} \tag{2.4}$$

For a distributed mass, such as a sphere, or any system of mass points, the total angular momentum is obtained by the usual integration

$$I' = \int dI' = \int \omega r^2 \, dM \tag{2.5}$$

Similarly, the magnetic moment of a system involving distributed charge is

$$\mu' = \int d\mu' = \frac{1}{2c} \int \omega r^2 \, dq \tag{2.6}$$

If the ratio of charge to mass dq/dM is constant and equal to q/M throughout the system, then $dq = (q/M) \, dM$, and the second integral becomes

$$\mu' = \frac{q}{2Mc} \int \omega r^2 \, dM = \frac{q}{2Mc} I' \tag{2.7}$$

Thus the classical gyromagnetic ratio γ is

$$\gamma \equiv \frac{\mu'}{I'} = \frac{q}{2Mc} \text{ gauss}^{-1} \text{ sec}^{-1} \tag{2.8}$$

for *any rotating system in which charge and mass are proportionately distributed*, such as in a rotating uniformly charged spherical shell or a rotating uniformly charged sphere, or the motion of a charged particle moving in a closed orbit.

b. Nuclear g Factor.   If the classical relationship between the angular momentum and magnetic dipole moment were valid for nuclear systems, the absolute magnetic dipole moment μ'_{I*}, which is collinear with the absolute angular momentum $I' = \hbar \sqrt{I(I+1)} \equiv \hbar I^*$, would be expected to have the absolute value

$$\mu'_{I*} = \gamma I' = \gamma \hbar I^* = \frac{eh}{4\pi Mc} I^* \qquad \text{if classical} \tag{2.9}$$

for the case of a spinning proton containing a uniformly distributed charge e and mass M.

However, the directly measured values for the magnetic dipole moment of the proton, and for the gyromagnetic ratios of various nuclides, do not follow so simple a relationship.   Indeed, a precise theory of the origin of nuclear magnetism is still lacking.   The principal experimental data consist of measurements of the nuclear gyromagnetic ratios for the proton, neutron, and for many nuclides.   What is commonly called either the *nuclear g factor* (or, in most of the pre-1950 literature, the *nuclear gyromagnetic ratio, g*) is equivalent to inserting a dimensionless correction factor g in the right-hand side of Eq. (2.9), so that it reads (P1)

$$\mu'_{I*} = \gamma_I I' = \gamma_I \hbar I^* = g \frac{eh}{4\pi Mc} I^* \qquad \text{for real nuclei} \tag{2.10}$$

where $\gamma_I = g(e/2Mc)$ gauss^{-1} sec^{-1} is now called the *nuclear gyromagnetic ratio* in absolute units.

By analogy with the *Bohr magneton* μ_β for atomic electrons, which has the value

$$\mu_\beta \equiv \frac{eh}{4\pi m_0 c} = 9.273 \times 10^{-21} \text{ erg/gauss} \tag{2.11a}$$

we define a *nuclear magneton* μ_M as

$$\mu_M \equiv \frac{eh}{4\pi Mc} = \mu_\beta \left(\frac{m_0}{M}\right) = 5.050 \times 10^{-24} \text{ erg/gauss}$$

$$= 3.152 \times 10^{-12} \text{ ev/gauss} \tag{2.11b}$$

where M is the mass of a *proton*. Note that the nuclear magneton is 1,836 times *smaller* than the Bohr magneton, because the nuclear magneton contains the proton mass instead of the electron mass.

Then the absolute value μ'_{I*} of the nuclear magnetic dipole moment can be expressed in units of nuclear magnetons as the dimensionless quantity μ_{I*}, where

$$\mu_{I*} \equiv \frac{\mu'_{I*}}{\mu_M} \qquad \text{nuclear magnetons} \qquad (2.12)$$

Actually, neither I^* nor its collinear magnetic moment μ_{I*} are directly observable quantities, but their ratio can be measured accurately in many different types of experiments which depend on the phenomenon of Larmor precession (Chap. 5). From Eqs. (2.10) and (2.12) we can write

$$g = \frac{\mu_{I*}}{I^*} \qquad (2.13)$$

c. Nuclear Magnetic Dipole Moment. The maximum observable component of I^* is I, and because I^* and μ_{I*} are collinear, the corresponding maximum observable component of μ_{I*} is

$$\mu_{I*}\left(\frac{I}{I^*}\right) = \mu_{I*}(\cos \beta)_{\max} \equiv \mu \qquad (2.14)$$

This maximum component, and not μ_{I*}, is, in fact, the quantity which is colloquially called the *"nuclear magnetic dipole moment"*; it is denoted by the symbol μ. We have then

$$g = \frac{\mu_{I*}}{I^*} = \frac{\mu}{I} \qquad (2.15)$$

The values of μ which are found in nuclear tables are all derived from measurements of I, combined with independent measurements of g, and represent the quantity

$$\mu = gI \qquad (2.16)$$

The units of μ are generally spoken of as "nuclear magnetons," because of the relationships in Eqs. (2.12) and (2.13). Actually μ, g, and I are all pure numbers. Thus g really expresses the ratio between the actual nuclear magnetic moment and the magnetic moment which would be expected if the nuclear angular momentum were entirely due to the orbital motion of a single proton, with angular-momentum quantum number I.

The nuclear magnetic moment is taken as positive if its direction with respect to the angular-momentum vector corresponds to the rotation of a positive electrical charge.

Problems

1. Assuming all the charge on a proton to be uniformly distributed on a spherical surface, 1.5×10^{-13} cm in radius, what should be the actual value of the magnetic dipole moment of the proton if the proton is a sphere of uniform density, having an angular momentum of $(\frac{1}{2}\sqrt{3})\hbar$?   If the maximum observable component of the angular momentum is $\frac{1}{2}\hbar$, what is the corresponding maximum observable component of the magnetic dipole moment, expressed in nuclear magnetons?   *Ans.:* $(5\sqrt{3}/6)(eh/4\pi Mc)$; $\frac{5}{6}\mu_M$.

2. Assuming all the charge on a proton to be uniformly distributed throughout a spherical volume, of radius 1.5×10^{-13} cm, what should be the actual value of the magnetic dipole moment of the proton if its angular momentum is $(\frac{1}{2}\sqrt{3})\hbar$ and if the proton has a uniform density?   If the maximum observable component of the angular momentum is $\frac{1}{2}\hbar$, what is the corresponding maximum observable component of the magnetic dipole moment, expressed in nuclear magnetons?   *Ans.:* $(\sqrt{3}/2)(eh/4\pi Mc)$; $\frac{1}{2}\mu_M$.

3. *Anomalous Magnetic Moments of Free Nucleons*

a. The Spin Magnetic Moment for Atomic Electrons. In a wide variety of experiments the magnetic dipole moment associated with the *orbital* angular momentum of atomic electrons always has the value expected from simple classical considerations, as illustrated by Eq. (2.8). This is equivalent to saying that the atomic *orbital g factor*, in an atomic analogue of Eq. (2.10), has the value $g_l = 1$. Such is not the case for the magnetic moment associated with the *spin* angular momentum of electrons. From the time of the introduction, in 1925, of the concept of electron spin, it was clear experimentally that the magnetic dipole moment of the spinning electron is very closely equal to one Bohr magneton. Because $s = \frac{1}{2}$ for the electron, the *spin g factor* g_s for an electron appeared therefore to be $g_s = 2$. When Dirac developed his relativistic quantum-mechanical theory of the electron, the value $g_s = 2$ also emerged from this theory in a natural way.

By atomic-beam methods it is possible to obtain very precise measurements of the separation of optical fine-structure levels, and such experiments first showed in 1947 (K51, L2) that the magnetic dipole moment of the spinning electron is slightly greater than one Bohr magneton and corresponds to $g_s \simeq 2.0023$. The following year, Schwinger showed (S21), from a reformulation of relativistic quantum electrodynamics, that the interaction energy between an electron and an external magnetic field must include a radiative correction term representing the interaction of the electron with the quantized electromagnetic field. The detailed application of the theory showed that in the atomic-beam experiments the effective value of the magnetic moment due to the spin of the electron should be greater than one Bohr magneton by the factor $(1 + \alpha/2\pi) = 1.001\,16$, where $\alpha = 2\pi e^2/hc \simeq \frac{1}{137}$ is the fine-structure constant.

This theoretical result concerning the increased effective value of the spin gyromagnetic ratio for the electron in a magnetic field is in agreement with the experimental value obtained from precision comparisons of the frequency of lines in the hyperfine-structure spectrum of gallium, indium, and sodium in a constant magnetic field (K51, M7). Thus, for atomic electrons, the spin g factor is

$$g_\varepsilon = 2(1 + \alpha/2\pi) = 2.002\,32 \tag{3.1}$$

while the orbital g factor has its classical value of $g_l = 1$, all the corresponding magnetic moments being in Bohr magnetons.

These observations on the electron-spin gyromagnetic ratio are important for two reasons. First, many nuclear gyromagnetic ratios are measured in terms of high-precision direct comparisons with electronic gyromagnetic ratios. Secondly, the anomalous spin gyromagnetic ratio for the electron is reasonably well understood in terms of existing theory.

b. The Spin Magnetic Moment for Protons. If the spinning proton behaved like a uniformly charged classical sphere, then $g_s = 1$, and its magnetic dipole moment should be one-half nuclear magneton, by Eq. (2.16). If the proton were a particle which followed Dirac's relativistic quantum mechanics, then $g_s = 2$, and its magnetic dipole moment should be one nuclear magneton. Actually, the spin magnetic dipole moment of the free proton has the nonintegral and "anomalous" value of slightly over 2.79 nuclear magnetons.

Direct Observation of the Proton Magnetic Moment. The magnetic dipole moments of atoms, due to the spin and orbital motion of atomic electrons, were first demonstrated and measured directly in the epochal experiments of Stern and Gerlach (p. 389 of R18). The same experimental principle of deflecting a beam of neutral molecules by passing it through a strongly inhomogeneous magnetic field was applied successfully to neutral hydrogen molecules in 1932 by Stern, Estermann, and Frisch (E16, E15).

These experiments are of great fundamental importance for two separate reasons. First, they remain the only measurements of a nuclear magnetic moment in which the interpretation is independent of the gyromagnetic ratio. The quantity measured is the force exerted on a neutral particle by a strong inhomogeneous magnetic field. This force is proportional to the classically defined magnetic dipole moment, without recourse to the presence or absence of angular momentum.

Second, these experiments were the first to reveal the anomalous value of the proton magnetic moment. The inadequacy of the Dirac wave equation or of any other theory for heavy elementary particles became apparent because these theories are unable to predict the correct magnetic dipole moment for the proton. This challenging situation remains unrelieved by theoretical efforts up to the present.

The essentials of the molecular-beam method for hydrogen developed by Estermann, Frisch, and Stern are the following: Normal hydrogen consists of a mixture of 75 per cent orthohydrogen and 25 per cent parahydrogen. Pure parahydrogen can be prepared by adsorption on charcoal at liquid-hydrogen temperature. The nuclear spins, and hence the nuclear magnetic moments, of the two hydrogen atoms are parallel in the *orthohydrogen* molecule and antiparallel in the *parahydrogen* molecule. Therefore in parahydrogen the nuclear moments cancel each other, and the angular momentum and magnetic moment of the molecule are due to the electrons and to molecular rotation. In orthohydrogen, however, the nuclear moments are parallel and reinforce each other, thus adding to the molecular moments.

The deflection of a beam of molecular hydrogen in a transverse inhomogeneous magnetic field depends on the total molecular magnetic moment. The contribution of electrons and molecular rotation is determined from the measurements on parahydrogen. In principle, these are then subtracted out of the deflections of orthohydrogen. The result is a direct measure, by differences, of the magnetic moment of the proton. In this way, the proton magnetic dipole moment μ_p was found to be 2.46 $\pm$ 0.08 nuclear magnetons. The result was confirmed by measurements on the HD molecule (E16) but is a little low in comparison with later studies of the proton gyromagnetic ratio by magnetic resonance methods. All the subsequent determinations of μ_p have been made by more accurate but less direct methods which involve measurements of the proton gyromagnetic ratio, usually by observing the Larmor precession frequency produced by a homogeneous magnetic field [Chap. 5, Eq. (2.3)].

Precision Measurements of the Proton Spin Magnetic Moment. All measurements of nuclear g factors are currently referred to the proton spin g factor as a reference standard. Consequently, the proton magnetic moment has fundamental importance, experimentally as well as theoretically.

A variety of experimental methods has been used (Chap. 5). Several of these are thought to have an accuracy of about 0.01 per cent. However, present results by various methods have a spread which approaches 0.1 per cent. Each author of a table or compilation of nuclear magnetic moments generally chooses one or another of these individual measurements as a *reference standard* for the entire compilation. Caution must therefore be used in comparing tables by various authors and tables of various dates by the same authors.

In 1953 one of the principal reference-standard values adopted for the proton magnetic moment was

$$\mu_p = 2.7934 \text{ nuclear magnetons} \qquad (3.2)$$

derived from comparisons by Gardner and Purcell (G9) of the Larmor precession frequency of protons (in mineral oil) with the cyclotron resonance frequency of free electrons measured in the same magnetic field. The observed value by Gardner and Purcell of

$$\mu_p = (1.521\ 00 \pm 0.000\ 02) \times 10^{-3} \text{ Bohr magneton} \qquad (3.3)$$

leads to Eq. (3.2) if the ratio of proton to electron mass is 1,836.6 (D43), although a more recent value for this mass ratio is 1,836.1 (D44). Equation (3.2) was the reference standard for the table of nuclear moments compiled by H. L. Poss (P27) and for the earlier issues of the widely used cumulative tables of new nuclear data which are published as a quarterly supplement in *Nuclear Science Abstracts* (N24). Note, however, that the parent table "Nuclear Data" (National Bureau of Standards Circular 499) has a different basis, namely,

$$\mu_p = 2.7926 \text{ nuclear magnetons} \qquad (3.4)$$

This value was based upon preliminary data on the ratio of the Larmor precession frequency for protons to the cyclotron resonance frequency for free protons, measured in the same magnetic field, by Hipple, Sommer, and Thomas (H55) in 1949. In Eq. (3.4) a correction of 0.003 per cent has been added to the observed value, to compensate for the estimated diamagnetic effect (L1) of the atomic electrons in hydrogen. In 1950, the same authors (S60) obtained by the same experimental method an improved value of

$$\mu_p = 2.792\ 68 \pm 0.000\ 06 \text{ nuclear magnetons} \tag{3.5}$$

No diamagnetic correction is included in Eqs. (3.2), (3.3), or (3.5).

By still different methods, other groups of workers have obtained values of μ_p which vary from one another often by more than the assigned experimental errors. But these slight differences are probably not of fundamental origin, and it is more important to stress the remarkable degree of agreement upon some figure very close to

$$\mu_p = 2.793 \text{ nuclear magnetons} \tag{3.6}$$

as obtained by a wide variety of methods. Equation (3.6) corresponds to an absolute gyromagnetic ratio γ_I for the proton of

$$\gamma_p = \frac{\mu_p}{I_p}\frac{e}{2Mc} = 2.675 \times 10^4 \text{ gauss}^{-1} \text{ sec}^{-1} \tag{3.6a}$$

Of course, the absolute value of the spin angular momentum of the proton is $(s')^* = \hbar \sqrt{s(s+1)} = \hbar(\sqrt{3}/2)$, rather than $\hbar/2$, and because $g = \mu/I = \mu_{I*}/I^*$, the absolute (but unobservable) magnetic dipole moment of the proton in the direction of s^* is $\mu_{s^*} = \mu_p \sqrt{3}$.

c. The Spin Magnetic Moment for Neutrons. It has been possible to obtain an accurate comparison of the Larmor precession frequencies, which are proportional to nuclear g factors [Chap. 5, Eq. (2.3)], for protons and for free neutrons in the same magnetic field by making use of the phenomenon of magnetic scattering of neutrons in magnetized iron (A24, A31). In this way it is found that the ratio of the nuclear magnetic dipole moments of the neutron and proton is (B76)

$$\frac{g_n}{g_p} = \frac{\mu_n}{\mu_p} = -0.685\ 00 \pm 0.000\ 03 \tag{3.7}$$

Taking Eq. (3.2) as the reference value of μ_p gives

$$\mu_n = -1.9135 \text{ nuclear magnetons} \tag{3.8}$$

Thus the neutron, whose net electric charge is exactly zero, possesses an unknown inner constitution such that its spin angular momentum, $s = \frac{1}{2}$, is associated with a fairly large magnetic dipole moment. The sign of this magnetic moment is negative and therefore simulates the rotation of negative charge in the spin direction.

Nonadditivity of Magnetic Moments. The nuclear g factor of the deuteron has been measured accurately with respect to that of the proton.

Combining the results leads to $\mu_d = 0.8576$ nuclear magneton for the deuteron. It is important to note that the neutron magnetic moment cannot be obtained by merely subtracting the proton moment from the deuteron moment. This would give

$$\mu_d - \mu_p = 0.8576 - 2.7934 = -1.9358 \text{ nuclear magnetons}$$

a value which differs from the directly measured $\mu_n = -1.9135$ by far more than the limits of error of the measurements. We shall see later (Chap. 10) that, in the case of the deuteron, the finite difference between μ_d and ($\mu_p + \mu_n$) can be interpreted as evidence in favor of the existence of a contribution of tensor (noncentral) force between nucleons in nuclei.

Problem

Evaluate the magnetic field, due to the intrinsic magnetic dipole moment of the proton, in gauss: (a) at the equator of the proton and (b) at the radius of the first Bohr orbit of hydrogen. *Ans.*: (a) $\sim 7 \times 10^{15}$ gauss; (b) 165 gauss.

4. *Relationships between I and μ*

The nuclear angular momentum and magnetic moment have been measured for the ground levels of more than 100 nuclides (K23, W2a) by the application of a variety of experimental methods. Many of these data are summarized in Tables 4.3 and 5.1. Some regularities have emerged from studies of these data. One generalization to which no exceptions have yet been found is that $I = 0$ for all even-Z even-N nuclides and for no others.

a. Classifications of the Experimental Data on I and μ. For convenience in systematizing many types of data, nuclides are divided into four classes according to whether the proton number Z and the neutron number N ($= A - Z$) are odd or even. A common arrangement of these four classes, and the population of each, is shown in Table 4.1, together with a gross summary of the experimental results on I and μ by classes.

Note that even-Z even-N is by far the most abundant class of stable nuclides. Among these nuclides, measurements of I have been obtained in about a dozen cases, usually by diatomic band spectroscopy (Chap. 5), and invariably with the result $I = 0$. This is the experimental basis for a fundamental assumption which is made in a number of nuclear models. An even number of protons are assumed always to find their lowest energy level by aligning their individual angular momenta so that they cancel by pairs, and hence also in the aggregate. Likewise, the individual angular momenta of neutrons within an unexcited nucleus are assumed to cancel by pairs and thus to total zero for any even number of neutrons.

Then an odd-Z even-N nucleus could be visualized as one odd proton outside a closed "*core*" of even-Z even-N. On this single-particle model, the core would contribute zero angular momentum and zero magnetic dipole moment. The nuclear I and μ would then be due entirely to the one odd proton in odd-Z even-N nuclei. Analogously, in even-Z odd-N

nuclei, the entire nuclear I and μ are attributable to the one odd neutron, in this single-particle model.　Mirror nuclei, in which Z and N are interchanged, will then have the same value of I.　This applies to the ordinary odd-A mirror nuclei, which are the adjacent isobars $A = 2Z \pm 1$, and also to the group of even-A mirror nuclei ($A = 2Z \pm 2$) which are the outer members of symmetrical isobaric *triads* such as $\mathrm{Be^{10}B^{10}C^{10}}$ and $\mathrm{C^{14}N^{14}O^{14}}$.

Odd-Z odd-N nuclei are generally unstable, except in the four cases $_1\mathrm{H^2}$, $_3\mathrm{Li^6}$, $_5\mathrm{B^{10}}$, $_7\mathrm{N^{14}}$ for which $Z = N$.　On the single-particle model, these odd-Z odd-N nuclei consist of an even-Z even-N core, with one proton and one neutron outside.　The angular momenta so far measured for

TABLE 4.1. SUMMARY OF THE FOUR "ODD-EVEN" CLASSES OF NUCLIDES AND
THE GROSS RESULTS OF MEASUREMENTS OF THEIR GROUND-LEVEL
NUCLEAR ANGULAR MOMENTA I AND MAGNETIC DIPOLE
MOMENTS μ
Compiled from (H61) and (K23)

	Nucleon classification				Nuclear moments			
Class	Mass number A	Proton number Z	Neutron number N	Number of known stable nuclides	Number of nuclides measured		I	μ
					Stable	Radioactive		
I	Odd	Odd	Even	50	50	11	$\frac{1}{2}, \frac{3}{2}, \frac{5}{2}, \frac{7}{2}, \frac{9}{2}$	Usually large, usually positive
II	Odd	Even	Odd	55	36	4	$\frac{1}{2}, \frac{3}{2}, \frac{5}{2}, \frac{7}{2}, \frac{9}{2}$	Usually small, often negative
III	Even	Odd	Odd	4	4	9	1, 2, 3, 4, 6	Usually positive
IV	Even	Even	Even	165	12	1	0	Indeterminate

such nuclei are all nonzero.　Thus, in general, the angular momenta of the single odd proton and neutron do not align for cancellation, as would a pair of protons or a pair of neutrons.

Schmidt Diagrams.　Schmidt (S14) first emphasized the guidance which can be obtained from plots of μ against I.　Figures 4.1 and 4.2 are modernizations of Schmidt's plots of the empirical dependence of μ on I for nuclei containing one odd nucleon.　The trend of μ against I is seen to be quite different when the odd nucleon is a proton (odd-Z even-N, Fig. 4.1) and when the odd nucleon is a neutron (even-Z odd-N, Fig. 4.2).

b. Single-particle Model, for Odd-A Nuclei.　If, with Schmidt, we assume a single-particle model, in which the total nuclear moments I and μ of odd-A nuclei are due to one odd nucleon, then I is simply $j = l \pm s$ of this one odd nucleon.　The dependence of the associated magnetic dipole moment on I can be determined in the following way.

Let μ_{l^*} be the value of the magnetic dipole moment which is collinear with the orbital angular momentum whose magnitude is denoted

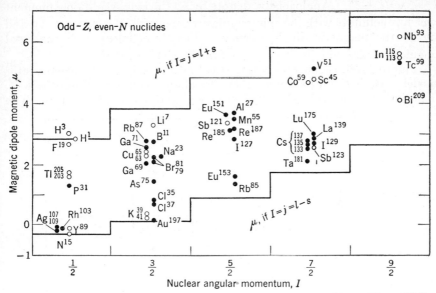

Fig. 4.1 Schmidt diagram of I and μ for odd-Z even-N nuclides. The solid-line histogram corresponds to the Schmidt limits for each value of I, if I and μ were due entirely to the motion of one odd *proton*, Table 4.2. Open circles represent nuclides with one proton in excess of, or with one proton less than, a "closed shell" of 2, 8, 20, 28, 40, 50, or 82 protons.

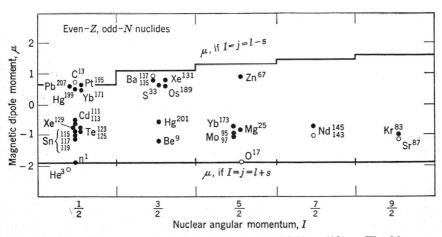

Fig. 4.2 Schmidt diagram of I and μ for even-Z odd-N nuclides. The histogram corresponds to the Schmidt limits for each value of I, if I and μ were due entirely to the motion of one odd *neutron*, Table 4.2. Open circles represent nuclides which have one neutron more, or one neutron less, than the number required to form a "closed shell" of 2, 8, 20, 28, 40, 50, 82, or 126 neutrons.

$l^* \equiv \sqrt{l(l + 1)}$. Analogously, denote by μ_{s^*} the magnetic dipole moment which is collinear with the spin angular momentum $s^* \equiv \sqrt{s(s + 1)}$, and by μ_{j^*} the magnetic dipole moment which is collinear with the total angular momentum $j^* \equiv \sqrt{j(j + 1)}$ of the single particle.

Figure 4.3 illustrates the geometrical relationships of the usual vector model. Both l^* and s^* precess (W39) about their vector resultant j^*. The time-average values of the components normal to j^* are zero. The

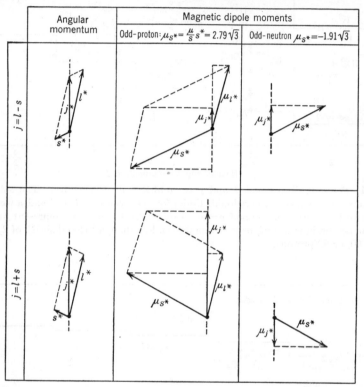

Angular momentum	Magnetic dipole moments	
	Odd-proton: $\mu_{s^*} = \frac{\mu}{s} s^* = 2.79\sqrt{3}$	Odd-neutron $\mu_{s^*} = -1.91\sqrt{3}$

Fig. 4.3 Vector diagrams (for $l = 3$) illustrating the composition of angular-momentum vectors, whose magnitudes are $l^* = \sqrt{l(l + 1)}$, $s^* = \sqrt{s(s + 1)}$, to form $j^* = \sqrt{j(j + 1)}$, for the "parallel" $j = l + s$ and "antiparallel" case $j = l - s$. Because of the anomalous values of the spin magnetic moments for the proton and the neutron, the magnetic moment μ_{j^*} for the antiparallel case, as shown graphically here, leads to the value of μ given by Eq. (4.10).

value of j^* is such that $j = l + s$ for the so-called "parallel" alignment of l and s, while $j = l - s$ for the "antiparallel" alignment of the orbit and spin angular momenta. Note that the quantum numbers l and s add as scalars, thus $j = l \pm s$; but the corresponding angular momenta l^* and s^* do not add as scalars ($j^* \neq l^* \pm s^*$) but only as vectors

$$\mathbf{j}^* = \mathbf{l}^* \pm \mathbf{s}^*$$

In turn, j^* is understood to precess about any arbitrary direction, such as that of an external magnetic field, in such a way that j is the maximum observable component of j^*. This is analogous to the vector-model diagram in Fig. 1.1 for I and I^*. In this single-particle model, $I = j$ and $I^* = j^*$.

In Fig. 4.3, the angle (l^*j^*) between l^* and j^* is given by the law of cosines as

$$\cos\,(l^*j^*) = \frac{l^{*2} + j^{*2} - s^{*2}}{2l^*j^*} \tag{4.1}$$

for both of the possible cases, $j = l + s$ and $j = l - s$. Similarly, the angle between s^* and j^* is given by

$$\cos\,(s^*j^*) = \frac{s^{*2} + j^{*2} - l^{*2}}{2s^*j^*} \tag{4.2}$$

The net component of the magnetic dipole moments which is parallel to j^* is given by

$$\mu_{j^*} = \mu_{l^*}\cos\,(l^*j^*) + \mu_{s^*}\cos\,(s^*j^*) \tag{4.3}$$

The g factor for the single particle is, by Eq. (2.15),

$$g = \frac{\mu}{I} = \frac{\mu}{j} = \frac{\mu_{j^*}}{j^*} \tag{4.4}$$

where μ is the observable component of the net magnetic dipole moment and the nuclear-angular-momentum quantum number I is the same as j for the single odd particle. By substituting Eqs. (4.1) to (4.3) into this equation, we can obtain the general relationship

$$g = \frac{g_l}{2}\left(1 + \frac{l^{*2} - s^{*2}}{j^{*2}}\right) + \frac{g_s}{2}\left(1 - \frac{l^{*2} - s^{*2}}{j^{*2}}\right) \tag{4.5}$$

in which the orbital and spin g factors are given by

$$g_l \equiv \frac{\mu_{l^*}}{l^*} = \frac{\mu_l}{l} \tag{4.6}$$

$$g_s \equiv \frac{\mu_{s^*}}{s^*} = \frac{\mu_s}{s} = 2\mu_s \tag{4.7}$$

Parallel Spin and Orbit. For the "parallel" case, $I = j = l + s$, and substitution of $j^{*2} = j(j + 1) = (l + \frac{1}{2})(l + \frac{3}{2})$ into Eq. (4.5) allows it to take on the simple special form

$$g = g_l\left(\frac{l}{I}\right) + g_s\left(\frac{s}{I}\right) \tag{4.8}$$

or $\mu = gI = g_l l + \mu_s \qquad$ for $I = l + \frac{1}{2}$ $\qquad$ (4.9)

This represents simple additivity of orbital and spin projected magnetic moments and is a result to be expected on naïve intuitive grounds. The antiparallel case turns out to be more subtle.

Antiparallel Spin and Orbit. For the "antiparallel" case,

$$I = j = l - s$$

and substitution of $j^{*2} = j(j + 1) = (l - \frac{1}{2})(l + \frac{1}{2})$ into Eq. (4.5) gives for this special case

$$g = g_l \left(\frac{l + 1}{I + 1} \right) - g_s \left(\frac{s}{I + 1} \right)$$

or $\qquad \mu = gI = g_l I - (\mu_s - \frac{1}{2} g_l) \left(\frac{I}{I + 1} \right) \qquad$ for $I = l - \frac{1}{2}$ $\qquad$ (4.10)

Schmidt Limits. When we substitute into Eqs. (4.9) and (4.10) the g factors which correspond to single nucleons, namely,

for protons: $\qquad g_l = 1 \qquad g_s = 2\mu_s = 2 \times 2.79$
for neutrons: $\qquad g_l = 0 \qquad g_s = 2\mu_s = 2(-1.91)$ $\qquad$ (4.11)

we obtain the predicted relationships between I and μ on the single-particle model. To each value of I, there correspond two values of μ, depending on whether $I = l + \frac{1}{2}$ or $I = l - \frac{1}{2}$. These two values of μ constitute the so-called *Schmidt limits*. They are summarized in Table 4.2 and are shown as solid lines in Figs. 4.1 and 4.2.

TABLE 4.2. THE SCHMIDT LIMITS, IN THE SINGLE-PARTICLE MODEL, FOR NUCLIDES HAVING ONE ODD NUCLEON

I	Odd proton	Odd neutron
$l + \frac{1}{2}$	$\mu = I + 2.29$	$\mu = -1.91$
$l - \frac{1}{2}$	$\mu = I - 2.29 \dfrac{I}{I + 1}$	$\mu = 1.91 \dfrac{I}{I + 1}$

Schmidt Groups. The 100-plus measured values of I and μ for the ground levels of nuclei are seen to fall generally between, but not on, the Schmidt limits. There is a tendency for the measured values to fall fairly clearly into two groups, each parallel to a Schmidt limit. These two "*Schmidt groups*" are presently assumed to correspond to the $I = l + \frac{1}{2}$ and the $I = l - \frac{1}{2}$ cases, in odd-A nuclides. Thus a measurement of μ and I affords a means of "measuring" the value of l for the odd particle.

For example, $_{27}\text{Co}^{59}$ has $I = \frac{7}{2}$ and $\mu = 4.64$. The high value of μ places this nuclide in the upper Schmidt group for odd-Z nuclides in Fig. 4.1. Hence $I = l + \frac{1}{2}$, and $l = 3$. It is then reasonably certain that the odd proton in Co^{59} is in an $f_{\frac{7}{2}}$ state and not a $g_{\frac{7}{2}}$ state. Such inferences of l are of great value in the development of theories of nucleon coupling and nuclear structure (Chap. 11).

Quenching of Nucleon Spin Magnetic Moment. The two Schmidt groups are approximately parallel to the Schmidt limits. Their slope is about unity for odd-proton nuclides and zero for odd-neutron nuclides. Thus the groups appear physically to represent μ_l due to orbital motion, plus or minus a magnetic moment due to spin. Except for H^3 and He^3, the total μ never exceeds what would be expected if all the I and μ were due to the one odd proton (or neutron), the rest of the nucleus forming a closed system, or core, with $I = 0$ and $\mu = 0$.

The spread of actual values of μ from lines corresponding only to μ_l is not as large as would be expected for μ_s. Thus, empirically, it appears that μ_s, as measured for free protons and neutrons, may not be fully effective when these nucleons aggregate into nuclei. This so-called *"quenching"* of the anomalous magnetic dipole moments is qualitatively understandable in the language of the meson theory of nuclear forces.

According to the meson theory, the attractive force between nucleons arises from the exchange of charged and uncharged mesons between nucleons. A free isolated nucleon then exhibits a virtual emission and absorption of mesons, and this meson current is the origin of the anomalous magnetic dipole moment. The intrinsic magnetic moment μ_s of the free nucleon may therefore be reduced, or partially quenched, when the odd nucleon is bound to the nuclear core (B74). Although these concepts have a welcome plausibility, their quantitative aspects have yet to emerge successfully from contemporary meson theory (F27).

Asymmetric Core. The two Schmidt groups each have a spread which is much greater than the observational uncertainties, and so most of the variations must be taken as real. Moreover, as can be seen from the points shown as open circles in Figs. 4.1 and 4.2, nuclides which have one odd nucleon above or below a "closed shell" of 2, 8, 20, . . . protons or neutrons seem to show no overwhelming distinction from nuclides whose core is not blessed by a "magic number." These observations suggest that the core does not always have exact spherical symmetry $I = 0$, $\mu = 0$ but contributes at least to the magnetic moment of the nucleus (D25).

The concept of an asymmetric core is strengthened also by the inability of a symmetrical-core model to account for the observed electric quadrupole moments of nuclei (Sec. 5). At least for the odd-proton nuclei, the single-orbit model would lead to negative electric quadrupole moments entirely, whereas most measured quadrupole moments are actually positive, and some are very large. Polarization of the core by the odd nucleon appears to be a principal mechanism in producing the asymmetric core.

At present, we have to interpret the Schmidt diagrams of Figs. 4.1 and 4.2 as supporting a single-particle model for odd-A nuclides, modified both by quenching of free-nucleon moments and by asymmetry of the even-even core. The quantitative aspects of these effects are not yet well understood in existing theories.

Uniform Model. The total magnetic dipole moment of a nucleus is composed of two intrinsically different parts, an orbital moment and a spin moment. Margenau and Wigner (M10) have considered some details of a nuclear model in which the orbital angular momentum is distributed uniformly over all the nucleons. This leads to an orbital gyromagnetic ratio $g_L = Z/A \simeq 0.4$, where Z is the number of protons and A is the number of nucleons in the nucleus. Replacing g_l in Eqs. (4.9) and (4.10) by g_L leads to the so-called Margenau-Wigner (M-W) limits. For odd-proton nuclei, the Margenau-Wigner limits do not follow at all the empirical slope of about unity which is displayed in the Schmidt diagrams. For odd-neutron nuclei the Margenau-Wigner limits predict an increase of μ with I which is very much steeper than the empirical values. Thus, on a basis of the general trends, there is no support for the uniform model in competition with the extreme single-particle model.

Within a particular nucleus the volumetric distribution of the density of magnetic dipole moment would generally be nonuniform. Various methods for measuring nuclear gyromagnetic ratios can depend in different ways on the volumetric distribution of the magnetic moment. Molecular-beam methods and Larmor frequency resonance methods generally (Chap. 5) can treat the total moment as a point dipole. On the other hand, the magnitude of the hyperfine-structure separations of an electronic s state are proportional to the average electron density at the location of the nuclear magnetic moment. Bitter (B60) has observed a finite difference between the relative hyperfine structure and the relative total moments of the isotopic nuclides Rb^{85} ($I = \frac{3}{2}$; $\mu = 2.75$) and Rb^{87} ($I = \frac{5}{2}$; $\mu = 1.35$) which can be traced to a dependence on the volumetric distribution of magnetic dipole moment. A. Bohr and Weisskopf (B90) were able to show that these differences are in somewhat better agreement with the simple Schmidt extreme single-particle model than with the uniform model.

c. Odd-Z Odd-N Nuclei. The angular momentum I and the nuclear g factor have been measured directly for the ground levels of about a dozen nuclides belonging to the odd-Z odd-N class. As indicated in Tables 4.1 and 4.3, all these nuclides exhibit $I > 0$, even in the four cases in which $Z = N$. The simplest case, of course, is $_1H^2$, for which $I = 1$. Both nucleons are surely in $s_{\frac{1}{2}}$ states, with $j = \frac{1}{2}$. The total I here is $j_1 + j_2 = 1$, with the proton spin and the neutron spin aligned parallel to one another.

Most nuclides in the odd-Z odd-N class are radioactive, and they decay by β-ray transitions to even-Z even-N nuclides which presumably have $I = 0$. From comparisons of the radioactive half-period and decay energy, assignments can be made in many cases of the angular momentum of the odd-Z odd-N nuclide (Chap. 6).

Nordheim's Rule. It is often possible to infer the state of the odd proton by comparison with a known odd-Z even-N nuclide having the same Z. For example, $_3Li^7$ ($I = \frac{3}{2}$) lies in the Schmidt diagram near the $I = l + \frac{1}{2}$ limit. Consequently, $l = I - \frac{1}{2} = 1$, and the odd proton is in a $p_{\frac{3}{2}}$ state. Analogously, the state of the odd neutron can often be inferred. Then if the angular momenta of the odd proton and the odd neutron are called j_p and j_n, Nordheim (N23) has pointed out that the following coupling rules apply in at least 60 clear cases, though there are a few established exceptions.

1. If the odd proton and neutron belong to *different* Schmidt groups (that is, $j_p = l + \frac{1}{2}$ and $j_n = l - \frac{1}{2}$, or the reverse), then $I = |j_p - j_n|$.

2. If the odd proton and neutron belong to the same Schmidt group (i.e., both $j = l + \frac{1}{2}$, or both $j = l - \frac{1}{2}$), then $I > |j_p - j_n|$.

In the first case, the spin angular momenta of the odd proton and neutron are aligned parallel. In the second case, there is still a tendency toward parallel alignment.

TABLE 4.3. NUCLEAR ANGULAR MOMENTUM I AND MAGNETIC DIPOLE MOMENT μ FOR SOME ODD-Z ODD-N NUCLIDES

(As obtained by direct measurement of I and $g = \mu/I$. The first four nuclides are stable; the others, radioactive.)

Nuclide	Z	N	I	μ
H²	1	1	1	0.857
Li⁶	3	3	1	0.822
B¹⁰	5	5	3	1.800
N¹⁴	7	7	1	0.404
Na²²	11	11	3	1.746
Na²⁴	11	13	4	$(-)1.7$
Cl³⁶	17	19	2	
K⁴⁰	19	21	4	-1.29
K⁴²	19	23	2	-1.41
V⁵⁰	23	27	6	3.34
Rb⁸⁶	37	49	2	-1.68
Cs¹³⁴	55	79	4	2.95
Lu¹⁷⁶	71	105	≥ 7	4

Problem

Show that the Schmidt limit, for the case $j = l - s$, is

$$\mu = gj = g_l \left[\frac{(l+1)(l - \frac{1}{2})}{l + \frac{1}{2}} \right] - \mu_s \left(\frac{l - \frac{1}{2}}{l + \frac{1}{2}} \right)$$

for both odd-neutron ($g_l = 0$; $\mu_s = -1.91$) and odd-proton ($g_l = 1$; $\mu_s = 2.79$) nuclei.

5. *Electric Quadrupole Moment*

If the time average of the volumetric distribution of electric charge within a nucleus deviates from perfect spherical symmetry, then the nucleus will possess finite electric multipole moments. The electrostatic field which is produced at the position of the nucleus by the atomic and molecular electron configurations is generally a nonuniform field. The electrostatic potential energy of a nuclear electric multipole moment, residing in this nonuniform field, makes a contribution to the energy of the electronic state. Measurable effects in the hyperfine structure of atomic and molecular spectra have been found which can be attributed to nuclear electric quadrupole moments.

Nuclear electric quadrupole moments were not discovered until 1935 when Schüler and Schmidt (S18) found them necessary in order to explain irregularities in the hyperfine spectra of Eu[151] and Eu[153]. Effects due to other electric multipole moments (dipole, octupole, etc.) are not expected and have not yet been found.

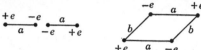

Fig. 5.1 Classical quadrupoles, composed of antiparallel paired dipoles, of equal dipole moment ea. The axial quadrupole, at the left, easily can be shown to produce a potential, at a distance $d \gg a$ along its extended axis, of $\varphi = 2a(ea)/d^3$. Its classical quadrupole moment φd^3 in the axial direction is therefore $2ea^2$.

a. Classical Multipole Moments for Point Charges. The simplest example of a classical electric quadrupole is the so-called axial quadrupole. This is composed of two electric dipoles, whose axes are collinear and antiparallel, as indicated in Fig. 5.1. In common with all quadrupoles, it produces a potential which varies inversely with the cube of distance, and its quadrupole moment has dimensions of (charge) × (area). A classical octupole can be formed by two closely spaced quadrupoles, and so on for the higher multipoles.

Multipole moments are also exhibited in the potential due to a single point charge, if that charge is not located at the origin of the coordinate system. Visualizing the atomic nucleus as an approximately spherical assembly of neutrons (charge, zero) and protons (charge, $+e$), we may specialize the general classical theory (p. 172 of S76) of electric multipole

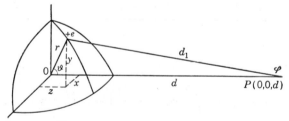

Fig. 5.2 To accompany Eq. (5.1) et seq. for the potential φ at P, due to the charge $+e$ at x, y, z. The coefficients of $1/d^{n+1}$ in Eq. (5.2) are the effective components in the z direction of the classical electric moments of multipole order 2^n.

moments. In rectangular coordinates x, y, z (Fig. 5.2) the scalar electrostatic potential φ at the external point $P(0,0,d)$ on the z axis, due to a charge $+e$ at the point (x,y,z), is

$$\varphi = \frac{e}{d_1} = \frac{e}{d}\left(1 - 2\frac{r}{d}\cos\vartheta + \frac{r^2}{d^2}\right)^{-\frac{1}{2}} \tag{5.1}$$

where $d_1 = (d^2 - 2rd\cos\vartheta + r^2)^{\frac{1}{2}}$ is the distance from the point P to the charge, $r = (x^2 + y^2 + z^2)^{\frac{1}{2}}$ is the distance from the origin (or mass centroid of a nucleus) to the charge, and $\cos\vartheta = z/r$ defines the angle between r and d.

Expanding Eq. (5.1) and collecting terms in $1/d^n$, we obtain the general expression

$$\varphi = \frac{e}{d} + \frac{er}{d^2}\cos\vartheta + \frac{er^2}{d^3}\left(\frac{3}{2}\cos^2\vartheta - \frac{1}{2}\right)$$

$$+ \frac{er^3}{d^4}\left(\frac{5}{2}\cos^3\vartheta - \frac{3}{2}\cos\vartheta\right) + \cdots \quad (5.2)$$

or, more generally,

$$\varphi = \sum_{n=0}^{\infty} \frac{er^n}{d^{n+1}} P_n(\cos\vartheta) \quad (5.3)$$

where $P_n(\cos\vartheta)$ are the Legendre polynomials and n (or, more exactly, 2^n) is the multipole order. Thus, in Eq. (5.2) the coefficient of $1/d$ is the monopole strength, of $1/d^2$ is the z component of the dipole moment, of $1/d^3$ is the z component of the quadrupole moment, of $1/d^4$ is the z component of the octupole moment, etc. The first term in Eq. (5.2) is the ordinary coulomb potential.

Thus even a single isolated charge, if not located at the origin of coordinates, exhibits a quadrupole and other moments; i.e., *the electric field due to an asymmetrically placed proton is identical with the electric field which would be produced by placing, at the center of the nucleus, one proton, and also an electric dipole, an electric quadrupole, an electric octupole, etc.* The total electric charge in such an equivalent structure would still be one proton, because the classical electric multipoles each have zero net charge.

If in Eq. (5.2) we now substitute $\cos\vartheta = z/r$, we obtain for the coefficient of $1/d^3$, which is the effective classical quadrupole moment $q^{(2)}$ in the direction z, as exhibited at $P(0,0,d)$,

$$q^{(2)} = \frac{e}{2}(3z^2 - r^2) \quad (5.4)$$

The classical quadrupole moment of such a nucleus would be taken along the body axis of total angular momentum, I^*. If a single proton were situated at the nuclear radius R, along the body axis, i.e., if $z = r = R$, and $x = y = 0$, then the classical quadrupole moment would be, from Eq. (5.4),

$$q^{(2)} = eR^2$$

Similarly, a single proton at the nuclear equator, $z = 0$, $r = R$, would have a classical quadrupole moment

$$q^{(2)} = -\tfrac{1}{2}eR^2$$

Thus if six protons were located symmetrically along the coordinate axes at distances $\pm R$ from the center, the two protons at $z = \pm R$ on the body axis of angular momentum would contribute $+2eR^2$ to the quadrupole moment, while the four protons in the equatorial plane, at $x = \pm R$

and $y = \pm R$, would contribute $4(-eR^2/2) = -2eR^2$. Thus, for this or any other *spherically symmetric* distribution of positive charge in the nucleus, the net quadrupole moment is zero.

If, in addition to a symmetric distribution, one or more nuclear protons are located asymmetrically, the nucleus will possess a net electric quadrupole moment. Thus both positive and negative nuclear quadrupole moments are to be expected. *Positive moments* correspond to an elongation of the nuclear charge distribution along the angular-momentum axis (football-shaped distribution). *Negative moments* correspond to a flattened, or oblate, distribution (discus-shaped distribution).

b. Nuclear Electric Quadrupole Moment. The potential energy of an electric quadrupole when placed in a nonuniform electric field can be shown to be proportional to the product of the gradient $\partial \mathcal{E}_z/\partial z$ of the electric field and the quadrupole moment in the z direction. The interaction energy between the field produced at the nucleus by the atomic or molecular electrons and the nuclear quadrupole moment can be measured accurately by several methods. It is much more difficult to evaluate the electronic field, and thus to obtain a quantitative measurement of the nuclear quadrupole moment.

The electronic field, the quadrupole moment, and their interaction energy are to be calculated quantum-mechanically. Then what is usually called the "quadrupole moment" Q receives in the quantum mechanics a definition which differs in some details from a classical definition. First, the quadrupole moment is not taken about the body axis of I^* but about the axis of its maximum projected component $m_I = I$. Second, the numerical factor $\frac{1}{2}$ in the classical expression Eq. (5.4) disappears. Third, the probability density for a proton at any position (x,y,z) in the nucleus is represented in terms of the square of a wave function $|\psi|^2$. The quantum-mechanical charge distribution is therefore continuous and can be represented by a mean charge density $\rho(x,y,z)$. Fourth, the integral over the charge distribution is divided by the proton charge e, which

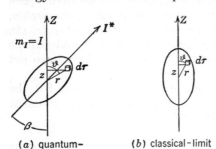

(a) quantum-mechanical   (b) classical-limit

Fig. 5.3 The nuclear electric quadrupole moment Q is evaluated in the quantum mechanics as an integration of Eq. (5.5) about the axis of $m_I = I$, which is the maximum projection of $I^* = \sqrt{I(I+1)}$. In the classical limit, $I^* \to I$, and the volume integral would be taken in the geometry shown at the right.

makes all nuclear quadrupole moments have dimensions of cm^2 only.

Then if ρ is the density of nuclear charge in the volume element $d\tau$ at the point (z,r), as illustrated in Fig. 5.3, the nuclear electric quadrupole moment Q is defined as the time average of

$$Q \equiv \frac{1}{e} \int \rho(3z^2 - r^2)\, d\tau = \frac{1}{e} \int \rho r^2(3\cos^2 \vartheta - 1)\, d\tau \qquad (5.5)$$

taken about $m_I = I$, as I^* precesses about I. This is often written in the equivalent forms

$$Q = \frac{1}{e} \left[\rho r^2 (3 \cos^2 \vartheta - 1) \right]_{\text{av}} = Z \langle 3z^2 - r^2 \rangle_{\text{av}} \qquad (5.6)$$

Certain other nonequivalent definitions of the nuclear quadrupole moment are used by some authors. Caution is necessary in comparing the results of various investigators, especially in the older literature. What we would call Q/Z is used by some as the quadrupole moment. Feld (F25), Bardeen and Townes (B10), and Ramsey (R3) have presented very helpful comparisons of the several expressions used by various authors for reporting quadrupole moments.

Relationships among Q, m_I, and I. The evaluation of the quadrupole moment Q in the quantum state $m_I = I$ is in harmony with the conventional definitions of the magnetic moment μ and the mechanical moment I. In the case of Q, the effective components for other magnetic quantum numbers $m_I = (I - 1), \ldots$, do not follow a simple cosine law, as they do for μ and I, because of the $\cos^2 \vartheta$ term in Eq. (5.5). If β is the angle between the body axis I^* and the z axis in space, then, as illustrated in Fig. 1.1,

$$\cos \beta = \frac{m_I}{\sqrt{I(I + 1)}}$$

and it can be shown (B68) that the effective value of the quadrupole moment is proportional to $(3 \cos^2 \beta - 1)$. Then the effective value $Q(m_I)$ in the state m_I is related to its value Q in the state $m_I = I$ by

$$Q(m_I) = \frac{3 \cos^2 \beta_m - 1}{3 \cos^2 \beta_I - 1} Q = \frac{3m_I^2 - I(I + 1)}{I(2I - 1)} Q \qquad (5.7)$$

Nuclei which have $I = 0$ or $I = \frac{1}{2}$ can exhibit no quadrupole moment Q in the state $m_I = I$. This can be seen from Eq. (5.7) or, more physically, by noting that, in the case of $I = \frac{1}{2}$, $\cos \beta_I = \frac{1}{2} / \sqrt{\frac{1}{2} \times \frac{3}{2}} = 1/\sqrt{3}$, and, from symmetry considerations, an average value of $(3 \cos^2 \vartheta - 1)$ in Eq. (5.5) becomes zero. This does not mean that nuclei with $I = \frac{1}{2}$ necessarily have perfectly spherical distributions of charge about their body axis I^*, but only that the maximum observable component Q is zero. *Finite electric quadrupole moments are therefore detectable only for nuclei which have angular momenta $I \geq 1$.*

Other Nuclear Electric Multipole Moments. When all nuclear electric multipole moments are defined quantum-mechanically in terms of the state $m_I = I$, it can be shown (p. 30 of B68) quite generally that all electric multipoles with even values of the multipole order (quadrupole, 2^4-pole, 2^n-pole) are zero unless $I \geq n/2$. Moreover, all electric multipoles of odd order (dipole, octupole, 2^5-pole, etc.) are identically zero, if we follow the reasonable assumption that nuclei have axial symmetry and that the center of mass and the center of charge coincide. We refer here to the "*static*" moment, or the "permanent" moment, of the stationary state of the quantum-mechanical system. The electric (and magnetic) multipole moments which characterize radiative transitions between excited nuclear levels are not similarly restricted.

c. Significance of the Experimental Data on Quadrupole Moments. Precise measurements of atomic and molecular hyperfine structure have permitted the evaluation of the quadrupole moment Q for the ground level of a number of nuclides. Mostly Q lies in the domain of 10^{-26} to 10^{-24} cm², which is of the order of the square of the nuclear radius. Such moments would therefore be produced by a nonspherical distribution of one or a few protons at distances of the order of the nuclear radius.

Ellipticity of Charge Distribution. In the constant-density model of nuclei (Chap. 2), we conventionally assume that all nuclei have a spherical distribution of both mass and charge. The finite quadrupole moments imply that some nuclei have a slightly ellipsoidal distribution of charge. We can relate Q semiquantitatively to this ellipticity (S15, F26, B68).

Let the nucleus be represented, as in Fig. 5.3*b*, as an ellipsoid, with semiaxis b parallel to the z direction and semiaxis a perpendicular to z. If we assume that the charge is uniformly distributed throughout this volume, with charge density

$$\rho = \frac{Ze}{\int d\tau} = \frac{3Ze}{4\pi a^2 b}$$

then the quadrupole moment in the direction z is

$$Q = \frac{\rho}{e} \int (3z^2 - r^2)\, d\tau = \tfrac{2}{5}Z(b^2 - a^2) \tag{5.8}$$

Because the semiaxes b and a will turn out to be nearly equal for real nuclei, it is convenient to define the nuclear radius R as their mean value

$$R \equiv \frac{b + a}{2} \tag{5.9}$$

and to measure the ellipticity in terms of a parameter η, defined by

$$\eta \equiv \frac{b - a}{R} = 2\frac{b - a}{b + a}. \tag{5.10}$$

The quadrupole moment of Eq. (5.8) can now be rewritten as

$$Q = \tfrac{4}{5}\eta Z R^2 \tag{5.11}$$

The quantity ηZ is then a rough measure of the number of protons whose cooperation is required in order to produce the observed quadrupole moment. Alternatively, the asymmetry of the charge distribution, as measured by the ratio of the major and minor axes of the ellipsoid, is given to a good approximation by

$$\frac{b}{a} \simeq 1 + \eta \tag{5.12}$$

The ellipticities η of nuclides for which Q has been measured are given in Table 5.1. Recall that for $I = 0$ and $\tfrac{1}{2}$, $Q = 0$ and $\eta = 0$.

For $I \geq 1$, the usual asymmetries are seen to be of the order of a few per cent. This is the extent of the experimental justification for the common simplifying assumption that nuclei are spherical.

It must be noted that the ellipticities calculated from Eq. (5.11) and shown in Table 5.1 correspond to the $m_I = I$ state and are therefore minimum estimates in regard to the actual nucleus when it is considered, for example, as a target in a nuclear reaction. This is because we have evaluated Eq. (5.8) in the classical limit of large quantum numbers, so that $I^* \to I$, and $\beta \to 0$. What might be called Q^*, the quadrupole moment about the body axis I^*, will always be larger than Q.

The Deuteron. The deuteron is included in Table 5.1 even though it cannot be assigned a well-defined radius. Far-reaching consequences are associated with the discovery (K13) in 1939 at Columbia University of the small, but finite, quadrupole moment of the deuteron,

$$Q = 0.273 \times 10^{-26} \text{ cm}^2$$

The ground level of the deuteron could no longer be regarded as simply the $^3S_1$ level ($L = 0$, $S = 1$), resulting from a central force between the neutron and proton, because an S state must be spherically symmetrical.

In this simplest of nucleon aggregations, the quadrupole moment can be accounted for by assuming that the force between the neutron and proton is partly a central force and partly a noncentral, or tensor, force (R6, R29, I4). The very existence of a noncentral force implies that the orbital angular momentum L is no longer a constant of the motion, although the total angular momentum I remains a "good" quantum number. The ground level of the deuteron becomes in this model a mixture of $^3S_1$ and $^3D_1$ ($L = 2$, $S = 1$, $I = 1$) levels. (No P-state admixture is present because the parity of a P state is odd, while the S and D levels both have even parity, as discussed in Sec. 6.)

It is found that the quadrupole moment of the deuteron can be attributed to an admixture of about 4 per cent $^3D_1$ level with 96 per cent $^3S_1$ level. This same admixture just accounts for the nonadditivity of the spin magnetic dipole moments of the neutron and proton in the deuteron by introducing a small contribution from orbital motion of the charged proton in the $^3D_1$ level. Then

$$\mu_d = \mu_n + \mu_p - \tfrac{3}{2}(\mu_n + \mu_p - \tfrac{1}{2})\Phi \tag{5.13}$$

where

$$\Phi \equiv \frac{\int \psi_D^2 \, d\tau}{\int (\psi_S^2 + \psi_D^2) \, d\tau} \simeq 0.039$$

is the so-called proportion of D level, ψ_S and ψ_D are the wave functions in the S and D levels, and $d\tau$ is the volume element in the relative coordinates between the proton and neutron (R6, S2, F48).

Shell Structure in Nuclei. The systematic variation of Q and η with Z was first pointed out by Schmidt (S15), who noted in 1940 that minima in the absolute magnitude of the nuclear quadrupole moments occur near $Z = 50$ and 82. Additional data, and the revival and improvement since

TABLE 5.1. NUCLEAR QUADRUPOLE MOMENTS Q, AND THE CORRESPONDING ELLIPTICITY η, IN THE QUANTUM STATE $m_I = I$, USING EQ. (5.11) WITH $R = 1.5 \times 10^{-13}$ CM

The measured values of I, μ, and Q, and the presumed state of the odd nucleon in the ground level, are from the compilation by Klinkenberg (K23).

Nuclide		Number of odd nucleons		I	μ	Q, 10^{-26} cm²	η	Ground level
Z	A	Odd-Z	Odd-N					
0 n	1†	..	1	$\frac{1}{2}$	-1.913	0	0	$s_{\frac{1}{2}}$
1 H	1	1	...	$\frac{1}{2}$	$+2.793$	0	0	$s_{\frac{1}{2}}$
1 H	2	1	1	1	$+0.857$	$+0.273$	$+0.095$	$(\frac{1}{2},\frac{1}{2})_1$
1 H	3	1	...	$\frac{1}{2}$	$+2.979$	0	0	$s_{\frac{1}{2}}$
3 Li	6	3	3	1	$+0.822$	<0.09	<0.005	$(\frac{3}{2},\frac{3}{2})_1$
3 Li	7	3	...	$\frac{3}{2}$	$+3.256$	$(+)2\ddagger$	$(+)0.10\ddagger$	$p_{\frac{3}{2}}$
5 B	10	5	5	3	$+1.800$	$+6$	$+0.14$	$(\frac{3}{2},\frac{3}{2})_3$
5 B	11	5	...	$\frac{3}{2}$	$+2.689$	$+3$	$+0.067$	$p_{\frac{3}{2}}$
7 N	14	7	7	1	$+0.404$	$+2$	$+0.027$	$(\frac{1}{2},\frac{1}{2})_1$
8 O	17	..	9	$\frac{5}{2}$	-1.894	-0.5	-0.005	$d_{\frac{5}{2}}$
13 Al	27	13	...	$\frac{5}{2}$	$+3.641$	$+15.6$	$+0.074$	$d_{\frac{5}{2}}$
16 S	33	..	17	$\frac{3}{2}$	$+0.644$	-8	-0.027	$d_{\frac{3}{2}}$
16 S	35†	..	19	$\frac{3}{2}$	....	$+6$	$+0.019$	$d_{\frac{3}{2}}$
17 Cl	35	17	...	$\frac{3}{2}$	$+0.822$	-7.89	-0.024	$d_{\frac{3}{2}}$
17 Cl	36†	17	19	2	....	-1.68	-0.005	$(\frac{3}{2},\frac{3}{2})_2$
17 Cl	37	17	...	$\frac{3}{2}$	$+0.684$	-6.21	-0.018	$d_{\frac{3}{2}}$
29 Cu	63	29	...	$\frac{3}{2}$	$+2.226$	-13	-0.016	$p_{\frac{3}{2}}$
29 Cu	65	29	...	$\frac{3}{2}$	$+2.385$	-12	-0.014	$p_{\frac{3}{2}}$
31 Ga	69	31	...	$\frac{3}{2}$	$+2.017$	$+23.2$	$+0.025$	$p_{\frac{3}{2}}$
31 Ga	71	31	...	$\frac{3}{2}$	$+2.561$	$+14.6$	$+0.015$	$p_{\frac{3}{2}}$
32 Ge	73	..	41	$\frac{9}{2}$	....	-20	-0.02	$g_{\frac{9}{2}}$
33 As	75	33	...	$\frac{3}{2}$	$+1.439$	$+30$	$+0.03$	$p_{\frac{3}{2}}$
35 Br	79	35	...	$\frac{3}{2}$	$+2.106$	$+26$	$+0.022$	$p_{\frac{3}{2}}$
35 Br	81	35	...	$\frac{3}{2}$	$+2.270$	$+21$	$+0.018$	$p_{\frac{3}{2}}$
36 Kr	83	..	47	$\frac{9}{2}$	-0.970	$+15$	$+0.012$	$g_{\frac{9}{2}}$
49 In	113	49	...	$\frac{9}{2}$	$+5.486$	$+114$	$+0.055$	$g_{\frac{9}{2}}$
49 In	115†	49	...	$\frac{9}{2}$	$+5.500$	$+116$	$+0.056$	$g_{\frac{9}{2}}$

† A radioactive nuclide.
‡ Parentheses indicate an uncertainty.
§ Os 189 is from Murakawa and Suwa (M75).

TABLE 5.1. NUCLEAR QUADRUPOLE MOMENTS Q, AND THE CORRESPONDING ELLIPTICITY η, IN THE QUANTUM STATE $m_I = I$, USING EQ. (5.11) WITH $R = 1.5 \times 10^{-13}$ CM (*Continued*)

Nuclide		Number of odd nucleons		I	μ	Q, 10^{-26} cm²	η	Ground level
Z	A	Odd-Z	Odd-N					
51 Sb	121	51	...	$\frac{5}{2}$	+3.360	−30	−0.013	$d_{\frac{5}{2}}$
51 Sb	123	51	...	$\frac{7}{2}$	+2.547	−120	−0.053	$g_{\frac{7}{2}}$
53 I	127	53	...	$\frac{5}{2}$	+2.809	−59	−0.025	$d_{\frac{5}{2}}$
53 I	129†	53	...	$\frac{7}{2}$	(+)2.618‡	−43	−0.018	$g_{\frac{7}{2}}$
54 Xe	131	..	77	$\frac{3}{2}$	+0.700	−15	−0.006	$d_{\frac{3}{2}}$
63 Eu	151	63	...	$\frac{5}{2}$	+3.6	+120	+0.037	$d_{\frac{5}{2}}$
63 Eu	153	63	...	$\frac{5}{2}$	+1.6	+250	+0.077	$d_{\frac{5}{2}}$
70 Yb	173	..	103	$\frac{5}{2}$	−0.65	+390	+0.100	$f_{\frac{5}{2}}$
71 Lu	175	71	...	$\frac{7}{2}$	+2.9	+590	+0.148	$g_{\frac{7}{2}}$
71 Lu	176†	71	105	≥7	+4.2	+700	+0.174	$(\frac{11}{2}, \frac{13}{2})_{10}$
73 Ta	181	73	...	$\frac{7}{2}$	+2.1	+600	+0.143	$g_{\frac{7}{2}}$
75 Re	185	75	...	$\frac{5}{2}$	+3.171	(+280)‡	+0.064	$d_{\frac{5}{2}}$
75 Re	187†	75	...	$\frac{5}{2}$	+3.204	+260	+0.059	$d_{\frac{5}{2}}$
76 Os	189§	..	113	$\frac{3}{2}$	(+)0.7‡	+200	+0.045	$p_{\frac{3}{2}}$
80 Hg	201	..	121	$\frac{3}{2}$	−0.559	+50	+0.010	$p_{\frac{3}{2}}$
83 Bi	209	83	...	$\frac{9}{2}$	+4.082	−40	−0.008	$h_{\frac{9}{2}}$

1948 of the earlier shell models, allow some interesting tentative correlations to be made between the presumed shell structure of nuclei and the observed quadrupole moments (H54, T26, M62). With some refinements, we may use the core-plus-single-particle model, which we have seen correlates fairly well with the observed relationships between the mechanical moment I and the magnetic moment μ (Figs. 4.1 and 4.2).

A core of even-Z, which in this model has $I = 0$, $\mu = 0$, cannot be expected, in general, also to cancel out its quadrupole moments to zero. Certain special even-Z cores do, however, contain protons in all possible m_j states and therefore could have spherical symmetry, and $Q = 0$, if the core were not distorted by the nucleons outside it. These are the so-called *closed shells*, corresponding in the shell model to the observed "magic numbers," 2, 8, 20, 28, 40, 50, 82.

For odd-Z even-N nuclides in which Z corresponds to a closed shell plus one proton, we would then expect a flattened, or disklike, charge distribution and consequently a negative Q. Positive quadrupole moments can also emerge from this model. If, in odd-Z even-N nuclides, Z corresponds to one proton *less* than a closed shell, then, by the so-called "*partial configuration method*" (F18), the "hole" in the proton shell behaves like a negatively charged particle. Thus for a sequence of odd-Z

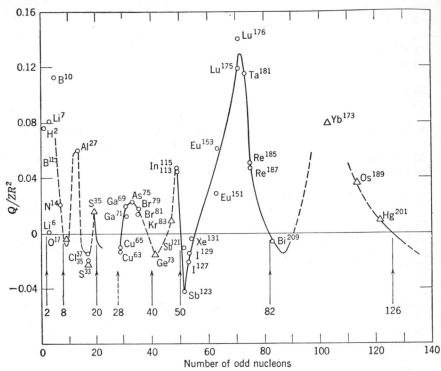

Fig. 5.4 The plotted points are the observed quadrupole moments Q divided by the nuclear charge Z and the square of the nuclear radius, which is taken as $R = 1.5 \times 10^{-13} A^{\frac{1}{3}}$. The ordinates are therefore proportional to the ellipticity and correspond to $0.8\eta \simeq 0.8 \ [(b/a) - 1]$ of Eqs. (5.11) and (5.12). Moments of odd-Z even-N nuclides and odd-Z odd-N nuclides are plotted as circles against Z. Moments of even-Z odd-N nuclides are plotted as triangles. Arrows indicate the closing of major nucleon shells. The solid curve represents regions where quadrupole-moment behavior seems established (T26, P27). The dashed curve represents more doubtful regions. [*Adapted from Townes, Foley, and Low* (T26).]

even-N nuclides, Q would be expected to be positive for Z slightly less than a closed shell of protons. As Z increases and passes just beyond a magic number, Q would change sign and become negative. This behavior is clearly displayed by $_{49}\text{In}^{115}$ ($Q = +1.16 \times 10^{-24}$ cm^2) and $_{51}\text{Sb}^{121}$ ($Q = -0.3 \times 10^{-24}$ cm^2) as Z passes through the well-established closed shell of 50 protons.

For even-Z odd-N nuclides we can expect a systematic variation of Q

with N only if the mean spatial distribution of the protons is somehow correlated with that of the uncharged neutrons.   Empirically, the correlation of Q with odd-N exists and is similar to the variation of Q with a corresponding number of odd protons.   This suggests that the strong attractive forces between protons and neutrons are such that a distortion of the neutron distribution produces a similar distortion in the proton distribution.

Q has been measured for only a few even-Z odd-N nuclides.   Among these, $_{16}S^{35}$ ($I = \frac{3}{2}$; $Q = +0.06 \times 10^{-24}$ cm^2; $N = 19$) is a clear example of a positive quadrupole moment just before the closing of a neutron shell at $N = 20$.   The case of $_8O^{17}$ ($I = \frac{5}{2}$; $Q = -0.005 \times 10^{-24}$ cm^2; $N = 9$) illustrates the negative Q observed just after the closing of a neutron shell.   This case is especially interesting because its even-Z proton configuration is the closed shell $Z = 8$.   Its core is the doubly closed-shell configuration $Z = 8$, $N = 8$, and so it should have spherical symmetry and $Q = 0$.   Even so, the odd neutron is able to distort this into a slightly flattened distribution of charge.   The absolute magnitude of this negative quadrupole moment is small, however.

This simple model leads to the following conclusions (T26):

1. For odd-Z even-N nuclides, the quadrupole moment is primarily dependent on the number of protons. Q is always positive immediately before, and always negative immediately after, a proton shell is filled.

2. For even-Z odd-N nuclides, the sign of Q is determined by the number of neutrons, but the absolute magnitude of Q depends on the number of protons.   The quadrupole moments behave in sign as though the neutrons were positively charged.

3. For odd-Z odd-N nuclides, estimation of Q is considerably more complex and depends in part on how the mechanical moments of the odd proton and odd neutron add.   If these moments are essentially parallel, Q should be of the same sign and approximately the same magnitude as for a similar odd-Z even-N nuclide (examples: B^{10}, N^{14}, Lu^{176}).   If the mechanical moments of the odd proton and odd neutron are not essentially parallel, the magnitude of Q should be considerably reduced (examples: Li^6, Cl^{36}).

4. For even-Z even-N nuclides, $I = 0$ and hence $Q = 0$ because $I < 1$.

The quadrupole moments for a number of nuclides are plotted in Fig. 5.4, where the sequence of positive and negative values of Q and the other features just discussed can be visualized.   The apparent distortion of the core, between closed shells, has been discussed on the collective model by Bohr and Mottelson (B89) and by Hill and Wheeler (H53).

Problems

1. What is the numerical value of the classical electric quadrupole moment of a nucleus having a finite angular momentum and containing one proton at the nuclear equator in addition to a spherically symmetric distribution of charge, if the nuclear radius is 4×10^{-13} cm?   What would be the quantum-mechanical value for this same quadrupole moment? *Ans.:* -0.08×10^{-24} cm²/electron; -0.16×10^{-24} cm².

2. Show that the quadrupole moment Q of a uniformly charged ellipsoid is $(2Z/5)(b^2 - a^2)$ as given by Eq. (5.8).

3. Show that the ellipticity parameter η is actually related to the ratio of the semiaxes of the ellipsoid, b/a, as

$$\eta = 2 \frac{(b/a) - 1}{(b/a) + 1} \quad \text{or} \quad \frac{b}{a} = 1 + \frac{\eta}{1 - (\eta/2)} \simeq 1 + \eta + \frac{\eta^2}{2} \cdots$$

4. Show that, in the model used for Eq. (5.7), the quadrupole moment Q^* along the body axis I^* of a nucleus is related to the usual quadrupole moment Q of the quantum state $m_I = I$ by

$$Q^* = \frac{2I + 2}{2I - 1} Q$$

Compute Q^* and the corresponding ellipticity η^* for a few nuclides from Table 5.1.

5. If the "actual" quadrupole moment Q^* about the body axis is positive, is there any value of I which permits the measurable quadrupole moment Q to be negative?

If Q is positive for a particular nuclide, whose angular-momentum quantum number is I, what are the magnetic quantum states m_I for which the effective quadrupole moment is negative?

6. (*a*) Show that the geometrical target area of a nucleus whose ellipticity about its body axis I^* is given by $\eta^* = 2(b - a)/(b + a)$ is

$$\sigma_\perp = \pi ab = \pi \left(\frac{\text{volume}}{4\pi/3} \right)^{\frac{2}{3}} (1 + \tfrac{1}{3}\eta^* + \cdots) \qquad \text{perpendicular to body axis}$$

$$\sigma_\parallel = \pi a^2 = \pi \left(\frac{\text{volume}}{4\pi/3} \right)^{\frac{2}{3}} (1 - \tfrac{2}{3}\eta^* + \cdots) \qquad \text{parallel to body axis}$$

(*b*) Look up data on the fast-neutron cross section of nuclei which have large quadrupole moments, such as some of the rare earths, and determine whether their ellipticities are detectable as anomalies in the progression of fast-neutron cross section with mass number.

6. *Parity*

The property called "parity" is a classification of wave functions into two groups, those of "even parity" and those of "odd parity." This classification is especially useful for quantum-mechanical systems containing two or more particles, such as a nucleus.

The parity of an *isolated* system is a constant of its motion and cannot be changed by any internal processes. Only if radiation or a particle enters or leaves the system, and hence the system is no longer isolated, can its parity change. We therefore refer to the "conservation of parity" in the same sense and with the same rigor as the conservation of charge and of angular momentum. Like the angular-momentum quantum number I, parity is spoken of as a "good" quantum number.

a. Definition of Parity. Wave mechanics gives a satisfactory description of many nuclear, atomic, and molecular systems. For very large quantum numbers, the wave mechanics goes over into the equations of ordinary mechanics. Thus we can visualize ordinary mechanical analogues of the nuclear angular momentum, the intrinsic spin of single particles, and some other mechanical properties of nuclear systems. The so-called *parity* of a system of elementary particles, such as a nucleus, atom, or molecule, is a fundamental property of the motion according to the wave-mechanical description, but it has no simple analogy in ordinary mechanics.

As was noted in Chap. 2, Eq. (5.43), the physical description of the system, particularly the probability of finding the particle at the position and with the spin orientation given by the coordinates (x,y,z,s), is proportional to the square of the absolute value of the wave function, $|\Psi|^2 = \Psi\Psi^* = \psi\psi^*$, where Ψ^* and ψ^* are the complex conjugates of Ψ and ψ.

Now the physical description of a particle or system of particles cannot depend, for example, on whether we are right-handed or left-handed, and hence $\psi\psi^*$ must be the same in coordinates (x,y,z,s) as in the coordinates $(-x,-y,-z,s)$. This transformation of coordinates is equivalent to *reflecting the particle at the origin* in the (x,y,z) system, an operation which must either leave the wave function unchanged, or only change its sign, so that its squared absolute value remains unaltered in either case.

To a good approximation, ψ is the product of a function depending on space coordinates and a function depending on spin orientation. When reflection of the particle at the origin does not change the sign of the spatial part of ψ, the motion of the particle is said to have *even parity*. When reflection changes the sign of the spatial part of ψ, the motion of the particle is said to have *odd parity*. Thus

$$\psi(-x,-y,-z,s) = \psi(x,y,z,s) \qquad \text{represents even parity}$$
$$\psi(-x,-y,-z,s) = -\psi(x,y,z,s) \qquad \text{represents odd parity} \qquad (6.1)$$

It can be shown that the spatial part of ψ, on reflection of the particle, does not change sign if the angular-momentum quantum number l is even, but it does change sign if l is odd. Hence, for a particle with an even value of l, the motion has *even parity* and, with an odd value of l, the motion has *odd parity*.

For a system of particles, the wave function becomes approximately the product of the wave functions for the several particles, $\psi = \psi_1\psi_2\psi_3$ . . . , or a linear combination of such products. Hence the parity of a system of particles such as a nucleus depends on the parity of the motion of its individual particles.

Visualizing reflection of the system as the successive reflection of each individual particle, one at a time, we conclude that a *system* will have *even parity* when the arithmetic sum of the individual numerical values l_i for all its particles Σl_i is even, and odd parity when Σl_i is odd. A system containing an even number of odd-parity particles, and any number of even-parity particles, will have even parity. A system with an odd number of odd-parity particles, and any number of even-parity particles, will have odd parity. The symbol $(+)$ is often used as a superscript on

I, for example, $I = 3^+$, to denote even parity, and the symbol $(-)$ to denote odd parity. The *intrinsic parity* of the electron is defined arbitrarily as even. From the properties of simple systems it has been found experimentally that the intrinsic parity of the proton, neutron, and neutrino is the same as that of the electron; hence, it is even. In contrast, the π meson is found to have odd intrinsic parity.

All that has been said thus far applies to the nonrelativistic case, i.e., to heavy particles, such as protons or neutrons at energies below about 50 Mev, and to electrons of energy less than about 0.04 Mev. The relativistic wave mechanics has been developed for electrons but not for heavy particles. For electrons having an energy greater than about 0.04 Mev the Dirac relativistic electron theory must be used. The wave function describing the Dirac electron is a four-component vector in phase space, which reduces to the simple wave function Ψ for the nonrelativistic case. For the relativistic Dirac electron, the mathematical concept of parity is retained, but the l values no longer determine the parity in the simple fashion discussed above for the nonrelativistic case.

b. Change of Parity. Parity is always conserved. Thus the parity of a system (e.g., a nucleus) can only be changed by the capture of photons or particles having odd total parity (intrinsic parity plus parity of motion with respect to the initial system) or by the emission of photons or particles having odd total parity.

The selection rules for all nuclear transitions involve a statement of whether or not the nucleus changes parity as a result of the transition. Thus the notation "*yes*" denotes that the nuclear parity changes (from even to odd or from odd to even), hence that the emitted or absorbed particles or quanta have odd total parity. For example, an emitted α ray, having $l = 1$ with respect to the emitting nucleus, will have odd parity and can be emitted only if the nuclear parity changes. Similarly, the selection rule "*no*" means that the initial and final nuclei have the same parity (both even or both odd). An emitted α ray, having $l = 2$ with respect to the emitting nucleus, will have even parity and can be emitted only if the nuclear parity does not change.

c. Determination of the Parity of Nuclear Levels. The quantum-mechanical parity classification to which a given nuclear level belongs cannot be "measured" with the directness that an experimentalist feels in the measurement of such classical properties as charge, mass, angular momentum, and kinetic energy. Nevertheless, every nuclear level is representable only as a stationary state of a quantum-mechanical system. Therefore, one of the most important parameters of each level is its parity.

The parity of a given nuclear level is determined by the odd or even character of Σl_i. The evaluation of Σl_i is reliable in many instances only to the extent that the nuclear model employed is valid in its designation of the orbital quantum numbers l_i for the individual nucleons not occurring in closed shells.

We have seen that the core-and-single-particle nuclear model gives reasonable agreement with the Schmidt groups of μ and I for the ground levels of nuclei.   A very high percentage of successful predictions of I for ground levels and for excited levels has given much support since 1949 to the extreme single-particle model, with jj coupling between nucleons.   This evidence will be examined in Chap. 11.   Here we may note that the single-particle model forms a reasonable basis for the determination of l for an odd-nucleon and predicts $\Sigma l_i = 0$ for the core, as discussed earlier in connection with the Schmidt limits.   On this basis, the parity classification of many nuclear levels can be made with reasonable assurance.

Parity of Ground Levels.   When I and μ have been measured, the Schmidt group classification determines l of the odd nucleon in odd-A nuclides.   The interesting nuclide $_{56}\mathrm{Ba}^{137}_{81}$, with one neutron lacking from a closed shell of 82 neutrons, is found in its ground level to have $I = \frac{3}{2}$, and $\mu = +0.93$ nuclear magneton.   Then, from Fig. 4.2, the ground level of this nuclide belongs to the $I = j = l - s$ Schmidt group.   Then the 81st neutron is taken to be in an $l = \frac{3}{2} + \frac{1}{2} = 2$ or a "d" orbit.   With $\Sigma l_i = 0$ for the core, this makes $\Sigma l_i = 2$ for the entire nucleus.   The ground level therefore has even parity and is denoted "$d_{\frac{3}{2}}$, even," or, more commonly, "$d^+_{\frac{3}{2}}$."

Parity of Excited Levels.   The selection rules for every type of nuclear reaction and transition involve parity as well as angular-momentum changes.   Parity and angular momentum I are two "good quantum numbers" for all nuclear interactions; both are rigorously conserved. An explicit example of the determination of I and parity for excited levels in Ba^{137} will be discussed in Chap. 6, Sec. 7.

7. *The Statistics of Nuclear Particles*

We have seen that the wave mechanical concept of parity arises from considerations of the reflection properties of the spatial part of solutions ψ of the wave equation.   Another important property of nuclei, *statistics*, arises from considerations of the *symmetry properties* of wave functions, i.e., the effect on the wave function ψ of the interchange of all the coordinates of two identical particles.   The wave functions which are solutions of Schrödinger's equation for a system of two or more identical particles may be divided into two symmetry classes, "symmetric" and "antisymmetric."   Transitions between these two classes are completely forbidden.   The symmetry class of a wave function does not change with time.   It is a constant of the motion.   The symmetry class to which a particle belongs is synonymous with its statistics.   The statistics, in turn, has a profound effect on the physical behavior of collections of the identical particles.   Every particle in nature must obey either one of the two types of statistics, Fermi-Dirac (antisymmetric) or Einstein-Bose (symmetric), and these two have the following principal characteristics.

a. Fermi-Dirac Statistics.   The wave function of a system obeying Fermi-Dirac statistics is *antisymmetric* in the coordinates (three spatial and one spin) of the particles.   This means that if all the coordinates of any pair of identical particles are interchanged in the wave function, the new wave function representing this new system will be identical with the original except for a change in sign. The probability density $\psi\psi^*$ is, of course, unaltered. Thus if $\psi(x_1, \ldots, x_i, \ldots, x_j, \ldots, x_n)$ is the wave function of a system of n identical particles obeying Fermi-Dirac statistics, and x_i stands for all the coordinates of the particle i, the new wave function $\psi(x_1, \ldots, x_j, \ldots, x_i, \ldots, x_n)$ resulting from interchanging the particles i and j will be given by

$$\psi(x_1, \ldots, x_j, \ldots, x_i, \ldots, x_n)$$
$$= -\psi(x_1, \ldots, x_i, \ldots, x_j, \ldots, x_n) \quad (7.1)$$

It can be shown (p. 491 of B87) that antisymmetry of the wave functions restricts the number of particles per quantum state to one. This is equivalent to saying that the *Pauli exclusion principle holds for Fermi-Dirac particles*, since two particles may not occupy the same quantum state.

Inferences from experiments show that nucleons (both protons and neutrons), electrons (both $+$ and $-$), μ mesons, and neutrinos are described only by antisymmetric wave functions and therefore have Fermi-Dirac statistics. Direct experiments on the relative intensity of the successive lines from the rotational levels of diatomic homonuclear molecules show that H^1, Li^7, F^{19}, Na^{23}, P^{31}, Cl^{35} obey the Fermi-Dirac statistics. Generalizing these observations with the aid of Sec. c below, we can expect that *all nuclei of odd mass number have Fermi-Dirac statistics*.

b. Einstein-Bose Statistics. A system whose wave function is *symmetric* is said to follow Einstein-Bose statistics. Interchange of two identical Einstein-Bose particles leaves the wave function for their system unaltered. In the notation of Eq. (7.1), this condition is expressed analytically as

$$\psi(x_1, \ldots, x_j, \ldots, x_i, \ldots, x_n)$$
$$= \psi(x_1, \ldots, x_i, \ldots, x_j, \ldots, x_n) \quad (7.2)$$

Einstein-Bose particles do not follow the Pauli exclusion principle. *Two or more such particles may be in the same quantum state;* in fact, they may be said to prefer joint occupancy of identical position and spin coordinates.

It is known from collision experiments that photons and α particles obey Einstein-Bose statistics. From diatomic band spectra, H^2, He^4, C^{12}, N^{14}, O^{16}, S^{32} are known to obey Einstein-Bose statistics. Generalizing, we can expect that photons and *all nuclei of even mass number have Einstein-Bose statistics*. The π meson, which is associated with the binding forces between nucleons, is an Einstein-Bose particle.

c. Statistics, Mass Number, and Angular Momentum. The two generalizations regarding the statistics of nuclei of odd and even mass number are easily demonstrated, provided that all nuclear constituent particles have Fermi-Dirac statistics. Consider two identical nuclei located near points a and b and each composed of Z protons and N neutrons. (Reasons will be summarized in Chap. 8 for believing that neutrons and protons are the only constituents of atomic nuclei.) The wave function describing this system of two nuclei will include the coordinates of each of these $2(Z + N)$ particles. We can conceptually interchange the position of the two nuclei by individually exchanging the identical particle constituents between the two nuclei until all have been exchanged. Each such individual exchange of a particle from nucleus a with its twin from nucleus b will simply change the sign of the wave function. If the total number of particles $(Z + N)$ in each nucleus is odd, the complete interchange of the two nuclei through this step-by-step process will result only in changing the sign of the wave function. Hence any nucleus which contains an odd number of constituent particles will have Fermi-Dirac statistics. If protons and neutrons are the only constituent particles in nuclei, such a nucleus must also have an odd mass number. In an exactly similar manner, nuclei of even mass number, containing an even number of nucleons, will provide a step-by-step exchange having an even number of stages. Because interchange of two such nuclei leaves the wave function unaltered, these nuclei must have Einstein-Bose statistics.

That the neutron is an elementary particle obeying Fermi-Dirac statistics is seen most directly from the experimental fact (band spectra) that the deuteron obeys Einstein-Bose statistics and consists only of one proton and one neutron. Because the proton has Fermi-Dirac statistics, the neutron must also.

Nucleons obey Fermi-Dirac statistics and also have a spin of $\frac{1}{2}$. Pauli (P9) has shown, from the relativistically invariant wave equation, that elementary particles with any odd half-integer spin ($s = \frac{1}{2}, \frac{3}{2}, \ldots$) must necessarily obey the Fermi-Dirac statistics, and further that elementary particles with any arbitrary integral spin ($s = 0, 1, 2, \ldots$) must obey the Einstein-Bose statistics. This is a far-reaching, fundamental generalization.

Due to the conservation (vectorially) of angular momentum, all nuclei having an odd number of nucleons also have an odd half-integer total angular momentum ($\frac{1}{2}, \frac{3}{2}, \frac{5}{2}, \ldots$). Similarly, all nuclei having an even number of nucleons have even half-integer total angular momentum ($0, 1, 2, 3, \ldots$). In tabular form we have, then,

Mass number	Angular momentum	Statistics
Odd............	$I = \frac{1}{2}, \frac{3}{2}, \frac{5}{2}, \ldots$	Fermi-Dirac
Even............	$I = 0, 1, 2, \ldots$	Einstein-Bose

d. β Rays and Atomic Electrons Are Identical Particles. An ingenious and definitive application of statistics, through the Pauli exclusion principle, has been carried out by Goldhaber (G26) in order to prove the complete identity of the electrons arising in β decay and ordinary atomic electrons. If β rays differed in any property, such as spin, from atomic electrons, then the Pauli principle should permit the capture of slow β rays into bound atomic states ($K, L, M, \ldots$ shells) even though the corresponding states are filled with atomic electrons. Goldhaber has shown that no anomalous X rays are emitted when the soft β rays of C^{14} are absorbed in lead. Hence these β rays obey the Pauli principle, have spin $\frac{1}{2}$, and must be identical with atomic electrons.

e. Fermions and Bosons. Time often tends to compress the language in which physical ideas are expressed. Fermi-Dirac statistics is now frequently called simply *Fermi statistics*, and Einstein-Bose statistics is shortened to *Bose statistics*. Time has also brought spontaneous transformations in the corresponding adjectives, as defined by the identities

$$(\text{Fermi-Dirac particle}) \to (\text{Fermi particle}) \to \text{fermion}$$
$$(\text{Einstein-Bose particle}) \to (\text{Bose particle}) \to \text{boson}$$

Thus a π meson ($s = 0$) is a type of *boson*, while a μ meson ($s = \frac{1}{2}$) is a type of *fermion*. Nucleons, electrons, and neutrinos are fermions.

Problem

A variety of experimental evidence has shown that electrons ($e^{\pm}, \beta^{\pm}$) and nucleons (p,n) have Fermi-Dirac statistics, while photons (γ) have Einstein-Bose statistics. With this information, determine the spin and statistics for the neutrino (ν), μ meson (μ), and π meson (π), from the following observed processes:

(a) β decay of neutron, $n \to p + \beta^- + \nu$. (Half-period agrees with theory of allowed transitions on Gamow-Teller selection rules; hence β^- and ν probably emitted with parallel spins.)

(b) Decay of μ mesons, $\mu^{\pm} \to e^{\pm} + 2\nu$.

(c) Decay of charged π mesons, $\pi^{\pm} \to \mu^{\pm} + \nu$.

(d) Decay of neutral π mesons, $\pi^0 \to 2\gamma$.

CHAPTER 5

Atomic and Molecular Effects of Nuclear Moments, Parity, and Statistics

The influence of the added energy due to the nuclear moments and the influence of the statistics of the nucleus are felt in a variety of molecular and atomic phenomena. These effects give rise to a variety of experimental methods for the determination of the *absolute* values of nuclear ground-level moments.

1. *Extranuclear Effects of Nuclear Angular Momentum and Statistics*

a. Number of Hyperfine-structure Components. The main features of atomic spectra, including the so-called fine structure (which is associated with electron spin), have been described adequately in terms of the energy states of atomic electrons in a central electrostatic field, of strictly coulomb nature, due to the charge on the small massive atomic nucleus. When this nucleus is given the added property of quantized angular momentum I, we have seen that a magnetic dipole moment μ will also be associated with it, because of the motion of internal electric charges in the nucleus. The interaction of this small nuclear magnetic moment with the electrons not appearing in closed shells, particularly with a penetrating s electron in the group of valence electrons, gives rise to a multiplicity of slightly separated energy states for this electron. This closely spaced group of energy levels of the atom is called a *hyperfine-structure multiplet*. The energy separations in this multiplet can be measured in a number of cases by molecular-beam magnetic-resonance methods, which we shall discuss later. When such a penetrating electron undergoes a transition to a state having a much smaller coupling with the nuclear moment, the hyperfine structure (hfs) of the resulting optical transition may be particularly clear and readily resolved by means of a Fabry-Pérot interferometer.

The *magnitude* of the hyperfine-structure separations, and hence the possibility of observing them, depends on the magnitude of μ.

The *number* of hyperfine states depends only on I and on the electronic angular-momentum quantum number J. J and I couple, in a manner which is completely analogous to LS coupling in atoms, to produce the total angular-momentum quantum number F. Thus F can take on the series of integer-spaced values from $I + J$ to $|I - J|$. The total number of possible values of F is the *multiplicity*, or number, of hyperfine states and is $(2I + 1)$ when $I \leq J$, or $(2J + 1)$ when $I > J$. The corresponding vector diagram is shown in Fig. 1.1.

We see that the number of hyperfine components in an atomic term is generally different for different terms in the same atom. $J = 0$ is

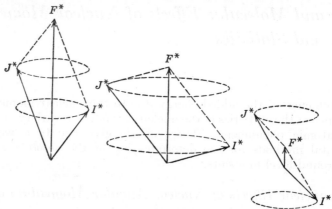

Fig. 1.1 Vector diagram illustrating the coupling of the resultant electronic angular momentum $J^* = \sqrt{J(J + 1)}$ with the nuclear angular momentum $I^* = \sqrt{I(I + 1)}$ to form the total angular momentum $F^* = \sqrt{F(F + 1)}$, about which both I^* and J^* precess (W39). The figure is drawn for the special case $J = \frac{3}{2}$, $I = 1$, which gives a hyperfine multiplet containing the three components $F = \frac{5}{2}, \frac{3}{2}, \frac{1}{2}$.

always single, but if J is at least as large as I then the nuclear moment uniquely determines the number of hyperfine levels as

$$\text{hyperfine multiplicity} = (2I + 1) \qquad \text{if } I \leq J \qquad (1.1)$$

b. Relative Separation of Hyperfine Levels. The magnetic field produced by the atomic electrons is of the order of 10^5 to 10^7 gauss at the position of the nucleus in the alkali atoms Li, Na, Rb, Cs, which have one valence electron. Although nuclei have very small magnetic dipole moments, the magnetic interaction energy between them and such huge fields is large enough to be measurable easily and constitutes the hyperfine-structure splitting of atomic levels.

For the energy of a dipole in a magnetic field we can write

$$W = \mu'_{I^*} H_{J^*} \cos (I^* J^*) \qquad (1.2)$$

where W = magnetic interaction energy
$\quad \mu'_{I^*}$ = nuclear magnetic dipole moment, Eq. (2.10), Chap. 4
$\quad H_{J^*}$ = magnetic field, parallel to J^*, produced by atomic electrons
$\quad (I^* J^*)$ = angle between I^* and J^*, Fig. 1.1
In general, H_{J^*} is proportional to J^*. From Eq. (2.15) of Chap. 4, we have $\mu'_{I^*} = g \mu_M I^*$, where $g \equiv \mu/I$ is the nuclear g factor. Then Eq. (1.2) becomes

$$W = aI^* J^* \cos (I^* J^*) \qquad (1.3)$$

where a is the so-called *interval factor* of hyperfine structure. The interval factor is proportional to g and involves constants of the J state of the atom which we will evaluate later, Eq. (1.10).

We see from Fig. 1.1 and the cosine law of trigonometry that

$$\cos (I^*J^*) = \frac{F^{*2} - I^{*2} - J^{*2}}{2I^*J^*} \tag{1.4}$$

Substituting in Eq. (1.3), the nuclear magnetic interaction energy of

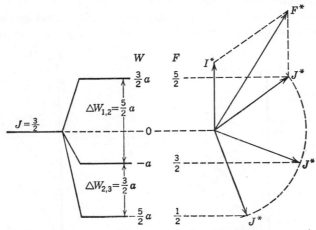

Fig. 1.2 Graphical illustration of the interval rule of hyperfine separations, based on Eq. (1.3), for the special case $I = 1$, $J = \frac{3}{2}$. The atomic level $J = \frac{3}{2}$ is split, because of the nuclear angular momentum I and an associated μ (assumed positive here), into $(2I + 1)$ hyperfine levels. These are characterized by the total-angular-momentum quantum numbers $F = \frac{5}{2}, \frac{3}{2}, \frac{1}{2}$ and are displaced in energy by the amounts W given by Eq. (1.6). The *relative separations* ΔW are $(5a/2):(3a/2) = 5:3$, as given by Eq. (1.7). (*Adapted from White, p. 355 of W39.*)

ordinary hyperfine structure can be rewritten as

$$W = \frac{a}{2} (F^{*2} - I^{*2} - J^{*2})$$

$$= \frac{a}{2} [F(F + 1) - I(I + 1) - J(J + 1)] \tag{1.5}$$

which is called the *interval rule* of hyperfine structure. Now, as F takes on its allowed values of $(I + J)$, $(I + J - 1)$, $(I + J - 2)$, . . . , $|I - J|$, the corresponding values of W become

for $F = (I + J)$, $W_1 = aIJ$
for $F = (I + J - 1)$, $W_2 = a[IJ - (I + J)]$ (1.6)
for $F = (I + J - 2)$, $W_3 = a[IJ - (I + J) - (I + J - 1)]$

The energy spacing between successive hyperfine levels is then

$$\begin{aligned}
\Delta W_{1,2} &= W_1 - W_2 = a(I + J) \\
\Delta W_{2,3} &= W_2 - W_3 = a(I + J - 1) \\
\Delta W_{3,4} &= W_3 - W_4 = a(I + J - 2)
\end{aligned} \tag{1.7}$$

Thus the *relative separation between successive hyperfine levels is proportional to the larger of the values of F for the two levels.*

For example, if the largest value of F happened to be, say, 5 (such as for $I = \frac{5}{2}$, $J = \frac{5}{2}$), then the relative separations of the hyperfine levels would be in the ratio $5:4:3:2:1$. In optical transitions to other atomic levels having a negligible hyperfine splitting, the relative separation of successive lines in the hyperfine-structure spectrum displays this same set of ratios, thus giving rise to the familiar "flag" pattern of optical hyperfine spectroscopy.

This *interval rule* of hyperfine structure is illustrated in Fig. 1.2. In many cases, an independent determination of I can be made from

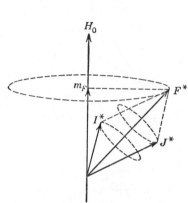

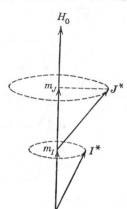

Fig. 1.3 Vector diagram of the Zeeman effect in hyperfine structure. In a *very weak* external magnetic field, I^* and J^* remain coupled to form F^*, about which both precess. F^* precesses about the direction of the external magnetic field H_0 and has $(2F + 1)$ magnetic substates $m_F = F$, $(F - 1)$, $(F - 2)$, . . . , $-F$.

Fig. 1.4 Vector diagram of the Paschen-Back effect in hyperfine structure. In a *weak* external magnetic field H_0, I^* and J^* become decoupled, and each precesses independently about H_0, with independent magnetic quantum numbers, m_I and m_J.

measurements of the relative separation of three or more hyperfine levels, J being inferred from other evidence. The absolute separations depend upon the interval factor a and hence are proportional to the nuclear g factor $g = \mu/I$.

c. Zeeman Effect in Hyperfine Structure. If an external magnetic field H_0 is now applied to the atom, the magnetic energy given by Eq. (1.2) changes, because the total magnetic field at the nucleus is now due to both the internal atomic field H_{J^*} and the applied field H_0. A variety of effects can occur, depending on the magnitude of H_0.

If H_0 is *very small*, then I^* and J^* will remain coupled to form F^*, while F^* will precess about the direction of H_0, as shown in Fig. 1.3. Then F^* can take up any of a series of possible orientations such that its projection in the direction of the external field is given by its magnetic quantum number m_F. Thus each hyperfine level F is broken up into $(2F + 1)$ magnetic substates, with magnetic quantum numbers $m_F = F$, $(F - 1)$, $(F - 2)$, . . . , $-F$. This is the *Zeeman effect* of hyperfine structure.

Paschen-Back Effect. As the external field H_0 is increased, the frequency of precession of F^* about H_0 increases. Because of the small absolute value of the nuclear magnetic dipole moment, the coupling between I^* and J^* is weak, and the frequency of their precession about F^* is not large. At sufficiently large external fields, the frequency of precession of F^* about H_0 exceeds that of I^* and J^* about F^*. Then I^* and J^* become decoupled, and each becomes space-quantized independently in the direction H_0, with independent magnetic quantum

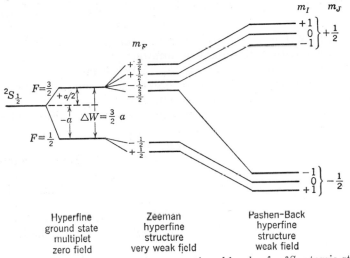

Fig. 1.5 Spectroscopic diagram of the magnetic sublevels of a $^2S_{\frac{1}{2}}$ atomic state, due to a nuclear angular momentum $I = 1$ with an associated positive magnetic dipole moment.

numbers m_I and m_J. This state of affairs is illustrated in Fig. 1.4 and is usually called the Paschen-Back effect of hyperfine structure.

Each level of a given m_J (which corresponds to the ordinary Zeeman effect of fine-structure spectra) is further split into a number of substates corresponding to the $(2I + 1)$ values of m_I, that is, $m_I = I$, $I - 1$, $I - 2$, . . . , $-I$. This number of substates $(2I + 1)$ is the same for all terms in an atom and thus constitutes a very direct method for determining the nuclear angular momentum, merely by counting up the number of line components. This elegant method was first used by Back and Goudsmit for determining $I = \frac{9}{2}$ for bismuth.

The shifts in the energy of the magnetic sublevels from very weak fields to weak fields are illustrated in Fig. 1.5 as they occur in optical spectroscopy.

Transitions between the magnetic sublevels follow the selection rules: $\Delta F = 0$, ± 1; $\Delta m_F = 0$, ± 1 in the Zeeman hyperfine-structure region, and $\Delta m_I = 0,\ \pm 1,$ or $\Delta m_J = 0,\ \pm 1,$ in the Paschen-Back hyperfine-structure region.

Breit-Rabi Formula. The region of intermediate fields (order of 1 to 1,000 gauss) has become of particular importance in recent years because the atomic-beam magnetic-resonance method (K12) makes it possible to measure the energy separation of the magnetic sublevels in the ground state of many atoms.   For atoms whose electronic angular momentum is $J = \frac{1}{2}$, the energy behavior in the Zeeman, Paschen-Back, and intermediate domains of hyperfine structure is given in closed form by a formula due to Breit and Rabi (B116, T8), which can be written in the form

$$W_{I \pm \frac{1}{2},\, m_F} = -\frac{a}{4} + m_F g \mu_M H \pm \frac{\Delta W}{2} \left(1 + \frac{4 m_F}{2I + 1}\, x + x^2 \right)^{\frac{1}{2}} \quad (1.8)$$

where a = hyperfine-structure interval factor, Eq. (1.3)

m_F = magnetic total quantum number

$g = \mu / I$ = nuclear g factor, Eq. (2.15), Chap. 4

$\mu_M = eh/4\pi Mc = 5.05 \times 10^{-24}$ erg/gauss = nuclear magneton

H = magnetic field intensity, gauss

$\Delta W = h\,\Delta\nu = a(I + \frac{1}{2})$ = hyperfine separation, Eqs. (1.7) and (1.11)

$x \equiv (g_J \mu_\beta - g\mu_M)H/\Delta W \simeq 2\mu_\beta H/\Delta W$

g_J = Landé atomic g factor = $+2(1 + \alpha/2\pi)$ Bohr magnetons for $^2S_{\frac{1}{2}}$ state

$\mu_\beta = eh/4\pi m_0 c = \mu_M(M/m_0) = 9.27 \times 10^{-21}$ erg/gauss = Bohr magneton

The $+$ is to be used for $F = I + J = I + \frac{1}{2}$, and the $-$ for $F = I - \frac{1}{2}$. The ordinary hyperfine splitting, at zero field, is given by the third term. With $H = 0$ and $x = 0$

$$W_{I+\frac{1}{2}} - W_{I-\frac{1}{2}} = \Delta W = a(I + \tfrac{1}{2}) \quad (1.9)$$

in agreement with Eq. (1.7).   Expansion of the square-root term in Eq. (1.8) will yield a term linear in x, which defines the Zeeman splitting and is the dominant field-dependent term when $x \ll 1$.   The higher terms in x, which become significant in "weak fields," $x < 1$, define the Paschen-Back effect.   If these higher terms are neglected in "very weak fields," $x \ll 1$, the Breit-Rabi formula then reduces to one for the Zeeman splitting of hyperfine structure.

The second term in Eq. (1.8), $m_F g\mu_M H$, represents a portion of the direct interaction energy between the nuclear magnetic dipole moment $\mu = gI$ and the external field. Because of the small value of the nuclear magneton μ_M, this energy is of the order of 1,000 times smaller than the Zeeman splitting. However, the high accuracy now attainable with the atomic-beam magnetic-resonance method permits Eq. (1.8) to be used to determine the hyperfine-structure separation ΔW of the ground state of certain atoms and both the magnitude and sign of the nuclear magnetic dipole moment (D9).

Note that x is a dimensionless parameter proportional to H. It is the ratio of two energies, namely, the magnetic energy of the whole atom in the external field and the zero-field hyperfine-structure splitting. Thus $x \ll 1$ defines magnetic splittings which are much less than the zero-field hyperfine structure. But this is just what we mean by the Zeeman domain. It is when the Zeeman splitting becomes of the same order of magnitude as the zero-field hyperfine structure (separation of levels of different F) that the onset of the Paschen-Back effect occurs. A "very

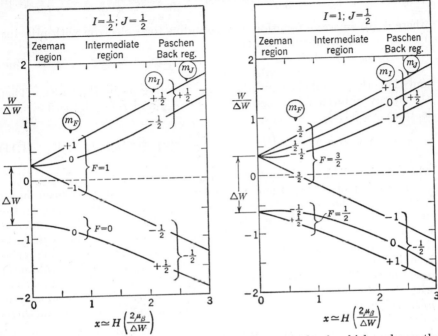

Fig. 1.6 The variation with magnetic field of the energy levels which make up the ground level $^2S_{\frac{1}{2}}$ of an atom with $J = \frac{1}{2}$ and $I = \frac{1}{2}$ (as in hydrogen, at left) or $I = 1$ (as in deuterium, at right). The nuclear magnetic dipole moment μ has been taken here as positive. The zero-field, very-weak-field (Zeeman hyperfine structure), and weak-field (Paschen-Back hyperfine structure) quantum numbers are marked on each curve. The curves show quantitatively the continuous variation of W with H, Eq. (1.8). The curves for $I = 1$ represent the same physical situation as shown in the conventional spectroscopic diagram of Fig. 1.5.

weak field" is thus defined as one for which $x \ll 1$, yielding the Zeeman levels. We see that the definition of a "very weak field" varies from atom to atom because of the different values of ΔW.

Figure 1.6 is a representative plot of the variation of the energy of the magnetic sublevels with applied field H, as given by Eq. (1.8).

Interval Factor of Hyperfine Structure. We noted in Eq. (1.3) that the hyperfine-structure interval factor a is proportional to $g = \mu/I$ and to the magnetic field which the atomic electrons produce at the position of the nucleus. It can be shown that this field is proportional to the average value of $1/r^3$, where r represents the electron's radial distance from an assumed "point" dipole located at the center of the nucleus. It is therefore very sensitive to the wave functions chosen to represent the probability density of an electron in the vicinity of the nucleus. Fermi (F31) and others (G38, C52) have shown that for a single s electron ($^2S_{\frac{1}{2}}$ state, $J = \frac{1}{2}$, as in the hydrogens and the alkali metals) the interval factor is

$$a = \frac{16\pi}{3} g\mu_M\mu_\beta|\psi_n(0)|^2 \simeq \frac{16}{3} g\mu_M\mu_\beta \frac{Z}{n^3 a_H^3} \tag{1.10}$$

where $\psi_n(0)$ = wave function at zero radius for s electron with principal quantum number n

$a_H = h^2/4\pi^2 e^2 m_0 = 0.529 \times 10^{-8}$ cm = radius of first Bohr orbit for hydrogen

and the other symbols have the same meaning as in Eq. (1.8). Then the energy difference between the $F = I + \frac{1}{2}$ and $I - \frac{1}{2}$ hyperfine levels is, from Eq. (1.7),

$$\Delta W \equiv h\,\Delta\nu = a\left(I + \frac{1}{2}\right) = \frac{8\pi}{3}\frac{\mu}{I}(2I + 1)\mu_M\mu_\beta|\psi_n(0)|^2 \tag{1.11}$$

where $\Delta\nu$ is called the *hyperfine-structure separation*.

A number of refined theoretical evaluations of $\psi_n(0)$ have been made, including, among other correction terms (K23, T8), the effect of the decrease of electron probability density at the center of the nucleus because of the finite volume of the nucleus and the assumed uniform distribution of charge in the nucleus (C52). With these correction terms included, the theoretical values of the hyperfine-structure interval factor a and of the hyperfine-structure separation $\Delta\nu$ are in excellent agreement with the very accurate experimental values of $\Delta\nu$, and independently of μ/I, which are obtainable by atomic-beam magnetic-resonance methods (T8).

Diamagnetic Correction. Whenever $\Delta\nu$ and μ/I are measured by a magnetic-resonance method, the added magnetic field intensity at the nucleus is slightly less than the externally applied field H as measured in the laboratory. This reduction is due to the diamagnetism of the atomic electrons. The induced field which is produced at the position of the nucleus by the induced Larmor precession of the atomic electrons is proportional to the external applied field H. Therefore the correction cannot be evaluated experimentally. Theoretical evaluations have been made by Lamb and others (L1, D37, R3), using various degrees of approximations for the electron wave functions. The Fermi-Thomas atom model leads to the simple relationship (L1)

$$g_{\text{observed}} = g_{\text{actual}}(1 - 3.19 \times 10^{-5}Z^{\frac{4}{3}}) \tag{1.12}$$

where the term in $Z^{\frac{4}{3}}$ is the ratio of the induced field at the nucleus to the external applied field. Hartree and Hartree-Fock wave functions have been used to obtain more accurate values for individual elements. The correction runs from 0.0018 per cent for atomic hydrogen to 1.16 per cent for uranium. The corrected values of g and μ are always larger than the raw observed values.

d. Relative Intensity of Hyperfine Lines. The probability of exciting each of the magnetic substates m_F is assumed, with good experimental justification, to be the same, i.e., the several magnetic substates are said to have the same *statistical weight*. If the externally applied magnetic field is reduced toward zero, the energy differences due to the magnetic interaction vanish. Therefore at zero magnetic field all the $(2F + 1)$ magnetic substates are superposed. Then, in the absence of an external field, each ordinary hyperfine state has a relative *statistical weight* of $(2F + 1)$.

In the hyperfine multiplet at zero field each state is characterized by a different statistical weight $(2F + 1)$. Hyperfine-structure lines in optical spectroscopy originate from transitions between two hyperfine multiplets (with the additional selection rule $\Delta F = 0, \pm 1$ allowed; $0 \to 0$ forbidden), the statistical weight of each level being determined by its F value. Hence the *relative intensity* of the lines in a hyperfine spectrum depends on the angular momenta J and I and not on the nuclear magnetic dipole moment. The relative-intensity relationships are analogous to those of fine-structure multiplets (p. 206 of W39).

e. Alternating Intensity in Diatomic Molecular Band Spectra. The relative intensity of each spectral line in the rotational band spectrum of a homonuclear diatomic molecule (for example, H^1H^1, $C^{12}C^{12}$, $N^{14}N^{14}$, $O^{16}O^{16}$, etc.) is determined by the statistical weight of the states involved in the transition.

Consider a homonuclear diatomic molecule. If I is the total intrinsic-angular-momentum quantum number of each nucleus, then the total nuclear-angular-momentum quantum number T of the diatomic molecule can have any of the values $T = 2I, 2I - 1, \ldots, 0$. It can be shown that the values $2I, 2I - 2, \ldots$ of T belong to one of the two types of rotational states (symmetric or antisymmetric in the space coordinates of the nuclei) and that the values $2I - 1, 2I - 3, \ldots$ belong to the other type. Each state with total nuclear angular momentum T consists of $2T + 1$ magnetic substates which coincide in the absence of an external magnetic field. Each of these substates has an equal chance of occurrence, so that the frequency of occurrence, or *statistical weight*, of the T state is $2T + 1$ times that of a state with $T = 0$. If the statistical weights $2T + 1$ for all the $2I, 2I - 2, \ldots$ values of T are added and compared with the total statistical weights for all the $2I - 1, 2I - 3,$ $\ldots$ values of T, it is found that the sums are in the ratio $(I + 1)/I$.

Now transitions between these two types of rotational states (symmetric to antisymmetric or vice versa) are almost completely forbidden (the mean life for such a transition is of the order of months or years), and transitions between states of the same type (e.g., symmetric) can occur only when accompanied by an electronic transition. Hence, homonuclear diatomic molecules do not have any pure rotational (or rotation-vibrational) spectra. Alternate lines in the rotational fine structure of the electronic spectra arise from transitions between states belonging to one of the symmetry types, depending on the electronic states involved. For example, the first, third, fifth, . . . lines may be from the symmetric rotational states, and the second, fourth, sixth, . . . lines from the anti-symmetric states. Accordingly, successive lines have an intensity ratio of $(I + 1)/I$. This is the ratio of symmetric lines to antisymmetric lines for nuclei obeying the Einstein-Bose statistics (for which I is 0, 1, 2, . . .). The ratio of the relative intensity of the symmetric lines to the antisymmetric lines for nuclei obeying the Fermi-Dirac statistics (for which I is $\frac{1}{2}$, $\frac{3}{2}$, . . .) is $I/(I + 1)$.

Thus, regardless of which type of statistics is obeyed by the nuclei in a homonuclear diatomic molecule, the average ratio of the intensity of the more intense to the less intense family of lines is always

$$\frac{I + 1}{I} \tag{1.13}$$

It is important to notice that the total nuclear angular momentum determines uniquely the relative intensity of successive lines in the rotational band spectrum of molecules composed of two identical atoms. Neither the pure rotational nor the rotation-vibrational bands are emitted, but the effect can be observed in either the electronic bands or the Raman spectra. A nuclear angular momentum of zero leads to an infinite intensity ratio for successive lines, i.e., alternate lines are missing.

The nuclear angular momentum has been obtained from band-spectrum studies for a number of nuclei, including H^1, H^2, He^4, Li^7, C^{12}, C^{13}, N^{14}, N^{15}, O^{16}, F^{19}, Na^{23}, P^{31}, S^{32}, Cl^{35}. A convenient review of the theory of alternating intensities of band spectra, together with illustrative data for F^{19}, has been compiled by Brown and Elliott (B133).

f. Specific Heat of Diatomic Gases. Two forms of the hydrogen molecule exist. In *orthohydrogen* the spins of the two protons are parallel, while in *parahydrogen* the proton spins are antiparallel. The statistical weighting of rotational states and recognition of the absence of transitions between the two types of hydrogen under ordinary conditions were necessary in order to explain the specific heat of hydrogen at very low temperatures (D24). A proton spin of $\frac{1}{2}$ accounts for the observed specific heat.

The ortho and para forms exist for all diatomic molecules whose atoms do not have zero spin. The general considerations applied to hydrogen are also applicable to other molecules.

Problems

1. Expand the Breit-Rabi formula, for the Zeeman separations in hyperfine structure, into a power series in H, as far as quadratic terms. Discuss the physical significance of each term. To the same approximation, obtain a formula for the energy of transition between $m_F = -F$ and $m_F = -F + 1$ in the $F = I + J$ levels. Discuss the dependence of this transition energy on μ and I and especially whether it depends on the sign of μ.

2. Calculate and plot the energies $W/|\Delta W|$ vs. magnetic field ($x = 0$ to 3) for the Zeeman effect of hyperfine structure for the case of *negative* nuclear magnetic dipole moment μ.   Take $J = \frac{1}{2}$, $I = \frac{1}{2}$ and 1.   Compare the result with the curves of Fig. 1.6 for positive μ, and state the general consequences of the sign of μ.

3. Calculate the hyperfine splitting $\Delta \nu$ expected for the ground state of the hydrogen atom, in units of (a) cycles per second, (b) cm^{-1}, and (c) $h \, \Delta \nu$ in ev. *Ans.*: 1,420 megacycles/sec; 0.0473 cm^{-1}; 6×10^{-6} ev.

4. Show that the "center of gravity" of a spectral line is unaltered by its hyperfine splitting in zero field, if each hyperfine-structure level is given a weight of $(2F + 1)$; i.e.,

$$\Sigma(2F + 1)W = 0$$

Verify this relationship for the hyperfine structure in hydrogen and deuterium (Fig. 1.6).

5. In Fig. 1.6, for $I = \frac{1}{2}$, identify the following two transitions:

$$\nu_1 = (F = 1, \, m_F = 0) \leftrightarrow (F = 1, \, m_F = -1),$$
and
$$\nu_2 = (F = 1, \, m_F = 1) \leftrightarrow (F = 0, \, m_F = 0)$$

Show from the Breit-Rabi formula that, if the frequencies ν_1 and ν_2 are measured in the same magnetic field H, then the hyperfine separation $\Delta \nu$ for zero field is given directly by $\Delta \nu = \nu_2 - \nu_1$.

2. *Extranuclear Effects of Nuclear Magnetic Dipole Moment*

a. Absolute Separation of Hyperfine-structure Components.   We have seen that the nuclear angular momentum I determines the number of hyperfine levels and also their relative separations.   The absolute magnitude of these separations, however, is proportional to the *interval factor a* of Eqs. (1.3) and (1.10) and therefore depends upon both the magnitude and sign of the nuclear magnetic moment and on factors related to the electronic states and the probability of the electron being near the nucleus.   Also, the effects of perturbations from other electronic states, as well as the presence of a nuclear electric quadrupole moment, may alter a.

To minimize these perturbations, spectroscopic observations are usually made on states having large hyperfine structure, as these are least perturbed.   In spite of the uncertainty in computing μ from observations of the optical hyperfine structure, many of our values of nuclear magnetic moment come from hyperfine-structure separations.

It must be emphasized that the absence of detectable optical hyperfine structure in some atoms may be due to the smallness of μ and cannot be taken as definite evidence for zero mechanical moment.

b. Absolute Separation of Atomic-beam Components.   The number of components into which an atomic beam is split by a magnetic field depends upon the nuclear mechanical moment.   The separation of these $(2I + 1)(2J + 1)$ components, however, is determined by the magnitude of the field gradient and the hyperfine-structure separation factor a for the *normal state* of the neutral atom, hence by the nuclear magnetic moment.

By the atomic-beam deflection method, Kellogg, Rabi, and Zacharias (K14) measured in 1936 the hyperfine-structure separation $\Delta \nu$ for the ground state of the hydrogen atom H^1, from which they obtained

$$\mu_p = 2.85 \pm 0.15$$

nuclear magnetons for the proton. The essential agreement between this value and the directly measured value of $\mu_p = 2.46 \pm 0.08$ obtained from the deflection of orthohydrogen molecules in an inhomogeneous field by Stern and his collaborators (Chap. 4, Sec. 3) gave the first *truly direct confirmation of the origin of atomic hyperfine structure in nuclear magnetic moments.*

From accurate measurements of the deflection patterns, Rabi and his coworkers (R1, K14, M47) have succeeded in obtaining the magnitude and sign of the nuclear magnetic moment of a number of atoms, some of whose hyperfine-structure separations are too small to be measured by optical methods. The atomic-beam deflection method has been used successfully on atoms having a single valence electron, i.e., the hydrogens and the alkalis H^1, H^2, Li, Na, K, Rb, and Cs. It has generally been superseded by the magnetic-resonance method as applied to both atomic and molecular beams.

c. Larmor Precession Frequency. Larmor showed in 1900 from classical electrodynamics that any gyromagnetic system which has angular momentum and a collinear magnetic dipole moment will be set into precessional motion when placed in a uniform magnetic field.

If the absolute angular-momentum vector I' makes an angle β with the direction of the magnetic field H, the Larmor precession is such that I' describes the surface of a cone having H as an axis, with the frequency ν which is given by

$$2\pi\nu = \gamma H = \frac{\mu'}{I'} H \tag{2.1}$$

where ν = frequency, cycles/second
H = magnetic field intensity, gauss
γ = absolute gyromagnetic ratio, gauss^{-1} sec^{-1}
μ' = absolute magnetic dipole moment, ergs/gauss
I' = absolute angular momentum, erg-sec

The kinetic energy added to the system by the Larmor precession is

$$W = \mu'H \cos \beta \tag{2.2}$$

The absolute value of the nuclear magnetic dipole moment which is collinear with the nuclear angular momentum is given by Eq. (2.10), Chap. 4. Substituting in Eq. (2.1) we have for the Larmor frequency of a nucleus

$$\nu = \frac{1}{2\pi} H \frac{\mu'_{I^*}}{(h/2\pi)I^*} = \frac{1}{2\pi} H \frac{g(eh/4\pi Mc)I^*}{(h/2\pi)I^*} = gH \frac{e}{4\pi Mc} \tag{2.3}$$

where $g = \mu/I$ is the usual nuclear g factor as defined in Eq. (2.15), Chap. 4. Substituting numerical values, we obtain

$$\frac{\nu}{H} = 762g \qquad \text{cycles/(sec)(gauss)} \tag{2.4}$$

Thus for nuclei the Larmor frequencies will be of the order of 10^3H, or about a megacycle per second for $H = 1,000$ gauss.

The kinetic energy of the Larmor precession is easily obtained by eliminating $\mu'H$ between Eqs. (2.1) and (2.2) and is

$$W = 2\pi\nu I' \cos \beta = h\nu I^* \cos \beta = m_I h\nu \qquad (2.5)$$

where $m_I = I^* \cos \beta$ is the magnetic quantum number for the projection of I^* on H in the usual vector model (Fig. 1.1, Chap. 4).

We see that quantization of the classical Larmor theorem leads to a precession energy which can have only a series of $(2I + 1)$ discrete values, as m_I takes on the integer-spaced values from $+I$ to $-I$. We note the very interesting facts that the Larmor precession frequency ν is independent of m_I, so that the precession energies have a uniform spacing equal to $h\nu$. Thus the Larmor frequency ν, which such a precessing system would radiate classically, is exactly equal to the Bohr frequency condition for the emission or absorption of electromagnetic radiation in transitions between adjacent levels.

d. Radio-frequency Spectroscopy. If nuclear magnets can be subjected to radiation at their Larmor frequency while they are in a constant magnetic field, a nucleus in a lower magnetic energy state may absorb a quantum of energy from the radiation field and make a transition to its next higher magnetic level. It turns out that this can be accomplished and detected experimentally in several different ways and that the resonances for absorption of energy at the Larmor frequency are sharp.

Indeed, transitions between molecular levels as well as atomic levels can be induced in this way. The Larmor precession frequency of the effective gyromagnetic system has only to match the Bohr frequency condition, namely, that $h\nu$ be the energy separation between the levels concerned in the transition.

The frequency range which is involved can be obtained from Eq. (2.3), which shows that for electronic systems

$$\frac{\nu}{H} \sim \frac{\mu_\beta}{h} \sim 1 \text{ megacycle/(sec)(gauss)} \qquad (2.6)$$

and for nuclear systems

$$\frac{\nu}{H} \sim \frac{\mu_M}{h} \sim 1 \text{ kilocycle/(sec)(gauss)} \qquad (2.7)$$

At ordinary laboratory magnetic field intensities of the order of 1 to 1,000 gauss, these frequencies lie in the radio-frequency domain. Studies of nuclear, atomic, and molecular properties by Larmor resonance methods have therefore come to be characterized as *radio-frequency spectroscopy.*

Three principal experimental arrangements are in current use: (1) molecular-beam magnetic-resonance method (Rabi et al., 1938), (2) the nuclear paramagnetic-resonance absorption method (Purcell et al., 1945), and (3) the nuclear resonance induction method (Bloch et al., 1945).

Molecular-beam Magnetic-resonance Method. Magnetic-resonance methods and radio-frequency spectroscopy got their start (R2, K52) with the method of "molecular beams," a generic term which now includes beams of neutral atoms as well as of neutral molecules. This technique has evolved into one of the most versatile, sensitive, and accurate methods for studying the hyperfine structure and Zeeman levels of atoms and molecules.

A schematic representation of one modern form of molecular-beam apparatus is shown in Fig. 2.1. With it, I and μ were first measured directly for the nuclear ground levels of the radioactive nuclides Na^{22}, Cs^{135}, and Cs^{137} (D9), and I, μ, and Q were measured for both the stable chlorine isotopes Cl^{35} and Cl^{37} (D8). A beam of neutral atoms diffuses at thermal velocities from the oven and passes successively through three magnetic fields. The first and last are inhomogeneous fields, whose

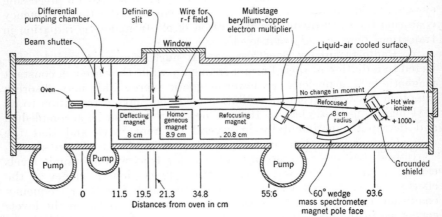

Fig. 2.1 Schematic diagram of a modern molecular-beam apparatus capable of determining I, μ, and Q on very small samples of material. (*From L. Davis, Jr., Massachusetts Institute of Technology, Research Laboratory of Electronics Technical Report 88,* 1948.)

purpose is to deflect and then refocus the beam. As used in this experiment, the final refocusing field was arranged to refocus only those atoms which had undergone a Zeeman transition involving a change of sign of their magnetic moment while passing through the centrally located homogeneous magnetic field H. In this homogeneous field H, the Larmor precession frequency ν can be determined as the frequency f of a small additional radio-frequency field, directed normal to H, which produces the sought-for Zeeman transition, and thus permits the final focusing magnet to bring the beam onto the detecting elements. At $f = \nu$, a sharp resonance peak in the transmitted beam is observed, and thus the Larmor frequency is determined.

The detecting elements consist of a narrow hot tungsten ribbon, on which surface ionization of the originally neutral atoms takes place. The ions thus formed are then sorted for mass by passing them through a single-focusing mass spectrometer.   Finally, the accelerated ions impinge on the first plate of a Be-Cu multistage electron multiplier, where they are detected as "counts" in the output circuit.

The sensitivity is so high that only 4×10^{-10} mole of Na^{22} was used up in obtaining the final measurements of the nuclear moments I and μ of the 3-yr radionuclide Na^{22}.   It is believed that measurements on other radionuclides can be accomplished with as little as 10^{13} atoms, which should now permit studies of a great many shorter-lived radioactive species.

With genetically similar molecular-beam apparatus, a number of nuclear, atomic, and molecular constants have been determined.   The details of this work will be found in *Physical Review* and in various summaries and reviews (H12, K12, R3).

Nuclear Paramagnetic-resonance Absorption Method.   Nuclear g-factors can be determined in bulk solid, liquid, or gaseous samples by two closely related methods: "nuclear resonance absorption" and "nuclear resonance induction."   The nuclear resonance absorption method stems from the work of Purcell, Torrey, and Pound (P37) who first demonstrated the attenuation of 29.8 megacycles/sec electromagnetic radiation by 850 cm³ of paraffin in a radio-frequency resonant cavity, when an external magnetic field of 7,100 gauss was impressed on the paraffin at right angles to the magnetic vector of the electromagnetic field.   These conditions correspond to the Larmor precession frequency of the proton.

It can be shown that the absorption of radiation by the protons is largely canceled by stimulated emission.   The net absorption effect is a small one and is attributable to the Boltzmann distribution, which favors a slightly greater population in the lower-energy levels.   As an illustrative numerical case (P1), for 1 million hydrogen atoms in thermal equilibrium at room temperature, and in a field of 20,000 gauss, an average of only seven more protons are in the lower magnetic state than in the upper state.   This slight asymmetry accounts for the net nuclear paramagnetism.   By utilizing a radio-frequency bridge circuit, and modulating the magnetic field at a low frequency, the nuclear resonance absorption can be clearly and very precisely measured.

The nuclear resonance absorption method (and also the nuclear induction method) each require moderately large samples, running at present in the neighborhood of $\sim 10^{18}$ nuclei.   The methods are therefore applicable to stable or very long-lived nuclides.   In order to eliminate the effects of electric quadrupole interactions, and to minimize the interactions of nuclei with their neighbors, these methods have so far been confined to nuclei with $I = \frac{1}{2}$ (which have no observable quadrupole moment) or to cubic crystals.

The techniques and results have been summarized in several excellent review articles (P1, P28), and further details may be found in the current periodical literature.

Nuclear Resonance Induction Method.   The "nuclear resonance induction" method developed by Bloch and coworkers (B73, B75) also is applicable to matter of ordinary density.   As in the nuclear resonance absorption method, a small sample (~ 1 cm³) is placed in a strong uniform magnetic field H, about which the nuclear magnets precess at the Larmor frequency ν which is proportional to their nuclear g factor $g = \mu/I$.

A radio-frequency field, whose frequency is f, is applied with its magnetic vector at right angles to H. At the resonant frequency $f = \nu$, changes occur in the orientation of the nuclear moments, corresponding to transitions between the magnetic substates, in accord with Eq. (2.5). In the resonance *absorption* method, these changes are observed by their reaction on the radio-frequency driving circuit. In the resonance *induction* method, these changes are observed directly by the electromotive force which they induce in a receiving coil, which is placed with its axis perpendicular to the plane containing H and the driving field f. The success of this very direct detection method gives a sense of immediate physical reality to the concept of space quantization of the Larmor precession of nuclei.

The thermal relaxation process, by which energy is exchanged between the nuclear magnets and the "lattice" of thermally vibrating atoms and molecules, has received extensive theoretical and experimental study (B73, B75, B79). The so-called *spin-lattice relaxation time*, as observed in both the nuclear resonance absorption and resonance induction methods, ranges from the order of 10^{-5} sec to several hours for various materials.

Values of the Larmor frequency for many nuclides relative to that of the proton in the same magnetic field can be obtained by the nuclear resonance absorption method, and by the closely related nuclear resonance induction method, with a precision of the order of 0.02 per cent. The corresponding relative values of the nuclear g factors $g = \mu/I$ and the nuclear magnetic dipole moments μ are not as accurately known, because of uncertainties in the corrections for the diamagnetism of the atomic electrons, Eq. (1.12).

For details, the reader will be well rewarded by the study of the original papers of Bloch (B73) and his colleagues (B75) and of later descriptions of routine determinations of I and μ, such as those of Tl, Sn, Cd, and Pb (P35).

e. Conversion of Parahydrogen and Orthodeuterium. Under ordinary conditions there are no transitions between the ortho and para states of either hydrogen or deuterium. Moreover, relatively pure parahydrogen and relatively pure orthodeuterium can be prepared by adsorption on charcoal at liquid-air temperatures. In these pure substances transitions leading to the equilibrium mixture of ortho and para materials can be induced by an inhomogeneous magnetic field. Such a field is supplied by the presence of the paramagnetic oxygen molecule.

The rate of conversion of para- to orthohydrogen and ortho- to para-deuterium depends only on the equilibrium concentrations and the mechanical and magnetic moments of the proton and deuteron. By observing the relative speeds of conversion for parahydrogen and ortho-deuterium, the ratio of the nuclear magnetic moments of proton and deuteron is found (F8) to be $\mu_p/\mu_d = 3.96 \pm 0.11$. This observation probably contains some unknown source of error, as the ratio obtained is definitely higher than is obtained by magnetic-resonance methods $\mu_p/\mu_d = 2.793/0.857 = 3.26$.

Problems

1. Derive the Larmor precession frequency and kinetic energy from classical electrodynamics.

2. Consider the hyperfine-structure separation $\Delta\nu$ as an energy difference due to Larmor precession of the nucleus in the magnetic field H_{J*} produced by the atomic electrons. Evaluate and plot H_{J*} in gauss against Z for hydrogen and the alkali metals.

Nuclide	$\Delta\nu$, megacycles/sec	μ, nuclear magnetons	I	Principal quantum number n of valence electron
H^1	1,420.5	2.793	$\frac{1}{2}$	1
H^2	327.4	0.857	1	1
Li^6	228.2	0.822	1	2
Li^7	803.5	3.256	$\frac{3}{2}$	2
Na^{23}	1,771.6	2.217	$\frac{3}{2}$	3
K^{39}	461.7	0.391	$\frac{3}{2}$	4
Rb^{85}	3,035.7	1.353	$\frac{5}{2}$	5
Rb^{87}	6,834	2.750	$\frac{3}{2}$	5
Cs^{133}	9,193	2.577	$\frac{7}{2}$	6

NOTE: Values of $\Delta\nu$ are from P. Kusch and H. Taub, *Phys. Rev.*, **75**: 1477 (1949).

Ans.: hydrogen, 0.289×10^6 gauss; . . . ; cesium, 3.54×10^6 gauss.

3. *Extranuclear Effects of Nuclear Electric Quadrupole Moment*

a. Deviations from the Interval Rule for Hyperfine-structure Separations. The relative separations of hyperfine-structure components are predicted by the interval rule of Eq. (1.5), which is derived from an energy term proportional to $\cos(I*J*)$. Two types of deviations from the interval rule have been observed. The first is due to perturbations in the individual hyperfine-structure levels when the energy difference between the parent term and an adjacent electronic state is comparable with the hyperfine-structure separations.

Observations by Schüler and Schmidt of the hyperfine structure of europium (S18) first revealed deviations which were different for the two isotopes Eu^{151} ($I = \frac{5}{2}$) and Eu^{153} ($I = \frac{5}{2}$) and therefore could not be explained as perturbations. However, the introduction of an additional interaction term which depends on $\cos^2(I*J*)$ satisfactorily accounts for these and many subsequent observations on other elements. The physical interpretation of this energy term implies, through Eq. (5.7), Chap. 4, that the deviations are due to a nonspherical distribution of positive charge in the nucleus, having the characteristics of a nuclear electric quadrupole moment.

The observed quadrupole deviations from the interval rule give the product of the nuclear electric quadrupole moment and the average charge distribution of the electronic states involved. Where these electronic charge distributions are not known accurately, the value determined for the nuclear quadrupole moment will reflect this uncertainty. Accordingly, much more reliance is to be placed on the *ratio* of the quadrupole moments for two isotopes of the same element, as Eu[151] and Eu[153], than on the absolute value for either of them. The electronic charge distribution, being the same in both isotopes, does not affect the value for the ratio of the quadrupole moments.

Only certain atomic states are affected by the nuclear electric quadrupole moment. Electronic states having $J = \frac{1}{2}$ have no quadrupole effect. Thus s and $p_{\frac{1}{2}}$ electrons do not show the quadrupole deviation in the

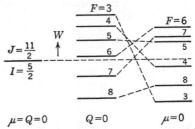

Fig. 3.1 Hyperfine splitting of an atomic energy level $J = \frac{11}{2}$, if $I = \frac{5}{2}$ (e.g., in U[235]). Left, the single level, in the absence of magnetic dipole μ and electric quadrupole moment Q. Center, normal hyperfine structure, with μ finite and Q absent. Right, pure electric quadrupole splitting. [*From McNally* (M38).]

hyperfine-structure spacings. Other states should be influenced approximately in proportion to their fine-structure doublet separation, leading to large deviations for the low $p_{\frac{3}{2}}$ and d electrons of the heavy elements.

According to Casimir (C6), the ordinary interval law of hyperfine structure, Eq. (1.5), is to be replaced by

$$W = \frac{a}{2}C + \frac{b}{8}\frac{3C(C + 1) - 4IJ(I + 1)(J + 1)}{IJ(2I - 1)(2J - 1)} \qquad (3.1)$$

where $C \equiv F(F + 1) - I(I + 1) - J(J + 1)$

a = hyperfine-structure interval factor, Eqs. (1.3) and (1.10)

b = electric quadrupole factor, proportional to Q

The effects of the electric quadrupole moment Q compared with those of the magnetic dipole moment μ are illustrated in Fig. 3.1.

An example of the determination of I, μ, and Q from optical hyperfine structure is shown in Fig. 3.2.

Deviations from the magnetic levels expected in the Zeeman effect of hyperfine structure (Fig. 1.6) can also be interpreted in terms of the nuclear electric quadrupole moment (F28, D8). In this way, the deuteron was first shown (K13) to have a quadrupole moment

$$Q = +0.273 \times 10^{-26} \text{ cm}^2$$

b. Hyperfine Structure of Molecular Rotational Spectra. In polyatomic molecules, the energy of interaction between the nuclear electric quadrupole moment and the gradient of the molecular electric field at the nucleus gives rise to a hyperfine structure in transitions between molecular rotational levels. This interaction energy depends on the relative orientation of the nuclear angular momentum I and the angular momentum of molecule rotation. The relative intensity and relative

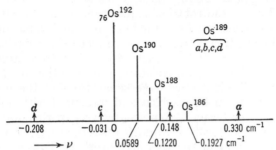

Fig. 3.2 Hyperfine structure and isotope shift, as measured with a Fabry-Pérot etalon, in the λ4,260 line of singly ionized osmium. The lines due to the even-Z even-N isotopes, 186, 188, 190, 192, are single, corresponding to nuclear angular momenta of $I = 0$, and display an approximately constant isotope shift of about 0.03 cm^{-1} per mass unit. The line due to Os^{189} is split into four hyperfine components, marked a, b, c, d, whose relative spacings show deviations from the interval rule. For Os^{189}, Murakawa and Suwa (M75) interpret their measurements of this and other osmium lines as: I: multiplicity $= (2I + 1) = 4$, $I = \frac{3}{2}$; μ: from absolute separations of a, b, c, d, $\mu = 0.7 \pm 0.1$; Q: from deviations from the interval rule, $Q = +(2.0 \pm 0.8) \times 10^{-24}$ cm^2.

spacing of the lines depend on I and provide an unambiguous measure of I.

The absolute values of the energy differences in the hyperfine-structure pattern are the product of a function of the quantum numbers of molecular rotation and of nuclear angular momentum, multiplied by the energy of the "*quadrupole coupling.*" The "quadrupole coupling" is defined in different ways by different investigators, and caution must be exercised in comparing their reported results. Helpful comparisons of the conventions used by different investigators have been compiled by Feld (F25) and by Bardeen and Townes (B10). The "quadrupole coupling" may usually be interpreted as $[eQ(\partial^2 U/\partial z^2)]$, where e is the electronic charge, Q is the quadrupole moment defined as in Eq. (5.6), Chap. 4, and $\partial^2 U/\partial z^2$ is the second derivative of the electric potential U due to *all* the electrons in the molecule, taken in the direction of the symmetry axis of the molecule.

Microwave Absorption Spectroscopy. For heavy molecules, the separation of successive rotational energy levels corresponds to frequencies of the order of 10^4 megacycles/sec, and hence wavelengths of the order of 1 cm. These frequencies lie in the so-called "microwave" domain where enormous advances in technique have been accomplished as a consequence of radar developments. Thus techniques are available which provide both accurate frequency measurements and high resolution, and these have been applied in the now rapidly expanding field of "microwave spectroscopy."

The pure rotation spectra of ICl^{35} and ICl^{37} were the first to be investigated by the methods of microwave spectroscopy. In ICl^{35} the transition between the molecular-rotation quantum numbers 3 and 4 has a frequency of about 27,200 megacycles/sec. The exact frequency depends not only on the rotational quantum numbers but also on the nuclear angular momentum I and the nuclear electric quadrupole moment Q. Thus each transition between any two successive rotational quantum numbers, e.g., $3 \rightarrow 4$ in ICl^{35}, is actually split into a large number of identifiable lines which give quantitative information on I and Q (but not μ). These individual lines have separations of the order of 10 to 100 megacycles and can be resolved and measured with an accuracy of 0.1 megacycle/sec or better. Representative experimental results, and their interpretation in terms of I and Q for N^{14}, O^{18}, $S^{33,34}$, $Cl^{35,37}$, $Br^{79,81}$, and I^{127}, will be found in the thorough work of Townes, Holden, and Merritt (T27).

These measurements are accomplished by observing the absorption of microwaves, in ICl, as a function of frequency. Microwaves of about 1-cm wavelength are passed through a waveguide 16 ft long which contains ICl vapor and acts as a 16-ft absorption cell. The minimum detectable absorption lines have absorption coefficients of about 4×10^{-7} cm^{-1}, and the corresponding differences of the order of 0.02 per cent in over-all transmission can be determined by the use of calibrated attenuators or by a balanced waveguide system. The techniques and results of microwave spectroscopy have been reviewed by Gordy and coworkers (G34, G37).

One of the outstanding achievements by this method was the discovery from the microwave-absorption spectrum of boron carbonyl, H_3BCO, that $I = 3$ for the ground level of B^{10} (G36, W19), whereas the value $I = 1$ had long been erroneously assumed for B^{10} by analogy with the only other stable nuclides which contain equal numbers of protons and neutrons, namely, H^2, Li^6, and N^{14}.

In a small number of cases it has been possible to place the absorption cell in a magnetic field of the order of 2,000 gauss and thus to observe Zeeman, or magnetic, splitting, superimposed on the electric quadrupole hyperfine structure of rotational transitions. In this way it is possible to determine some nuclear *magnetic dipole moments* μ by microwave-absorption methods (G35), but the accuracy is not competitive with the magnetic-resonance methods of radio-frequency spectroscopy.

Because isotopic molecules, such as ICl^{35} and ICl^{37}, have an appreciable difference in rotational moment of inertia, there is a relatively large frequency separation between analogous groups of lines from the two similar molecules containing different isotopes of the atom in question. The microwave-absorption data possess such high resolution and accuracy that they permit the determination of atomic *mass ratios* (for example, Cl^{35}/Cl^{37}) and *isotopic abundance ratios* with an accuracy comparable with that obtained from mass spectroscopy (L35).

Molecular-beam Electric-resonance Method.   The electric moments of molecules can be measured also by a molecular-beam resonance method, in which all the fields are electric instead of magnetic.   These electrical resonance methods of molecular-beam spectroscopy were first applied to the fluorides of the alkali metals CsF (H71, T28) and RbF (H72).   The nuclear electric quadrupole moment Q can thus be measured, as well as the molecular electric dipole moment, moment of inertia, and internuclear distance.

Problem

Show that electronic states having $J = 0$ or $\frac{1}{2}$ have no quadrupole effect, even if the nuclear quadrupole moment is finite.

CHAPTER 6

Effects of Nuclear Moments and Parity on Nuclear Transitions

Differences of angular momentum and parity between nuclear levels produce profound effects on the relative probability of various competing nuclear transitions. Studies of these transitions provide the experimental basis for the determination of *relative* values of nuclear angular momentum and parity. These purely nuclear effects are especially useful for evaluating excited levels in nuclei, as well as some ground levels.

The total energy, total angular momentum, and parity of any isolated set of nuclear particles are always conserved in all nuclear interactions and transformations. Any changes of nuclear angular momentum and parity which may occur in a nucleus must therefore be found associated with an emitted or absorbed particle.

The probability of any type of nuclear transformation depends on a number of factors, the best understood of which are: (1) the energy available, (2) the vector difference $\mathbf{I}_A - \mathbf{I}_B$ between the angular momentum of the initial and final levels, (3) the relative parity of the initial and final levels, (4) the charge Ze of the nucleus and ze of any emitted particle, and (5) the nuclear radius.

From measurements of the relative *probability* of various nuclear transformations, quantitative inferences can often be made concerning the difference in angular momentum and parity between two nuclear levels. The *angular distribution* of reaction products, and of successive nuclear radiations, is also markedly dependent upon angular-momentum and parity considerations. In these two general ways *relative* values of nuclear angular momentum and parity can be determined. Conversion to absolute values usually is made by reference to ground-level values of I and parity, which have been determined through the measurement of hyperfine structure or other extranuclear effects. In these ways, nuclear transformations provide a means of studying the moments of short-lived excited levels, which are generally inaccessible to methods of radio-frequency spectroscopy, band spectroscopy, and microwave absorption.

Nuclear transformations of substantially every type are impaired if the change in angular momentum is large and are easiest and most probable for transformations in which $I_A = I_B$ or $I_B \pm 1$.

The vector change in angular momentum $\mathbf{I}_A - \mathbf{I}_B$ can have any absolute value from $|I_A - I_B|$ to $|I_A + I_B|$, depending on the relative spatial orientation of the angular momenta $\mathbf{I}_A$ and $\mathbf{I}_B$ of the initial and final levels. Because the smallest value of $\mathbf{I}_A - \mathbf{I}_B$ is usually the most probable, most nuclear transformations involve a change in angular momentum which is simply the minimum possible value, namely,

$$\Delta I \equiv |I_A - I_B|$$

The principal exceptions to this general rule occur when $I_A = I_B$ in the case of γ-ray emission and will be summarized in Table 4.2.

1. *Conservation of Parity and Angular Momentum*

A few of the reactions of Li^7, when bombarded by protons, will serve as examples of the effectiveness of parity conservation in prohibiting some nuclear reactions, even though an abundance of energy is available.

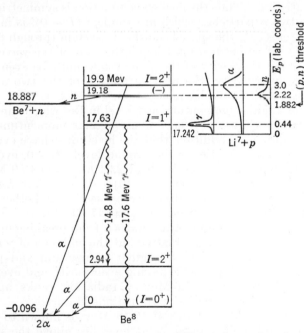

Fig. 1.1 Some of the known energy levels of Be^8 and reactions involved in their formation and dissociation (A10).

Figure 1.1 depicts a few of the known (A10) resonance reactions, $\mathrm{Li}^7(p,\alpha)\mathrm{He}^4$, $\mathrm{Li}^7(p,n)\mathrm{Be}^7$, and $\mathrm{Li}^7(p,\gamma)\mathrm{Be}^8$, followed by the fission of Be^8 into two α particles, $\mathrm{Be}^8 \to \mathrm{He}^4 + \mathrm{He}^4$. The scales and manner of plotting are the same as those used in Chap. 3, Figs. 4.1 and 4.8. In addition, the dependence of reaction cross section on proton bombarding energy E_p is shown above the ground level of ($\mathrm{Li}^7 + p$). The numerical values of E_p are shown, for convenience, in laboratory coordinates, alongside the vertical energy scale which, of course, is actually plotted in center-of-mass coordinates.

We note particularly here the sharp resonance at $E_p = 441$ kev, whose measured width is only 12 kev. The excited level of the compound nucleus Be^8, formed of $(Li^7 + p)$ at this particular bombarding energy, has an excitation energy of 17.63 Mev above the ground level of Be^8. The ground level of Be^8 disintegrates spontaneously into two He^4 nuclei with a half-period of less than 10^{-14} sec and a decay energy of about 96 kev. Yet when Be^8 is in its excited level at 17.63 Mev it is completely unable to disintegrate into two He^4 nuclei. This experimental fact can be understood and accepted only in terms of the quantum-mechanical ideas of parity and statistics.

The dissociation of Be^8 into two α particles gives a final system composed only of two identical α particles. In the wave function of the final system, the interchange of these two identical particles must leave the sign of the wave function unaltered, because α particles have Einstein-Bose statistics. Thus the final wave function is symmetric. Interchanging the two <u>α particles, which are spinless ($I = 0$)</u>, is in this case equivalent to reflecting the spatial coordinate system through the origin, and hence this reflection also must leave the sign of the wave function unchanged. Thus the parity of the final system must be even.

To possess even parity, the relative motion of the two α particles must have even orbital angular momentum, $l = 0, 2, 4, \ldots$. Due to conservation of angular momentum, any level in Be^8 which can break up into two α particles must also have even angular momentum. Parity conservation requires, in addition, that the level must have even parity. Hence only such levels in Be^8 as the ground level ($I = 0$, even parity; denoted $I = 0^+$) and the excited levels at 2.94 Mev and 19.9 Mev [both $I = 2^+$ from independent evidence (A10)] can dissociate into two α particles. Evidence from the scattering cross section and other considerations shows (W10) that the excited level at 17.63 Mev is $I = 1^+$. Its odd angular momentum completely excludes it from breaking up into two α particles. It has no other alternative but the emission of γ radiation, which can carry changes of both angular momentum and parity, in order to arrive at some lower level having even parity and even angular momentum. The resulting 17.6-Mev γ radiation ranks among the highest known energies for radiative transitions in nuclei.

Another resonance level of Be^8, at 19.18 Mev, is known to have odd parity and does not emit α rays. This level lies above the separation energy for a neutron; hence it can and does emit a neutron in accord with the reaction $Li^7(p,n)Be^7$.

2. *Penetration of Nuclear Barrier*

We have seen in Appendix C, Fig. 10 and Eq. (103), and Chap. 2, Eq. (5.79), that the mutual orbital angular momentum l of two nuclear particles corresponds to an energy which is not available for penetration of a coulomb barrier and is known as the *centrifugal barrier*, $(h/2\pi)^2 l(l + 1)/2Mr^2$. Thus barrier transmission is simplest, and reaction cross sections are largest, when the formation of the compound nucleus and its subsequent dissociation both correspond to s-wave interactions ($l = 0$).

For α-ray disintegrations in the heavy elements, numerical substitution in Eq. (103) of Appendix C shows that the transition probability varies about as $e^{-0.1l(l+1)}$. Thus even an angular-momentum change of

$$l = \Delta I = 5$$

produces only about a 20-fold reduction in the α-ray decay constant. This feeble effect is completely swamped by the much larger effects due to slight variations in nuclear radius and by shell effects relating to the probability of formation of the α ray (P15). Hence the fine structure which is present in some α-ray spectra (ThC, ThC', RaC, RaC', etc.) cannot be used for quantitative evaluation of the angular momenta of excited levels of the nuclei involved, as was once thought possible. Nevertheless, Gamow's interpretation of the fine structure of α-ray spectra in terms of changes in nuclear angular momentum was of great historical value. It led him later to initiate analogous considerations regarding β-ray transformations, where nuclear angular momentum plays a predominating role.

In the lighter elements, whose coulomb barriers are lower, the centrifugal barrier can exert more profound effects.

3. Lifetime in β Decay

a. Allowed and Forbidden Transitions. The concept of allowed and forbidden nuclear transitions first came to prominence in the empirical correlation known as the Sargent diagram, Fig. 3.1, between the half-period and the energy of β decay. In 1933 only the β-ray emitters of the uranium, thorium, and actinium families were known. These were shown by Sargent (S4) to fall into two groups. For a given energy ($E_{\max}$ of the β-ray spectrum), one group has about 100 times the half-period of the other group. As a specific illustration that some parameter besides disintegration energy plays a predominant role in the lifetime for β decay, we may compare the energy and lifetime of RaB and RaE. These have

Parent nuclide	$E_{\max}$, Mev	Half-period	Class
RaB ($= {}_{82}Pb^{214}$)	0.7	27 min	Allowed
RaE ($= {}_{83}Bi^{210}$)	1.17	5.0 d	Forbidden

Even though the RaE decay is more energetic, its half-period is more than 200 times that of RaB. In 1934, in the light of Fermi's newly proposed theory of β decay, Gamow (G4) proposed that nuclear angular momentum was responsible for the existence of the two groups. He suggested that the shorter-lived group are "*permitted*," or "*allowed*," transitions, with a selection rule ($\Delta I = 0$, no), while the longer-lived group are "*not-permitted*," or "*forbidden*," transitions, with ($\Delta I = \pm 1$, yes).

With the discovery of artificial radioactivity in 1934 and the subsequent study of several hundred β-ray emitters, the situation is known to be much more complicated than it seemed in the beginning. In particular, the clear separation into two groups has vanished. Newly found radionuclides are scattered over the entire area of the Sargent diagram, beneath an upper envelope, or ceiling, on the decay constant λ for a particular value of E_{max}. The forbidden transitions are subdivided into first-forbidden, second-forbidden, third-forbidden, etc., and each of these classes is further subdivided into "favored" and "unfavored" transitions, in consonance with Wigner's (W47, K39) theory of supermultiplets. A

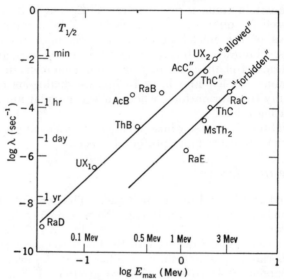

Fig. 3.1 Original form of the Sargent diagram for some of the naturally occurring β-ray emitters. The maximum energy of the β-ray spectrum E_{max} is plotted against the partial decay constant λ for the principal branch of the β decay. The half-period $T_{\frac{1}{2}} = 0.693/\lambda$ is also shown. [*From Sargent* (S4).]

vast amount of experimental and theoretical work has enlightened the topic of β decay, but some fundamental problems remain unsolved.

b. Comparative Half-periods in β Decay. Two forms of empirical classification of β emitters have emerged so far. One is based on the relationships between E_{max} and the half-period, and the other on the shape of the β-ray spectrum. Both classifications are in acceptable agreement with present theories of the lifetime and shape of forbidden β-ray spectra (Chap. 17).

The classification by "comparative half-periods," or "*ft value*," was introduced by Konopinski (K37) in connection with his theory of forbidden β-ray transitions. It permits comparison of the observed half-periods "*t*" after due allowance is made through the function "*f*" for differences in nuclear charge Z and the energy of the β transition.

From the theory of *allowed* β spectra, there emerges the relationship

$$\frac{0.693}{t} = \lambda = \frac{|P|^2}{\tau_0} f(Z, W_0) \tag{3.1}$$

where t = half-period in seconds
$|P|^2$ = nuclear matrix element for transition
$W_0 = (E_{max} + m_0c^2)/m_0c^2 = $ *total* energy of β transition
Z = atomic number of *decay* product
τ_0 = universal time constant determined by electron and neutrino interaction with nucleons

The somewhat complicated analytical form of the so-called "Fermi function" $f(Z, W_0)$ is discussed in Chap. 17. This function $f(Z, W_0)$ is very strongly dependent upon W_0, varying approximately as W_0^5. Graphs (F22) and a useful nomogram (M61, H61) of $f(Z, W_0)$ are now available in the literature. The nuclear matrix element $|P|^2$ can be visualized physically (Chap. 17) as representing the degree of overlap of the wave functions of the transforming nucleon ($n \rightarrow p + \beta^- + \nu$, or $p \rightarrow n + \beta^+ + \nu$) in its initial and final state. $|P|^2$ is of the order of unity for allowed transitions.

Rewriting Eq. (3.1) in the form

$$ft = \frac{\text{universal constants}}{|P|^2} \tag{3.2}$$

shows that all allowed β-ray transitions should have the same ft value, except for minor variations in $|P|^2$. This is found to be the case. Indeed, the transitions between the mirror isobars ($Z = N \pm 1$) constitute a special class of superallowed, or *allowed and favored, transitions*, for which ft lies between 1,000 and 5,000 sec (K39). The so-called *allowed and unfavored* transitions have larger ft values, mostly in the domain of 5,000 to 500,000 sec. Remembering that, even for allowed transitions, f and t individually vary by factors of the order of 10^8 ($t = 0.8$ sec for He^6; $t = 12$ yr for H^3), the constancy of ft within a factor of about 100 represents an exceptionally good accomplishment for the theory. In view of the large numbers involved in the ft values, it is often more convenient to use only the exponents, i.e., the "log ft" value, as is done in Table 3.1. The *first-forbidden* transitions lie generally around 10^6 to 10^8 sec, or log ft = 6 to 8.

c. Selection Rules for β Decay. In the theory of forbidden β decay (K39, K41, K37) the transition probability can be expanded in a rapidly convergent series of terms characterized by successive integral values for the angular momentum of the electron-neutrino field with respect to the emitting nucleus. The largest term represents the allowed transitions; the successively smaller terms represent the forbidden transitions. The selection rules follow from inspection of the character of each term. The ultimate nature of the nucleon-electron-neutrino interaction (Y3) is not yet perfectly understood. Comparisons between experiment and various theoretical formulations at present narrow the choices to two possible sets of selection rules, known as "Fermi selection rules" and the "Gamow-Teller (G-T) selection rules."

The Gamow-Teller rules (G8) emerge when the intrinsic spin of the transforming nucleon is introduced into the Hamiltonian which describes the transformation. This couples the electron-neutrino spin directly to the nucleonic spin. The Fermi rules (F34) emerge when this is omitted. In allowed transitions, Fermi rules imply that the electron-neutrino pairs are emitted with antiparallel spins (singlet state), while in Gamow-Teller rules they are emitted with parallel spins (triplet state) in the nonrelativistic limit (p. 679 of B68). At present, Gamow-Teller rules appear to describe most cases of β decay, especially among all but the lightest elements, but there are a few instances where Fermi rules or a mixture of Fermi and Gamow-Teller rules are required to describe the observations (B66, S33) (C^{10} and O^{14}, allowed and favored, $I = 0 \to 0$, no, transitions). These selection rules are summarized in Table 3.1.

TABLE 3.1. SELECTION RULES FOR β DECAY, ACCORDING TO THE CLASSIFICATION BY KONOPINSKI (K37)

For classification on the basis of the "order" Δl of the transition, see Blatt and Weisskopf (p. 705 of B68).

Class of transition	Parity change	ΔI		Approximate log ft values (M27)
		Gamow-Teller (tensor and axial vector)	Fermi (scalar and polar vector)	
Allowed	No	0, ±1 (but not $0 \to 0$)	0	3–6
First-forbidden	Yes	0, ±1, ±2 (not $0 \to 0$, $\frac{1}{2} \to \frac{1}{2}$, $0 \leftrightarrow 1$)	0, ±1 (not $0 \to 0$)	6–10
Second-forbidden	No	±2, ±3; $0 \to 0$ (not $0 \leftrightarrow 2$)	±1, ±2, (not $0 \leftrightarrow 1$)	>10
nth-forbidden n odd n even	Yes No	±n, ±($n + 1$)	±($n - 1$), ±n	

The Gamow-Teller rules are characteristic of a tensor or an axial-vector interaction, while the Fermi rules represent a scalar or an ordinary vector interaction between the transforming nucleon and the electron-neutrino field (K37, L5, S43).

It will be noted that the selection rule on a parity change in the transforming nucleus is the same for either type of selection rules and alternates in the successive degrees of forbiddenness. This corresponds to the emission of the electron-neutrino pair with successively larger values of orbital angular momentum.

d. Shell Structure. From measurements of the β-ray energy and half-period, log ft values are now available for over 140 odd-A radionuclides and over 100 even-A nuclides. These provide empirical evi-

dence on the degree of forbiddenness for the various transitions.   With
the help of the selection rules, this evidence can be interpreted in terms
of the parity and angular-momentum differences between the parent and
daughter nuclides.   Many absolute reference values are available from

TABLE 3.2. ILLUSTRATIVE ALLOWED AND FORBIDDEN β TRANSFORMATIONS

Correlation of β-decay log ft values with assignments of odd-nucleon states on the
single-particle shell model with jj coupling, and with Gamow-Teller selection rules
(selected from M27, K39, and K18a compilations for odd-A nuclides).   The nucleon
states marked * have been determined from Schmidt group classification, following
direct measurement of I and μ.   When the odd nucleon is a neutron, the neutron
number is given as a subscript beneath the mass number of the nuclide.   The energy-
level diagram and decay scheme for the two transitions of Cs^{137} are given in Chap. 6,
Fig. 7.1.

β transition		E_{max}, Mev	Log ft	Odd-nucleon states			Parity change of the odd nucleon
				Initial $\rightarrow$ final	ΔI	Δl	
Super-allowed	$_0n_1^1 \xrightarrow{\beta^-} {}_1H^1$	0.78	3.1	$s_{\frac{1}{2}}* \rightarrow s_{\frac{1}{2}}*$	0	0	No
	$_9F^{17} \xrightarrow{\beta^+} {}_8O_9^{17}$	1.72	3.4	$d_{\frac{5}{2}} \rightarrow d_{\frac{5}{2}}*$	0	0	No
Allowed unfavored	$_{16}S_{19}^{35} \xrightarrow{\beta^-} {}_{17}Cl^{35}$	0.17	5.0	$d_{\frac{3}{2}} \rightarrow d_{\frac{3}{2}}*$	0	0	No
	$_{32}Ge_{43}^{75} \xrightarrow{\beta^-} {}_{33}As^{75}$	1.1	5.0	$p_{\frac{1}{2}} \rightarrow p_{\frac{3}{2}}*$	1	0	No
l-forbidden	$_{28}Ni_{37}^{65} \xrightarrow{\beta^-} {}_{29}Cu^{65}$	2.10	6.6	$f_{\frac{5}{2}} \rightarrow p_{\frac{3}{2}}*$	1	2	No
First-forbidden	$_{56}Ba_{83}^{139} \xrightarrow{\beta^-} {}_{57}La^{139}$	2.27	6.7	$f_{\frac{7}{2}} \rightarrow g_{\frac{7}{2}}*$	0	1	Yes
	$_{36}Kr_{51}^{87} \xrightarrow{\beta^-} {}_{37}Rb^{87}$	3.6	7.0	$d_{\frac{5}{2}} \rightarrow p_{\frac{3}{2}}*$	1	1	Yes
	$_{38}Sr_{51}^{89} \xrightarrow{\beta^-} {}_{39}Y^{89}$	1.46	8.5	$d_{\frac{5}{2}} \rightarrow p_{\frac{1}{2}}*$	2	1	Yes
	$_{55}Cs^{137} \xrightarrow{\beta^-} {}_{56}Ba_{81}^{137}$	0.51	9.6	$g_{\frac{7}{2}}* \rightarrow h_{\frac{11}{2}}$	2	1	Yes
Second-forbidden	$_{55}Cs^{137} \xrightarrow{\beta^-} {}_{56}Ba_{81}^{137}$	1.17	12.2	$g_{\frac{7}{2}}* \rightarrow d_{\frac{3}{2}}*$	2	2	No
Third-forbidden	$_{37}Rb^{87} \xrightarrow{\beta^-} {}_{38}Sr_{49}^{87}$	0.27	17.6	$p_{\frac{3}{2}}* \rightarrow g_{\frac{9}{2}}*$	3	3	Yes
Fourth-forbidden	$_{49}In^{115} \xrightarrow{\beta^-} {}_{50}Sn_{65}^{115}$	0.63	23.2	$g_{\frac{9}{2}}* \rightarrow s_{\frac{1}{2}}*$	4	4	No

the directly measured values of I and μ, which can be interpreted in
terms of total angular momentum I, orbital angular momentum l of the
odd nucleon, and parity, with the help of the Schmidt groups and the
single-particle model (Chap. 4, Figs. 4.1 and 4.2).

The results of these multilateral correlations (M27, N23, K39) have been most encouraging. They have greatly strengthened the case for the single-particle model, with *jj* coupling, and closed shells at 2, 8, (14), 20, (28), 50, 82, and 126 nucleons.

The careful study of a few examples will give the flavor of the correlations. Table 3.2 contains well-verified cases in which the log *ft* values are quite reliable and the nuclear I, l, and parity of the odd nucleon have been determined for either the initial or final state (or both). The other

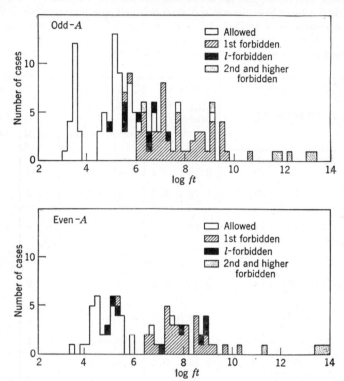

Fig. 3.2 Frequency histograms of log *ft* values for odd-*A* and even-*A* radionuclides. [*Compiled by D. R. Wiles* (W52).]

state in the transition is that predicted by the shell model with *jj* coupling (Chap. 11).

In all these cases Gamow-Teller selection rules agree with the differential assignment between the initial and final states. Fermi selection rules would agree in some cases and not in others. The preference is clearly in favor of Gamow-Teller selection rules in these cases and in most, but not all, other cases.

In the superallowed group, the initial and final odd nucleons always belong to the same shell. In the allowed but unfavored group, the odd nucleon is usually in a different shell before and after the transition. The overlap of initial and final nucleon wave functions therefore cannot be as complete as for the superallowed group, and the matrix element $|P|^2$ is of the order of 0.01.

Note that in the allowed but unfavored transitions there is no distinction between the transition probability, as measured by $\log ft$, for $\Delta I = 0$ and for $\Delta I = 1$. The controlling condition appears to be $\Delta l = 0$, that is, zero orbital momentum change in the transforming nucleus, hence also no parity change, and zero orbital angular momentum for the β-ray electron-neutrino pair with respect to the emitting nucleus. Analogously, the first-forbidden transitions all have $\Delta l = 1$, second-forbidden, $\Delta l = 2$, etc.

The so-called *l-forbidden* transitions (N23, M27, K39) constitute at present a small subgroup, closely related to the allowed unfavored transitions, and obeying the Gamow-Teller selection rules on ΔI for allowed transitions but having $\Delta l = 2$ on the single-particle shell model. These *l*-forbidden transitions ($\Delta I = 1$, no, $\Delta l = 2$) have $\log ft \simeq 5$ to 9, hence half-periods which are usually somewhat longer than would be expected for ordinary allowed transitions ($\Delta I = 0$ or 1, no, $\Delta l = 0$).

Figure 3.2 collects the presently evaluated $\log ft$ values (M27, N23) in a frequency histogram. This figure is equivalent to sighting up a modern Sargent diagram in the direction of the line of allowed transitions, so that the scale of energy disappears. The spike at $\log ft = 3.5 \pm 0.2$ contains the superallowed transitions, with no over-all trend from H^3 to $Ti.^{43}$ The allowed but unfavored transitions are mainly in the band $\log ft = 5.0 \pm 0.3$, with very few values above 6. The first-forbidden transitions are mostly above $\log ft = 6$ and tend to cluster between 6 and 10.

4. *Radiative Transitions in Nuclei*

In the early days, even the origin of γ radiation was a mystery. It was first pointed out by C. D. Ellis and by Lise Meitner in 1922 that the complex γ rays from some radioactive substances, such as RaB, exhibit simple additive rules, $h\nu_1 + h\nu_2 = h\nu_3$, and hence that γ rays represent radiative transitions between quantized energy levels in nuclei.

After the development of the quantum theory of radiation, it became possible to classify γ radiations into electric and magnetic multipole radiations of various orders and to associate these with the difference in angular momentum and parity between the two states involved in the transition.

The quantum theory of radiation borrows the classical representation of a radiation source as an oscillating electric or magnetic moment. The complicated spatial distribution of the corresponding electric charges and currents is represented by spherical harmonics of order 1, 2, 3, . . . , and the names dipole, quadrupole, octupole, . . . are applied both to these equivalent nuclear moments and to the resulting radiation. Convergence of the expansion (p. 248 of S11) is assured by the fact that the wavelength of γ radiation ($\lambdabar = \lambda/2\pi \sim 200 \times 10^{-13}$ cm for 1 Mev) is generally much larger than the dimensions of the nucleus in which the radiation originates, that is $(R/\lambdabar) \ll 1$.

a. Angular Momentum and Multipole Order of γ Radiation. It can be shown (p. 802 of B68) that the angular momentum of γ radiation with respect to an emitting (or absorbing) system is determined by the same type of quantum numbers l, m as the angular momentum of a material particle. For photons, l can have only nonzero values. Thus the angular momentum of a quantum of light is $\hbar \sqrt{l(l+1)}$, and its projection on any arbitrary axis is $m\hbar$ with maximum component $l\hbar$. The probability of emission (or absorption) decreases rapidly as l increases, roughly as $(R/\lambda)^{2l}$.

Angular momentum is conserved between the γ ray and the emitting (or absorbing) system, so that l is the vector difference between the angular momentum of the initial and final nuclear levels, or

$$l = |\mathbf{I}_A - \mathbf{I}_B| \tag{4.1}$$

Thus, between levels I_A and I_B, l can have any nonzero integer value given by

$$\Delta I \equiv |I_A - I_B| \leq l \leq I_A + I_B \tag{4.2}$$

The magnetic quantum number m of the radiation is the difference between the magnetic-angular-momentum quantum numbers of the levels I_A and I_B, or

$$m = m_B - m_A \tag{4.3}$$

In practice, l is usually confined by relative transition probabilities to $l = \Delta I$. In exceptional circumstances, a measurable fraction of the transitions may have $l = \Delta I + 1$, in competition with $l = \Delta I$. If either I_A or I_B is 0 and the other is nonzero, then there is only one possible value, namely, $l = \Delta I$. This simplifying circumstance is met, for example, in all transitions to the ground level of even-Z even-N nuclei.

The *multipole order* of γ radiation is 2^l; thus $l = 1$ is called *dipole* radiation, $l = 2$ is *quadrupole*, etc.

One of the consequences of the transverse nature of an electromagnetic wave is that it contains no $l = 0$ multipole. Hence, from conservation of angular momentum as represented in Eq. (4.2), γ-ray transitions between two levels $I_A = I_B = 0$ are absolutely excluded.

b. Electric and Magnetic Multipoles. Parity of γ Radiation. For each multipole order two different waves are possible. These are called the "electric" and "magnetic" multipole radiations. For each value of l, a quantum of electric and one of magnetic radiation have the same angular momentum but differing parity. *The parity of an electric multipole is the same as that of a material particle having the same l.* Thus any electric multipole has even parity when l is even and odd parity when l is odd. *Magnetic* multipole radiation has the opposite parity, i.e., odd parity when l is even and even parity when l is odd. This can be summarized as

$$\begin{array}{l} \text{parity of electric multipole} = \quad (-1)^l \\ \text{parity of magnetic multipole} = -(-1)^l \end{array} \tag{4.4}$$

where $+1$ means even parity and -1 denotes odd parity.

c. Selection Rules for γ-Ray Emission (or Absorption). The probability of any transition from the state Ψ_A to Ψ_B in a system of particles is proportional to the integral $\int \Psi_A q \Psi_B^* \, d\tau$, where Ψ_B^* is the complex conjugate of Ψ_B, $d\tau$ is a volume element, and q depends on the nature of the transition. Thus, for electric dipole transitions, q is the effective electric dipole moment $\Sigma e_i x_i$ and changes sign on reflection, i.e., when x becomes $-x$. For electric quadrupole transitions, q is the effective electric quadrupole moment, symbolically $\Sigma e_i x_i^2$, and does not change sign with reflection of the particles in the origin of coordinates.

The value of a definite integral cannot possibly change by an alteration of the system of coordinates. Hence, if for electric dipole radiation the integral $\int \Psi_A (\Sigma e_i x_i) \Psi_B^* \, d\tau$ changes sign with reflection, it can have no other value than zero. Consequently if Ψ_A represents a state having even parity, Ψ_B (and Ψ_B^*) must represent a state of odd parity, or vice versa, to allow a finite transition probability. That is, the parity of the

TABLE 4.1. SELECTION RULES AND SYMBOLS FOR γ RADIATION

Classification	Symbol	l	Parity change in nucleus
Electric dipole	E1	1	Yes
Magnetic dipole	M1	1	No
Electric quadrupole	E2	2	No
Magnetic quadrupole	M2	2	Yes
Electric octupole	E3	3	Yes
Magnetic octupole	M3	3	No
Electric 2^l-pole	El	l	No for l even Yes for l odd
Magnetic 2^l-pole	Ml	l	Yes for l even No for l odd

final state must be opposite to that of the initial state for emission of electric dipole radiation. Conservation of parity in the system as a whole (i.e., nucleus and quantum of radiation) then requires that for electric dipole radiation the photon must have odd parity with respect to the system it leaves (or the system it enters in an absorption or excitation process).

Similar considerations for the emission of electric quadrupole and magnetic dipole radiation show that for each of these radiations to be possible the parity of the final state of the nucleus must be the same as that of the initial state.

The selection rules for emission (or absorption) of γ-ray photons are those combinations of l and parity which give nonvanishing values of the transition probability. These are summarized in Table 4.1.

d. γ-Ray Emission Probability. Although we saw in Chap. 4 that the "static" electromagnetic moments of nuclei are generally confined to a magnetic dipole and an electric quadrupole, this restriction does not apply to the "dynamic" electromagnetic moments which are involved in the γ-ray transitions.   These electromagnetic effects have their origin in the motions of individual protons, in the intrinsic magnetic moment of neutrons and protons, and probably also in an "exchange current" which would be associated with the exchange of charge between neutrons and protons in connection with the exchange forces between nucleons.

The absolute values of the theoretically predicted transition probabilities are proportional to these electromagnetic multipole moments, and the estimation of these moments depends strongly on the nuclear model which is assumed in the calculation.   The most recent of these theories, and one which agrees with experimental results in some areas where earlier theories failed (G27), was developed in 1951 by Weisskopf and is based on the single-particle shell model of nuclei.   In the single-particle theory, a γ-ray transition is associated with a change in the quantum numbers of only one nucleon.

Electric Multipoles.   Weisskopf (W23, B68) has shown that for electric multipole transitions of order 2^l, the partial mean life τ_{el} (reciprocal of the partial decay constant) for the emission of a γ ray whose energy is $h\nu$ is given very approximately (perhaps within a factor of 10 to 100) as

$$\frac{1}{\tau_{el}} = S \frac{2\pi\nu}{137} \left(\frac{R}{\lambda}\right)^{2l} \tag{4.5}$$

where $R = R_0 A^{\frac{1}{3}}$ is the nuclear radius and S is a statistical factor given by

$$S \equiv \frac{2(l+1)}{l[1 \times 3 \times 5 \cdots (2l+1)]^2} \left(\frac{3}{l+3}\right)^2 \tag{4.6}$$

From Eq. (4.6) the numerical values of $1/S$ are as follows:

l	1	2	3	4	5
$1/S$	4	2.1×10^2	1.6×10^4	1.9×10^6	3.2×10^8

Note that $1/S$ increases by roughly 10^2 for an increase of l by unity. The energy W of the nuclear transition can be expressed alternatively in terms of the frequency ν or the rationalized wavelength λ of the radiation as

$$\lambda = 2\pi\lambda = \frac{c}{\nu} = \frac{ch}{W} = \frac{(h/m_0 c)}{(W/m_0 c^2)} = \frac{1{,}240 \times 10^{-13} \text{ cm}}{W \text{ (in Mev)}} \tag{4.7}$$

Equation (4.5) refers to a transition in which a proton jumps from an initial state $I_1 = j_1 = l + \frac{1}{2}$ to a final state $I_2 = j_2 = \frac{1}{2}(l_2 = 0)$, and it is regarded by Weisskopf as representing a *minimum value of the theoretical mean life* of the level against γ-ray emission.

Equation (4.5) can be put into the convenient equivalent form

$$\tau_{el} = \frac{1}{S} \left[\frac{137}{(W/m_0 c^2)}\right]^{2l+1} \left[\frac{r_0}{R_0 A^{\frac{1}{3}}}\right]^{2l} \frac{\hbar}{m_0 c^2} \tag{4.8}$$

$$\simeq \left[\frac{70}{W \text{ (in Mev)}}\right]^{2l+1} \left[\frac{2}{A^{\frac{1}{3}}}\right]^{2l} \frac{1.29 \times 10^{-21}}{S} \quad \text{sec} \tag{4.9}$$

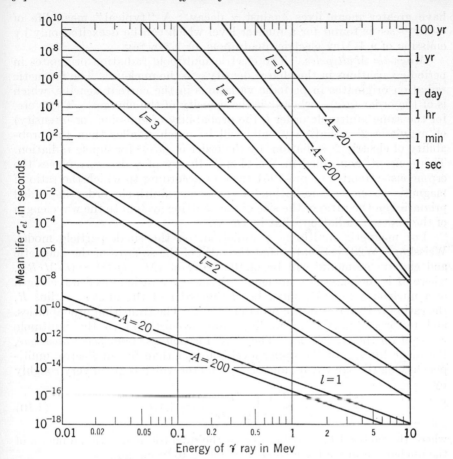

Fig. 4.1 The minimum estimated partial mean life τ_{el} of nuclear levels for deexcitation by the emission of electric multipole γ radiation, of order 2^l, on the single-particle model, Eq. (4.9).   For each value of l, the lower curve gives τ_{el} for $A = 200$, while the upper curve is for $A = 20$.   For electric multipole transitions, the values plotted here are not remarkably different from the predictions of the liquid-drop model, as plotted by Moon (M54).   For magnetic multipoles, see Eq. (4.10).

where the ratio of the classical electron radius

$$r_0 = \left(\frac{e^2}{m_0 c^2}\right) = 2.82 \times 10^{-13} \text{ cm}$$

to the nuclear unit radius R_0 is taken as $(r_0/R_0) \simeq 2$, and

$$\frac{\hbar}{m_0 c^2} = 1.29 \times 10^{-21} \text{ sec}$$

Figure 4.1 expresses Eq. (4.9) in graphical form.   For each value of l, the variation of τ_{el} with mass number A is indicated by curves for $A = 20$ and $A = 200$.   Note that the smaller nuclei are expected to have greater mean lives against γ decay. A "typical" mean life of $\sim 10^{-11}$ sec is found for a nuclear level which can be deexcited only by emission of a 1-Mev electric quadrupole, or E2, γ ray.

Magnetic Multipoles. The electric multipole radiation originates in periodic variations in the charge density ρ in the nucleus. The magnetic radiation originates in periodic variations in the current density, which is of the order $(v/c)\rho$, where v is the velocity of the charges. Therefore, for the same multipole order l, the probability of emission (or intensity) of magnetic 2^l radiation usually will be much smaller than the probability of electric 2^l radiation, by the order of $(v/c)^2$ for dipole radiation. This concept, contained in Weisskopf's theory of γ decay, replaces the erroneous estimates of pre-1951 theories according to which the ratio of magnetic to electric radiation of the same multipole order depended primarily on the ratio of the size of the emitting system to the wavelength of the emitted radiation, that is, (R/λ).

For magnetic multipole γ radiation, on the single-particle model, Weisskopf (W23) estimates that the ratio of the squares of the magnetic and electric moments will be of the order of $(M_{lm}/Q_{lm})^2 \simeq (\hbar/McR)^2$, where M is the mass of a nucleon. Because the rationalized wavelength of a nucleon $\lambda \simeq \hbar/Mv$ must be of the order of the nuclear radius R, the ratio $(\hbar/McR)^2$ is of the order of $(v/c)^2$. The transition probabilities, and reciprocal partial mean lives, are proportional to the multipole moment for the transition. Therefore, for *magnetic multipole transitions*, the mean life τ_{mag} of the upper level is longer than for an electric multipole having the same l, W, and A, by a factor which is given very roughly by

$$\frac{\tau_{mag}}{\tau_{el}} \simeq \frac{1}{10}\left[\frac{R}{(\hbar/Mc)}\right]^2 \simeq 4.4A^{\frac{2}{3}} \tag{4.10}$$

where the factor 10 arises because of the intrinsic magnetic moments of the nucleons and we have used $R \simeq 1.4 \times 10^{-13}$ cm and

$$\frac{\hbar}{Mc} = 0.211 \times 10^{-13} \text{ cm}$$

Notice that the ratio in Eq. (4.10) is independent of both the transition energy W and the multipole index l. The curves in Fig. 4.1 may therefore be used for estimating the partial mean life τ_{mag} of a level against magnetic multipole γ radiation, simply by multiplying each curve by $4.4A^{\frac{2}{3}}$. This is a factor of about 30 for $A = 20$ and of about 150 for $A = 200$.

Predominant Transitions. In all theories, the probability of γ emission per unit time decreases very rapidly with increasing l, the dependence being roughly as $(R/\lambda)^{2l}$. The multipole radiation which is actually observed in a transition from an initial nuclear level, with angular-momentum quantum number I_A, to a final level I_B therefore will correspond primarily to the smallest value of l which is consistent with conservation of angular momentum, Eq. (4.2), and parity, Eq. (4.4). Often this will be simply $l = |I_A - I_B| \equiv \Delta I$.

The transitions which correspond to the smallest value of l can be enumerated by reference to the conservation laws as embodied in the selection rules, combined with the principle that 2^l-pole radiation is much more probable than $2^{(l+1)}$-pole radiation, and that the intensity of magnetic 2^l-pole radiation is smaller than the intensity of electric 2^l-pole radiation by a considerable factor (though not as much as in pre-1951 theories, especially for low energies).

TABLE 4.2. THE TYPE OF MULTIPOLE RADIATION EMITTED IN TRANSITIONS BETWEEN NUCLEAR LEVELS WHOSE ANGULAR-MOMENTUM QUANTUM NUMBERS ARE I_A AND I_B AND WHOSE PARITY IS THE SAME (NO CHANGE) OR WHOSE PARITY IS OPPOSITE (YES)

The types of multipole radiation are indicated by the usual symbols as given in Table 4.1. Transitions $\Delta I = 0$ are possible between levels $I_A = I_B$ only if both have nonzero values, so that $|m| \geq 1$, Eq. (4.3). Transitions $0 \to 0$ are absolutely excluded. The rules are the same for emission and for absorption of photons by a nuclear system.

Parity	$\Delta I \equiv \|I_A - I_B\|$	Spin change in nucleus ΔS	Parity change in nucleus	Pre-dominant radiation	Weak admixture of
Favored	Even (not zero)	0	No	EΔI	M($\Delta I + 1$); absent if I_A or $I_B = 0$
	Zero	0	No	M1	E2; absent if $I_A = I_B = \frac{1}{2}$
	Odd	0	Yes	EΔI	M($\Delta I + 1$); absent if I_A or $I_B = 0$
Unfavored	Even (not zero)	± 1	Yes	MΔI	E($\Delta I + 1$); absent if I_A or $I_B = 0$
	Zero	± 1	Yes	E1	M2; absent if $I_A = I_B = \frac{1}{2}$
	Odd	± 1	No	MΔI	E($\Delta I + 1$); absent if I_A or $I_B = 0$

The results are summarized in Table 4.2, which shows also the classification which can be made into *parity-favored* transitions (no "spin flip") and *parity-unfavored* transitions for which, in the single-particle model, one unit of the angular momentum contained in l has to arise from the reversal of the direction of intrinsic spin of the odd nucleon; thus $\Delta S = \pm 1$ within the emitting nucleus.

For example, the transition $f_{\frac{7}{2}} \to d_{\frac{5}{2}}$ involves a change of only the orbital motion of the odd nucleon and would be "parity-favored," whereas $f_{\frac{7}{2}} \to f_{\frac{5}{2}}$ would involve a "spin flip" ($\Delta S = \pm 1$) and would be "parity-unfavored."

e. Mixed Transitions. Admixtures of the predominant multipole with the weaker competing multipole shown in the right-hand column of Table 4.2 are expected, in the theory, to be of the same order of magnitude only when the predominant radiation is a magnetic multipole. The fact that the competing electric multipole has to be one order higher than the magnetic, i.e., $2^{(l+1)}$ instead of 2^l in order to conserve parity, may be only partially compensated in suitable cases by the factor of the order of $(v/c)^2$ between the squares of the effective "dynamic" magnetic and electric moments for the transition.

When the predominant radiation is an electric multipole, the competing magnetic multipole is at a double disadvantage. Then the radiation can be expected to be substantially the pure electric multipole.

Experimentally, the only mixed transitions found have been M1 + E2, in a classification of over 90 isomeric γ-ray transitions by Goldhaber and Sunyar (G27).

f. Forbidden Transitions. In ordinary optical spectroscopy the selection rules for allowed transitions are simply those for the electric dipole $l = 1$, yes, which correspond to the usual selection rules for electronic transitions in atoms: $\Delta J = 0, \pm 1$, (not $0 \rightarrow 0$); $\Delta m = 0, \pm 1$, yes. The so-called forbidden transitions involve all the other electric and magnetic multipoles. These all involve longer lifetimes for the excited level. Under ordinary laboratory conditions of temperature and pressure, these longer-lived atomic levels generally lose their excitation energy in collisions with other atoms and thus are deexcited by nonradiative collision processes. The forbidden electron transitions only show up strongly where the pressures are much lower than those attainable on earth, such as in the nebulae. Thus the nebular spectrum lines which were once attributed to "nebulium" were shown by Bowen to be forbidden transitions in ionized oxygen atoms (B104).

In nuclei, analogous thermal collision processes are not accessible for nonradiative deexcitation. Hence the forbidden radiative transitions are observed. Indeed, they are so ordinary that they usually are not referred to as forbidden; in fact, electric quadrupole radiation, or E2, is probably the most common type of nuclear γ radiation.

Nuclei do have available several types of deexcitation which do not involve the emission of γ radiation. The most common of these is internal conversion. Here the nuclear excitation energy is given, in a nonradiative process, to a penetrating electron as discussed in the next section. In $0 \rightarrow 0$ transitions, which are truly and absolutely forbidden in any radiative process, all the transitions must proceed by nonradiative processes, usually internal conversion within the nuclear volume.

5. *Internal Conversion*

The transition from an excited level of a nucleus to a lower level of the same nucleus can also be accomplished without the emission of a photon. The energy W involved in the nuclear transition can be transferred directly to a bound electron of the same atom. This energy transfer is a direct interaction between the bound atomic electron and the same nuclear multipole field which otherwise would have resulted in the emission of a photon. All nuclear γ-ray transitions are accomplished in competition with this direct coupling process, which is called *internal conversion*.

The nuclear energy difference W is "converted" to energy of an atomic electron, which is ejected forthwith from the atom with a kinetic energy E_i given by

$$E_i = W - B_i \qquad (5.1)$$

where B_i is the original atomic binding energy of the electron. Figure 5.1 shows the spectrum of conversion electrons which are ejected from the K, L, and M shells of indium by internal conversion of the 392-kev transition in In^{113}. After the ejection of the photoelectron, the atom emits the energy B_i as characteristic X rays or as Auger electrons.

Equation (5.1) rests simply on the law of conservation of energy. No photon is involved. The process of internal conversion has intervened and won over a competing radiative transition. However, Eq. (5.1) is identical in form with Einstein's photoelectric equation, if W is replaced by the energy $h\nu$ of the unsuccessful photon. This fact led to many years, even decades, of misinterpretation of the mechanism of internal conversion. Equation (5.1) began its important career as a purely empirical relationship in 1922, when C. D. Ellis (E8) and Lise Meitner (M39) independently showed that it held for what was then called the "line spectrum of β rays" (now called conversion electrons) from RaB (Ellis) and ThB, RaD, RdTh, and Ra (Meitner). These experiments were the first to prove the presently accepted views on the origin and nature of γ rays. Up until that time γ rays were thought to be bremsstrahlung (continuous X rays) associated with the passage of β rays through the electron configuration of the emitting atom. Meitner,

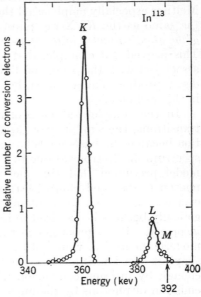

Fig. 5.1 Internal-conversion electron spectrum for the 392-kev transition in In^{113}. [*Graves, Langer, and Moffat* (G41).] The energy differences for the electron groups from the K, L, M shells correspond to the differences in binding energy of these atomic shells in In. Conversion in the L_I, L_{II}, . . . and M_I, M_{II}, . . . subshells are not resolved in this particular work. The observed ratio of conversion in the K shell to that in the $(L + M)$ shells is 4.21 for this transition, which has been identified as an M4 transition (magnetic 2^4-pole; $\Delta I = 4$, yes) in agreement with single-particle shell model predictions of $p_{\frac{1}{2}} \rightarrow g_{\frac{9}{2}}$ (G25). [The interlocked decay schemes of the isobars $_{47}$Ag^{113}, $_{48}$Cd^{113}, $_{49}$In^{113}, and $_{50}$Sn^{113} have been correlated by Goldhaber and Hill (G25).]

especially, disproved this view by showing that line spectra of electrons were associated with some α-ray emitters, which possess no continuous β-ray spectrum. Both Ellis and Meitner resolved the conversion electron groups from the L_I, L_{II}, L_{III} and M_I, M_{II}, M_{III} subshells, as well as N_I and O shell conversions, and proved the rigorous validity of Eq. (5.1). Meitner especially emphasized the fact that *the $K - L$ difference* has to be the same as the K_α X-ray photon energy and hence *is a direct measure of the atomic number of the atom in which the nuclear transition takes place.* This proved, for example, that the conversion electrons and the γ rays associated with the β rays of ThB ($_{82}Pb^{212}$) in fact are emitted from the decay product ThC ($_{83}Bi^{212}$), hence that the γ decay *follows* the β decay in this radionuclide.

In the complete absence of any theory of the probability of γ-ray transitions, the similarity of Eq. (5.1) with Einstein's photoelectric equation became the basis for Ellis's and Meitner's interpretation of the line spectrum of electrons as due to an "internal photoelectric effect." This model presumed that the nucleus first emits a photon but that this photon is absorbed photoelectrically in the inner electron shells without ever escaping from the emitting atom. This model was all right energetically because it does lead to Eq. (5.1); nevertheless this model is quite incorrect. Its disproof lies in the agreement between experimental and modern theoretical values of the "internal-conversion coefficient." The simplest decisive situation is the $0 \rightarrow 0$ transition which proceeds readily enough by internal conversion within the nuclear volume although the emission of photons by the nucleus is completely forbidden.

a. Internal-conversion Coefficient. After the development of the quantum mechanics, Taylor and Mott (T10) first clearly pointed out in 1933 that the theoretical probability of the "internal photoelectric effect" was generally negligible compared with that of the "direct-coupling" mechanism of internal conversion. The quantum mechanics was able to provide a theory for the relative probability of internal conversion by direct coupling as compared with the probability of photon emission.

Let the decay constant λ_γ represent the probability per unit time for the emission of a photon, whose energy is $W = h\nu$, by a radiative nuclear multipole transition. Let the decay constant λ_e represent the probability per unit time that this same nuclear multipole field will transfer its energy W to any bound electron in its own atom. Then the total *internal-conversion coefficient* α is defined as

$$\alpha \equiv \frac{\lambda_e}{\lambda_\gamma} = \frac{N_e}{N_\gamma} \tag{5.2}$$

where experimentally N_e and N_γ are the numbers of conversion electrons and of photons emitted in the same time interval, from the same sample, in which identical nuclei are undergoing the same nuclear transformation characterized by the energy W. The total transition probability λ is

$$\lambda = \lambda_\gamma + \lambda_e = \lambda_\gamma(1 + \alpha) \tag{5.3}$$

and the total number of nuclei transforming is $N_\gamma + N_e$.

The theoretical value of the internal-conversion coefficient depends on

W, the energy of the transition
Z, the atomic number of the transforming nucleus
l, the multipole order of the transition
parity-favored (electric multipole) or parity-unfavored (magnetic multipole)
atomic shell (K, L_I, L_II, . . . , M_I, M_II, . . .) in which conversion takes place

Happily, the conversion coefficient for each atomic shell does not depend on the value of the nuclear electric or magnetic multipole moment for the transition, because this moment enters both λ_e and λ_γ and cancels out when only the relative transition probability α is sought.

A potentially confusing residue of the disproved "internal-photo-electric-effect" model of internal conversion is the occasional reappearance of the pre-1933 definition of internal-conversion coefficient, which we may call α_p, where $\alpha_p = N_e/(N_e + N_\gamma)$. Then $\alpha = \alpha_p/(1 - \alpha_p)$. The possible values of α_p are only $0 \leq \alpha_p \leq 1$, in comparison with $0 \leq \alpha \leq \infty$. Expressions such as "80 per cent converted" mean $\alpha_p = 0.8$, hence $\alpha = N_e/N_\gamma = 0.8/0.2 = 4$, not $\alpha = 0.8$.

b. K-shell Conversion. Equation (5.2) represents the total internal-conversion coefficient α, which in fact is made up of the sum of individual coefficients acting separately for each atomic subshell. In present experimental work, such as Fig. 5.1, conversion in the separate subshells is usually not resolved; the L_I, L_II, L_III conversions therefore often are lumped as L conversion. Accordingly, the shell-conversion coefficients become important in theory and experiment, where

$$\alpha = \alpha_K + \alpha_L + \alpha_M + \cdots \tag{5.4}$$

and α_K is the shell-conversion coefficient for *both* K electrons, α_L is the shell-conversion coefficient for all L electrons, and so forth.

Exact theoretical values of α_K, α_L, . . . cannot be expressed in closed form. A number of approximate formulas have been developed. Although their usefulness is limited, they have served for many years as rough guides. One helpful example is the relativistic treatment by Dancoff and Morrison (D2) whose result, for a transition energy W which is small compared with m_0c^2, and neglecting the binding energy of the K electron, reduces to

$$(\alpha_K)_\mathrm{el} \simeq \frac{l}{l+1} Z^3 \left(\frac{1}{137}\right)^4 \left(\frac{2m_0c^2}{W}\right)^{l+\frac{5}{2}} \tag{5.5}$$

for two K electrons, and $m_0c^2 \gg W \gg B_K$. Equation (5.5) applies only to electric multipoles, of order 2^l, with $l = 1, 2, 3, \ldots$. For magnetic multipoles (parity-unfavored, as shown in Table 4.2), the K-shell internal-conversion coefficient for $m_0c^2 \gg W \gg B_K$ reduces to

$$(\alpha_K)_\mathrm{mag} \simeq Z^3 \left(\frac{1}{137}\right)^4 \left(\frac{2m_0c^2}{W}\right)^{l+\frac{3}{2}} \tag{5.6}$$

Both Eqs. (5.5) and (5.6) involve the Born approximation in their derivation. Therefore their validity is further restricted by the usual Born condition $[Z/137(v/c)] \ll 1$, where v is the emission velocity of the conversion electron.

Qualitatively, Eqs. (5.5) and (5.6) bring out several essential points. They correctly imply a strong increase of α_K with increasing multipole order, hence with increasing angular-momentum change ΔI in the nuclear transition. Also α_K increases strongly as Z increases and as W decreases.

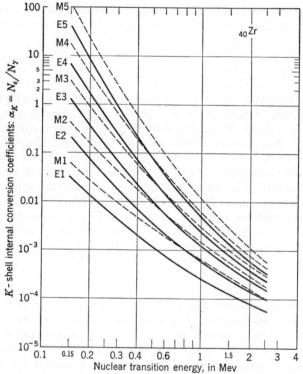

Fig. 5.2 K-shell internal-conversion coefficients $(\alpha_K)_{el}$ and $(\alpha_K)_{mag}$, for $Z = 40$ and $l = 1$ to 5. [*From tables by M. E. Rose et al.* (R32, R31).]

The conversion coefficients for electric and for magnetic multipoles vary in a slightly different way with l and W, and usually, but not always, $(\alpha_K)_{mag} > (\alpha_K)_{el}$ for the same W and l ($= \Delta I$). See Fig. 5.2.

Internal conversion was well known in the natural radioactive nuclides long before the discovery of the artificial β-ray emitters in 1934. The strong Z dependence ($\sim Z^3$) made the observation of internal conversion in the new low-Z artificially radioactive bodies seem unlikely. Alvarez (A23) obtained the first experimental evidence of internal conversion in artificial radionuclides in connection with his experimental proof of the existence of electron-capture transitions, such as in Ga⁶⁷. With the gradual improvement of experimental methods, internal conversion has become a process of first-rank importance in the study of the angular momentum and parity of nuclear energy levels (G25, M33).

Exact theoretical values of $(\alpha_K)_{el}$ and $(\alpha_K)_{mag}$ for $1 \leq l \leq 5$, $10 \leq Z \leq 96$, and $0.3 m_0 c^2 \leq W \leq 5 m_0 c^2$ have been obtained with an automatic sequence relay calculator by M. E. Rose and coworkers (R32, R31). These exact numerical values cover a domain of about 10^8, from $\alpha_K \sim 10^{-6}$ for small Z, small l, and large W, to $\sim 10^2$ for large Z, large l, and small W.

Figure 5.2 shows the strong dependence of $(\alpha_K)_{el}$ and $(\alpha_K)_{mag}$ on the transition energy, and on the multipole order, for the particular case of $Z = 40$ (zirconium). The shapes of the curves are qualitatively similar for other values of Z. Quantitatively, Fig. 5.3 depicts the increase of α_K with Z for four illustrative cases.

c. L-shell Conversion. If the transition energy is adequate, that is, $W > B_K$, conversion is usually more probable in the K shell than in the L shell, because the K electrons have the greater probability of being near the nucleus. Approximate calculations of α_L have been made by Hebb and Nelson and others (H27, G16). Exact calculations by M. E. Rose et al., including the effect of screening by the K electrons, are in progress (R32).

K/L Ratio. It is well established both experimentally and theoretically that α_L depends on l, W, and Z in a markedly different way than does α_K. Then the so-called "K/L ratio" α_K/α_L becomes also a function of W, Z, and the multipole order of the transition. This im-

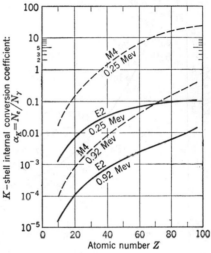

Fig. 5.3 Variation of K-shell internal-conversion coefficients with atomic number for two common types of multipole, E2 ($\Delta I = 2$, no) and M4 ($\Delta I = 4$, yes), and for two representative values of the transition energy. [*From tables by M. E. Rose et al.* (R32, R31).]

portant point was first emphasized by Hebb and Nelson (H27), who also made approximate calculations of α_L and of α_K/α_L under the same simplifying assumptions as those of Eqs. (5.5) and (5.6).

Experimental determinations of the K/L ratio

$$\frac{\alpha_K}{\alpha_L} = \frac{(N_K/N_\gamma)}{(N_L/N_\gamma)} = \frac{N_K}{N_L} \tag{5.7}$$

where N_K and N_L are the relative numbers of K-conversion electrons and of L-conversion electrons, are much simpler and more reliable than absolute measurements of either α_K or α_L. Figure 5.1 illustrates the directness with which α_K/α_L can be determined. Such methods provide one of our best procedures for determining the angular-momentum difference ΔI between levels in the same nucleus. This approach has both experimental and theoretical advantages. Experimentally, the difficult determination of N_γ is made unnecessary because it cancels out. On the theoretical side, the uncertainties surrounding the estimation of the nuclear multipole moments are also circumvented, because these moments cancel out in the definition of the total internal-conversion coefficient, Eq. (5.2), and of the shell-conversion coefficients, Eq. (5.4).

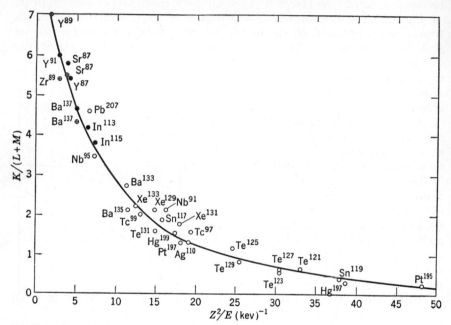

Fig. 5.4 Empirical values of the ratio of conversion electrons $K/(L + M) = \alpha_K/(\alpha_L + \alpha_M)$ for transitions which have been otherwise identified as M4 ($\Delta I = 4$, yes). E is the transition energy in kev; Z is the atomic number. [*From Graves, Langer, and Moffat (G41).*]

Two generalizations can be made. First, as $l = \Delta I$ increases, α_L becomes more pronounced in comparison with α_K. Thus, for the same W and Z,

$$\frac{\alpha_K}{\alpha_L} \text{ decreases as } \Delta I \text{ increases} \tag{5.8}$$

Second, as $l = \Delta I$ increases, the decrease in α_K/α_L is more pronounced for electric 2^l-pole transitions than for magnetic 2^l-pole transitions. Thus, for the same W, Z, and ΔI,

$$\left(\frac{\alpha_K}{\alpha_L}\right)_{\text{el}} < \left(\frac{\alpha_K}{\alpha_L}\right)_{\text{mag}} \tag{5.9}$$

The experimental values of the K/L ratio range between 10 (large W, small ΔI, small Z) and 0.1 (small W, large ΔI, large Z).

Pending completion and testing of the exact theoretical values of α_L and α_K/α_L, empirical values of the K/L ratio have been accumulated (G27, G41) on over 60 transitions, including E1 to E5 and M1 to M4, in which ΔI and parity can be established from other types of experimental evidence or can be inferred from the single-particle shell model. An example of this procedure, for the case of $Cs^{137} \rightarrow Ba^{137}$, will be discussed in Sec. 7. Figure 5.4 is a representative compilation of empirical ratios for M4 transitions in which α_L and α_M are treated as unresolved.

d. Pair Internal Conversion. The creation of a positron-negatron pair in the external field of a nucleus is energetically possible whenever more than the rest energy $2m_0c^2$ ($= 1.02$ Mev) of two electrons is available. If the nuclear excitation energy W exceeds $2m_0c^2$, then nuclear deexcitation can occur by an additional process, related to internal conversion, in which an electron is lifted from an occupied negative energy state into the continuum of possible positive energy states. The resulting "hole" in the negative energy states is the experimentally observed positron, while the electron in a positive energy state is the negatron member of the observed positron-negatron pair.

The energy W of the nuclear transition then appears as a positron-negatron pair, whose total energy is

$$W = E_+ + E_- + 2m_0c^2 \tag{5.10}$$

where E_+ and E_- are the kinetic energies of the positron and the negatron.

Momentum is conserved between the nucleus and the electron pair. Although the *pair internal-conversion* process (or, synonymously, *internal pair formation*) can take place anywhere in the coulomb field of the nucleus, the probability is greatest at a distance from the nucleus which is of the order of $(Z/137)^2$ times the radius of the K shell of atomic electrons (J5).

The energy distribution of E_+ tends to be symmetric with E_- for small Z. For large Z there is a strong preponderance of high-energy positrons (J5, R34) as a consequence of the action of the nuclear coulomb field on the pair.

The angular distribution is strongly peaked in favor of small angles, $\vartheta \rightarrow 0$, between the directions of the emerging positron and negatron (R34, R30).

In the deexcitation of a nuclear level for which $W > 2m_0c^2$, the processes of ordinary (atomic) internal conversion and of pair internal conversion compete with and supplement one another, and both compete with γ-ray emission. The absolute probability of internal pair formation *is greatest where the probability of ordinary internal conversion is least*, i.e., for large W, for small Z, and for small l. For $Z \sim 40$ and $W \sim 2.5$ Mev, the two processes are of roughly equal importance, the pair internal-conversion coefficient being between about 1.0×10^{-3} pair per photon for an E1 transition, and 1.8×10^{-4} for an E5 transition. The absolute value of the pair-conversion coefficient is almost independent of Z; indeed, it decreases slightly with increasing Z. Convenient graphs of the pair internal-conversion coefficient, from $W = 1.02$ Mev to 10.2 Mev, and for both electric and magnetic multipoles from $l = 1$ to 5 inclusive, have been published by M. E. Rose (R30). Figure 5.5 shows illustrative values of the pair internal-conversion coefficient.

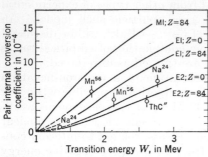

Fig. **5.5** Representative theoretical curves and experimental points for the pair internal-conversion coefficient. Note the strong contrasts with the ordinary internal-conversion coefficient, as plotted in Figs. 5.2 and 5.3. [*From Slätis and Siegbahn* (S46).]

Experimentally, the radioactive nuclides provide only a few γ-ray transitions whose energy is great enough (say, > 2 Mev) to make pair internal conversion an important process in competition with ordinary atomic internal conversion. Among these, Alichanow et al. (A13, L12) first reported that RaC emits about three positrons per 10^4 γ rays in its 1.76-Mev and 2.2-Mev transitions, and that the 2.62-Mev γ-ray transition which follows the β decay of ThC'' emits about four positrons per 10^4 γ rays, in agreement with the theory of Jaeger and Hulme and the known E2 character of this transition. Pair internal-conversion coefficients have been measured by Slätis and Siegbahn (S46) for the following well-known γ-ray transitions:

TABLE 5.1. PAIR INTERNAL-CONVERSION COEFFICIENTS

Parent radionuclide	Transition energy W, Mev	Number of positrons per γ ray	Multipole character of transition
ThC'' ($_{81}$Tl^{208})	2.62	4.3×10^{-4}	E2
Co^{60}	1.33	Detectable	E2
Co^{60}	1.17	Detectable	E2
Mn^{56}	2.13	4.6×10^{-4}	?
Mn^{56}	1.81	5.6×10^{-4}	?
Na^{24}	2.76	8.0×10^{-4}	E2
Na^{24}	1.38	0.3×10^{-4}	E2

Figure 5.6 shows the energy spectra of the positrons which compete with the 2.76-Mev and 1.38-Mev γ-ray transitions in Na$^{24} \xrightarrow{\beta,\gamma}$ Mg^{24}, as determined in a careful experimental study of the shape and relative intensity of the positron and negatron spectra by Bloom (B80).

At even higher energies, the pair internal-conversion coefficient is rather insensitive to the multipole order of the transition (R30). Hence there has been little incentive to study internal pair formation in the higher-energy transitions which accompany some nuclear reactions.

e. $0 \to 0$ Transitions. Internal Conversion within the Nuclear Volume. For any l, there is a contribution to the matrix element of internal conversion by the region within the nucleus, $r < R$. This contribution is usually negligible in comparison with the region outside the nucleus, $r > R$. But in the special case where $I = 0$ for both the initial and final states there is no electromagnetic field outside the nucleus (because $l = 0$) and consequently no internal conversion in the extranuclear region. Then the energy transfer to an atomic electron (e.g., to an s electron from the K shell or L shell) can take place only inside the nucleus. Thus,

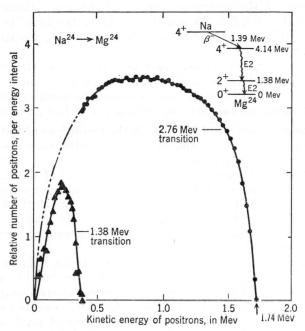

Fig. 5.6 Energy spectra of the positrons produced by pair internal conversion, in competition with the 2.76-Mev and 1.38-Mev γ-ray transitions which follow the β decay of Na²⁴. The area under these curves, when compared with the area under the associated negatron spectrum of β rays and pair conversion negatrons, gives for the pair internal-conversion coefficients 7.1×10^{-4} for the 2.76-Mev transition and 0.6×10^{-4} for the 1.38-Mev transition. [*From S. D. Bloom* (B80).] The predominant mode of decay of Na²⁴ is shown in the inset. Both the γ transitions are E2 (based on K-shell internal-conversion coefficients, pair internal-conversion coefficients, and γ-γ angular correlation); the β transition is allowed (log $ft = 6.1$). A competing feeble (0.003 per cent) 4.17-Mev, second-forbidden β transition is omitted in the figure, as is also a 0.04-per cent crossover E4 γ-ray transition.

in $0 \rightarrow 0$ transitions, ordinary single quantum γ-ray emission is absolutely forbidden. Internal conversion can take place, but the probability per unit time is small because the region in which the energy transfer can take place is restricted to the interior of the nucleus. The $0 \rightarrow 0$ transitions are distinguished experimentally by the emission of conversion electrons and the complete absence of γ-ray emission. Thus the internal-conversion coefficient is infinite.

Emission of a Single Nuclear Internal-conversion Electron. The mean life τ_{e^-} for a $0 \to 0$ transition, if both levels have the same parity, is approximately (B68)

$$\tau_{e^-} \sim \frac{2}{Z^3} \left(\frac{4}{A^{\frac{1}{3}}}\right)^4 \left(\frac{m_0 c^2}{W - B_e}\right)^{\frac{1}{2}} 10^{-4} \qquad \text{sec} \qquad (5.11)$$

where all symbols have their customary meaning, and $W - B_e$ is the kinetic energy of the emerging conversion electron. Equation (5.11) says that for $A \sim 64$, $Z \sim 30$, and $W \sim 1$ Mev, the mean life for K-shell conversion within the nuclear volume in a $0 \to 0$, no, transition is $\sim 5 \times 10^{-9}$ sec.

Experimentally, the classical case of a $0 \to 0$, no, transition is the 1.412-Mev excited level in RaC′ ($_{84}Po^{214}$), which was first studied by C. D. Ellis (E9). This level is one of some 12 known excited levels in RaC′, all of which are produced in the β decay of RaC, and all of which emit long-range α rays (see Chap. 16) in the transitions of RaC′ $\xrightarrow{\alpha}$ RaD. In addition to α rays, γ rays and conversion electrons are observed from all these levels except the one at an excitation energy of 1.412 Mev. This one level, in its transitions to the ground level of RaC′, emits conversion electrons but no γ rays. The mean life of the level is markedly increased by the prohibition of γ transitions. Although the β-branching ratios of RaC are not fully studied, it is noteworthy that the 1.412-Mev level in RaC′ emits more than twice as many long-range α rays as all the other 11 excited levels put together.

A second experimental example of the $0 \to 0$, no, transition appears to be the 0.7-Mev level in $_{32}Ge^{72}$. This level is produced in an ~ 1 per cent branch in the β decay of $_{31}Ga^{72}$. Conversion electrons are observed, but no γ rays, and the level has a mean life of 0.3 μsec as measured by delayed coincidence techniques (G25). The ground level of $_{32}Ge^{72}$ is presumed to be $I = 0$, even, because of the even-Z even-N composition of this nucleus. Because of the absence of γ rays, the 0.7-Mev metastable level is also assumed to be $I = 0$, even. At present, this is the only known case of nuclear isomerism which is attributable to the slowness of $0 \to 0$ transitions.

Nuclear Pair Formation. When the transition energy W exceeds $2m_0 c^2$, deexcitation by positron-negatron pair production can occur in the $0 \to 0$, no, transitions. Exactly as in the case of nuclear K-electron conversion, the pair can be produced only within the nuclear volume, because there is no multipole field external to the nucleus. These "*nuclear pairs*" can be distinguished experimentally from pairs produced outside the nuclear volume by the ordinary process of pair internal conversion. The nuclear pairs have a much narrower energy distribution (O5, O3).

The one clear and carefully studied case of nuclear pair formation in a $0 \to 0$, no, transition is the 6.04-Mev-excited level in O^{16}. Because of the low Z and high W, no single-electron "nuclear" internal conversion has been observed in this instance. The level is produced by the $F^{19}(p,\alpha)O^{16}$

reaction, has a measured mean life of about 7×10^{-11} sec (D36), and emits positron-negatron pairs whose total kinetic energy is

$$6.04 - 1.02 = 5.0 \text{ Mev}$$

The moderately extensive literature on this transition has been summarized by Bennett et al. (B34) and by Rasmussen et al. (R9). Figure 5.7 shows the narrow momentum distribution of the positron members of the nuclear pairs which are produced in this 6.04-Mev $0 \rightarrow 0$, no, transition.

$0 \rightarrow 0$, *Yes, Transitions.* The two types of nuclear internal conversion which we have just discussed apply only to $0 \rightarrow 0$ transitions in

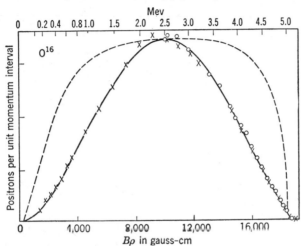

Fig. 5.7 Momentum spectrum of the positrons from the "nuclear pair" formation transition in O^{16}. The dotted curve shows the broader and flatter distribution which would be expected if these pairs had been produced in the external field of the O^{16} nucleus by pair internal conversion of dipole radiation (compare Fig. 5.6). [*From Rasmussen, Hornyak, Lauritsen, and Lauritsen* (R9).]

which there is no change in parity. A $0 \rightarrow 0$ transition between levels of different parity cannot occur at all by internal conversion. However, the mean life for such a transition is not infinite, as deexcitation can be accomplished by various processes involving the emission of two simultaneous radiations, such as two quanta, or one quantum and one internal-conversion electron. The probability of these processes is extremely small, and they do not compete effectively except for the $0 \rightarrow 0$, yes, transition, for which *both* γ radiation and internal conversion are absolutely forbidden.

6. *Nuclear Isomers*

The existence of isotopic isobars (same-Z, same-A), with clearly distinguishable properties such as different radioactive half-periods, was anticipated in 1917 when Soddy proposed that such nuclei be called *isomers* if and when found. The prediction that some nuclei would be found which have one or more long-lived excited levels was first made on sound theoretical grounds by Weizsächer (W27), who pointed out in 1936 that γ-ray decay of levels whose excitation energy W is small should be delayed by an easily measurable amount if the angular-momentum change ΔI is large.

a. Long-lived Metastable Levels. Experimentally, the first case of nuclear isomerism was discovered in 1938, when Feather and Bretscher (F14) unraveled the interlocked decay schemes of UX$_1$, UX$_2$, UZ, and UII ($_{90}$Th^{234}, $_{91}$Pa^{234m}, $_{91}$Pa^{234}, and $_{92}$U^{234}) and showed that UX$_2$ ($T_{\frac{1}{2}} = 1.14$ min) is only a long-lived excited level of UZ ($T_{\frac{1}{2}} = 6.7$ hr).

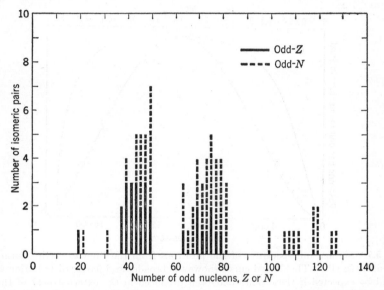

Fig. 6.1 The frequency distribution of odd-A isomeric pairs displays "islands of isomerism" (F18) in which the odd-nucleon number is less than 50, or less than 82. The solid bars represent the number of odd-Z even-N cases, while the even-Z odd-N isomeric pairs are shown dotted. [*The data are from the tabulation by Goldhaber and Hill* (G25).]

As experimental techniques have improved, a large number of isomers have been found and studied in artificial radionuclides and in the stable nuclides.

Figure 6.1 shows the frequency of isomerism in odd-A nuclides as a function of the number of odd nucleons. The so-called *islands of isomerism* appear here as two principal groups, in which the number of odd nucleons is just below the magic numbers 50 and 82.

$\rightarrow$ By 1951 Goldhaber and coworkers (G27, G25) could classify the nuclear properties of 77 isomers for which the half-period of the excited metastable level is between 1 sec and 8 months. About half these are M4 transitions ($\Delta I = 4$, yes), and the remainder are M3, E3, and E4. Most of them occur in odd-A nuclides. The correlation of nuclear angular-momentum values with the single-particle shell model (Chap. 11, Sec. 2) is excellent.

This systematic classification of known isomers, by multipole type, has provided important empirical evaluations of the decay constant λ_γ for γ-ray emission and of the internal-conversion coefficients α, α_K, and α_K/α_L. Comparison with Weisskopf's theory for λ_γ, and Rose's calculations of α_K, shows acceptable agreement, whereas pre-1951 theories were valid only in a few limiting cases.

b. Short-lived Metastable Levels. By the usual definition, an isomeric level is one whose half-period is "measurably" long. The development of experimental techniques utilizing scintillation counters in delayed coincidence circuits has made accurate measurements of half-periods possible in the microsecond domain. Thus some 16 cases whose half-periods lie between 10^{-5} and 10^{-9} sec have been added to the lists of studied "isomers" (G27). This shorter-lived group is made up of M1, M2, and E2 transitions. Experimental techniques for exploration of the millisecond domain await development and systematic utilization.

c. Half-period for Isomeric Transitions. The half-period would be that of γ decay if the excited nucleus were stripped of its atomic electrons. Internal conversion shortens the half-period by providing an alternative mode of deexcitation. Then, from Eq. (5.3), the half-period $T_{\frac{1}{2}}$ for a simple isomeric transition becomes

$$T_{\frac{1}{2}} = \frac{\ln 2}{\lambda} = \frac{0.693}{\lambda_\gamma(1 + \alpha)} = \frac{0.693}{1 + \alpha} \tau_\gamma \qquad (6.1)$$

where τ_γ is τ_{el} or τ_{mag} of Fig. 4.1 and Eqs. (4.9) and (4.10). If there is branching, i.e., several modes of decay of the metastable level, then λ in Eq. (6.1) is to be replaced by the sum of the decay constants for all competing modes. Because both α and $T_{\frac{1}{2}}$ are measurable quantities, studies of the isomeric transitions give values of λ_γ for direct comparison with the theory of γ decay.

d. Experimental Identification of Multipole Order of a γ Transition. The qualitative effects of the change in nuclear angular momentum $\Delta I = |I_A - I_B|$ can now be summarized. For fixed energy W and charge Z, with increasing ΔI,

$$\begin{array}{ll} \lambda_\gamma \text{ decreases} & \alpha_K \text{ increases} \\ \lambda_e \text{ decreases} & \alpha_L \text{ increases} \\ T_{\frac{1}{2}} \text{ increases} & \alpha_K/\alpha_L \text{ decreases} \end{array} \qquad (6.2)$$

The two general experimental approaches for the evaluation of ΔI involve measurement of

$$\alpha \qquad \text{or} \qquad \alpha_K/\alpha_L \qquad (6.3)$$

or $\qquad \lambda_\gamma \qquad$ through $T_{\frac{1}{2}}$ and Eq. (6.1) $\qquad (6.4)$

Theory and empirical correlations with ΔI are now available for the quantitative appraisal of most cases (G27, G25). As an illustration, the 2.6-min isomeric level in Ba^{137} is worked out in the following section.

7. Determination of Angular Momentum and Parity of Excited Levels from β- and γ-Transition Probabilities

We illustrate the conventional methods for determining I and parity for excited levels, and also for the ground levels of some radionuclides, by detailed consideration of the $Cs^{137} \rightarrow Ba^{137}$ transitions. Ba^{137} is the stable end product of the β decay of the important radionuclide $_{55}Cs^{137}$, whose long half-period (33 yr) and accurately measured monoenergetic γ rays (0.6616 Mev) make it a very useful and common substance. The decay scheme is shown in Fig. 7.1. The ground level of Ba^{137} is $I = \frac{3}{2}$, $\mu = +0.93$, therefore $d_{\frac{3}{2}}^+$, as was shown in Chap. 4, Sec. 6.

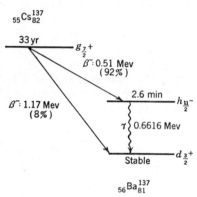

Fig. 7.1 Decay scheme of Cs^{137}, with angular-momentum and parity assignments for all levels.

a. β Decay of Cs^{137}. Two modes of β decay are in competition. The high-energy β transition directly to the ground level of Ba^{137} occurs in only about 8 per cent of the disintegrations of Cs^{137}. This transition therefore has a partial half-period of 33 yr/0.08 $\simeq$ 400 yr. This is an exceptionally long life for a β transition involving 1.17 Mev. The log ft value is 12.2 and corresponds in the theory of β decay (Table 3.2) to a second-forbidden transition, for which the selection rule involves no parity change. The shape (L5) of the β-ray spectrum is characteristic of $\Delta I = \pm 2$, no, in agreement with this assignment (Chap. 17, Sec. 3). The angular momentum of the ground level of Cs^{137} therefore has the same parity (even) as the ground level of Ba^{137}, and an angular momentum $I = \frac{3}{2} + \Delta I = \frac{7}{2}$.

The low-energy β transition of Cs^{137} has a measured decay energy of 0.51 Mev and a partial half-period of 33 yr/0.92 $\simeq$ 36 yr. The shape (O6, L8) of the β-ray spectrum corresponds in the theory of forbidden β decay [Chap. 17, Eq. (3.22)] to an angular-momentum change of 2, accompanied by a change in parity ($\Delta I = 2$, yes). This is a first-forbidden transition according to Gamow-Teller selection rules and is in quantitative agreement with the long half-period, log $ft = 9.6$. Then the excited level at 0.66 Mev in Ba^{137} must have odd parity. Its angular momentum should be that of $Cs^{137} \pm 2$, that is, $I = \frac{7}{2} \pm 2 = \frac{11}{2}$, or $\frac{3}{2}$.

b. γ Decay of Ba^{137}. Decision regarding I for the 0.66-Mev excited level in Ba^{137} can be made by several methods. In the first place, γ decay to the ground level is long delayed; the excited level is a well-recognized isomeric level whose half-period is 2.6 min. This implies that there is an angular-momentum difference of several units between the ground level and the 0.66-Mev level in Ba^{137}. Among the choices available for the 0.66-Mev level we must elect $I = \frac{11}{2}$. This decision is independently established by measurements of the internal-conversion coefficients for the transition to the ground level.   For a 0.66-Mev transition at $Z \simeq 55$, the K conversion coefficient is large ($\alpha_K = N_K/N_\gamma \simeq 0.08$) and also the K/L ratio is small ($\alpha_K/\alpha_L = 4.6$).   Therefore, a large change in angular momentum is involved.   All these data, when interpreted quantitatively (W1, G27, G25), support the conclusion that this transition is a magnetic 2^4-pole or, more briefly, an M4 transition (Fig. 5.4), for which the selection rule is $\Delta I = 4$, yes.   This confirms the choice $I = \frac{11}{2}$, odd, for the 0.66-Mev excited level in Ba^{137}.   Because the parity is odd, l must be odd, and so $l = \frac{11}{2} - \frac{1}{2} = 5$.   Then the 81st neutron is in an $h_{\frac{11}{2}}$ state, as shown in Fig. 7.1.

Knowledge of I and parity for the 0.66-Mev level of Ba^{137} permits us to estimate μ and Q for this level, but there are as yet no measurements

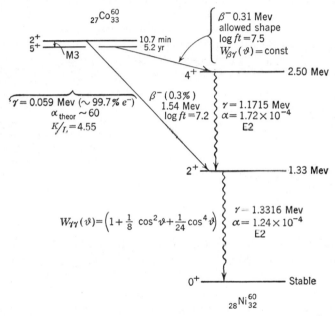

Fig. 7.2   Decay scheme of Co$^{60} \rightarrow$ Ni^{60}.   See also Figs. 8.6 and 8.8.

of the magnetic and electric moments of this excited level with which to make comparisons.

This experimental evidence on the β decay and γ decay of Cs^{137} $\rightarrow$ Ba^{137} is seen to be sufficient to overdetermine the angular-momentum and parity assignments given in Fig. 7.1.   In addition, experimental confirmation of the $g_{\frac{7}{2}}^+$ character of the ground level of Cs^{137} has been obtained by direct measurement of $I = \frac{7}{2}$, $\mu = +2.84$, using the atomic-beam magnetic-resonance method (D9).

c. β-γ **Decay of Co$^{60} \rightarrow$ Ni^{60}.**   The decay scheme of the very important radionuclide Co^{60} has been studied by substantially every available experimental method.   We shall have many occasions to refer to its decay scheme.   Figure 7.2 summarizes the presently known data on the isomers of Co^{60} and on the excited levels in their decay product, Ni^{60}.

Under irradiation of Co^{59} ($I = \frac{7}{2}$) with thermal neutrons (D32) the cross section for the formation of the 10.7-min isomeric level in Co^{60} is nearly the same as the cross section for formation of the 5.2-yr ground level of Co^{60}, both through the reaction Co^{59} $(n,\gamma)Co^{60}$. The 10.7-min level has an excitation energy of only 59 kev and transforms almost entirely to the ground level of Co^{60} by internal conversion. The half-period of 10.7 min is consistent with an M3 or E3 transition, and the K/L ratio of 4.55 implies that this is an M3 transition (magnetic octu-pole). The upper isomeric level transforms by β decay also; 0.3 per cent of the isomeric nuclei go by β decay to the 1.33-Mev level in Ni^{60}. Less than one in 10^6 isomeric nuclei transform by β decay to the ground level of Ni^{60} (D32). These data are consistent with assignments of 2^+ and 5^+ for the angular momentum and parity of the isomeric levels of Co^{60}. Both β transitions are then allowed. In Ni^{60}, the 2.50-Mev "crossover" γ ray is not observed and has an abundance less than 2.5×10^{-7} of that of the 1.17 plus 1.33-Mev cascade (F55).

Problems

1. On a basis of the single-particle shell model, make semiempirical estimates of the magnetic dipole moment μ and the electric quadrupole moment Q of the isomeric level at 0.66 Mev in Ba^{137}, knowing that this level is $h_{1\!\!/\!_1}$ with odd parity.

$l = 5$
$s = \frac{1}{2}$

2. Look up the data on the nuclides Cs^{135} and Ba^{135}, especially the determina-tions of angular momentum and parity for the levels which are analogous to those of $Cs^{137} \rightarrow Ba^{137}$ shown in Fig. 7.1. Account qualitatively for the similarities and the differences.

3. Compute the theoretical mean life of the 2.50-Mev excited level in Ni^{60}.

8. *Angular Correlation of Successive Radiations*

The photons emitted by a sample in which a large number of nuclei are undergoing identical γ-ray transitions will be isotropic in the labora-tory coordinates. There is no preferred direction of emission for the γ-ray photon from the individual transition $I_A \xrightarrow{\gamma} I_B$, because the atoms and nuclei are oriented at random. The same is true for α-ray, β-ray, and conversion-electron emission. If the transition $I_A \rightarrow I_B$ is followed by a second transition $I_B \rightarrow I_C$, the individual radiations from the second transition are likewise isotropic in the laboratory coordinates.

However, in a two-step cascade transition, such as $I_A \xrightarrow{\gamma_1} I_B \xrightarrow{\gamma_2} I_C$, there is often an angular correlation between the directions of emission of two successive γ-ray photons, γ_1 and γ_2, which are emitted from the same nucleus. Often there are similar angular correlations for other pairs of successive radiations, such as α-γ, β-γ, β-e^- (where e^- means a conver-sion electron), γ-e^-, ... Many of the details of the complicated theory of these angular correlations have been worked out. Experi-mental and theoretical developments have been summarized in a number of excellent review articles (D29, F66, B67).

The existence of an angular correlation arises because the direction of the first radiation is related to the orientation of the angular momentum

I_B of the intermediate level.   This orientation can be expressed in terms of the magnetic-angular-momentum quantum number m_B with respect to some laboratory direction such as that of the first radiation.   If I_B is not zero, and if the lifetime of the intermediate level is short enough so that the orientation of I_B persists, then the direction of emission of the second radiation will be related to the direction of I_B and hence to that of the first radiation.

a. Dipole-Dipole Angular Correlation.   Any pure γ-γ cascade can be represented in the obvious notation $I_A(l_1) I_B(l_2) I_C$, where l_1 and l_2 are the angular momenta of the two succes-sive γ rays.   As the simplest pos-sible example, we shall consider two successive dipole γ rays ($l_1 = l_2 = 1$) in the cascade $0(1)1(1)0$.

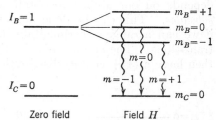

At first, imagine that measure-ments are made only on the second γ ray, and that the source is in a magnetic field H, which serves here to give a fixed direction in the lab-oratory.   The magnetic sublevels $m_B = 0$, ± 1 of the excited level $I_B = 1$ are shown schematically in Fig. 8.1.   The relative populations

Fig. 8.1   Magnetic sublevels m_B of the level $I_B = 1$.   Transitions $I_B \rightarrow I_C$ in-volve the emission of the dipoles l, m with $l - 1$, and $m - m_C - m_B - +1$, 0, or -1.

of these sublevels will be proportional to the Boltzman factor

$$e^{-\mu\mu_M H m_B/kT I_B} \tag{8.1}$$

where μ = magnetic dipole moment, nuclear magnetons
  μ_M = nuclear magneton
  k = Boltzman constant

Equation (8.1) is substantially unity except at the strongest fields H and lowest temperatures T which are now available.   Otherwise the mag-netic energy $\mu(m_B/I_B)\mu_M H$ is negligible compared with the thermal agitation energy kT.   The magnetic sublevels are therefore equally popu-lated under ordinary experimental conditions, and the transitions $\Delta m = 0$, $+1$, and -1 will have equal abundance.

The angular distribution of the intensity of electric multipole radia-tion is given by known analytic functions (p. 594 of B68, p. 251 of S11) and is the *same* for electric 2^l-pole and magnetic 2^l-pole radiation.   The electric and magnetic multipoles differ mathematically only in their par-ity and physically only in the orientation of their plane of polarization.   For dipole radiation the angular distribution is

$$w^0(\vartheta)\, d\Omega = \frac{3}{8\pi} \sin^2 \vartheta \, d\Omega \qquad \text{for } m = 0 \tag{8.2a}$$

$$w^{+1}(\vartheta)\, d\Omega = \frac{3}{16\pi} (1 + \cos^2 \vartheta)\, d\Omega \qquad \text{for } m = +1 \tag{8.2b}$$

$$w^{-1}(\vartheta)\, d\Omega = \frac{3}{16\pi} (1 + \cos^2 \vartheta)\, d\Omega \qquad \text{for } m = -1 \tag{8.2c}$$

where ϑ is the angle between H and the direction of emission of the photon and $w(\vartheta)$ is the probability per unit solid angle that the photon will be emitted into the solid angle $d\Omega$ at ϑ. Equation (8.2a) is the common expression for the intensity of radiation from a classical linear dipole, when $\vartheta = 0$ denotes the direction of the axis of the dipole.

If the states are equally populated, the total angular distribution is the sum of Eqs. (8.2), which is a constant. Hence, even in the presence of the ordinary magnetic field, the total radiation is still isotropic. We see that the ability to observe anisotropy in the angular distribution depends on our ability to obtain a *nonuniform population of magnetic substates*. This can be done most simply in the dipole case of Fig. 8.1 if we can arrange experimentally to exclude observation of the $m = 0$ transitions. The angular distribution of the $m = \pm 1$ transitions would then have a $(1 + \cos^2 \vartheta)$ distribution.

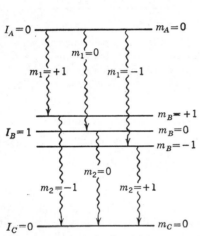

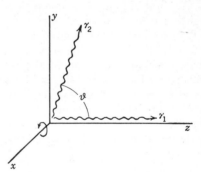

Fig. 8.3 In the dipole-dipole, γ_1-γ_2 cascade, $0(1)1(1)0$, the intermediate state has one unit of angular momentum, which must be annulled by the emission of the second quantum. This requirement imposes an angular dependence on the direction of emission of the second quantum relative to the first.

Fig. 8.2 Method of exciting the magnetic sublevels of I_B by means of a previous dipole transition from $I_A = 0$.

We can do this experimentally by forming the $m_B = 0$ sublevel in a preceding transition $I_A \xrightarrow{\gamma_1} I_B$, as shown in Fig. 8.2. No external magnetic field is used. In its absence, the m_B sublevels are degenerate, and the transition probabilities from $I_A = 0$, $m_A = 0$, to each of the m_B levels are equal. Also the direction of $\vartheta = 0$ in the laboratory is arbitrary, and we will now take it as the direction of emission of the first quantum γ_1. The first transition cannot lead to the sublevel $m_B = 0$ in this particular coordinate system, because by Eq. (8.2a) its intensity in the $\vartheta = 0$ direction is zero. All the photons in the $\vartheta = 0$ direction therefore correspond to $m_1 = \pm 1$ transitions. The $m_1 = +1$ transition has to be followed by $m_2 = -1$, and $m_1 = -1$ by $m_2 = +1$, in order to reach $I_C = 0$. Both these second transitions have a $(1 + \cos^2 \vartheta)$ distribution, by Eqs. (8.2b, c). Thus if γ_1 is detected in a counter whose direction from the source is called $\vartheta = 0$, the probability that γ_2 will traverse a second counter set at an angle ϑ will vary as $(1 + \cos^2 \vartheta)$.

These considerations can be reduced to pictorial terms as in Figs. 8.3 and 8.4. In Fig. 8.3, if γ_1 is emitted in the z direction ($\vartheta = 0$), its dipole character ($l_1 = 1$) requires it to leave the residual system with one unit of angular momentum normal to the direction of propagation. (This corresponds in the previous argument to $m_1 = \pm 1$.) Let the arbitrary direction of this unit of angular momentum be chosen as the x axis. The second radiation γ_2 must remove this unit of angular momentum, in order to reach $I_c = 0$. The direction of γ_2 can therefore be any direction which is normal to the x axis, i.e., in the yz plane. If γ_1 and γ_2 are detected with instruments which are not sensitive to the plane of polarization of γ_1 and γ_2, then the observed γ_1-γ_2 coincidence counts will include all possible orientations of the x axis. For unpolarized detection we must remove the arbitrary selection of the x direction by rotating the xy plane about the z axis. This averaging operation must lead then to the angular correlation function

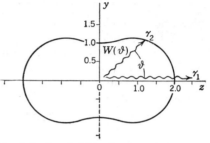

$$W(\vartheta)\, d\Omega$$
$$= W(90°)(1 + \cos^2 \vartheta)\, d\Omega \quad (8.3)$$

where $W(\vartheta)$ is the probability, per unit solid angle, that the second quantum is directed into the element of solid angle $d\Omega$ at any angle ϑ with the first quantum. This spatial distribution is indicated in Fig. 8.4, where the fore-and-aft symmetry which arises from even powers of $\cos \vartheta$ is evident. This

Fig. 8.4   Spatial distribution of the angular correlation for a dipole-dipole, γ-γ cascade. The length of the radius vector $W(\vartheta)$ gives the probability, per unit solid angle, that the angle between the directions of the two successive photons will be ϑ. The directions of the two photons γ_1 and γ_2 are, of course, interchangeable. Note the fore-and-aft symmetry. The angle ϑ is actually in center-of-mass coordinates, but the nuclear recoil from γ-ray emission is so slight that the difference for laboratory coordinates is negligible.

fore-and-aft symmetry, in center-of-mass coordinates, is, in fact, characteristic of most angular correlation distributions.

Equation (8.3) is applicable only to the 0(1)1(1)0 cascade. There are as yet no known nuclear examples of two successive dipole γ rays. Most of the γ-γ cascades which have been measured thus far are 4(2)2(2)0, or quadrupole-quadrupole cascades, in even-Z even-N nuclides such as Mg^{24}, Ni^{60}, etc.

b. General Case for γ-γ Angular Correlation. The principles which we have just outlined can be applied to any γ-γ cascade involving arbitrary multipole orders. The mathematical complications rapidly become insuperable unless more sophisticated methods are invoked. Yang (Y1) first applied group theory to obtain the form of the general angular-correlation function. For the generalized γ-γ cascade $I_A(l_1)I_B(l_2)I_c$ the angular-correlation function $W(\vartheta)$ for the angle ϑ between the successive γ rays can be shown to be (Y1, F5, B67)

$$W(\vartheta)\, d\Omega = \sum_{i=0}^{i=L} A_{2i} P_{2i}(\cos \vartheta)\, d\Omega \qquad (8.4)$$

where A_{2i} are coefficients which depend on l_1 and l_2, and $P_{2i}(\cos \vartheta)$ are the even Legendre polynomials. While this form is convenient for the theory, an equivalent and more common form is usually used for comparison with experiments. This is a power series in *even* powers of $\cos \vartheta$, and normalized to $W(90°) = 1$, as follows

$$W(\vartheta)\, d\Omega = (1 + a_2 \cos^2 \vartheta + a_4 \cos^4 \vartheta + \cdots + a_{2L} \cos^{2L} \vartheta)\, d\Omega \qquad (8.5)$$

where the coefficients a_2, a_4, ... are functions of the angular momenta I_A, I_B, I_C, l_1, and l_2 but not of the relative parity of the levels.

There are rigorous restrictions on the number of terms in Eqs. (8.4) and (8.5); the highest even power of $\cos \vartheta$ is determined by l_1, I_B, or l_2, whichever is *smallest*. Thus $2L$ is not larger than $2l_1$ or $2I_B$, or $2l_2$, and will be one unit less than the smallest if the smallest is odd. For example, if $I_B = 0$ or $\frac{1}{2}$, $W(\vartheta) = 1$, and the angular correlation distribution will be isotropic.

A rough over-all index of the complexity of the angular distribution is given by the so-called *anisotropy*, defined as

$$\text{Anisotropy} = \frac{W(180°)}{W(90°)} - 1 = a_2 + a_4 + \cdots + a_{2L} \qquad (8.6)$$

This is a convenient quantity experimentally as it involves measurements for only two values of ϑ, corresponding to "back-to-back" and "normal" directions. However, this simple index may conceal some of the true complexity of the distribution, because the coefficients a_2, a_4, ... can have negative as well as positive values.

We shall see that Eqs. (8.4) and (8.5) are very general indeed and that with appropriate evaluation of a_2, a_4, ... they apply to all two-step cascades, α-γ, β-γ, γ-γ, γ-e^-, e^--e^-, etc., as well as to nuclear scattering experiments and nuclear disintegrations.

The *conditions of validity* of Eq. (8.4) or (8.5) entail all the assumptions made in its derivation. These are:

1. The magnetic sublevels m_A of the initial level I_A are equally populated. This is generally true for ordinary radioactive sources at room temperature but can be altered deliberately in suitable cases by the influence of very low temperatures combined with very large magnetic fields, Eq. (8.1).

2. Each nuclear level I_A, I_B, and I_C must be a single level with well-defined parity and angular momentum. Violations of this condition, caused by the occasional overlap of broad nuclear levels at high excitation energies, may give rise to interference effects and to the appearance of terms in odd powers of $\cos \vartheta$ in $W(\vartheta)$.

3. Each of the radiations l_1 and l_2 must correspond to a pure multi-

pole.   Mixed radiations of opposite parity can give rise to interference effects and odd powers of cos ϑ.

4. Equation (8.5) restricts its attention to the relative directions of the two radiations, without cognizance of their states of polarization.   Therefore Eq. (8.5) applies only to the usual experimental situations in which both detectors are insensitive to the plane of polarization of the radiations.

5. The half-period of the intermediate level I_B must be short enough to permit the orientation of I_B to remain undisturbed.   We have seen that $I_B \geq 1$ if any anisotropy exists.   The finite magnetic dipole moment μ of this intermediate level will therefore give rise to a Larmor precession of I_B with Larmor frequency ν in the field of the atomic electrons or in any applied strong external field. The half-period $T_{\frac{1}{2}}$ of the intermediate level must be short compared with the reciprocal of the angular velocity $2\pi\nu$ of the Larmor precession if there is to be no influence on $W(\vartheta)$.

c. Magnetic Dipole Moment of an Excited Nuclear Level.   Between $T_{\frac{1}{2}} \sim 10^{-8}$ sec and a lower limit of $\sim 10^{-5}$ sec (set experimentally by the accidental coincidence rate due to the resolving time of the coincidence circuits) it is possible in a few selected cases to influence the angular correlation by a known external field and thus to determine the nuclear g factor for the excited level.   This has been done in the case of the 243-kev level in Cd^{111} (Fig. 8.5), where the reduction in anisotropy with field strength (0 to 7,000 gauss), applied perpendicular to the plane of the two γ rays, leads to the value $g = -(0.28 \pm 0.05)$ (F66).   The

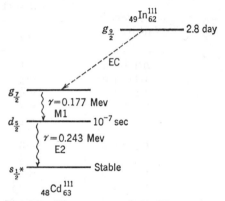

Fig. 8.5   The γ-γ cascade in Cd^{111}, following the electron-capture transition $In^{111} \rightarrow Cd^{111}$.   The influence of an external magnetic field on the γ-γ angular correlation leads to a value of $\mu \simeq -0.7$ nuclear magneton for the magnetic dipole moment of the $d_{\frac{5}{2}}$ level at 0.243 Mev. Cd^{111} also has another isomeric level (not shown here) lying 0.149 Mev above the $d_{\frac{5}{2}}$ level.   This is an $h_{\frac{11}{2}}$ level, produced by $Cd^{110}(n,\gamma)Cd^{111}$, and decaying to the $d_{\frac{5}{2}}$ level with a half-period of 48 min (G25).

ground level of Cd^{111} has the directly measured values $I = \frac{1}{2}, \mu = -0.595$ and therefore is an $s_{\frac{1}{2}}$ level in the shell model (Chap. 11, Sec. 2).   The angular momentum of the intermediate level is $I_B = \frac{5}{2}$ from the angular correlation measurements on $W(\vartheta)$ without an external field.   The negative sign for g makes the intermediate level $d_{\frac{5}{2}}$ (in agreement with the single-particle shell model) and gives for the excited level at 243 kev in Cd^{111}

$$\mu(d_{\frac{5}{2}}) = -(0.7 \pm 0.1) \text{ nuclear magneton}$$

This is the first measurement of the *magnetic dipole moment* for an excited nuclear level.   In magnitude, it is comparable with μ of the ground level in this case.

d. γ-γ Angular-correlation Coefficients. Hamilton (H14), Falkoff (F4), and others have deduced the angular-correlation coefficients a_2, a_4, . . . for most of the multipoles expected in γ-γ cascades. As illustrations, we give in Table 8.1 the coefficients (H14) for some of the possible dipole and quadrupole γ-γ cascades for the important case $I_C = 0$, as met in even-Z even-N nuclei.

TABLE 8.1. ANGULAR-CORRELATION COEFFICIENTS FOR SOME DIPOLE AND QUADRUPOLE γ-γ CASCADE TRANSITIONS

[When the angular-momentum quantum number $I_C = 0$ for the final level, such as the ground level of even-Z even-N nuclides (H14, B107).]

γ-γ cascade $I_A(l_1)I_B(l_2)I_C$	$W(\vartheta)\, d\Omega = (1 + a_2 \cos^2\vartheta + a_4 \cos^4\vartheta)\, d\Omega$	
	a_2	a_4
0(1)1(1)0	1	0
1(1)1(1)0	$-\frac{1}{3}$	0
1(2)1(1)0	$-\frac{1}{3}$	0
2(1)1(1)0	$-\frac{1}{3}$	0
3(2)1(1)0	$-\frac{3}{29}$	0
0(2)2(2)0	-3	$+4$
1(1)2(2)0	$-\frac{1}{3}$	0
2(1)2(2)0	$+\frac{3}{7}$	0
2(2)2(2)0	$-\frac{15}{13}$	$+\frac{16}{13}$
3(1)2(2)0	$-\frac{3}{29}$	0
4(2)2(2)0	$+\frac{1}{8}$	$+\frac{1}{24}$

Experimentally, the application of scintillation counters to the problem of angular correlation of successive γ rays, by Deutsch and coworkers (B107, M20), first gave the required combination of high sensitivity and good resolving time which facilitates routine coincidence counting. With these techniques $W(\vartheta)$ was found to be anisotropic for the γ-γ cascades which follow the β-ray transitions: $Na^{24} \rightarrow Mg^{24}$, $Sc^{46} \rightarrow Ti^{46}$, $Co^{60} \rightarrow Ni^{60}$, $Sr^{88} \rightarrow Y^{88}$, $Rh^{106} \rightarrow Pd^{106}$, and $Cs^{134} \rightarrow Ba^{134}$.

Figure 8.6 shows the measured dependence of the coincidence counting rate on ϑ, for the γ-γ cascade in Ni^{60}, and is in agreement with a quadrupole-quadrupole transition 4(2)2(2)0. This observation fixes the angular momenta of the excited levels at 1.33 and 2.50 Mev in Ni^{60} as $I_B = 2$ and $I_A = 4$, as was shown in Fig. 7.2. The γ-γ cascades in Mg^{24}, Ti^{46}, Ba^{134}, and Ce^{140} have also been shown to be 4(2)2(2)0. In Hf^{177}, the γ-γ cascade appears to be $\frac{5}{2}(1)\frac{7}{2}(2)\frac{3}{2}$, while in Cd^{111} (Fig. 8.5) the γ-γ cascade $g_{\frac{7}{2}}(1)d_{\frac{5}{2}}(2)s_{\frac{1}{2}}$ seems well established (F66).

e. Parity of Excited Levels. γ-γ **Polarization-direction Correlation.** The γ-γ angular-correlation coefficients of Table 8.1 depend only on multipole order and not on parity. This is because, for the same multipole order, magnetic and electric multipoles have the same angular distribution. They differ in their parities and in the corresponding orien-

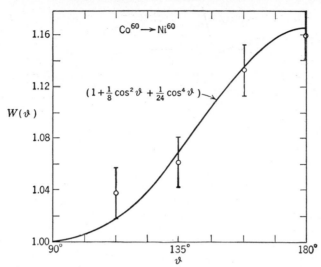

Fig. 8.6 Coincidence counting rate, proportional to $W(\vartheta)$, for the γ-γ cascade in Ni^{60}, following the β decay of Co^{60}. The observations are in agreement with the unique angular correlation distribution for a 4(2)2(2)0 cascade (Table 8.1). These measurements determine the angular momentum of the 1.33 Mev and 2.50-Mev excited levels in Ni^{60}, which were shown in Fig. 7.2. [*Data from Brady and Deutsch* (B107).]

tation of the plane of polarization of the electromagnetic radiation. By measuring the orientation of the polarization vector (here defined as the $\mathcal{E}$ vector of the electromagnetic radiation) relative to the plane of the two successive γ rays, it can be determined whether the successive multipoles are electric or magnetic (H14). Hence the relative parity of the nuclear levels can be measured.

Experimentally, Metzger and Deutsch (M44) developed a successful γ-ray triple coincidence polarimeter, shown in Fig. 8.7, and measured the polarization-direction correlation of the γ-γ cascades in Ti^{46}, Ni^{60}, Pd^{106}, and Ba^{134}.

Hamilton's (H14) theory of the polarization-direction correlation can be expressed qualitatively in terms of the measurable ratio $\mathcal{E}_{\parallel}/\mathcal{E}_{\perp}$, which is the ratio of the polarization of γ_1 parallel ($\mathcal{E}_{\parallel}$) to the ϑ plane containing the two γ rays, and perpendicular ($\mathcal{E}_{\perp}$) to the plane of the two γ rays. In a quadrupole-quadrupole cascade, the polarization-correlation when $\vartheta = 90°$ is

$$\frac{\mathcal{E}_{\parallel}}{\mathcal{E}_{\perp}} > 1 \text{ for E2-E2} \qquad (I_A \text{ and } I_C \text{ have same parity})$$

$$\frac{\mathcal{E}_{\parallel}}{\mathcal{E}_{\perp}} = 1 \text{ for E2-M2, or M2-E2} \ (I_A \text{ and } I_C \text{ have opposite parity})$$

$$\frac{\mathcal{E}_{\parallel}}{\mathcal{E}_{\perp}} < 1 \text{ for M2-M2} \qquad (I_A \text{ and } I_C \text{ have same parity})$$

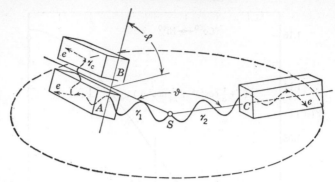

Fig. 8.7 The γ-ray triple-coincidence polarimeter of Metzger and Deutsch (M44). Triple coincidences are registered between the three scintillation counters A, B, and C. (1) The source S sends a photon γ_1 into counter A, where γ_1 projects a Compton electron in the scintillator, thus producing a count in A. The Compton scattered photon γ_C will be preferentially directed with its electric vector ε_C parallel to the electric vector ε_1 of the primary photon γ_1 [see the Klein-Nishina formula, Chap. 23, Sec. 2, Eq. (2.3) and Fig. 2.2]. Thus if ε_1 lies *normal* to the plane of counters A and B, there is a maximum probability that γ_C will be directed toward counter B. (2) In counter B, γ_C must produce a countable secondary electron, either by photoelectric absorption or another Compton collision. (3) In counter C, located at angle ϑ from the direction of A and B, the second photon γ_2 from the γ-γ cascade in the source S must also produce a countable secondary electron. Counters C and A form a coincidence pair which is insensitive to polarization, as in ordinary angular correlation experiments.

Thus *for two electric quadrupoles*, E2-E2, *the plane of the* ε *vector tends to lie parallel to the plane of the two* γ *rays*. For two magnetic quadrupoles M2-M2, the plane of the ε vector tends to lie perpendicular to the plane of the two γ rays. When $\vartheta = 180°$, $\varepsilon_\parallel / \varepsilon_\perp = 1$, independent of the electric or magnetic character of the successive quadrupoles.

Figure 8.8 shows the polarization-direction correlation of the cascade γ rays in Ni^{60}, following the β decay of Co^{60}. Unambiguously, $\varepsilon_\parallel / \varepsilon_\perp > 1$, showing that both γ rays are electric quadrupoles. Now this cascade can be written more explicitly as 4(E2)2(E2)0. This proves that the intermediate level at 1.33 Mev has the same parity as the ground level, and so does also the upper level at 2.50 Mev. Because Ni^{60} is an even-Z

TABLE 8.2. β-γ ANGULAR CORRELATION (F5)

Note that the angular distribution of β-γ coincidences is isotropic unless the β spectrum has a *forbidden shape*.

β Transition	γ Multipole	$W(\vartheta)/W(90°)$
Allowed β..........................	Any	1
Forbidden by selection rules, but having allowed spectrum shape..............	Any	1
First-forbidden.......................	Any	$1 + a_2 \cos^2 \vartheta$
Second-forbidden....................	Dipole	$1 + a_2 \cos^2 \vartheta$
Second-forbidden....................	$\geq$Quadrupole	$1 + c_2 \cos^2 \vartheta + a_4 \cos^4 \vartheta$

even-N nucleus, it is assumed from the shell model that the ground level is $I_c = 0$, even, or $I = 0^+$. This is the experimental basis for the parity assignments given this nuclide in Fig. 7.2.

f. β-γ Angular-correlation Coefficients. Angular-correlation coefficients for the successive emission of any two nuclear radiations, such as α-γ, β-γ, γ-e^-, . . . , have been developed and tabulated by Falkoff and Uhlenbeck (F5) and others. In general, the coefficients a_2, a_4, . . . of Eq. (8.5) are found to be functions of the angular momenta of the three nuclear levels and the two emitted radiations, as well as the interaction between the emitted particles and the nucleus.

For β-γ angular correlations, irrespective of the character of the β interaction, the generalizations shown in Table 8.2 apply to the complexity of the angular-distribution function $W(\vartheta)$ of Eq. (8.5). Near the low-energy end of the β spectrum there is no β-γ angular correlation; the strongest correlation occurs for β rays near the maximum energy of their spectrum, where the neutrino takes little energy and momentum. Anisotropic β-γ angular correlations have been observed in K^{42}, As^{76}, Rb^{86}, Sb^{122}, Sb^{124}, I^{126}, Tm^{170}, ...

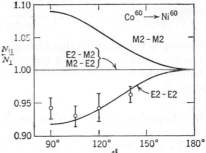

Fig. 8.8 Polarization-direction correlation of the two quadrupole γ rays in Ni^{60}, which follow the β decay of Co^{60} (Fig. 7.2). The ordinates are the experimental triple-coincidence counting ratios $N_{\parallel}/N_{\perp}$. For $N_{\parallel}$ the polarimeter *counters* are parallel to the plane of the γ rays ($\varphi = 0$ in Fig. 8.7). Thus $N_{\parallel}$ corresponds to $\mathcal{E}_{\perp}$. For $N_{\perp}$, the *counters* are at $\varphi = 90°$ to the plane of the γ. The data show $N_{\parallel}/N_{\perp} < 1$ at $\vartheta = 90°$, hence $\mathcal{E}_{\parallel}/\mathcal{E}_{\perp} > 1$. The electric vector tends to lie parallel to the plane of the two γ rays, which must both be electric quadrupoles. The three curves show the different possible parity assignments for the two successive transitions, which are known from the directional correlation alone to be two quadrupoles. [*Adapted from Metzger and Deutsch* (M44).]

Problems

1. Show that the most probable plane *angle*, ϑ to $\vartheta + d\vartheta$, between two successive dipole γ-ray quanta, in the $0(1)1(1)0$ cascade is about $55°$.

2. In a γ-γ angular-correlation experiment show that the directional correlation will be disturbed if the half-period $T_{\frac{1}{2}}$ of the intermediate level does not satisfy the inequality

$$T_{\frac{1}{2}} \ll \frac{1}{2\pi\Delta\nu}$$

where $\Delta\nu$ is the hyperfine-structure separation for an atom with $J = \frac{1}{2}$, Eq. (1.11) of Chap. 5. Determine the restriction on $T_{\frac{1}{2}}$ in seconds for a middleweight nucleus, such as cesium. *Ans.:* $\sim 10^{-11}$ sec.

3. Under the same conditions as the previous problem, show that, if a strong external magnetic field H is applied, the angular correlation may be influenced if the half-period $T_{\frac{1}{2}}$ of the intermediate state is

$$T_{\frac{1}{2}} \sim \frac{I}{\mu}\frac{\hbar}{\mu_M}\frac{1}{H} = \frac{2 \times 10^{-4} \text{ sec}}{gH}$$

where μ is the magnetic dipole moment in units of the nuclear magneton μ_M and I is the angular-momentum quantum number of the intermediate level. Determine a typical critical value for $T_{\frac{1}{2}}$ if the applied field is 10^5 gauss. *Ans.:* $\sim 10^{-9}$ sec.

9. *Angular Distribution in Nuclear Reactions*

In any nuclear reaction, such as $B^{10}(\alpha,p)C^{13}$, the direction of the incident particle provides a reference axis for angular distribution studies. If we write out such a reaction in full, some obvious analogies appear with the case of the successive emission of two radiations. Thus, in

$$_5B^{10} + {_2}He^4 \rightarrow (_7N^{14}) \rightarrow {_1}H^1 + {_6}C^{13} \tag{9.1}$$

the excited compound nucleus $(_7N^{14})$ plays the role of the intermediate level I_B of the previous discussion. Generalizing, we can symbolize a large class of nuclear reactions as

$$A + a \rightarrow B \rightarrow c + C \tag{9.2}$$

Elastic- and inelastic-resonance-scattering processes are included by noting that a and c may be identical particles.

a. Channel Spin. In the dissociation of B, the products c and C have mutual orbital angular momentum l_2. Analogously, in the formation of B, we may represent by l_1 the mutual orbital angular momentum between A and a. Each of the four particles A, a, c, C may have a finite intrinsic nuclear angular momentum, denoted by the quantum numbers I_1, i_1, i_2, I_2, respectively. The vector sum of I_1 and i_1 may have any value between $|I_1 - i_1|$ and $|I_1 + i_1|$, and the particular value which it does have is called the entrance *channel spin* s_1. Similarly, the exit channel spin s_2 is the vector sum of I_2 and i_2 for the outgoing particles. These concepts and notation can be summarized mnemonically

$$
\begin{aligned}
(A + a) \quad &\rightarrow \quad B \quad \rightarrow \quad (c + C) & (9.2a)\\
(\mathbf{I}_1 + \mathbf{i}_1) + \mathbf{l}_1 &= \mathbf{I}_0 = \mathbf{l}_2 + (\mathbf{i}_2 + \mathbf{I}_2) & (9.2b)\\
\mathbf{s}_1 \quad + \mathbf{l}_1 &= \mathbf{I}_0 = \mathbf{l}_2 + \quad \mathbf{s}_2 & (9.2c)
\end{aligned}
$$

where the quantum number I_0 denotes the angular momentum of the intermediate compound level. I_0 is preserved throughout the reaction. The analogy is now complete. Our previous notation $I_A(l_1)I_B(l_2)I_C$ for the two-step process now becomes

$$s_1(l_1)I_0(l_2)s_2 \tag{9.2d}$$

and is applicable to all nuclear reactions and scattering processes in which a compound intermediate level is formed and has definite parity and angular momentum. The angular distribution of reaction products is measured in terms of cos ϑ, where ϑ is the angle between the directions of a and c, in center-of-mass coordinates.

b. Elastic Resonance Scattering. We may consider the case of elastic scattering between spinless particles without significant loss of generality (B67). The differential cross section $d\sigma$ for scattering into the solid angle $d\Omega$, at angle ϑ, is developed in Appendix C [Eq. (107)] and is

$$d\sigma = |f(\vartheta)|^2 \, d\Omega \tag{9.3}$$

where the complex scattering amplitude $f(\vartheta)$ is a summation of functions of the phase shifts δ_l, which are real quantities whose values depend on the nature of the central scattering force $U(r)$ and on the wave number $k = 1/\lambda$ of the colliding particles, as given by Eq. (118) of Appendix C. The summation over various partial waves l, and evaluation of

$$|f(\vartheta)|^2 = f^*(\vartheta)f(\vartheta)$$

can be carried through rigorously and leads to the more convenient form

$$d\sigma = \lambda^2 \sum_{i=0}^{\infty} B_i P_i(\cos \vartheta) \, d\Omega \tag{9.4}$$

in which $P_i (\cos \vartheta)$ are the Legendre polynomials and B_i is a real but complicated quantity which depends on the angular momenta and the phase shifts. There are rigorous restrictions which limit severely the number of terms in Eq. (9.4), as discussed below.

c. Angular Distribution for Reactions in Which a Compound Nucleus Is Formed. Under conditions of validity which are the complete analogues of those given for Eqs. (8.4) and (8.5), Eq. (9.4) is applicable to all collision processes of the type $A + a \rightarrow B \rightarrow c + C$. As a consequence of conservation of parity, only the terms involving even powers of cos ϑ are finite if I_0 is a pure level with single-valued parity and angular momentum. For convenience in comparisons with experiment, Eq. (9.4) can be put in the more common form

$$\frac{W(\vartheta)}{W(90°)} \, d\Omega = [1 + A(E) \cos^2 \vartheta + B(E) \cos^4 \vartheta + \cdots] \, d\Omega \tag{9.5}$$

where the real coefficients $A(E)$, $B(E)$, . . . are complicated functions of the energy E of the incident particle, of the angular momenta s_1, I_0, s_2, l_1, and l_2, and of the nature of the forces between the particles (Y1, B67). The highest power, $\cos^{2L} \vartheta$, is restricted by l_1, I_0, or l_2, whichever is *smallest*, and $2L$ is not greater than $2l_1$, $2I_0$, or $2l_2$. These restrictions are analogous to those which apply to Eq. (8.5). If $I_0 = 0$ or $\frac{1}{2}$, the distribution is isotropic in center-of-mass coordinates. Also, if $l_1 = 0$, or $l_2 = 0$ (s waves), the distribution is isotropic.

Thus, in all nuclear reactions, information on l_1 or I_0 or l_2 is obtained directly by noting how many terms in $\cos^2 \vartheta$ are required to match the observed angular distribution. Interference terms in odd powers of cos ϑ may enter Eq. (9.5) if the compound state is a mixture of levels of opposite parity, and if the incoming or outgoing particle waves contain mixtures of opposite parity. Examples of such mixtures have been observed in $Li^6(d,p)Li^7$, $Li^6(p,\alpha)He^3$, and $Li^7(p,n)Be^7$, for example, (A10).

d. Angular Distribution for $Li^7(p,\alpha)He^4$. The angular momentum and parity of the resonance level at 19.9 Mev above ground in Be^8 was given in Fig 1.1 as $I = 2^+$. This is determined by the angular distribution of the α rays from the reaction $Li^7(p,\alpha)He^4$, which has been the object of many careful experimental and theoretical studies, although several details require further work. Here we wish only to show how qualitative interpretation of angular-distribution data suffices to determine $I = 2^+$ for the 19.9-Mev level.

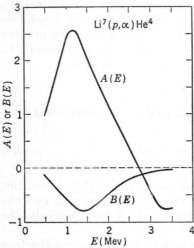

From $E = 0.5$ to 3.5 Mev, the experimentally determined angular distribution follows $1 + A(E)\cos^2\vartheta + B(E)\cos^4\vartheta$, where $A(E)$ and $B(E)$ are empirical coefficients whose observed dependence on E is shown in Fig. 9.1. The shape of these curves can be matched by a detailed theory of the reaction (I3, H50). Here we note only that a $\cos^4\vartheta$ term is required, and that there is no positive experimental evidence for a $\cos^6\vartheta$ term. Then, from the conditions on the highest power of $\cos^2\vartheta$, $l_1 \geq 2$, $I_0 \geq 2$, and $l_2 \geq 2$.

We have noted in Sec. 1 that the Bose statistics and spinless character of the two α particles from this reaction require l_2 to be even. Because the intrinsic spin of the α particles is zero, the exit channel spin is zero, and therefore $I_0 = l_2$. Any level in Be^8 which can dissociate into two α parti-

Fig. 9.1 The observed angular-distribution coefficients $A(E)$ and $B(E)$ in $W(\vartheta)/W(90°) = 1 + A(E)\cos^2\vartheta + B(E)\cos^4\vartheta$, for the reaction $Li^7(p,\alpha)He^4$. E is the kinetic energy of the incident protons in laboratory coordinates; ϑ is the angle between p and α in center-of-mass coordinates. [*Data are a composite of several authors in various energy ranges* (H50, T1, A10).]

cles is obliged by conservation of parity and of angular momentum to have *even parity* and even total angular momentum $I_0 = 0, 2, 4, \ldots$.

In the entrance channel, the ground level of Li^7 is $I_1 = \frac{3}{2}$, and it has odd intrinsic parity in every reasonable nuclear model, while the proton has $i_1 = \frac{1}{2}$ and even intrinsic parity. Thus the entrance-channel spin has odd parity and is $s_1 = \frac{3}{2} \pm \frac{1}{2}^+ = 1^-$ or 2^-. This restricts the incident orbital angular momentum to the odd values $l_1 = 1, 3, 5, \ldots$, of which only $l_1 = 3, 5, \ldots$ are possible because of the $\cos^4\vartheta$ term. The absence of a $\cos^6\vartheta$ term is therefore not dictated by l_1 but means $I_0 < 3$. The only possible assignment for the resonance level is therefore $I_0 = 2$, even.

The yield of the $Li^7(p,\alpha)He^4$ reaction, as a function of bombarding energy E, was shown in Fig. 1.1. The resonance peak in the yield at $E \sim 3$ Mev is attributed to the level with $I_0 = 2^+$, at 19.9 Mev above ground in Be^8. Detailed analysis of the influence of E on the yield and on $A(E)$ and $B(E)$ indicates that this level, which has a width Γ at half maximum of ~ 1 Mev, is superimposed on a much broader level $I_0 = 0^+$, which underlies the whole region. Both levels can be produced by both p-wave and f-wave protons ($l_1 = 1, 3$).

e. Angular Distribution in Photodisintegration of the Deuteron. Two mechanisms for the disintegration of the deuteron by γ rays are experimentally distinguishable, if the γ-ray energy is only slightly greater than the binding energy (2.22 Mev) of the deuteron. The proton and neutron have parallel spins ($^3S_1$ level) in the ground level of the deuteron. The antiparallel-spin state ($^1S_0$) is an excited level which is unstable by about 65 kev against dissociation. There is a continuum corresponding to a wide ^3P state. The incident photon can be absorbed either as an electric dipole or as a magnetic dipole, and these two processes produce different angular distributions.

In the *photoelectric* disintegration, the deuteron absorbs the incident photon as an electric dipole. This involves a change in parity and $\Delta I = 1$ (Table 4.2). Hence, in the struck deuteron, $\Delta S = 0$, $\Delta L = 1$, yes, and the ($^3S_1$, even) level is converted to (^3P, odd), the dissociation of which is observed to have a $(1 - \cos^2 \vartheta) = \sin^2 \vartheta$ angular distribution (F72). This corresponds classically to ejection of the proton by interaction with the electric vector of the incident γ ray and is peaked at 90° from the direction of the incident Poynting vector.

The *photomagnetic* disintegration results from absorption of the incident photon as a magnetic dipole, $\Delta I = 1$, no. Then in the struck deuteron, $\Delta S = 1$, $\Delta L = 0$, no, and the ($^3S_1$, even) level is converted by the spin flip to ($^1S_0$, even). This level is unstable and dissociates with an isotropic distribution in center-of-mass coordinates because the intermediate level has $I_0 = 0$. The photomagnetic disintegration corresponds classically to an interaction between the magnetic vector of the incident photon and the spin magnetic dipole moments of the proton and neutron. Being of opposite sign, these magnetic moments are antiparallel in the $^3S_1$ ground level and parallel in the $^1S_0$ excited level.

The photomagnetic cross section is largest just above the γ-ray threshold at 2.22 Mev and falls as the γ-ray energy increases, as shown in Fig. 4.1 of Chap. 10. Above about 2.5 Mev, photoelectric disintegration becomes the dominant process (W70).

f. Deuteron Stripping Reactions. The outstanding peculiarities of the deuteron as a nuclear projectile are its small internal binding energy and the large average separation ($\sim 4 \times 10^{-13}$ cm) between the constituent proton and neutron, which actually spend most of their time outside the "range" of their attractive mutual force (Chap. 10, Fig. 2.1).

In nuclear reactions of the (d,α) type the incident deuteron joins the target nucleus to form a compound nucleus, in the manner of most other nuclear reactions. Much more commonly, the loosely joined deuteron structure dissociates in the external field of the target nucleus, and only one of its constituents is captured. These are the very common *"stripping reactions,"* (d,p) and (d,n).

Energetics of Stripping Reactions. In the (d,p) stripping reaction, the target nucleus accepts a neutron of orbital angular momentum l_n directly into one of the levels of the *final* nucleus. The proton proceeds in a direction determined by l_n and with an energy determined by the reaction energy Q for the formation of the level into which its partner was captured. Analogously, in (d,n) stripping reactions, the target nucleus accepts a proton of orbital angular momentum l_p directly into one of the excited levels or the ground level of the final nucleus. Thus the energetics of the stripping reaction are indistinguishable from those in which a compound nucleus is formed and subsequently dissociates.

Angular Distribution in Stripping Reactions. The angular distributions of the product particles are entirely different in stripping reactions and in compound nucleus reactions. The direction of the uncaptured particle in stripping reactions is determined by the angular momentum l_n or l_p transferred to the final nucleus by the captured particle. The angular distribution does not have fore-and-aft symmetry about $\vartheta = 90°$ but shows a pronounced forward maximum. This maximum lies directly forward at $\vartheta = 0°$, if l_n or $l_p = 0$, and moves out to progressively larger angles for larger values of l_n or l_p. There are also secondary maxima, for each l_n or l_p value, as shown in Fig. 9.2. The theory of the angular distribution in (d,p) and (d,n) stripping reactions has been developed by

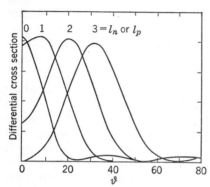

Fig. 9.2 Angular distribution of the uncaptured particle in the stripping reactions (d,p) and (d,n). The captured particle transfers orbital angular momentum l_n or l_p directly into a level in the final nucleus. In general, the differential cross section is largest for l_n or $l_p = 0$ and decreases as the angular-momentum transfer increases. The illustrative angular distributions shown refer to any stripping reaction for which the incident deuteron energy is 14.9 Mev and the uncaptured particle has 19.4 Mev, both in center-of-mass coordinates. [*From Butler* (B146).]

Butler, using approximations which are equivalent to the Born approximation (B146, G18). Agreement with experiment is excellent over a wide range of target nuclei and deuteron energies, and the method is rapidly adding to our knowledge of the energy, angular momentum, and parity of excited levels in nuclei (A10, B128, B127, S31).

Problems

1. In the nuclear reaction $A + a \rightarrow B \rightarrow c + C$, show that, in center-of-mass coordinates, $\cos \vartheta$ has the same absolute value, whether ϑ is defined as the angle between the directions of the particles (a,c), or (a,C), or (A,c), or (A,C).

2. In the reaction $Li^7(p,\alpha)He^4$, compare the height of the coulomb barrier with that of the centrifugal barrier for incident s-, p-, and f-wave protons, measuring each in Mev at the nuclear radius.   *Ans.:* $B_{coul} = 1.5$ Mev; $B_{cent} = l(l + 1)$ 2.88 Mev.

3. Explain qualitatively, in terms of angular momenta and parity of partial waves, why Rutherford scattering shows a characteristically forward distribution, $\csc^4 (\vartheta/2)$, instead of fore-and-aft symmetry in center-of-mass coordinates.

4. When Li^6 (whose ground level is $I = 1$, even) is bombarded by deuterons whose kinetic energy in laboratory coordinates is $E_d = 0$ to 1 Mev, the yield of the reaction $Li^6(d,\alpha)$ He^4 shows a moderate resonance peak at $E_d \simeq 0.6$ Mev. If ϑ is the center-of-mass angle between the direction of the incident deuterons and that of the observed α rays, the number of α rays per unit solid angle, at mean angle ϑ, is found to be proportional to $1 + A \cos^2 \vartheta$, where the coefficient A is a smoothly varying function of E_d. If any $\cos^4 \vartheta$ term is present, its coefficient in this energy domain is negligible compared with A. From this information alone, and the masses of the reacting constituents, determine systematically and clearly the energy, angular momentum, and parity of the excited resonance level in the compound nucleus. Which partial waves of deuterons (s, p, d, etc.) are effective in producing this excited level?

CHAPTER 7

Isotopic Abundance Ratios

We have seen that many of the chemical elements consist of mixtures of isotopes. For nearly every element, the relative abundance of its several isotopes appears to be constant and completely independent of the ultimate geographical and geological origin of the specimen. Even in meteorites, the isotopic abundance ratios of all elements so far measured are the same as in the earth (E18).

The principal exceptions to this generalization occur in specimens where radioactive disintegration processes result in the accumulation of stable isotopes as decay products. These include Sr^{87} in rubidium micas (H6, M20), Ca^{40} and A^{40} in potassium minerals, He^4 in gas wells where the ratio of He^4/He^3 is about ten times greater than in atmospheric helium (A26, A12, C39), and the well-known radiogenic leads (N14) which are found in uranium and thorium ores.

Also, very slight variations in the normal isotopic ratios have been reported for some of the lightest elements (T13). The O^{18}/O^{16} ratio is slightly greater in atmospheric oxygen than in fresh water. Various carbon sources show maximum variations of 5 per cent in the C^{12}/C^{13} ratio, limestone having a slightly higher ratio and plants a slightly lower ratio than the average of all sources (N20). Some minute differences in the lightest elements may well arise from natural evaporation and distillation processes occurring geologically over long periods of time. In several cases the variations can be correlated with the equilibrium constant for isotopic exchange reactions (Sec. 8), such as that between water and carbonate ion. These physical-chemical equilibrium constants are temperature-dependent. Then precision measurements of isotopic abundance ratios, such as O^{18}/O^{16} and S^{32}/S^{34}, can be used to determine climatic conditions in the geological past (U3, T16, N6).

The relative abundance of isotopes in nature, by virtue of its almost universal constancy, seems to be closely related to the basic problems of nuclear stability and of the origin of the elements. Because of the wide range of abundance ratios, several experimental methods have been used in their determination.

1. Ratios from Mass Spectroscopy

By far the most accurate abundance ratios are obtained from mass spectroscopes especially designed for this purpose. Particular precautions must be taken with the ion source to assure proper representation in the ion beam of all the isotopes present in the source material. For this reason, sources depending on the evaporation of the element from a solid state are often unsatisfactory, because of the slightly greater volatility of the light isotopes. The presence of hydrides in the ion beam has to be particularly guarded against. The most reliable method is to secure the element in a suitable gaseous compound, to dissociate and ionize a portion of this gas by bombardment with a well-collimated beam of high-energy electrons, to withdraw electrostatically the ions so formed, and to send them through the usual energy and momentum filters.

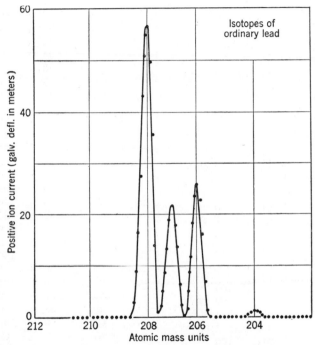

Fig. 1.1 The relative abundance of the isotopes (204, 206, 207, 208) of ordinary lead The numerical values of the relative abundances are 204:206:207:208 = 1.48:23.59: 22.64:52.29. [*From Nier* (N12).]

Best results usually are obtained using a single-focusing mass spectrometer, such as that shown in Fig. 3.5 of Chap. 3. Ions of various ne/M values may be brought into the collecting electrode through a fixed exit slit by varying the electrostatic field in the energy filter. Using modern vacuum-tube electrometer circuits, the relative ion currents can be determined with high accuracy, and the linearity of the electrical method is particularly suited to the study of very weak isotopes, such as K^{40}, which has an abundance of only about 1 part in 8,600 parts of K^{39}.

Absolute values of relative abundance can now be obtained with an accuracy of 1 per cent, and abundances relative to a reference standard

TABLE 1.1. RELATIVE ABUNDANCE OF THE ISOTOPES OF THE ELEMENTS
FOUND IN NATURE

[As compiled in 1950 by Bainbridge and Nier (B6). An asterisk denotes a naturally occurring radioactive nuclide. Parentheses denote questionable data.]

Nuclide			Relative abundance in atom per cent	Nuclide			Relative abundance in atom per cent
Z	Element	A		Z	Element	A	
1	H	1	99.9851	19	K	39	93.08
		2	0.0149			40*	0.0119
2	He	3	0.000 13			41	6.91
		4	99.9999	20	Ca	40	96.97
3	Li	6	7.52			42	0.64
		7	92.47			43	0.145
4	Be	9	100			44	2.06
5	B†	10	18.98 to 18.45			46	0.0033
		11	81.02 to 81.55			48	0.185
6	C‡	12	98.892	21	Sc	45	100
		13	1.108	22	Ti	46	7.95
7	N	14	99.635			47	7.75
		15	0.365			48	73.45
8	O§	16	99.758			49	5.51
		17	0.0373			50	5.34
		18	0.2039	23	V	50*	0.24
9	F	19	100			51	99.76
10	Ne	20	90.92	24	Cr	50	4.31
		21	0.257			52	83.76
		22	8.82			53	9.55
11	Na	23	100			54	2.38
12	Mg	24	78.60	25	Mn	55	100
		25	10.11	26	Fe	54	5.84
		26	11.29			56	91.68
13	Al	27	100			57	2.17
14	Si	28	92.27			58	0.31
		29	4.68	27	Co	59	100
		30	3.05	28	Ni	58	67.76
15	P	31	100			60	26.16
16	S	32	95.1			61	1.25
		33	0.74			62	3.66
		34	4.2			64	1.16
		36	0.016	29	Cu	63	69.1
17	Cl	35	75.4			65	30.9
		37	24.6	30	Zn	64	48.89
18	A	36	0.337			66	27.81
		38	0.063			67	4.11
		40	99.600				

† Abundances vary from different sources.
‡ As found in limestone.
§ As found in air.
‖ These abundances are recommended tentatively (B6).

TABLE 1.1. RELATIVE ABUNDANCE OF THE ISOTOPES OF THE ELEMENTS
FOUND IN NATURE (*Continued*)

Nuclide			Relative abundance in atom per cent	Nuclide			Relative abundance in atom per cent
Z	Element	A		Z	Element	A	
		68	18.56	44	Ru‖	96	(5.68)
		70	0.62			98	(2.22)
31	Ga	69	60.2			99	(12.81)
		71	39.8			100	(12.70)
32	Ge	70	20.55			101	(16.98)
		72	27.37			102	(31.34)
		73	7.61			104	(18.27)
		74	36.74	45	Rh	103	100
		76	7.67	46	Pd	102	0.8
33	As	75	100			104	9.3
34	Se	74	0.87			105	22.6
		76	9.02			106	27.2
		77	7.58			108	26.8
		78	23.52			110	13.5
		80	49.82	47	Ag	107	51.35
		82	9.19			109	48.65
35	Br	79	50.52	48	Cd	106	1.215
		81	49.48			108	0.875
36	Kr	78	0.354			110	12.39
		80	2.27			111	12.75
		82	11.56			112	24.07
		83	11.55			113	12.26
		84	56.90			114	28.86
		86	17.37			116	7.58
37	Rb	85	72.15	49	In	113	4.23
		87*	27.85			115*	95.77
38	Sr	84	0.56	50	Sn	112	0.95
		86	9.86			114	0.65
		87	7.02			115	0.34
		88	82.56			116	14.24
39	Y	89	100			117	7.57
40	Zr	90	51.46			118	24.01
		91	11.23			119	8.58
		92	17.11			120	32.97
		94	17.40			122	4.71
		96	2.80			124	5.98
41	Nb	93	100	51	Sb	121	57.25
42	Mo	92	15.86			123	42.75
		94	9.12	52	Te	120	0.089
		95	15.70			122	2.46
		96	16.50			123	0.87
		97	9.45			124	4.61
		98	23.75			125	6.99
		100	9.62			126	18.71

TABLE 1.1. RELATIVE ABUNDANCE OF THE ISOTOPES OF THE ELEMENTS
FOUND IN NATURE (*Continued*)

Z	Element	A	Relative abundance in atom per cent	Z	Element	A	Relative abundance in atom per cent
		128	31.79	64	Gd	152	0.20
		130*	34.49			154	2.15
53	I	127	100			155	14.73
54	Xe	124	0.096			156	20.47
		126	0.090			157	15.68
		128	1.919			158	24.87
		129	26.44			160	21.90
		130	4.08	65	Tb	159	100
		131	21.18	66	Dy	156	0.0524
		132	26.89			158	0.0902
		134	10.44			160	2.294
		136	8.87			161	18.88
55	Cs	133	100			162	25.53
56	Ba	130	0.101			163	24.97
		132	0.097			164	28.18
		134	2.42	67	Ho	165	100
		135	6.59	68	Er	162	0.136
		136	7.81			164	1.56
		137	11.32			166	33.41
		138	71.66			167	22.94
57	La	138*	0.089			168	27.07
		139	99.911			170	14.88
58	Ce	136	0.193	69	Tm	169	100
		138	0.250	70	Yb	168	0.140
		140	88.48			170	3.03
		142	11.07			171	14.31
59	Pr	141	100			172	21.82
60	Nd	142	27.13			173	16.13
		143	12.20			174	31.84
		144*	23.87			176	12.73
		145	8.30	71	Lu	175	97.40
		146	17.18			176*	2.60
		148	5.72	72	Hf	174	0.18
		150	5.60			176	5.15
62	Sm	144	3.16			177	18.39
		147*	15.07			178	27.08
		148	11.27			179	13.78
		149	13.84			180	35.44
		150	7.47	73	Ta	181	100
		152	26.63	74	W	180	0.135
		154	22.53			182	26.4
63	Eu	151	47.77			183	14.4
		153	52.23			184	30.6
						186	28.4

TABLE 1.1. RELATIVE ABUNDANCE OF THE ISOTOPES OF THE ELEMENTS
FOUND IN NATURE (*Continued*)

Nuclide			Relative abundance in atom per cent	Nuclide			Relative abundance in atom per cent
Z	Element	A		Z	Element	A	
75	Re	185	37.07	80	Hg	196	0.146
		187*	62.93			198	10.02
76	Os	184	0.018			199	16.84
		186	1.59			200	23.13
		187	1.64			201	13.22
		188	13.3			202	29.80
		189	16.1			204	6.85
		190	26.4	81	Tl	203	29.50
		192	41.0			205	70.50
77	Ir	191	38.5	82	Pb†	204	1.48
		193	61.5			206	23.6
78	Pt	190	0.012			207	22.6
		192	0.78			208	52.3
		194	32.8	83	Bi	209	100
		195	33.7	90	Th	232*	100
		196	25.4	92	U	234*	0.0058
		198	7.23			235*	0.715
79	Au	197	100			238*	99.28

† From nonradiogenic galena, Great Bear Lake.

can often be relied on to about 0.1 per cent or better. Excellent reviews of the technical problems and of current results have been published by Thode and Shields (T17) and by Bainbridge (B4).

A typical contemporary result of high quality is illustrated in Fig. 1.1, which is from Nier's precision study of ordinary (nonradiogenic) lead (N12) and shows the existence of only four isotopes, of mass numbers 204, 206, 207, and 208. The additional masses 203, 205, 209, 210 originally reported by Aston appear to have been spurious, some of them certainly due to the presence of hydrides.

a. Tables of Relative Isotopic Abundance. Most of the currently accepted data on the relative abundances of isotopes in nature have been obtained by mass-spectroscopic methods. The measurements have now been extended to all the elements, although the results on some are still tentative. An excellent compilation and critical review of the results obtained up to 1950 by all methods was prepared by Bainbridge and Nier (B6). Table 1.1 summarizes the values which they adopted for each of the elements found in nature. Future work can be expected to produce some changes, but these will probably be minor.

It is sometimes important to review the experimental evidence that a given nuclide, such as He^5 or Co^{57}, does *not* occur in nature. The experimental upper limits for the relative abundance of the nonoccurring nuclides are given in the excellent isotope tables by Bainbridge (B4).

Problem:

Ordinary carbon monoxide is to be analyzed in a mass spectrometer. What fraction of the molecules will have atomic weights of 28, 29, 30, and 31? *Ans.:* $(0.9865):(0.011\ 42):(0.002\ 02):(0.000\ 02)$.

2. *Isotope Shift in Line Spectra*

A number of rare but very important nuclides have been discovered by optical spectroscopic methods, after eluding early mass-spectroscopic searches.

Isotope shifts in optical line spectra arise from two distinct causes: (a) an effect of reduced mass and (b) an effect of nuclear volume.

a. In Light Elements. Bohr's theory of the atomic hydrogen spectra leads to an expression for the Rydberg constant, governing the frequency of the emission lines, which contains as a factor the reduced mass M_0 of the electron and nuclear system. If the mass of the nucleus is M, and of the electron m_0, then the moment of inertia about the center of mass of the system is $M_0 a^2$, where a is the separation of the nucleus and electron and the reduced mass M_0 is

$$M_0 \equiv \frac{m_0 M}{M + m_0} = \frac{m_0}{1 + (m_0/M)} \tag{2.1}$$

It is well known that this expression, when combined with the experimentally determined Rydberg constants for hydrogen and for singly ionized helium, leads to an independent estimate of about 1,836 for the ratio of masses of the proton and the electron. It is also clear from Eq. (2.1) that the Balmer series lines for the deuterium atom will have a slightly shorter wavelength than the same lines in the light hydrogen spectrum. Deuterium owes its discovery (U5) to this slight difference in emission frequency in the Balmer series, which corresponds to 1.79 A for $H_\alpha^1 - H_\alpha^2$ and 1.33 A for $H_\beta^1 - H_\beta^2$, the H^2 satellites gaining in intensity as the heavy hydrogen was concentrated by fractional distillations.

This spectroscopic method enjoyed dramatic success in the discovery of the very rare isotope H^2. From the relative intensity of the lines, it further indicated that the atomic abundance of H^2 in ordinary hydrogen is only about 0.02 per cent. The observations cannot, however, be used for an accurate mass determination.

The Bohr formula applies only to atoms or ions having a single electron. The theory of isotope shift in the line spectra of the two- and three-electron systems of Li^+ and Li has been worked out and is in reasonable agreement with the separations of the Li^6 and Li^7 lines (H70). The separations are several times smaller than for the hydrogen isotopes. For heavier atoms the reduced mass correction will be very small and has not been deduced.

b. In Heavy Elements. There is, however, an isotope shift in heavy elements which can be observed readily with the aid of the Fabry-Pérot interferometer. This isotope shift depends primarily on nuclear volume

(Chap. 2, Sec. 3) rather than nuclear mass.   As we go from the lightest isotope of an element, an increase in mass causes a proportionate increase in nuclear volume such that the density remains approximately constant. The *isotope shift*, originating in departures from the coulomb distribution in the interior of the nucleus, is then proportional to the increment of nuclear volume, and each spectral line so affected will be represented by as many components as there are isotopes of the element.

Each of these isotope-shifted lines may be further split by hyperfine structure, unless the line is due to an isotope for which the nuclear angular momentum $I = 0$ (Chap. 5, Sec. 1).   Even for odd-A nuclides some spectral lines have very small hyperfine-structure splittings, and these can be used when the isotope shift is of major experimental interest.

Exact masses are not given by investigations of the isotope structure of line spectra, but under carefully controlled conditions relative abundances in some cases may be obtained with as much accuracy as intensity measurements on photographic plates will permit, say 1 to 5 per cent. Thus the routine assay of enriched samples of U^{235} in U^{238} is based on intensity measurements of the 4,244-A line where $U^{238} - U^{235} = 0.251$ A (B145).

Isotope   Shift   in   Samarium. That the isotope shift in heavy elements is *not due to nuclear mass alone* is well illustrated by comparison of the mass-spectroscopic and atomic spectra observations on samarium.   This element consists of a mixture of seven isotopes, having mass numbers of 144, 147, 148, 149, 150, 152, and 154, with relative abundances as indicated in Fig. (2.1a).   Careful observations (S17) of the samarium atomic spectral line at λ5,321 clearly show the isotope shift in the lines from the isotopes of even atomic weight, while those due to the isotopes 147 and 149 of odd atomic weight are split by hyperfine structure because of their finite nuclear moments, so that they spread over the region

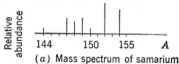

(a) Mass spectrum of samarium

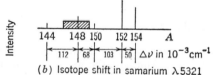

(b) Isotope shift in samarium λ5321

Fig. 2.1   Comparison of the mass spectrum and isotope shift in the line spectrum of samarium.   Except for the hyperfine splitting of the lines due to the isotopes of odd mass number, the two spectra parallel each other in intensity. The isotope shift between mass 150 and 152 is, however, anomalously large, indicating a larger change in nuclear radius between these two isotopes.   [*Schüler and Schmidt* (S17).]

corresponding to masses between 146 and 149.   The observed spectrum is indicated in an idealized fashion in Fig. (2.1b) for comparison with the mass spectrum of Fig. (2.1a).

It will be seen at once that the isotope shift per atomic mass unit is nearly constant (0.03 cm^{-1}), except between the two isotopes having mass numbers 150 and 152 where the isotope shift is nearly twice as great. This anomaly precludes an explanation of isotope shift on a simple basis of changes in nuclear mass and lends additional support to the interpretation in terms of a change in nuclear volume and hence alteration of the coulomb field near the origin.

Anomalous Isotope Shift in Sm, Nd, *and* Eu. Samarium does have one isotope which is α-radioactive, and for a time this activity was thought to be associated with the isotope-shift anomaly and to be due to Sm^{152}. However, further studies, using enriched isotopes, have now proved that Sm^{147} is the α-active isotope (R7, W13). The implications of the anomalously large isotope shift between $_{62}Sm_{88}^{150}$ and $_{62}Sm_{90}^{152}$ seem to be related to the neutron-shell configuration, because a similarly large isotope shift has been found between $_{60}Nd_{88}^{148}$ and $_{60}Nd_{90}^{150}$, and between $_{63}Eu_{88}^{151}$ and $_{63}Eu_{90}^{153}$ (S48, K22). In every case, the anomalous shift occurs between the isotopes which have 88 and 90 neutrons. In fact, for the same neutron numbers, all the relative shifts in Nd, Sm, and Eu agree within their experimental errors (F59).

Direction of Isotope Shift. The nuclear-volume effect, as seen in the heaviest elements, is such that the largest isotope has the greatest wavelength. This is in the opposite direction to the mass effect, as seen in the lightest elements, where the lightest isotope has the longest wavelength in the isotope-shifted pattern. Some intermediate-weight elements exhibit combined effects; for example, in $_{36}Kr$ the heaviest isotopes have the shortest wavelength while in $_{54}Xe$ the heaviest isotopes have the longest wavelength (K27). The isotope shift in Xe is therefore predominantly due to the nuclear-volume effect rather than to the nuclear-mass effect.

Problem

Taking the Rydberg constant for an infinitely heavy nucleus as $R_\infty = 109,737$ cm^{-1}, compute the wavelength of H_α and H_β for H^1. Compute the isotope shift for tritium (H^3) as $(H_\alpha^1 - H_\alpha^3)$ and $(H_\beta^1 - H_\beta^3)$ in cm^{-1} and in angstroms. [H_α and H_β are the Balmer series lines involving transitions between total quantum numbers 3 and 2, 4 and 2, respectively. The Bohr formula is

$$\frac{\nu}{c} = R\left(\frac{1}{n_1^2} - \frac{1}{n_2^2}\right) \quad cm^{-1}$$

where $R = (M_0/m_0)R_\infty$ and M_0 is the reduced mass of the electron.] Compare with the measured tritium shift of 2.36 ± 0.05 A from H_α (6,562.8 A) reported by Pomerance and Terranova, *Am. J. Phys.*, **18**: 466L (1950).

3. *Isotope Shift in the Band Spectra of Diatomic Molecules*

The total energy W of any diatomic molecule is made up of a contribution E_e from the electronic structure, together with energy E_v due to states of vibration along the internuclear axis of the molecule, and energy E_r due to states of rotation about an axis at right angles to the internuclear axis. Each of these energy states is quantized, and the total energy $h\nu$ emitted or absorbed when all three states change is

$$h\nu = W - W' = (E_e + E_v + E_r) - (E_e' + E_v' + E_r')$$
$$= (E_e - E_e') + (E_v - E_v') + (E_r - E_r') \quad (3.1)$$

a. **Isotope Shift in Pure Rotational Band Spectra.** Considering the pure rotational term $(E_r - E_r')$ first, we may write

$$E_r = \frac{1}{2} I\omega^2 = \frac{(I\omega)^2}{2I}$$

where I is the moment of inertia of the molecule about its center of mass and ω is the angular velocity of rotation. According to the principles of wave mechanics, the angular momentum $I\omega$ can have only certain discrete values

$$I\omega = \hbar \sqrt{L(L + 1)} \tag{3.2}$$

where the integer L is the rotational-angular-momentum quantum number. Then a quantum $h\nu_r$ in the pure rotational spectrum would have the energy

$$h\nu_r = E_r - E_r' = \frac{\hbar^2}{2I} [L(L + 1) - L'(L' + 1)] \tag{3.3}$$

where L and L' are the rotational quantum numbers of the two states between which the transition takes place.

The selection rule for the rotational quantum numbers requires that $L - L' = \pm 1$; hence, there can be a series of lines in the *pure rotation spectrum* in which no electronic or vibrational energy changes take place. Substitution in Eq. (3.3) of successive quantum numbers shows that these individual lines have an energy *separation* of $\hbar^2/I$. The rotational quanta $h\nu_r$ are very small, and hence the wavelength of these lines is very long. They occur in the far infrared, usually in the neighborhood of 50 to 100 μ for molecules of small mass, and are, therefore, difficult to study by optical methods.

The moment of inertia I about the center of mass of a diatomic molecule composed of atoms of mass M_a and M_b is $M_0 b^2$, where b is the separation between the nuclei and M_0 is the *reduced mass* $M_a M_b/(M_a + M_b)$ of the system. It has been established experimentally that the internuclear distance b depends almost entirely on the electronic wave functions, rather than on the masses of the nuclei. Accordingly, the ratio of the moments of inertia of two isotopic molecules (M_b, M_a) and (M_c, M_a), in one of which the atom M_b is replaced by one of its isotopes M_c, will be given by the ratio of the reduced masses of the two molecules, i.e.,

$$\frac{I_c}{I_b} = \frac{(M_0)_c b^2}{(M_0)_b b^2} = \frac{(M_0)_c}{(M_0)_b} = \frac{M_c M_a}{M_c + M_a} \frac{M_b + M_a}{M_b M_a} \tag{3.4}$$

The difference in the rotational energy $h\nu_r$ of Eq. (3.3), due to the same quantum transition $L' \to L$ in two such molecules, for example, H^1Cl^{35} and H^1Cl^{37}, is therefore obtained from the difference between two expressions based on Eq. (3.3), and, with appropriate subscripts, is

$$(h\nu_r)_b - (h\nu_r)_c = \left(\frac{1}{I_b} - \frac{1}{I_c}\right) \frac{\hbar^2}{2} [L(L + 1) - L'(L' + 1)]$$

$$= \left(\frac{I_c}{I_b} - 1\right) \frac{\hbar^2}{2I_c} [L(L + 1) - L'(L' + 1)] \tag{3.5}$$

where Eq. (3.4) at once gives its dependence on the atomic masses M_a, M_b, and M_c. When observed by optical methods, the isotope effect is most readily studied in the vibration-rotation bands. The new techniques of microwave spectroscopy (Chap. 5, Sec. 3) have made it possible to obtain precision mass data and relative abundance data from the rotational spectra of some molecules.

Fig. 3.1 The isotope effect in the electronic bands of diatomic carbon. [*King and Birge* (K18).]

b. Isotope Shift in the Vibration-Rotation Bands. Returning to Eq. (3.1), we examine the consequences of changes in vibrational energy. These vibrational quanta are, in general, considerably larger than the rotation quanta. Therefore, any given vibrational quantum change $(E_v - E'_v)$ will be accompanied by a dozen or so smaller rotational quantum changes $(E_r - E'_r)$, and the rotational effects impose a sort of fine structure on the vibrational levels. Within this fine structure, the rotational isotope effects will appear as a further splitting of each of the levels.

The vibration frequencies also depend on the masses of the nuclei composing the molecule, being inversely proportional to the square root of the reduced mass, i.e.,

$$h\nu_v \propto M_0^{-\frac{1}{2}} = \left(\frac{1}{M_a} + \frac{1}{M_b}\right)^{\frac{1}{2}} \tag{3.6}$$

The vibration-rotation bands occur in the near infrared, in the neighborhood of 2.5- to 10-μ wavelengths, and the isotope effects in the vibrational levels correspond to splittings of the order of 2 cm^{-1}.

c. Isotope Shift in Electronic Bands.   Returning again to Eq. (3.1), we consider the consequences of changes in electronic energy states, $(E_e - E_e')$.   These quanta are, in general, much larger than those due to the vibrational levels, and the electronic band spectra occur in the visible or ultraviolet regions.   Each electronic transition, being a large energy change, is accompanied by several changes in vibrational energy, and in turn each of these vibrational transitions is accompanied by many rotational transitions.   The result is a very complex band spectrum, the details of which may be reviewed in any of the standard treatises on band spectra (J15, H43).

One of the great values of diatomic band spectra to nuclear physics has been in the discovery of rare isotopes which had escaped detection in the earlier mass-spectroscopic studies, for example, C^{13}, N^{15}, O^{17}, and O^{18}.   Figure 3.1 illustrates the isotope effect in the electronic bands of $C^{12}C^{12}$, showing the presence of the $C^{13}C^{12}$ components which accounted for the discovery of C^{13}.

There are also important deductions from band spectra concerning nuclear angular momenta, nuclear statistics, and nuclear electric quadrupole moments (Chap. 5, Sec. 3).

Problems

1. Compare the effectiveness of the nuclear mass of deuterium in producing isotope shift in a pure rotational band spectrum, say of HF, and in producing isotope shift in the emission spectrum of atomic hydrogen.   Specifically, calculate the fractional change $(h\nu_2 - h\nu_1)/h\nu_1$ in the energy of the photons emitted as a result of (a) transitions between the same two rotational states $(L' \to L)$ for H^2F and for H^1F and (b) transitions in the Balmer series of atomic H^2 and of H^1.

2. Certain lines of the spectra of diatomic molecules are due to the vibrations of the molecules along their internuclear axis.   In the quantum theory, these are due to transitions of the molecule from one state of vibrational energy to another. Assuming that the molecule is a harmonic oscillator (and this is only roughly true), the energy levels for pure vibration can be shown by wave mechanics (L. Pauling and E. B. Wilson, "Introduction to Quantum Mechanics," pp. 267–274, McGraw-Hill Book Company, Inc., New York, 1935) to be

$$W_n = (n + \tfrac{1}{2})h\nu_0$$

where $n = 0, 1, 2, \ldots$

$$\nu_0 = \frac{1}{2\pi}\sqrt{\frac{k}{M_0}}$$

k = force constant
M_0 = reduced mass

Thus ν_0 is the classical natural frequency. The selection rule is $\Delta n = \pm 1$. Thus the energy levels are equally spaced and the frequency of the emission line is given by

$$\text{Emission frequency } \nu = \frac{W_{n+1} - W_n}{h} = \nu_0$$

Actually, the observed vibrational levels show a convergence for increasing n. The fault with the above theory is the assumption of a parabolic potential function (constant k); a better potential is the Morse function described in Pauling and Wilson. This leads to very accurate energy levels.

Since HCl molecules contain both Cl^{35} and Cl^{37}, there will be an isotopic splitting of the vibrational levels. Assuming the simplified model ($k = $ const), show that the separation in angstroms of the two components of the 17,600-A line is about 14 A. This is close to the observed value.

4. *Isotope Ratios from Radioactive Decay Constants*

Among the naturally radioactive elements many isotopes exist in such minute amounts as to defy detection by mass-spectroscopic or spectroscopic methods. Their relative abundance can be obtained by computation from their decay constants. For example, uranium consists of a mixture of three isotopes, two of which are members of the uranium series of radioactive element, while the third is the independent parent of the actinium series. When radioactive equilibrium (see Chap. 15) is present, the same number of atoms of each type decay in unit time. Hence their relative abundances are inversely proportional to their decay constants. Thus, taking the decay constants of U^{238} and U^{234} as 4.8×10^{-18} sec^{-1} and $\sim 2 \times 10^{-14}$ sec^{-1}, the relative abundance of U^{234} to U^{238} in ordinary uranium would be about 1 to 4,000. Employing the same basic ideas, but in a somewhat more complicated manner (see Chap. 15), the computed value of the relative abundance of U^{235} was first thought to be about 1 in 280. These abundances were the best available until Nier's successful mass-spectroscopic study (N13) showing that the ratios $U^{238}/U^{234} = 17,000 \pm 2,000$ and $U^{238}/U^{235} = 139 \pm 1$. These new data may now be used to improve the values assumed for the decay constants of U^{234} and U^{235}, which were extremely difficult to observe directly until isotopically enriched samples became available.

5. *Chemical and Physical Scales of Atomic Weight*

The chemical-atomic-weight scale is based on the arbitrary selection of the atomic weight 16.000 for oxygen, and all other chemical atomic weights are obtained from measurements of the combining weights of the elements, using this oxygen standard. Band spectroscopic studies in 1929 (G22) first showed that ordinary oxygen is a mixture of three isotopes having mass numbers 16, 17, and 18, mass 16 being by far the most abundant. Moreover, there are variations of the order of 4 per cent in the relative abundance of O^{18}/O^{16} obtained from different sources. The O^{18}/O^{16} ratio is lowest in fresh water, intermediate in sea water, and highest in limestone and in atmospheric oxygen (B6, T13). A more precise definition of the standard of atomic weight then became necessary. At present the chemical scale retains its traditional basis, O = 16, but the physical scale assigns a mass of exactly 16.000 to the most abundant oxygen isotope. Thus $O^{16} = 16$ represents the physical-atomic-weight (or "isotopic mass") scale.

The conversion factor between the chemical and physical scales of atomic weight depends upon the source of the oxygen used to define the chemical scale. As Bainbridge and Nier (B6) have said: "It becomes meaningless to give a conversion factor, or for that matter to make an atomic-weight determination, to more than five significant figures unless the isotopic composition of the oxygen used as a reference is clearly specified."

The currently favored reference standard of oxygen is atmospheric oxygen, for which the relative isotopic abundances found by Nier (N18) are

$$\frac{O^{16}}{O^{18}} = 489.2 \pm 0.7$$

$$\frac{O^{16}}{O^{17}} = 2{,}670 \pm 20$$

(5.1)

Combining these data with the isotopic masses of O^{17} and O^{18} from Table 5.1 of Chap. 3, we have for atmospheric oxygen

Isotope	Mass	Atom per cent
O^{16}	16.000 000	99.758
O^{17}	17.004 533	0.0373
O^{18}	18.004 857	0.2039

The arithmetic average mass of this mixture of atmospheric-oxygen isotopes, as computed from the relative abundances, is 16.004 452 (± 7) on the physical scale. Since this quantity is taken as exactly 16 in the chemical scale, we have for the ratio between the chemical- and physical-atomic-weight scales

(Mass on physical scale) = 1.000 278 × (mass on chemical scale)   (5.2)

This ratio has fundamental consequences in many directions whenever the small correction ($\frac{1}{40}$ per cent) is numerically justified. Bearing in mind that the absolute mass of any single atom is independent of the scale on which it is measured, we note that one gram-equivalent weight of any element involves more atoms on the physical scale than on the chemical scale. For example, 1 mole (chemical scale) of oxygen is 16.000 g of oxygen, but 1 mole (physical scale) of oxygen is 16.004 45 g of oxygen. This means that Avogadro's number and the faraday are both larger on the physical scale (Chap. 3, Sec. 4) than on the chemical scale. Thus, with $e = 4.803 \times 10^{-10}$ esu (D44), we obtain the values given in Table 5.1.

TABLE 5.1. COMPARISON OF PHYSICAL AND CHEMICAL SCALES
(ATMOSPHERIC OXYGEN)

	Chemical scale	Physical scale (D44)
1 mole of atmospheric O_2......	16.000 00 g	16.004 45 g
Avogadro's number...........	$6.023\ 05 \times 10^{23}$ mole^{-1}	$6.024\ 72 \times 10^{23}$ mole^{-1}
Faraday.....................	96,493.3 coulombs	96,520.1 coulombs
1 amu......................	931.42 Mev	931.16 Mev

Problems

1. The density ratio between liquid $H^1O^{16}H^1$, $H^1O^{17}H^1$, and $H^1O^{18}H^1$ is assumed to be equal to the ratio of the molecular weights, i.e., $18:19:20$. Water derived from atmospheric oxygen is about 6.6 parts per million more dense than fresh water. What is the mean atomic weight of fresh-water oxygen on the physical scale? If the density differences arise mainly from variations in the O^{16}/O^{18} abundance ratio, while $O^{18}/O^{17} \simeq$ const., what is the O^{18}/O^{16} ratio in fresh water?

2. Chlorine is a mixture of two isotopes whose percentage abundances and masses on the *physical* scale are

$$Cl^{35}: 75.4 \text{ atom per cent, } 34.980\ 04 \text{ amu}$$
$$Cl^{37}: 24.6 \text{ atom per cent, } 36.977\ 66 \text{ amu}$$

Calculate the *chemical* atomic weight of chlorine. (A slide rule combined with a little algebra will give a sufficiently accurate result for comparison with the chemists' gravimetric value of 35.457.) *Ans.:* 35.461.

6. *Mass-spectrographic Identification of Nuclides in Nuclear Reactions*

a. Direct Identification of Radionuclides. Dempster first used the mass spectrograph in 1938 for determining the mass number of a radioactive isotope by postponing the photographic development of the plate used for recording the ions of Sm until the radioactive isotope of Sm had produced latent α-ray tracks in the photographic emulsion. This combination of the mass spectrograph and autoradiographic techniques is especially useful for the identification of the mass number of long-lived β-ray-emitting isotopes produced in nuclear reactions (H25, L22).

b. Identification of Nuclides with Large (n,γ) Cross Sections. Several elements, such as Cd, Sm, Gd, have a number of stable isotopes, one of which has an unusually large capture cross section for slow neutrons. The particular isotope which accounts for the high nuclear reactivity of the element can be identified by comparing the relative abundance of the stable isotopes before and after intense irradiation with slow neutrons in a uranium reactor. For example, when normal Cd is exposed to thermal neutrons, Fig. 6.1 shows that there is an impoverishment in Cd^{113} and a corresponding enhancement of Cd^{114}, because of the very large cross section for the reaction $Cd^{113}(n,\gamma)Cd^{114}$ (D23). In this way, the exceptionally large thermal neutron-capture cross sections of Cd, Sm,

and Gd have been shown to belong to

Nuclide........................	Cd[113]	Sm[149]	Gd[155]	Gd[157]
$\sigma(n,\gamma)$ in 10^{-24} cm²/nucleus........	20,000	65,000	69,000	240,000

It is interesting to note that the usefulness of Cd in the control rods of a uranium reactor depends on the absorption of slow neutrons by the isotope Cd[113], which comprises only 12.3 per cent of the atoms of normal

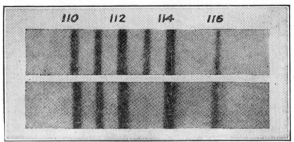

Fig. 6.1 Mass spectrum of normal cadmium (above) and of cadmium after intense irradiation by thermal neutrons (below), showing the alteration produced in cadmium by its absorption of neutrons, predominantly through the reaction Cd[113](n,γ)Cd[114]. [*Dempster* (D23).]

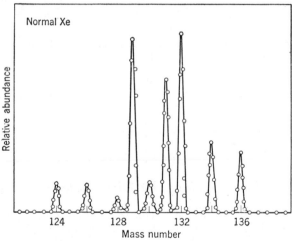

Fig. 6.2 Mass spectrum of normal xenon gas. [*Thode and Graham* (T14).]

Cd, while the seven other stable isotopes of Cd have relatively unimportant (n,γ) cross sections.

    c. Identification of End Products of Radioactive Series. By showing that Pb[207], as well as Pb[206], is an end product of the decay of uranium, Aston (A35) first proved the existence of U[235].

    In an analogous way, the mass identification of several series of radionuclides, which result from the fission of U[235] by thermal neutrons, has been made by Thode and coworkers (T14). Figure 6.2 shows the mass spectrogram of normal xenon gas, which has nine stable isotopes. Figure 6.3 is the mass spectrogram of the xenon gas which accumulates in uranium after irradiation with thermal neutrons. It is seen that the stable end products of four of the fission-product decay chains are Xe of mass number 131, 132, 134, and 136. If mass spectrograms are obtained directly after irradiation, Xe^{133} is also found and can be shown with the mass spectrometer to decay with a half-period of 5.270 ± 0.002 days.

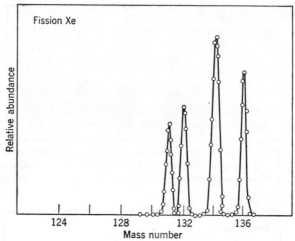

Fig. 6.3 Mass spectrum of xenon accumulated from the fission of U^{235}. [*Thode and Graham* (T14).]

From measurements of the absolute abundances of the Xe obtained in these five chains, the corresponding absolute fission yields can be determined to be (M1):

Mass number, A	131	132	133	134	136
Per cent of U^{235} fissions which give mass A	2.8	4.2	6.3	7.4	6.1

7. *The Separation of Isotopes by Direct Selection Methods*

The name isotope (from the Greek isos, equal, and topos, place) was selected by Soddy and connotes the chemical inseparability of various forms of the same element because they occupy the same place in the periodic table of the elements. In the ordinary sense, purely chemical methods will not successfully separate the isotopes of an element. Because the *nuclear* properties of the isotopes of any one element are usually highly dissimilar, the success of many nuclear studies depends on the availability of separated isotopes.

Separation techniques must utilize the difference in mass, or in some physical or physicochemical property which, in its turn, depends on mass. These techniques divide into two groups, the "direct selection methods," and the "enrichment methods." The direct selection methods, by which a single isotope is produced at substantially 100 per cent isotopic purity, are discussed in this section. Complete separation in chemical quantities was first achieved on a laboratory scale for the isotopes of H, Li, Ne, Cl, K, and Rb prior to 1940. Then the military significance of separated U^{235} resulted in the extension of established laboratory methods to full industrial-plant scale. As an enormously useful by-product of this great technical development, the isotopes of any element can now be separated with the equipment at Oak Ridge (K10) whenever the operating expense is economically justified. Many separated or enriched isotopes are now catalogue items and are widely used both for studies of their nuclear properties and for the enormous field of tracer applications in chemistry, biology, and industry (H48, E3).

a. The Mass Spectrograph. The mass spectrograph depends only on atomic mass and deals directly with the individual atoms. Therefore it effects complete separation regardless of the number of isotopes which an element may possess. Complete separation of isotopes *in weighable quantities* demands very intense ion sources, as wide slits as are possible without loss of complete resolution, and a method of "freezing" the atoms to a target which replaces the usual photographic plate or Faraday cup. Separated isotopes, in quantities of more than 1 mg, were first obtained for nuclear studies in the cases of lithium (R39), potassium (S53), and rubidium (H30) by high-intensity mass spectrographs. The electromagnetic mass separators, or "calutrons" (S52), at Oak Ridge are essentially large mass spectrographs combining high-intensity ion sources (K11) with filter systems of types *b* (accelerator energy filter) and *c* (180° magnetic momentum filter) of Fig. 3.1, Chap. 3. It has been pointed out (S50) that beam-current limitations imposed by the space charge within an intense beam of positive ions can be minimized by providing an auxiliary supply of free electrons which can be attracted into the beam and trapped there by the strong potential gradients associated with the beam's positive space charge.

The cyclotron acts as a mass spectrograph, since its resonant condition is equivalent to a series of electrostatic accelerators and 180° momentum filters. The rare stable isotope He^3 was discovered by Alvarez and Cornog with the cyclotron (A26).

b. Radioactive Recoil. Because of the conservation of momentum in each individual radioactive disintegration, the emission of an α ray imparts kinetic energy to the residual nucleus. Such recoil atoms, ionized by recoil or by collision, are positively charged and hence may be collected on a negatively charged plate.

The recoils from α disintegration of the heavy elements have about 2 per cent of the kinetic energy of the α ray and a range of about 0.1 to 0.2 mm of air at atmospheric pressure. Separation of a radioactive decay product by recoil is applicable to any α emitter (for example, ThC″ from the α disintegration of ThC) and has even been used successfully on a few β-emitting elements, although the recoil atoms then have very small energy. The quantities separated are extremely minute and are unweighable by many orders of magnitude. They are, however, adequate for radioactive studies of the recoil products and may be thought of as "physical quantities," in contrast to weighable "chemical quantities." It is conceivable that application of the recoil method to very intense artificially radioactive sources might result in the collection of sufficient quantities of the stable decay products to permit nuclear experiments to be conducted on them.

Of course, the fission of uranium results in two fragments of comparable mass M_1 and M_2 having equal momenta and therefore sharing the total kinetic energy $(E_1 + E_2)$ available to them such that $M_1E_1 = M_2E_2$. Thus the radioactive fission products may be obtained by recoil from a uranium target experiencing neutron irradiation.

c. Production of Isotopes by Radioactive Decay. Gold consists of only a single stable isotope, of mass number 197. When bombarded by slow neutrons, the gold nucleus captures a neutron, becoming radioactive $_{79}Au^{198}$, which has a half-period of 2.7 days and transforms into $_{80}Hg^{198}$ by β-ray decay. The complete decay of 1 curie of Au^{198} produces only 4.1 μg of Hg^{198}, but this mercury isotope is unaccompanied by the six other stable isotopes of mercury. Substantial quantities of spectroscopically pure Hg^{198} have been produced by this method, and these have been used as spectroscopic sources of monochromatic radiation because of the absence of isotope shift and hyperfine structure.

All the elements of odd-Z have one or, at most, two stable isotopes. The elements of even-Z often have many stable isotopes. Thus there are many cases in which one or two pure isotopes of elements having even-Z might be obtained through the decay of artificially radioactive isotopes of neighboring elements of odd-Z.

In minerals containing rubidium, but no original strontium, pure Sr^{87} accumulates in weighable amounts by the radioactive decay of Rb^{87}, whose half-period is about 6×10^{10} yr. Similarly, substantially pure Pb^{208} is found in some thorium minerals as the end product of radioactive disintegration.

d. Photochemical Excitation. Slight differences (isotope shift) exist between some of the optical levels of certain isotopes. By irradiating a photosensitive material, e.g., mercury vapor in oxygen, with a resonance line of a particular isotope, this isotope alone may become excited, may undergo a chemical reaction, and subsequently may be removed by chemical methods. While sound in principle, this method is difficult to apply, the yields are discouragingly small, and the separations are incomplete (Z3).

e. Molecular-beam Method. A method of separating pure isotopes by a combination of an opposing magnetic field and the gravitational field or centrifugal force, which might have future implications, has been suggested by Stern (S72).

Problems

1. How many total milliamperes of singly charged iron ions would be needed in order to permit the collection of 1 g of Fe^{54} in 24 hr of operation of a mass spectrometer, if the slits and focusing arrangements allow the collection of 60 per cent of all ions emitted by the source? *Ans.:* 590 ma.

2. (*a*) Derive a general expression for the recoil kinetic energy T_r of an atom of mass M as a result of its having emitted a γ ray of energy E ($= h\nu$).

(*b*) Derive a similar expression for the case of α emission.

(*c*) Derive a similar expression for the maximum kinetic energy of recoil following β-ray emission, if E is the maximum energy of the β-ray spectrum.

(*d*) Plot on a single graph three curves of (MT_r) vs. E (energy of emitted radiations) over the energy range $0 < E < 5$ Mev, for (1) α rays, (2) β rays (plot maximum recoil energy), and (3) γ rays.

3. (*a*) What is the kinetic energy of recoil for a Br^{80} atom recoiling after the emission of a 0.049-Mev γ ray?

(*b*) If the 0.049-Mev transition in Br^{80} takes place by internal conversion in the K shell, what will be the kinetic energy of recoil of the residual Br^{80} atom? The K edge of Br is 0.918 A, or 13.5 kev.   *Ans.:* (*a*) 0.016 ev.; (*b*) 0.24 ev.

8. *The Separation of Isotopes by Enrichment Methods*

Partial separation of isotopes may be achieved sometimes by methods based on the statistical properties of a group of atoms.   For example, in the gaseous state, the mean velocity of the lightest isotope of argon exceeds that of the heavier isotopes because of the equipartition of kinetic energy.   The efficiency of some of these methods is greatly increased by operating at the lowest possible temperature, since then the fractional velocity differences become greater than at high temperatures.   Enrichment methods are most suitable for the separation of isotopes when the element has only two abundant isotopes.   Some enrichment methods depend upon slight differences in chemical equilibrium constants between isotopic ions.   The existence of such chemical differences was first recognized after the discovery of deuterium and the comparison of the physico chemical properties of heavy water and ordinary water.   Isotope substitution also exerts measurable effects on the rates of certain organic reactions (R27).

a. Enrichment Factor and Separation Factor.   The effectiveness of any enrichment process is characterized by the *enrichment factor R*, by the time necessary for the apparatus to come to equilibrium, and by the time required to produce unit quantity at this enrichment.   If the mole fraction of the one isotope which we wish to separate is N_0 in the original material, N_1 in one (e.g., the heavy) fraction, and N_2 in the other fraction, then the *enrichment factor* R_1 for this isotope in the first fraction is defined as

$$R_1 = \frac{N_1/(1 - N_1)}{N_0/(1 - N_0)} \tag{8.1}$$

Accordingly $R_1 = 1$ represents no separation, while $R_1 = \infty$ represents complete separation.   If $R_1 > 1$, then there is a corresponding impoverishment of the same isotope in the other fraction, where the enrichment factor

$$R_2 = \frac{N_2/(1 - N_2)}{N_0/(1 - N_0)} \tag{8.2}$$

will be less than unity.

In the theoretical analyses of various enrichment methods for separating isotopes, the process fractionation factor, or *separation factor* α, where

$$\alpha = \frac{N_1/(1 - N_1)}{N_2/(1 - N_2)} \tag{8.3}$$

is often a useful parameter.   Comparison with Eqs. (8.1) and (8.2) shows

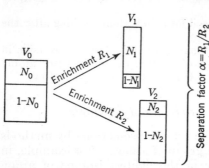

that the process separation factor α is always greater than the corresponding useful enrichment factor R_1, since

$$\alpha = \frac{R_1}{R_2} \tag{8.4}$$

The relationships between enrichment and separation factors are shown in Fig. 8.1.

When the enrichment process can be repeated n times, as by connecting several units in series, the over-all enrichment becomes R^n. Significant enrichment can thus be achieved even where R is small, since $100 = 2^{6.6} = 1.5^{11} = 1.1^{48} = 1.01^{463}$, etc.

Fig. 8.1   Schematic diagram representing the general class of enrichment processes. An original amount V_0 of isotopic material having N_0 mole fraction of the interesting isotope and $(1 - N_0)$ of all other isotopes is separated into two fractions of amount V_1 and V_2.   The significance of the two "enrichment factors" and the "separation factor" is indicated on the diagram.   Application of the principle of conservation of total material, $N_0 V_0 = N_1 V_1 + N_2 V_2$ and $V_0 = V_1 + V_2$, allows one to deduce an analytical relationship between (V_1/V_2), N_0, R_1, and α, as defined by Eqs. (8.1) and (8.2).   Note that if the feed is infinite, and only a small fraction V_1 is drawn off, then $V_2 \simeq V_0$, $N_2 \simeq N_0$, and $R_1 \simeq \alpha$.

Essentially complete separation of H^1 and H^2, Ne^{20} and Ne^{22}, Cl^{35} and Cl^{37}, as well as partial enrichment of the rare isotopes C^{13}, N^{15}, O^{18}, S^{34}, Kr^{86} and minute changes in the mean atomic weight of K, Zn, Hg, and Pb, had been obtained by repeated applications of various enrichment processes on a laboratory scale prior to 1940.   Using many enrichment stages in cascade, the U^{235} and U^{238} isotopes were successfully separated in significant quantities at Oak Ridge (S52).

b. Gaseous Diffusion.   Continuous diffusion and recirculation through a series of porous tubes (H41, H18), Fig. 8.2, or through streaming mercury vapor (H42), was ably introduced in 1932 by Hertz and his coworkers for the essentially complete separation of Ne^{20} and Ne^{22} at a rate of 1 liter per 8 hr of operation.   Over-all enrichments of the order of 10 to 20 were obtained for C^{13}, N^{15}, and O^{18} on laboratory scale equipment prior to 1938 by diffusion of methane, ammonia, and water vapor, respectively.

The lighter isotope, having a mean velocity inversely proportional to the square root of its molecular weight, diffuses slightly more rapidly than a heavier isotope.   For a single diffusion stage, and if only a small fraction of the feed material is permitted to diffuse, the enrichment factor R is given approximately by

$$R \simeq \sqrt{\frac{H}{L}} \tag{8.5}$$

where H and L are the molecular weights of the heavy and light gases. The process separation factor α for a single diffusion stage may therefore be somewhat larger than the square root of the ratio of the molecular weights; thus $\alpha = 1.1$ was obtained in the case of methane by Sherr (S32). In multistage apparatus, approximately one-half the gas entering each stage may be allowed to diffuse through the porous barrier, after which it is pumped back to the feed of the adjacent stage, Fig. 8.2. The

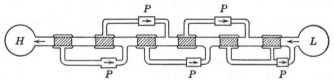

Fig. 8.2 Schematic presentation of the Hertz multiple-stage porous-tube apparatus for separating isotopes by diffusion. The progress of the main volume of gas is from right to left, as it becomes enriched in the heavy fractions. The lighter fractions diffuse out through the porous tubes (crosshatched) and are returned by the recirculating pumps P to the previous stage, eventually collecting in the reservoir L. The heavier fractions progress from stage to stage, eventually collecting in the reservoir H. The over-all enrichment increases exponentially with the number of stages. Depending on the isotopes to be separated, some 10 to 50 or more stages may be used.

effective enrichment factor per stage is then less than the ideal value for a single stage with negligible throughput. As is well known, multistage gaseous diffusion methods have been applied successfully to obtain large-scale enrichments of U^{235} from uranium hexafluoride vapor (S52, B32).

    c. Electrolysis. Electrolytic methods have thus far proved useful only in the case of the hydrogen isotopes. The commercial separation of heavy water D_2O is carried out by the electrolysis of water. The hydrogen liberated at the cathode is greatly enriched in H^1, and by long continued electrolysis D_2O of any desired purity can be attained in the liquid residues. A number of isotope-discriminating processes appear to be involved in electrolysis, but the controlling process is thought to be a preferential adsorption of light hydrogen ions on the cathode and their subsequent combination to form neutral hydrogen molecules (U7). About 1 cc of 99.9 per cent pure D_2O can be obtained from 25 liters of ordinary water.

    d. Exchange Reactions and Free Evaporation. The isotopes of an element which is present in two phases in equilibrium usually have different concentrations in the two phases. For example, the equilibrium between gaseous ammonia NH_3 and aqueous ammonium ion NH_4^+

$$N^{15}H_3 + N^{14}H_4^+ \leftrightarrows N^{14}H_3 + N^{15}H_4^+ \tag{8.6}$$

has an observed (T15) equilibrium constant

$$k = \frac{[N^{14}H_3][N^{15}H_4^+]}{[N^{15}H_3][N^{14}H_4^+]} = 1.031 \tag{8.7}$$

which leads to an enrichment of N^{15} in the liquid phase and makes possible separation of the nitrogen isotopes by repeated fractional distillation. Similarly, the equilibrium between gaseous SO_2 and aqueous HSO_3^- ion, and gaseous CO_2 and aqueous HCO_3^- ion, has equilibrium constants which favor slightly the concentration of the heavier isotope S^{34} and C^{13} in the solution (C25). In these particular cases the separation factor is the same as the equilibrium constant and is about 1.01 to 1.03 in the most favorable cases. The theory of such separation has been treated in detail by Urey and Greiff (U6) and by Cohen (C30).

Similarly, the exchange may take place between the liquid and vapor phases of a single substance. For example, the vapor pressure of H_2O is 5 per cent greater than the vapor pressure of D_2O; hence partial evaporation will result in enrichment of the liquid phase in D_2O. Again, the vapor pressure of H_2 exceeds that of D_2, and deuterium was first discovered by concentrating it by evaporation of hydrogen near the triple point (U5).

The principles of exchange equilibrium have led to the erection of large multiplate fractionating columns for the enrichment of certain isotopes by substantially the same principles of fractional distillation which have long been applied in the petroleum and other chemical industries. If complete equilibrium between liquid and vapor were realized at each plate, then n plates, each giving a small enrichment R, would yield an over-all enrichment of R^n. Actually, the number of plates required exceeds this theoretical number by some 20 to 100 per cent, because of lack of complete equilibrium. Straight columns, packed with glass helices, provide an inexpensive fractionating column which gives excellent results (U2). Fractional distillation has been applied to H, Li, C, N, O, Ne, S, and others with good enrichments of the heavier isotopes, while free evaporation methods have also been used on K, Cl, Hg, Zn, and Pb with slight changes in atomic weight. From the standpoint of the commercial production of enriched isotopes, Urey (U2) finds the chemical exchange methods the most economical.

e. The Centrifuge. The ultracentrifuge offers separation factors of the order of 1.1 to 1.7 at 300°K for ideal gases having a mass difference of 1 to 4 amu (B21, B23, B22, H76). The *enrichment increases with decreasing temperature;* for example, at 200°K these separation factors increase to 1.2 for unit mass difference and 2.2 for a mass difference of four units.

The separation factor for the single-stage centrifuge in terms of the equilibrium mole fractions of the light isotope at the axis and at the periphery of the rotor is

$$\alpha = e^{(M_2-M_1)(v^2/2kT)} \tag{8.8}$$

where $M_2 - M_1$ is the difference in mass of the heavy and light isotopes,

v is the peripheral velocity ($\sim 8 \times 10^4$ cm/sec), k is the gas constant, and T is the absolute temperature. In this case the enrichment depends on the absolute value of the *difference in mass*, not on the ratio of the masses as in the diffusion process. This characteristic gives the centrifuge a great advantage, particularly for heavy elements. If centrifuges could be operated in series at extremely low temperatures, very high over-all enrichment factors could be realized.

f. Thermal Diffusion. Self-diffusion and thermal diffusion in a mixture of two gases of different molecular weights, placed between a hot and a cold surface, result in a higher relative concentration of the heavier gas at the cold surface. Theory shows that this should be true for all molecules between which the interaction force varies more rapidly than the inverse fifth power of the separation of the molecules (J18, S41).

The use of this thermal diffusion for the separation of isotopes was first suggested by Chapman, but it was not practical until ingeniously combined with nonturbulent thermal convection by Clusius and Dickel (C26) when it became one of the simplest and most effective methods available for isotope separation.

Clusius and Dickel used a cooled vertical glass tube with an electrically heated wire along its axis. Optimum dimensions of this simple apparatus, shown schematically in Fig. 8.3, have been deduced subsequently (K45). The process separation factor α, in terms of the equilibrium mole concentrations in the heavy and light reservoirs, is

$$\alpha = e^{lA(M_2-M_1)/(M_2+M_1)} \qquad (8.9)$$

where M_1 and M_2 are the masses of the light and heavy isotopic molecules being separated, l is the length of the column, and A is a function of the viscosity, self-diffusion, and density of the gas, the temperatures and radii of the cylindrical walls, and the gravitational constant. The method owes some of its success to

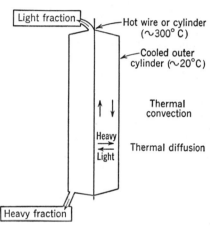

Fig. **8.3** Schematic explanation of the Clusius-Dickel thermal-diffusion isotope separator. By thermal diffusion, the heavier fraction tends to concentrate at the cool outer wall while the lighter fraction concentrates at the hot inner cylinder or wire. The action of gravity then causes thermal convection which provides an effective downward transport for the heavy fraction at the cool outer wall and an upward transport for the light fraction along the axis. The pressure is maintained at a low enough value to avoid turbulence in the thermal convective flow.

the fortunate fact that the separations achieved depend on the *difference in mass*, Eq. (8.9), of the substances being separated. A single column 2 in. in diameter and 24 ft high gives an enrichment $R = 4$ for C^{13} in methane (N15), and longer columns should easily yield 10 mg of C^{13} per day, with about a 10-fold enrichment over the normal C^{13}/C^{12} ratio.

Rapid and substantially complete separations of the heavy isotopes of H, Ne, Cl, Kr have been obtained, and some extensions of the method to the separation of isotopes in liquid instead of gaseous phase have been undertaken with moderate success.

Problems

1. By an enrichment method, it is desired to produce chlorine which is at least 95 atom per cent Cl^{37}. What is the over-all enrichment factor for such an apparatus? If the enrichment process selected has an enrichment factor of 1.5 per stage, how many stages must be used in series? *Ans.: $R \simeq 58$; 10 stages required.*

2. In a uranium separation process, a sample of the ingoing material gives $10^4 \alpha$ counts per second per gram with a certain experimental arrangement of counter and sample, in which are U^{238} ($\lambda = 1.527 \times 10^{-10}$ yr^{-1}), U^{235} ($\lambda = 9.82 \times 10^{-10}$ yr^{-1}), U^{234} ($\lambda = 2.980 \times 10^{-6}$ yr^{-1}); the ratio $U^{238}/U^{235} = 139$, and $U^{234}/U^{238} = 5 \times 10^{-5}$. A sample of the outgoing material, measured under exactly the same experimental conditions, gives $3 \times 10^4 \alpha$ counts per second per gram. Assuming that the apparatus is one which does not alter the U^{234}/U^{235} ratio, find the enrichment factor R for U^{235}. *Ans.: $R \simeq 5.1$.*

3. Assume that a single-stage apparatus for the separation of isotopes by gaseous diffusion has a separation factor α equal to the ratio of the mean kinetic velocities of the molecules being separated. What is the minimum number of stages of such gaseous diffusion apparatus required theoretically to produce uranium having 20 atom per cent U^{235}, if uranium hexafluoride is the diffusing gas? *Ans.: 824 stages.*

4. It can be shown [e.g., from Eq. 1 of Humphreys, *Phys. Rev.*, **56**: 684 (1939)] that, in a hollow cylindrical centrifuge, the density ρ_1 g/cm^3 of a light molecule, at any distance r from the axis, is

$$\rho_1 = \rho_{10} e^{M_1 \omega^2 r^2 / 2kT}$$

where ρ_{10} is the density of the light molecules at the axis, M_1 is the mass of one molecule, ω is the angular velocity, k is the gas constant, and T is the absolute temperature. A similar equation holds for the density ρ_2 of the heavy molecule, that is, $\rho_2 = \rho_{20} e^{M_2 \omega^2 r^2 / 2kT}$. If the separation factor at equilibrium is

$$\alpha = e^{(M_2 - M_1) v^2 / 2kT}$$

compute the enrichment factor R for the light isotopic molecule at the axis, in terms of the separation factor. *Ans.: $R \simeq (M_1/M_2)\alpha$.*

5. A centrifuge is to be used at 20°C for the enrichment of U^{235} in normal uranium hexafluoride vapor. If a hollow cylindrical rotor is used, having an inside radius of 5 cm and a speed of 1,000 rps, what separation factor α can be expected when equilibrium has been reached within the cylinder? How many times greater than the force of gravity is the radial force on a molecule at the periphery of this rotor? *Ans.: $\alpha \simeq 1.063$; 2×10^5.*

6. A certain thermal diffusion column, with a large reservoir of feed gas (so that $R_1 \simeq \alpha$) and having a height l_1, is fed CH_4 containing the normal proportion of C^{13} (1.1 atom per cent C^{13}, 98.9 atom per cent C^{12}). The carbon contained in the heavy fraction of methane leaving the column contains 10 atom per cent C^{13}, 90 atom per cent C^{12}. A completely similar column, except for its length, is to be built for the enrichment of radioactive C^{14}. If the feed material for the new column is methane containing the normal isotopic ratio of C^{12} and C^{13} and also 1 atom of C^{14} per 10,000 stable atoms (this corresponds to a specific radioactivity of about 0.1 mc/g), how long a column (in units of l_1) must be built to give a 100-fold enrichment of the C^{14}?   Neglect the effects of deuterium in the system. *Ans.: $l_2 \simeq 1.03 l_1$.*

7. Assume that an ion source which produces singly ionized Li^6 and Li^7 is available.   The ions so produced are accelerated in vacuum through a potential difference of 2×10^6 volts and are then allowed to pass through a very thin metal foil.   A fraction of the ions will be reflected (i.e., elastically scattered through 90° or more in the laboratory coordinates) by the foil.   We shall collect these reflected ions.   Compare the isotopic abundance of Li^6 in these reflected ions with that in the incident beam.   What is the enrichment factor for Li^6 in this isotope separating process if (a) the reflecting foil is of beryllium ($_4Be^9$) and (b) the reflecting foil is of gold ($_{79}Au^{197}$)?

(c) Comment briefly on the relative practicability of this method of separating isotopes, in comparison with existing production methods.

9. *Szilard-Chalmers Reaction for the Enrichment of Radioactive Isotopes*

When the nucleus of an atom which is present in an organic molecule, e.g., iodine in ethyl iodide, becomes radioactive by the capture of a slow neutron, the molecular bond is usually broken either by recoil from the neutron collision or by recoil from a γ ray or other radiation emitted by the nucleus immediately after capturing the neutron.   The radioactive atom thus set free from the molecule can then be made to combine with other ions present as "acceptors" in the solution, as was first shown by Szilard and Chalmers (S83).   Thus, following the neutron irradiation of ethyl iodide, if water containing a trace of iodide ion be added and the two immiscible phases (water and ethyl iodide) be shaken together and then allowed to separate, the bulk of the radioactive iodine will be found in the water layer.   Thus it is possible to separate those iodine atoms (I^{128}) which have become radioactive from the overwhelmingly greater number of stable iodine atoms (I^{127}) in the target, because all the iodine atoms which have not been made radioactive remain bound in their original molecules while the activated atoms are liberated (S83, L29).

This general method of enriching a radioactive isotope is widely used and often dictates the composition of the target material chosen for nuclear bombardment when the main objective is the production of radioactive material in a concentrated and useful form (M34).

10. *Separation of Radioactive Isomers*

Nuclear isomers have both the same mass number and atomic number.   Their separation offers special challenges to the radiochemist.   It is often possible to separate the radioactive isomers by having the element combined in an organic molecule and then taking advantage of the disruption of the molecular bonds which takes place during an isomeric transition to the ground level (S26).   The mechanism by which the transforming atom breaks its molecular bond probably is its acquisition of a large positive charge, owing to the emission of an internal-conversion electron and several Auger electrons (C41, E4).

CHAPTER 8

Systematics of Stable Nuclei

Many of the basic properties of the subnuclear constituents of matter emerge from a systematic catalogue of the nuclei found in nature.

1. Constituents of Atomic Nuclei

Before Chadwick's discovery of the neutron in 1932 it was assumed that nuclei were composed of protons and electrons. This incorrect notion arose from overinterpretation of the early studies of radioactivity. By 1932 there was enough evidence at hand to make nuclear electrons a distasteful concept. The neutron gained substantially immediate acceptance as the proper subnuclear teammate for protons. The simplest and most compelling arguments concerning the subnuclear constituents of matter are reviewed in this section.

We assume throughout that if a neutron, proton, electron, neutrino, or meson enters a nucleus, the particle retains its identity and extranuclear characteristics of spin, statistics, magnetic moment, and rest mass.

a. Nonexistence of Nuclear Electrons. When α rays and β rays were first identified as helium nuclei and electrons, the presumption was that both were contained in nuclei, because both were expelled from nuclei. This led to the incorrect notion that nuclei were composed of protons and electrons. Then the nucleus of $_7N^{14}$, for example, would contain $A = 14$ protons and $A - Z = 7$ electrons, or a total of $(2A - Z)$ elementary particles. Note that on the proton-electron model, all odd-Z nuclei would contain an odd total number of protons plus electrons.

Both the proton and electron are known from direct evidence to be Fermi-Dirac particles (fermions) and to have spin $\frac{1}{2}$. Any nuclear aggregation of an odd number of fermions would have to obey Fermi-Dirac statistics and possess half-integer nuclear angular momentum, I (Chap. 4).

Nuclear Angular Momentum of N^{14}. The earliest and soundest experimental contradiction to the proton-electron model came from observations in 1928 of the band spectrum of $N^{14}N^{14}$, for which the intensity ratio of alternate lines, $(I + 1)/I$, has the value 2. Then $I = 1$ for $_7N^{14}$, and this nucleus cannot be composed of an odd number $(2A - Z)$ of fermions.

Statistics of N^{14}. From band spectra and Raman spectra the statistics of $_7N^{14}$ was found to be Einstein-Bose. Again there was disagreement with any model which involves an odd number of fermions.

Magnetic Dipole Moment of N^{14}. All nuclei have magnetic dipole moments μ which are of the order of one nuclear magneton $\mu_M = eh/4\pi Mc$ (Chap. 4). For N^{14} in particular, $\mu = 0.40$ nuclear magneton. The magnetic dipole moment of a single electron is one Bohr magneton, or roughly 2,000 times larger. Therefore there cannot be an unpaired odd electron in any nucleus, for example, N^{14}. These three arguments (I, statistics, and μ) apply equally to any other odd-Z nuclide, such as deuterium.

β Decay. The argument that electrons are contained in nuclei because electrons are emitted in β decay lost its force when positron β decay was found to be common. Indeed, dual β decay is exhibited by many nuclides, such as Cu^{64}, which can emit either positron β rays or negatron β rays. If both positive and negative electrons were in nuclei, they should annihilate each other.

Electron-Neutrino Pairs. By differential measurements (B63, M14), the neutrino is a fermion with spin $\frac{1}{2}$, like the electron, proton, and neutron. Fermi's interpretation of β decay in terms of the emission of an electron-neutrino pair (Chap. 17) gives a satisfactory over-all account of the emission of both positron and negatron β rays. The mechanism by which the electron-neutrino pair arises during the nucleon transition is as yet obscure. It is clear, however, that the electron-neutrino pair originates during the transition and was not present initially in the nucleus. Cowan (C47a) has shown experimentally that if the neutrino has any magnetic dipole moment it is less than 10^{-7} Bohr magneton. Therefore electron-neutrino pairs, residing in a nucleus, would still possess a net magnetic dipole moment of one Bohr magneton, and μ for odd-Z nuclei, such as N^{14}, would have to be in the neighborhood of one Bohr magneton, or about 2,000 nuclear magnetons, if there were electron-neutrino pairs in nuclei.

De Broglie Wavelength. In order to be confined within a nucleus, a particle must have a rationalized de Broglie wavelength $\lambda = \hbar/p$ which is not greater than the nuclear dimensions. A 1-Mev electron has $\lambda \sim 140 \times 10^{-13}$ cm. This could not possibly be retained within nuclei whose radii are all smaller than 10×10^{-13} cm (Chap. 2). To be confined within a nuclear volume, a nuclear electron would have to have a kinetic energy of ~ 30 Mev ($\lambda \sim 7 \times 10^{-13}$ cm). Such energies are too large to be admissible in any satisfactory model of mass defects and binding energies of nuclei (Chap. 9).

b. Acceptability of Neutrons and Protons as Subnuclear Particles.
We have seen previously that neutrons and protons are both Fermi-Dirac particles (fermions) with spin $\frac{1}{2}$ and that their combination gives values of nuclear angular momentum, statistics, and of magnetic dipole moment (Chap. 4) which agree with observations.

De Broglie Wavelength. In the neutron-proton model of nuclei, the binding energy is about 7 to 8 Mev/nucleon (Chap. 9). The kinetic energy of the nucleon is greater than this, because the binding energy is the difference between the potential and kinetic energy of the nucleons. A nucleon of only 8 Mev has a rationalized *de Broglie* wavelength of $\lambda \sim 1.7 \times 10^{-13}$ cm and therefore easily can be localized within a nuclear volume.

Nuclear Reactions. Many nuclear reactions involve only the addition or subtraction of one neutron or of one proton with respect to a target nucleus. For example,

$$\mathrm{Na}^{23}(n,\gamma)\mathrm{Na}^{24} \qquad \mathrm{C}^{12}(p,\gamma)\mathrm{N}^{13}$$
$$\mathrm{O}^{16}(\gamma,n)\mathrm{O}^{15} \qquad \mathrm{Mg}^{25}(\gamma,p)\mathrm{Na}^{24}$$

The mere qualitative existence of such reactions does not of itself demonstrate the necessity of a neutron-proton model of nuclear constitution. Quantitatively, however, the detailed course of such reactions is in accord with theoretical deductions based on the neutron-proton model.

Pions. The binding forces between nucleons are now thought to be due to the exchange of π mesons, or "pions," between protons and neutrons. At any given instant, pions may be "in transit" between nucleons, thus producing a meson current in nuclei which may have effects on the nuclear multipole moments (Chap. 4, Sec. 4). The pion has $I = 0$ and Einstein-Bose statistics (B63); therefore it does not contribute to I, μ, or the statistics of nuclei.

c. Comparison of Possible Models. Actually, at least three forms of nuclear-electron model require consideration. These are:

1*a*. A protons $+ (A - Z)$ electrons $= (2A - Z)$ fermions.
1*b*. A neutrons $+ Z$ positrons $= (A + Z)$ fermions.
1*c*. A protons $+ (A - Z)$ electron-neutrino pairs $= (3A - 2Z)$ fermions.

Models 1*a* and 1*b* are excluded by considerations such as the statistics and angular momentum of N^{14}. Model 1*c*, however, offers the statistics and angular momenta which are actually observed in nuclei. The neutrino could conceivably cancel the spin of its electron companion, but it cannot cancel the electron's large magnetic dipole moment. Therefore model 1*c* fails also.

In disproving the existence of nuclear electrons, we establish at the same time that a neutron is not a close combination of a proton and electron, nor is a proton a close combination of a neutron and a positron (with or without a companion neutrino).

The neutron-proton model can also be visualized in several modifications, chiefly:

2*a*. Z protons $+ (A - Z)$ neutrons.
2*b*. Z protons $+ (A - Z)$ neutrons $+$ any number of π mesons.

Because the π meson has $I = 0$ and Einstein-Bose statistics, either 2*a* or 2*b* matches all known simple requirements.

d. Summary of Physical Properties. We collect in Table 1.1 the known static properties of nucleons and other closely related particles.

e. Structure of Nucleons. Contemporary theoretical and experimental work is exploring the substructure of protons and neutrons. In the language of present theory (B63), the individual nucleon is composed of a core, or "nucleor," surrounded by a pion "cloud" made up of one or more π mesons. If the nucleor were found to obey the Dirac equation, then it would have a magnetic dipole moment of one nuclear magneton. The anomalous magnetic dipole moment of protons and neutrons would then be attributed to the contributions from the orbital moments of the circulating pion or pions.

TABLE 1.1. STATIC PHYSICAL PROPERTIES OF SUBNUCLEAR PARTICLES AND THEIR CLOSE RELATIVES

Particle	Charge	Rest mass, amu	Spin	Magnetic dipole moment, nuclear magnetons	Statistics	Intrinsic parity
Proton......	$+e$	$1.008\ 14 - m_0$ $=1.007\ 59$	$\frac{1}{2}$	$+2.793$	Fermi	Even
Neutron....	0	$1.008\ 98$	$\frac{1}{2}$	-1.913	Fermi	Even
Electron....	$\pm e$	$m_0 = 0.000\ 55$	$\frac{1}{2}$	$\pm 1,836$	Fermi	Even
Neutrino....	0	0	$\frac{1}{2}$	$<10^{-3}$	Fermi	Even
π meson.....	$\pm e$	$276\ m_0$	0	0	Bose	Odd(B63)
π^0 meson....	0	$265\ m_0$	0	0	Bose	Odd
μ meson.....	$\pm e$	$212\ m_0$	$\frac{1}{2}$	?	Fermi	?

In any case, these concepts are congenial with the experimental observation, from the $\pi^- + \text{H}^2 \to 2n$ reaction, that the pion has $I = 0$, Bose statistics, and intrinsic *negative parity*. A pion would therefore have to circulate in a p orbit ($l = 1$) about a bare nucleor in order that the overall parity of the nucleon could be even. Such circulation of a charged pion would contribute to the magnetic dipole moment of the nucleon. We have already noted in Chap. 4 some possible consequences of this model, in terms of the partial "quenching" of the anomalous nucleon magnetic moments when nucleons aggregate in nuclei. Quantitatively, the theory of the structure of nucleons is as yet very shaky, but progress is being made, and new experiments on pion-nucleon interactions will supply valuable new information.

2. *Relative Abundance of the Chemical Elements*

The observed abundance distribution of stable nuclides must be closely related to the mechanism by which the elements originated and also to the ultimate characteristics of nuclear forces.

The experimental data consist mainly of measurements of the relative abundance of the elements in meteorites and in the earth's crust, hydrosphere, and atmosphere. Astrophysical observations of solar and stellar spectra add some data and support the hypothesis that the earth is a reasonably typical cosmic sample. Among the individual elements, the relative isotopic abundances are found to be the same in terrestrial and meteoritic samples. As a working hypothesis, the isotopic constitution of each element is therefore taken as a constant of nature.

The observed relative abundances of the elements show no systematic relationship with their chemical properties, but instead they are clearly related to the nuclear properties of their stable isotopes.

Such obvious facts as the preponderance in the universe of even-Z even-N nuclides, and of lightweight elements such as oxygen, must emerge as necessary consequences of any acceptable theory of nuclear forces and of the origin of the elements.

a. Relative Abundance of Elements in the Earth's Crust. All available relative abundance measurements on terrestrial materials were compiled in 1932 by Hevesy (H47) and in 1938 by Goldschmidt (G28). One clear-cut generalization from these data is that by weight *more than 85 per cent of the sampled earth consists of even-Z even-N nuclides.* Representative data for the eight most abundant elements in the earth's crust are given in Table 2.1. These alone account for 98 per cent of the earth's total mass. The hydrogen in the oceans makes up but a small part of the remaining 2 per cent (R40).

We have noted previously that over 60 per cent of the known stable nuclides are even-Z even-N nuclides (Chap. 4, Table 4.1) and that of the remainder all but four have either even-Z or even-N.

TABLE 2.1. ABUNDANCE OF THE EIGHT ELEMENTS IN THE EARTH'S CRUSTAL ROCKS WHICH HAVE AN AVERAGE WEIGHT ABUNDANCE GREATER THAN 1 PER CENT

[These account for ∼98 per cent of the earth's mass (G28).]

	Even-Z					Odd-Z		
Element	$_8$O	$_{14}$Si	$_{26}$Fe	$_{20}$Ca	$_{12}$Mg	$_{13}$Al	$_{11}$Na	$_{19}$K
Weight per cent abundance	48	26	5	3.5	2.0	8.5	2.8	2.5
Principal isotope	16	28	56	40	24	27	23	39

b. Cosmic Abundance of the Elements. All available data on the relative abundance of the elements, from terrestrial, meteoritic, and stellar measurements, were compiled and summarized in 1949 by Harrison Brown (B131). A number of interpolations and judicious appraisals had to be made. Except for volatile constituents, such as the noble gases and the light elements which participate in thermonuclear reactions in the stars, stellar matter appears to be fairly well represented by average meteoritic matter, and meteoritic matter by terrestrial matter. Brown's tables have been reviewed and extended by Alpher and Herman (A20, A21), whose estimates of the mean cosmic abundance of nuclei are shown in Fig. 2.1. The abundance distribution is shown in terms of mass number A, which is the parameter used in most theories of the origin of the elements. Values which differ in detail but not in general trend have been compiled by Urey (U4).

The general trend of these isobaric abundances clearly approximates an exponential decrease with increasing A, until $A \sim 100$, above which the relative abundance is roughly independent of A. There is no overwhelming distinction between even-A and odd-A.

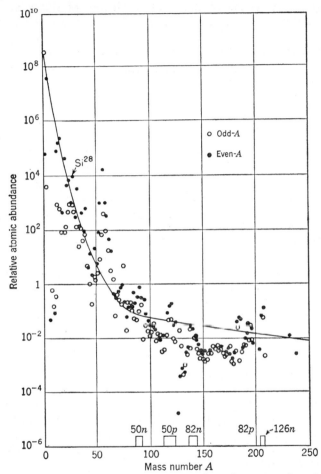

Fig. 2.1 Mean cosmic relative abundance of nuclides, of mass number A, normalized to 10,000 atoms of silicon (hence, 9,227 atoms of Si^{28}). The nonequilibrium model of the origin of the elements, by successive (n,γ) capture processes, leads to predicted abundances which are in semiquantitative agreement with this observed distribution. The solid curve shows a typical theoretical result, if the initial conditions at the starting time of the element-building process involved $\sim$88 per cent free neutrons and $\sim$12 per cent free protons, at a total nucleon concentration of $\sim 1.07 \times 10^{17}$ cm^{-3} ($\sim 1.8 \times 10^{-7}$ g/cm^3) and at a temperature of $\sim 1.28 \times 10^9$ °K (0.11 Mev). [*Adapted from Alpher and Herman* (A21).]

c. The Origin of the Elements.   Accompanying the gradual improvement of nuclear experimental data, the quantity and quality of theories of the origin of the elements have advanced markedly.

Among the nuclear and astrophysical data which have to be matched by a proper theory are the relative abundances of nuclides, the binding energy of nuclei, certain nuclear reaction cross sections, time scales which are compatible with the half-periods for β decay of unstable nuclides, and the age and rate of expansion of the universe.

The age of formation of the solid earth and of the solar system is about 3×10^9 yr, based on radioactivity studies of terrestrial and meteoritic samples (P2, A33). This age scale is confirmed by many other types of evidence and is also in agreement with the cosmic time scale derived from the Hubble red shift (L34). It has been shown experimentally (E18) that the age of the *atoms* of potassium and of uranium found in the Pultusk meteorites is the same as the age of the atoms of terrestrial samples of these elements.

These and other experimental facts point to a "great event" of creation which took place somewhat abruptly, about 3×10^9 yr ago. A number of very different theories have been developed, but none of these is yet free from serious difficulties. Details will be found in the interesting reviews by Alpher and Herman (A20, A21). Among the theories which invoke a great event rather than a continuum of creation, there are two broad classes: equilibrium and nonequilibrium theories.

Equilibrium Hypothesis. Using as parameters the observed nuclear binding energies, and an assumed initial temperature and density, methods of thermodynamics and statistical mechanics have been applied to the problem by Tolman and many others. Nuclear binding energies are of the order of 7 to 8 Mev/nucleon for most of the elements; hence in heavy elements the binding energies approach 2,000 Mcv. Equilibrium conditions in a thermodynamic system would therefore require very high temperatures. The trend of the relative abundance data for $A < 40$ can be matched by an initial temperature of $\sim 8 \times 10^9$ °K and an initial density of $\sim 10^7$ g/cm³. Because of the linear relationship between binding energy and mass number, the predicted abundance continues to fall exponentially with increasing A and for heavy nuclei is $\sim 10^{50}$ smaller than the observed abundances. No single combination of initial temperature and density can account for the observed abundances, and there are also important difficulties concerning the time scale and the mechanism for "freezing-in" a final mixture to give us the isotopically uniform cosmos in which we live.

Nonequilibrium Hypothesis. A mechanism which does match the trend of the relative abundance data for all values of A was proposed by Gamow (G5). This is a nonequilibrium process, taking place during a very brief period of time. The subsequent quantitative development of this theory by Alpher, Herman, Gamow, Fermi, Turkevich, and others has been fruitful (A21).

As initial conditions, the nonequilibrium theory contemplates a very small localized region of space containing mostly neutrons, at a concentration of $\sim 10^{17}$ cm⁻³ ($\sim 10^{-7}$ g/cm³), a temperature of $\sim 10^9$ °K (~ 0.1 Mev), and an initial rate of universal expansion corresponding to the present Hubble red shift. Within the first few minutes some neutrons have already undergone β decay into protons, and these capture further neutrons to form deuterons H(n,γ)D. The heavier nuclides are built up by successive (n,γ) reactions followed by β decay to stable nuclides, and in competition with neutron decay. In the course of an hour or so the process is essentially terminated, due to β decay of the uncaptured neutrons (half-period $\sim$ 13 min), and to the reduction in mean density and reaction probability caused by universal expansion.

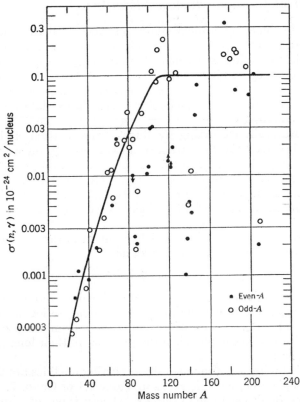

Fig. 2.2 Radiative-capture cross sections for 1-Mev neutrons (n,γ) as a function of mass number A. The isolated points with extremely small (n,γ) cross sections are due to nuclides containing closed shells of neutrons, $N = 50, 82,$ or 126. [*Data from Hughes, Garth, Eggler, and Levin* (H68, H69).]

Today, 3×10^9 yr later, we find the products of this nonequilibrium great event have a mean cosmic density of $\sim 10^{-30}$ g/cm³ and are still expanding. The isotopic constitution of the resulting mixture in this theory depends strongly on the fast neutron radiative-capture (n,γ) cross sections. These have been compiled by Hughes (H68) and coworkers and are shown in Fig. 2.2. A trend which correlates visually with the abundance data of Fig. 2.1 is evident. The fast (n,γ) cross sections rise roughly exponentially with A up to $A \sim 100$, then level off to a substantially constant value of ~ 0.1 barn per nucleus. Using the (n,γ) cross sections of Fig. 2.2, and an initial nucleon concentration of 1.07×10^{17}

cm^{-3} at $t = 0$, the predicted relative abundance distribution is shown by the solid line in Fig. 2.1.

Many details remain to be clarified, but the nonequilibrium model for the origin of the elements appears to be an important step toward ultimate clarification of the origin of the elements.

3. *Empirical Rules of Nuclear Stability*

There are some 274 known stable nuclides. All these are found in natural terrestrial samples. As a result of extensive nuclear transmutation and disintegration experiments, more than 800 new nuclides have been produced and studied. All these are radioactive. *No previously unknown stable nuclides have been produced by nuclear reactions.* The characteristics of the stable nuclides are basic input data for all theories of nuclear structure.

a. The Naturally Occurring Nuclides. The creation of the elements must have involved the formation of all conceivable nuclear aggregates of neutrons and protons. Most of these were unstable and have undergone radioactive decay into stable forms. There remain in nature today not only those nuclides which are truly stable but also the unstable nuclides whose radioactive half-periods are comparable with the age of the universe.

Half-periods. The nuclides which occur in nature can therefore be defined in terms of their half-period $T_{\frac{1}{2}}$ as

$$\sim 10^9 \text{ yr} \leq T_{\frac{1}{2}} \leq \infty \tag{3.1}$$

In addition, there are in nature some 40 shorter-lived radioactive nuclides, such as radium, which are members of the decay series of thorium and uranium (Chap. 16, Sec. 2). We exclude these from our present survey because their existence depends on the presence of their long-lived parent Th^{232}, U^{235}, or U^{238}.

With this limitation, the naturally occurring nuclides are those whose relative isotopic abundance is given in Table 1.1 of Chap. 7.

Symmetry in Protons and Neutrons. Many types of visual arrangement of these data have been used. Of these we select, as the most physical, the plot of neutron number N vs. proton number Z, Fig. 3.1. This arrangement emphasizes the important general symmetry in protons and neutrons which is displayed by stable nuclides. The relative frequency distribution of isotopes (constant Z) is similar to the distribution of isotones (constant N).

Radioactive Nuclides. Immediately after the discovery of radioactivity in uranium and thorium, all the then available elements were surveyed for this new property of matter. Most of the elements were reported to emit radioactive radiations. Gradually it became evident that these radiations were usually due to the nearly universal contamination of all materials by radium, in detectable but minute amounts ($\sim 10^{-13}$ g Ra/g). All reports were withdrawn or disproved except for the cases of potassium and rubidium, which remained for several decades as the only known radioactive substances outside the thorium and uranium series.

In recent years several especially interesting nuclides, which seemed at first to form exceptions to the empirical rules of nuclear stability, have been restudied, using greatly improved chemical and physical techniques. By the end of 1954 most of these had been shown to be measurably unstable, although the half-periods of some exceed 10^{12} yr. In addition to the "stable" adjacent isobars Cd^{113}, In^{113} and Sb^{123}, Te^{123}, the only remaining exception is V^{50}. Radioactive radiations have yet to be found from V^{50}, although this nuclide satisfies other criteria for instability. Mass data, obtained from mass-spectroscopic doublets (J17), show that both positron and negatron β decay are to be expected:

$$_{23}V^{50} \rightarrow \beta^+ + {}_{22}Ti^{50} + 2.4 \text{ Mev}$$
$$_{23}V^{50} \rightarrow \beta^- + {}_{24}Cr^{50} + 1.2 \text{ Mev} \tag{3.2}$$

However, the nuclear angular momentum of V^{50} is $I = 6$, while both decay products are even-Z even-N, hence probably $I = 0$. The β transitions against $\Delta I = 6$ may well have such a long half-period that they will frustrate radiation detection techniques for some time to come. Because of the energetics of Eq. (3.2), and because stability or radioactivity at these levels becomes a matter of degree, we arbitrarily include V^{50} in Table 3.1, which summarizes the naturally occurring parent radioactive nuclides. We shall exclude these nuclides from further consideration in connection with empirical rules of stability.

b. Stability Rules Relating to Mass Number. Turning to Fig. 3.1, we note that the stable nuclides are confined to a narrow region of the N vs. Z diagram. Artificially radioactive nuclides have already been produced and studied which fill in most of the blank values of (N,Z) within this region and which also line the borders of the region for a distance of several neutron numbers above and below the region of stability. These nuclides transform by β-ray emission, along lines of constant A, hence diagonally in Fig. 3.1, toward the center of the region of stability.

Nuclear Energy Surface. When the N vs. Z diagram is viewed diagonally, along any isobaric line of constant A, it is noted that for odd-A nuclides there is generally only one stable nuclide. However, for even-A nuclides there are often two and occasionally three stable nuclides which have the same mass number. We can understand this consistent behavior most easily by adding atomic mass M, as a third coordinate, normal to the (N,Z) plane in Fig. 3.1. Then the region of stability becomes a valley, with the stable nuclides at the bottom of the mass-energy valley and the unstable nuclides lining the sides and rims of the valley. Such a mass-energy valley is called a *nuclear energy surface*.

Relative Mass of Odd-A Isobars. Cross sections of the valley, in planes of constant A, have a characteristic appearance. For odd-A, the relationship between atomic mass M and nuclear charge Z is as shown in Fig. 3.2. The lowest isobar in the mass-energy valley is the stable nuclide for the particular *odd* mass number A. Isobars of larger Z decay by positron β rays or by electron capture. Isobars of smaller Z decay to the stable nuclide by successive negatron β decay. Note that for odd-A each isobar is either even-Z odd-N or odd-Z even-N.

The smoothed relationship between M and Z, for constant A, can be shown to be parabolic (Chap. 11), with a minimum lying at some value of nuclear charge Z_0 which determines the "most stable isobar," and

TABLE 3.1. PARENT RADIOACTIVE NUCLIDES WHICH ARE FOUND IN NATURE
References to the original literature will be found in (H61) and (N6)

Nuclide		Atom per cent abundance	Half-period, yr	Radiation observed	Disinte-gration energy Q, Mev	Change in nuclear angular momentum I
Z	A					
19 K	40	0.0119	1.2×10^9	β^-, EC	1.4	4
23 V	50	0.24	?	?	2.4	6
37 Rb	87	27.85	6×10^{10}	β^-	~ 0.3	3
49 In	115	95.77	6×10^{14}	β^-	0.6	4
52 Te	130	34.49	$\sim 10^{21}$	Growth of $_{54}Xe^{130}$	~ 1.6	0
57 La	138	0.089	$\sim 2 \times 10^{11}$	β^-, EC	~ 3	?
60 Nd	144	23.9	$\sim 1.5 \times 10^{15}$	α (W3)	1.9	0
62 Sm	147	15.07	1.4×10^{11}	α	2.1	?
71 Lu	176	2.6	7.5×10^{10}	β^-, γ	0.9	≥ 7
75 Re	187	62.93	4×10^{12}	β^-	0.4	?
90 Th	232	100	1.39×10^{10}	α	4.05	0
92 U	235	0.715	7.13×10^8	α	4.66	?
92 U	238	99.28	4.49×10^9	α	4.25	0

which usually is noninteger. The integer Z which lies nearest Z_0 determines the stable isobar of odd-A. In the case shown in Fig. 3.2 the mass of $_{53}I_{82}^{135}$ lies below the smooth parabolic relationship which the other isobars follow. This is attributed to the closed shell of $N = 82$ neutrons in I^{135}.

Adjacent Stable Isobars. Figure 3.2 shows graphically why there is, in general, only one stable isobar for any particular odd-A. If two odd-A isobars were to lie nearly symmetrically in the bottom of the energy valley, straddling Z_0, then the energy available for a β transition between

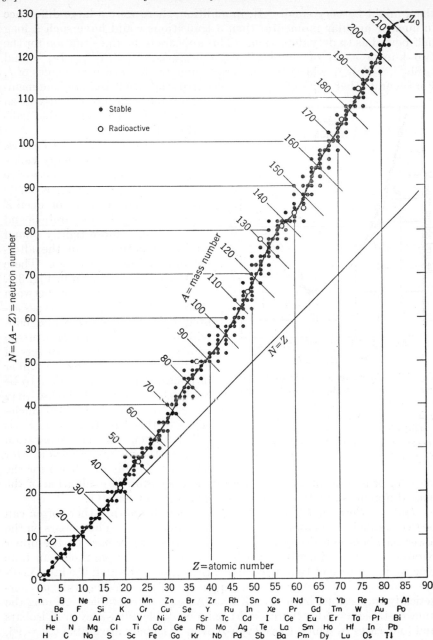

Fig. 3.1 The naturally occurring nuclides for $Z \leq 83$. Open circles show the radioactive nuclides listed in Table 3.1. For $Z > 80$, all naturally occurring nuclides and artificial nuclides will be found in another NZ diagram which is given in Chap. 16, Fig. 3.1. The solid line shows the course of Z_0, which is the bottom of the mass-energy valley, or the "line of β stability" (Chap. 11), (S80, K33). The chemical elements are identified by their symbols along the Z axis.

them might be very small.   If, in addition, there were a large difference in nuclear angular momenta, then β transitions could have such a long half-period as to defy detection.   This appears to be the situation for the two known cases of "stable" *adjacent isobars,* ($_{48}Cd_{\frac{1}{2}}^{113}$, $_{49}In_{\frac{9}{2}}^{113}$) and ($_{51}Sb_{\frac{7}{2}}^{123}$, $_{52}Te_{\frac{1}{2}}^{123}$), where the subscripts denote the measured values of I. For several other pairs of naturally occurring adjacent isobars, one member of the pair has recently been shown to have a measurable half-period (Table 3.1).

Relative Mass of Even-A Isobars. For even-A the mass-energy valley is more complicated.   Successive isobars no longer fall on a single parabola.   The isobars of even-Z even-N fall on a lower parabola and therefore have more tightly bound nuclear structures than the alternating odd-Z odd-N isobars.   These relationships are shown in Fig. 3.3.

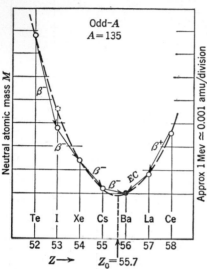

Fig. 3.2   Characteristic relationship between atomic mass M and nuclear charge Z for odd-A isobars.   For $A = 135$, the only stable isobar is $_{56}Ba$, shown here as a solid circle.   The bottom of the mass-energy valley for $A = 135$ occurs at $Z_0 = 55.7$.

The mass separation between these two parabolas is to be associated with the even-even and odd-odd character of the proton-neutron configurations in these two sets of even-A isobars.   An even number of identical nucleons is seen to be relatively more tightly bound than an odd number of identical nucleons.   If this "pairing energy" is called δ, then the mass separation between the two parabolas is δ for the even-Z, plus another δ for the even-N, or a total of 2δ.   We shall give a generalized evaluation of the mass differences due to nucleon pairing energy in Chap. 11.

Isobaric Pairs and Trios.   Figure 3.3 also shows that there often can be two stable isobars for a particular *even* value of A.   The isobars on the lower parabola can decay only by β transitions to isobars on the upper parabola.   Transitions between isobars on the lower parabola can take place only by way of two successive β transitions, through the intermediate odd-Z odd-N isobar on the upper parabola.   When this is energetically impossible, both even-Z even-N isobars are stable.   Among the known stable nuclides there are 54 pairs of stable even-Z even-N isobars and four cases in which three even-Z even-N isobars are stable ($A = 96$, 124, 130, 136).

Double β Decay.   The only alternative transitions between a pair of "stable" even-Z even-N isobars would be by the simultaneous emission of two β rays, or *double β decay.*   The theoretical half-period for the emission of two electron-neutrino pairs, in a double β transition, is $\sim 10^{24}$

yr for an allowed transition with 1.6 Mev of available energy. Presently available radiation-detection techniques, arranged for the observation of β-β coincidences, can at best explore down to a half-period of $\sim 10^{18}$ yr. Within this domain, no unequivocal cases of double β decay have been found by radiation measurements. In the experimentally more favorable case of $_{52}\text{Te}^{130} \rightarrow \beta^-\beta^- + {}_{54}\text{Xe}^{130}$ ($Q \sim 1.6$ Mev), Ingrahm and Reynolds (I2) have observed a measurable accumulation of Xe^{130} in a Bi_2Te_3 mineral whose geological age is $\sim 1.5 \times 10^9$ yr. The data lead to a half-period of $\sim 1 \times 10^{21}$ yr for the double β decay of Te^{130}.

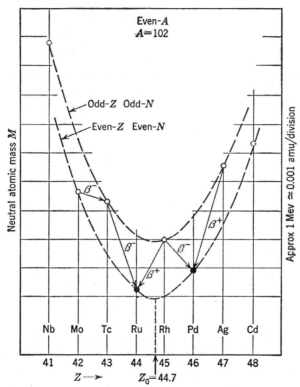

Fig. 3.3 Cross section of the energy valley for even-A isobars, showing the characteristic double-valued relationship between atomic mass M and nuclear charge Z. For $A = 102$, *both* $_{44}\text{Ru}$ and $_{46}\text{Pd}$ are stable (solid circles). The bottom of the mass-energy valley is at $Z_0 = 44.7$ for $A = 102$.

Antineutrinos in Double β Decay. We may note here that the observation of double β decay with a half-period $> 10^{20}$ yr is presently the only positive experimental evidence which distinguishes between two formulations of β-decay theory (K39). If the neutrino is a particle which satisfies Dirac's equation for electrons (after setting the charge and rest mass equal to zero), then there would be two distinguishable solutions, a "neutrino," ν, and an "*antineutrino,*" $\bar{\nu}$. The antineutrino may be regarded as a "hole," just as a positron is a "hole" in Dirac electron theory. Then positron β decay involves the emission of a positron-neutrino pair, while in negatron β decay a negatron-antineutrino pair is emitted:

$$p \rightarrow n + \beta^+ + \nu$$
$$n \rightarrow p + \beta^- + \bar{\nu}$$

(3.3)

Double β^- decay requires the emission of two Dirac antineutrinos, and the calculated half-periods are generally $> 10^{20}$ yr.

In a modification due to Majorana, there is no distinction between a neutrino and an antineutrino. Then in double β decay, the neutrino emitted by one transforming nucleon can be absorbed by the other transforming nucleon. This type of double β^- decay would involve only the emission of two β rays but no neutrinos. This model leads to very much shorter predicted half-periods, $\sim 10^{12}$ yr, for double β decay (P34). Because these have not been found experimentally, the presumption is presently against Majorana neutrinos and in favor of distinguishable Dirac neutrinos and antineutrinos.

Colloquially, the expression "electron-neutrino pair," as used in discussions of ordinary single β decay, can be understood to include either form of neutrino, wherever the distinction between neutrino and antineutrino is significant.

Frequency Distribution of Stable Isobars. Returning again to the NZ diagram of Fig. 3.1, study of the details of the distribution brings out several simple and important generalizations concerning the stability of nuclei. With respect to mass number A, these can be summarized for $1 \leq A \leq 209$ as follows:

1. For even-A: *There are always one, two, or three stable values of Z, always with even-Z* [exceptions: (a) H^2, Li^6, B^{10}, N^{14}, which have odd-Z but are stable because $N = Z$; (b) no stable nuclide exists for $A = 8$].

2. For odd-A: *There is only one stable value of Z, and this value of Z can be either odd or even* [exceptions: (a) Cd^{113}, In^{113} and Sb^{123}, Te^{123}; (b) no stable nuclide exists for $A = 5$ and 147].

c. Stability Rules Relating to Proton Number and Neutron Number. Empirical rules for the distribution of stable isotopes and isotones also emerge from a study of Fig. 3.1. These rules are particularly significant for the theory of nuclear forces.

Frequency of Stable Isotopes. Stable nuclides are found for all proton numbers in the range $1 \leq Z \leq 83$, except for $Z = 43$ (technetium, Tc) and $Z = 61$ (promethium, Pm). The following generalizations can be made:

1. For even-Z: *There are always at least two values of N which give stable isotopes* (exception: $_4Be^9$ is simple). Usually two or more of these isotopes have even-N (up to seven for $Z = 50$, Sn). There may also be stable odd-N isotopes, numbering 0, 1, 2 (for 15 elements), or 3 (for $Z = 50$, Sn, only).

2. For odd-Z: *There are never more than two stable isotopes.* The element is usually simple, and if so its only stable isotope is invariably even-N. In 10 cases there are two stable isotopes, both even-N (Cl, K,

Cu, Ga, Br, Ag, Sb, Eu, Ir, Tl).   In two cases there are no stable isotopes (Tc, Pm).   All odd-N isotopes are unstable (exceptions: H^2, Li^6, B^{10}, N^{14}, for which $N = Z$).

Frequency of Stable Isotones.   Stable isotones are found for all neutron numbers in the range $0 \leq N \leq 126$, except for nine values, all of which are odd-N.   The following generalizations can be made:

1. For even-N: *There are always at least two values of Z which give stable isotones* (exceptions: $N = 2$ and 4, where $_2He_2^4$ and $_3Li_4^7$ are the only stable isotones).   Usually two or more of these isotones have even-Z (up to five for $N = 82$).   There may also be stable odd-Z isotones, numbering 0, 1, or 2 (only for $N = 20$ and $N = 82$).

2. For odd-N: *There are never more than two stable isotones.*   Usually there is only one stable isotone (example: $_8O_9^{17}$), and if so this is invariably even-Z (exception: $_3Li_3^6$, where $N = Z$).   In nine cases there are no stable isotones ($N = 19, 21, 35, 39, 45, 61, 89, 115, 123$).   All odd-$Z$ isotones are unstable (exceptions: H^2, Li^6, B^{10}, N^{14}, for which $N = Z$).

Correlation of Isobar, Isotope, and Isotone Distributions.   The empirical stability rules from the standpoint of mass number derive actually from the nuclear behavior of neutrons and protons, hence from the stability rules regarding isotopes and isotones.   These can now be assembled in the symmetric form given in Table 3.2.

TABLE 3.2. THE OBSERVED FREQUENCY DISTRIBUTION OF STABLE NUCLIDES
(According to the odd and even character of the neutron number N, proton number Z, and mass number A.   The underscoring indicates the most abundant cases.)

A	Z	N	Total number of stable nuclides	Number of stable *isotopes* for a particular value of Z	Number of stable *isotones* for a particular value of N
Odd	Odd	Even	50	0, 1, 2	0, 1, 2 (2 for $N = 20, 82$)
Odd	Even	Odd	55	0, 1, 2, 3 (3 for $Z = 50$)	0, 1, 2
Even	Odd	Odd	4	0, 1	0,1
Even	Even	Even	165	1, 2, 3, . . . , 7 (7 for $Z = 50$)	1, 2, 3, 4, 5 (5 for $N = 82$)

d. Conclusions from the Empirical Frequency Distributions of Isobars, Isotopes, and Isotones.   The principal exceptions to the simplest generalizations about the occurrence of stable nuclei arise from two small groups of nuclides.   These deserve special mention.   The four lowest odd-Z elements (H, Li, B, N) are able to form stable nuclides which contain equal odd numbers of protons and neutrons.   For larger Z, and hence greater disruptive coulomb forces, nuclides containing equal numbers of protons and neutrons are stable only if both are even.   This implication that even numbers of identical nucleons are more tightly bound than odd numbers is confirmed by the nonoccurrence of stable odd-Z odd-N nuclides, when $N > Z$. The second unique group of nuclides comprises the stable adjacent isobars $_{48}Cd^{113}$, $_{49}In^{113}$ and $_{51}Sb^{123}$, $_{52}Te^{123}$, whose existence is attributable to their large difference in nuclear angular momentum. Note that these bracket the closed shell of protons at $Z = 50$.

Detailed comparison of the stability rules for isotopes with those for isotones shows that neutrons exhibit a behavior in nuclei which is substantially identical with the behavior of protons. The missing elements $Z = 43$ and 61 are the analogues of the missing isotones $N = 19$,

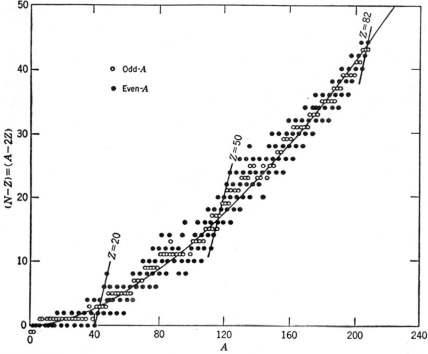

Fig. 3.4 The excess-neutron number $N - Z$ as a function of mass number A for the stable nuclides shown in Fig. 3.1. The smooth curve is $N - Z = 0.0060 \, A^{\frac{5}{3}}$, as given by Eq. (3.27) of Chap. 11.

$21, \ldots, 123$. The marked tendency of other odd-Z elements to be simple and even-N is the analogue of the tendency for the odd-N isotones to be simple and to have even-Z. The large number of stable isotopes found for even-Z elements is the analogue of the large number of stable even-N isotones. These large frequencies for even-Z, and analogously but independently for even-N, reach their maximum values for Z or $N = 20, 28, 50,$ and 82. This observation was one of the earliest identifications of the "magic numbers," or closed shells, in nuclei.

We can draw at least three principal conclusions from the frequency distribution of stable nuclides.

1. Neutrons in nuclei behave in a manner which is similar, if not identical, to the behavior of protons in nuclei. There is every reason to regard neutrons and protons as two forms of a more fundamental particle, the nucleon.

2. Even numbers of identical nucleons are more stable than odd numbers of the same nucleons.

3. Exceptional stability is associated with certain even numbers of identical nucleons, especially 20, 28, 50, and 82, and these magic numbers identify some of the closed-shell configurations of identical nucleons.

e. Neutron Excess in Stable Nuclides. Only the lightest nuclei tend to have equal numbers of protons and neutrons. As Z increases, the disruptive forces due to coulomb repulsion between all the protons would prohibit the formation of stable nuclides if some extra attractive forces were not brought into the nuclear structure. These extra attractive forces are provided by neutrons, whose number N exceeds Z by a larger and larger amount as Z increases. In the NZ diagram of Fig. 3.1, the excess-neutron number, $N - Z$, is seen as the vertical distance between the stable nuclides and the diagonal $N = Z$ line.

The empirical relationship between $N - Z$ and the mass number A becomes an important parameter in the liquid-drop model of nuclei (Chap. 11). From the data of Fig. 3.1 we can construct the graphical relationship between $N - Z$ and A, as shown in Fig. 3.4. Empirically, a good fit is obtained from the simple relationship

$$N - Z = \text{const } A^{\frac{2}{3}} \tag{3.4}$$

A slightly more sophisticated form emerges from the liquid-drop model and is given in Chap. 11. Equation (3.4) is of interest here because it contains fundamental information about nuclear forces. The coulomb disruptive energy of a charge Ze, distributed throughout a volume of radius R, is proportional to $(Ze)^2/R$. If nuclear matter has a constant density, then R is proportional to $A^{\frac{1}{3}}$. To a first approximation, Fig. 3.1 shows that A is proportional to Z. Then the coulomb energy should be approximately proportional to $A^2/A^{\frac{1}{3}} = A^{\frac{5}{3}}$. It is a well-founded presumption that the major role for the excess neutrons $N - Z$ is to neutralize the coulomb repulsion energy.

CHAPTER 9

Binding Energy of Nuclei

The aggregate of protons and neutrons within nuclei is held together by strong forces of mutual attraction between the nucleons.   There must also be short-range repulsive forces between nucleons within nuclei, such that the balance between attractive and repulsive forces causes nuclei to exhibit an approximately constant density and a radius which is proportional to $A^{\frac{1}{3}}$.   If short-range repulsion were absent, all nuclei should collapse into a small radius of the order of the range of the nucleon-nucleon force ($\sim 2 \times 10^{-13}$ cm).

Some of the characteristics of the *net forces* between nucleons are accessible to evaluation through an examination of the masses of nuclei, as compared with the masses of the constituent neutrons and protons.

1. Packing Fraction

Accurate values of the "isotopic weight," or "neutral atomic mass" M, were first obtained by Aston in "preneutron" days, when the nuclear constituents were thought to be protons and electrons.   Aston expressed his results in terms of the quantity actually measured by his mass spectrograph, the so-called *packing fraction P*, defined by

$$P \equiv \frac{M - A}{A} \tag{1.1}$$

where A is the mass number.   By rearrangement of Eq. (1.1), the packing fraction can be regarded physically as a small correction term ($\sim 10^{-3}$ for many nuclides) which relates the isotopic mass M to the mass number A

$$M \equiv A(1 + P) \tag{1.2}$$

Aston correctly pointed out that the measured packing fraction P is connected in some way with the stability of nuclei, but the actual relationship to nuclear forces could not be inferred because the constituents of nuclei were unknown.

The packing fraction is seen from Eq. (1.2) to be zero, by definition, for O^{16}.   Curves of P vs. A have been compiled by Aston (A36), Dempster (D22), Mattauch (M22), Collins, Johnson, and Nier (C34), and others to represent the accumulated mass-spectroscopic data on nuclear

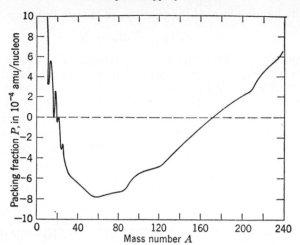

Fig. 1.1 The general trend of the variation of packing fraction P (in units of 10^{-4} amu/nucleon) with mass number A, from mass-spectroscopic data.

masses. Figure 1.1 illustrates the general character of the packing-fraction curve. Note that P has a minimum value of about -8×10^{-4} in the vicinity of iron, cobalt, and nickel.

2. *Total Binding Energy*

Aston's early data (A36) were sufficiently accurate to establish what he justly called the "failure of the additive law with regard to mass." Thus, the isotopic mass of O^{16} is clearly not four times that of He^4, and He^4 is not four times H^1. These mass deficiencies were recognized as analogous to the heat of formation of a chemical compound and attributable to the energy liberated when the elementary nuclear constituents aggregate. What Aston called the *mass defect*, or loss of mass upon coalescence of the elementary constituents, can be evaluated quantitatively only after the nuclear constituents have been identified or assumed.

a. Binding Energy on the Proton-Neutron Model. When protons and neutrons are assumed to be the elementary constituents of all nuclei, the mass defect,† or *binding energy B*, of the nucleus is

$$B \equiv ZM_p + NM_n - M' \tag{2.1}$$

where M_p, M_n, and M' are the masses of the proton, neutron, and bare nucleus. It is convenient to introduce the mass of Z atomic electrons

---

† According to its original definition (A36) and some current usage (M22), "mass defect" is synonymous with binding energy. Some contemporary mass spectros-copists (C35, C36) have used the name "mass defect" to mean $(M - A)$ and $(A - M)$. To minimize confusion, $(M - A)$, when it needs a name, can be called the *mass excess* (R18).

into the right-hand side of this equation, so that it becomes

$$B = ZM_H + NM_n - M \qquad (2.2)$$

where M_H and M are the neutral atomic masses of hydrogen and of the nuclide in question. This conventional procedure allows binding energies to be evaluated from tables of neutral atomic mass, such as those of Chap. 3, Sec. 5. Rigorously, the binding energy $B_e(Z)$ of the atomic electrons belongs in Eq. (2.2), both for M_H and for M. This refinement is customarily omitted because $B_e(Z)$ is at most about 3 kev/nucleon [Eq. (2.2) of Chap. 3], whereas B is of the order of 8 Mev/nucleon.

Physically, we define the binding energy as the (positive) work necessary to disassemble a nucleus into neutrons and protons. Equivalently, it is the energy liberated when Z protons and N neutrons combine to form a nucleus. For visualization, the simplest examples are the photodisintegration of the deuteron $H^2(\gamma,n)H^1$ and the radiative capture of neutrons by hydrogen $H^1(n,\gamma)H^2$. The binding energy of the deuteron (2.22 Mev) is the Q value of the synthesis reaction $H^1(n,\gamma)H^2$, or $-Q$ for the dissociation reaction $H^2(\gamma,n)H^1$, as evaluated in Chap. 3, Sec. 4.

With respect to the interior of a nucleus, the binding energy is the difference between the mutual potential energy (taken as a positive quantity) and the total kinetic energy of the constituent nucleons.

We emphasize that the definition of B is arbitrary and that the value of B depends on the model assumed. Even in the proton-neutron model, B is the energy liberated on coalescence only if the starting materials are exactly Z protons and N neutrons. If the nucleus $_ZX^A$ is made, not by combining Z protons and $N = (A - Z)$ neutrons, but by combining $(Z - 1)$ protons and $(A - Z + 1)$ neutrons to form $_{Z-1}X^A$, which then liberates an additional energy Q_β in a β transition to $_ZX^A$, the total energy liberated will *not* be equal to the binding energy B of $_ZX^A$.

b. Binding Energy of the Lightest Nuclei. We can evaluate B from Eq. (2.2) for a number of nuclei, using the mass values M from Table 5.1 of Chap. 3. For the lightest nuclides, the resulting values of B, and the average binding energy per nucleon B/A, are given in Table 2.1.

TABLE 2.1. BINDING ENERGY B, AND AVERAGE BINDING ENERGY PER NUCLEON B/A, FOR THE LIGHTEST NUCLIDES

Nuclide..................	n	H^1	H^2	H^3	He^3	He^4	Li^6	Li^7
B(Mev)..................	0	0	2.22	8.48	7.72	28.3	32.0	39.2
B/A (Mev/nucleon)........	0	0	1.11	2.83	2.57	7.07	5.33	5.60

The Deuteron. We note especially the very small binding energy of the deuteron. This can be correlated with other evidence, to be discussed in Chap. 10, which shows that the deuteron is a loosely joined structure in which the proton and neutron have an unusually large separation during a major portion of the time. In any nucleus, the rationalized de Broglie wavelength λ of the constituent particles must not be greater than the nuclear dimensions. A large kinetic energy may be required in order to achieve a sufficiently small λ. This is the case in the deuteron, where the kinetic energy is nearly as great as the potential energy. Therefore the net binding energy (PE − KE) is small.

The α Particle. The number of possible attractive bonds between pairs of nucleons is one in H^2, three in H^3 and He^3, six in He^4, and 15 in Li^6. Clearly, the number of possible bonds for these lightest nuclides is not in proportion to the observed binding energies. He^4 stands out clearly as an exceptionally tightly bound configuration. In He^4, the attractive forces have pulled the nucleons into a smaller and fully bound structure. He^4 contains the maximum possible number of $1s$ nucleons, the four particles differing only with respect to their two possible spin orientations and their two possible values of charge, in accord with the Pauli principle. There is no orbital angular momentum in He^4; otherwise there would be a repulsion due to centrifugal force, and something other than He^4 would be the most stable simple configuration. He^4 then represents the smallest nuclear configuration of totally closed neutron and proton shells.

c. Change of Binding Energy in Nuclear Transitions. Spontaneous nuclear transitions, such as β decay and α decay, generally, but not necessarily, progress in the direction of increasing B. For example, H^3 is β-active but has a greater binding energy than its decay product He^3. It can be shown easily that if Q_β is the $(\beta + \gamma)$ energy released in β^- decay between a parent and daughter nuclide identified by the subscripts 1 and 2, then

$$Q_\beta = M_1 - M_2 = (B_2 - B_1) + (M_n - M_H) \qquad (2.3)$$

Because the neutron-hydrogen mass difference $(M_n - M_H)$ is about 0.78 Mev [Eq. (4.42), Chap. 3], all β^- transitions for which the total β-ray and γ-ray energies is $Q_\beta < 0.78$ Mev will involve a *decrease* in binding energy. The criterion for β instability (either β^- or electron capture) is

$$(M_1 - M_2) > 0 \qquad \text{not} \qquad (B_2 - B_1) > 0 \qquad (2.4)$$

Problem

Consider the energy released in the formation of any nuclide $_ZX^A$ by two alternative processes: (*a*) combination of Z protons and electrons with $(A - Z)$ neutrons, with release of binding energy B, and (*b*) combination of $(Z + 1)$ protons and electrons with $(A - Z - 1)$ neutrons, followed by positron β decay. Show that the total energy released in processes (*b*) is $B - (M_n - M_H) = B - 0.78$ Mev. Explain physically why the energy released in the formation of $_ZX^A$ by the processes (*b*) is *not* equal to the "binding energy" of $_ZX^A$.

3. *Average Binding Energy*

In middleweight and heavy nuclei $(A \geq 40)$ the average binding energy per nucleon becomes an important empirical parameter in several theories of nuclear structure.

a. Approximate Constancy of Average Binding Energy per Nucleon. From Eq. (2.2) the total binding energy, in terms of the mass number A

and atomic number Z, is

$$
\begin{aligned}
B &= ZM_H + (A - Z)M_n - M \\
&= AM_n - Z(M_n - M_H) - M
\end{aligned} \tag{3.1}
$$

The average binding energy per nucleon can be expressed in several useful forms, including

$$
\begin{aligned}
\frac{B}{A} &= M_n - \frac{Z}{A}(M_n - M_H) - \frac{M}{A} \\
&= (M_n - 1) - \frac{Z}{A}(M_n - M_H) - \frac{M - A}{A} \\
&= (M_n - 1) - \frac{Z}{A}(M_n - M_H) - P
\end{aligned} \tag{3.2}
$$

where P is the packing fraction of Eq. (1.1) and Fig. 1.1, in units of atomic mass units per nucleon. For the nuclides from Ca^{40} to Sn^{120}, Z/A varies only between 0.50 and 0.42; say its mean value is $Z/A \simeq 0.46$. In the same region, $P \simeq -6 \times 10^{-4}$ amu/nucleon. Then numerically Eq. (3.2) becomes

$$
\begin{aligned}
\frac{B}{A} &\simeq 0.008\,982 - 0.46(0.000\,840) + 0.0006 \\
&= 0.0092 \text{ amu/nucleon} \\
&= 8.5 \text{ Mev/nucleon}
\end{aligned} \tag{3.3}
$$

The mass excess $(M_n - 1)$ of the neutron is clearly the predominant term in Eq. (3.3). The small observed values of the packing fraction P and the small neutron-hydrogen mass difference $(M_n - M_H)$ act only as small correction terms. We see here the importance of accurate knowledge of the neutron mass M_n, because to a first approximation $(M_n - 1)$ is the average binding energy (B/A) of the nucleons in all nuclei except the very lightest.

Figure 3.1 shows the variation of B/A with A, for $1 \leq A \leq 238$. For $A < 28$ there is a prominent cyclic recurrence of peaks, corresponding to maximum binding for nuclides in which A is a multiple of four. Each of these most tightly bound nuclides is even-Z even-N, and $N = Z$. They correspond to a sequence of completed "four-shells" and suggest an α model for light nuclei. The existence of these peaks is a compelling experimental demonstration of the applicability of the Pauli exclusion principle in nuclei, because each four-shell contains just two neutrons (with spin "up" and spin "down") and two protons (with spin "up" and spin "down").

Pairs of stable isobars first appear at $_{16}S^{36}$, $_{18}A^{36}$ and become frequent as A increases. Then B/A is no longer single-valued with respect to A, even for stable nuclides. Also, for $A \geq 30$ ($_{14}Si^{30}_{16}$), the B/A values begin to exhibit other effects, probably attributable to closed shells in jj coupling (N or $Z = 14, 20, 28, 40, 50, 82, 126$). Above $A \sim 60$, accurate mass values are as yet available for only a small portion of the known nuclides (M22, B4).   Figure 3.1 therefore indicates only the smoothed general trend of B/A for $30 \leq A \leq 240$, without explicit representation of significant fine variations which undoubtedly will be quantified later.   Even so, this region already shows several significant features. There is a broad maximum near $A \simeq 60$ (Fe, Ni, Co) where $B/A \simeq 8.7$ Mev/nucleon.   Above this region the mean B/A values fall monotonically.   Note also that B/A declines among the heavy emitters of α rays to a low of 7.3 Mev/nucleon for U^{238}.   This small value of B/A approaches, but does not equal, the $B/A = 7.07$ Mev/nucleon exhibited in the α particle itself.   Nuclides having A appreciably larger than 238,

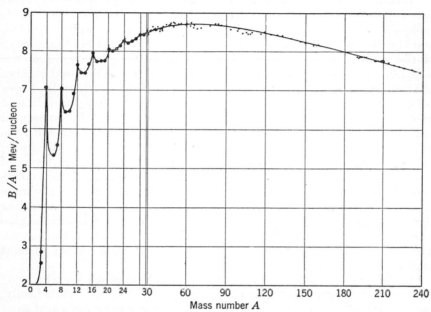

Fig. 3.1   Average binding energy B/A in Mev per nucleon for the naturally occurring nuclides (and Be^8), as a function of mass number A.   Note the change of magnification in the A scale at $A = 30$.   The Pauli four-shells in the lightest nuclei are evident.   For $A \geq 16$, B/A is roughly constant; hence, to a first approximation, B is proportional to A.

and correspondingly smaller values of B/A, could be expected to be energetically unstable against total disruption into α particles.   Thus there is a natural limitation on the maximum achievable value of A (and Z), even in the absence of the boundary set by spontaneous two-body fission, which is discussed in Chap. 11.

   b. Saturation of Nuclear Forces.   If each nucleon exerted the same attractive force on all other nucleons in its nucleus, then there would be $A(A - 1)/2$ attractive bonds.   For $A \gg 1$, the binding energy would then increase at least as rapidly as A^2, even assuming that in larger nuclei the nucleons are not drawn closer together, where they could experience still stronger forces.   Experimentally, this square law is distinctly not realized, because B/A is not proportional to A. Instead B/A is substantially constant. To a good approximation, the total binding energy B is proportional to the number of nucleons, or

$$B \simeq \text{const} \times A \tag{3.4}$$

This is analogous to the chemical binding energy between the atoms in a liquid, which is known to be proportional to the total number of atoms present. We therefore take this analogy as a guide in our selection of the mathematical methods and terminology for the discussion of the fundamental forces between nucleons.

In a drop of liquid hydrogen we find a strong *homopolar binding* (H44) between individual pairs of hydrogen atoms, with the formation of H_2 molecules. A third hydrogen atom is not nearly so strongly attracted, and the H_2 molecule is said to be *saturated*. The total binding energy of the drop is approximately equal to the combined energies of the individual pairs of hydrogen atoms, i.e., proportional to the total number of atoms present. The total energy is only slightly increased by forces between the molecules. The successful mathematical representation of homopolar binding is that of *exchange forces*, which physically correspond to a continued process of exchanging the electrons of one atom with the other atom in the molecule. It is therefore assumed that the forces between nucleons may also be represented mathematically in terms of *exchange operators*, which perform the operation of exchanging the coordinates, between pairs of nucleons, in the potential energy term of the wave equation. This adoption of the concept of exchange forces in nuclear theory was made principally because such methods were known to give forces which show saturation. Its justification lies only in the success which the method has already had in dealing with the theory of light nuclei.

Exchange Forces between Nucleons. The particle which is exchanged† between two nucleons is assumed to be a π meson, or pion. Symbolically, the exchange force between a proton and neutron can be described as

$$p + n \rightarrow n' + \pi^+ + n \rightarrow n' + p' \tag{3.5}$$

Here the initial proton becomes a neutron, by losing a positive pion, which then joins the original neutron and converts it into a proton. The original proton and neutron have now exchanged their coordinates.

Negative pions and neutral pions can also be involved in the exchange force between nucleons, according to

$$\begin{aligned}
n + p &\rightarrow p' + \pi^- + p \rightarrow p' + n' \\
n + n &\rightarrow n' + \pi^0 + n \rightarrow n' + n' \\
p + p &\rightarrow p' + \pi^0 + p \rightarrow p' + p'
\end{aligned} \tag{3.6}$$

Dependence of Nuclear Forces on Spatial and Spin Coordinates. The nuclear unit which shows saturation does not contain two particles, as in

---

† Falkoff's (F3) qualitative explanations of the concepts of exchange forces in billiard-ball and nucleon collisions should prove especially useful to those who have dealt previously with classical forces only.

the hydrogen molecule, but four. This is evident from the binding energies, which attain their first maximum for the α particle, an additional neutron or proton being less tightly bound. Nucleons are seen to exert strong forces upon each other only if they are in the *same quantum state with regard to their spatial coordinates.* These internucleon forces are moderately indifferent to relative spin orientations. If, for example, the force between a neutron and proton were strong only when their spins were parallel, then the deuteron should be the saturated subunit, and an additional proton or neutron, as in He³ and H³, should not be strongly bound. Therefore the forces between nucleons can *depend only moderately on the relative spin directions of the two nucleons.*

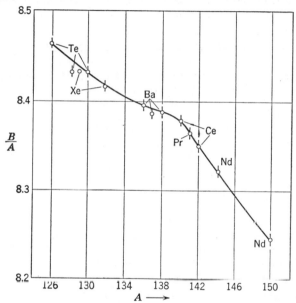

Fig. 3.2 Detail of a portion of the curve of binding energy per nucleon B/A in Mev per nucleon, against A, showing a discontinuity at $_{58}Ce_{82}^{140}$. The curve is drawn through the points for the family of even-Z even-N nuclides. [*From Duckworth et al.* (D41).]

c. Shell Structure and Binding Energy. The detailed behavior of the B/A vs. A curve of Fig. 3.1 has been explored over several restricted regions of A. For the heavier elements, the absolute values of M, and hence of B/A, obtained by different laboratories often disagree by more than the assigned errors of measurement. But by confining attention to any one self-consistent set of mass values, the systematic variations of binding energy with mass number may be revealed. In this way, Fig. 3.2 shows the discontinuity in B/A vs. A which has been reported by Duckworth et al. (D41) at $_{58}Ce_{82}^{140}$, and which apparently marks the closing of a shell of $N = 82$ neutrons.

Similar discontinuities have been observed elsewhere, e.g., by Nier and coworkers at Z or $N = 20$ and 28 (C35, C36), and at $Z = 50$ (H11), and by Dempster (D22) at the "doubly magic" Pb²⁰⁸ ($Z = 82, N = 126$).

The systematics of nuclear moments (Chap. 4, Sec. 4) has been fruitful in the development of the shell model of nuclei, but for all even-Z even-N nuclides these methods give only the information that $I = 0$. Mass values, and the binding energies derived from them, provide explicit quantitative data on families of even-Z even-N nuclides and therefore supply complementary information on the location of closed shells in nuclei.

Problems

1. In Fig. 3.1, Li⁶ has an average binding energy B/A which is less than that for the α particle. Why does Li⁶ not undergo spontaneous α decay?

2. Show that

$$\frac{B}{A} = \frac{N}{A}(M_n - M_H) + (M_H - 1) - P$$

and that the uncertainty in B/A with respect to uncertainties δM_n or δM_H, in M_n or M_H, is of the order of $\delta M_n/2$ and $\delta M_H/2$.

3. From mass data, compute and plot the average binding energy per nucleon B/A against N in the vicinity of $N = 20$, 28 (C35 and C36, or Table 5.2, Chap. 3) or B/A against Z in the neighborhood of $Z = 50$ (H11). Comment on any closed-shell effects which may be displayed by your graph.

4. (a) Show that for a nucleus A_1 to be energetically unstable against α-ray emission, the slope of the B/A vs. A curve must be negative, and its absolute value must exceed

$$\frac{1}{A_1}\left(7.07 - \frac{B_2}{A_2}\right)$$

where B_2/A_2 refers to the decay product of the transition.

(b) Show from a similar argument that the slope of the B/A vs. A curve must be negative and that its absolute value must exceed

$$\frac{1}{A_1}\left(1.11 - \frac{B_2}{A_2}\right)$$

if the radioactive emission of a deuteron is to be possible energetically.

(c) What conclusions can be drawn from (a) and (b) concerning the types of heavy-particle radioactivity which one can expect to observe?

4. Separation Energy for One Nucleon

A somewhat more detailed view of nuclear forces is given by the variations in the binding energy of the "last" proton or neutron in a group of nuclides. The energy required to remove one neutron from the nucleus (Z,N) is called the *neutron separation energy* S_n, and can be written

$$S_n(Z,N) = \frac{\Delta B}{\Delta N} = M(Z, N - 1) + M_n - M(Z,N) \qquad (4.1)$$

where M_n is the neutron mass, $M(Z,N)$ is the atomic mass of the nuclide, and $M(Z, N - 1)$ is the atomic mass of the lighter isotope which results when one neutron is removed from the nucleus (Z,N). In terms of binding energies, the neutron separation energy $S_n(Z,N)$ is the increment in total nuclear binding energy when one neutron is added to the lower isotope $(Z, N - 1)$, thus

$$S_n(Z,N) = B(Z,N) - B(Z, N - 1) \qquad (4.2)$$

For this reason S_n is also called the "binding energy of the last neutron."

In a completely analogous fashion, S_p is the *proton separation energy* or the binding energy of the last proton, and is given by

$$S_p(Z,N) = M(Z - 1, N) + M_{\mathrm{H}} - M(Z,N) \qquad (4.3)$$

or $\qquad\quad S_p(Z,N) = B(Z,N) - B(Z - 1, N) \qquad (4.4)$

Nucleon separation energies are the nuclear analogues of the first ionization potential of atoms. As is well known, the atomic ionization potentials exhibit a systematic cyclic behavior with increasing Z (p. 217 of H44). The largest values of the first ionization potential occur for the atoms which have closed shells of electrons: He, Ne, A, Kr, Xe, Rn. In each case the next higher atomic number displays the smallest ionization potential, or "last electron binding energy," in the sequence.

The sequence of S_n and S_p for successive nuclides shows a cyclic behavior and provides information on the nature of the forces between nucleons.

a. Separation Energy in the Lightest Nuclides. Figure 4.1 shows the neutron and proton separation energies for the stable nuclides $1 \leq A$

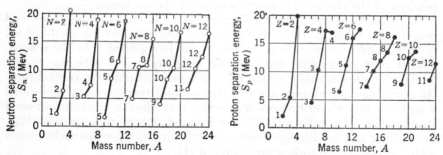

Fig. 4.1 The left-hand diagram shows the energy S_n in Mev required to separate one neutron from the lightest stable nuclides and from H^3 and Be^8. Each point is further identified by its neutron number N. The right-hand diagram shows the analogous separation energy S_p in Mev required to remove the last proton from the same nuclides (except that He^3 replaces H^3), each point being marked with its proton number Z. In each diagram, note that the even-Z even-N nuclides are at or near the top and the odd-Z or odd-N nuclides form the lower envelope.

≤ 24, as computed from the self-consistent mass data of Table 5.1 of Chap. 3. Several principles emerge with dramatic clarity from these simple data.

1. In odd-N nuclides, the final neutron is lightly bound; for example, $S_n = 5.4$ Mev in $_3\mathrm{Li}_3^6$.

2. In even-N nuclides, the last neutron is more tightly bound; for example, in $_3\text{Li}_4^7$, $S_n = 7.2$ Mev. When, in addition, the nuclide has even-Z, then $S_n > 15$ Mev. These are the even-Z even-N nuclides which occupy the peaks of the B/A curve, Fig. 3.1, and also form the upper envelope of S_n in Fig. 4.1. The exceptionally tight binding of the second neutron, which completes an even-N pair, is the origin of the *pairing energy* δ, whose qualitative presence in heavier nuclides we noted in Fig. 3.3 of Chap. 8. The pairing energy for neutrons can be expressed as

$$\delta_n = \tfrac{1}{2}[S_n(\text{even-}N) - S_n(\text{odd-}N)]$$

and is seen to be ~ 2 Mev for many of these lightest nuclides. The factor of one-half arises because each S_n represents the difference between an even-N and an odd-N nucleus.

3. There is a complete parallelism between S_n for odd-N and even-N nuclides and the behavior of the *proton* separation energies S_p in odd-Z and even-Z nuclides. The separation energies S_n and S_p are similar in absolute magnitude, and so are the neutron pairing energies δ_n and the proton pairing energies δ_p.

4. The addition of a *proton*, as between $_6\text{C}_7^{13}$ and $_7\text{N}_7^{14}$, increases the separation energy S_n of the last *neutron*. Similarly, the presence of an additional neutron, as between $_7\text{N}_7^{14}$ and $_7\text{N}_8^{15}$, generally tightens the binding S_p of the last proton.

5. These close similarities between S_n and S_p, δ_n and δ_p suggest that fundamentally the forces between any pair of nucleons are nearly independent of the charge character (n or p) of the nucleons.

b. Models of the Lightest Nuclei. The $1s$ shells of neutrons and protons are filled at He^4. Between He^4 and O^{16}, the $1p$ shells of six neutrons and protons (Chap. 4, Sec. 1) are being filled. In the p shell, neither pure jj coupling nor pure LS coupling agrees with the energy levels which are actually observed. Independent-particle, central-force (Hartree) models, whose wave functions do not correspond to preformed α particles but whose first-order energies may show a marked four-shell structure in LS coupling (F23), are favored over pure α models (H2). For a closer match with experimental results, independent-particle models with intermediate coupling are required (I4).

As a simplification of this complexity, we may visualize the rough but illuminating model for the $1s$ and $1p$ shells which is shown in Fig. 4.2. The four-shell structure which was exhibited by B/A in Fig. 3.1, and by S_n or S_p in Fig. 4.1, is represented here as a sequence of levels, each capable of accepting at most two protons and two neutrons. In an LS-coupling model, these four lowest levels correspond to the orbital quantum numbers $l = 0$, and $l = 1$, $m_l = -1$, 0, $+1$.

Point-by-point comparisons between Figs. 4.1 and 4.2 show in every case that nucleons are strongly bound only to other nucleons within the same subshell. There is very little net binding between nucleons which are not in the same quantum state l, m_l of orbital motion. We can say that *the elementary forces between nucleons are nonadditive.* This unique and fundamental characteristic of the "specifically nuclear" forces is not exhibited by the other known basic types of interaction, i.e., by gravitational forces and by electromagnetic forces.

The *saturation character* of the nuclear forces is emphasized by the nonexistence of stable nuclides with $A = 5$ and 8. The fully saturated He^4 structure declines to bind either an additional neutron or proton, so that He^5 and Li^5 have no bound levels. Even when two four-shells are offered, as in Be^8, there is insufficient binding force between subshells to form a stable nucleus. Three four-shells are required, as in C^{12}, before the forces between subshells are sufficient to form a stable even-Z even-N nuclide. Again, in two nuclides such as B^{11} and N^{15}, Fig. 4.2 suggests

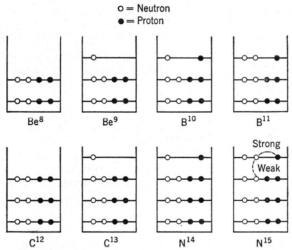

Fig. 4.2 Pictorial models of the $1s$ shell and $1p$ subshells in some of the lightest stable nuclides and Be^8. In accord with the Pauli principle, each "level" can accommodate two neutrons (spin "up" and spin "down") and two protons (spin "up" and spin "down") at the same "spatial position" (l, m_l) in the configuration. The forces between nucleons in the same level are strong, while those between nucleons in different levels are weak, as is suggested schematically in the N^{15} diagram.

that if the forces between nucleons in different subshells were appreciable, the last nucleons in N^{15} should be more tightly bound than those in B^{11}. However, Fig. 4.1 shows that S_n and S_p are the same, or possibly smaller, in N^{15} than in B^{11}.

We should also visualize in the models of Fig. 4.2 all the generalizations drawn earlier from the S_n and S_p diagrams of Fig. 4.1. For example, the last neutron in C^{13} is very loosely bound, whereas the last proton in both C^{12} and C^{13} is tightly bound and gets only a little extra binding from the extra neutron in C^{13}.

c. Separation Energy in Heavy Nuclides. The nucleon separation energies S_n and S_p can be evaluated for many of the heavier nuclides, even where atomic-mass values are unknown, by using nuclear-reaction energetics. For example, the threshold energy for photoneutron production is $-Q(\gamma,n)$, where $Q(\gamma,n)$ is the energy released in the (γ,n) reaction on the target nuclide (Z,N). Then

$$S_n(Z,N) = -Q(\gamma,n) \tag{4.5}$$

It can be shown easily that

$$S_p(Z + 1, N) - S_n(Z + 1, N) = Q(p,n) \tag{4.6}$$

where $Q(p,n)$ is the energy released in the ground-to-ground level (p,n) reaction on the target nuclide (Z,N). Similarly,

$$S_p(Z + 1, N) - S_n(Z + 1, N) = Q_\beta - (M_n - M_H) \tag{4.7}$$

where Q_β is the total $\beta + \gamma$ decay energy for a β^- transition of the parent nuclide (Z,N), and $(M_n - M_H)$ is the neutron-hydrogen mass difference.

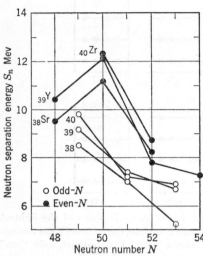

Fig. 4.3 Neutron separation energy S_n in Mev for the stable and radioactive isotopes of $_{38}$Sr, $_{39}$Y, and $_{40}$Zr ($86 \leq A \leq 93$), which involve nuclides containing about 50 neutrons. Isotones of odd N are shown as open circles. These have S_n values which pass monotonically through $N = 50$, whereas the even-N isotones exhibit maxima at $N = 50$, which is identified as a major closed shell of neutrons. [*From tables by Feather* (F13).]

By utilizing all available reaction energetics, Feather (F13) was able by 1953 to compile values of S_n or S_p in some 600 cases covering all values of Z from 1 to 98, except for the usual hiatus including $61 \leq Z \leq 72$. A large proportion of the separation energies are in the domain of 8 ± 2 Mev for middleweight nuclides, while for the heaviest nuclides S_n and S_p fall to the domain of 5 ± 2 Mev.

In Fig. 4.3 the neutron separation energies in the vicinity of $N = 50$ ($86 \leq A \leq 93$) are plotted from Feather's tables. Qualitatively, the same physical phenomena which were so evident in the lightest nuclides, Fig. 4.1, are still present, but their magnitude is somewhat subdued. There is a clear maximum of S_n at $N = 50$, marking the closing of a major neutron shell. For a given N, the neutron separation energy generally increases slightly with Z, hence with the total number of nucleons offering binding forces. S_n is still clearly greater for even-N than for odd-N, although the neutron pairing energy is now down to ~ 1 Mev.

We conclude that in nuclei of any A the forces between nucleons are nonadditive. Only nucleons which have the same "spatial position" are strongly bound to one another. These forces become saturated when, at most, two protons and two neutrons have the same spatial coordinates. We therefore assume that the fundamental forces between nucleons are of an exchange character.

Problems

1. In the (d,p) reaction on a target nuclide (Z,N), show that the neutron separation energy $S_n(Z, N + 1)$ of the *product* nuclide is given by

$$S_n(Z, N + 1) = Q(d,p) + B(H^2)$$

where $Q(d,p)$ is the energy released in the ground-to-ground level reaction and $B(H^2)$ is the binding energy of the deuteron.

2. When $_{79}Au^{197}$ is bombarded with deuterons, a (d,p) reaction takes place, forming Au^{198} which decays to stable Hg^{198} with a half-period of 2.7 days. Au^{198} emits a simple negatron spectrum with a maximum energy of 0.963 Mev followed by one 0.412-Mev γ ray. Take the neutral atomic masses to be

$$_{79}Au^{197} = 197.0394 \text{ amu} \qquad _{80}Hg^{198} = 198.0421 \text{ amu}$$

(*a*) Find the neutral atomic mass of Au^{198}.

(*b*) Find the Q value of the reaction $Au^{197}(d,p)Au^{198}$.

(*c*) Find the separation energy of the last neutron in Au^{198} and compare it with the average binding energy per nucleon.

(*d*) Explain *briefly* the *basic* physical reason for the large variation found in (*c*).

3. Three of the five stable isotopes of nickel $(Z = 28)$ have the following neutral atomic masses: $Ni^{60} = 59.949\ 01$, $Ni^{61} = 60.949\ 07$, $Ni^{62} = 61.946\ 81$.

(*a*) Determine the *total* nuclear binding energy, and the average binding energy per nucleon, in Ni^{60}.

(*b*) Determine the increase in the *total* nuclear binding energy when one neutron is added to Ni^{60} to form Ni^{61}.

(*c*) Determine the increase in the *total* nuclear binding energy when one neutron is added to Ni^{61} to form Ni^{62}.

(*d*) Explain the difference noted in the numerical answers to (*b*) and (*c*), in terms of the corresponding separation energies.

(*e*) Ni^{58} is stable, but Ni^{59} transforms by electron capture to stable Co^{59}. What type of nuclear force may be regarded as primarily responsible for the radioactivity of Ni^{59}?

4. (*a*) Show clearly how you obtain the separation energy for one neutron from Pb^{207}, knowing that the reaction $Pb^{206}(d,p)Pb^{207}$ has a measured value of $Q = +4.5$ Mev for the protons which correspond to the formation of Pb^{207} in its ground level.

(*b*) What would be the quantum energy of the γ rays emitted when thermal neutrons are captured by Pb^{206}, in the reaction $Pb^{206}(n,\gamma)Pb^{207}$, for the Pb^{207} nuclei which are formed in the ground level?

(*c*) Measured values of the separation energy for one neutron from each of several nuclides are given in the following table:

Nuclide	$_{82}Pb^{207}$	$_{82}Pb^{208}$	$_{82}Pb^{209}$	$_{83}Bi^{210}$
Separation energy, Mev	6.7	7.4	4.0	4.2

From general concepts regarding the shell structure of nuclei, explain why these energies are not constant, and why each value deviates from the average in a way which is reasonable for the particular nuclide in question.

5. The elements $Z = 52$ to 56 have the following stable isotopes:

52 Te: 120, 122, 123, 124, 125, 126, 128, 130
53 I: 127
54 Xe: 124, 126, 128, 129, 130, 131, 132, 134, 136
55 Cs: 133
56 Ba: 130, 132, 134, 135, 136, 137, 138

(*a*) Draw a schematic graph of mass vs. Z for the isobars of $A = 130$, and show why Te, Xe, and Ba can all be stable.

(*b*) Show from the Pauli exclusion principle and other contemporary concepts of nuclear structure why elements having odd-Z have so few stable isotopes (and none of even-A unless $A = 2Z$), while neighboring elements of even-Z have many stable isotopes.

CHAPTER 10

Forces between Nucleons

The ground levels and excited levels of all nuclei can be explained by a quantitative theory only after we understand the simplest cases involving just the interaction between two nucleons. As Inglis (I4) has pointed out, our progress toward a full understanding of nuclear spectroscopy involves three major steps. *First*, we have to see which of several possible forms of interaction best fits the experimental data on two-body nucleon-nucleon interactions ("phenomenological theory of nucleon interactions"). *Second*, we must develop a theory of the structure of nucleons which will lead to the selected interaction in a natural way ("meson theory," or other, of the nucleon-force field). *Third*, we must apply the nucleon-structure theory to the general problem of calculating nuclear energy levels.

The main features of nucleon-nucleon interactions have become clear as a result of much experimental and theoretical work, but the two-body forces are still not completely understood. Thus, the first step is not finished, although the choices of interaction have been narrowed greatly in the two decades since the discovery of the neutron. The second step is in progress, but meson theory is still in an unsatisfactory state. Step 3 has seen only exploratory sorties.

In this chapter we make use of the experimental information previously discussed, plus additional results on two-body interactions, in order to determine the principal characteristics of the interaction between individual nucleons.

1. General Characteristics of Specifically Nuclear Forces

Prior to the discovery of the strange and intriguing character of intranuclear forces, substantially all types of material interactions could be described quantitatively in terms of either gravitational forces or electromagnetic forces. Nuclear forces present a new, third major category of fundamental forces.

a. Comparison of Atomic and Nuclear Forces. Atomic electrons are bound into atoms in a manner which is well understood in terms of coulomb forces and simple quantum-mechanical effects associated with spin. The atom possesses a predominant central particle which is the origin of a long-range coulomb field. The atomic electrons spend their time at relatively large distances from this force center and have only a weak interaction with it.   Thus the separation energy for valence electrons is only a few electron volts, while that of the innermost electrons in the heaviest elements does not exceed 0.1 Mev.

In sharp contrast, the nucleus contains *no predominant central particle*. The forces which hold it together have to be mutual forces between the individual nucleons in the ensemble.   These forces have a very *short range* of action, of the order of 10^{-13} cm.   Consequently, the nucleons find themselves closely packed together, with very *small spacings*.   In order to confine a nucleon to a region of this size, its rationalized de Broglie wavelength λ must be correspondingly small, and its kinetic energy must be of the order of $p^2/2M = \hbar^2/2M\lambda^2 \sim 20$ Mev.   This requires a very *large average potential energy*, of the order of 30 Mev if the residual average binding energy is to be ~ 8 Mev.

Clearly, the intranuclear forces cannot be dealt with as small perturbations, with consequent mathematical simplifications.   The many-body problem here presented is prohibitive mathematically.   What can be done is to deal with only the lightest nuclei and especially with the two-body problem represented by the deuteron.

b. Inadequacy of Classical Forces.   The force between nucleons cannot be a classical force which depends only on distance, because the total binding energy of nuclei is proportional to the number of nucleons A and not to A^2.   This qualitative conclusion is strengthened by simple quantitative considerations.

The *gravitational* potential energy between a proton and neutron which are $\sim 2 \times 10^{-13}$ cm apart is smaller than 8 Mev by a factor of $\sim 10^{36}$.   The *electrostatic* potential energy between the same two nucleons is identically zero, because the neutron is uncharged.   The *magnetic* potential energy corresponding to the intrinsic magnetic moments μ'_n and μ'_p of the neutron and proton is of the order of $\mu'_n\mu'_p/r^3$ and, at a separation of $r \sim 2 \times 10^{-13}$ cm, amounts to about 0.03 Mev.   Whether the magnetic force is attractive or disruptive depends on an average over the relative orientation of the neutron and proton but is clearly of opposite sign for parallel and antiparallel spin orientations.   From our evaluation of the separation energies we have found that the force between a neutron and protron is attractive for both parallel and antiparallel spin orientations.   Hence the nuclear force cannot be of magnetic origin.

We conclude that gravitational, electrostatic, and magnetic forces are quantitatively inadequate to act as anything more than very minor perturbations on the specifically nuclear forces.

c. The Singlet and Triplet Two-body Forces between Nucleons. The number of important two-body forces which we must evaluate is fortunately limited.   In nuclei, the proton and neutron separation energies (Chap. 9) show that the important forces are those between nucleons which are in the same spatial quantum state.   Nucleons are strongly bound only to the small number of other nucleons which have the same l values.   We are justified, therefore, in focusing our attention on the forces between nucleons which have zero angular momentum relative to each other, the so-called S states of even parity. Because the nucleons are fermions and obey the Pauli exclusion principle, there can be involved at most two neutrons (spin "up" and spin "down") and two protons in such a group. The possible forces therefore include three types of *singlet force* (antiparallel spins), designated by the superscript 1:

$^1(np)$ between a proton and neutron
$^1(nn)$ between two neutrons
$^1(pp)$ between two protons

The triplet forces (parallel spins) are restricted to one type for S states, namely,

$^3(np)$ between a proton and neutron

because the Pauli principle excludes a $^3(nn)$ and $^3(pp)$ force by providing that no two identical particles can have identical quantum numbers. As long as we restrict our attention to even-parity, S-state interactions, we have only four forces to evaluate: $^3(np)$, $^1(np)$, $^1(nn)$, and $^1(pp)$. We may hereafter drop the singlet superscript from (nn) and (pp) when only S states are under consideration.

In states of nonzero angular momentum the forces between identical particles (nn) and (pp) are restricted by the Pauli exclusion principle to singlet interactions for even-l and to triplet interactions for odd-l.

The (pp) force represents the specifically nuclear attractive force between two protons and does not include their purely classical coulomb interaction. The attractive (pp) interaction greatly exceeds the coulomb interaction, in consonance with the observation that protons are not concentrated on the surface of nuclei but appear to be more or less uniformly distributed throughout the nuclear volume (isotope shift, Chap. 2). That there exists also a strong attractive force (nn) between neutrons is shown by the fact that the neutron excess $(N - Z)$ in nuclei varies approximately as $A^{\frac{2}{3}}$ and appears to counterbalance the disruptive coulomb forces in heavy nuclei (Chap. 8). The finite strength and approximate equality of the (pp) and (nn) forces in nuclei are also shown qualitatively by the isotopic mass (Chap. 2) and excitation levels (B130) of mirror nuclei and by the presence of a proton-pairing energy and an approximately equal neutron-pairing energy in nuclei of any A (Chap. 9).

d. Exchange Forces. The clear experimental evidence that nuclear forces show saturation directs our attention toward the purely quantum-mechanical concept of exchange forces (Chap. 9).

Three types of exchange force have been studied extensively, and these are commonly named for the investigators who first explored their characteristics. They are:

1. *Heisenberg forces*, in which there is exchange of both the *position and spin* coordinates of the two interacting nucleons. Heisenberg forces are attractive for triplet interactions and repulsive for singlet interactions (antiparallel spins). This would be acceptable if the deuteron were the saturated subunit, but pure Heisenberg forces are ruled out by the clear experimental evidence that the α particle is the saturated subunit.

2. *Majorana forces*, in which there is exchange of the *position* coordinates but not of spin. They can be visualized physically in terms of the exchange of π mesons and appear to have an important place in nuclei. The Majorana force is attractive for two particles with even relative angular momentum (for example, S states) and repulsive for interactions involving odd relative angular momentum.

3. *Bartlett forces*, in which there is exchange of the *spin* coordinates but not of the position coordinates.

The effect of the exchange operator on the sign of the force is summarized in Table 1.1, where for completeness we include also the entire class of short-range nonexchange forces, which are now generally known as *Wigner forces*. The Wigner exchange operator is unity and does nothing to the force. Taking the plus sign as representing an attractive force, the minus sign connotes a force of equal magnitude but repulsive. The two-nucleon system can usually be represented as a mixture of Majorana and Wigner forces.

TABLE 1.1. EFFECT OF THE EXCHANGE OPERATORS ON THE SIGN OF THE
NUCLEAR FORCE, IN THE TWO-BODY SYSTEM

Force	Operator	State			
		Even-l		Odd-l	
		Triplet	Singlet	Triplet	Singlet
Heisenberg.............	P_H	1	-1	-1	1
Majorana..............	P_M	1	1	-1	-1
Bartlett...............	P_B	1	-1	1	-1
Wigner................	P_W	1	1	1	1

e. Tensor Forces. With central forces, the probability density of nucleons in S states must be spherically symmetric (Appendix C). The main features of the measured interactions between two nucleons can be described in terms of central forces with or without exchange. However, there are a few small but absolutely definite effects whose existence cannot be explained in terms of central forces alone. Foremost among these are the finite electric quadrupole moment of the deuteron and the nonadditivity of the magnetic dipole moments of the neutron and proton in the deuteron (Chap. 4, Sec. 5). These and some other small effects are explicable if there is admixed with the dominant central force a small amount of a noncentral force.

The strength of this noncentral force, or *tensor force*, depends not only on the separation between the interacting pair of particles but also on the angle between the spins of the particles and the line joining the particles, like the force between two bar magnets, Eq. (8.2). The tensor force can be represented with or without exchange, as in the case of central forces.

f. Charge Independence of Singlet Forces between Nucleons. In the following sections we shall consider a variety of experimental evidence, principally that which concerns S-state interactions between all pairs of nucleons. The theoretical interpretation of these data depends somewhat on the assumed character of the interaction. At low energies (< 10 Mev) many of the results are quite insensitive to the choice of interaction potential, so long as it is short-range. It is found that the singlet forces between all pairs of nucleons are substantially equal, i.e.,

$$^1(np) = {}^1(nn) = {}^1(pp) \tag{1.1}$$

This equality is spoken of as the "*charge independence*" of nuclear forces, and the extent and causes of small deviations from Eq. (1.1) continue to be the object of many theoretical and experimental investigations. Equality between $^1(nn)$ and $^1(pp)$, without consideration of $^1(np)$, is spoken of as the "*charge symmetry*" of nuclear forces.

The main features of the nucleon-nucleon interactions can be visualized from simple considerations outlined below, using a central-force, nonexchange (Wigner-force) approximation. The bound-state $^3(np)$ interaction is obtained most simply from the theory of the deuteron, while the continuum of unbound states is explored in n-p and p-p scattering experiments.

2. *Ground Level of the Deuteron*

a. Wave Function for the Rectangular-well Approximation. The wave function of the bound state of the deuteron is not markedly dependent on the exact shape of the potential $U(r)$ between a proton and neutron, provided that a potential of short range is chosen. For simplicity, we may choose at first the rectangular potential well, of depth D and radius b, given by

$$\begin{aligned} U(r) &= -D \qquad r < b \\ U(r) &= 0 \qquad\;\; r > b \end{aligned} \tag{2.1}$$

where r is the distance between the proton and neutron.

The wave function $\psi(r,\vartheta,\varphi)$ which describes the relative motion of the proton and neutron can be separated into its radial $\psi_1(r)$ and angular $\psi_2(\vartheta,\varphi)$ parts, because we have assumed a radially symmetric potential $U(r)$. In our approximation we are interested only in the S state, $l = 0$, for which there is spherical symmetry and $\psi_2(\vartheta,\varphi)$ is constant. Then if $u(r)$ is the modified radial wave function, defined by

$$u(r) = r\,\psi_1(r) \qquad\qquad \tag{2.2}$$

see bottom P66 White

the probability of finding the proton and neutron at a separation between r and $r + dr$ is proportional to $u^2(r)\,dr$. The boundary conditions on $u(r)$ are

$$u(r) = 0 \qquad \text{for } r = 0 \text{ and for } r \to \infty \tag{2.3}$$

so that $\psi_1(r)$ will be noninfinite at $r = 0$ and will be zero at $r = \infty$.

The radial wave equation [Appendix C, Eq. (54)] for the relative motion becomes

$$\frac{d^2u}{dr^2} + \frac{2M}{\hbar^2}[W - U(r)]u = 0 \tag{2.4}$$

where M is the reduced mass of the proton and neutron $(2M \simeq M_n \simeq M_p)$ and W is their total energy in C coordinates.

For the ground level of the deuteron, the total energy W is restricted to the single constant value

$$W = -B \tag{2.5}$$

where $B = 2.225 \pm 0.002$ Mev is the observed binding energy of the deuteron. Then, for the regions inside and outside the rectangular potential well, the radial wave equation is

$$\frac{d^2u}{dr^2} + \frac{2M}{\hbar^2}(D - B)u = 0 \qquad r < b \tag{2.6}$$

$$\frac{d^2u}{dr^2} - \frac{2M}{\hbar^2}Bu = 0 \qquad r > b \tag{2.7}$$

The solutions which satisfy the boundary conditions of Eq. (2.3) on $u(r)$ are

$$u = A_1 \sin Kr \qquad r < b \tag{2.8}$$
$$u = A_2 e^{-(r/\rho)} \qquad r > b \tag{2.9}$$

where A_1 and A_2 are arbitrary amplitudes, K is the effective wave number inside the potential well

$$K = \frac{1}{\lambda} = \frac{\sqrt{2M(D - B)}}{\hbar} \tag{2.10}$$

and

$$\rho = \frac{\hbar}{\sqrt{2MB}} \tag{2.11}$$

Physically, ρ is equivalent to the rationalized de Broglie wavelength λ of the relative motion of two particles having reduced mass M and sharing kinetic energy equal to the binding energy B of the deuteron. At $r = b$ the usual boundary conditions [Appendix C, Eqs. (15), (16)] require that ψ and $d\psi/dr$, and therefore u and du/dr, be continuous. Therefore

$$A_1 \sin Kb = A_2 e^{-(b/\rho)} \tag{2.12}$$

$$KA_1 \cos Kb = -\frac{A_2}{\rho}e^{-(b/\rho)} \tag{2.13}$$

Dividing, in order to eliminate A_1 and A_2, we obtain

$$K \cot Kb = -\frac{1}{\rho} \tag{2.14}$$

b. Relationship between Depth and Range of Potential. Equation (2.14) represents the relationship between the binding energy B of the deuteron and the depth D and radius b of a rectangular potential well.

The explicit relationship is obtained by substituting Eqs. (2.10) and (2.11) into Eq. (2.14) and is

$$\cot \left[\frac{2M(D - B)b^2}{\hbar^2} \right]^{\frac{1}{2}} = - \left[\frac{B}{D - B} \right]^{\frac{1}{2}} \qquad (2.15)$$

This does not give explicit separate solutions for D and b, and it is helpful to develop an approximation to Eq. (2.15). From many lines of evidence, the range of the nuclear forces is of the order of 2×10^{-13} cm. Substituting $b \sim 2 \times 10^{-13}$ cm and $B = 2.22$ Mev in Eq. (2.15) gives for the depth of the rectangular potential well $D \sim 35$ Mev. Then, in general, $D \gg B$; the right-hand side of Eq. (2.15) is small compared with unity, and the left-hand side can be roughly represented by $\cot (\pi/2)$. Then, approximately,

$$Db^2 \simeq \left(\frac{\pi}{2} \right)^2 \frac{\hbar^2}{2M} = 1.0 \times 10^{-24} \text{ Mev-cm}^2 \qquad (2.16)$$

c. Shape of the Deuteron Ground-level Wave Function. The shape of the modified radial wave function $u(r)$ is given by Eqs. (2.8) and (2.9) and is shown schematically in Fig. 2.1. Going out from $r = 0$, $u(r)$ behaves like $\sin Kr$ for slightly more than one-quarter wavelength; then at and beyond the range of the force, $u(r)$ becomes proportional to the exponentially decreasing function $e^{-(r/\rho)}$. The relaxation length ρ of the external part of $u(r)$ is often referred to as the "*radius of the deuteron.*"

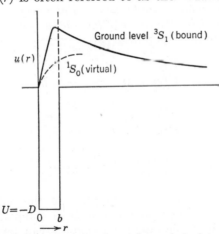

Fig. 2.1 The radial wave functions for the triplet and singlet states of the deuteron, in the rectangular-potential-well approximation. The probability of finding the neutron and proton at a separation r is proportional to $u^2(r)\ dr$. The external part of the triplet (ground level) wave function is nearly independent of the assumed potential and is proportional to $e^{-(r/\rho)}$, where the length ρ is called the radius of the deuteron.

From Eq. (2.11), with $2M \simeq M_n$, and $B = 2.22$ Mev, the radius of the deuteron becomes

$$\rho = \frac{\hbar}{\sqrt{2MB}} = 4.31 \times 10^{-13} \text{ cm} \qquad (2.17)$$

It is remarkable that the "radius" ρ of the deuteron is considerably larger than the range of the nuclear force. The neutron and proton actually spend the order of half the time at a separation greater than the range of the force which binds them together. This could not occur classically. It is a wave-mechanical phenomenon and is to be associated with the wave penetration, or tunneling, of potential barriers. The deuteron is seen to be a loosely bound, greatly extended structure, in which the average kinetic energy and the average potential energy of its constituents both greatly exceed the binding energy.

d. Singlet State of the Deuteron. The ground level of the deuteron has nuclear angular momentum $I = 1$ and is therefore the $^3S_1$ state. Another $l = 0$ state is formed when the proton and neutron have antiparallel spins. Measurements of the cross section for the scattering of slow neutrons by hydrogen, to be discussed in Sec. 3, show that this $^1S_0$ singlet state of the deuteron is definitely not a bound state but is unstable by the order of 50 kev. Its wave function may be represented schematically by the dotted line in Fig. 2.1, which does not quite reach a phase of $\pi/2$ at the edge of the well.

e. Conventional Central-force Potential Wells. A number of potentials $U(r)$ besides the rectangular well have been studied extensively. As long as these correspond to short-range forces the results are nearly independent of the exact potential $U(r)$ assumed. In particular, it is always found that (a) *the potential energy must be much greater than the binding energy of the deuteron and* (b) *the radial wave function of the deuteron decreases as* $e^{-(r/\rho)}$ *outside the range of the nuclear force.*

The four most common potentials are

Rectangular well:
$$U(r) = -U_0 \qquad r < b$$
$$U(r) = 0 \qquad r > b \tag{2.18}$$

Gaussian well:
$$U(r) = -U_0 e^{-(r/b)^2} \tag{2.19}$$

Exponential well:
$$U(r) = -U_0 e^{-2(r/b)} \tag{2.20}$$

Yukawa well:
$$U(r) = -U_0 \frac{e^{-(r/b)}}{(r/b)} \tag{2.21}$$

In each case, U_0 represents the "depth" of the potential and b the "range" of the force. For precise studies, a comparative "well-depth parameter" and "intrinsic-range parameter" can be assigned to each form of potential (B68).

Problem

Recall that $b \sim \lambda/4 \sim \pi/2K$ for the ground level of the deuteron. From this, show that the radius of the deuteron, in the rectangular-well model, is given approximately by

$$\rho \simeq \frac{2}{\pi} b \sqrt{\frac{D}{B}}$$

3. *Neutron-Proton Scattering at 0 to 10 Mev*

The binding energy of the deuteron gives us a relationship between the depth and range of the $^3(np)$ force but does not suffice to determine either quantity uniquely, Eq. (2.16). To separate these parameters, and also to obtain information on the singlet interaction $^1(np)$, we turn to experiments on the scattering of neutrons by free protons.

a. Energy Dependence of the n-p Scattering Cross Section. For incident neutron energies up to 10 Mev or somewhat greater, the angular distribution of the observed scattering is isotropic in the center-of-mass coordinates (A19). This means that only S-state interactions ($l = 0$) are involved in this energy range. On the reasonable assumption that some P-state interaction exists in nature, the failure to observe it at energies of $\sim$10 Mev shows directly that the range of the (np) force is small. This is because a neutron and proton which share only 10 Mev of kinetic energy (laboratory coordinates) must be at a separation of at least $l \times 2.83 \times 10^{-13}$ cm if they are to have a mutual angular momentum of $l\hbar$. As the $l = 1$ interaction is not observed, this minimum separation of 2.83×10^{-13} cm is greater than the range of the (np) force.

A great many careful measurements have been made of the attenuation of monoenergetic neutrons by the hydrogen atoms in a variety of absorbers. From these, the total cross section σ_t for neutron-proton interactions has been determined as a function of the laboratory kinetic energy of the incident neutrons. These values are shown in Fig. 3.1.

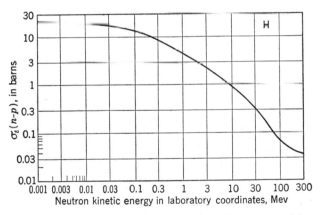

Fig. 3.1 Observed total cross section for interaction of neutrons with protons, as a function of laboratory kinetic energy of the incident neutrons. [*From Adair* (A2).]

The predominant contribution to the total cross section σ_t is the n-p scattering cross section. The cross section for the competing radiative-capture reaction $H^1(n,\gamma)H^2$ is only 0.05 barn per proton for 1-ev neutrons and decreases with $1/V$, where V is the neutron velocity.

The scattering of very slow neutrons by free protons is of special interest. The proton-containing absorber is commonly hydrogen gas, hydrocarbon gases and liquids, or liquid water. If thermal neutrons ($\sim 1/40$ ev) are used, there are opportunities for exchanges of energy with molecular vibration levels, whose spacing is of the order of 0.1 ev. For neutrons whose energy is ≥ 1 ev ("*epithermal neutrons*"), the proton may be considered to be unbound. From 1 ev to about 1,000 ev, the n-p scattering cross section, as measured with a slow neutron velocity spectrometer (M41), is nearly independent of neutron energy (Fig. 3.1). The hydrogen cross section in the energy range from 0.8 to 15 ev, after extrapolating out the small effects due to molecular binding, is variously identified as the scattering cross section σ_0 for "zero-energy neutrons," or for "epithermal neutrons" by free protons, for which the measured value by Melkonian (M41) is

$$\sigma_0 = 20.36 \pm 0.1 \text{ barns/proton} \tag{3.1}$$

b. Phase-shift Analysis of n-p Scattering. The theoretical description of s-wave, elastic n-p scattering emerges from the radial wave equation (2.4) when the total energy W is taken as the (positive) mutual kinetic energy of the neutron and proton in C coordinates. The incident neutrons are represented as the plane wave e^{ikz}, and the total disturbance ψ_{total} consists of the incident and scattered waves

$$\psi_{\text{total}} \equiv \frac{u(r)}{r} = e^{ikz} + f(\vartheta)\frac{e^{ikr}}{r} \tag{3.2}$$

where the complex quantity $f(\vartheta)$ is the scattering amplitude in the direction ϑ and k is the wave number of relative motion, given by

$$k^2 = \frac{2M}{\hbar^2}W \tag{3.3}$$

where M = reduced mass $\simeq M_n/2 \simeq M_p/2$
  W = incident kinetic energy in C coordinates
  $W \simeq \frac{1}{2}$ (incident neutron energy E_n in L coordinates)
  The corresponding solutions are developed in Appendix C, Sec. 6. We quote here only the pertinent results. For s-wave ($l = 0$) interactions, the scattering amplitude $f(\vartheta)$ is isotropic and for any short-range central force has the value

$$f_0 = \frac{e^{2i\delta_0} - 1}{2ik} = \frac{e^{i\delta_0}\sin\delta_0}{k} \tag{3.4}$$

where the purely real quantity δ_0 is the phase shift for s-wave scattering. The s-wave total-elastic-scattering cross section σ then becomes a function of δ_0, and of the incident neutron energy as represented by k,

$$\sigma = 4\pi|f_0|^2 = \frac{4\pi}{k^2}\sin^2\delta_0 \tag{3.5}$$

An experimental determination of σ can therefore be expressed equally well as a measured phase shift δ_0. It is then the task of theory to predict matching values of δ_0, which will be expected to depend on k and on the shape, range, and depth of the assumed nuclear potential well. The measured phase shifts δ_0 have become the "common meeting ground" of experiment and theory.

c. Scattering Length. In the limit of very small neutron energies $E_n \to 0$ (and hence $k \to 0$), the scattering amplitude Eq. (3.4) takes on a particularly simple form. It can be seen from Eq. (3.4) that as $k \to 0$, δ_0 must also approach zero, otherwise f_0 would become infinite. Then, in the limit, $e^{i\delta_0} \to 1$ and Eq. (3.4) becomes

$$f_0 \to \frac{\delta_0}{k} \equiv -a \qquad \text{as } k \to 0 \tag{3.6}$$

where the length $+a$ is called the *scattering length* in the convention of Fermi and Marshall (F40). Although f_0 is, in general, a complex quantity, the scattering length a is to a very good approximation a real length. (Exceptions occur only in unusual cases near a resonance level where a large amount of absorption competes with the elastic scattering.)

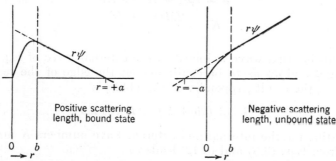

Fig. 3.2 The "scattering length" a, or extrapolated Fermi intercept, is positive for scattering from a bound state and negative for scattering from an unbound state.

A simple geometrical interpretation of the scattering length can be visualized. Outside the range of the nuclear force, $U(r) = 0$ and the total wave function Eq. (3.2) has the value [Appendix C, Eq. (131)]

$$\psi_{\text{total}} = \frac{e^{i\delta_0}}{kr} \sin (kr + \delta_0) \tag{3.7}$$

In the limit of $k \to 0$, this becomes

$$r\psi_{\text{total}} \to r + \frac{\delta_0}{k} \equiv r - a \tag{3.8}$$

which is the equation of a straight line crossing the r axis at $r = a$. Figure 3.2 shows that the scattering length can be interpreted physically as the intercept of $r\psi_{\text{total}}$ on the r axis, for zero-energy particles, when a linear extrapolation of $r\psi_{\text{total}}$ is made from a distance just outside the range of the nuclear force. For this reason, the scattering length is sometimes called the *Fermi intercept* of $r \psi(r)$.

From Eqs. (3.5) and (3.6) the zero-energy scattering cross section becomes

$$\sigma_0 = 4\pi a^2 \tag{3.9}$$

which is the same as the zero-energy scattering from an impenetrable sphere of radius a. We see from Eq. (3.9) that σ_0 *determines the magnitude of the scattering length* a, *but not its sign*.

d. *n-p* Scattering for a Rectangular Potential Well. For any potential well, the phase shift δ_0 can be evaluated by joining the external wave function Eq. (3.7) to an internal wave function ψ_{in} whose form is determined by the parameters of the potential well. Inside a rectangular potential well of depth D and radius b, the radial wave equation (2.4), for particles whose total energy has the positive value W, is

$$\frac{d^2u}{dr^2} + \frac{2M}{\hbar^2}(W + D)u = 0 \tag{3.10}$$

and has the solution

$$u = r\psi_{in} = A_1 \sin Kr \tag{3.11}$$

where

$$K^2 = \frac{2M(W + D)}{\hbar^2} \tag{3.12}$$

When this internal wave is joined to the external wave of Eq. (3.7) by requiring ψ and $d\psi/dr$ to be continuous at the edge of the rectangular well $r = b$, the result [Appendix C, Eq. (142)] is

$$k \cot (kb + \delta_0) = K \cot Kb \tag{3.13}$$

Substituting for the internal and external wave numbers K and k their values from Eqs. (3.3) and (3.12) leads to

$$\cot\left(\frac{\sqrt{2MW}}{\hbar}b + \delta_0\right) = \left(\frac{W + D}{W}\right)^{\frac{1}{2}} \cot\left(\frac{\sqrt{2M(W + D)}}{\hbar}b\right) \tag{3.14}$$

as an implicit relationship which gives the phase shift δ_0 produced at a collision energy W by a rectangular well of depth D and radius b. This relationship is analogous in form to Eq. (2.15) which describes the binding energy B of the deuteron in terms of the same rectangular well D, b.

By algebraically combining Eqs. (3.14) and (2.15) we can eliminate the well depth D. Then we can evaluate δ_0 and the *n-p* cross section σ in terms of the remaining parameters. The result, after making use of the approximations $D \gg B$, $D \gg W$, and for low-energy neutrons such that $kb \ll 1$, is

$$\sigma = \frac{4\pi}{k^2}\sin^2\delta_0 = 2\pi\frac{\hbar^2}{M}\frac{1}{W + B}\left(1 + \frac{b}{\rho} - \cdots\right) \tag{3.15}$$

where $\rho = \hbar/\sqrt{2MB} = 4.31 \times 10^{-13}$ cm = deuteron radius, Eq. (2.17)

$$M \simeq M_n/2 \simeq M_p/2 = \text{reduced mass}$$
$$W \simeq E_n/2 = \text{kinetic energy in } C \text{ coordinates}$$

This relationship is found to be in satisfactory agreement with measured n-p scattering cross sections for neutrons whose kinetic energy is large enough so that the denominator $(W + B)$ is *not* dominated by the binding energy B. Thus there is good agreement for $E_n \sim 5$ to 10 Mev.

e. Spin Dependence of Nuclear Forces. At low energies, however, the situation is very different. Numerical substitution in Eq. (3.15) of $B = 2.22$ Mev, $M \simeq M_n/2$, $b \sim 2 \times 10^{-13}$ cm gives a predicted value for "zero-energy neutrons," $W = 0$,

$$\sigma_0 \simeq 3.5 \text{ barns} \qquad \text{for } B = 2.22 \text{ Mev} \tag{3.16}$$

which is in violent disagreement with the measured value $\sigma_0 = 20.4$ barns. Wigner first pointed out that this disagreement is due to the tacit assumption that singlet and triplet s-wave interactions are equal. The binding energy B, which dominates W in the evaluation of σ_0, applies only to the ground level of the deuteron, hence to a triplet interaction between the colliding neutron and proton.

When unpolarized neutrons strike randomly oriented protons, their uncorrelated spins add up to unity in three-fourths of the collisions and to zero in one-fourth of the collisions. This is equivalent to saying that the triplet state ($S = 1$) has three times the statistical weight $(2S + 1)$ of a singlet ($S = 0$) state. Accordingly, the average cross section σ_0 for "zero-energy neutrons" should be written

$$\begin{aligned} \sigma_0 &= \tfrac{3}{4}(^3\sigma_0) + \tfrac{1}{4}(^1\sigma_0) \\ &= \pi[3(^3a)^2 + (^1a)^2] \end{aligned} \tag{3.17}$$

where $^3\sigma_0$ and ^3a refer to triplet collisions, while $^1\sigma_0$ and ^1a apply to singlet collisions. Then Eq. (3.16) becomes $^3\sigma_0 \sim 3.5$ barns, and it is clear that $^1\sigma_0 \gg {}^3\sigma_0$.

To the extent that the simple central-force rectangular potential well is at all representative of the true character of nuclear forces, one would have to conclude that the $^3(np)$ and $^1(np)$ potentials are quite different. For orientation, one typical set of rectangular-well parameters, which is derived by making use of additional types of scattering experiments, is (C3)

$^3b = 2.0 \times 10^{-13}$ cm, to match neutron scattering by parahydrogen
$^3D = 36.6$ Mev, combined with ^3b to match $B \simeq 2.22$ Mev for the deuteron
$^1b = 2.8 \times 10^{-13}$ cm, to match p-p scattering
$^1D = 11.9$ Mev, to match $\sigma_0 \simeq 20$ barns for n-p scattering

The "zero-energy neutron" cross section σ_0 shows that the singlet scattering length ^1a must be large but, because of the squares in Eq. (3.17), σ_0 does not tell the sign of ^1a. This can be done by neutron scattering in parahydrogen, as will be discussed later. It is found that ^1a is negative and that therefore the singlet state of the deuteron is not bound.

f. Effective Range of Nuclear Forces. The various commonly used shapes of nuclear potential, Eqs. (2.18) to (2.21), have been blended by Schwinger, Bethe (B45), and others (B68) in an "effective-range theory

of nuclear forces," or "shape-independent approximation," by the introduction of a second parameter (in addition to the scattering length a)
called the *effective range* r_0.

Recall Eq. (3.13). It can be shown quite generally (B45, B68) that
for any reasonable shape of potential well

$$k \cot \delta_0 = -\frac{1}{a} + k^2 \int_0^\infty (vv_0 - uu_0) \, dr \qquad (3.18)$$

where v = modified radial wave function $r\psi$, *outside* range of nuclear
       potential, where $U(r) = 0$

    $v_0 = v$, for zero incident energy $W = 0$

    u = modified radial wave function $r\psi$, *inside* range of nuclear
       potential $U(r)$

    $u_0 = u$, for zero incident energy $W = 0$

Equation (3.18) is exact. The significant contribution to the integral
comes from inside the range of the nuclear force, $0 \leq r \leq b$. In this
region, and for collision energies W which are not too large, $U(r) \gg W$,
and we can make the approximations $v \simeq v_0$ and $u \simeq u_0$. Then the
length r_0, called the *effective range*, is defined by

$$r_0 \equiv 2 \int_0^\infty (v_0^2 - u_0^2) \, dr \qquad (3.19)$$

where the factor 2 is arbitrarily inserted so that the approximation will
give an effective range r_0 which is near the outer "edge" of the potential
well. Thus r_0 is generally comparable in magnitude with b in Eqs. (2.18)
to (2.21). The phase shift δ_0 of Eq. (3.18) is given to good approximation
($W \leq 10$ Mev) by

$$k \cot \delta_0 = -\frac{1}{a} + \frac{1}{2} k^2 r_0 \qquad (3.20)$$

where δ_0 = s-wave phase shift
    k = wave number of relative motion, Eq. (3.3)
    a = scattering length of nuclear potential
    r_0 = effective range of nuclear potential

The effective range r_0 depends upon the width and depth of the potential well $U(r)$, as Eq. (3.19) shows, but not upon the incident energy,
which is given by k^2. The experimental values of δ_0 and k serve to
determine the two parameters a and r_0. Any reasonable potential shape,
such as those of Eqs. (2.18) to (2.21), can be made to give matching
values of a and r_0 by suitable choice of its depth U_0 and range b. Hence
*the two experimentally determined lengths a and r_0 do not determine the
shape of the nuclear potential, but if the shape is chosen arbitrarily then a and
r_0 fix the depth U_0 and range b*. For this reason, Eq. (3.20) is known as
the "*shape-independent approximation*."

**g. Ground Level of the Deuteron in the Shape-independent Approxi-
mation.** By replacing the radial wave functions in Eq. (3.19) by those
which are appropriate to the bound triplet state of the deuteron, for

which $W = -B$, the shape-independent approximation leads to

$$\frac{1}{\rho} = + \frac{1}{(^3a)} + \frac{1}{2} \frac{(^3r_0)}{\rho^2} \qquad (3.21)$$

where $\rho = \hbar/\sqrt{2MB} = 4.31 \times 10^{-13}$ cm is again the "radius" of the deuteron as defined by Eq. (2.17).

h. n-p Scattering Cross Section in the Shape-independent Approximation. For the s-wave, n-p scattering cross section σ we can now write a more general expression than Eq. (3.15), which was derived for a rectangular potential well. In order to introduce the binding energy of the deuteron, we eliminate the scattering length a, between Eqs. (3.20) and (3.21), and substitute the resulting value of $\cot \delta_0$ into

$$^3\sigma = \frac{4\pi}{k^2} \sin^2 \delta_0 = \frac{4\pi}{k^2} \frac{1}{1 + \cot^2 \delta_0} \qquad (3.22)$$

The result is

$$^3\sigma = \left(\frac{4\pi\rho^2}{1 + k^2\rho^2} \right) \left[\frac{1}{1 - (^3r_0/\rho) + (^3r_0/2\rho)^2(1 + k^2\rho^2)} \right] \qquad (3.23)$$

where $\rho = \hbar/\sqrt{2MB}$
$k^2\rho^2 = W/B$

from Eqs. (2.17) and (3.3). Notice that Eq. (3.23) is essentially the same as Eq. (3.15), the difference being that the radius b of the rectangular well is replaced by the effective range r_0, and a second-order range correction term in $(^3r_0/2\rho)^2$ appears in the final bracket of Eq. (3.23).

Equation (3.23) and also the rectangular-well approximation Eq. (3.15) apply rigorously only to the triplet scattering, which involves the binding energy B of the ground level of the deuteron. If there were also a bound singlet state, with binding energy ^1B, Eqs. (3.23) and (3.15) could be applied for $^1\sigma$ by using ^1B in place of B. In the absence of a bound singlet state, it is best to return to Eq. (3.20) and thus to express the singlet n-p scattering cross section in terms of the singlet effective range $^1r_0$ and the singlet scattering length ^1a. Then

$$^1\sigma = \frac{4\pi}{k^2} \frac{1}{1 + \cot^2 \delta_0} = \frac{4\pi(^1a)^2}{[1 - k^2(^1a)(^1r_0)/2]^2 + k^2(^1a)^2} \qquad (3.24)$$

The total cross section is then given by

$$\sigma = \tfrac{3}{4}(^3\sigma) + \tfrac{1}{4}(^1\sigma) \qquad (3.25)$$

i. Coherent Scattering of Slow Neutrons. An experimental decision on the sign of the singlet n-p scattering length ^1a, and hence whether the singlet state of the deuteron is bound ($^1a > 0$) or virtual ($^1a < 0$), can be obtained by measurements on any phenomenon which has a strong dependence on the first power of ^1a. Such effects occur in several important types of experiments on the coherent scattering of neutrons.

Scattering of Neutrons by Para- and Orthohydrogen. The internuclear distance in the hydrogen molecule is 0.78×10^{-8} cm. Coherent scattering, in which the amplitudes instead of the intensities add, may be obtained from the pair of protons in the hydrogen molecule provided that the de Broglie wavelength of the neutrons is much greater than the internuclear distance.   Neutron velocity selector techniques can be used to conduct scattering experiments with "cold" neutrons, in the energy domain 0.0008 ev ($\sim$10°K) to 0.0025 ev ($\sim$30°K).   Here the de Broglie wavelength is 10 to 5.7 $\times$ 10^{-8} cm, and only a small correction ($\sim$10 per cent) needs to be made for the relative phase introduced by the finite separation of the two protons in the hydrogen molecule.

In the parahydrogen molecule, the nuclear spins of the two protons are antiparallel.   Then an incident unpolarized neutron can have, so to speak, a triplet collision with one of the protons and a singlet collision with the other proton.   The actual interference effects can be determined by using the Pauli spin operators of the neutron and protons.   Then it can be shown that (S23, B43, B68) the coherent scattering cross section for cold neutrons by parahydrogen is

$$\sigma_{\text{para}} = \tfrac{16}{9} 4\pi (a_{\text{para}})^2 \tag{3.26}$$

where the *coherent scattering length* a_{para} is

$$a_{\text{para}} = 2[\tfrac{3}{4}(^3a) + \tfrac{1}{4}(^1a)] \tag{3.27}$$

Here ^3a and ^1a are the usual triplet and singlet n-p scattering lengths Eq. (3.6) for *free* protons.   The factor 2 in Eq. (3.27) represents the two protons in each hydrogen molecule.   In Eq. (3.26), the factor $\tfrac{16}{9} = (\tfrac{4}{3})^2$ corrects for the reduced mass M in the neutron–hydrogen-molecule collision where $M = \tfrac{2}{3}M_n$, as compared with the reduced mass in the neutron–free-proton collision where $M = \tfrac{1}{2}M_n$.

In the orthohydrogen molecule, the proton spins are parallel, and the neutron coherent scattering cross section is

$$\sigma_{\text{ortho}} = \tfrac{16}{9} 4\pi (a_{\text{ortho}})^2 \tag{3.28}$$

where the coherent ortho scattering length a_{ortho} can be shown to be

$$a_{\text{ortho}} = 2\{[\tfrac{3}{4}(^3a) + \tfrac{1}{4}(^1a)]^2 + 2[\tfrac{1}{4}(^3a) - \tfrac{1}{4}(^1a)]^2\}^{\frac{1}{2}} \tag{3.29}$$

Here the factor 2 at the second square brackets represents physically $T(T + 1)$, where T is the total nuclear spin of the hydrogen molecule. This term is present only for orthohydrogen ($T = 1$).   Equation (3.29) is physically the same as Eq. (3.27), except that, for parahydrogen $T = 0$, the second square-bracket term disappears, and the general form which is implicit in Eq. (3.29) reduces to Eq. (3.27).

The ratio of the cross sections given by Eqs. (3.26) and (3.28), for elastic coherent neutron scattering from the two forms of molecular hydrogen, then reduces to

$$\frac{\sigma_{\text{ortho}}}{\sigma_{\text{para}}} = 1 + 2\left[\frac{^3a - {}^1a}{3(^3a) + (^1a)}\right]^2 \tag{3.30}$$

Several clear-cut predictions follow at once.

1. If the total (np) forces are spin-independent, i.e., if $^3(np) = {^1(np)}$, then there should be no physical difference between ortho and para scattering

$$\frac{\sigma_{\text{ortho}}}{\sigma_{\text{para}}} = 1 \qquad \text{if } {^3a} = {^1a} \tag{3.31}$$

2. When the measured cross section of $\sigma_0 \sim 20$ barns for elastic scattering of epithermal neutrons by free protons and the measured binding energy of the deuteron $B = 2.22$ Mev are combined with the theory of the (np) force in the shape-independent approximation Eqs. (3.23) and (3.24), one would conclude that for purely central forces

$$\begin{aligned} {^3a} &\simeq \rho = +4.3 \times 10^{-13} \text{ cm} \\ {^1a} &\simeq \pm 24 \times 10^{-13} \text{ cm} \end{aligned} \tag{3.32}$$

where the sign of ^1a cannot be determined because ^1a occurs only quadratically in Eq. (3.24) for very slow neutrons $k \to 0$. Making use of these orders of magnitude in Eq. (3.30), we find that the ratio $\sigma_{\text{ortho}}/\sigma_{\text{para}}$ is extremely sensitive to the sign of the singlet scattering length. Indeed

$$\frac{\sigma_{\text{ortho}}}{\sigma_{\text{para}}} \simeq 1.5 \qquad \text{if } {^1a} \simeq +20 \times 10^{-13} \text{ cm} \tag{3.33}$$

$$\frac{\sigma_{\text{ortho}}}{\sigma_{\text{para}}} \simeq 14 \qquad \text{if } {^1a} \simeq -20 \times 10^{-13} \text{ cm} \tag{3.34}$$

The experimental values for the effective cross sections, at 0.002 ev, are (S81)

$$\sigma_{\text{ortho}} \simeq 120 \text{ barns} \tag{3.35}$$
$$\sigma_{\text{para}} \simeq 4 \text{ barns} \tag{3.36}$$

Hence
$$\frac{\sigma_{\text{ortho}}}{\sigma_{\text{para}}} \simeq 30 \tag{3.37}$$

Unequivocally, these observations prove that:
1. The total (np) forces are spin-dependent, $^3(np) \neq {^1(np)}$.
2. The singlet $n\text{-}p$ scattering length ^1a is negative; therefore the singlet state of the deuteron is unbound.

An additional consequence of the large observed value of $\sigma_{\text{ortho}}/\sigma_{\text{para}}$ relates to the spin of the neutron. The ground state of the deuteron could still have $l = 0$ and $I = 1$ if the neutron spin were $s_n = \frac{3}{2}$ and were aligned antiparallel to the proton spin (which is known definitely from band spectra to be $s_p = \frac{1}{2}$). In such a model the relative statistical weights for $n\text{-}p$ collisions with free protons would change from their values of $\frac{3}{4}$ and $\frac{1}{4}$ in Eq. (3.17) to values of $\frac{5}{8}$ and $\frac{3}{8}$. Analogous reweightings would occur in the ortho- and parahydrogen scattering cross sections. The over-all result of these reweightings is

$$\frac{\sigma_{\text{ortho}}}{\sigma_{\text{para}}} \simeq 2 \qquad \text{if } s_n = \frac{3}{2} \tag{3.38}$$

The observations therefore serve a third purpose, by showing that:
3. The neutron has spin $\frac{1}{2}$, not $\frac{3}{2}$.

Experimentally, there are many complications in the ortho- and para-hydrogen experiment. Among others, these include: (1) transitions between orthohydrogen (ground-state molecular-rotation quantum number $L = 1$) and parahydrogen (ground-state molecular-rotation quantum number $L = 0$) induced by inelastic collisions with neutrons; (2) Doppler corrections for the thermal motion of hydrogen molecules, even at the usual operating temperatures of $\sim 20°K$; (3) possible intermolecular forces between adjacent hydrogen molecules; and (4) radiative-capture reactions $H^1(n,\gamma)H^2$ in which a neutron is removed from the incident beam and a deuteron is formed.

Scattering of Slow Neutrons by Crystals. The de Broglie wavelength of a 0.1-ev neutron is 0.9 A, which is comparable with the atomic separations in solids and liquids. Therefore diffraction studies can be carried out using slow neutrons (H68, B1) under physical principles which are entirely analogous to those involved in the Bragg coherent scattering of X rays.

The neutron scattering amplitudes, for various atoms, depend upon nuclear properties, whereas the corresponding X-ray scattering amplitudes depend upon the number of electrons in the atom. There are therefore important differences in the relative intensity of neutron and of X-ray scattering by different types of atoms in a crystal. For example, in crystalline sodium hydride NaH the X-ray diffraction patterns are dominated by the scattering from Na and give no information on the location or behavior of H. On the other hand, the neutron scattering amplitude of Na is small enough that the neutron diffraction pattern is clearly influenced by scattering from H and serves to determine both the position of H in the crystal structure and the neutron scattering amplitude of H (S36).

Neutron-diffraction studies on crystalline powders can now be carried out routinely by utilizing the strong neutron flux available from uranium reactors. Monoenergetic beams of neutrons, in the angstrom region of wavelengths, are obtainable by Bragg reflection from crystals in the same manner as X rays are monochromatized.

The incoherent (diffuse) scattering cross section for a mixture containing several nuclides is

$$\sigma_{\text{inc}} = 4\pi(p_1 a_1^2 + p_2 a_2^2 + \cdots) \tag{3.39}$$

where p_1, p_2, . . . are the relative abundances of nuclides whose *bound* scattering lengths are a_1, a_2, ... These bound scattering lengths correspond to the scattering which would be observed if the struck nucleus were infinitely heavy, so that the reduced mass for a neutron and a bound atom is equal to the mass of the neutron. Therefore the bound scattering lengths differ from the scattering lengths for a free atom, and

$$a_{\text{bound}} = \left(\frac{A + 1}{A}\right) a_{\text{free}} \tag{3.40}$$

where A is the mass number of the atom.

The coherent (Bragg) scattering is observed only at the appropriate Bragg angles and has the cross section

$$\sigma_{\text{coh}} = 4\pi(p_1 a_1 + p_2 a_2 + \cdots)^2 \tag{3.41}$$

where the p's are the relative abundances and the a's are the bound scattering lengths.

For nuclei with nonzero nuclear angular momenta I, each bound scattering length is the statistically weighted sum for the $(I + \frac{1}{2})$ and $(I - \frac{1}{2})$ interaction with the incident neutron. Thus the *bound* coherent scattering length for hydrogen a_{H} becomes

$$a_{\text{H}} = 2[\tfrac{3}{4}(^3a) + \tfrac{1}{4}(^1a)] \tag{3.42}$$

where ^3a and ^1a are the usual triplet and singlet scattering lengths for free protons and the factor 2 arises from the reduced mass correction of Eq. (3.40). Recall Eq. (3.27) and note that a_{H} is identical with a_{para}, the coherent scattering length for both atoms in the parahydrogen molecule.

Coherent neutron scattering from crystalline powders such as NaH can therefore be used to evaluate $a_{\text{H}} = a_{\text{para}}$ by experimental methods which are free from many of the difficulties of the low-temperature parahydrogen scattering experiment. In this way, Shull and coworkers (S36) obtained in 1948 the value

$$a_{\text{H}} = \tfrac{1}{2}[3(^3a) + ^1a] = (-3.96 \pm 0.2) \times 10^{-13} \text{ cm} \tag{3.43}$$

which is an improvement on the parahydrogen result, Eq. (3.36), but, in the light of later evidence, Eq. (3.43) appears to contain a small but significant systematic error.

Reflection of Slow Neutrons from Liquid Mirrors. It can be shown that, if absorption is small compared with scattering, the index of refraction n for neutron waves on a homogeneous material is

$$n = 1 - \frac{a\lambda^2 N}{2\pi} \tag{3.44}$$

where a = average *bound* coherent scattering length
λ = de Broglie wavelength of incident neutrons
N = scattering nuclei per cm³

If a is positive, so that n is less than one, there will be a critical angle ϑ_c given by

$$\cos \vartheta_c = n \tag{3.45}$$

at which neutrons impinging on the material will experience total specular reflection back into the air. A material from which neutrons incident at a glancing angle are totally reflected is spoken of as a neutron "mirror." The angle ϑ_c is always small, e.g., in the case of beryllium $a = 7.7 \times 10^{-13}$ cm, and for neutrons of 1-A wavelength, $1 - n = 1.5 \times 10^{-6}$, and $\vartheta_c \sim 0.1°$.

The critical angle for total neutron reflection can be measured in a straightforward way. Various incoherent effects which might seriously disturb other types of scattering experiments are less troublesome because they only reduce the intensity of the reflected beam, without changing ϑ_c which is the quantity measured. Observations on substances whose bound coherent scattering length is negative can be accomplished by mixing them with substances which have sufficiently positive scattering lengths to give a net positive value, and hence observable total reflection. In this way, Hughes, Burgy, and Ringo (H68) have measured the bound coherent scattering length for hydrogen a_H, by using various liquid "mirrors" of the hydrocarbons $C_{12}H_{18}$, C_6H_{10}, C_6H_{12}, and taking advantage of the accurately known positive bound coherent scattering length of carbon $a_C = (+6.63 \pm 0.03) \times 10^{-13}$ cm. These experiments gave $a_C/a_H = (-1.753 \pm 0.005)$ and therefore

$$a_H = \tfrac{1}{2}[3(^3a) + {}^1a] = (-3.78 \pm 0.02) \times 10^{-13} \text{ cm} \qquad (3.46)$$

which is currently regarded as the best available measurement of the coherent scattering lengths for the (np) interaction.

This important experimental parameter of the (np) interaction has recently been confirmed by very careful ortho- and parahydrogen neutron scattering experiments at the Cavendish Laboratory (S75), which give for the coherent scattering length

$$a_{\text{para}} = (-3.80 \pm 0.05) \times 10^{-13} \text{ cm}$$

in good agreement with Eq. (3.46).

j. Nuclear-force Parameters in the Shape-independent Central-force Approximation. We now have enough experimental data and interconnecting theory to permit evaluation of the four parameters which enter the "shape-independent approximation" or "effective-range theory" of nuclear forces. We summarize the theoretical and experimental relationships, with their original equation numbers for ease of reference.

1. *n-p* scattering cross section for free protons, extrapolated to "zero energy neutrons"

$$\sigma_0 = \pi[3(^3a)^2 + ({}^1a)^2] \qquad (3.17)$$
$$\sigma_0 = 20.36 \times 10^{-24} \text{ cm}^2 \qquad (3.1)$$

2. Bound coherent *n-p* scattering length

$$a_{\text{para}} = a_H = \tfrac{1}{2}[3(^3a) + {}^1a]^2 \qquad (3.27), (3.42)$$
$$a_H = (-3.78 \pm 0.02) \times 10^{-13} \text{ cm} \qquad (3.46)$$

3. Binding energy of the deuteron

$$B = H^1 + n - H^2$$
$$= 2.225 \pm 0.002 \text{ Mev} \qquad \text{Chap. 3, Eq. (4.46)}$$

4. Radius of the deuteron

$$\rho = \frac{\hbar}{\sqrt{2MB}} = 4.31 \times 10^{-13} \text{ cm} \qquad (2.17)$$

5. Effective range $^3r_0$ of triplet (np) force

$$\frac{1}{\rho} = + \frac{1}{(^3a)} + \frac{1}{2}\frac{(^3r_0)}{\rho^2} \tag{3.21}$$

6. Variation of total n-p scattering cross section with neutron energy

$$\sigma = \tfrac{3}{4}(^3\sigma) + \tfrac{1}{4}(^1\sigma) \tag{3.25}$$

$$^3\sigma = \frac{4\pi\rho^2}{1 + k^2\rho^2}\left[\frac{1}{1 - (^3r_0/\rho) + (^3r_0/2\rho)^2(1 + k^2\rho^2)}\right] \tag{3.23}$$

$$^1\sigma = 4\pi(^1a)^2\left\{\frac{1}{[1 - k^2(^1a)(^1r_0)/2]^2 + k^2(^1a)^2}\right\} \tag{3.24}$$

Simultaneous solution of items 1 and 2 gives the two triplet and singlet scattering lengths ^3a and ^1a. With ^3a determined, item 5 gives the triplet effective range $^3r_0$. The experimental variation of σ, for neutron energies from 0.8 to 5 Mev (L3), gives the singlet effective range $^1r_0$. The "1952 best values" for the central-force, shape-independent approximation to the (np) nuclear force are (S3, B114)

For $^3(np)$
$$^3a = +5.378(1 \pm 0.0038) \times 10^{-13} \text{ cm}$$
$$^3r_0 = +1.70(1 \pm 0.018) \times 10^{-13} \text{ cm} \tag{3.47}$$

and for $^1(np)$
$$^1a = -23.69(1 \pm 0.0022) \times 10^{-13} \text{ cm}$$
$$^1r_0 = +2.7(1 \pm 0.19) \times 10^{-13} \text{ cm} \tag{3.48}$$

Problems

1. In the collision of a neutron with a proton, show that the classical impact parameter x must exceed $(9l/\sqrt{E_n}) \times 10^{-13}$ cm, if l is the angular-momentum quantum number for the collision and E_n is the laboratory kinetic energy of the incident neutron in Mev.

2. When neutrons of the order of 1 Mev are scattered by hydrogen, it is found that the angular distribution of recoil protons is isotropic in the center-of-mass coordinates. Thus, in the C coordinates, the differential cross section per unit solid angle is independent of the angle of scattering. This could be written $d\sigma = c\, d\Omega = c2\pi \sin\Theta\, d\Theta$, where c is a constant whose value is $\sigma/4\pi$, if the total scattering cross section is σ. If E_n is the kinetic energy of an incident neutron, show that the differential cross section for the production of a recoil proton with kinetic energy between E_p and $E_p + dE_p$ in the laboratory coordinates is *independent of E_p* and is equal to

$$d\sigma = \sigma\frac{dE_p}{E_n}$$

3. Carry through the derivation of the total n-p scattering cross section σ as given by Eq. (3.15), using the phase-shift relationship of Eq. (3.14) as starting point.

4. Using the parameters of the shape-independent approximation, determine the absolute value of the (negative) binding energy $|^1B|$ of the singlet state of the deuteron.

4. *Electromagnetic Transitions in the n-p System*

The $^3(np)$ and $^1(np)$ forces also govern two other basic processes in the neutron-proton system:

$$n + \mathrm{H}^1 \rightarrow \mathrm{H}^2 + h\nu \qquad \text{radiative capture} \qquad (4.1)$$

and the inverse process

$$\mathrm{H}^2 + h\nu \rightarrow n + \mathrm{H}^1 \qquad \text{photodisintegration} \qquad (4.2)$$

From a study of these two interactions we can:

1. Confirm that $^3(np) \neq {}^1(np)$
2. Show that the singlet state of the deuteron is unbound
3. Obtain a rough measurement of $(^3r_0 - {}^1r_0)$

a. Selection Rules for Transitions below 10 Mev. The cross section σ_{cap} for the radiative-capture process, Eq. (4.1), is only significant for very-low-energy neutrons. Even then, it is very small compared with the elastic n-p scattering cross section σ_0. For thermal neutrons ($E_n = 0.025$ ev) $\sigma_{\mathrm{cap}} = 0.3$ barn, whereas σ_0 is over 60 times as large. Physically, the radiative-capture cross section is small because the coupling between matter and electromagnetic radiation is always weak, being represented in general by the appearance of the fine-structure constant $2\pi e^2/hc = \frac{1}{137}$ in the formulas for all types of radiative processes.

Magnetic Dipole Radiative Capture. The capture of a neutron by a proton is a radiative transition from the continuum of unbound n-p states to the $^3S_1$ ground state of the deuteron. In principle, the initial state may have angular momentum $L = 0, 1, 2, \ldots$ and either parallel or antiparallel spins. However, for $L \geq 1$, and incident neutron energies below about 10 Mev, the n-p separation exceeds the range of the (np) force. Consequently, capture is only important from S states ($L = 0$) in the continuum. Then the initial and final states both have even parity, and the γ-ray transition between them has no change in parity. This restricts the important radiative-capture transitions to the magnetic dipole, or M1, transition, for which $\Delta L = 0$, $\Delta S = 1$, $\Delta I = 1$, no (Chap. 6, Sec. 4). This M1 transition involves only a spin flip and takes place between a singlet in the continuum and the triplet deuteron ground state, $^1S_0 \rightarrow {}^3S_1$.

Photomagnetic Disintegration of the Deuteron. In the inverse process, Eq. (4.2), the "photomagnetic disintegration" consists of M1 transitions from the deuteron ground state $^3S_1$ to $^1S_0$ states in the continuum.

Photoelectric Disintegration of the Deuteron. An additional process can be effective if the incident photon energy $h\nu$ is clearly greater than the binding energy of the deuteron. Then an E1, or electric dipole, transition ($\Delta L = 1$, $\Delta S = 0$, $\Delta I = 1$, yes) can carry the n-p system from the $^3S_1$ ground state to a ^3P state in the continuum.

Quadrupole transitions, M2 and E2, are generally much less probable than dipole transitions (Chap. 6, Sec. 4); hence at moderate photon energies (≤ 10 Mev) only the M1 and E1 transitions can be expected to be significant.

b. Cross Section for Photomagnetic Capture. The matrix element which governs the probability of the "spin-flip" magnetic dipole transition can be shown to be proportional to the net magnetic dipole moment in the singlet state (B68). For the central-force model the net magnetic dipole moment is

$$\frac{eh}{4\pi M_p c}(\mu_p - \mu_n) \qquad\qquad \text{(4.3)}$$

where μ_p and μ_n are the magnetic dipole moments of the proton and neutron in units of the nuclear magneton $eh/4\pi M_p c$. It is interesting to note that the $^1S \rightarrow {}^3S$ transition probability would be zero if the neutron and proton had equal magnetic dipole moments.

The matrix element for the photomagnetic-capture transition is also proportional to the integral over all space of the product of the singlet and triplet wave functions $(^1\psi)(^3\psi)$. This integral has a nonzero value because the singlet potential differs from the triplet potential. The $^1S \rightarrow {}^3S$ transition probability and the corresponding radiative-capture cross section are *finite because the nuclear force is spin-dependent*, that is, $^3(np) \neq {}^1(np)$, as well as because $\mu_p \neq \mu_n$. The principal contribution to the integral over all space comes from the region outside the range of the nuclear forces. Then a good approximation can be obtained simply by assuming that the external wave functions are valid all the way from $r = \infty$ in to the origin, $r = 0$. This procedure is equivalent to neglecting the effective ranges $^1r_0$ and $^3r_0$ of the nuclear force. In this *central-force zero-range approximation*, the cross section σ_{cap} for photomagnetic capture of a neutron by a proton is (R4, B68)

$$\sigma_{\text{cap}} = \frac{\pi}{137}(\mu_p - \mu_n)^2 \left(\frac{\hbar}{2Mc}\right)^4 \frac{[1 + (\rho k)^2]}{k\rho^3} \frac{[1 - (^1a/\rho)]^2}{[1 + (^1ak)^2]} \qquad \text{(4.4)}$$

where the definition of each symbol remains the same as in Sec. 3.

The physical behavior of σ_{cap} is more apparent if we replace the wave number k of the colliding neutron and proton, and the radius ρ of the deuteron, by their energy equivalents

$$k^2 = \frac{2MW}{\hbar^2} \qquad \text{and} \qquad \rho^2 = \frac{\hbar^2}{2MB} \qquad \text{(4.5)}$$

where W = incident kinetic energy in C coordinates
  B = binding energy of deuteron
  M = reduced mass of neutron and proton

After some algebra, Eq. (4.4) becomes

$$\sigma_{cap} = \frac{\pi}{137} (\mu_p - \mu_n)^2 \left(\frac{\hbar}{2Mc}\right)^2 \left(\frac{W+B}{2Mc^2}\right) \left(\frac{B}{W}\right)^{\frac{1}{2}} \frac{[1 - (^1a/\rho)]^2}{[1 + (^1ak)^2]} \quad (4.6)$$

Several important results emerge from the comparison of Eq. (4.6) with the experimentally determined value (W43, H20)

$$\sigma_{cap} = 0.332(1 \pm 0.02) \text{ barn} \qquad \text{for 0.025-ev neutrons} \quad (4.7)$$

Singlet State of the Deuteron. First, consider the factor $[1 - (^1a/\rho)]^2$ in Eq. (4.6). Using the numerical values of the singlet scattering length ^1a and the deuteron radius ρ as given by Eqs. (3.48) and (2.17), we find $(^1a/\rho) = -5.50$. Then the expression in the square brackets has the value $[6.50]^2 = 42.25$, and Eq. (4.6) gives $\sigma_{cap} = 0.30$ barn for 0.025-ev neutrons, in fair agreement with the experimental values. If we were to use the same absolute value of ^1a, but with a positive sign (corresponding physically to a bound singlet state of the deuteron), then the square brackets become $[4.50]^2 = 20.25$, and $\sigma_{cap} = 0.14$ barn. This is clearly excluded.

Historically, the first experimental proof that the ^1S state of the deuteron is virtual was obtained by Fermi (F35) who showed in 1935 that (1) the lifetime of slow neutrons in paraffin is only about 10^{-4} sec, (2) their disappearance is due to photomagnetic capture by protons, (3) the cross section for capture is ~ 0.3 barn, and (4) therefore the singlet state of the deuteron is unbound.

The 1/V Law. For low-energy neutrons, $W \ll B$ and also $(^1ak)^2 \ll 1$ in Eq. (4.6). Then the velocity V of the neutron is proportional to $W^{\frac{1}{2}}$, and the cross section for neutron capture takes on the particularly simple form

$$\sigma_{cap} = \frac{\text{const}}{V} \qquad \text{for } W \ll B \quad (4.8)$$

Physically, this says that the probability of neutron capture is proportional to 1/velocity, i.e., to the length of time which the neutron spends in the vicinity of the target proton. The $1/V$ law is applicable not only to the simple $H^1(n,\gamma)H^2$ capture reaction but to neutron-capture reactions generally. All such reactions (n,γ), (n,α), etc., exhibit a $1/V$ cross section for slow neutrons. In addition, there may be peaks, superimposed on the $1/V$ cross section, at particular neutron energies which correspond to the resonance capture of the neutron into a level of the compound nucleus [Chap. 14, Eq. (1.1)].

Effective Range of Nuclear Forces. Approximate expressions for the correction to Eq. (4.6) for the finite effective ranges $^1r_0$ and $^3r_0$ of the nuclear force were first obtained by Bethe and Longmire (B50). The first-order correction does not depend on the absolute value of $^1r_0$ or $^3r_0$ but upon their difference $(^1r_0 - ^3r_0)$. From the presently available data (B50, S3) $(^1r_0 - ^3r_0) = (0.8 \pm 0.4) \times 10^{-13}$ cm, which is in acceptable agreement with the values of effective range obtained from scattering experiments, Eqs. (3.47) and (3.48), as interpreted on the central-force shape-independent model.

Additional corrections for the effects of tensor forces, and for the additional (exchange) magnetic moment, which can be associated with the exchange of charge between the nucleons (F48), are small and are presently comparable with the ~6 per cent uncertainty in the experimental value of σ_{cap}, Eq. (4.7).

c. Reciprocity Relationship between Cross Sections for Inverse Processes. The reactions Eqs. (4.1) and (4.2) are illustrative of inverse nuclear processes, and their cross sections obey a universal reciprocity relationship. Symbolically, consider any two inverse reactions

$$a + A \rightarrow B + b + Q \qquad (4.9)$$
$$b + B \rightarrow A + a - Q \qquad (4.10)$$

where Q is the energy release in the "direct" reaction $A \rightarrow B$. Then if the particles a, A, B, b are all spinless, it can be shown that (F41, B43, B52, B68) the cross section $\sigma(B \rightarrow A)$ for the inverse reaction Eq. (4.10) is

$$\frac{\sigma(B \rightarrow A)}{\sigma(A \rightarrow B)} = \left(\frac{p_a}{p_b}\right)^2 \qquad (4.11)$$

where $\sigma(A \rightarrow B)$ is the cross section for the direct reaction Eq. (4.9) and p_a is the momentum of relative motion of the incident particle a in the entrance channel which produces the momentum p_b of b in the exit channel of the direct reaction. More explicitly, the momentum p_a is related to the channel wavelength $\lambda_a = h/p_a$ and is given by

$$p_a^2 = 2M_a W_a \qquad (4.12)$$

where M_a = reduced mass of $a + A$
  W_a = kinetic energy of $a + A$, in C coordinates
Analogously, the exit channel wavelength is $\lambda_b = h/p_b$ and

$$p_b^2 = 2M_b W_b \qquad (4.13)$$

where M_b = reduced mass of $b + B$
  W_b = kinetic energy of $b + B$, in C coordinates
From conservation of energy, the kinetic energies follow the usual relationship

$$W_a + Q = W_b \qquad (4.14)$$

If the particles have intrinsic angular momenta I, but the reaction cross sections are independent of the relative orientations of the I's, then the cross sections are each to be multiplied by the statistical weight of all the states in their respective channel. Thus, for particles with angular momenta I_a, I_A, I_B, I_b, the general relationship which replaces Eq. (4.11) is

$$(2I_b + 1)(2I_B + 1)p_b^2 \, \sigma(B \rightarrow A)$$
$$= (2I_a + 1)(2I_A + 1)p_a^2 \, \sigma(A \rightarrow B) \qquad (4.15)\dagger$$

† An interesting experimental example of Eq. (4.15) is the detailed correspondence between the reaction $Al^{27}(p,\alpha)Mg^{24}$ ($Q = +1.61$ Mev; $I_a = \frac{1}{2}$; $I_A = \frac{5}{2}$) and its inverse reaction $Mg^{24}(\alpha,p)Al^{27}$, as reported by Kaufmann and coworkers (K8). See Fig. 1.4 of Chap. 14.

If a or b is an unpolarized photon, its statistical weight $(2I_a + 1)$ or $(2I_b + 1)$ is to be taken as 2, which corresponds physically to the two possible directions of polarization which remain after the direction of propagation has been fixed.

The angular distribution, in C coordinates, will be the same for both the direct and inverse reactions, and so Eqs. (4.11) and (4.15) apply equally well to differential cross sections or to total cross sections.

d. Photomagnetic Disintegration of the Deuteron. Fermi first pointed out that the disintegration of the deuteron by photons must include a photomagnetic disintegration process $^3S \to {}^1S$ which is the inverse of the $^1S \to {}^3S$ photomagnetic-capture reaction. From Eq. (4.15), the cross section $\sigma_{dis}(\text{M1})$ for the magnetic dipole absorption $^3S \to {}^1S$ must be given by $\sigma(B \to A)$,

where $$p_a = k\hbar \qquad\qquad p_b = \frac{h\nu}{c}$$

$$\cdot (2I_a + 1) = 2 \text{ (proton)} \qquad (2I_b + 1) = 2 \text{ (photon)}$$
$$(2I_A + 1) = 2 \text{ (neutron)} \qquad (2I_B + 1) = 3 \text{ (deuteron)}$$

Hence, by Eq. (4.15)

$$\frac{\sigma_{dis}(\text{M1})}{\sigma_{cap}} = \frac{2}{3}\left(\frac{k\hbar}{h\nu/c}\right)^2 \tag{4.16}$$

Substituting $k^2 = 2MW/\hbar^2$, and $W + B = h\nu$ [because B is the Q value of the $H^1(n,\gamma)H^2$ reaction], we find

$$\frac{\sigma_{dis}(\text{M1})}{\sigma_{cap}} = \frac{2}{3}\frac{W(2Mc^2)}{(W + B)^2} \tag{4.17}$$

in which the reduced mass M is given to good approximation by

$$2M = \tfrac{1}{2}(M_n + M_p)$$

and the corresponding rest energy is $2Mc^2 \simeq 939$ Mev. Recall Eq. (4.8), $\sigma_{cap} \propto 1/W^{\frac{1}{2}}$, for slow neutrons. Then for the photomagnetic disintegration, Eq. (4.17) shows that $\sigma_{dis}(\text{M1})$ is zero at the threshold $h\nu = B$, and for small values of $W = h\nu - B$, σ_{dis} rises linearly with $W^{\frac{1}{2}}$, that is, with the velocity V of the disintegration particles.

The general expression for the photomagnetic cross section is obtained by substituting σ_{cap} from Eq. (4.4) into Eq. (4.17). This gives

$$\sigma_{dis}(\text{M1}) = \frac{2}{3}\frac{\pi}{137}(\mu_p - \mu_n)^2\left(\frac{\hbar}{2Mc}\right)^2\left\{\frac{\rho k}{[1 + (\rho k)^2]}\frac{[1 - ({}^1a/\rho)]^2}{[1 + ({}^1ak)^2]}\right\} \tag{4.18}$$

or, expressing k and ρ in terms of $h\nu$ and B,

$$\sigma_{dis}(\text{M1})$$
$$= \frac{2}{3}\frac{\pi}{137}(\mu_p - \mu_n)^2\left(\frac{\hbar}{2Mc}\right)^2\left\{\frac{\sqrt{B}\sqrt{h\nu - B}}{h\nu}\frac{[1 - ({}^1a/\rho)]^2}{[1 + ({}^1ak)^2]}\right\} \tag{4.19}$$

These cross sections, like σ_{cap}, correspond to the central-force zero-range model and are subject to the same small corrections for the finite range of nuclear forces, for exchange magnetic moments, and for tensor forces.

The photomagnetic disintegration cross section increases as $(h\nu - B)^{\frac{1}{2}}$ near the threshold at $h\nu = B$. In contrast with σ_{cap}, the term in $[1 + (^1ak)^2]$ therefore becomes important. The cross section $\sigma_{\text{dis}}(M1)$ reaches a maximum when $^1ak \simeq 1$, i.e., when $h\nu \simeq B + |^1B|$, where

$$|^1B| = \frac{\hbar^2}{2M\,(^1a)^2} \simeq 37 \text{ kev}$$

is the absolute value of the "binding energy," $-{}^1B$, of the virtual ^1S level of the n-p system, in the zero-range, central-force approximation. The variation of $\sigma_{\text{dis}}(M1)$ with $h\nu$ is shown graphically in Fig. 4.1.

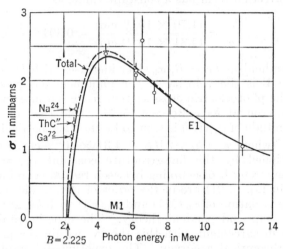

Fig. 4.1 Photodisintegration of the deuteron. Solid curves: theory, Eq. (4.21) for electric dipole (E1); Eq. (4.19) for magnetic dipole (M1). Points: representative experimental data (B58, P21, F48).

e. Photoelectric Disintegration of the Deuteron. We have noted that the electric dipole capture reaction $^3P \rightarrow {}^3S$ has a negligible cross section because of the small interaction energy of the P state. The inverse reaction is the photoelectric disintegration of the deuteron by the absorption of E1 radiation. The ratios of the cross sections for E1 disintegration and for E1 capture are the same as the corresponding ratios for M1 disintegration and capture. Then Eq. (4.17) shows that for $W \sim B$, $[\sigma_{\text{dis}}(E1)]/[\sigma_{\text{cap}}(E1)] \sim 150$. The photoelectric disintegration therefore becomes significant.

Derivation of the cross section $\sigma_{\text{dis}}(E1)$ is completely analogous to the procedure we have followed for $\sigma_{\text{dis}}(M1)$. In the matrix element for the $^3P \rightarrow {}^3S$ capture transition, the interaction energy between the neutron and proton in the P state is set equal to zero. The correction for the effective range $^3r_0$ of the ^3S interaction can be made easily. Including this, the cross section for disintegration of the deuteron by electric dipole absorption is (B68)

$$\sigma_{\text{dis}}(\text{E1}) = \frac{8\pi}{3}\frac{1}{137}\rho^2\left[\frac{k\rho}{1+(k\rho)^2}\right]^3\frac{1}{(1-{}^3r_0/\rho)} \qquad (4.20)$$

The variation with photon energy $h\nu$ is seen more clearly by expressing k and ρ in terms of $W\ (=h\nu-B)$ and B. From Eq. (4.5), $k\rho = \sqrt{W/B}$; hence Eq. (4.20) becomes

$$\sigma_{\text{dis}}(\text{E1}) = \frac{8\pi}{3}\frac{\rho^2}{137}\left[\frac{\sqrt{B(h\nu-B)}}{h\nu}\right]^3\frac{1}{(1-{}^3r_0/\rho)} \qquad (4.21)$$

The range correction term has a constant value, as

$$\frac{{}^3r_0}{\rho} = \frac{(1.70\times10^{-13}\text{ cm})}{(4.31\times10^{-13}\text{ cm})} = 0.394$$

Near the threshold at $h\nu = B$, $\sigma_{\text{dis}}(\text{E1})$ increases with k^3, or $(h\nu-B)^{\frac{3}{2}}$, or V^3, where V is the velocity of the photoneutrons produced in the reaction. The photoelectric cross section reaches a maximum of 0.0023 barn per deuteron at $h\nu = 2B \simeq 4.45$ Mev and then decreases. The order of magnitude of $\sigma_{\text{dis}}(\text{E1})$ is seen to be the "geometrical area" of the deuteron $\pi\rho^2$ (where $\rho = \hbar/\sqrt{2MB} = 4.31\times10^{-13}$ cm is the deuteron radius) multiplied by the fine-structure constant $\frac{1}{137} = e^2/\hbar c$ which represents the strength of coupling between radiation and matter. The other terms in Eq. (4.21) are of the order of magnitude unity. Figure 4.1 shows the variation of $\sigma_{\text{dis}}(\text{M1})$ and $\sigma_{\text{dis}}(\text{E1})$ with $h\nu$, according to the central-force shape-independent theory. The experimental data so far available are in agreement with this theory, within the present experimental and theoretical accuracy. The experimental results of Bishop et al. (B58), at photon energies just above the threshold, are summarized in Table 4.1.

TABLE 4.1. EXPERIMENTAL AND THEORETICAL TOTAL CROSS SECTIONS $\sigma = \sigma_{\text{dis}}(\text{M1}) + \sigma_{\text{dis}}(\text{E1})$ FOR THE PHOTODISINTEGRATION OF DEUTERIUM (B58)

These theoretical values were based on $B = 2.231 \pm 0.005$ Mev. This will depress the theoretical values somewhat as compared with the more recent value of $B = 2.225$ Mev [Chap. 3, Sec. 4; Eq. (4.46)].

Source of γ rays	$h\nu$, Mev	σ (observed), millibarns	σ (theory), millibarns
Ga^{72}	2.504	1.19 ± 0.08	1.01 ± 0.03
ThC''	2.618	1.39 ± 0.06	1.25 ± 0.03
Na^{24}	2.757	1.59 ± 0.06	1.51 ± 0.03

f. Angular Distribution of Photoneutrons. The ratio of the photomagnetic to photoelectric cross sections is determined from measurements of the angular distribution of the photoneutrons (G39).   Recall from Chap. 6, Sec. 9, that the angular distribution in C coordinates is isotropic for M1 and varies as $\sin^2 \vartheta$ for the E1 transition.   Then the observed differential cross section $d\sigma (\vartheta)$ is

$$d\sigma (\vartheta) = d\sigma(M1) + d\sigma(E1)$$

$$= \left[\frac{1}{4\pi} \sigma(M1) + \frac{3}{8\pi} \sigma(E1) \sin^2 \vartheta \right] d\Omega$$

$$= \frac{1}{4\pi} \sigma(E1) \left[\frac{\sigma(M1)}{\sigma(E1)} + \frac{3}{2} \sin^2 \vartheta \right] d\Omega \qquad (4.22)$$

Much of the experimental work on angular distribution has been summarized by Bishop and coworkers (B59), who add the value

$$\frac{\sigma(M1)}{\sigma(E1)} = 0.61 \pm 0.04$$

for $h\nu = 2.504$ Mev (Ga^{72}), based on measurements of the relative photoneutron intensities at $\vartheta = 45°$, $90°$, and $135°$.   Figure 4.2 shows that the measurements are well fitted by the central-force shape-independent model, within the present accuracy of both the experimental and theoretical values.

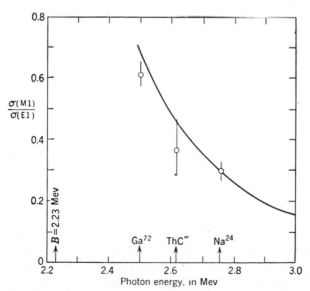

Fig. 4.2   Ratio of magnetic to electric photodisintegration of the deuteron, as a function of $h\nu$.   Points: measured values determined from the angular distribution of photoneutrons (B59).   Curve: the shape-independent (effective-range) theory (B50) calculated with $B = 2.231$ Mev by Bishop et al. (B59).

Problems

√**1.** From the cross section for the photoelectric disintegration of the deuteron $\sigma_{dis}(E1)$, derive an expression for the photoelectric-capture cross section $\sigma_{cap}(E1)$ and evaluate $\sigma_{cap}(E1)$ in barns per proton for thermal neutrons. Compare with the photomagnetic-capture cross section $\sigma_{cap}(M1) = 0.30$ barn per proton for thermal neutrons. *Ans.:* $\sigma_{cap}(E1) \simeq 5 \times 10^{-9}$ barn per proton for 0.025-ev neutrons.

√**2.** Numerically evaluate σ_{cap} for the photomagnetic capture of thermal neutrons (0.025 ev in L coordinates) by protons, using the central-force zero-range model, Eq. (4.6). *Ans.:* 0.30 barn per proton.

5. *The Proton-Proton Force at* 0 *to* 10 *Mev*

The energy domain up to ~10 Mev corresponds roughly to the separation energies for a proton from a heavy nucleus and should involve most of the main characteristics of the force between two protons.

Because of the saturation character and finite range of the (pp) force, as seen qualitatively in the constancy of the average binding energy B/A per nucleon (Chap. 9), we can anticipate that the (pp) force for S-state $(l = 0)$ interactions will be overwhelmingly stronger than the (pp) force for P-state and higher $(l = 1, 2, \ldots)$ interactions so long as the energy is small.

In the S state, the Pauli exclusion principle confines the possible interactions to the $^1(pp)$, or singlet, interaction, because the two protons are identical particles. In general (J2), singlet (pp) interactions can occur only in states of even-l $(S, D, \ldots)$, while triplet interactions $^3(pp)$ can occur only in states of odd-l $(P, F, \ldots)$.

With primary interest thus centered in only one mode of interaction, the singlet S state, detailed information on the (pp) two-body forces can be obtained best from experiments on the scattering of protons by protons. These experiments involve the production and detection of charged particles only and hence can be conducted with greater accuracy than the analogous n-p scattering experiments. However, the theoretical interpretation of the low-energy p-p scattering is much more complicated than for n-p scattering. This is due in part to wave interference effects produced by the joint action of the short-range (pp) force and the "infinite-range" coulomb force.

Studies of p-p scattering entail a tremendous field of experimental and theoretical activity. Excellent comprehensive reviews appear with reasonable frequency. The details of the present situation will be found in such reviews as those of Breit (B113), Jackson and Blatt (J2), Breit and Gluckstern (B114), Breit and Hull (B115), and Squires (S64). We shall have to be content here with a qualitative description of the main phenomena.

a. Theory of *p-p* Scattering at 0 to 10 Mev. It can be shown from general arguments similar to those developed in Appendix C, Sec. 6, that the differential cross section $d\sigma(\vartheta)$ for the projection of a proton into the solid angle $d\Omega$, at mean angle ϑ (in C coordinates), is (M69, B117, J2)

$$\frac{d\sigma(\vartheta)}{d\Omega} = \left(\frac{e^2}{2MV}\right)^2 \left(\frac{1}{\sin^4(\vartheta/2)} + \frac{1}{\cos^4(\vartheta/2)} - \frac{\cos[\eta \ln \tan^2(\vartheta/2)]}{\sin^2(\vartheta/2)\cos^2(\vartheta/2)}\right.$$

$$-\frac{2}{\eta}\sin\delta_0 \left\{\frac{\cos[\delta_0 + \eta \ln \sin^2(\vartheta/2)]}{\sin^2(\vartheta/2)} + \frac{\cos[\delta_0 + \eta \ln \cos^2(\vartheta/2)]}{\cos^2(\vartheta/2)}\right\}$$

$$\left.+\frac{4}{\eta^2}\sin^2\delta_0\right) \qquad (5.1)$$

where M = reduced mass $(2M = M_p)$
V = incident relative velocity
ϑ = scattering angle in C coordinates
$\eta = e^2/\hbar V = 1/137\beta$
δ_0 = nuclear phase shift for $l = 0$ collision

The phase shift δ_0 which we have used heretofore (Chap. 10, Sec. 3; Appendix C, Sec. 6; etc.) represented the departure of the total wave function from the wave function of the incident particles. However, in Eq. (5.1) δ_0 represents only the effect of turning on the specifically nuclear (pp) force. The entire phase shift between the incident wave and the total wave function includes both δ_0 and a phase shift δ_c due to the effect of the coulomb force. The coulomb phase shift does not appear explicitly in Eq. (5.1), having been eliminated algebraically by use of the known form of the coulomb potential. The predicted value of δ_0, for a given proton energy, depends upon the shape, depth, and range of the nuclear potential.

The term in $\eta \ln \tan^2 (\vartheta/2)$ is small for proton energies above 1 Mev and for angles ϑ not too close to 0° or 180°. When each of the three logarithmic terms is assumed to be zero, a commonly seen approximate form emerges.

Equation (5.1) is applicable when only the s-wave phase shift is appreciable, and when the nuclear forces are central forces. The physical origin of each term is indicated explicitly in Eq. (5.1). These can be visualized with the help of Fig. 5.1, which corresponds to Eq. (5.1) when the incident proton energy is 2.4 Mev in L coordinates, hence 1.2 Mev in C coordinates.

For small incident energies (large η), or for small scattering angles, the scattering is essentially classical. The first term in Eq. (5.1) is the standard Rutherford scattering [Chap. 1, Eq. (3.10)]. The second term arises because the projectile and target proton are indistinguishable. Scattering of the incident proton at ϑ or at $\pi - \vartheta$ results in the partner proton emerging from the collision at angle $\pi - \vartheta$ or at ϑ. The first two terms are entirely classical. However the third term is completely nonclassical. It is the result of wave interference between two identical particles with spin $\frac{1}{2}$, such as two protons or two electrons. This term was originally developed by Mott (M65); hence the first three terms are

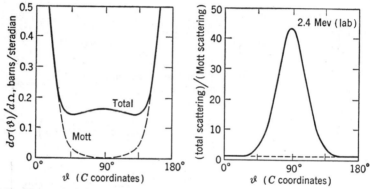

Fig. 5.1 Theoretical differential cross section for scattering of 2.4-Mev protons (laboratory energy) by protons vs. scattering angle ϑ in C coordinates. Near $\vartheta = 90°$ (laboratory angle 45°) the scattering is mainly nuclear. Near $\vartheta = 0°$ and 180° (laboratory, 0° and 90°) the scattering is substantially coulomb. The dips at intermediate angles, $\vartheta \sim 45°$ and 135°, are due to destructive interference between nuclear and Mott scattering. [*The curves are from Jackson and Blatt* (J2).]

commonly known as *Mott scattering*. Note that the Mott scattering has fore-and-aft symmetry about 90°, because of the identity of the two particles, even though the interaction forces are purely coulomb.

At higher incident energies (small η), or for nearly head-on collisions, the specifically nuclear forces become effective. There are two results. The scattering amplitude is now the sum of coulomb and nuclear (pp) effects. As shown in Appendix C, Sec. 6, a cross term appears, representing the intensity due to interference between the coulomb and nuclear scattering amplitudes. Secondly, a term due purely to nuclear potential scattering also appears in Eq. (5.1). At moderate energies, as in Fig. 5.1, the observed total scattering differs from Mott scattering predominantly near $\vartheta = 90°$ and is therefore due mainly to the cross term in Eq. (5.1). This cross term makes the nuclear effect important by coupling it to the coulomb effect. The purely nuclear term $(4/\eta^2) \sin^2 \delta_0$ is smaller than the cross term at moderate energies and is independent of scattering angle, because of the spherical symmetry of s-wave interactions.

In comparisons with experimental values, the sign of the cross term gives immediate information about the nature of the (pp) nuclear force. Positive values of δ_0 correspond to an attractive interaction; negative values of δ_0 signify a repulsive force (Appendix C, Sec. 6, Fig. 11).

b. Experimental Results on p-p Scattering from 0 to 10 Mev. The existence of a short-range attraction between protons was demonstrated in 1936 when White (W40) and Tuve, Heydenburg, and Hafstad (T32) first observed the anomalous (non-Mott) scattering of protons by hydrogen, beginning at about 0.7 ± 0.1 Mev. These findings were confirmed and extended in experimental studies by Herb, Kerst, Parkinson, and Plain (H37), and in 1939 all available data in the energy range from 0.8 to 2.4 Mev were compared with the predictions of a variety of assumed nuclear potentials by Breit, Thaxton, and Eisenbud (B117), and Hoisington, Share, and Breit (H60). The essential results of this analysis remain unaltered and have been confirmed by much further work. It was found that:

1. Cross sections having an accuracy of a few per cent can be fitted by Eq. (5.1) and therefore correspond to s-wave ($l = 0$) interactions, with no significant contribution from p waves.

2. The observed phase shifts δ_0 could be accounted for by any of several shapes of central-force potential wells, with suitable adjustment of the depth and range Eqs. (2.18) to (2.21), e.g., by a rectangular well of 11 Mev depth and 2.8×10^{-13} cm radius.

3. The $^1(pp)$ interaction was found to be nearly equal to the $^1(np)$ interaction but about 2 per cent weaker, the difference being independent of the assumed shape of the potential well.

Figure 5.2 shows the differential p-p cross section, measured with an accuracy of ± 0.3 per cent, at incident proton energies from about 1.8 to 4.2 Mev (W71). The general physical effects noted in Fig. 5.1 are evident. The curves are fitted from Eq. (5.1) for s-wave nuclear interactions only, with the "nuclear phase shift" δ_0 as the only adjustable parameter. The resulting nuclear phase shifts (H7) δ_0 are plotted in Fig. 5.3 as a function of the incident proton energy.

c. Scattering Length and Effective Range of the (pp) Singlet Force. In the interpretation of the p-p scattering results, the phase shifts δ_0 are, as usual, the common meeting ground of experiment and theory. As is shown in detail by Jackson and Blatt (J2), the observed variation of δ_0 with incident proton energy can be matched by any of the conventional shapes of potential well, with suitable choices of depth and range. A shape-independent theory therefore has a natural attractiveness. For the (pp) interaction, such a theory contains as parameters the effective range r_0 and a constant a which is the (pp) analogue of the singlet scattering length in the (np) interaction. The best fit to the data of Fig. 5.3 is obtained with

$$r_0 = 2.65(1 \pm 0.03) \times 10^{-13} \text{ cm} \qquad (5.2)$$
$$a = -7.7(1 \pm 0.07) \times 10^{-13} \text{ cm} \qquad (5.3)$$

Within the present accuracy of measurement, the singlet effective range

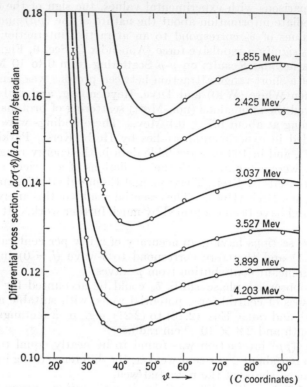

Fig. 5.2 Angular distribution of *p-p* scattering, at angles ϑ (in *C* coordinates), for the incident proton energies (in *L* coordinates) marked on each curve. [*Adapted from Worthington, McGruer, and Findley* (W71).]

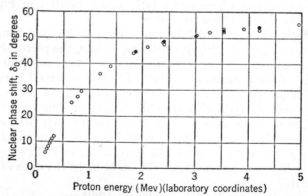

Fig. 5.3 Experimental *p-p* differential scattering cross sections as represented by the nuclear phase shift δ_0, Eq. (5.1), as a function of the incident proton energy. *Open circles* represent the data compiled by Jackson and Blatt (J2); *solid circles* are from data of Worthington et al. (W71) as interpreted by Hall and Powell (H7).

r_0 for the (pp) interaction is seen to be the same as for the $^1(np)$ interaction, Eq. (3.48).

The p-p scattering length a is of special interest. It turns out to be negative in sign. This tells us at once (compare Fig. 3.2) that the singlet p-p system is unbound. Therefore the di-proton, or He², has no stable bound level. The absolute value of a requires further interpretation because it includes coulomb as well as specifically nuclear effects. The specifically nuclear effects can be isolated by treating the coulomb force, within the range of the nuclear force, as a small perturbation. When this is done (J2, B68), the specifically nuclear scattering length a' for the $^1(pp)$ interaction is increased to the value

$$a' \simeq -17 \times 10^{-13} \text{ cm} \tag{5.4}$$

d. Equivalence of the (pp) **and** (np) **Singlet Forces.** Quantitative comparison of a' with the singlet $^1(np)$ scattering length

$$^1a = -23.69 \times 10^{-13} \text{ cm}$$

Eq. (3.48), shows that both interactions have virtual singlet states whose (negative) binding energy is close to zero (~ 50 kev). Also, if the potential wells for the $^1(pp)$ and $^1(np)$ interactions are assumed to have the same shape and range, then the potential well for $^1(np)$ is only slightly deeper (1.5 to 3 per cent) than for the $^1(pp)$ interaction.

Finally, Schwinger (S22) has drawn attention to the difference in the magnetic forces between $^1(np)$ and $^1(pp)$, which arises because the intrinsic magnetic dipole moments of the neutron and proton are of opposite sign. By a variational method, Schwinger has evaluated a net *attractive* magnetic interaction in the observed $^1(np)$ force and a net *repulsive* magnetic interaction in the observed $^1(pp)$ force. If the Yukawa shape, Eq. (2.21), is chosen for the nuclear potential, then the small observed difference between $^1(pp)$ and $^1(np)$ is exactly ($\pm\frac{1}{2}$ per cent) accounted for.

This equality of the parameters of the (pp) and (np) singlet interactions is the central evidence on which rests the *hypothesis of the charge independence of nuclear forces*. The evidence is valid within present experimental and theoretical accuracy. There is supportive experimental evidence, of a less accurate kind, that the (nn) singlet force equals the (pp) singlet force.

The hypothesis of charge independence implies that the forces between two protons, or two neutrons, or a neutron and proton, are all equal in ^1S states and are all equal in ^3P states, etc. While there is as yet no contradictory evidence, the present experimental evidence must be regarded as inadequate to prove so sweeping a generalization. In the meantime, the hypothesis of charge independence has proved fruitful in some theories of the heavier nuclei.

e. P-state p-p Repulsion. In Fig. 5.2, the observed p-p scattering cross sections have been well matched by a ^1S phase shift δ_0 appropriate to each bombarding energy. However, there are slight discrepancies, of the order of 1 per cent, especially for scattering angles near $\vartheta \simeq 30° \pm 15°$. Figure 5.4 illustrates these small deviations from a pure s-wave effect.

Upon analysis (H7), these effects are interpreted as evidence for a small negative p-wave nuclear phase shift whose value is about $\delta_1 \simeq -0.1°$ at 4 Mev. The negative sign means that the ^3P interaction is repulsive. These inferences are not inconsistent with the interpretation of very-high-energy proton-proton scattering experiments to be discussed in Sec. 9.

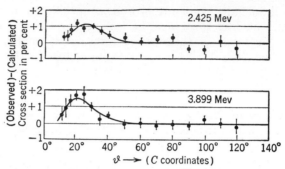

Fig. 5.4 Experimental evidence for a small nuclear repulsive force between two protons in a ^3P state. The points represent the difference between the observed and calculated p-p differential scattering cross sections which are not apparent on the scale of Fig. 5.2. [*Adapted from Worthington, McGruer, and Findley* (W71).]

Problem

Show under what conditions the p-p differential cross section at $\vartheta = 90°$ (C coordinates) should vary as $1/$(incident proton energy) and compare with the experimental findings of Cork, *Phys. Rev.*, **80**: 321 (1950) ($d\sigma/d\Omega \propto 1/E_p$ between 19 and 32 Mev), and with Figs. 5.3 and 9.4.

6. *Equivalence of* (nn) *and* (pp) *Forces*

Direct two-body evidence on the force between two neutrons is extremely limited. Scattering experiments, analogous to the n-p and p-p scattering studies, seem permanently excluded. This is because a thermal neutron flux of 10^{13} neutrons/(cm²)(sec), such as is attainable in present reactors, corresponds in neutron density only to a monatomic gas at 10^{-12}-atm pressure.

a. The Di-neutron. There is one piece of negative evidence, the nonexistence of a stable di-neutron (C29). This might be expected by analogy with the nonexistence of the di-proton He², because, even with the coulomb field turned off, the p-p scattering length a' is negative, Eq. (5.4). The scattering length for the (nn) interaction appears at least to have the same (negative) sign as that for the (pp) interaction.

b. Binding Energy of H³ and He³. The lightest pair of adjacent mirror nuclei, H³ and He³, provide the most direct evidence on the equivalence of $^1(nn)$ and $^1(pp)$. Counting up the number of possible two-body interactions, we have in H³, $^3(np) + {}^1(np) + {}^1(nn)$, and in He³, $^3(np) + {}^1(np) + {}^1(pp)$. These are all S-state interactions because neither nucleus has any orbital angular momentum. The binding energy of the two nuclides should therefore differ only by the coulomb energy and by any difference which may exist between $^1(nn)$ and $^1(pp)$. The observed binding-energy difference is 0.76 Mev (Chap. 9). If this is attributed to the coulomb energy of two discrete protons, then, by Chap. 2, Eq. (2.3),

$$W_{\text{coul}} = \frac{3}{5}\frac{e^2}{R}\,Z(Z-1) \qquad (6.1)$$

and $R \simeq 2.3 \times 10^{-13}$ cm. This is a reasonable radius for H^3 or He^3 and suggests that $^1(nn) = {}^1(pp)$. When tensor forces are included, and charge independence is assumed, the detailed theory of H^3 by Pease and Feshbach (P11) shows that the binding-energy difference between H^3 and He^3 can be attributed entirely to the coulomb interaction between the two protons in He^3.

c. Coulomb-energy Difference of Heavier Mirror Nuclides. The heavier mirror nuclides, such as $_{16}S^{31}_{15}$ and $_{15}P^{31}_{16}$, differ from each other only by the interchange of one proton for a neutron. This interchange alters the number of p-p and n-n bonds, but in a manner whose details depend on the coupling scheme. In any case, we have found in Chap. 2, Eq. (2.13) and Fig. 2.1, that the difference in total binding due to specifically nuclear forces is negligible between mirror nuclides, and this supports the hypothesis of charge symmetry, i.e., the presumed equality of $^1(nn)$ and $^1(pp)$.

d. Neutron-Deuteron Interactions. Neutron scattering by deuterons provides a means of exploring the (nn) force. At present, clear-cut quantitative conclusions have yet to emerge from the theoretical and experimental work on elastic n-d scattering (A6, A19, C20, T29). Inelastic scattering, i.e., the disruption of H^2 according to the reaction $H^2(n,p)2n$ by neutrons of the order of 90 Mev, has given quantitative support to the equivalence of (nn) and (pp) forces (C19).

e. H^3 and He^3 in Nuclear Reactions. The differential cross sections at $\sim$10 Mev for the reactions $H^3(d,n)He^4$ and $He^3(d,p)He^4$ show marked asymmetries which are very similar for both reactions. These observations have been interpreted (A18) as also supporting the equality of (nn) and (pp).

f. Excited Levels in Mirror Nuclei. In each of the mirror nuclei $_3Li^7_4$ and $_4Be^7_3$, the first excited level has $I = \frac{1}{2}-$ and appears to form a ^2P spin doublet with the ground level $I = \frac{3}{2}-$. The excitation energies differ by only 10 per cent, most of which may be accounted for by magnetic interactions. This evidence (B130) and an analogous but more complicated situation in the several heavier mirror nuclei (A10, T19, E14) add further support to the hypothesis of charge symmetry, $^1(nn) = {}^1(pp)$.

7. *Summary of Central Forces*

Thus far in this chapter we have dealt analytically only with the ordinary (nonexchange), central (nontensor) forces. These forces between individual nucleons can be represented by many explicit potential shapes (rectangular, Gaussian, exponential, Yukawa, . . .) or by their shape-independent approximation, which characterizes the effective-range theory.

a. Interactions at Energies Comparable with the Nucleon Binding Energy. Insofar as phenomena below the order of 10 Mev are concerned, these considerations now give quite satisfactory explanations for a wide variety of two-body phenomena, including:

1. Small binding energy of the deuteron
2. Large size of the deuteron
3. Large epithermal n-p cross section σ_0 of free protons
4. Small coherent scattering cross section of cold neutrons by parahydrogen
5. Coherent scattering of slow neutrons by bound protons in crystals
6. Total reflection of neutrons from "neutron mirrors"
7. Radiative capture of neutrons by protons
8. Photomagnetic disintegration of the deuteron
9. Photoelectric disintegration of the deuteron
10. Singlet phase shift δ_0 in p-p scattering
11. Instability of the di-proton and di-neutron
12. Difference in binding energy of H^3 and He^3

b. Charge Independence. All the dramatic surprises in this group of experiments have now been explained in terms of short-range triplet and singlet central forces between nucleons in S states. Within the accuracy of theory and experiment, the singlet forces between all pairs of nucleons are found to be equal, and we can write

$$^1(pp) = {}^1(nn) \qquad \text{``charge symmetry''} \qquad (7.1a)$$

and $\qquad ^1(np) = {}^1(pp) = {}^1(nn) \qquad \text{``charge independence''} \qquad (7.1b)$

c. Spin Dependence. The total (np) force is clearly stronger in the triplet state than in the singlet state. This is a clear experimental result which is almost independent of any type of theory, because the ground level of the deuteron has angular momentum $I = 1$ and is a ^3S level, whereas the ^1S level is unbound. The conclusion

$$^3(np) > {}^1(np) \qquad (7.2)$$

is supported by the theoretical interpretation of all n-p collision phenomena.

d. Exchange Forces. The nuclear force must be some type of saturated force in order that heavy nuclei may have a binding energy proportional to the number of nucleons. This is most simply achieved by invoking exchange forces of the Majorana type, for which the nucleon-nucleon force is attractive in S states and all other states of even-l but changes sign and is repulsive for P states and all other states of odd-l. To the extent that the low-energy interactions involve only S states, the introduction of exchange forces produces no change in the theoretical interpretation based on ordinary forces.

From other evidence, the actual central force appears to be neither a pure ordinary force nor a pure exchange force but instead contains a proportion of ordinary force plus enough exchange force to provide a saturation mechanism. The introduction of exchange forces does not produce any significant change in the bulk of the low-energy predictions, and it is in accord with the small P-state repulsion seen in the p-p scattering data of Fig. 5.4.

The physical picture of the exchange force lies in a meson field surrounding the nucleon and in the actual exchange of a meson between two nucleons which approach each other very closely. For visualizing the relationship between the range of the nuclear force and the mass of the meson, a simple consideration due to Wick (W45) is useful. Imagine that a proton spontaneously emits a π meson of mass M_π, according to the reaction

$$p \to n + M_\pi$$

This would violate conservation of energy because an amount of energy $\Delta E \sim M_\pi c^2$ has appeared spontaneously. Thus, classically, the reaction cannot take place. But we can imagine the "virtual" emission of the π meson, followed by its recapture within a time Δt, according to

$$p \rightleftarrows n + M_\pi \tag{7.3}$$

Now if Δt is a sufficiently short time so that the uncertainty principle

$$\Delta E \, \Delta t \sim \hbar \tag{7.4}$$

is satisfied, we have no experimental way of contradicting Eq. (7.3), because any experiment performed in a time Δt will disturb the energy of the system by at least $\Delta E \sim \hbar / \Delta t$. We then ask how far away from the proton the meson could travel in the time Δt and still get back without its individual journey being detectable. The distance b traveled in time Δt is $b \sim v \, \Delta t$, where v is the velocity of the meson. The uncertainty ΔE in energy must be at least as large as the rest energy $M_\pi c^2$ if the virtual emission is to take place without violation of conservation of energy. Then

$$\Delta E \sim \frac{\hbar}{\Delta t} \sim \frac{\hbar v}{b} \geq M_\pi c^2 \tag{7.5}$$

The maximum value of v is c; hence Eq. (7.5) becomes

$$b \leq \frac{\hbar}{M_\pi c} = \frac{1}{2\pi} \left(\frac{h}{m_0 c} \right) \frac{m_0}{M_\pi} \tag{7.6}$$

where $(h/m_0 c) = 2{,}426 \times 10^{-13}$ cm is the Compton wavelength of the electron. Then, for a meson of mass $M_\pi = 276 m_0$, the travel distance of a meson in virtual emission is about

$$b \sim 1.4 \times 10^{-13} \text{ cm} \tag{7.7}$$

which agrees more than qualitatively with the observed range of the nuclear forces.

We may note in passing how this "meson field" is simply related to the more common electromagnetic fields of classical experience. Consider the Yukawa potential, Eq. (2.21), and identify the range b of the potential with the rationalized Compton wavelength of the meson, that is, $b = \hbar/M_\pi c$. If we reduce the mass of the field particle M_π toward zero, then the $e^{-(r/b)}$ term approaches unity, and the Yukawa potential becomes the conventional $1/r$ potential of electrodynamics, in which the field quantum $h\nu$ does have zero rest mass. The Yukawa potential is thus seen to be a more generalized potential in which the field is associated with a particle whose rest mass is finite.

Problems

1. State very briefly the principal types of evidence which show that the (np) binding force in nuclei is (*a*) short-range, (*b*) nonelectric, (*c*) nongravitational, (*d*) nonmagnetic, and (*e*) spin-dependent.

2. What experimental evidence shows that the (nn) and (pp) forces are substantially equal?

8. *Effects of Tensor Forces*

Among the low-energy data there are two experimental results for which central forces, with or without exchange, are completely inadequate. With central forces, in a spherically symmetric S state, the deuteron should have a magnetic moment $\mu_d = \mu_n + \mu_p$ and an electric quadrupole moment $Q = 0$. The experimentally observed departures from these conditions are small, but they are also very certain (Chap. 4, Sec. 5).

a. The Tensor Operator. In order to obtain a representation of these nonspherical effects, one adds to the central force a small amount of a noncentral force. Then the total potential has the form (R6, R29, B68)

$$U(r) = U_1(r) + U_2(r)\mathbf{d}_1 \cdot \mathbf{d}_2 + U_3(r)S_{12} \tag{8.1}$$

where $U_1(r)$, $U_2(r)$, and $U_3(r)$ = ordinary functions of r [such as one of the potential wells of Eqs. (2.18) to (2.21)]

$\mathbf{d}_1$ and $\mathbf{d}_2$ = spin operators of the two nucleons

$\mathbf{d}_1 \cdot \mathbf{d}_2$ = 1 for a triplet state and -3 for a singlet state

The noncentral character of the interaction is contained in the tensor operator

$$S_{12} = \frac{[3(\mathbf{d}_1 \cdot \mathbf{r}_{12})(\mathbf{d}_2 \cdot \mathbf{r}_{12})]}{r_{12}^2} - (\mathbf{d}_1 \cdot \mathbf{d}_2) \tag{8.2}$$

which gives a dependence on the direction of the spin vectors $\mathbf{d}_1$ and $\mathbf{d}_2$ relative to the separation $\mathbf{r}_{12}$ between the two nucleons.

Note that S_{12} is a scalar. It can be shown that when $U_3(r)$ is finite the total angular momentum I and the parity remain good quantum numbers but that the orbital angular momentum L is no longer a constant

of the motion.   There also emerges from Eq. (8.2) the valuable generalization

$$S_{12} = 0 \qquad \text{for all singlet states } (^1S, \, ^1P, \, ^1D, \, \ldots) \qquad (8.3)$$

Hence *all tensor effects are to be found in triplet states only.*

   b. Magnetic and Electric Moments of the Deuteron.   The effect of a
finite tensor force on the low-energy data was first studied in detail by
Rarita and Schwinger (R6), who used a rectangular potential well of
radius $b = 2.8 \times 10^{-13}$ cm for both the central and tensor potentials.
With this rectangular potential, the magnetic dipole moment and the
electric quadrupole moment of the deuteron emerged correctly, without
disturbing markedly the theoretical match with the other low-energy
data, by assuming that the ground state of the deuteron is an admixture
of about 4 per cent ^3D state plus 96 per cent ^3S state.

   Other potential shapes and ranges have been studied by many investigators.   These are summarized by Feshbach and Schwinger (F48), who
have made detailed calculations for the low-energy phenomena, using a
Yukawa shape in both the central and tensor potentials.   With these
potentials, the magnetic and electric moments of the deuteron can be
matched, within experimental and theoretical uncertainties, by an admixture of 4 ± 1.6 per cent ^3D state in the ground state of the deuteron.
The experimentally determined triplet scattering length ^3a and effective
range $^3r_0$ of Eq. (3.47) are found to require that

$$b_t > b_c \qquad (8.4)$$

where b_t and b_c are the triplet ranges of the tensor and central Yukawa
potentials, Eq. (2.21).

   c. Binding Energy of H³, He³, and He⁴.   These same potentials can
be applied to the three-body problem, H³ and He³, and the four-body
problem He⁴, by variational methods.   It is well established generally
that the observed binding energy of these nuclei is distinctly smaller than
is predicted by any purely central interaction which will at the same time
match the properties of the deuteron and the low-energy scattering data.
Also, any admixture of *noncentral force reduces the theoretical binding
energy* and brings it closer to the experimentally determined values.

   The Yukawa potential shapes studied by Feshbach and Schwinger
(F48) have been applied to H³ and He³ by Pease and Feshbach (P11)
and to He⁴ by Irving (I6).   It is found that the following potential is
one which matches all the low-energy scattering data, as well as the
properties of the deuteron, and the binding energy of H³, He³, and He⁴

$$\text{singlet: } \, ^1U(r) = -U_c \frac{e^{-(r/b_c)}}{(r/b_c)} \qquad (8.5)$$

$$\text{triplet: } \, ^3U(r) = -U_c \frac{e^{-(r/b_c)}}{(r/b_c)} - U_t \frac{e^{-(r/b_t)}}{(r/b_t)} S_{12} \qquad (8.6)$$

where

$$
\begin{aligned}
&\text{central: } \; U_c = 47 \text{ Mev} \qquad b_c = 1.18 \times 10^{-13} \text{ cm} \\
&\text{tensor: } \; U_t = 24 \text{ Mev} \qquad b_t = 1.70 \times 10^{-13} \text{ cm}
\end{aligned}
\qquad (8.7)
$$

Note that the central parts of the triplet Yukawa potential $^3U(r)$ and the singlet Yukawa potential $^1U(r)$ are equal. This means that the well-established spin dependence of nuclear forces

$$^3(np) > {}^1(np)$$

can be ascribed entirely to the additional tensor force, which is effective only for the triplet state.

Note that the depth of the tensor potential U_t is about half that of the central potential U_c, but that the tensor range b_t is greater than the central range b_c. The small effects of the tensor force are to be associated with its small percentage admixture, which for Yukawa wells is of the order of 3 per cent D state in H^2, H^3, He^3, and He^4, and the balance S state (F48, I6).

d. Exchange Tensor Forces. Exchange interactions of the Majorana type leave the attractive forces unaltered in states of even-l (S, D, . . .) and only change the sign of the force to a repulsion for states of odd-l (P, F, . . .). The low-energy data involve a P state only in the photoelectric disintegration of the deuteron ($^3S \rightarrow {}^3P$), where the P-state interaction was taken as negligible in Eq. (4.20), and in the small (≤ 1 per cent) anomaly in the p-p scattering, Fig. 5.4. Therefore the inclusion or omission of exchange forces in Eqs. (8.5) and (8.6) is a matter of relative indifference in the low-energy domain. For simplicity, exchange is ordinarily omitted here, and no dire consequences result even though the potentials in Eqs. (8.5) and (8.6) are unsaturated.

9. *High-energy n-p and p-p Scattering*

The (np) and (pp) two-body interactions for states of nonzero angular momentum l can be explored in scattering experiments at very high energies. For example, to achieve an angular momentum as large as $2\hbar$ in an n-p collision whose impact parameter is as small as 1×10^{-13} cm requires an incident kinetic energy of at least 320 Mev. Such energies are so much greater than those encountered in a heavy nucleus that there may be little direct connection between the high-energy scattering and conditions within an average nucleus.

Both n-p and p-p scattering experiments have now been carried out at energies up to several hundred Mev. The results have been, in the words of Blatt and Weisskopf, "strange and unexpected," and were definitely not predicted from the low-energy data. We shall indicate here the general character of the experimental findings. The interpretation of these high-energy scattering experiments is as yet by no means complete, but one or two important and clear facts about the nature of nuclear forces have already emerged.

a. n-p Scattering above 10 Mev. Incident neutrons up to 20-Mev laboratory kinetic energy are scattered isotropically (in C coordinates) by protons (B8). At energies of 27 Mev, deviations from spherically symmetric scattering are clearly measurable (B126). At still higher energies the angular distribution of the scattered neutrons takes on a characteristic "valley" shape. This is the prominent experimental feature of Fig. 9.1 which shows the differential cross section for neutrons of 40-, 90-, and 260-Mev laboratory kinetic energy, as scattered by protons (H1, K15). The pronounced minimum in the vicinity of 90° is to be associated with the effects of exchange forces and not with scattering in higher-angular-momentum states. At 90 Mev, for example, some 90 per cent of the total cross section is still attributable to S-state scattering (C21).

Exchange Forces in High-energy n-p Scattering. The influence of exchange forces and of ordinary forces on high-energy scattering can be

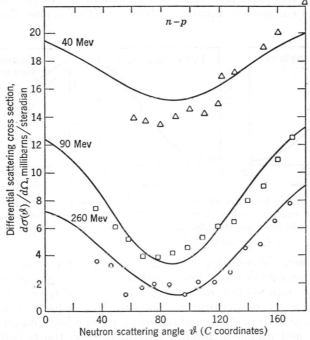

Fig. 9.1 Angular distribution of neutrons scattered by protons, for incident neutrons of 40-, 90-, and 260-Mev laboratory kinetic energy. [*From Jastrow's* (J8) *compilation of the measurements by Hadley, Kelly, Leith, Segrè, Wiegand, and York* (H1, K15).]

understood qualitatively in the following way. We have seen from the low-energy collision data that the depth of the n-p potential well $-U_0$ is of the order of, say, 20 to 50 Mev, depending on the shape of the well. This depth is a measure of the strength of the interaction between a neutron and proton. It therefore is a rough measure of the maximum energy transfer, in laboratory coordinates, between a colliding neutron and proton. At incident kinetic energies which are greatly in excess of $-U_0$, only a limited fraction of the incident kinetic energy can possibly be transferred in the collision, if ordinary (nonexchange) forces govern the interaction. Then, by Eq. 28 of Appendix B, the center-of-mass angle through which the neutron can be deflected is limited to small values.

For ordinary forces there should be substantially no scattering of the neutron through large angles, if the interaction is weak compared with the mutual kinetic energy. Thus we are led to predict an angular distribution like that shown in Fig. 9.2.

For an exchange force the situation is entirely different. Now the interaction mechanism involves an exchange of identity between the incident neutron and the struck proton. With weak interaction the particles which travel predominantly along in their initial direction have exchanged their identity and are protons after the interaction. The particles which emerge from the collision at large angles, such as 90° to 180°, are struck particles, which exchanged their identity during the collision and emerged as neutrons. This situation is also illustrated in Fig. 9.2.

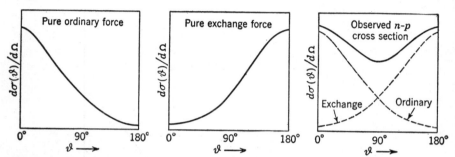

Fig. 9.2 Schematic behavior of the angular distribution of neutrons scattered by protons, when the interaction energy is weak compared with the incident kinetic energy. The observed angular distribution represents a mixture of ordinary and exchange forces. [*After Fermi* (F41).]

Serber Force. The observed angular distribution has neutron maxima both at 0° (as for an ordinary force) and at 180° (as for an exchange force) and therefore represents a mixture of both types of force. Reasonable fits with the observed neutron angular distribution have been obtained by Christian and Hart (C21) and others by using a half-and-half mixture of ordinary and exchange force. This mixture is the so-called *Serber force* and is represented analytically by the operator

$$\tfrac{1}{2}(1 + P_M) \tag{9.1}$$

where P_M is the Majorana exchange operator whose value is $+1$ for $l = 0, 2, 4, \ldots$ (attractive force) and is -1 for $l = 1, 3, 5, \ldots$ (repulsive force). The Serber force is therefore zero for odd states $(P, F, \ldots)$. Although this gives a reasonable match with the high-energy n-p scattering, the Serber force does not contain enough exchange force to give a repulsion in odd states, and hence it cannot account for the saturation which is definitely seen in the binding energy of heavy nuclei.

In contrast with n-p scattering below ~ 10 Mev, the effective range for high-energy scattering is dependent on the assumed shape of the potential well. Analytically (p. 501 of R4) this corresponds to the addition of a shape-dependent term $Pk^4r_0^3$ to the right-hand side of Eq. (3.20).

Christian and Hart have used several potential shapes, all with Majorana space exchange (Serber force) in the central-force part of the interaction. With pure central forces, the predicted distribution near 90° is too flat. The addition of some tensor force, either with or without exchange, makes the theoretical curve less flat near 90°. Although this recipe matches the observed *n-p* scattering distribution, it fails completely when applied to high-energy *p-p* scattering.

The fundamentally important result of the high-energy *n-p* scattering studies has been *the most suggestive experimental demonstration of exchange forces in a two-body interaction.*

b. *p-p* Scattering above 10 Mev. In *p-p* scattering the identity of the two particles produces three effects which are not present in *n-p* scattering.

1. For each proton scattered at any angle ϑ (*C* coordinates) the partner is scattered at $\pi - \vartheta$. Therefore the experimental results always display fore-and-aft symmetry about 90° and are ordinarily reported for only 0° to 90° even when the measurements involve a wider angular range.

2. Coherence between the scattered amplitudes

$$|f|^2 = |f(\vartheta) + f(\pi - \vartheta)|^2$$

for the two identical protons makes the singlet and triplet *p-p* cross sections inherently four times larger than the corresponding *n-p* cross sections.

3. The Pauli principle excludes all odd-*l* singlet states and all even-*l* triplet states. Therefore the *p-p* scattering can take place only from ^1S, ^3P, ^1D, ^3F, . . . states. Among these possibilities, the ^3F state is still ineffective at ~320 Mev, because for $l = 3$ the colliding protons are widely separated, compared with the effective range of the nuclear forces. Among the remaining ^1S, ^3P, ^1D interactions, only the ^3P can partake of a tensor interaction or can display a repulsion if Majorana space exchange is mixed in adequate amounts with a central force.

The experimental results for *p-p* scattering up to 340 Mev differ sharply from what would be expected on a basis of the *n-p* results at comparable energies.

1. The angular distribution is roughly isotropic between 20° and 90°.

2. The absolute magnitude of the observed differential cross section clearly exceeds the maximum possible *S*-state value $d\sigma = \lambda^2 \, d\Omega$, where $\lambda = \hbar/MV$, which is predicted by Eq. (5.1) for angles $\vartheta \sim 90°$ where coulomb scattering is unimportant.

3. The expected variation of $d\sigma$ with $1/E_p$, where E_p is the incident proton kinetic energy in laboratory coordinates, is seen in the domain $19 \leq E_p \leq 32$ Mev (C44), but $d\sigma$ is substantially independent of E_p for $E_p \geq 100$ Mev (C7, C15, O9, M70, H21). These general characteristics appear definite. The pioneer work at Berkeley in the energy domains

$$E_p \simeq 30 \text{ Mev} \qquad \text{(C44, P5)}$$
$$E_p \simeq 120, 164, 250, 345 \text{ Mev} \qquad \text{(C15)}$$

has been "confirmed" for

$$E_p \simeq 75, 105 \text{ Mev} \qquad \text{at Harvard (B57)}$$
$$E_p \simeq 147 \text{ Mev} \qquad \text{at Harwell (C7)}$$
$$E_p \simeq 240 \text{ Mev} \qquad \text{at Rochester (O9)}$$
$$E_p \simeq 435 \text{ Mev} \qquad \text{at Carnegie Tech (M70, H21)}$$

Illustrative experimental results are shown in Fig. 9.3 (angular variation of $d\sigma$) and Fig. 9.4 (energy variation of $d\sigma$).

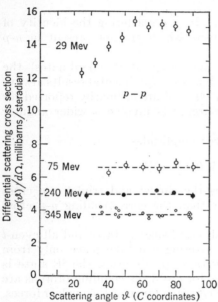

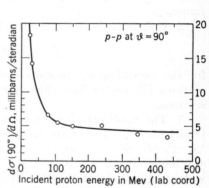

Fig. 9.3 Angular variation of p-p scattering at high energies. In general, the absolute values of the cross sections reported from Berkeley are $\sim$20 per cent smaller than the initial results from some other laboratories. The important finding is that the trends of $d\sigma$ with angle, and with energy (Fig. 9.4), are found to be the same from all laboratories.

Fig. 9.4 Variation of the differential p-p scattering cross section at $\vartheta = 90°$ (C coordinates) with incident proton kinetic energy E_p (laboratory coordinates).

The absence of the expected minimum in $d\sigma$ (ϑ) for p-p scattering at 90° cannot be explained (C22) by potentials of the types used by Christian and Hart (C21) for n-p scattering unless the hypothesis of charge independence, $^1(np) = {}^1(pp)$, is given up. This breakdown of the standard forms of potential well, with recipes involving admixtures of central and tensor forces, with and without exchange, has stimulated a theoretical search for some new formulation which will preserve charge independence and at the same time will fit the p-p and n-p scattering data at all energies.

c. Short-range Repulsion between Nucleons. One method of preserving charge independence is the introduction of a new form of potential well. Jastrow (J8, J9) has made progress toward the discovery of a potential which will fit all experimental results by *adding a very short-range repulsive core* to the interior of the standard forms of potential well. Such a composite potential is shown schematically in Fig. 9.5, where it can be seen that a spin-independent core radius can result in an effective hard-core repulsion in singlet states and in its essential absence in the triplet states.

In order to reduce the mathematical difficulties, Jastrow has tested a composite potential which represents an impenetrable spherical core of

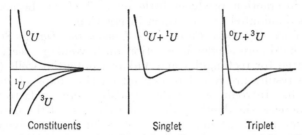

Fig. 9.5 The addition of a spin-independent short-range repulsion ^0U to the spin-dependent attractive potentials ^1U (singlet) or ^3U (triplet) can result in a singlet potential $^0U + {}^1U$ with an effective hard-core repulsion, and a triplet potential $^0U + {}^3U$ with a negligible hard-core repulsion. [*After Jastrow* (J8).]

radius r_0, surrounded by a standard exponential well with Serber exchange for the singlet interaction. Thus

$$\text{singlet: } U(r) = +\infty \qquad r < r_0 = 0.6 \times 10^{-13} \text{ cm}$$
$$U(r) = -{}^1U_0 e^{-(r-r_0)/({}^1b)}[\tfrac{1}{2}(1 + P_H)] \qquad r > r_0 \qquad (9.2)$$

For the triplet interaction, the hard core is assumed to be negligible. Good semiquantitative agreement with the high-energy n-p and p-p scattering is obtained using a triplet potential containing exchange in both a central and tensor part, and given by

$$\text{triplet: } U(r) = -{}^3U_0 e^{-r/({}^3b)}[\tfrac{1}{2}(1 + P_H) + (0.3 + 0.7P_H)1.84S_{12}] \qquad (9.3)$$

where $^1U_0$ = 375-Mev singlet depth
$^3U_0$ = 69-Mev triplet depth
r_0 = 0.60 × 10^{-13} cm hard-core radius
^1b = 0.40 × 10^{-13} cm singlet exponential range
^3b = 0.75 × 10^{-13} cm triplet exponential range

Qualitative Effects of the Repulsive Core on High-energy p-p Scattering. At sufficiently high energies, the singlet S-wave phase shift is negative because of the singlet repulsive core. States of higher angular momentum still experience an attractive force due to the outer part of the potential well. In this energy region interference between the ^1S and ^1D scattered amplitudes tends to suppress the forward scattering and to increase the scattering at 90°. In addition, the tensor scattering of the

^3P interaction builds up the intensity in the vicinity of 55°. Thus, qualitatively, the angular distribution of p-p scattering takes on the flat character which is seen experimentally, and also the absolute cross sections are of the order of 4 millibarns/steradian, as observed. Although the repulsive-core model best predicts the observed single-scattering cross sections, it does not appear possible at present to match the experiments on p-p *double scattering* with this same potential (O8).

Qualitative Effects on the Repulsive Core on High-energy n-p Scattering. In contrast with p-p scattering, the n-p scattering involves both ^3S and ^1S states, and the triplet scattering enjoys three times the statistical weight of singlet scattering. Thus the addition of the repulsive core to the singlet interaction produces little over-all effect, because the n-p scattering is dominated by the triplet interaction.

Effects of the Repulsive Core on the Low-energy Data. Some of the effects of a hard-core singlet interaction on low-energy scattering have been calculated for rectangular and Yukawa potential wells (H73). In general, the results are found to depend on the shape of the assumed potential well. Introduction of the repulsive core tends to reduce the range and increase the depth of the attractive part of the potential well. There is as yet no indication that parameters for the repulsive-core model cannot eventually be found which will simultaneously satisfy the low-energy and high-energy data. This work remains for the future.

CHAPTER 11

Models of Nuclei

The complex interrelationships between nucleons when they aggregate to form medium and heavy nuclei will continue to defy precise analysis for a long time to come. In the absence of an exact theory, a number of nuclear models have been developed. These utilize different sets of simplifying assumptions. Each model is capable of explaining only a portion of our experimental knowledge about nuclei.

If it is assumed that in the ground level and in the lowest excited levels of a nucleus the nucleons have very little interaction, then the *independent-particle models* emerge. We shall discuss the shell model as an example from the broad group of independent-particle models.

The extreme opposite view is that of very strong interaction between all the nucleons in a nucleus. As representatives of the *strong-interaction models*, some aspects of the liquid-drop model and of the statistical model will be examined.

1. *Summary of Experimental Evidence Which Should Be Represented by the Model*

The main experimental characteristics of nuclei, which we should like to see described by as few models as possible, may be summarized briefly, as a base line for the appraisal of presently available models.

1. Nuclear *angular momenta* I of ground levels

> For even-Z even-N nuclides, $I = 0$.
> For odd-Z odd-N nuclides, $I = 1, 2, 3, \ldots$
> For odd-A nuclides, $I = \frac{1}{2}, \frac{3}{2}, \ldots$
> Mirror nuclei have equal I.
> Extremes of triads have equal I.

2. *Magnetic dipole moments* μ, and their approximate two-valued relationship with I, as summarized in Schmidt diagrams (Chap. 4, Figs. 4.1 and 4.2)

3. *Electric quadrupole moments* Q, and their systematic empirical variation with Z or N (Chap. 4, Fig. 5.4)

4. Existence of *isomers*, and their statistical concentration in the

regions of N or $Z = 40$ to 50 and 70 to 80 (the so-called "islands of isomerism," Chap. 6, Fig. 6.1)

5. Relative *parity* of nuclear levels, as seen in β decay and γ decay (Chap. 6, Table 3.2)

6. *Discontinuities of nuclear binding energy* and of neutron or proton separation energy, as seen for particular values of N or Z, especially 50, 82, and 126 (Chap. 9, Figs. 3.2 and 4.3)

7. *Frequency of stable isotones and isotopes*, especially the statistical concentration for particular values of N and Z (Chap. 8, Fig. 3.1)

8. *Pairing energy* for identical nucleons, as seen in the occurrence of stable, nonadjacent, isobars (Chap. 8, Fig. 3.3)

9. Substantially *constant density* of nuclei, with radius $R \propto A^{\frac{1}{3}}$ (Chap. 2)

10. Systematic dependence of the *neutron excess* $(N - Z)$ on $A^{\frac{2}{3}}$ for stable nuclides (Chap. 8, Fig. 3.4)

11. Approximate constancy of the *binding energy per nucleon* B/A, as well as its small but definite systematic trends with A (Chap. 9, Fig. 3.1)

12. *Mass differences in families of isobars* and the energies of cascade β transitions (Chap. 8, Figs. 3.2 and 3.3)

13. *Systematic variation of α decay energies* with N and Z (Chap. 2, Fig. 6.2)

14. *Fission* by thermal neutrons of U^{235} and other odd-N nuclides (Chap. 11, Sec. 3)

15. *Finite upper bound on Z and N* of heavy nuclides produced in reactions and the nonexistence in nature of nuclides heavier than U^{238}

16. Wide spacing of low-lying *excited levels in nuclei*, in contrast with the close spacing of highly excited levels (Chap. 11, Fig. 4.1)

17. Existence of resonance-capture reactions, such as (n,γ). Constancy of the fast-neutron-capture cross section for $A > 100$, except for its anomalously small value for the isotones in which $N = 50, 82,$ or 126 (Chap. 8, Fig. 2.2)

Experimental items 1 through 8 are well represented by the independent-particle shell model. The liquid-drop model is built to account for items 9 through 15. Item 16 forms the main basis of the statistical model. Item 17 finds its best representation in the strong-interaction models (liquid-drop and statistical) but must draw on the independent-particle model also, in order to represent the effects of $N = 50, 82,$ and 126.

2. *The Nuclear Shell Model*

In 1932, Chadwick's discovery of the neutron opened the way for the development of models of nuclear structure. Drawing heavily upon analogies with the extranuclear electronic structure of atoms, Bartlett, Guggenheimer, Elsasser, and others developed early individual-particle models (F54) involving closed shells of $2(2l + 1)$ neutrons or protons, where l is the angular-momentum quantum number of the nucleons.

The order of filling of shells having various l values was expected to differ from that found in the electronic structure, because of the different type of forces involved.   With LS coupling, the theoretical order of levels for simple potential shapes was able to account for the then known nuclear discontinuities, or "magic numbers," only as far as O^{16}, where the first p shell closes.   Because of the small absolute values of the nucleon magnetic moments, jj coupling was not expected theoretically.

From roughly 1936 until 1948 interest in nuclear models turned away from individual-particle models and centered around the development of Bohr's idea of a liquid-drop nucleus and around Wigner's (W47) uniform-model, supermultiplet, and isobaric-spin concepts.

Attention was drawn forcefully by Maria Mayer in 1948 to the accumulation of experimental evidence for closed shells in nuclei at the higher magic numbers, especially 50, 82, and 126 identical nucleons (M23).   The liquid-drop model and the uniform model are inherently incapable of predicting such discontinuities.   Attention swung sharply back to the individual-particle models.   Important contributions were promptly made by Feenberg, Hammack, Nordheim (F20, F21, N22, F18), and many others.

It remained for Mrs. Mayer (M24) herself, and independently for Haxel, Jensen, and Suess (H24), to take the important step of introducing jj coupling.   By assuming strong spin-orbit forces for individual nucleons, a sequence of independent-particle states emerges which matches the experimentally known "magic numbers."   The justification for introducing a strong spin-orbit interaction and its jj-coupling scheme lies only in its success in matching experimental facts, which has been noteworthy.   No adequate theoretical basis for jj coupling in nuclei has been found, although the introduction of tensor forces appears to hold promise (K9) for a possible future explanation.

   a. Assumptions in the Independent-particle Model.   In contrast with the situation with atoms, the nucleus contains no massive central body which can act as a force center.   This deficiency is circumvented by the bold assumption that each nucleon experiences a central attractive force which can be ascribed to the average effect of all the other $(A - 1)$ nucleons in the nucleus.   On this assumption, each nucleon behaves as though it were moving independently in a central field, which is describable as a short-range potential well.   Secondly, this potential is assumed to be the same for all values of l.

   The Weak-interaction Paradox for Low-lying States.   In the assumed central potential, each nucleon is imagined to be capable of describing an orbit of well-defined energy and angular momentum, in a manner analogous to the behavior of atomic electrons.   This condition implies that each nucleon can describe at least several revolutions without being disturbed or scattered in collisions with other nucleons.   The assumed "mean free path" between collisions therefore has to be at least several times the nuclear radius.   In such a model, the interaction between individual nucleons has to be weak.   This assumption seems to be in clear conflict with the well-demonstrated strong interaction between nucleons, as seen in scattering experiments, and in nuclear reactions generally. To an incident nucleon, the struck nucleus is not "transparent," as would be implied by a mean free path exceeding the nuclear radius, but on the contrary is nearly opaque. All incident particles are scattered or captured. The mean free path for an *incident* nucleon is therefore short, compared with the nuclear radius.

Weisskopf (W24) has drawn attention to the Pauli exclusion principle as a means of resolving the weak-interaction paradox. Amongst individual nucleons within a nucleus in its ground level, or a level having small excitation energy, the expected strong interaction may be present but unable to manifest itself, because all the quantum states into which the nucleon might be scattered are already occupied. Contrariwise, an incident nucleon can be scattered or captured into a previously unoccupied, and highly excited, quantum state. Thus it is possible to accept the model of weak interaction between the constituent nucleons within a nucleus at low excitation energies, without denying the inherently strong character of the interaction between free nucleons.

b. The Sequence of Nucleon States for the Ground Levels of Successive Isotopes and Isotones. The value of the independent-particle model lies mainly in its ability to give a nearly correct energy sequence for nucleon states having different values of l. It turns out that the order of the nucleon states is quite insensitive to the detailed shape of the assumed potential, so long as the potential decreases rapidly outside the nuclear radius.

A simple rectangular well having a great depth $-U_0$ and a radius about equal to the nuclear radius R is a sufficiently good representation of such a short-range force. The wave functions for independent particles within such a well obey the radial wave equation [Chap. 2, Eq. (5.75)] for $r < R$ and are zero at the well boundary $r = R$, as well as outside the well $r > R$. The allowed energy states then correspond to the sequence of solutions of the radial wave equation (Bessel functions) which have zero values at $r = R$.

Each state with orbital angular momentum l is degenerate (same energy) with respect to m_l, since m does not occur in the radial wave equation. Therefore, in each state of a given l, there can be $(2l + 1)$ identical nucleons when spin is neglected or $2(2l + 1)$ identical nucleons if the energy is independent of spin orientation. The order of energy states for the deep rectangular well turns out to be

Order of states	$1s$	$1p$	$1d$	$2s$	$1f$	$2p$	$1g$
Occupation number $2(2l + 1)$	2	6	10	2	14	6	18
Aggregate number of nucleons $\Sigma 2(2l + 1)$	2	8	18	20	34	40	58

where the letter gives the l value and the integer prefix gives the radial quantum number, as defined in Chap. 4. This sequence fails to give any indication of a closed shell at 50 nucleons and fails even more clearly for still larger nucleon numbers.

Sequence of States in the Spin-orbit-coupling Model. Additional assumptions are needed if the sequence of energy states is to match the empirically known "magic numbers" 50, 82, and 126. It was noted independently by Mayer and by Haxel, Jensen, and Suess that this match could be obtained by postulating strong spin-orbit coupling for nucleons. Then, for the same l value, the energy of the $j = l + \frac{1}{2}$ state may be quite different from the energy of the $j = l - \frac{1}{2}$ state. As presently visualized, the "shell model," or "spin-orbit-coupling model," or "jj-coupling model," involves the following assumptions (M25, M26), in addition to those which are inherent in every independent-particle model:

1. For the same value of the orbital angular momentum l, the $j = l + \frac{1}{2}$ state ("parallel" orbit and spin) is deeper lying, or more tightly bound, than the $j = l - \frac{1}{2}$ state.

2. The energy separation between $j = l + \frac{1}{2}$ and $j = l - \frac{1}{2}$ increases with increasing values of l, being then approximately proportional to $(2l + 1)/A^{\frac{1}{3}}$.

3. An even number of identical nucleons having the same l and j will always couple to give even parity, zero total angular momentum, and zero magnetic moment.

4. An odd number of identical nucleons having the same l and j will always couple to give odd parity if l is odd and even parity if l is even, a total angular momentum j, and a magnetic moment equal to that of a single nucleon in the state j [Chap. 4, Eqs. (4.9) and (4.10)].

5. There is an additional binding energy, or *pairing energy*, δ associated with double occupancy of any state l, j, by two identical nucleons. In any nucleus, the pairing energy is greatest for states of largest j. This extra binding energy δ for an even nucleon compared with an odd nucleon is approximately proportional to $(2j + 1)/A$.

The primary purpose of assumptions 1 and 2 is to match the higher magic numbers 50, 82, and 126. Assumptions 3, 4, and 5 are refinements which provide agreement with the experimentally known values of parity, nuclear angular momentum I, and magnetic dipole moment μ, for the ground levels of nuclei as well as for many low-lying excited levels.

Figure 2.1 illustrates the succession of states in a very deep rectangular potential well and the general nature of their splitting by the spin-orbit coupling, according to assumptions 1 and 2. The level order is independent of the depth and radius of the well, as long as it is deep ($U_0 \sim 30$ Mev) and narrow ($b \sim R$). The same level sequence is given by many other short-range potentials, such as a three-dimensional harmonic oscillator potential $U = -U_0 + ar^2$ (B48, H24), or hybrids of oscillator and rectangular-well potentials (M6).

In accord with the Pauli exclusion principle, each state is permitted to contain a maximum of $(2j + 1)$ identical particles, corresponding to the number of possible values of m_j (Chap. 4). The occupation numbers $(2j + 1)$ are given in Fig. 2.1 for each state and shell. Note that for any l value the total occupation of the $j = l + \frac{1}{2}$ and the $j = l - \frac{1}{2}$ levels always has the value $2(2l + 1)$, which is independent of the assumed coupling scheme.

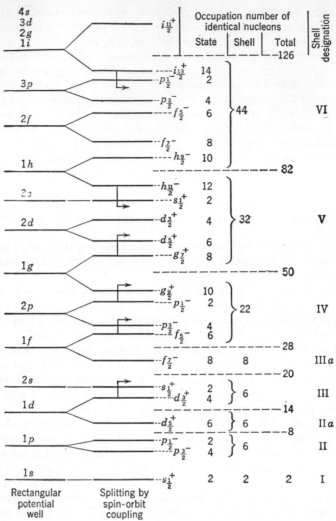

Fig. 2.1 Order of energy states (denoted by their radial and orbital quantum numbers) for identical nucleons in an independent-particle model using a deep rectangular potential well (left). Center, the empirical splitting of $j = l + \frac{1}{2}$ and $j = l - \frac{1}{2}$ states, which is attributed to spin-orbit coupling. The energies are not to scale. The exact order of the states is subject to variations, particularly with respect to the crossovers shown by bent arrows. For convenience, the parity of each state is indicated by the superscript, $(-)$ denoting odd for p, f, h states and $(+)$ denoting even parity for s, d, g, i states.

Major Closed Shells. Figure 2.1 shows that the higher magic numbers 50, 82, and 126 can be obtained from the spin-orbit- or jj-coupling hypothesis by asuming that the major shells close with a $j = l + \frac{1}{2}$ state and that the next shell begins with the corresponding $j = l - \frac{1}{2}$ state. For example, the state of the last odd proton in the $Z = 50$ shell is shown by the nuclear moments of odd-A isotopes of indium, $Z = 49$.   These properties are

$$_{49}\mathrm{In}_{64}^{113}: I = \tfrac{9}{2} \qquad \mu = +5.49$$
$$_{49}\mathrm{In}_{66}^{115}: I = \tfrac{9}{2} \qquad \mu = +5.50$$

and in accord with the Schmidt limits [Chap. 4, Eq. (4.9)] the 49th proton is in a $g_{\frac{9}{2}}$ state, which is $j = l + \tfrac{1}{2}$ with $l = 4$.   After the $Z = 50$ shell is filled, the state of the first proton in the next shell is shown by the nuclear moments of odd-A isotopes of antimony, $Z = 51$.   Here we find

$$_{51}\mathrm{Sb}_{72}^{123}: I = \tfrac{7}{2} \qquad \mu = +2.55$$

and therefore this 51st proton is in a $g_{\frac{7}{2}}$ state, which is $j = l - \tfrac{1}{2}$ with $l = 4$.

Crossovers within Major Shells.   Within each shell the exact order of the energy states is somewhat flexible.   Some adjacent levels lie very close to one another in energy, and their actual order in any given nucleus may depend upon factors which are as yet unknown.   The magnitude of the spin-orbit splitting may cause states which arise from adjacent l values in the same shell to cross over.   Several apparently frequent instances of such crossovers, or inversions of the elementary order of energy levels, are shown in Fig. 2.1 by the bent arrows.   As an example, consider again the 51st proton but in another odd-A isotope of antimony

$$_{51}\mathrm{Sb}_{70}^{121}: I = \tfrac{5}{2} \qquad \mu = 3.36$$

whose moments correspond to a $d_{\frac{5}{2}}$ state, rather than to the $g_{\frac{7}{2}}$ state shown by the 51st proton in $_{51}\mathrm{Sb}^{123}$.   In these two Sb isotopes, the shell just above 50 protons can therefore begin with either a $g_{\frac{7}{2}}$ or a $d_{\frac{5}{2}}$ proton, and the relative energy of these two states depends upon some factor other than the proton number Z, possibly the neutron number N.

Minor Shells.   Figure 2.1 shows also how minor discontinuities in nuclear properties, e.g., the possible cases at 14, 28, and 40 identical nucleons, can be accommodated as subshells in the jj-coupling model.

Pairing Energy in the Shell Model.   Assumption 5 states that the pairing energy δ is finite and increases with j.   This is physically the same pairing energy which we noted in our discussion of binding energies in Chap. 9.   The shell model provides no information on the absolute separation of nuclear energy levels nor on binding energies.   We may wonder why the pairing energy is pertinent to the shell model.

The pairing energy is invoked in the shell model in order to account for the observed nuclear moments.   Although Fig. 2.1 shows that shell V (between 51 and 82 identical nucleons) has places for 12 particles with $j = \tfrac{11}{2}$, no nuclide is known which actually has a ground-level nuclear angular momentum $I = \tfrac{11}{2}$.   The inference is that the nucleons do not always fill up the lowest states first in a shell.

As an example of the action of pairing energy, consider the nuclide

$$_{52}\mathrm{Te}_{71}^{123}: I = \tfrac{1}{2} \qquad \mu = -0.74$$

in which the values of I and μ show that the 71st neutron is in an $s_{\frac{1}{2}}$ state.

In Fig. 2.1 we may count up the available states in shell V and note that the 71st particle must be in $h_{\frac{11}{2}}$ if the states fill up in order, regardless of the presence or absence of a crossover between $s_{\frac{1}{2}}$ and $h_{\frac{11}{2}}$. The experimental values of I and μ show then that for ground levels the $h_{\frac{11}{2}}$ state always contains an even number of identical nucleons. In the case of Te^{123}, this is accomplished by drawing one neutron out of the $s_{\frac{1}{2}}$ state in order to complete the pairing in the $h_{\frac{11}{2}}$ state.

A very approximate calculation by Mayer (M26), assuming a short-range attractive potential between identical nucleons, gives an interaction energy per pair of identical nucleons which is proportional to $(2j + 1)/A$, and an interaction energy of zero for any odd nucleon. Then the pairing energy δ is approximately proportional to $(2j + 1)/A$, and the pairing of identical nucleons is energetically favored for states of large j over states of smaller j. This is in accord with the observation that for ground levels the $h_{\frac{11}{2}}$ state, if confronted with occupancy by an odd nucleon, will always rob a state of smaller j, in order to make up an even number of nucleons in $h_{\frac{11}{2}}$.

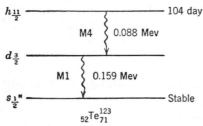

Excited Levels in the Shell Model. Some of the low-lying excited levels of odd-A nuclei correspond to occupation of higher-energy states by the odd nucleon. Figure 2.2 shows the known excited levels of Te^{123}, whose observed angular momenta and parities are consistent with occupancy by the 71st neutron of the $s_{\frac{1}{2}}$ state (ground level), the $d_{\frac{3}{2}}$ state (excited level at 0.159 Mev), and the $h_{\frac{11}{2}}$ state (104-day isomeric level). All these states are available in shell V.

Fig. 2.2 The excited levels of Te^{123} correspond to an occupancy by the odd neutron of a $d_{\frac{3}{2}}$ and an $h_{\frac{11}{2}}$ state, within the same shell V as the $s_{\frac{1}{2}}$ ground state. The asterisk denotes an assignment of l and j based on direct measurements of I and μ.

Recall also the decay scheme of $_{49}In^{111}_{62} \rightarrow {}_{48}Cd^{111}_{63}$, given in Fig. 8.5 of Chap. 6. The $g_{\frac{9}{2}}$ state for $_{49}In^{111}$ shows that in this case (and in shell IV) the proton pairing energy does not overcome the lower states. In the ground level of the decay product $_{48}Cd^{111}_{63}$, the 63d neutron occupies the $s_{\frac{1}{2}}$ state (due clearly to the effect of neutron pairing energy), and the excited states shown in Fig. 8.5 correspond to occupancy by the 63d neutron of other states ($d_{\frac{5}{2}}$ and $g_{\frac{7}{2}}$) in the same shell. In addition, two other low-lying levels are known in Cd^{111}, and the angular momentum and parity of these correspond to the $d_{\frac{3}{2}}$ and $h_{\frac{11}{2}}$ states which are also available in shell V.

Excited levels may also correspond to occupancy by the odd nucleon of states belonging to the ground-level configurations of higher shells. For example, $_{49}In^{115}$ has known excited levels (G25) for which the state of the 49th proton is $p_{\frac{1}{2}}$, $d_{\frac{5}{2}}$, $d_{\frac{3}{2}}$, and $g_{\frac{7}{2}}$. The $p_{\frac{1}{2}}$ state is available in shell IV, while the others are typical of ground-level configurations in shell V.

Domain of Success of the Shell Model. The successes of the present shell model extend through the first eight items of experimental information listed in Sec. 1 of this chapter. These are the phenomena associated with the magic numbers, or the "periodic system for nuclei," and with nuclear moments. The shell model, with strong spin-orbit coupling, gives the first satisfactory representation of the angular momentum, parity, and magnetic dipole moment of the ground levels and the low-lying excited levels of nuclei. This model also gives the best representation found so far of the "dynamic" electric and magnetic moments which account for the γ-ray transition probabilities between different levels in nuclei (Chap. 6). Besides the original literature, a number of useful reviews (F18, F19, F54) may be consulted for additional details.

Problems

1. Predict the following characteristics of the ground levels of (a) $_{12}Mg^{25}$ and (b) $_{29}Cu^{63}$: (1) state of the odd nucleon, (2) total nuclear angular momentum, (3) nuclear magnetic dipole moment, (4) sign of the nuclear electric quadrupole moment, and (5) parity of the ground level. Explain the probable cause of any important discrepancies between your predictions and the following measured values of the moments

	I	μ	Q
$_{12}Mg^{25}$	$\frac{5}{2}$	-0.96	Not reported
$_{29}Cu^{63}$	$\frac{3}{2}$	$+2.22$	-0.1

2. The observed nuclear moments of $_{83}Bi^{209}$ are: $I = \frac{9}{2}$, $\mu = +4.1$, and $Q = -0.4 \times 10^{-24}$ cm². What are the expected values on the independent-particle model? Comment on any significant discrepancies. Why would you expect Bi²⁰⁹ to have an unusually low cross section (~0.003 barn) for the capture of 1-Mev neutrons, as compared with an "average" heavy nuclide (~0.10 barn)?

3. *The Liquid-drop Model*

The liquid-drop model provides reasonable explanations for many nuclear phenomena which are inaccessible to the shell model. In the main, these phenomena are items 9 through 15 of the tabulation in Sec. 1, involving the masses and binding energy of nuclear ground levels; the energetics of β decay, α decay, and nuclear reactions; the cross sections for resonance reactions; and the energetics of nuclear fission.

The liquid-drop model is the antithesis of the independent-particle models. The interactions between nucleons are assumed to be strong instead of weak. Nuclear levels are represented as quantized states of the nuclear system as a whole and not as states of a single particle in an average field. The liquid-drop model originated in Bohr's concept of the compound nucleus in nuclear reactions. When an incident particle is captured by a target nucleus, its energy appears to be quickly shared by all the nucleons. The captured particle has a mean free path in nuclear matter which is much smaller than the nuclear radius. To account for such behavior, interactions between nucleons have to be strong, and the particles cannot behave independently, with negligible cross sections for collisions and interactions with their neighbors.

Application of the strong-interaction, liquid-drop model to the cross sections for nuclear reactions will be considered in Chap. 14. We shall devote our attention in this section mainly to those restricted aspects of the liquid-drop model which are fruitful in quantitative discussions of nuclear masses, the nuclear energy surface, and the energetics of spontaneous and induced nuclear reactions. Primarily, this involves the development and use of a modern version of Weizsäcker's (W26) so-called *semiempirical mass formula*.

a. Qualitative Basis of the Semiempirical Mass Formula. The mass M of a neutral atom whose nucleus contains Z protons and N neutrons is

$$M = ZM_H + NM_n - B \tag{3.1}$$

where the binding energy B is made up of a number of terms, each of which represents some general characteristic of nuclei, as seen in the empirical data on the binding energy of stable nuclei. Thus

$$B = B_0 + B_1 + B_2 + \cdots \tag{3.2}$$

Under a reasonable set of simplifying assumptions, we can develop a quantitative model which describes the binding energy B of the ground levels of all but the lightest nuclei, say, $A \geq 30$. The initial assumptions are:

1. The nucleus is like a droplet of *incompressible* matter, and all nuclei have the same density.

2. The distinction between the triplet (np) and singlet (np) force is ignored; forces between nucleons are considered to be *spin-independent* as well as *charge-independent*. If the coulomb force is turned off,

$$(np) = (nn) = (pp)$$

3. These nuclear forces have a *short-range* character and are effective only between nearest neighbors. Each nucleon interacts with all its nearest neighbors.

4. Additional assumptions will be introduced later to provide refinements in the model.

Volume Energy. The first approximation to B, and the largest term in the binding energy, is identified as due to the saturated exchange force. We have seen (Chap. 9) that the average binding energy per nucleon is approximately constant (± 10 per cent) in all nuclei ($A \geq 16$). Then we write

$$B_0 = a_v A \qquad \text{volume energy} \tag{3.3}$$

where the arbitrary constant a_v is to be evaluated empirically. The subscript v connotes "volume" energy. (With equal justification, what we here call volume energy is often called the "exchange energy.")

Surface Energy. Those nucleons which are visualized as being at the nuclear surface have fewer near neighbors than nucleons which are deep within the nuclear volume. We can expect a deficit of binding energy for these surface nucleons. We interpret the exchange energy term B_0 as a "volume energy" representing the binding of nucleons which are totally within the nuclear volume. Then we deduct a correction term for the nucleons which constitute the nuclear surface. The radius of the nucleus is $R = R_0 A^{\frac{1}{3}}$ under the assumption of constant density. If the range of the nuclear forces is b, we can take the effective radius of a nucleon as about $b/2$ if the nucleons are presumed to be essentially in contact with each other. Then the volume of a nucleus would be

$$\frac{4\pi}{3} R^3 = \frac{4\pi}{3} R_0^3 A = \frac{4\pi}{3} \left(\frac{b}{2}\right)^3 A \tag{3.4}$$

and the effective radius of one nucleon $b/2$ is about equal to the nuclear unit radius $R_0 \simeq 1.5 \times 10^{-13}$ cm.

The surface area of the nucleus is

$$4\pi R^2 = 4\pi R_0^2 A^{\frac{2}{3}} \tag{3.5}$$

Then the number of nucleons on the surface would be approximately

$$\frac{4\pi R_0^2 A^{\frac{2}{3}}}{\pi R_0^2} = 4A^{\frac{2}{3}} \tag{3.6}$$

and the fraction of the nucleons which are in contact with the surface is of the order of

$$\frac{4A^{\frac{2}{3}}}{A} = \frac{4}{A^{\frac{1}{3}}} \tag{3.7}$$

Thus for light nuclei nearly all the nucleons are at the surface, while for heavy nuclei about half the nucleons are at the surface and half are in the interior of the nucleus. We introduce a negative correction term B_1 representing the loss of binding energy by the nucleons at the surface

$$B_1 = -a_s A^{\frac{2}{3}} \qquad \text{surface energy} \tag{3.8}$$

where a_s is an arbitrary constant to be evaluated from empirical data. The subscript s means "surface energy." Occasionally this surface energy is referred to as "surface tension," by analogy with these two concepts in ordinary liquids. It should be remembered, however, that "surface energy" is generally a larger quantity than "surface tension" even though the two do have the same physical dimensions (M35).

Coulomb Energy. The only known long-range force in nuclei is the coulomb repulsion between protons. We have seen in Chap. 2 that in evaluating the coulomb energy for nuclei we are justified in regarding the total nuclear charge Ze as spread approximately uniformly throughout the nuclear volume. Again assuming a constant-density nuclear radius, $R_0 A^{\frac{1}{3}}$, the loss of binding energy due to the disruptive coulomb energy is

$$B_2 = -\frac{3}{5}\frac{e^2 Z^2}{R_0 A^{\frac{1}{3}}} \equiv -a_c \frac{Z^2}{A^{\frac{1}{3}}} \qquad \text{coulomb energy} \tag{3.9}$$

where a_c is to be evaluated and the subscript c designates coulomb energy

Asymmetry Energy. Another deficit in binding energy depends on the neutron excess $(N - Z)$ and is proportional to $(N - Z)^2/A$. This "asymmetry energy" is a purely quantum-mechanical effect, in contrast with the simple classical effects of surface energy and coulomb energy.

Among the lightest elements, there is a clear tendency for the number of neutrons and protons to be equal, as in $_6C^{12}, _7N^{14}, _8O^{16}$. This is properly interpreted as showing that the (np) force can dominate (nn) and (pp) forces. But it is the triplet (np) force which is involved in the $N = Z$ relationship for the lightest nuclides. In the liquid-drop model for heavier nuclei we are neglecting the difference between the (np) triplet and the (np) singlet.

Heavy nuclei always contain appreciably more neutrons than protons. If we were to attempt to build a heavy nucleus out of equal numbers of protons and neutrons we should find it violently unstable, because the large disruptive coulomb energy could not be overcome by the available (np), (nn), and (pp) attractive forces. It is necessary to introduce a neutron excess $(N - Z)$ to provide enough total attractive force to dominate adequately the coulomb repulsion. At the same time one must not add too many neutrons or instability is again achieved.

For a medium or heavyweight nucleus, of predetermined mass number A, the approximate mass, based only on Eqs. (3.1) to (3.9),

$$M = ZM_H + NM_n - B = ZM_H + (A - Z)M_n - B$$

$$= AM_n - Z(M_n - M_H) - a_vA + a_sA^{\frac{2}{3}} + a_c\frac{Z^2}{A^{\frac{1}{3}}} + \cdots \quad (3.10)$$

has only two terms which depend on Z. These terms are of opposite sign, so that by differentiation a value of Z can be found for which M is a minimum. If this equation really represented all the dominant effects, then we would have to expect ridiculously small values of Z. For example, for $A = 125$, Eq. (3.10) gives a minimum M, hence greatest stability for $Z = 3$. Clearly, some important term is still missing, and its sign must be such as to increase Z for a given A.

The physical phenomena which have been neglected so far are the quantization of the energy states of the individual nucleons in the nucleus and the application of the Pauli exclusion principle. If we put Z protons into a nucleus, these will occupy the lowest Z energy states. If we add an equal number of neutrons $N = Z$, these neutrons will occupy the same group of lowest-energy states. If we now add one or more excess neutrons, these $(N - Z)$ neutrons must go into previously unoccupied quantum states. In general, these will be *states of larger kinetic energy* (KE) *and smaller potential energy* (PE) *than those already occupied.* The binding energy of each nucleon is the difference (PE − KE) between its potential and kinetic energies. Hence these $(N - Z)$ excess neutrons will have less average binding energy than the first $2Z$ nucleons which occupy the deepest-lying energy levels. If there should happen to be more protons than neutrons, the $(Z - N)$ excess protons would have to go into higher-energy states, in a completely similar way.   The reasoning is then independent of the sign of $(N - Z)$.

The form $(N - Z)^2/A$ of the asymmetry-energy term can be "derived" in a variety of ways, depending on what assumptions one is willing to make (W26, F41, B48, W48).   In every case the asymmetry term expresses the physical fact that, in a quantized system of neutrons and protons, any "excess" nucleons are pushed up to levels which they occupy alone.   They are thus deprived of the fullness of binding which was implied in Eq. (3.3).

The simplest approach to the form of the asymmetry energy is probably the following: If the $|N - Z|$ excess nucleons are regarded as producing a deficit of binding energy because they are "out of reach" of the other nucleons (quantically), the fraction of the nuclear volume so affected is $|N - Z|/A$, and the total deficit is proportional to the product of these, or

$$B_3 = -a_u \frac{(N - Z)^2}{A} = -a_a \frac{(A - 2Z)^2}{A} \qquad (3.11)$$

where the asymmetry coefficient a_a is to be evaluated empirically.

Wigner's "uniform model" of nuclei (W47, W48), from which emerges a reasonably satisfactory account of the mass difference of isobars in the domain $16 \leq A \leq 60$ (I4, F71, W17), goes over smoothly for larger A (W48) into the semiempirical mass formula of the liquid-drop model. In Wigner's theory, the isobaric-spin quantum number T, when projected onto the ζ axis in a hypothetical isobaric-spin space, has the value $T_\zeta = \frac{1}{2}(N - Z)$, or one-half the neutron excess.   For large A, the difference between the total potential energy and kinetic energy contains the term T_ζ^2/A, which again gives an asymmetry energy proportional to $(N - Z)^2/A$.

In heavy nuclei, the asymmetry energy will be found later (Table 3.2) to be of the order of one-quarter as large as the coulomb energy.   The presence of this "unbinding," or disruptive, energy term, containing $(N - Z)^2$, greatly favors proton numbers Z which are comparable with N.

From a purely empirical point of view, it can be shown readily that the systematic dependence of $(N - Z)$ on A, as shown in Fig. 3.4 of Chap. 8, can only be had if in Eq. (3.11) the coefficient a_a is positive and if the exponent in the numerator is exactly 2.   Also empirically, the parabolic relationship between Z and the masses M_Z of a family of isobars, as shown in Figs. 3.2 and 3.3 of Chap. 8, only emerges if the exponent of $(N - Z)$ in Eq. (3.11) is exactly 2.

Pairing Energy.   All our energy terms thus far have involved a smooth variation of the total binding energy every time Z or N changes. This is contrary to two sets of empirical facts: first, the finite pairing energy δ between odd-A and even-A nuclei and, second, the anomalously large binding energy of nuclei which contain a "magic number" of neutrons or protons.   These facts fail to appear in the liquid-drop model because we have omitted the intrinsic spin of the nucleons and have based the development, up to now, on spin-independent forces. To correct for this omission, we add the pairing energy δ as another correction term B_4 for the total binding energy. Conventionally, the pairing-energy correction is usually taken as zero for odd-A nuclides (F38, B96, K35). Then for even-A nuclides

$$B_4 = \begin{cases} +\delta \text{ for even-}Z \text{ even-}N \\ -\delta \text{ for odd-}Z \text{ odd-}N \end{cases} \qquad (3.12)$$

When δ is regarded as a correction to the mass rather than to the binding energy, the sign of δ is given by

$$\begin{aligned} \delta &= 0 & \text{for odd-}A \\ &-\delta & \text{for even-}Z \text{ even-}N \\ &+\delta & \text{for odd-}Z \text{ odd-}N \end{aligned} \qquad (3.13)$$

From the shell model, the pairing energy δ appears to be roughly proportional to $(2j + 1)/A$. As no information on angular momenta j is implied in the liquid-drop model, the average pairing energy should be expressed as some smooth function of A. Fermi's (F41) empirical value

$$\delta \simeq a_p \frac{1}{A^{\frac{3}{4}}} \qquad (3.14)$$

where a_p is an approximately constant empirical coefficient, has been used widely and is in consonance with the general trend of increasing j with increasing A in the approximate expression $(2j + 1)/A$. Equation (3.14) is only a rough representation of δ, as will be seen later in Fig. 3.4.

In a refined treatment of the pairing energy, Kohman (K35) has given quantitative recognition to slight differences between those odd-A nuclides which have odd-Z and those which have odd-N. In a given heavy odd-A nucleus the $(N - Z)$ excess causes an unpaired neutron to lie in a higher state than does an unpaired proton. This leads to a slight difference ϵ between the pairing energy for neutrons and for protons, which Kohman evaluates empirically by replacing $\delta = 0$ for odd-A nuclides by $\delta = +\epsilon/2$ for odd-Z even-N nuclides, and by $\delta = -\epsilon/2$ for even-Z odd-N nuclides. In the present discussion we shall omit this interesting (C46) refinement.

Closed Shells. The liquid-drop model takes no cognizance of shell structure. Therefore the extra binding energy (~ 1 to 2 Mev) of nuclei which contain fully closed shells of neutrons or protons is not represented in the semiempirical mass equation. For those who desire it, a "coefficient of magicity" could be added as a final correction term B_5, to be used only when N or $Z = 20, 28, 40, 50, 82,$ or 126 (see Table 3.4). More commonly, one simply notes that these nuclides will have an abnormally small mass when compared with their isobars.

b. Empirical Evaluation of the Coulomb and Asymmetry Coefficients. Assembling the results of the previous paragraphs, we have for the *semiempirical mass formula* of the liquid-drop model

$$M(Z,A) = ZM_H + (A - Z)M_n - B$$
$$= ZM_H + (A - Z)M_n - a_v A + a_s A^{\frac{2}{3}} + a_c \frac{Z^2}{A^{\frac{1}{3}}}$$
$$+ a_a \frac{(A - 2Z)^2}{A} \pm \delta \quad (3.15)$$

where δ is defined by Eq. (3.13) or (3.32).

The five empirical coefficients are to be evaluated by comparison of Eq. (3.15) with data on the masses of stable nuclides and the energetics of nuclear reactions. In principle, the five constants, determined from five masses or reactions, will then serve to predict hundreds of other masses and reactions. In practice, Eq. (3.15) gives an extremely good *average* representation of nuclear energetics over a wide range of A.

The Coulomb Energy of Nuclei. The nuclear unit radius R_0, as derived from those types of experimental evidence which involve coulomb effects, has been discussed in detail in Chap. 2. The unit radius which is usually chosen as appropriate to the semiempirical mass formula is the coulomb-energy unit radius, Eq. (2.14) of Chap. 2, which is

$$R_0 = (1.45 \pm 0.05) \times 10^{-13} \text{ cm} \qquad 10 < A < 240 \quad (3.16)$$

Then the coulomb coefficient a_c in Eq. (3.9) becomes

$$a_c = \frac{3}{5} \frac{(e^2/m_0 c^2)}{R_0} m_0 c^2 = \frac{3}{5} \frac{2.82 \times 10^{-13} \text{ cm}}{1.45 \times 10^{-13} \text{ cm}} 0.51 \text{ Mev}$$
$$= (0.595 \pm 0.02) \text{ Mev} = (0.64 \pm 0.02) \times 10^{-3} \text{ amu} \quad (3.17)$$

The Neutron Excess in Stable Odd-A Nuclides. The asymmetry-energy term is evaluated by adjusting its coefficient a_a so that Eq. (3.15) will predict stability against β decay for the naturally occurring stable nuclides.

For any odd-A, the correction for pairing energy δ is taken as zero. Then Eq. (3.15) becomes an analytical relationship between the masses M and the nuclear charge Z of any group of odd-A isobars. Equation (3.15) is quadratic in Z; hence for each fixed value of A there is some particular value of Z for which M is minimum. The Z value which corresponds to minimum mass M is called the *nuclear charge of the most stable isobar*, denoted Z_0. By setting

$$\left(\frac{\partial M}{\partial Z}\right)_{A \text{ const}} = 0 \quad (3.18)$$

Eq. (3.15) gives the following relationship, for odd-A,

$$2a_c \frac{Z_0}{A^{\frac{1}{3}}} - 4a_a \frac{(A - 2Z_0)}{A} = M_n - M_H \quad (3.19)$$

On rearrangement, this becomes

$$\frac{a_a}{a_c} = \frac{1}{2}\left(\frac{Z_0 A^{\frac{2}{3}}}{A - 2Z_0}\right) - \left(\frac{A}{A - 2Z_0}\right)\frac{(M_n - M_H)}{4a_c} \quad (3.20)$$

In actual nuclei Z is an integer, but the charge Z_0 of the "most stable isobar" was obtained by minimizing M; hence Z_0 is generally some hypothetical noninteger charge. The atomic number Z of the actual stable nuclide of odd mass number A is the integer which is nearest to Z_0. Therefore Z must lie within the bandwidth $Z_0 \pm 0.5$. In Eq. (3.20) a mean value of a_a can be obtained by averaging the (Z_0, A) functions over a number of stable nuclides.

In evaluating Eq. (3.20) we find that the first term, $Z_0 A^{\frac{2}{3}}/2(A - 2Z_0)$, is predominant. The second term acts as a correction of about 5 per cent for heavy nuclides to 10 per cent for light nuclides. Therefore the value of the *ratio* a_a/a_c is substantially independent of the value of a_c chosen for the correction term. Using $a_c = 0.595$ Mev from Eq. (3.17), the dimensionless numerical coefficient of $A/(A - 2Z_0)$ is

$$\frac{(M_n - M_H)}{4a_c} = \frac{0.78 \text{ Mev}}{4 \times 0.595 \text{ Mev}} = 0.33$$

Table 3.1 shows a representative calculation of an average value of a_a/a_c. Note how the individual values vary more or less randomly from the average value. This is due in part to variations in $Z - Z_0$ and in

TABLE 3.1. EVALUATION OF THE ASYMMETRY-ENERGY COEFFICIENT a_a, FROM Z AND A OF STABLE ODD-A NUCLIDES, THROUGH EQ. (3.20)

Z	A	$A - 2Z$	$\dfrac{ZA^{\frac{2}{3}}}{A - 2Z}$	$\dfrac{A}{A - 2Z}$	$\dfrac{a_a}{a_c}$
33 As	75	9	65.2	8.3	29.9
35 Br	79	9	71.6	8.8	32.9
35 Br	81	11	59.5	7.4	27.4
41 Nb	93	11	76.5	8.5	35.4
45 Rh	103	13	76.3	7.9	35.5
53 I	127	21	63.8	6.1	29.9
55 Cs	133	23	62.3	5.8	29.3
65 Tb	159	29	65.9	5.5	31.1
67 Ho	165	31	65.1	5.3	30.8
69 Tm	169	31	68.1	5.5	32.3
73 Ta	181	35	66.7	5.2	31.7
77 Ir	191	37	69.0	5.2	32.8
77 Ir	193	39	65.9	4.9	31.3
79 Au	197	39	68.7	5.1	32.7
83 Bi	209	43	68.0	4.9	32.4
			Avg. = 67.5		Avg. = 31.7

part to true nuclear effects. The value $a_a/a_c \simeq 32$ can be used with Eq. (3.20) for the determination of Z_0 for any A. Then calculations of the type shown in Table 3.1 can be repeated, using Z_0 instead of Z. When this is done (F17), the average value of a_a/a_c remains essentially unchanged, and the fluctuations in a_a/a_c are reduced but not eliminated. The important physical fact is that the "local values" of a_a/a_c for various values of A do possess true variations of the order of 2 to 5 per cent from the average value.

We conclude that the ratio of the asymmetry-energy coefficient a_a to the coulomb-energy coefficient a_c is given on the average by

$$\frac{a_a}{a_c} = 32 \pm 1 \tag{3.21}$$

Then if $a_c = (0.595 \pm 0.02)$ Mev, we have

$$\begin{aligned} a_a &= (19.0 \pm 0.9) \text{ Mev} \\ &= (20.4 \pm 0.9) \times 10^{-3} \text{ amu} \end{aligned} \tag{3.22}$$

Two relationships which have general utility may be obtained by rearrangement of Eq. (3.19) and substitution of the empirical values of a_a and a_c. The first is a general expression for Z_0, the nuclear charge of the most stable isobar having odd mass number A, which reads

$$Z_0 = \frac{A}{2} \left[\frac{1 + (M_n - M_H)/4a_a}{1 + (a_c/4a_a)A^{\frac{2}{3}}} \right] \tag{3.23}$$

$$Z_0 = \frac{A}{1.98 + 0.0155A^{\frac{2}{3}}} \tag{3.24}$$

This equation is an analytical refinement of the rough rule $A \simeq 2Z$. The second generalization is an analytical expression for the neutron excess $N - Z_0 = A - 2Z_0$, which is

$$A - 2Z_0 = A \left[\frac{(a_c/4a_a)A^{\frac{2}{3}} - (M_n - M_H)/4a_a}{1 + (a_c/4a_a)A^{\frac{2}{3}}} \right] \tag{3.25}$$

$$A - 2Z_0 = A \left(\frac{0.0078A^{\frac{2}{3}} - 0.0103}{1 + 0.0078A^{\frac{2}{3}}} \right)$$

$$= 0.0078A^{\frac{2}{3}} \left(\frac{1 - 1.32/A^{\frac{2}{3}}}{1 + 0.0078A^{\frac{2}{3}}} \right) \tag{3.26}$$

The terms containing $A^{\frac{2}{3}}$ are both small, and their variations with A tend to cancel, so that over the mass range $60 < A < 210$, a good approximation (± 4 per cent) is

$$A - 2Z_0 \simeq 0.0060A^{\frac{4}{3}} \tag{3.27}$$

Equation (3.27) agrees in form and magnitude with the empirical variation of the neutron excess $N - Z$ with $A^{\frac{4}{3}}$, as was seen in Fig. 3.4 of Chap. 8.

c. **Equation of the Mass Parabolas for Constant A.** The parabolic relationship between isobaric mass $M(Z,A)$ and atomic number Z is contained in the semiempirical mass formula of Eq. (3.15). In order to simplify the nomenclature, we rewrite Eq. (3.15) as

$$M(Z,A) = Z(M_H - M_n) + A(M_n - a_v) + a_s A^{\frac{2}{3}} + a_c \frac{Z^2}{A^{\frac{1}{3}}} + a_a A$$

$$- a_a 4Z + a_a \frac{4Z^2}{A} \pm \varepsilon$$

$$\equiv \alpha A + \beta Z + \gamma Z^2 \pm \delta \tag{3.28}$$

where $\alpha \equiv M_n - \left(a_v - a_a - \dfrac{a_s}{A^{\frac{1}{3}}} \right)$ (3.29)

$\beta \equiv -4a_a - (M_n - M_H)$ (3.30)

$\gamma \equiv \left(\dfrac{4a_a}{A} + \dfrac{a_c}{A^{\frac{1}{3}}} \right) = \dfrac{4a_a}{A}\left(1 + \dfrac{A^{\frac{2}{3}}}{4a_a/a_c} \right)$ (3.31)

$$\pm \delta \equiv \text{pairing energy} = \begin{cases} +\delta \text{ for odd-}Z \text{ odd-}N:\text{even-}A \\ 0 \text{ for odd-}Z \text{ even-}N:\text{odd-}A \\ 0 \text{ for even-}Z \text{ odd-}N:\text{odd-}A \\ -\delta \text{ for even-}Z \text{ even-}N:\text{even-}A \end{cases}$$ (3.32)

For constant A, Eq. (3.28) is the equation of a parabola.   The coefficients α, β, γ have dimensions of energy (or of mass).   We note that β is independent of A, α is nearly independent of A, and γ varies approximately inversely with A.   The coefficients for surface energy a_s and volume energy a_v are contained only in α.   These are accessible to empirical evaluation, then, only when A varies, as in α decay systematics, nuclear reactions such as (α,p) or (γ,n) or fission, or a sequence of exact atomic-mass values.   The coefficients a_c and a_a/a_c have been evaluated, on the average, so we can at once write the *average values* of β and γ, which are

$$\begin{aligned} \beta_{av} &= -[4a_a + (M_n - M_H)] \\ &= -[4(19.0 \pm 0.9) + 0.78] \\ &= -(77 \pm 4) \text{ Mev} \qquad A \geq 60 \end{aligned}$$ (3.33)

We can expect local variations of at least 5 per cent about this mean value. Note that 99 per cent of β comes from the asymmetry term $4a_a$.   Like a_a, β tends to be larger than average for small values of A, say, $A < 60$. The average value of γ is

$$\begin{aligned} \gamma_{av} &= \frac{4a_a}{A}\left(1 + \frac{A^{\frac{2}{3}}}{4a_a/a_c} \right) \\ &= \frac{76 \pm 4}{A}\left(1 + \frac{A^{\frac{2}{3}}}{128} \right) \text{ Mev} \qquad A \geq 60 \end{aligned}$$ (3.34)

with about 5 per cent fluctuations expected in local values.

The coefficients α and δ could be evaluated here if accurate mass data were available for a number of middleweight and heavy elements.   In the absence of such data, we can turn our attention to differential forms of Eq. (3.28).   Then local values of β, γ, and δ can be obtained by comparison with the energetics of nuclear reactions in which A does not change, e.g., in (p,n), (n,p), $(d,2n)$ reactions, and in β decay.

Local Values of the Energy Coefficients.   In the simplified notation of Eq. (3.28) the charge Z_0 of the most stable isobar is

$$\left(\frac{\partial M}{\partial Z} \right)_{A \text{ const}} = \beta + 2\gamma Z_0 = 0$$ (3.35)

or $Z_0 = \dfrac{-\beta}{2\gamma}$ (3.36)

Equation (3.36) is the algebraic equivalent of Eq. (3.23). In the average

$$2\gamma_{av}Z_0 = -\beta_{av} = 77 \text{ Mev} = \text{constant for all } A \qquad (3.37)$$

For odd-A (hence $\delta = 0$), the mass $M(Z_0, A)$ of the hypothetical "most stable isobar" is given by Eq. (3.28), with $\beta = -2\gamma Z_0$, and is

$$\begin{aligned} M(Z_0, A) &= \alpha A - 2\gamma Z_0 Z_0 + \gamma Z_0^2 \\ &= \alpha A - \gamma Z_0^2 \qquad \text{odd-}A \end{aligned} \qquad (3.38)$$

On the same basis, the mass $M(Z, A)$ of a real nuclide, with an integer value of Z, is given by Eq. (3.28). Then αA can be eliminated between Eqs. (3.28) and (3.38), giving

$$\begin{aligned} M(Z, A) - M(Z_0, A) &= \beta Z + \gamma Z^2 + \gamma Z_0^2 \\ &= -2\gamma Z_0 Z + \gamma Z^2 + \gamma Z_0^2 \\ &= \gamma (Z - Z_0)^2 \qquad \text{odd-}A \end{aligned} \qquad (3.39)$$

Equation (3.39) is the parabolic mass relationship for odd-A isobars, with vertex at Z_0, $M(Z_0, A)$, as shown in Fig. 3.1.

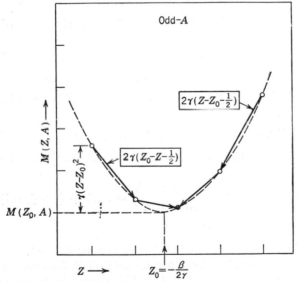

Fig. 3.1 The parabolic relationship between the masses $M(Z, A)$ of odd-A isobars, Eqs. (3.39) and (3.42). The two possible values of the β disintegration energy Q_β are shown in boxes, where Z is the atomic number of the initial nuclide.

 Transitions between Odd-A Isobars. Reactions in which $Z \to (Z + 1)$, at constant A, such as (p,n), $(d,2n)$, and β^- decay, will involve an energy release which for β^- decay is given by

$$\begin{aligned} Q_{\beta^-} &\equiv M(Z, A) - M(Z + 1, A) = \gamma[(Z - Z_0)^2 - (Z + 1 - Z_0)^2] \\ &= 2\gamma(Z_0 - Z - \tfrac{1}{2}) \qquad \text{for odd-}A \end{aligned} \qquad (3.40)$$

In a similar way, the energy release for all $Z \to (Z - 1)$ reactions, at constant A, such as (n,p), β^+ decay, and electron-capture transitions, is related to that for β^+ decay.

$$Q_{\beta^+} \equiv M(Z,A) - M(Z - 1, A) = \gamma[(Z - Z_0)^2 - (Z - 1 - Z_0)^2]$$
$$= 2\gamma(Z - Z_0 - \tfrac{1}{2}) \qquad \text{for odd-}A \qquad (3.41)$$

Both types can be summarized as

$$Q_\beta = M(Z,A) - M(Z \pm 1, A)$$
$$= 2\gamma[\pm(Z_0 - Z) - \tfrac{1}{2}] \qquad \text{for odd-}A \quad (3.42)$$

where the $+$ sign in $\pm(Z_0 - Z)$ is to be used with the $+$ sign in $Z \rightarrow (Z \pm 1)$. The graphical implication of Eq. (3.42) is indicated in Fig. 3.1.

For any odd-A, two measured Q values suffice to determine the local values of both unknowns Z_0 and γ. For example, the β decay schemes of Te^{131} and I^{131} involve complex β spectra and γ radiation, for which the total energy release, or Q values, are

$$_{52}Te^{131} \rightarrow \beta^- + _{53}I^{131} + (2.16 \pm 0.1) \text{ Mev} \qquad (3.43)$$
$$_{53}I^{131} \rightarrow \beta^- + _{54}Xe^{131} + (0.97 \pm 0.01) \text{ Mev} \qquad (3.44)$$

Expressing the energetics of these reactions in the form of Eq. (3.42), we have

for $_{52}Te^{131}$: $(2.16 \pm 0.1) = 2\gamma(Z_0 - 52 - \tfrac{1}{2})$ (3.45)
for $_{53}I^{131}$: $(0.97 \pm 0.01) = 2\gamma(Z_0 - 53 - \tfrac{1}{2})$ (3.46)

The local solution for γ is given at once by the difference between these two equations,

$$\gamma = \tfrac{1}{2}[(2.16 \pm 0.1) - (0.97 \pm 0.01)] = 0.60 \pm 0.05 \text{ Mev} \quad (3.47)$$

while the local solution for Z_0 follows from the quotient of the two equations and is

$$Z_0 = 52.5 + \left(\frac{2.16}{2.16 - 0.97}\right) = 52.5 + (1.8 \pm 0.1)$$
$$= 54.3 \pm 0.1 \qquad (3.48)$$

The stable isobar of $A = 131$ is actually xenon, $Z = 54$.

Prediction of Reaction Energetics among Odd-A Isobars. These empirical local values of γ and Z_0, for $A = 131$, should be compared with predictions based on γ_{av} and β_{av} for which Eqs. (3.33), (3.34), and (3.36) give

$$\gamma_{av}(A = 131) = 0.70 \pm 0.04 \text{ Mev}$$
$$Z_0(A = 131) = 55 \pm 3 \qquad (3.49)$$

The rather wide uncertainties implied here are reflections of the conservative view taken in Eq. (3.21) regarding $(a_a/a_c)_{av}$. For the prediction of local values of Z_0, the use of γ_{av} and β_{av} is seen to be of little value.

However, if the energetics is known for any one reaction at constant mass number A, then usefully accurate estimates of the energetics for all isobars at mass number A can be made, using γ_{av}. For example, if we assume that at $A = 131$ only Eq. (3.46) is known, then the energetics of the Te^{131} β decay can be predicted, using only γ_{av}. By generalizing Eqs. (3.45) and (3.46) we can write

$$Q_\beta\text{-}(Z_1, A) = Q_\beta\text{-}(Z_2, A) + 2\gamma_{av}(Z_2 - Z_1) \qquad (3.50)$$

Then
$$\begin{aligned} Q_\beta\text{-}(\mathrm{Te}^{131}) &= Q_\beta\text{-}(\mathrm{I}^{131}) + 2(0.70 \pm 0.04)(53 - 52) \\ &= 0.97 + (1.40 \pm 0.08) \\ &= 2.37 \pm 0.08 \text{ Mev} \end{aligned} \qquad (3.51)$$

We see that such predictions have an inherent uncertainty of only about 0.1 Mev.

Transitions between Even-A Isobars. Isobaric masses for even-A nuclides follow the same pattern as for odd-A, except for the introduction

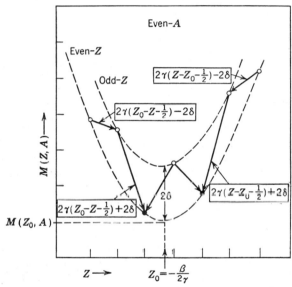

Fig. 3.2 Energetics of the even-A mass parabolas, Eqs. (3.52) and (3.54). The four forms of the β disintegration energy Q_β are shown in boxes, where Z is the atomic number of the initial isobar.

of the pairing energy δ. Then in Eqs. (3.28) to (3.38), β_{av}, γ_{av}, and Z_0 remain unchanged. The mass of the hypothetical "most stable isobar," Eq. (3.38), becomes

$$M(Z_0, A) = \alpha A - \gamma Z_0^2 - \delta \qquad \text{even-}A \qquad (3.52)$$

the negative pairing energy $-\delta$ being chosen so that $M(Z_0, A)$ will have the smallest possible value. Then the parameters $M(Z_0, A)$ and Z_0 locate the vertex of the lower, or even-Z even-N, mass parabola, as shown in Fig. 3.2.

In place of Eq. (3.39) we obtain, from Eqs. (3.28), (3.52), and

$$\beta = -2\gamma Z_0$$

the even-A mass parabolas

$$M(Z,A) - M(Z_0,A) = \gamma(Z - Z_0)^2$$
$$+ \begin{Bmatrix} 2\delta \text{ for odd-}Z \\ 0 \text{ for even-}Z \end{Bmatrix} \quad \text{even-}A \quad (3.53)$$

The reaction energy Q, for $Z \rightarrow (Z \pm 1)$ at constant even-A, becomes

$$Q_\beta \equiv M(Z,A) - M(Z \pm 1, A)$$
$$= 2\gamma[\pm (Z_0 - Z) - \tfrac{1}{2}] + \begin{Bmatrix} +2\delta \text{ for odd-}Z \\ -2\delta \text{ for even-}Z \end{Bmatrix} \quad \text{even-}A \quad (3.54)$$

The $+$ sign in $\pm (Z_0 - Z)$ is to be used with the $+$ sign in $Z \rightarrow (Z \pm 1)$, that is, for β^- decay, (p,n) and $(d,2n)$ reactions, etc., while the $-$ sign corresponds to $Z \rightarrow (Z - 1)$ transitions such as β^+ decay, (n,p) reactions, etc. When heavy particles are involved, their mass differences must, of course, be added into Eq. (3.54). For example,

$$Q_{(p,n)} = Q_{\beta^-} - (M_n - M_H) \qquad (3.54a)$$

d. Determination of Local Values of δ, Z_0, and γ. Historically, the original evaluations of the most stable charge Z_0, and the pairing energy δ, were based on the catalogue of known stable nuclides (F38, B96, F17, K33).

Limits of β Stability. The main features of the variation of Z_0 with A can be determined from the systematics of stable nuclides. In a Z vs. A diagram, the path of Z_0 is determined within rather narrow limits by the atomic numbers Z of the known stable nuclides, Fig. 3.3. For all odd-A nuclides Z_0 is confined to the narrow region

$$(Z - \tfrac{1}{2}) \leq Z_0 \leq (Z + \tfrac{1}{2}) \qquad \text{odd-}A \qquad (3.55)$$

For even-A, the odd-Z odd-N nuclides are unstable, so that we need study only the even-Z even-N species. Among these, each value of A may correspond to one, two, or three stable isobars. Figure 3.3 shows the Z and A values for all stable nuclides, in a form devised by Kohman (K33) to emphasize the limits of β stability.

The breadth of the variations in Z which can correspond to stable even-Z even-N nuclides is contained implicitly in Eq. (3.54). For all β-stable nuclides, $Q_\beta \leq 0$. Then from Eq. (3.54),

$$\left(\frac{\delta}{\gamma}\right)_A + \frac{1}{2} > |Z_0 - Z| \qquad (3.56)$$

for stable even-Z even-N nuclides, while

$$\left(\frac{\delta}{\gamma}\right)_A + \frac{1}{2} < |Z_0 - Z| \qquad (3.57)$$

for unstable even-Z even-N nuclides. Thus δ/γ is bracketed for all A.

Inspection of Fig. 3.3 shows that for constant A the approximate half width of the region of stability is $\delta/\gamma \simeq 1.5$ for heavy and middleweight elements and is smaller for the lightest elements.

Energetics of β Decay. For even-A isobars, Eq. (3.54) shows that the energetics of any reaction $Z \rightarrow Z \pm 1$ is determined by Z and three parameters: (1) the pairing energy δ, (2) the charge of the "most stable isobar" Z_0, and (3) the energy coefficient γ which is defined by Eq. (3.31). All three parameters δ, Z_0, and γ are functions of A. Each varies smoothly over a broad domain of A and also exhibits local variations. For any particular A, the energetics of at least three independent

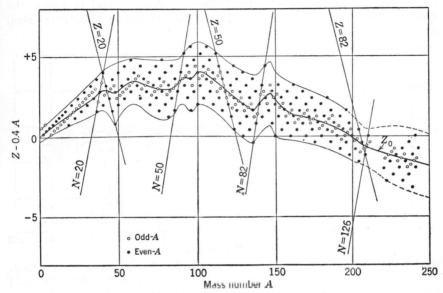

Fig. 3.3 β-stability diagram of the naturally occurring nuclides. The vertical scale is $(Z - 0.4A)$ instead of Z, in order to compress the diagram into a rectangular shape and to enhance the local variations. The line of "greatest stability" Z_0 passes always within $Z \pm \frac{1}{2}$ of each stable odd-A nuclide and otherwise is adjusted to pass about midway between the outer limits of β stability which are set by the even-A (even-Z even-N) nuclides. In Fig. 3.1 of Chap. 8 the line of β stability Z_0 is the central line Z_0 of this diagram. [*Adapted from Kohman (K33).*]

reactions are needed for the numerical determination of the three local parameters, δ, Z_0, and γ.

As an illustration, the decay schemes for three radioactive isobars at $A = 106$ have been studied carefully, with the results (H61)

$$_{44}Ru^{106} \rightarrow \beta^- + _{45}Rh^{106} + 0.0392 \text{ Mev}$$
$$_{45}Rh^{106} \rightarrow \beta^- + _{46}Pd^{106} + 3.53 \text{ Mev} \qquad (3.58)$$
$$_{47}Ag^{106} \rightarrow \beta^+ + _{46}Pd^{106} + (1.95 + 1.02) \text{ Mev}$$

These provide the data for three simultaneous equations in δ, Z_0, and γ, based on Eq. (3.54)

$$_{44}Ru^{106} \rightarrow \beta^-: 0.0392 = 2\gamma(Z_0 - 44 - 0.5) - 2\delta$$
$$_{45}Rh^{106} \rightarrow \beta^-: 3.53 = 2\gamma(Z_0 - 45 - 0.5) + 2\delta \qquad (3.59)$$
$$_{47}Ag^{106} \rightarrow \beta^+: 2.97 = 2\gamma(-Z_0 + 47 - 0.5) + 2\delta$$

The simultaneous solution gives, for the local values at $A = 106$,

$$\delta = 1.25 \text{ Mev} \qquad Z_0 = 46.19 \qquad \gamma = 0.752 \text{ Mev} \qquad (3.60)$$

As experimental data on β decay and nuclear reactions accumulate, these methods have been applied systematically by various workers. Figure 3.4 shows the numerical data on the pairing energy δ, plotted as δ/γ for $44 \leq A \leq 242$, as computed by Coryell (C46) from β-decay data. From the same survey, the local values of Z_0 are found to follow the general trends seen in Fig. 3.3 and to be influenced clearly by shell structure.

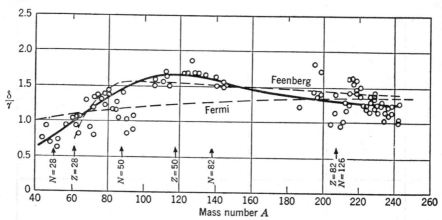

Fig. 3.4 The pairing energy δ, expressed as δ/γ, for $A > 40$. The circles are individual local values computed from β-decay energetics by Coryell (C46). The solid line represents the trend of these individual values. The dotted lines provide comparisons with Feenberg's (F17) evaluation of δ/γ from the limits of β stability, and with Fermi's (F38, F41) analytical approximation $\delta = 33.5/A^{\frac{3}{4}}$ Mev. [*Adapted from Coryell* (C46).]

e. Total Binding Energy for Stable Nuclides. We return to the full semiempirical mass formula, Eq. (3.15). The coefficients a_v (of "volume energy") and a_s (of "surface energy") are still to be evaluated. When this has been done, Eq. (3.15) will give predicted values for

1. The atomic mass $M(Z,A)$ and total nuclear binding energy B of any nuclide having $A \geq 40$
2. The energy release, or Q value, for nuclear reactions in which A changes, for example, (α,d), . . .
3. The energetics of α decay
4. The energetics of nuclear fission

In order to evaluate the two remaining coefficients a_v and a_s, we require a minimum of two independent experimental data concerning any phenomena in which A is not a constant. We elect, arbitrarily, to use mass values.

Masses of Stable Nuclides. It is convenient to express the observed neutral atomic mass M in terms of the average binding energy per nucleon B/A. Then, from Eq. (3.2) of Chap. 9, we have

$$\left(\frac{B}{A}\right)_{exp} = (M_n - 1) - (M_n - M_H)\frac{Z}{A} - \frac{M - A}{A} \tag{3.61}$$

The corresponding theoretical value, from Eq. (3.15), is, for odd-A,

$$\left(\frac{B}{A}\right)_{cal} = a_v - a_s\frac{1}{A^{\frac{1}{3}}} - a_c\frac{Z^2}{A^{\frac{4}{3}}} - a_a\left(1 - \frac{2Z}{A}\right)^2 \tag{3.62}$$

with $a_c = (0.595 \pm 0.02)$ Mev and $a_a = (32 \pm 1)a_c = (19.0 \pm 0.9)$ Mev, as previously evaluated.

Table 3.2 shows the masses of a few odd-A nuclides, selected to avoid proximity to magic numbers of Z or N. Any two masses suffice for a

TABLE 3.2. EXPERIMENTAL VALUES OF MASS AND BINDING ENERGY,
Eq. (3.61)

Compared with the values calculated from the semiempirical mass formula, Eq. (3.62), with energy coefficients as shown above each energy column.

Z	A	Volume B_0/A a_v $a_v =$ 14.1 Mev	Surface B_2/A $a_s/A^{\frac{1}{3}}$ $a_s =$ 13 Mev	Coulomb B_1/A $a_c Z^2/A^{\frac{4}{3}}$ $a_c =$ 0.595 Mev	Asymmetry B_3/A $a_a\left(1 - \frac{2Z}{A}\right)^2$ $a_a =$ 19 Mev	$(B/A)_{cal}$	$(B/A)_{exp}$	M_{exp}	Refs. for M_{exp}
8 O	17	14.1	5.05	0.87	0.07	8.11	7.75	17.004 533 ±7	(L27)
16 S	33	14.1	4.06	1.44	0.02	8.58	8.50	32.981 88 ±4	(C35)
25 Mn	55	11.1	0.42	1.78	0.16	8.74	8.75	54.955 8 ±1	(C36)
29 Cu	65	14.1	3.22	1.92	0.22	8.74	8.75	64.948 35 ±6	(C36)
53 I	127	14.1	2.59	2.62	0.52	8.37	8.43	126.945 3 ±1	(H11)
78 Pt	195	14.1	2.24	3.20	0.76	7.90	7.92	195.026 4 ±8	(B4)
97 Bk	245	14.1	2.08	3.66	0.82	7.54	7.52	245.142 ±1	(B4)

determination of a_v and a_s. The masses of Cu^{65} and I^{127} were determined in the same laboratory, using the same standards. Simultaneous solution of Eq. (3.62) for Cu^{65} and I^{127}, whose masses correspond to $(B/A)_{exp} = 8.75$ Mev and 8.43 Mev, gives $a_s = 13.6$ Mev and $a_v = 14.28$ Mev. If, as a check, we compare I^{127} with a heavier nuclide Pt^{195} (whose mass has been determined in another laboratory), Eq. (3.62) leads to the values $a_s = 11.7$ Mev and $a_v = 13.90$ Mev. The difference appears to be well outside the reported uncertainties in the masses of Cu^{65}, I^{127}, and Pt^{195} and may be taken as a rough index of the true variations of a_v and a_s. We adopt as representative mean values for $A \geq 40$

$$a_s = (13 \pm 1) \text{ Mev} \tag{3.63}$$
$$a_v = (14.1 \pm 0.2) \text{ Mev} \tag{3.64}$$

Table 3.2 also gives the observed and theoretical B/A for a few lighter and heavier nuclides. Note that over the entire range of A from S^{33} to Bk^{245}, the semiempirical mass formula, with the coefficients given in Table 3.2, predicts average binding energies B/A which are everywhere within 1 per cent of the observed values. This is a remarkable achievement for so simple a theory. Equation (3.15) can therefore serve as a smoothed base line against which local variations in M and B/A can be compared. In this way, discontinuities due to the shell structure of nuclei become prominently displayed, as we shall see shortly.

Evaluation of Components of the Total Binding Energy. Table 3.2 also lists the separate contributions of the four energy terms, volume, coulomb, surface, and asymmetry, for odd-A nuclides. The pairing

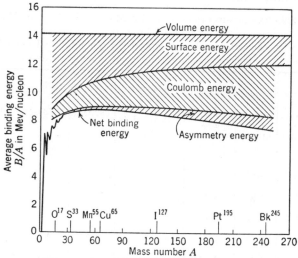

Fig. 3.5 Summary of the semiempirical liquid-drop-model treatment of the average binding-energy curve from Fig. 3.1 of Chap. 9. Note how the decrease in surface energy and the increase in coulomb energy conspire to produce the maximum observed in B/A at $A \sim 60$. For these curves, the constants used in the semiempirical mass formula are given in the last line of Table 3.3.

energy, for even-A nuclides, is best determined from Fig. 3.4 and added in as an empirical local value.

Figure 3.5 shows the separate contributions of each of the four energy terms to the average binding energy per nucleon B/A, for all A. The initial rise of B/A with A, which we first noted empirically in Fig. 3.1 of Chap. 9, is seen to be attributable mainly to the decreasing importance of surface energy as A increases. At still larger A, the importance of the disruptive coulomb energy becomes dominant, causing a maximum in B/A at $A \sim 60$ and a subsequent decline in B/A at larger A. Throughout the entire range of A above $A \sim 40$ the semiempirical mass formula matches the observed binding energies within about 1 per cent.

Summary of Evaluations of Energy Coefficients. Table 3.3 collects the evaluations of the energy coefficients of Eq. (3.15). For comparison and reference purposes, the values used by the principal contributors to this field are also given.   Among these, Fowler and Green avoided the conventional practice of determining a_c from the coulomb-energy difference of light mirror nuclei, Eq. (3.16), and determined all four energy coefficients from a least-squares adjustment to the mass data for β-stable

TABLE 3.3. COMPARATIVE EVALUATIONS (IN MEV) OF THE ENERGY
COEFFICIENTS OF THE SEMIEMPIRICAL MASS FORMULA

	Volume a_v	Surface a_s	Coulomb a_c	Asymmetry a_a	Pairing δ
1936 Bethe and Bacher† (B48)	13.86	13.2	0.58	19.5	
1939 Feenberg (F16)	......	13.3	0.62		
1939 Bohr and Wheeler (B96)	......	14	0.59	(Table of γ)	(Table)
1942 Fluegge (M22)	14.66	15.4	0.602	20.5	
1945 Fermi (F38, F41)	14.0	13.0	0.583	19.3	$33.5/A^{\frac{3}{4}}$
1950 Metropolis and Reitwiesner‡ (M43)	14.0	13.0	0.583	19.3	$33.5/A^{\frac{3}{4}}$
1947 Feenberg§ (F17)	14.1	13.1	0.585	18.1	(Graph)
1947 Fowler‖	15.3	16.7	0.69	22.6	
1949 Friedlander and Kennedy (F69)	14.1	13.1	0.585	18.1	132/A
1949 L. Rosenfeld (R36)	14.66	15.4	0.602	20.54	
1945 Canadian National Research Council (P36)	14.05	14.0	0.61	19.6	
1953 Coryell (C46)	......	......	......	(Table of γ)	(Graph)
1954 Green (G46)	15.75	17.8	0.71	23.7	
1955 Eqs. (3.17), (3.22), (3.63), (3.64)	14.1 ±0.2	13 ±1	0.595 ±0.02	19.0 ±0.9	(Fig. 3.4)

† Constants were fitted for even-N even-Z.   Pairing energy recognized but not evaluated.

‡ These voluminous ENIAC computations of $M(Z,A)$ for every conceivable value of Z and A use Fermi's 1945 constants, including $M_n = 1.008\ 93$ amu and $M_n - M_H = 0.000\ 81$ amu.

§ The particular values given here are for the incompressible fluid model, as used by all others in this tabulation.   Feenberg (F17) also studied extensively the effects of finite nuclear compressibility.

‖ All four coefficients determined from a least-squares fit with packing fractions by Mattauch and Fluegge (M22) for Ne^{20}, S^{34}, Fe^{56}, Kr^{84}, Xe^{132}, Gd^{158}, Hg^{200}, U^{238} (1947, unpublished).

nuclides.   This procedure leads to a larger value for a_c and corresponds to a smaller nuclear unit radius in the neighborhood of $R_0 \simeq 1.2 \times 10^{-13}$ cm for the heavy nuclides.   All but these two determinations fall clearly within the uncertainties assigned in Eqs. (3.17), (3.22), (3.63), and (3.64), in which our general objective has been to set up an average base line with which local variations and shell discontinuities can be compared.   The remarkable fact is that so simple a theory, with only four adjustable constants for odd-A and one additional parameter for even-A, can match the broad general behavior of the mass and binding energy of nearly a thousand stable and radioactive nuclides. The important point then becomes the extent and cause of local variations from this smooth base line.

f. Effects of Closed Shells. The semiempirical mass formula provides a base line from which shell effects can be quantified.

Energetics of β Decay and α Decay. In any group of isobars, the parabolic variation of mass $M(Z)$ with nuclear charge Z (Figs. 3.1 and 3.2) is an accurate representation if no isobar contains a magic number of neutrons or protons. However, the mass of any isobar which has Z or $N = 20, 28, 50, 82$, or 126 will lie about 1 to 2 Mev below the mass predicted by the smooth parabolic relationships of Eqs. (3.39) and (3.53).

TABLE 3.4. DECREASE ΔM IN NEUTRAL ATOMIC MASS FOR AN ISOBAR CONTAINING A CLOSED SHELL OF NEUTRONS OR PROTONS

[As compared with the expected mass $M(Z,A)$ of Eqs. (3.39) and (3.53) with local values of γ and Z_0. Coryell (C46).]

Z	$\Delta M = \Delta Q_\beta$, Mev	N	$\Delta M = \Delta Q_\beta$, Mev
20	1.1	20	1.1
28	1.1	28	1.0
50	1.5	50	1.9
82	(1.5)	82	1.8
		126	(1.8)

This state of affairs is illustrated graphically for the case of $A = 135$ by Fig. 3.2 of Chap. 8. There the atomic mass of $_{53}\mathrm{I}_{82}^{135}$ lies clearly below the parabola which correlates the masses and β decay energies of its isobars.

From a systematic survey of β decay energetics Coryell (C46) has obtained estimates of the magnitude of the shell discontinuities, as shown in Table 3.4. There are analogous discontinuities in the energetics of α decay, as has been shown clearly by Perlman, Ghiorso, and Seaborg (P15) and by Pryce (P36). The heaviest stable element bismuth undoubtedly owes its one stable isotope $_{83}\mathrm{Bi}_{126}^{209}$ to the closed shell of 126 neutrons. All other bismuth isotopes are unstable.

Neutron Separation Energy. As in Chap. 9, we define the neutron separation energy S_n as the work required to remove the last neutron from a nucleus which contains N neutrons and Z protons. Then

$$S_n(Z,N) = M(Z, N-1) + M_n - M(Z,N)$$
$$= B(Z,N) - B(Z, N-1)$$
$$= \left(\frac{\Delta B}{\Delta A}\right)_{Z \text{ const}} \tag{3.65}$$

The predicted value $(S_n)_{\text{cal}}$ is obtained from Eq. (3.65) by using B from

Eq. (3.15). This is to be compared with experimental values $(S_n)_{\text{exp}}$ computed from the Q values of (γ,n), (d,H^3), (d,p), and (n,γ) reactions as well as interlocking β decay and α decay energetics. The differences

$$\Delta S_n \equiv (S_n)_{\text{exp}} - (S_n)_{\text{cal}} \qquad (3.66)$$

are plotted in Fig. 3.6 as a function of N. Sharp discontinuities are evident. The 127th neutron is loosely bound and has a separation energy which is about 2.2 Mev less than that of the 126th neutron. A discontinuity of about the same size is seen between the 83d and 82d neutron, and between the 51st and 50th neutron. From the present data, no equally abrupt change in S_n is seen at $N = 28$.

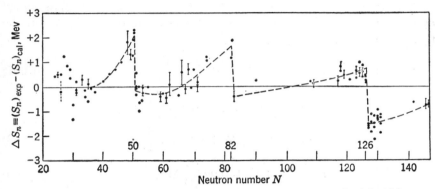

Fig. 3.6 Observed neutron separation energies $(S_n)_{\text{exp}}$ compared with $(S_n)_{\text{cal}}$ predicted by the smooth variation of the semiempirical mass formula, using Fermi 1945 coefficients (Table 3.3) in Eq. (3.65). Discontinuities of the order of 2 Mev are evident for $N = 50$, 82, and 126. Evidence for a shell closure at $N = 28$ is inconclusive. [*Adapted from Harvey* (H22).]

g. Stability Limits against Spontaneous Fission. When the nucleus is visualized as a droplet of incompressible liquid, the main features of the ground-level energetics are quite well represented by Eq. (3.15). However, the liquid-drop model fails to give an acceptable representation of the *excited levels* of nuclei. The excitation energy has to be visualized as due to surface vibrations, which correspond to periodic deformations of the droplet. The energy of these oscillations is proportional to the surface tension, hence to the surface-energy coefficient a_s. It can be shown (B68) that the lowest permissible mode of surface vibration corresponds to an excitation energy which is many times greater than the observed excitation energy of low-lying excited levels in nuclei. The liquid-drop model cannot match the observed close spacing of nuclear excited levels, even if an additional parameter, corresponding to a finite compressibility of nuclear matter, is introduced in the model.

However, the possibly superficial resemblance between the nucleus and an oscillating drop of incompressible liquid does lead quite directly to a plausible model which describes the stability limits of very heavy nuclei and the energetics of the nuclear-fission process.

Energy Available for Nuclear Fission. The maximum binding energy per nucleon occurs in nuclei which have $A \sim 60$ (Fig. 3.5). In heavier nuclei, say, $A > 100$, the total binding energy of the A nucleons can be increased by dividing the original nucleus into two smaller nuclei. Thus, if U^{238} is divided into two nuclei, having mass numbers $A = \frac{238}{2}$, the binding energy per nucleon will increase from $B/A \simeq 7.6$ to $B/A \simeq 8.5$ Mev/nucleon. This is an increase of ~ 0.9 Mev/nucleon, or some 210 Mev for division of the single U^{238} nucleus.

In general, the division of any nucleus (Z,A) into two lighter nuclei is energetically advantageous if $A \geq 85$. These spontaneous fission reactions do not take place in the common elements because they are opposed by a potential barrier, which we shall discuss presently.

The division of a nucleus (Z,A) into halves $(Z/2, A/2)$ is called *symmetric fission.* From the semiempirical mass formula Eq. (3.15) the energy Q released in symmetric fission is

$$Q = M(Z,A) - 2M\left(\frac{Z}{2}, \frac{A}{2}\right) \tag{3.67}$$

$$Q = a_s A^{\frac{2}{3}}(1 - 2^{\frac{1}{3}}) + a_c \frac{Z^2}{A^{\frac{1}{3}}}\left(1 - \frac{1}{2^{\frac{2}{3}}}\right)$$

$$= -0.260 a_s A^{\frac{2}{3}} + 0.370 a_c \frac{Z^2}{A^{\frac{1}{3}}} \tag{3.68}$$

$$Q = -3.4 A^{\frac{2}{3}} + 0.22 \frac{Z^2}{A^{\frac{1}{3}}} \text{ Mev} \tag{3.69}$$

In Eq. (3.68) we have not specified the odd or even character of Z and A and have therefore omitted a possible small contribution from the pairing energy δ. Applying Eq. (3.69), we have for the energy release on symmetric fission of $_{92}U^{238}$

$$Q = -3.4(238)^{\frac{2}{3}} + 0.22 \frac{(92)^2}{(238)^{\frac{1}{3}}}$$

$$= -130 + 300 = 170 \text{ Mev} \tag{3.70}$$

This is less than the 210 Mev estimated from the change in B/A, because the B/A values corresponded to stable nuclides. The fission fragments $(Z/2, A/2)$ will have too large a neutron excess for stability. They will release additional energy in several forms, including an average of about 2.5 "prompt" neutrons per fission, and a cascade of two or three β disintegrations in each fission fragment. Symmetric fission does take place, but asymmetric fission is more probable. The energy released is only slightly different.

In Eq. (3.70) we note that the positive energy release Q is the result of a large diminution in coulomb disruptive energy (300 Mev), which overrides a smaller change in the opposite direction (-130 Mev) due to the increased ratio of surface to volume. The energetics of nuclear fission is seen to depend mainly on the interplay between coulomb energy and surface energy.

Potential Barrier Opposing Spontaneous Fission. The origin and behavior of the potential barrier can be visualized more clearly by reversing the fission process. We shall consider the mutual potential energy between two fission fragments which approach each other from a large distance and finally coalesce to form a $_{92}U^{238}$ nucleus.

In Fig. 3.7, assume for simplicity that each fission fragment has the mass number $A/2$, nuclear charge $Z/2$, and radius $R = R_0(A/2)^{\frac{1}{3}}$. When the separation r between the centers of two particles is large compared with their radii R, their mutual potential is simply the coulomb energy $E_c = e^2(Z/2)^2/r$. When r decreases until the two particles are nearly touching, $r \geq 2R$, nuclear attractive forces begin to act. Then the mutual potential energy is less than the coulomb value, as indicated between positions b and c in Fig. 3.7.

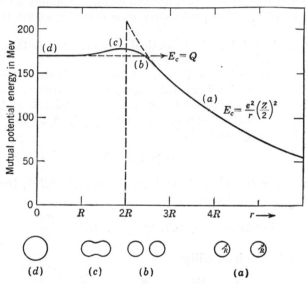

Fig. 3.7 Representation of the potential barrier opposing the spontaneous fission of U^{238}. Pictorially, the conditions at a, b, c, and d are illustrated on a reduced scale below.

If the particles remained spherical, and no attractive forces entered, then the coulomb energy when the two spheres just touched, that is, $r = 2R$, would be

$$E_c = \frac{e^2(Z/2)^2}{2R_0(A/2)^{\frac{1}{3}}} = \frac{2^{\frac{1}{3}}}{8}\frac{e^2}{R_0}\frac{Z^2}{A^{\frac{1}{3}}} \tag{3.71}$$

Remembering that $a_c \equiv 3e^2/5R_0 \simeq 0.595$ Mev, Eq. (3.71) becomes

$$E_c = \frac{2^{\frac{1}{3}}}{8}\left(\frac{5}{3}a_c\right)\frac{Z^2}{A^{\frac{1}{3}}} = 0.262a_c\frac{Z^2}{A^{\frac{1}{3}}} \simeq 210 \text{ Mev} \tag{3.72}$$

for spheres $(Z/2, A/2)$ in contact. This is shown as the extrapolated E_c curve at $r = 2R$ in Fig. 3.7. Actually, the coulomb energy for undeformed spheres is just equal to $Q \simeq 170$ Mev at position b in Fig. 3.7, where $r \simeq 2.5R$ for the case of U^{238}.

As the two particles come closer together, $r < 2R$, the nuclear attractive forces become stronger and the two halves coalesce into the (Z,A) nucleus, whose energy of symmetric fission, d in Fig. 3.7, is below the barrier height.

The nucleus (Z,A) will generally be essentially stable against spontaneous fission if its dissociation energy Q is a few Mev below the barrier height. Experimentally, fission can be induced in U^{238} by adding an excitation energy of only a few Mev. The threshold for the (γ,f), or "photofission" reaction, in which the required excitation energy is acquired by the capture of a photon, is only 5.1 Mev for U^{238}. Therefore the barrier is only about 5.1 Mev above Q. U^{238} does show a half-period of about 10^{16} yr for spontaneous fission, or about 25 fissions per hour in 1 g of U^{238}. The probability of α decay is about 10^7 times as great.

Many experimental and theoretical aspects of spontaneous fission have been summarized by Segrè (S25).

Stability Limits for Heavy Nuclei. A rough estimate of the mass and charge of a nucleus which is unstable against spontaneous fission can be had by finding (Z,A) such that Q for symmetric fission is as large as the coulomb energy E_c for undeformed spheres $(Z/2, A/2)$ in contact. A nucleus will be clearly unstable if

$$Q \geq E_c \tag{3.73}$$

Upon substituting Q and E_c from Eqs. (3.68) and (3.72), the condition for absolute instability becomes

$$-0.260a_s A^{\frac{2}{3}} + 0.370a_c \frac{Z^2}{A^{\frac{1}{3}}} \geq 0.262a_c \frac{Z^2}{A^{\frac{1}{3}}} \tag{3.74}$$

which reduces to the inequality

$$\frac{Z^2}{A} \geq 2.4 \frac{a_s}{a_c} = 53 \tag{3.75}$$

This is an upper limiting value, because it ignores the possibility of finite penetration of the barrier. The important point here is the character and dimension of the critical parameter Z^2/A and its dependence solely on the relative effective strengths of the forces associated with the coulomb energy ($\propto Z^2/A^{\frac{1}{3}}$) and with the surface energy ($\propto A^{\frac{2}{3}}$).

A much better estimate of the critical value of Z^2/A is based on the modes of oscillation of a drop of incompressible fluid, under the joint influence of short-range forces, as represented by surface tension, and the long-range coulomb forces [Bohr and Wheeler (B96) and others]. Oscillations of the type illustrated in Fig. 3.8 will be unstable and will result in division of the drop if small displacements from sphericity increase the total binding energy of the constituents of the drop.

The volume of the sphere $\frac{4}{3}\pi R^3$ is the same as that of the ellipsoid

$\frac{4}{3}\pi ab^2$, if the drop is incompressible.   The major and minor semiaxes of the ellipsoid can be represented by $a = R(1 + \epsilon)$ and $b = R/(1 + \epsilon)^{\frac{1}{2}}$, where ϵ measures the eccentricity and $\epsilon = 0$ for the sphere.   Then the surface energy can be shown to be

$$B_s = 4\pi R^2(1 + \tfrac{2}{5}\epsilon^2 + \cdots) \times \text{surface tension}$$
$$= a_s A^{\frac{2}{3}}(1 + \tfrac{2}{5}\epsilon^2 + \cdots) \tag{3.76}$$

while the coulomb energy of the ellipsoid is

$$B_c = \frac{3}{5}\frac{e^2 Z^2}{R}\left(1 - \frac{1}{5}\epsilon^2 + \cdots\right)$$
$$= a_c \frac{Z^2}{A^{\frac{1}{3}}}\left(1 - \frac{1}{5}\epsilon^2 + \cdots\right) \tag{3.77}$$

Thus the ellipsoidal form has less disruptive coulomb energy, because the charges are farther apart on the average.   Contrariwise, the ellipsoidal surface area is greater than that of the sphere; hence the deformation involves some loss of binding energy, because the surface deficit is increased.

Fig. 3.8   Oscillation of an incompressible liquid drop, for considerations of stability against spontaneous fission.

Taking only the terms in ϵ^2, we see that the sphere (Z,A) ceases to be the stable configuration and undergoes fission when nudged, if

$$a_c \frac{Z^2}{A^{\frac{1}{3}}}\left(\frac{1}{5}\epsilon^2\right) \geq a_s A^{\frac{2}{3}}\left(\frac{2}{5}\epsilon^2\right) \tag{3.78}$$

which reduces to the inequality

$$\frac{Z^2}{A} \geq 2\frac{a_s}{a_c} = 44 \tag{3.79}$$

Nuclei for which $Z^2/A < 44$ will be stable against small deformations, but a larger deformation will give the long-range coulomb force a greater advantage over the short-range forces which are represented by surface tension.   It may be expected that nuclei which are essentially stable against spontaneous fission will have values of Z^2/A which are clearly less than the limiting value.

In Fig. 3.9 the *fission parameter* Z^2/A is plotted against Z for representative elements.   The heaviest nuclide $_{98}Cf^{246}$ decays primarily by α-ray emission, with a half-period of 1.5 days.   As would be expected from its Z^2/A value of 39.0, it also undergoes spontaneous fission, against which its partial half-period is only about 2,000 yr.

Figure 3.10 illustrates the empirical correlation between the fission parameter Z^2/A and the measured values of the partial half-period for

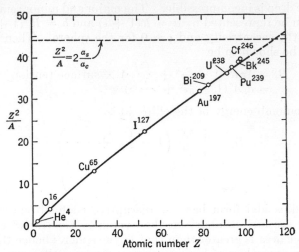

Fig. 3.9 The fission parameter Z^2/A for some representative nuclides. The limiting value, $Z^2/A = 2a_s/a_c = 44$, from the incompressible liquid-drop model is shown dotted. All the nuclides shown above $Z = 90$ exhibit spontaneous fission but not as their major mode of decay.

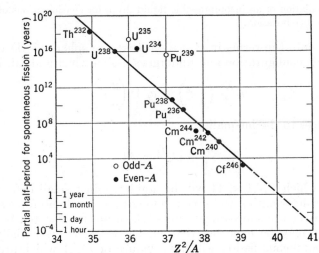

Fig. 3.10 Systematics of spontaneous fission in the heavy even-Z nuclides. The partial half-periods which have been reported thus far (H61) extend from 1.4×10^{18} yr for $_{90}\text{Th}^{232}$ to 2,000 yr for $_{98}\text{Cf}^{246}$. Accurate values are not yet available for odd-Z nuclides. Empirically, the logarithm of the half-period is a linear function of the fission parameter Z^2/A for all measured even-Z even-N nuclides except $_{92}\text{U}^{234}$. [*Adapted from Seaborg and collaborators* (S24, G20).]

spontaneous fission, in heavy even-Z nuclides from $Z = 90$ to 98.   This systematic relationship was first pointed out by Seaborg (S24, G20) and is useful in predicting the spontaneous-fission rates for undiscovered nuclides.   In general, the odd-A nuclides have longer partial half-periods than the even-Z even-N nuclides, for the same value of Z^2/A. It appears from Figs. 3.9 and 3.10 that nuclides having $Z = 100$ may be reached, or exceeded somewhat, before spontaneous fission becomes the major mode of decay.

Excitation Energy for Induced Fission.   Returning to Fig. 3.7, we note that a relatively small excitation energy ($\sim$5 Mev in the heaviest nuclides) (K28) is sufficient to induce fission.   This excitation energy can be supplied in many ways.   For example, immediately after the capture of a thermal neutron the compound nucleus has an excitation energy equal to S_n, the neutron separation energy from the ground level of the compound nucleus.   If the probability of fission from this excited level competes favorably with deexcitation by γ-ray emission, then fission may be a principal consequence of the neutron capture.

We have seen that S_n is appreciably greater for even-N than for odd-N nuclides.   This is a consequence of the pairing energy δ.   The excitation energy in the compound nucleus (Z,A) immediately following the capture of a thermal neutron is

$$S_n = M(Z, N - 1) + M_n - M(Z,N) \qquad (3.80)$$

where the neutron number of the *target* nucleus is $N - 1$.   Note that the neutron separation energy S_n from the ground level of the compound nucleus (Z,N) is the same as the Q value for the (n,γ) reaction on the target nucleus $(Z, N - 1)$.

Consider the excitation energy produced when a thermal neutron is captured by an odd-N target (say $_{92}U^{235}$) compared with an even-N target (say $_{92}U^{238}$) of approximately the same mass number.   It is easy to show, by inserting Eq. (3.15) into Eq. (3.80), that the excitation energy in

$$_{92}U^{235} + n \rightarrow U^{236}$$

is substantially 2δ greater than the excitation energy in the compound nucleus formed by

$$_{92}U^{238} + n \rightarrow U^{239}$$

This relationship is quite a general one.   If the mass numbers of two nuclides are nearly alike, the excitation energy is 2δ greater in a *compound* nucleus which has even-N than in one having odd-N.   In the domain of $A \sim 236$, the pairing energy δ is of the order of 0.5 Mev, so that the difference in excitation energy 2δ is about 1 Mev.   The fact that U^{235} undergoes fission with thermal neutrons but U^{238} requires bombardment by fast neutrons of $\sim$1 Mev in order to undergo fission is attributed to this expected difference of 2δ in the excitation energies.

Asymmetric Mass Yield in Low-energy Fission.   Symmetric fission, as contemplated in Eqs. (3.67) et seq., is actually an uncommon mode of cleavage when nuclear fission takes place from a level which has low-to-moderate excitation energy (C47, W42, M57).

The fission of U^{235} by thermal neutrons ($\sim\frac{1}{40}$ ev) has been most exhaustively studied, because of its present practical importance in nuclear reactors. When U^{235} captures a thermal neutron, the resulting excited nucleus U^{236} transforms to its ground level by γ-ray emission in only $\sim$15 per cent of the cases. Predominantly, the excited U^{236} nucleus undergoes fission. The immediate products of this fission process generally are two middleweight nuclei (the so-called *"fission fragments"*) and, on the average, 2.5 ± 0.1 *prompt neutrons* which are emitted instantly by the fission fragments.

The prompt neutrons have a continuous energy spectrum, with a maximum intensity near 1 Mev, and an approximately exponential decrease in intensity at higher energies, such that the relative intensity at 14 Mev is only about 10^{-4} of the intensity at 1 Mev (B97, H52, W11). Each of the fission fragments is "neutron-rich," because N/Z is appreciably greater for β-stable heavy nuclei than for β-stable middleweight nuclei.

TABLE 3.5. ASYMMETRY CHARACTERISTICS OF THE MASS-YIELD CURVES FOR
LOW-ENERGY FISSION OF SEVERAL TARGET NUCLIDES
[From Turkevich and Niday (T31)]

Target nuclide	Most probable light mass	Most probable heavy mass	Ratio of most probable masses	Mass width at half height	Ratio of peak-to-trough yields
Th^{232}	91	140	1.54	14	110
U^{233}	93	137	1.48	14	400
U^{235}	97	138	1.42	15	600
U^{238}	98	140	1.43	17	100
Pu^{239}	99	138	1.39	16	140

On the average, a fission product undergoes about three successive β transformations before becoming a stable middleweight nuclide (W12).

The *mass yield* in nuclear fission is the sum of all the independent fission yields of nuclides having the same mass number. Figure 3.11 shows this percentage yield of isobars, between mass number $A \sim 70$ and $A \sim 160$, which results from the fission of U^{235} by thermal neutrons (P24, R11). The outstanding characteristic of Fig. 3.11 is its double-peak mass distribution. This "asymmetric fission" is characteristic of all cases of low-energy fission. It is also observed in the mass-yield curves for the spontaneous fission of U^{238} and Th^{232}, which have been evaluated by mass-spectroscopic measurements on the Xe and Kr isotopes which have accumulated in ancient Th and U minerals (F53, W28).

Table 3.5 shows the magnitude of the asymmetry characteristics for the low-energy fission of U^{233}, U^{235}, and Pu^{239} by thermal neutrons, and for the low-energy fission of Th^{232} and U^{238} by "pile neutrons," i.e., by slightly moderated prompt neutrons from the fission of U^{235} by thermal neutrons.

The dramatic asymmetry of the mass-yield curves for low-energy fission gradually disappears as the excitation energy of the fissioning nucleus is increased. This trend is illustrated by the dotted curve in Fig. 3.11, which shows the mass-yield distribution for the fission of excited U^{236} compound nuclei which are produced by bombardment of Th^{232} by 37-Mev α particles (N9). The threshold for this reaction, Th^{232}

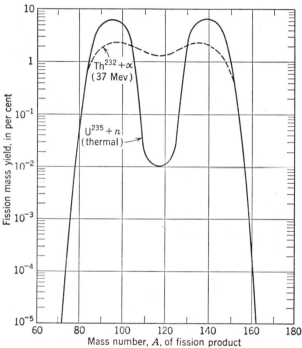

Fig. 3.11 Mass yield in the low-energy fission of U^{235} by thermal neutrons (solid curve). The asymmetry is reduced when fission takes place from more highly excited levels of the compound nucleus. The dotted curve shows the mass yield for Th^{232} + 37-Mev α particles, which also involves the compound nucleus U^{236}. [*From the Plutonium Project Reports* (P24) *and Newton* (N9).]

(α,f), is about 23 Mev; hence the compound U^{236} nucleus is of the order of 14 Mev more highly excited than the U^{236} formed from U^{235} plus thermal neutrons. This is sufficient to reduce the peak-to-trough ratio from 600 to about 2. For very-high-energy fission, e.g., that of Bi^{209} bombarded by 400-Mev α particles, symmetric fission predominates (S62).

A wide variety of tentative theories have been advanced in efforts to match the asymmetric mass yields which are seen in low-energy fission. These have been summarized and their inadequacies discussed by Hill and Wheeler (H53), in connection with their discussion of the so-called *collective model* of nuclei, which blends somewhat the individual-particle and the liquid-drop models of nuclei. At present, a simple and wholly acceptable theory of asymmetric fission remains a task for the future.

Problems

1. Consider the semiempirical mass formula of Eq. (3.15), but with the asymmetry term written as $a_a(A - 2Z)^n/A$, with the arbitrary exponent n (instead of 2).

(a) For any given odd value of A, derive an expression for the neutron excess $(A - 2Z_0)$ for minimum neutral atomic mass.

(b) Show that n must equal 2 for heavy nuclei, by assuming Z_0 substantially proportional to A, and recalling that $(A - 2Z_0)$ is empirically proportional to $A^{\frac{2}{3}}$.

2. (a) Show that the experimentally observed parabolic relationship

$$(M_Z - M_{Z_0}) = \gamma(Z - Z_0)^2$$

of Eq. (3.39), between mass M_Z and atomic number Z, for odd-A isobars, will emerge from the semiempirical mass formula Eq. (3.15) only if the exponent n, in the asymmetry term $(a_a/A)(A - 2Z)^n$, has the value $n = 2$ exactly.

(b) Would a parabolic relationship emerge if there were no asymmetry term, i.e., if $a_a = 0$?

3. A portion of the very complicated decay scheme of $_{32}\text{Ge}^{77}$ is shown below [from A. B. Smith, *Phys. Rev.*, **86**: 98 (1952)], together with the simple β decay scheme of $_{33}\text{As}^{77}$.

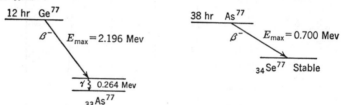

(a) From this evidence alone, evaluate the local values at mass number $A = 77$ for the semiempirical mass parameters Z_0 and γ.

(b) Plot a reasonably accurate graph of the neutral atomic mass differences $(M_Z - M_{Z_0})$ in Mev, against Z, for $A = 77$ and $Z = 32$ to 36.

(c) Predict the decay energy of $_{36}\text{Kr}^{77}$ and the maximum energy of the positron spectrum which it can emit in those transitions which go directly to the ground level of $_{35}\text{Br}^{77}$. Compare with recent measurements of the Kr^{77} decay spectrum.

(d) Predict the Q value for the nuclear reaction $\text{Se}^{77}(d,2n)\text{Br}^{77}$.

4. The principal modes of decay of As^{74} are as shown. Evaluate the pairing energy δ for the last neutron and proton in Ge^{74} and Se^{74}.

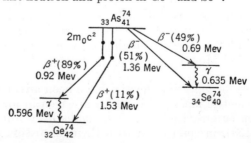

5. (*a*) Look up the disintegration scheme for the dual β decay of Cu^{64}. From the β^+ and β^- disintegration energies, determine the pairing energy δ at $A = 64$. Locate the resulting value of δ/γ_{av} on Fig. 3.4.

(*b*) Do likewise for the dual β decay of $_{45}Rh^{102}$.

6. Examine the chain of fission products having mass number 140: $Xe^{140} \rightarrow Cs \rightarrow Ba \rightarrow La \rightarrow Ce^{140}$. From the properties of Ba^{140}, La^{140}, and Pr^{140}, as given below (H61), evaluate the parameters Z_0, γ, and δ of the nuclear energy surface at $A = 140$. Predict the decay energy of Xe^{140} and Cs^{140}. Comment on any "magic-number effects."

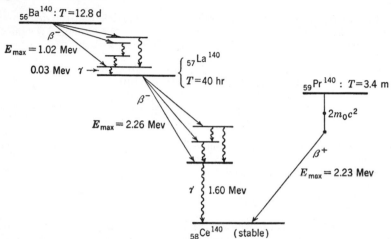

7. The reaction $V^{51}(p,n)Cr^{51}$ has a Q value of -1.534 ± 0.003 Mev, as determined from the threshold energy. The 5.8-min β^- emitter Ti^{51} is reported (H61) to give $E_{max} = 2.2$ Mev in transitions to the ground level of V^{51}. From these data alone:

(*a*) Determine the local value of γ, and compare with γ_{av} at $A = 51$.

(*b*) Determine the most stable nuclear charge Z_0 at $A = 51$ and compare with the line of β stability in Fig. 3.1 of Chap. 8.

(*c*) Determine the decay energy for electron-capture transitions of Cr^{51} and whether positron decay is permitted.

(*d*) Predict the positron decay energy Q_{β^+} of Mn^{51} and compare with reported values.

8. γ-ray photons of sufficiently large quantum energy can be reliably detected without interference from low-energy radiations by the use of so-called "threshold detectors." For example, copper becomes radioactive when exposed to γ rays of sufficiently high quantum energy, which produce $_{29}Cu^{64}$ by the photonuclear reaction

$$_{29}Cu^{65}(\gamma,n)_{29}Cu^{64}$$

(*a*) Make appropriate use of the concepts of separation energy and of the quantitative formulation of the liquid-drop model to predict (say, ± 0.5 Mev) the minimum photon energy which can produce the 12-hr Cu^{64} activity in metallic copper.

(*b*) The measured value of the threshold photon energy for this reaction is 10.2 ± 0.2 Mev [McElhinney et al., *Phys. Rev.*, **75**: 542 (1949)]. Point out clearly what components of the nuclear binding energies cause this to exceed the average binding energy per nucleon, which is about 8.5 Mev in Cu^{65}.

(c) Qualitatively, would you expect the separation energy of a neutron from the stable nuclide $_{30}Zn^{67}$ to be appreciably greater or less than that of $_{29}Cu^{65}$? State why clearly but briefly.

9. (a) Show that the Q value of a (d,α) reaction on a target nucleus $M(Z,A)$ is

$$Q(d,\alpha) = B_\alpha - B_d - 2a_v + a_s[A^{\frac{2}{3}} - (A-2)^{\frac{2}{3}}]$$

$$+ a_c\left[\frac{Z^2}{A^{\frac{1}{3}}} - \frac{(Z-1)^2}{(A-2)^{\frac{1}{3}}}\right] - a_a\left[\frac{2(A-2Z)^2}{A(A-2)}\right] + \begin{cases} 2\delta: A \text{ even, } Z \text{ odd} \\ -2\delta: A \text{ even, } Z \text{ even} \\ 0: A \text{ odd, } Z \text{ anything} \end{cases}$$

where B_α and B_d are the binding energies of the α particle and the deuteron.

(b) Evaluate the local values of a_v, a_s, and δ from the measured Q values for the following reactions, by assuming that a_c and a_a are known.

$$\begin{aligned}
&Mg^{25}(d,\alpha)Na^{23}: Q = 7.019 \pm 0.013 \text{ Mev} \\
&Al^{27}(d,\alpha)Mg^{25}: \qquad\quad 6.694 \pm 0.010 \\
&Si^{29}(d,\alpha)Al^{27}: \qquad\quad 5.994 \pm 0.011 \\
&Si^{30}(d,\alpha)Al^{28}: \qquad\quad 3.120 \pm 0.010 \\
&P^{31}(d,\alpha)Si^{29}: \qquad\quad 8.158 \pm 0.011
\end{aligned}$$

10. (a) Derive from the semiempirical mass formula a general expression for the Q value of a (d,p) reaction on a target nucleus $M(Z,A)$. Evaluate the coefficients a_v and a_s by utilizing tabulated data on the Q value of (d,p) reactions (e.g., references B4, H22, and V3a).

(b) Will the Q values of (d,p) reactions give independent information on the pairing energy δ?

(c) Will the Q values of (d,n), (γ,n), and (n,γ) reactions give information on δ?

11. Show that the average binding energy per nucleon can be represented by

$$\frac{B}{A} = a_v - \frac{a_s}{A^{\frac{1}{3}}} - a_c\frac{Z^2}{A^{\frac{4}{3}}} - a_a\left(1 - \frac{2Z}{A}\right)^2 \mp \frac{\delta}{A}$$

Assuming that only a_c and a_a are known, derive for odd-A nuclides an expression for a_s as a function only of a_c, a_a, and A_0 (the mass number for which B/A has its empirical maximum), that is,

$$a_s = a_s(a_c, a_a, A_0)$$

and evaluate a_s in Mev.

12. (a) Reevaluate the coefficients a_c, a_a, a_s, and a_v under the assumption that the nuclear unit radius is $R_0 = 1.1 \times 10^{-13}$ cm. Note from Eq. (3.21) that a_a/a_c will remain unchanged. Evaluate a_s and a_v, using the masses of Cu^{65}, I^{127}, and Pt^{195} as given in Table 3.2.

(b) Estimate the masses of $_{82}Pb^{208}$ and $_{83}Bi^{209}$, using the coefficients derived above, and making allowances for the closed shells involved in both nuclides. Compare with the values reported by Richards, Hays, and Goudsmit (R17), from time-of-flight measurements, based on $C^{12} = 12.003\ 895$:

$$\begin{aligned}
Pb^{208} &= 208.0416 \pm 0.0015 \text{ amu} \\
Bi^{209} &= 209.0466 \pm 0.0015 \text{ amu}
\end{aligned}$$

13. From the considerations involved in Eq. (3.67) et seq., evaluate the minimum mass number A for which symmetric fission would result in a net release of energy. *Ans.:* $A \sim 85$.

14. Show that the neutron separation energy S_n is substantially 2δ greater in an **even-Z** even-N nuclide, such as U^{236}, than it is in a nearby even-Z odd-N nuclide, such as U^{239}. What consequences does this generalization have in the utilization of normal uranium as a nuclear fuel?

15. Estimate the partial half-period $(T_{\frac{1}{2}})_{\text{fission}}$ for spontaneous fission of $_{94}Pu^{240}$. What fraction of the Pu^{240} nuclei will be expected to decay by spontaneous fission if Pu^{240} is β-stable and has a half-period for α decay of $(T_{\frac{1}{2}})_{\alpha} = 6{,}580$ yr? *Ans.:* $\sim 5 \times 10^{11}$ yr; $\sim 1 \times 10^{-8}$.

16. If you were setting out to produce a β-stable isotope of the element $Z = 102$, approximately what mass number A would you probably have to produce? For this nuclide, what would be the approximate partial half-period against spontaneous fission? *Ans.:* $A \sim 266$; $T_{\frac{1}{2}} \sim 10^3$ yr.

4. *Statistical Model of Excited Levels*

The lowest excited level in most nuclei usually lies well above the ground level, a separation of the order of several hundred kilovolts being common. We have seen, for example, in the case of Cd^{111} (Fig. 8.5 of Chap. 6), that the angular momentum and parity of the lowest-lying excited levels in many nuclei are described correctly by the shell model, with jj coupling. In odd-A nuclides, the shell model represents these excited levels as due to the independent motion of the single odd-nucleon, which then occupies some higher quantum state. In its present stage of development, the shell model does not make general predictions about the magnitude of the excitation energy for these discrete low-lying levels.

At moderate excitation energies, in the domain, say, of 2 to 6 Mev, the excited levels are found to be more closely spaced (A10). In this region, a generally acceptable theory is not presently known. At still higher excitation energies, say, above about 6 Mev, the energy difference between successive levels is often as small as 10 to 100 ev. This is the energy domain of many nuclear reactions, and especially of the radiative capture of slow neutrons. In these (n,γ) reactions the compound nucleus is formed with an excitation energy equal to the neutron separation energy S_n, say, 6 to 8 Mev in all but the lightest nuclides.

At these higher excitation energies the independent-particle model becomes entirely inadequate. The very formation of a compound nucleus, whose subsequent behavior is found to be independent of its mode of formation, shows that the incident particle interacts strongly with all the nucleons in the target nucleus. These more highly excited levels are best viewed as quantized levels of the compound nucleus as a whole. The individual nucleons in the excited compound nucleus have strong interactions. They share the total excitation energy in some way which is too complicated for detailed analysis. One turns then to the methods of statistical mechanics and thermodynamics for aid in developing a qualitative model of the energetics of highly excited nuclear levels.

a. Bound and Virtual Levels. Bound levels are those for which the excitation energy E is insufficient to permit dissociation of the excited nucleus by particle emission $(n, p, \alpha, \ldots)$. Deexcitation of a *bound level* can occur only by γ-ray emission or by its competing internal conversion.

Figure 4.1 shows the presently known excited levels in N^{14}. Energetically, any level above 7.542 Mev (which equals the mass difference $C^{13} + H^1 - N^{14}$) is capable of dissociating by the emission of a proton, even though selection rules may prevent it for certain levels. Any level whose *excitation energy* exceeds the lowest dissociation energy, in this

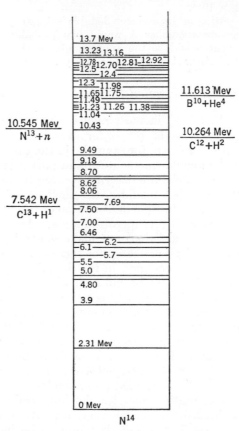

Fig. 4.1 The known excited levels in N^{14} and the mass difference (in Mev) between various possible dissociation products and the ground level of N^{14}. The *bound* levels are those below 7.542 Mev. Deexcitation of these can take place only by γ-ray emission or its ever-present competitor, internal conversion. Above 7.542 Mev all levels are called *virtual* because dissociation by particle emission is energetically possible. The gaps near 10 Mev represent a region which is not yet explored experimentally. [*Adapted from Ajzenberg and Lauritsen* (A10).]

case, 7.542 Mev, is called a *virtual level*. The virtual levels have many competing modes of deexcitation. For example, a virtual level at $E \sim 15$ Mev in N^{14} could transform by γ-ray emission or internal conversion to *any* lower-lying level, or by p, n, d, or α emission. In the cases of particle emission, the transition could be to the ground level or to an excited level in the product nuclei C^{13}, N^{13}, C^{12}, and B^{10}. Clearly, the higher the excitation energy, the larger is the number of possible competing modes of decay, or "exit channels."

b. **Level Width.** The width of a nuclear level is a completely quantum-mechanical concept. When the probability of deexcitation is included, a particular level can be represented by a wave function of the form

$$\Psi = \psi e^{-i(W-i\Gamma/2)t/\hbar} \tag{4.1}$$

where the energy $(W - i\Gamma/2)$ is complex. The probability $\Psi\Psi^*$ of finding the level intact after a time t will be proportional to $e^{-\Gamma t/\hbar}$. Thus $\Gamma/\hbar$ is the probability of decay per unit time, or the reciprocal of the mean life τ of the level. The energy Γ is called the *width* of the level and is related to the mean life τ by

$$\Gamma\tau = \hbar \tag{4.2}$$

This means that, because of its finite lifetime, the level cannot be said to have a perfectly sharply defined energy, and the uncertainties in energy and time are related as in the Heisenberg uncertainty principle, $\Delta E\, \Delta t \geq \hbar$. Inserting the numerical value of $\hbar$, Eq. (4.2) becomes

$$\Gamma = \frac{0.66 \times 10^{-15}}{\tau(\text{sec})} \qquad \text{ev} \tag{4.3}$$

Thus a bound level whose mean life against γ decay is 10^{-12} sec will have a width of only $\sim 10^{-3}$ ev. Even ground levels have a nonvanishing width because of the finite, though very small, probability of their transformation by fission, β decay, or other nuclear reaction.

It has not yet been possible to measure both Γ and τ for the same nuclear level, because $\hbar$ is so small. The width Γ has been measured for a number of excited levels. In N^{14}, for example, the levels whose excitation energy is in the domain of 11 to 13 Mev have measured widths of ~ 200 to 20 kev (Chap. 13, Table 4.1). The mean life of such levels is of the order of 10^{-20} sec.

Partial Width. Any level which has a number of possible competing modes of decay will have a corresponding number of "partial widths" Γ_i, each corresponding to the probability of decay by a particular mode. Then the *total width* of the level, which corresponds to the total probability of decay, is the sum of all the partial widths, or

$$\Gamma = \Gamma_1 + \Gamma_2 + \Gamma_3 + \cdots \tag{4.4}$$

c. **Relationship between Average Level Spacing and Level Width.** As the excitation energy increases, it is found experimentally that the level width Γ increases and that the average spacing between levels decreases. The levels are not uniformly spaced in energy, but for pictorial purposes it is convenient to think of an average energy spacing, or average "level distance," D in any particular region of excitation energy.

Recurrence Time for an Excited Configuration. Weisskopf (W22) has suggested a very simple semiclassical model, from which one may visualize the main features of a relationship between the average spacing D

of levels in a highly excited nucleus, the level width Γ, and the transparency T_l of the nuclear barrier at this excitation energy. Suppose that, within a *very large group of equally spaced levels*, all having the same value of total angular momentum and parity, the total energy of the nth level is $W_n = W_0 + nD$. Then a wave packet which represents a relatively well-defined grouping and motion of the nucleons can be constructed from a linear combination of the wave functions of a number of adjacent stationary states whose spatial dependence is φ_n. The total wave function will be of the form

$$\Psi = \sum_{n=1}^{n=N} a_n \varphi_n e^{-iW_n t/\hbar}$$

$$= e^{-iW_0 t/\hbar} \left(\sum_{n=1}^{n=N} a_n \varphi_n e^{-inDt/\hbar} \right) \tag{4.5}$$

where $e^{-iW_n t/\hbar}$ is the time-dependent part of the wave function for each of the neighboring states φ_n. The time dependence of the total wave function is seen from Eq. (4.5) to be such that $|\Psi|^2$ has the same value at time t and at a later time $t + 2\pi\hbar/D$. Thus the wave packet does not represent a stationary configuration but rather one which repeats itself, with a recurrence time Δt given by

$$\Delta t = \frac{2\pi\hbar}{D} \tag{4.6}$$

According to Bohr's correspondence principle, the motion for highly excited states, with very large quantum numbers, approaches a corresponding classical motion, which we can describe in this case as oscillation between the walls of a potential discontinuity at the edge of the nucleus. If we consider, for example, a spacing of $D = 10$ ev, then the recurrence time from Eq. (4.6) is $\sim 10^{-16}$ sec. In such a time interval, a nucleon traveling at the order of one-tenth the velocity of light (a few Mev of kinetic energy) would travel some 10^{-6} cm, or about a million nuclear diameters. This serves to emphasize, in a semiclassical way, the enormous complexity of the nuclear motion in a highly excited level. By way of contrast, the lowest-lying levels, with spacings of a few hundred kilovolts, would have much shorter recurrence times and therefore shorter recurrence path lengths, corresponding roughly to only some tens of nuclear diameters. This would be compatible with the orbital motion of independent particles, as visualized in the shell model for low-lying nuclear levels.

Transparency of the Nuclear Surface and Coulomb Barrier. Now we must recognize that these configurations are not exactly stationary states but that they have a finite probability of decay, which is $\Gamma/\hbar$ per unit time. For definiteness, we may think of a level at some 8-Mev excitation, which has just been produced by the capture of an incident nucleon. After a recurrence time $\Delta t = 2\pi\hbar/D$ this initial configuration will be repeated, and the nucleon would be back at the nuclear surface,

with its original velocity reestablished, and ready to leave the nucleus
if it is capable of penetrating the nuclear surface.   However, there is at
the nuclear surface a rapid change of potential, corresponding to the
absence outside the nucleus of the strong nuclear forces.   At this potential step the de Broglie wave, which represents the nucleon, suffers
reflection, and the nucleon returns to traverse once again its long path
through the nucleus.

Each time the nucleon reappears at the edge of the nucleus, it has a
finite probability of traversing the potential step and escaping from the
excited nucleus.   This event would correspond to the deexcitation of the
virtual level by dissociation.   The concept of a well-defined quasi-stationary virtual level is only possible if the reflection coefficient at the nuclear
surface is large.   Then the complicated motions visualized between
recurrence times will be repeated many times, and a well-defined level
could be found experimentally.   The transmission coefficient is given
by the familiar formula for a step barrier (Appendix C, Sec. 1, Prob. 6),
which reduces to simply $4k/K$ when the wave number k outside the
nucleus is small compared with the wave number K inside the nucleus.
If the emerging particle is charged, there will be a coulomb barrier to be
penetrated also.   Symbolically, we can represent the over-all transmission coefficient T_{al} for a particle a with emergent angular momentum l
as

$$\mathsf{T}_{al} \simeq \frac{4k}{K} P_{al} \qquad (4.7)$$

where P_{al} is the appropriate Gamow-type penetration factor for the combined coulomb and centrifugal barrier.   Then the excited level will have
a probability of decay per unit time $\Gamma/\hbar$ which is given semiclassically
by the transmission T_{al} times the number of recurrences per unit time,
$1/\Delta t = D/2\pi\hbar$, from which the partial width Γ_{al} is

$$\Gamma_{al} \simeq \mathsf{T}_{al} \frac{D_l}{2\pi}$$

$$\simeq \frac{4k}{K} P_{al} \frac{D_l}{2\pi} \qquad (4.8)$$

Reduced Width.   The factors which characterize the interior of the
nucleus may be conveniently grouped as a so-called *reduced width* γ_{al} by
rewriting Eq. (4.8) as

$$\Gamma_{al} = (2kRP_{al})\gamma_{al}$$

with
$$\gamma_{al} \equiv \frac{D_l}{\pi K R} \qquad (4.9)$$

where the nuclear radius R is introduced so that the reduced width has
the dimensions of energy and the first factor is dimensionless.†   Experi-

---

† The particular definition of reduced width given here is due to Blatt and Weisskopf (p. 390 of B68).   It differs only by the factor $1/R$ from the reduced width
defined earlier by Wigner, which has dimensions of Mev-centimeters and is usually
denoted in the periodical literature by the symbol γ^2, where $\gamma^2 = \Gamma_{al}/2kP_{al} \equiv R\gamma_{al}$.

mental data compiled by Wigner (W50) show that the ratio γ/D is roughly constant while γ and D individually vary over a range of $\sim 10^5$.

For the important special case of the emission or capture of s-wave neutrons ($l = 0$, $P_{al} = 1$), the particle width Γ_{al} is seen to vary with k and hence linearly with the velocity of the emitted or incident neutron. A well-defined resonance level for neutrons can be expected only when the width Γ_{al} is small compared with the level separation D_l. We see from Eq. (4.8) that this implies $k \ll K$, that is, an external neutron momentum $p = \hbar k$ which is small compared with the momentum of a nucleon inside the nucleus. Because the *total* width of the level is the sum of all the partial widths, the total width Γ can exceed the average separation D_l even when $k < K$.

d. Relationship between Excitation Energy and Average Level Spacing. As the excitation energy E increases, the total width Γ of the

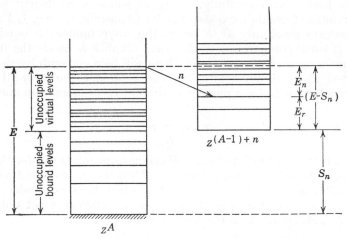

Fig. 4.2 Energetics of neutron dissociation of a virtual level. The kinetic energy E_n and the wave number k of the emitted neutron are given by Eq. (4.10).

excited level increases. Two distinct factors contribute to this increasing breadth. First, as E increases, more competing modes of deexcitation are available to the level. Second, as E increases, the barrier transparency T_{al} increases for each mode involving particle emission.

It is well demonstrated experimentally that the average spacing D_l of the levels decreases as we go up in excitation energy. This would mean, in Eq. (4.8), that the partial level width Γ_{al} would become narrower with increasing excitation energy, were it not for the fact that the increase in transparency T_{al} overrides the decrease in level spacing D_l as the excitation energy E increases. Physically, this can occur because a small change in E, and hence in D_l, can correspond to a very large change in k.

The physical situation is shown in Fig. 4.2. For definiteness, consider the nucleus $_zA$ in a virtual level whose excitation energy is E. Suppose that a neutron is emitted. Then the maximum kinetic energy of the emitted neutron will be $E - S_n$, where S_n is the neutron separation energy from $_zA$. But if the neutron emission leaves the residual nucleus $_z(A - 1)$ in an excited level E_r, then the kinetic energy $E_n = p^2/2M_n$ of the emitted neutron will be reduced to

$$E_n = \frac{p^2}{2M_n} = k^2 \frac{\hbar^2}{2M_n} = E - S_n - E_r \tag{4.10}$$

As long as $E_n \ll E$, the reduced width γ_{al} and the level spacing D_l will be only slightly influenced by small changes in E. On the other hand, E_n and k vary rapidly with E, especially just above the dissociation energy, where $E = S_n$.

Evaporation Model and Nuclear Temperature. Where a large number of closely spaced levels are involved, the methods of statistical mechanics may be applied as a guide to the possible behavior of highly excited nuclei. The emission of a neutron from an excited nucleus then becomes analogous to the evaporation of a molecule from a heated liquid droplet. The usual thermodynamic concepts of temperature, entropy, and heat capacity are applied to the nucleus. A clear summary of several forms of the theory has been given by Morrison (M57).

A general formulation of the statistical model has been developed by Weisskopf (W20, W25, W21, B68). For highly excited nuclear levels, the energy distribution of emitted neutrons is expected to be of the form

$$n \, d(E_n) \simeq \text{const} \times E_n e^{-E_n/T} \, d(E_n) \tag{4.11}$$

where $n \, d(E_n)$ neutrons should be emitted within the energy range E_n to $E_n + dE_n$. Here the quantity T is the *nuclear temperature of the residual nucleus*, evaluated at its maximum residual excitation energy

$$(E_r)_{\max} = E - S_n$$

(see Fig. 4.2). From Eq. (4.11) it is seen that T has the dimensions of an energy, as does its counterpart kT in the classical Maxwellian distribution of the energies of molecules evaporated from a surface at temperature T.

Figure 4.3 shows the general character of the expected energy distribution of neutrons "evaporated" from a highly excited nucleus. The statistical theory appears to be a good general guide for, say, $A > 50$. The smoothed, or continuous, spectrum represented by Eq. (4.11) should apply when the levels in the residual nucleus are so closely spaced that individual peaks in the neutron spectrum are not resolved. The preponderance of low-energy neutrons (small E_n in Fig. 4.2) is to be attributed to the joint influence of the larger number of excited levels available in the residual nucleus when E_n is small and E_r is large, and to the relatively much smaller dependence of the transparency T_{nl} on E_n. The maximum of the energy distribution is therefore shifted toward values of E_n which are small compared with its maximum possible value $(E_n)_{\max} = E - S_n$.

If the evaporated nucleons are protons instead of neutrons, then the coulomb barrier suppresses the low-energy protons, and the maximum of the expected distribution shifts to higher energies, as shown schematically in Fig. 4.3.

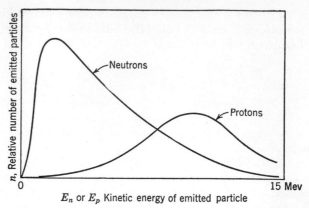

Fig. 4.3 Schematic energy spectrum for nucleons evaporated from a highly excited nucleus, as predicted by the statistical model.

The application of these considerations to real nuclei can be illustrated by Fig. 4.4, which shows the observed energy spectrum of neutrons emitted in the reaction $Au^{197}(p,n)Hg^{197}$ when a thin foil of gold is trav-

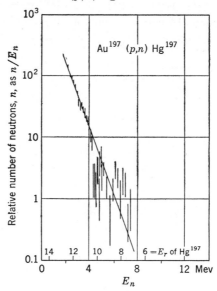

Fig. 4.4 Energy distribution of neutrons emitted in the reaction $Au^{197}(p,n)Hg^{197}$ with 16-Mev protons. E_n is the kinetic energy of the emitted neutrons; $E_r = 14.6 - E_n$ Mev is the excitation energy of the residual Hg^{197} nucleus. The slope of the experimental points corresponds to a nuclear "temperature" of $T = 0.8 \pm 0.1$ Mev in the residual Hg^{197} nucleus. [*Adapted from Gugelot (G47).*]

ersed by 16-Mev protons (G47). The Q value of this reaction is -1.4 Mev. Therefore the maximum neutron energy [compare Fig. 4.2 and Eq. (4.10)] is $(E_n)_{max} = E - S_n = 16 - 1.4$ Mev $= 14.6$ Mev. It will be seen from Fig. 4.4 that the smoothed distribution of unresolved neutron peaks is fairly well represented by an exponential function like that of Eq. (4.11). From the average slope of Fig. 4.4, the "nuclear temperature" of the residual Hg^{197} is $T = 0.8 \pm 0.1$ Mev.

Calculated Density of Levels in the Statistical Model. It also follows from Weisskopf's formulation of the statistical theory that, at large excitation energy E, the density of excited levels $1/D$, where D is the average distance between levels, should be roughly of the form

$$\frac{1}{D} = C e^{2(aE)^{\frac{1}{2}}} = C e^{2E/T} \tag{4.12}$$

where C and a are parameters which are functions of the mass number A and which are to be adjusted empirically. Generally C is evaluated from the observed level density at low excitation ($E \sim 1$ Mev), and a is adjusted to represent the spacing of levels found from the resonance capture of slow neutrons ($E \sim 6$ to 8 Mev).

Observed Density of (n,γ) Resonance Levels. Several experimental methods are accessible for determining the average spacing of highly excited levels in real nuclei (D35). One method depends upon measuring the average (n,γ) capture cross section for neutrons having a broad energy distribution centering about ~ 1 Mev. For each discrete excited level in the compound nucleus the capture cross section is described by the one-level resonance formula of Breit and Wigner (B118, F45, B141), which may be written [Chap. 14, Eqs. (1.10) and (1.13)]

$$\sigma(n,\gamma) = \pi \lambda^2 \left[\frac{2I_c + 1}{(2I_n + 1)(2I_t + 1)} \right] \frac{\Gamma_n \Gamma_\gamma}{(E_n - E_0)^2 + (\Gamma/2)^2} \tag{4.13}$$

where λ = rationalized de Broglie wavelength ($\lambda/2\pi$) of incident neutrons
$I_n = \frac{1}{2}$ = intrinsic angular momentum (spin) of bombarding neutron
I_t = intrinsic angular momentum (spin) of target nucleus
I_c = angular momentum of compound nucleus
E_n = kinetic energy of incident neutron
E_0 = kinetic energy of incident neutron which just forms excited level E of compound nucleus ($E_0 = E - S_n$)
Γ_γ = width of excited level for γ-ray emission
Γ_n = width of excited level for neutron emission
Γ = total width of excited level

When Eq. (4.13) is averaged over a number of resonance levels, whose average spacing is D_0, the result for the case of s-wave neutrons ($l = 0$) is simply (F45, H69)

$$\sigma(n,\gamma) = 2\pi^2 \lambda^2 \frac{\Gamma_\gamma}{D_0} \tag{4.14}$$

Hughes, Garth, and Levin (H68, H69) have measured the capture cross section $\sigma(n,\gamma)$ of a large number of nuclides for the prompt neutrons emitted during the fission of U^{235}. These neutrons have a continuous distribution of energy, with an effective value of ~ 1 Mev; hence they cover a number of adjacent resonances. The main effects are due to the capture of $l = 0$ or s-wave neutrons. The observed (n,γ) cross sections have been presented in Fig. 2.2 of Chap. 8. When these are inserted in Eq. (4.14), D_0 can be estimated, provided that the γ-radiation width Γ_γ is known. The experimental values of Γ_γ are about 0.1 ev for $A \simeq 100$ at an excitation energy of $E \sim 6$ to 8 Mev, and Γ_γ decreases slowly as A

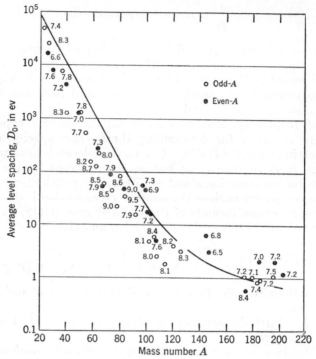

Fig. 4.5 Average spacing D_0 of excited levels in "nonmagic" nuclides, as determined from experimental values of $\sigma(n,\gamma)$ combined with Eq. (4.14). The experimental errors in $\sigma(n,\gamma)$ are of the order of 50 per cent, and so no significance is attached to deviations from the general trend. The actual excitation energy for each compound nucleus is shown numerically beside the individual points. The solid curve represents Eq. (4.12) with $E = 8.0$ Mev and Weisskopf's empirical evaluations of C and a from independent experimental data. [*From Hughes, Garth, and Levin* (H69).]

increases. Inserting these values, the average level spacings D_0 shown in Fig. 4.5 are found for "normal" nuclides, i.e., nuclides which do not involve a closed shell of neutrons. Within the accuracy of these values, there is no marked dependence of D_0 on the angular momentum I of the target nucleus, nor on whether Z is odd or even (so long as Z is not a closed shell).

All the target nuclides studied have even-N (except $_{71}Lu^{176}_{105}$). Those which have $N = 50$, 82, or 126 exhibit abnormally small capture cross sections $\sigma(n,\gamma)$. This is to be correlated with the relatively small binding of the 51st, 83rd, or 127th neutron, whose separation energy we have formerly found to be abnormally small. The compound nucleus $(Z, N + 1)$ therefore has a smaller excitation energy E when $N = 50$, 82, or 126. Consequently its level separation is expected to be greater and its $\sigma(n,\gamma)$ smaller than for nonmagic target nuclides. The experimental data suggest that, in addition to this expected effect, the level spacing in the compound nucleus $(Z, N + 1)$, when $N = 50$, 82, or 126, is about four times larger than expected on a basis of Eq. (4.12). This unusually wide separation of the levels in magic-plus-one compound nuclei provides additional information concerning the lower excited levels in the shell model.

It is significant that the variation of $\sigma(n,\gamma)$ with Z and N, for $\sim$1-Mev neutrons, simultaneously reveals features of the statistical model and of the shell model. Yet in their underlying assumptions these two models appear to be contradictory because the statistical model presupposes strong interactions between all nucleons, while the shell model is based on the presumption of noninteracting independent particles. In the transition region between small excitation energies, where the shell model is most applicable, and large excitation energies where the statistical model is applicable, we find physical phenomena which reflect some characteristics of both types of model.

CHAPTER 12

Conservation Laws for Nuclear Reactions

Much of our present knowledge of the structure of nuclei comes from experiments in which a particular chosen nuclide is bombarded with various types of projectiles. These projectiles may merely interact elastically (elastic scattering), or they may enter the nucleus and be reemitted with less energy (inelastic scattering), or one or more other types of particle may be emitted (nuclear reactions). We have considered in Chap. 6 the role played by nuclear angular momentum and parity in determining the course of nuclear reactions. We shall be concerned in the following three chapters mainly with the energetics of nuclear reactions, including the excitation energy of nuclear levels, the width of nuclear levels, and the cross sections for nuclear reactions.

Experiments have shown that there are a number of physical quantities which are rigorously conserved in all nuclear reactions. By "nuclear reaction" we understand for the present discussion any interaction between nucleons or aggregates of nucleons. We include elastic and inelastic scattering, ordinary reactions such as $B^{10}(\alpha,p)C^{13}$ in which a compound nucleus is formed, deuteron-stripping reactions, spallation reactions, and nuclear fission. We exclude temporarily radioactive β decay and those nuclear interactions which involve meson production or capture.

1. Physical Quantities Which Are Conserved in Nuclear Reactions

The conservation laws may be stated and illustrated by reference to some specific nuclear reaction, say,

$$_5B^{10} + {}_2He^4 \rightarrow ({}_7N^{14}) \rightarrow {}_1H^1 + {}_6C^{13} + Q \tag{1.1}$$

which is representative of the large and important class of reactions in which a compound nucleus is formed.

a. Charge. Total charge is conserved in every type of nuclear reaction. In $B^{10}(\alpha,p)C^{13}$ there are seven protons initially, also seven in the compound nucleus and in the products of the reaction. In all such reactions, we may say for brevity

$$\Sigma Z = \text{const} \tag{1.2}$$

b. Mass Number. The total number of nucleons entering and leaving the reaction is constant. In $B^{10}(\alpha,p)C^{13}$, we find 14 nucleons at each stage of the reaction. Generalizing, we write

$$\Sigma A = \text{const} \tag{1.3}$$

where A is mass number. When the total number of protons is conserved, Eq. (1.3) implies that the total number of neutrons ΣN also is conserved, or

$$\Sigma N = \text{const} \tag{1.4}$$

In β decay and in charged meson production or capture, Eq. (1.3) is still valid, but ΣZ and ΣN are not separately conserved. With the exception of Eqs. (1.2) and (1.4), all the conservation laws which are under review here are applicable to every type of nuclear transformation and reaction.

c. Statistics. Both sides of a reaction such as Eq. (1.1) involve the same total number of fermions; hence the statistics is either Fermi-Dirac throughout (for odd ΣA) or Einstein-Bose throughout (for even ΣA).

d. Angular Momentum. The total nuclear angular momentum is always a constant of the motion. In Eq. (1.1), B^{10} has $I = 3$, while the α particle is spinless. If the incident capture is by s wave ($l_i = 0$), then the compound intermediate nucleus must have $I_c = 3$. Both C^{13} and H^1 have $I = \frac{1}{2}$ and can therefore add vectorially to either 1 or 0. Then the mutual angular momentum l_f of the final products C^{13} and H^1 is restricted by angular-momentum conservation to $l_f = 2$, 3, or 4, if $I_c = 3$.

e. Parity. In every type of nuclear reaction, total parity is conserved. From the shell model, the parity of the ground level of B^{10}, He^4, and H^1 is even, while that of C^{13} is odd. In the $B^{10}(\alpha,p)C^{13}$ reaction, the input parity, for s-wave capture of the α particle, is therefore even. Then the particular excited level in the compound nucleus N^{14} must also have even parity. In the exit channel, C^{13} has odd parity; hence the requirement of even total parity puts an additional restriction on l_f and permits only $l_f = 3$, if $l_i = 0$.

f. Linear Momentum. As in all isolated mechanical systems, linear momentum is found to be conserved in every type of nuclear interaction. If the target particle is initially at rest, the linear momentum brought into the reaction by the projectile will later be found distributed among the reaction products. In the center-of-mass coordinates, the total linear momentum is zero at all times.

g. Mass-Energy. In nuclear reactions neither kinetic energy nor rest mass is conserved by itself. But their total is always conserved. The clear experimental evidence was reviewed in Chap. 3, Sec. 4. The kinetic energy Q "liberated" in any reaction is always equal to the reduction in the total rest mass of all the constituents of the reaction, the equivalence being given by

$$1 \text{ Mev} = 0.001\ 074 \text{ amu} \tag{1.5}$$

In Eq. (1.1), the Q value of the reaction is

$$M_{\text{B}^{10}} + M_{\text{He}^4} = M_{\text{H}^1} + M_{\text{C}^{13}} + Q \tag{1.6}$$

where all masses are rest masses for the corresponding neutral atoms. If relativistic masses were used in Eq. (1.6), then the Q value for every reaction would be identically zero.

h. Isobaric Spin. To the extent that the specifically nuclear forces are truly charge-independent, it is expected theoretically that total isobaric spin is conserved in any nuclear reaction, in a manner analogous to the conservation of total angular momentum. There is increasing experimental evidence that isobaric-spin selection rules may operate in all nuclear reactions (A4, I4, A10, E14). For example, the reaction $\text{O}^{16}(d,\alpha)\text{N}^{14*}$ seems never to go to the particular excited level at 2.3 Mev in N^{14}, although this is not forbidden by angular momentum, parity, or energy considerations. Because the isobaric spin is zero for O^{16}, the deuteron, and the α particle, it is consistent with other evidence to infer that the 2.3-Mev level in N^{14} is the isobaric-spin state $T = 1$ analogous to the ground levels of its isobars C^{14} and O^{14}.

i. Quantities Not Conserved. The most prominent physical characteristics which are *not* conserved in nuclear reactions are the magnetic dipole moments and the electric quadrupole moments of the reacting nuclei. These moments depend upon the internal distribution of mass, charge, and current within the nuclei involved and are not subject to conservation laws.

2. *Determination of the Q Value for Nuclear Reactions*

The Q value, or "nuclear disintegration energy," is expressed in center-of-mass coordinates by Eq. (4.17) of Chap. 3 as the change in total kinetic energy, $Q = (T_0)_{\text{out}} - (T_0)_{\text{in}}$. Because Q is also the change in total rest mass, Q must have the same value in laboratory coordinates as it has in center-of-mass coordinates.

a. The Q Equation. The so-called Q equation for nuclear reactions is an analytical relationship between the nuclear disintegration energy Q and the kinetic energy of the incident and product particles, as measured in the laboratory coordinates. We consider here the nonrelativistic case, in which the kinetic energy E_i of each particle is small compared with its rest energy $M_i c^2$.

In the following equations, we adopt the notation shown in Fig. 2.1. Conservation of mass-energy gives

$$E_1 + Q = E_3 + E_4 \tag{2.1}$$

Conservation of linear momentum, in the direction of the incident particle, gives

$$\sqrt{2M_1 E_1} = \sqrt{2M_3 E_3} \cos \vartheta + \sqrt{2M_4 E_4} \cos \varphi \tag{2.2}$$

The linear momentum, in a direction normal to the plane containing ϑ, is zero.   Therefore ϑ and φ are coplanar.   Conservation of linear momentum in the ϑ, φ plane gives

$$0 = \sqrt{2M_3E_3}\,\sin\vartheta - \sqrt{2M_4E_4}\,\sin\varphi \qquad (2.3)$$

These three conservation equations are valid only if the system (M_1, M_2, M_c, M_3, M_4) is an isolated system.   Collisions by any of these particles with other atoms or nuclei (as in a dense target) could result in energy losses or momentum changes which would invalidate one or more of Eqs. (2.1) to (2.3).   Usually the mean life of the compound nucleus (or of the intermediate system when no compound nucleus is actually formed) is so short that M_c loses no appreciable energy by ionization prior to its dissociation into M_3 and M_4.

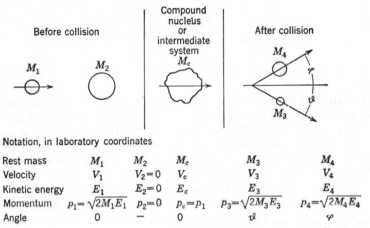

Notation, in laboratory coordinates					
Rest mass	M_1	M_2	M_c	M_3	M_4
Velocity	V_1	$V_2=0$	V_c	V_3	V_4
Kinetic energy	E_1	$E_2=0$	E_c	E_3	E_4
Momentum	$p_1=\sqrt{2M_1E_1}$	$p_2=0$	$p_c=p_1$	$p_3=\sqrt{2M_3E_3}$	$p_4=\sqrt{2M_4E_4}$
Angle	0	—	0	ϑ	φ

Fig. 2.1   Dynamics of two-body nuclear reactions, in laboratory coordinates.   Some reactions do not involve the formation of a well-defined compound nucleus, but this is not necessary for the validity of the Q equation.

By a simultaneous solution of Eqs. (2.1), (2.2), and (2.3), we can eliminate *any two* parameters.   In the most common experimental situation, measurements are made at chosen angles ϑ on the energy E_3 of the lighter particle [e.g., the emitted proton in Eq. (1.1)].   If we algebraically eliminate the energy E_4 and direction φ of the residual nucleus [the C^{13} nucleus in Eq. (1.1)], then the simultaneous solution of Eqs. (2.1), (2.2), and (2.3) is

$$Q = E_3\left(1 + \frac{M_3}{M_4}\right) - E_1\left(1 - \frac{M_1}{M_4}\right) - \frac{2\sqrt{M_1E_1M_3E_3}}{M_4}\cos\vartheta \qquad (2.4)$$

This is the conventional form of "the Q equation."   Here the kinetic energies E_1 of the incident particle and E_3 of the product particle, as well as the angle ϑ, are all *measured in laboratory coordinates*.   Equation (2.4) is independent of the mechanism of the reaction (compound nucleus, stripping, scattering, fission, etc.).   The mass factors can be viewed as momentum correction terms.   In many applications of the Q equation, the masses may be replaced without significant error by the corresponding integer-valued mass numbers A_1, A_2, A_3, A_4. For more accurate work, the neutral atomic masses M_i are used. Corrections to M_i for ionized atoms (e.g., a proton, not a neutral hydrogen atom) may occasionally be justified, but at this degree of accuracy other uncertainties usually become of comparable or greater magnitude. Notice that the third term in Eq. (2.4) vanishes at $\vartheta = 90°$.

b. General Solution of the Q Equation. The variation of E_3 with E_1, for a fixed Q, can be visualized most readily by regarding the Q equation as a quadratic in $\sqrt{E_3}$. Then its general solution can be put in the form

$$\sqrt{E_3} = v \pm \sqrt{v^2 + w} \tag{2.5}$$

where

$$v \equiv \frac{\sqrt{M_1 M_3 E_1}}{M_3 + M_4} \cos \vartheta \tag{2.6}$$

$$w \equiv \frac{M_4 Q + E_1(M_4 - M_1)}{M_3 + M_4} \tag{2.7}$$

The energetically possible reactions are those for which $\sqrt{E_3}$ is real and positive.

The physical factors which can contribute toward making a particular angle of emission of M_3 energetically impossible are seen to be a negative Q value, a heavy projectile such that $(M_4 - M_1)$ is negative, and a large angle of observation ϑ such that $\cos \vartheta$ is negative. The behavior of Eq. (2.5), in various energy domains E_1 of the incident particle, provides a guide to the types of nuclear reactions which can occur.

At relativistic velocities, the Q equation and its solutions become much more complicated. Relativistic treatments have been given by Bacon (B2), Blaton (B65), Morrison (M57), and others. Brown et al. (B130) have pointed out that all the nonrelativistic equations become relativistically correct if one substitutes for each rest mass M_i the quantity $M_i + E_i/2c^2$, where E_i is the particle's kinetic energy in L coordinates. This method is convenient for mildly relativistic cases, where the resulting equations can usually be solved by successive approximations. If one of the "particles" is a photon, it is always correct to give it an effective rest mass of $h\nu/2c^2$.

c. Energetics of Exoergic Reactions. Nuclear reactions are divided energetically into two classes. *Exoergic reactions* have positive Q values; the kinetic energy of the products exceeds that of the input particles. *Endoergic reactions* have negative Q values, and a corresponding excess kinetic energy must be put into the reaction, through the projectile particle, in order to make the reaction energetically possible.

In summarizing the energetic behavior of all exoergic reactions we focus our attention on the energy E_3 and direction ϑ of one of the disintegration particles, as the incident energy E_1 is gradually increased. The following cases, for $Q > 0$, then arise directly from the Q equation as expressed in Eq. (2.5).

"Zero" Bombarding Energy $(E_1 \simeq 0)$. These cases are illustrated best by certain thermal neutron reactions, such as $B^{10}(n,\alpha)Li^7$, for which

$Q = +2.8$ Mev. Then for $E_1 \to 0$, Eqs. (2.5) to (2.7) give $v \to 0$, $w \to QM_4/(M_3 + M_4)$, and

$$E_3 = Q \frac{M_4}{M_3 + M_4} \qquad Q > 0 \qquad (2.8)$$

The kinetic energy E_3 is the same for all angles ϑ. Physically, this is because the total momentum in L coordinates is effectively zero when $E_1 \to 0$. Then also

$$E_3 + E_4 = Q \qquad \text{and} \qquad \vartheta + \varphi = 180° \qquad (2.9)$$

Finite Bombarding Energy. The most common case is that in which the projectile M_1 is lighter than the unobserved particle M_4. Then, by Eq. (2.7), w is positive for all values of the bombarding energy. In turn, only one of the two solutions offered by Eq. (2.5) will be positive. Then E_3 is single-valued for all values of the bombarding energy and is given by

$$\sqrt{E_3} = v + \sqrt{v^2 + w} \qquad Q > 0, \, M_4 > M_1 \qquad (2.10)$$

Here E_3 depends on $\cos \vartheta$, through Eq. (2.6), and is smallest in the backward direction $\vartheta = 180°$. At $\vartheta = 90°$, $E_3 = w$. The reaction $B^{10}(\alpha,p)C^{13}$, for which $Q = +4.0$ Mev, is illustrative of Eq. (2.10) when the proton is the observed particle M_3.

Double Values of E_3. A number of situations arise in which E_3 is not single-valued. For example, in the reaction $B^{10}(\alpha,p)C^{13}$, if the observed particle M_3 is chosen as the residual C^{13}, then $M_3 \simeq A_3 = 13$, and $M_4 \simeq A_4 = 1$. Then Eq. (2.7) becomes

$$w = \frac{Q - 3E_1}{14} \qquad (2.11)$$

which is *negative* for all α-ray bombarding energies greater than

$$E_1 = \frac{Q}{3} = 1.33 \text{ Mev}$$

For E_1 greater than 1.33 Mev, Eq. (2.5) now gives two real positive values of $\sqrt{E_3}$ at $\vartheta = 0$. Thus in the forward direction there are *two monoenergetic groups* of C^{13} nuclei. Physically, these two groups correspond to C^{13} nuclei which, in the center-of-mass coordinates, are projected straight forward and straight backward. The backward-directed group is carried forward in the laboratory coordinates whenever the velocity of the center of mass is larger than the velocity of C^{13} in the C coordinates. Note also from Eq. (2.5) that, for $\cos \vartheta < 0$, and $E_1 > Q/3$, $\sqrt{E_3}$ is always negative, and there are no C^{13} particles projected at $\vartheta \geq 90°$ in L coordinates.

d. **Energetics of Endoergic Reactions.** For every nuclear reaction with a positive Q value, the inverse reaction has a negative Q value of exactly equal absolute magnitude. Thus $C^{13}(p,\alpha)B^{10}$ must have $Q = -4.0$ Mev, as the inverse of Eq. (1.1).

The number of endoergic reactions for which negative Q values have been precisely measured is not large, but several of these reactions are of special importance. As an example, the value $Q = -1.6457 \pm 0.002$ Mev for the reaction $Li^7(p,n)Be^7$ serves as a reference standard for the determination of the Q values of a number of other reactions, in the determination of mass values from nuclear disintegration data (L27).

The energetics of the negative Q reactions can be summarized also by reference to Eq. (2.5).

"Zero" Bombarding Energy. When Q is negative, and $E_1 \to 0$, Eq. (2.7) gives a negative value for $v^2 + w$. Hence $\sqrt{E_3}$ is imaginary. No reaction occurs. Physically, there is insufficient incident kinetic energy to provide for the required increase in rest mass.

Threshold Energy. The smallest value of bombarding energy at which the reaction can take place is called the threshold energy, $(E_1)_{thres}$. In terms of Eq. (2.5), the reaction first becomes possible when E_1 is large enough to make $v^2 + w = 0$. This occurs, in general, when

$$(E_1)_\vartheta = -Q\left[\frac{M_3 + M_4}{M_3 + M_4 - M_1 - (M_1 M_3/M_4)\sin^2\vartheta}\right] \tag{2.12}$$

If the product particle M_3 is observed at $\vartheta = 0$, then E_1 has its minimum possible value, which is the *threshold energy*

$$(E_1)_{thres} = -Q\left(\frac{M_3 + M_4}{M_3 + M_4 - M_1}\right) \tag{2.13}$$

This can be simplified somewhat by utilizing the general relationship between Q and the rest masses, which is

$$M_1 + M_2 = M_3 + M_4 + \frac{Q}{c^2} \tag{2.14}$$

Then, to an excellent approximation (namely, $M_2 \gg Q/c^2$), Eq. (2.13) becomes

$$(E_1)_{thres} = -Q\left(\frac{M_1 + M_2}{M_2}\right) \tag{2.15}$$

Physically, the kinetic energy $(T_0)_{in}$ available in the C coordinates is always

$$(T_0)_{in} = E_1 - E_c = E_1 \frac{M_0}{M_1} = E_1 \frac{M_2}{M_1 + M_2} \tag{2.16}$$

where M_0 is the reduced mass of M_1 and M_2. Therefore the kinetic energy of the reaction products, in C coordinates, is always

$$(T_0)_{out} = E_1 \frac{M_2}{M_1 + M_2} + Q \tag{2.17}$$

and Eq. (2.15) merely expresses the physical fact that, at the reaction threshold, $(T_0)_{out} = 0$. Thus, at threshold, the products of the reaction are formed with zero mutual velocity in the C coordinates. The velocity which they have in the L coordinates is due entirely to the motion of the center of mass.

At the threshold of the reaction, particles first appear, in the $\vartheta = 0$ direction, with the kinetic energy

$$E_3 = v^2 = (E_1)_{\text{thres}} \left[\frac{M_1 M_3}{(M_3 + M_4)^2} \right] \tag{2.18}$$

As the bombarding energy is raised, particles M_3 begin to appear at $\vartheta > 0$. In accord with Eq. (2.12), the particles first appear at $\vartheta \geq 90°$ (and with zero energy E_3) when $w = 0$, which is equivalent to

$$(E_1)_{90°} = -Q \left(\frac{M_4}{M_4 - M_1} \right) \tag{2.19}$$

Double Values of E_3. As the bombarding energy E_1 is increased above threshold, the disintegration particle designated by M_3 can appear in the forward direction with either of two discrete values of kinetic energy E_3. These two monoenergetic groups correspond mathematically to the two real and positive values of $\sqrt{E_3}$, given by Eq. (2.5) within a domain of bombarding energy E_1 which is specified by the inequalities

$$0 \leq (v^2 + w) \leq v^2 \tag{2.20}$$

This can be shown to be equivalent to

$$(E_1)_\vartheta \leq E_1 \leq (E_1)_{90°} \tag{2.21}$$

where $(E_1)_\vartheta$ and $(E_1)_{90°}$ are given by Eqs. (2.12) and (2.19).

Of course, in the C coordinates there is only one possible value for the kinetic energy of M_3 at any particular bombarding energy E_1. But some of these M_3 particles are moving "forward" and some "backward" in C coordinates. When their velocities are added vectorially to the velocity V_c of the center of mass, two monoenergetic groups of M_3 particles can appear in the forward direction in L coordinates whenever V_c is more than the velocity of M_3 in C coordinates. This is the domain of E_1 between $(E_1)_\vartheta$ and $(E_1)_{90°}$. Over this domain there are no M_3 particles emitted at $\vartheta > 90°$ in L coordinates.

All these generalizations concerning the energetics of negative Q reactions are illustrated by Fig. 2.2, which is drawn for the particular case of $\text{Li}^7(p,n)\text{Be}^7$.

Higher Bombarding Energies. In endoergic reactions, E_3 becomes single-valued for all laboratory directions ϑ when the bombarding energy E_1 exceeds $(E_1)_{90°}$, as given by Eq. (2.19). This corresponds to values of E_1 which are large enough to make w positive in Eq. (2.5). Physically, the kinetic energy of the reaction products is now large enough that M_3 can be projected in the backward direction in L coordinates. For this to be possible, it is also necessary that M_3 be lighter than the target nucleus. The heavy fragment from a negative Q reaction can never be projected in the backward direction $\vartheta > 90°$. This is evident from contemplation of the momenta involved, or it can be asserted as a direct consequence of Eq. (2.7). When $Q < 0$, w is always negative if $M_4 < M_1$; hence $M_3 > M_2$.

e. Energetics of Scattering. The general Q equation and its solutions for $\sqrt{E_3}$ describe also the L-coordinate energetics of all scattering interactions.

For *elastic scattering*, $Q = 0$. If the angular distribution of the incident particle M_1 is observed, then $M_3 = M_1$. The kinetic energy E_3 of the elastically scattered particle is then given as a function of scattering angle ϑ by Eq. (2.5), with $Q = 0$, $M_3 = M_1$, and $M_4 = M_2$.

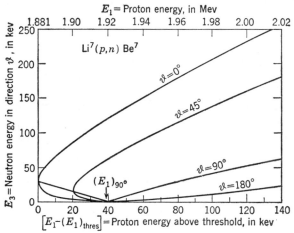

Fig. 2.2 Energetics of negative Q reactions, illustrated by the case of $Li^7(p,n)Be^7$, for which $Q = -1.646$ Mev (L27). All energies and angles are in laboratory coordinates. Note that the reaction first takes place at the threshold bombarding energy of $(E_1)_{thres} = 1.881$ Mev, when neutrons of energy $E_3 = 0.0294$ Mev suddenly appear in the $\vartheta = 0$ direction. As E_1 is further increased, neutrons can be emitted within a small forward cone, whose angle increases as E_1 increases, until at $(E_1)_{90°} = 1.920$ Mev all directions of neutron emission become energetically allowed. In the double-valued region, the diagonal straight line relates the neutron energy E_3 to the smallest bombarding energy $(E_1)\vartheta$ at which neutrons can be emitted in the direction ϑ, as given by Eq. (2.12).

Analogously, the energy of the recoiling target particle is given also by Eq. (2.5) by writing $M_3 = M_2$, $M_4 = M_1$.

In *inelastic scattering*, the struck nucleus is left in an excited level after the collision. If W is the excitation energy given to M_2 in the collision, then the angular dependence of the kinetic energy of the scattered particles is described by the Q equation with $Q = -W$, $M_3 = M_1$, and $M_4 = M_2$.

f. Measurement of Q Values. The experimental problems encountered in the measurement of Q values for various types of nuclear reactions are many and varied. We can review here only the fundamental objectives and a few of the basic experimental approaches. The reader will be well rewarded by a study of the original experimental papers in the periodical literature. An abundant bibliography will be found in any recent compilation of experimental results of Q-value measurements (A10, B13, B141, V3a).

Usually the masses M_1, M_2, M_3, and M_4 can be taken as known with sufficient accuracy for the momentum correction terms in the Q equation. Indeed, the corresponding mass numbers A_1, A_2, A_3, and A_4 are often sufficient. The incident energy E_1 of the projectile must be known accurately. Originally, the α rays from radioactive substances were the only projectiles available. E_1 was then determined by the nature of the α-ray source (polonium, RaC', etc.). With artificially accelerated particles, E_1 has to be determined for each experiment. This is accomplished by range measurements or, much more accurately, by magnetic deflection or electrostatic deflection and focusing of the accelerated particles. The magnetic and electrostatic elements are similar in principle to those used in mass spectroscopy (Chap. 3).

The measurement of the energy E_3 of the emitted particle, at selected angles ϑ, is accomplished also by range measurements, or by magnetic deflection, or by electrostatic deflection (B138, B106, W61). If the emitted radiation is uncharged (neutron, or γ ray), then the energy measurements have to be carried out on charged secondary radiations, produced in "converter" materials by these uncharged primaries.

Special attention must also be given to the target preparation. Usually a very thin target is desirable, so that the incident and emergent particles will lose as little energy as possible by ionization in the depth of the target. The chemical and physical composition of the target presents many special problems. In general, the physical target will contain many nuclides besides the one on which measurements are desired. The effects of "unwanted" nuclides may have to be identified and excluded by measurements on several targets in which the wanted nuclide appears in varying proportion.

Problems

1. The following reaction takes place in a target of a cyclotron whose deuteron-beam energy is not known accurately but is nearly homogeneous.

$$H^2 + C^{12} \rightarrow He^4 + B^{10}$$

From the known behavior of α rays, the energy of the emitted light particles can be determined with considerable accuracy. It is found that at 90° from the deuteron beam the mean energy of the α-ray group of greatest energy is 8.18 Mev. At 60° from the deuteron beam, the energy of the same group of α rays is 10.84 Mev. From these data alone, find the energy of the deuteron beam and also the Q value of the $C^{12}(d,\alpha)B^{10}$ reaction. *Ans.*: $E_1 = 16.00$ Mev; $Q = -1.35$ Mev.

2. (*a*) Calculate the Q value for the reaction $H^3(d,n)He^4$, based on the masses of the reacting particles.

(*b*) Write an expression for the neutron energy for this particular reaction, in terms of the deuteron energy E_1 and the angle ϑ between the direction of the deuteron and the neutron.

(*c*) In what direction will the neutron energy be smallest?

(*d*) Deuterons of any energy between $E_1 = 1$ Mev and 6 Mev are available. At what deuteron energy will this neutron energy be smallest? Why?

(*e*) What is this smallest possible energy?

(*f*) Explain physically why the smallest possible neutron energy does *not* occur at the smallest possible deuteron energy.

Ans.: (*d*) $E_1 = Q/3 = 5.87$ Mev; (*e*) 11.7 Mev.

3. The reaction $H^3(p,n)He^3$ has a negative Q value of $Q = -0.764$ Mev.

(*a*) What is the minimum energy of a proton, in the laboratory coordinates, which will just produce He^3 by bombardment of H^3?

(*b*) What is the minimum energy of a triton (H^3), in the laboratory coordinates, which will just produce He^3 by bombardment of H^1?

4. Neutrons from the $Li^7(p,n)Be^7$ reaction are to be observed at a laboratory angle of $\vartheta = 30°$.

(*a*) Compute and plot a graph of E_3 (neutron energy) vs. E_1 (proton energy) for $1.88 \leq E_1 \leq 2.02$ Mev.

(*b*) At what bombarding energy are neutrons of zero energy obtained?

5. Show that the "*d*-on-*d*" reaction ($H^2 + H^2 \rightarrow n + He^3$) gives monoenergetic neutrons, of energy E_n, at 90° to the direction of incident deuterons of energy E_1, where

$$E_n = 2.45 + \frac{E_1}{4} \qquad \text{Mev}$$

6. Use the Q equation to show that, in an elastic collision, the kinetic energy acquired by the struck particle is

$$E_2 = 4E_1 \frac{M_1 M_2}{(M_1 + M_2)^2} \cos^2 \vartheta$$

Compare with Eq. (29) of Appendix B.

7. The radioactive isotope $_{18}A^{37}$ can be produced by $_{17}Cl^{37}(d,2n)$. In its disintegration back into Cl^{37}, A^{37} emits only a very soft radiation which may be very-low-energy positron β rays or may be X rays or a possible soft γ ray following orbital electron capture. Show that the threshold deuteron energy for producing $Cl^{37}(d,2n)A^{37}$ must be (*a*) greater than 4.25 Mev if A^{37} emits positrons and (*b*) between 3.17 and 4.25 Mev if A^{37} decays by electron capture only. (*c*) Why is the difference between the limits in (*b*) *not* equal to $2m_0c^2$?

✓**8.** A number of nuclear reactions of the (p,n) type result in the formation of a radioactive nuclide which transforms by positron emission and thus returns to identity with the original target nucleus. For example,

$$_{29}Cu^{63}(p,n)_{30}Zn^{63}, \text{ followed by } _{30}Zn^{63} \rightarrow \beta^+ + _{29}Cu^{63}$$

The same nuclides can often be produced by a $(d,2n)$ reaction, thus,

$$_{29}Cu^{63}(d,2n)_{30}Zn^{63}$$

followed by the positron β-ray transformation back to $_{29}Cu^{63}$. Show that the Q value for the $(d,2n)$ reaction is always

$$Q = -4.02 - U \qquad \text{Mev}$$

where U is the sum of the maximum energy of the positron spectrum plus the energy of any γ rays emitted by the final nucleus in reaching ground level after the positron is emitted. Compare this result with the analogous relationship $Q = -1.80 - U$ (Mev) for the (p,n) reaction, and explain the physical basis for the difference of $4.02 - 1.80 = 2.22$ Mev in the constant terms of the two expressions.

9. About 35 per cent of the disintegrations of Mn^{52} follow the β^+ decay scheme shown (there is also $\sim$65 per cent EC).

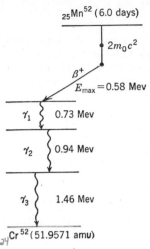

$_{25}Mn^{52}$ (6.0 days)

$2m_0c^2$

β^+

$E_{max} = 0.58$ Mev

γ_1 0.73 Mev

γ_2 0.94 Mev

γ_3 1.46 Mev

$_{24}Cr^{52}$ (51.9571 amu)

(a) Compute the mass of the neutral atom of Mn^{52}.
(b) Find the threshold proton bombarding energy for the reaction

$$Cr^{52}(p,n)Mn^{52}$$

10. Assume that the fission of U^{235}, following capture of a thermal neutron, releases 170 Mev of kinetic energy and that the resulting fission fragments have mass numbers 139 and 97. What is the kinetic energy of the lighter fission fragment?

11. In the spontaneous decay of π^+ mesons at rest, according to $\pi^+ \rightarrow \mu^+ + \nu$, the μ^+ mesons are observed to have a kinetic energy of 4.0 Mev. If the rest mass of the μ^+ meson is taken as $212m_0$, and that of the neutrino ν is taken as zero, what is the rest mass of the π^+ meson in units of the electron mass m_0?

12. A neutral π meson of rest mass M_0 is moving at velocity βc in the laboratory coordinates and hence has relativistic total energy $Mc^2 = M_0c^2/(1 - \beta^2)^{\frac{1}{2}}$, when it dissociates into two photons according to the reaction $\pi^0 \rightarrow 2h\nu$. Show from

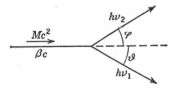

Mc^2

βc

$h\nu_2$

φ

ϑ

$h\nu_1$

conservation of momentum and energy that a photon emitted at angle ϑ in the laboratory coordinates will have an energy $h\nu = Mc^2(1 - \beta^2)/2(1 - \beta \cos \vartheta)$ and that the maximum and minimum photon energies are

$$h\nu(max) = \tfrac{1}{2}Mc^2(1 + \beta) \qquad \text{for } \vartheta = 0$$
$$h\nu(min) = \tfrac{1}{2}Mc^2(1 - \beta) \qquad \text{for } \vartheta = 180°$$

13. It is assumed that neutral π mesons, when at rest, emit quanta isotropically; $\pi^0 \rightarrow 2h\nu$. If the mesons are moving with velocity βc in the laboratory coordinates, show that the number of quanta per unit solid angle, observed at the

laboratory angle ϑ, is given by

$$I(\vartheta) = k \left[\frac{M_0}{M} \frac{1}{(1 - \beta \cos \vartheta)} \right]^2$$

where k is a constant.

14. Mesons are produced by bombarding a target nucleus M_2 with an energetic particle M_1. The product particles are the meson M_3 and the residual mass M_4. Let E_1 be the kinetic energy of M_1 in the laboratory system.

(a) Using *relativistic* relations, show that the velocity V_c of the center of mass is given by

$$\frac{M_1 V_1}{\sqrt{1 - V_1^2/c^2}} = V_c \left(M_2 + \frac{M_1}{\sqrt{1 - V_1^2/c^2}} \right)$$

where V_1 is the velocity of M_1 in the laboratory, and that the total kinetic energy in the center-of-mass coordinates is

$$E_0 = (M_1 + M_2)c^2 \left[\sqrt{1 + \frac{2M_2 E_1}{(M_1 + M_2)^2 c^2}} - 1 \right]$$

(b) At threshold $E_0 = -Q$, show that the threshold energy in laboratory coordinates is

$$E_1 = \frac{[(M_3 + M_4)^2 - (M_1 + M_2)^2]c^2}{2M_2}$$

Either use the results of (a) or derive the expression for threshold energy directly from relativistic conservation of momentum and energy in the laboratory system alone.

(c) Calculate the threshold energy for meson production for the following reactions:

$$p(\gamma,\pi^+)n$$
$$C^{12}(d,\pi^+)C^{14}$$

using a π^+ meson mass of 276 electron masses.

15. Suppose the compound nucleus formed by 5-Mev α rays in the reaction $B^{10}(\alpha,p)C^{13}$ has a level width $\Gamma_p \sim 1$ kev. What is the average linear distance traveled by the compound nucleus before it dissociates into $p + C^{13}$? Discuss semiqualitatively the probability of a significant loss of kinetic energy by the compound nucleus as a result of ionizing collisions in (a) a solid boron target and (b) a gaseous target of, say, BF_3.

16. Show that the general solution of the Q equation, for E_3, can also be written as

$$\sqrt{E_3} = \frac{\sqrt{M_1 M_3 E_1}}{M_3 + M_4} \cos \vartheta \left(1 \pm \left\{ 1 + \frac{1 + M_4/M_3}{\cos^2 \vartheta} \left[\frac{M_4}{M_1} \left(1 + \frac{Q}{E_1} \right) - 1 \right] \right\}^{\frac{1}{2}} \right)$$

17. The relationships between laboratory (L) and center-of-mass (C) coordinates take on simple forms which are independent of the nature of the forces and are derivable easily from the conservation laws. Consider nonrelativistic nuclear interactions, in which $Q = (M_1 + M_2 - M_3 - M_4)c^2$ is small compared with the rest energy $M_i c^2$ of any of the particles involved.

(a) If the angle of emission of M_3 is ϑ in L coordinates, and Θ in C coordinates, show that

$$\cot \vartheta = \frac{\gamma + \cos \Theta}{\sin \Theta} \qquad \text{and} \qquad \sin (\Theta - \vartheta) = \gamma \sin \vartheta$$

where $\gamma = \dfrac{\text{velocity } V_c \text{ of center of mass in } L \text{ coordinates}}{\text{velocity of } M_3 \text{ in } C \text{ coordinates}}$

$$= \left(\frac{M_1 M_3}{M_2 M_4} \frac{T_0}{T_0 + Q}\right)^{\frac{1}{2}} = \left[\frac{M_1 M_3}{M_2 M_4} \frac{E_1}{E_1 + Q(1 + M_1/M_2)}\right]^{\frac{1}{2}}$$

Here $T_0 = E_1 M_2 / (M_1 + M_2)$ is the incident kinetic energy in C coordinates, and all other symbols are as defined in Fig. 2.1. Show that $\gamma = M_1/M_2$ for elastic scattering, when the angular relationships reduce to Eq. (23) of Appendix B.

(b) If the differential cross section for the interaction is

$$d\sigma = \xi(\vartheta)\, d\omega = \xi(\Theta)\, d\Omega,$$

where $d\omega = 2\pi \sin \vartheta\, d\vartheta$ and $d\Omega = 2\pi \sin \Theta\, d\Theta$ are the solid angles in L and C coordinates, show that the general relationship between the angular distribution functions in L and C coordinates, $\xi(\vartheta)$ and $\xi(\Theta)$, is

$$\frac{\xi(\vartheta)}{\xi(\Theta)} = \frac{d\Omega}{d\omega} = \frac{\sin^3 \Theta}{\sin^3 \vartheta} \frac{1}{(1 + \gamma \cos \Theta)}$$

Compare with Prob. 2 of Appendix B, Sec. 4, for the special case of elastic scattering.

(c) The differential cross section can also be expressed as

$$d\sigma = \xi(\Theta)\, d\Omega = \xi(E_3)\, dE_3$$

where $\xi(E_3)$ is the energy distribution function for the kinetic energy E_3 of the emitted particle M_3, as observed in L coordinates. Show that, in general,

$$\xi(\Theta) = \frac{M_3 V_3 V_c}{2\pi} \xi(E_3) = \text{const } \xi(E_3)$$

where V_3 is the velocity of M_3 in C coordinates, and that therefore the distribution in energy E_3 of the emitted particle M_3, as measured in L coordinates, has exactly the same shape as the angular distribution of M_3 per unit solid angle in the C coordinates.

NOTE: Barschall and Powell (B15a) have pointed out that $\xi(\Theta)$ is proportional to $\xi(E_3)$ in all the relativistic cases, as well as in the elastic and inelastic nonrelativistic collisions and reactions treated here.

CHAPTER 13

Nuclear Reactions, Illustrated by $_5\mathrm{B}^{10}(\alpha,p)$ and Its Associates

The general features of several large classes of nuclear reactions will be explored here by centering our attention on a particular case, namely, the reactions of boron under bombardment by α rays. This selection has three related but discrete purposes: (1) to study the fundamental physical processes in terms of a prototype, (2) to observe the anatomy of discovery in physics, and (3) to glimpse a historically important "golden era" (1930 to 1936) in the development of nuclear physics.

The student of nuclear physics can acquire a pleasant and useful historical perspective of our science by studying the discoveries of the period centering around 1930 to 1936. Then occurred the experimental discovery of excited levels in light nuclei and the discovery of the neutron, of the positron, and of artificial radioactivity. Deuterium was discovered and isolated, and nuclear disintegrations were produced with accelerated protons and deuterons. On the theoretical side, the first successful theory of β decay, the independent-particle and the liquid-drop nuclear models, and the first theory of resonance reactions emerged. Many of these experimental and theoretical developments arose in connection with continuing studies of the bombardment of light elements, especially boron, nitrogen, and aluminum, by α rays. Much of the history of this era was charmingly and accurately recorded at the time by K. K. Darrow (D3).

Rutherford's epochal discovery in 1919, that the α-ray bombardment of nitrogen produces long-range protons, opened the field of man-made nuclear reactions. Thirteen years later this earliest discovered type, the (α,p) reaction, had been found to take place when 13 of the 19 lightest elements were used as targets, but no other kinds of induced nuclear reactions were known. Then the continuing systematic study of the details of these reactions resulted in a sequence of basic discoveries.

In 1936 Bohr pointed out that all the then known nuclear reactions could be best described as taking place in two sequential steps: (1) the formation of a *compound nucleus*, in a highly excited virtual level, and (2) the dissociation of this compound nucleus. Bohr assumed, and it has been well verified since, that:

1. The same compound nucleus can be formed in a variety of ways.

For example, a particular excited level in the compound nucleus N^{14}, designated as (N^{14}), can be produced by

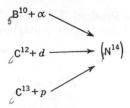

2. The compound nucleus has a lifetime which is very long ($\sim 10^{-16\pm3}$ sec) compared with the time for a proton to cross the nucleus ($\sim 10^{-22}$ sec).

3. The products of the reaction are independent of the manner in which the compound nucleus was formed. For example, (N^{14}) may dissociate in any of several competing "channels," including

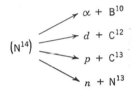

1. *Energy Distribution of Protons from* $B^{10}(\alpha,p)C^{13}$

The first evidence of a group structure in the energy distribution of the protons from (α,p) reactions was obtained by Bothe and Fränz in 1928 to 1930 (B100, B102, F65), using boron targets. Although normal boron is a mixture of B^{10} (18.8 per cent) and B^{11} (81.2 per cent), the (α,p) reaction was assumed to be due to only the B^{10} constituent, because this leads to the known nuclide C^{13}, whereas the $B^{11}(\alpha,p)C^{14}$ reaction would lead to the then-unheard-of nuclide C^{14}. Actually, both reactions take place. Bothe and Fränz correctly interpreted their observations as indicating that in some $B^{10}(\alpha,p)C^{13}$ disintegrations the residual C^{13} nucleus is left in an excited level after the emission of a low-energy proton.

a. Fine Structure of Protons from $B^{10}(\alpha,p)C^{13}$. Figure 1.1 shows some results of contemporary experiments on the energy distribution of protons from the $B^{10}(\alpha,p)C^{13}$ reaction. Isotopically enriched targets containing 98 per cent B^{10} were prepared by evaporation of amorphous boron onto a Formvar backing and were bombarded by 4.77-Mev α particles, obtained as accelerated helium ions from an electrostatic generator. The energy of the protons was determined by magnetic deflection, detection being by NTA photographic plates.

Four groups of protons are found, whose energies at $\vartheta = 90°$ are 6.84, 3.98, 3.43, and 3.23 Mev in the laboratory coordinates. The highest-energy proton group is assumed, with good justification, to correspond to the formation of C^{13} in its ground level.   From the Q equation, Eq. (2.4) of Chap. 12, with $E_3 = 6.84$ Mev, the ground-level Q value is $Q_0 = 4.07$ Mev.

b. Energy Levels in the Product Nucleus.   The three smaller values of E_3, when substituted into the Q equation, give $Q_1 = 0.98$ Mev,

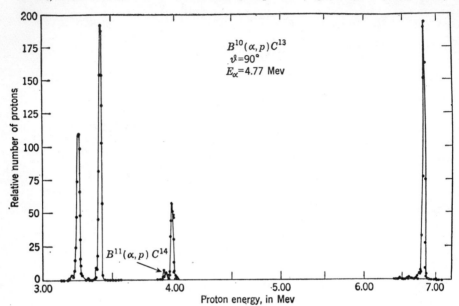

Fig. 1.1   Energy distribution of protons from $B^{10}(\alpha,p)C^{13}$ observed at $\vartheta = 90°$.   A minor proton group, due to the 2 per cent B^{11} present in the target and corresponding to the ground-level transition in $B^{11}(\alpha,p)C^{14}$, is seen near $E_p = 3.9$ Mev.   [*From Fader and Sperduto* (F1).]

$Q_2 = 0.39$ Mev, and $Q_3 = 0.22$ Mev.   These would correspond to dissociations in which the residual C^{13} nucleus is left in three excited levels whose excitation energies are

$$Q_0 - Q_1 = 3.09 \text{ Mev}$$
$$Q_0 - Q_2 = 3.68 \text{ Mev}$$
$$Q_0 - Q_3 = 3.85 \text{ Mev}$$

Figure 1.2 portrays the energetics of the reaction $B^{10}(\alpha,p)C^{13}$ in a standard form (A10) of energy-level diagram.   The important generalization here is that *energy levels in the product nucleus determine the "fine structure," or energy groups, of the reaction products.*   The excitation energy of the product nucleus is given, not by the energy difference of the proton groups, but by the energy difference of the corresponding Q values.

These results agree with the C^{13} levels (A10) determined by accurate measurements on the proton groups from the reaction $C^{12}(d,p)C^{13}$, which involves the same compound nucleus (N^{14}) and the same residual nucleus C^{13} (Fig. 4.2).

c. γ Rays from C¹³. When the $B^{10}(\alpha,p)C^{13}$ reaction leaves the residual C^{13} nucleus in an excited level, we can expect a γ-ray transition to some lower level. Creagan (C53) has shown by coincidence measurements (resolving time $\sim 10^{-7}$ sec) that the low-energy protons in Fig. 1.1

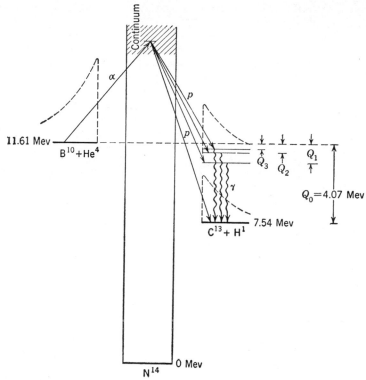

Fig. 1.2 Reaction energy-level diagram to illustrate the method for determining energy levels in C^{13}, as based on the energies of proton groups from $B^{10}(\alpha,p)C^{13}$. The vertical scale is linear in mass (and energy, as marked in Mev). Compare Chap. 3, Fig. 4.8. The height of the coulomb potential barriers $B = Zze^2/R$ which have to be penetrated or surmounted by the entering α particle and by the departing proton is indicated by the height of the dotted schematic barriers at pertinent energy levels.

are accompanied by γ rays, while the high-energy proton group is not. A γ-ray energy of $Q_0 - Q_i = 3.09, 3.68,$ and 3.85 Mev would be expected. In other noncoincidence experiments, a γ ray of about 3.8 Mev has been reported (A10), in agreement with these expectations.

Problems

1. When aluminum is bombarded with α rays from RaC' (7.68 Mev) a nuclear reaction takes place in which protons are emitted. At right angles to the direction of the α rays, the protons are found experimentally to consist of four groups having energies of 8.63, 6.41, 5.15, and 3.98 Mev.

(a) Write the nuclear reaction involved.

(b) Determine the energy liberated (Q value) for each proton group.

(c) What is the origin of the three low-energy proton groups?

(d) What are the energies of the γ rays which should accompany the reaction?

2. Potassium, when bombarded by α rays from ThC′, undergoes the transformation $_{19}K^{39}(\alpha,p)$. The protons observed at 90° to the α-ray beam exhibit three range groups, as follows:

Mean range of protons at 90°, air-cm [Pollard and Brasefield, *Phys. Rev.*, **50**: 890 (1936)]	Corresponding proton energy, Mev
59 ± 1	6.85 ± 0.1
41 ± 1	5.60 ± 0.1
25 ± 1	4.20 ± 0.1

(a) Assume that the mean energy of the α particles in the potassium target was 8.68 ± 0.1 Mev. Compute the Q values corresponding to the three proton groups. (Carry the probable errors of ±0.1 Mev in proton and α-ray energy along in the calculation, in order to see approximately how they propagate into all the derived results.)

(b) What are the energies (and approximate probable errors) of the first two excited levels shown by these observations? In what nucleus are they?

(c) Draw an energy-level diagram showing the initial particles, the compound nucleus, and the product nucleus. Show which energy-level differences correspond to Q_0, Q_1, Q_2 for this reaction.

(d) $_{19}K^{42}$ is a radioactive nuclide whose decay scheme is as shown. Is the energy of the 1.51 ± 0.02-Mev γ ray consistent with the results on the fine structure of protons from $K^{39}(\alpha,p)$?

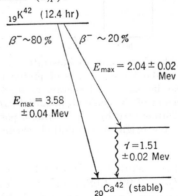

(e) What other γ rays would you expect to be energetically allowed in the radioactive decay of K^{42}? Why do you think they have not been found in the observations reported to date for K^{42}?

2. *Discovery of the Neutron from* B + α

One of the more fascinating and instructive tales of discovery in nuclear physics is the series of experiments in three countries, between

1930 and 1932, initiated for the purpose of measuring the γ radiation from $B^{10}(\alpha,p)C^{13}$ and similar reactions but culminating in the discovery of the neutron from the accompanying $B^{10}(\alpha,n)N^{13}$ and $B^{11}(\alpha,n)N^{14}$ reactions.

a. Discovery of the Penetrating Radiation from B + α. The sequence began in Berlin, where in 1930 Bothe and Fränz had found the low-energy proton groups from $B^{10}(\alpha,p)C^{13}$. The logical next step was to look for the expected γ radiation. This was done by Bothe and Becker (B101) who, using a Geiger point counter as detector, observed a radiation capable of penetrating the 2 mm of brass in which a Li, Be, or B target and a Po α-ray source were mounted. Their interpretation was that the penetrating radiation was entirely electromagnetic in character, because no other type of penetrating radiation was known, and γ radiation was expected from the excited product nuclei. This observation was confirmed in Paris the following year by Irene Curie (C58), with the same interpretation.

At the Cavendish Laboratory, in Cambridge, England, Webster (W16) undertook, in 1932, measurements of the quantum energy of this presumed γ radiation. Using Pb and Fe absorbers and both ionization chambers and Geiger-Müller counters as detectors, Webster found that the penetration of the radiation from B + α corresponded to that expected for 10-Mev γ rays. From the analogous Be + α reaction, γ radiation of 7 Mev was indicated. These high values were startling. But the interpretation in terms of known types of radiation became even more improbable when Curie and Joliot (C59) performed transmission experiments using a wider variety of absorbing materials. They found that the penetrating radiation from B + α and from Be + α was not reduced by thin absorbers containing hydrogen, such as paraffin, but, indeed, was enhanced. They showed that the penetrating radiation could eject protons from paraffin and that these protons have a range in air of 8 cm for B + α and 26 cm for Be + α. This observation was interpreted by Curie and Joliot as a type of high-energy Compton effect, and the quanta held responsible for projecting the protons had to be assigned a quantum energy of 35 Mev from B + α and 50 Mev from Be + α. The twin difficulties, that the energies were far too high and that the cross sections for an elastic collision between a photon and a proton were much too large, were noted.

At this point, Chadwick (C12) solved the riddle of the penetrating radiations from B + α in a series of magnificently direct and compelling experiments at the Cavendish Laboratory.

b. The Penetrating Radiation from B + α and Be + α Is Identified As Neutrons. For a given α-ray source, the yield of penetrating radiation from Be + α is several times as great as from B + α. Most of Chadwick's measurements on the character of the radiation were therefore done with the Be + α reaction, following which all the essential features were shown to be the same for the B + α reaction. Chadwick found that the penetrating radiation ejects ionizing particles not only from hydrogen but from all other light elements which were examined. Energy measurements on these ejected atoms provided an experimental measure of both the mass and the energy of the particles (neutrons) which form a portion of the penetrating radiation from Be + α and B + α.

Figure 2.1 shows the essential features of Chadwick's apparatus. In an evacuated chamber at the left, the 5.3-Mev α rays from a polonium source strike a thick target of Be or of B. The ensuing nuclear reaction produces a penetrating radiation which emerges in all directions. Some of this radiation travels toward a small ionization chamber, in which the passage of individual ionizing particles (such as recoil protons and recoil nitrogen nuclei) produces an ionization pulse of several thousand ion pairs. This pulse is amplified electronically and fed to an output oscillograph. The height of each pulse is then a measure of the ionization produced by a single recoil atom in the ionization chamber.

With no foils interposed between the source vessel and the ionization chamber, pulses were observed which could be ascribed to recoil nitrogen atoms, produced in the gas with which the ionization chamber was filled.

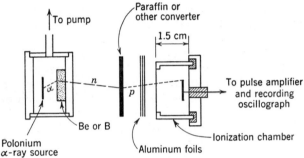

Fig. 2.1 Chadwick's apparatus for identifying the neutron as the penetrating radiation from the Be + α and B + α reactions.

When as much as 2 cm of Pb was interposed between the source and the detector, this counting rate remained sensibly unchanged, thus verifying the highly penetrating character of the radiation from the source vessel.

When a 2-mm-thick sheet of paraffin was interposed between the source vessel and the ionization counter, the counting rate showed a substantial increase, and the pulse heights could be identified as characteristic of protons in the ionization chamber. The range of these recoil protons was determined by interposing thin foils of Al between the paraffin and the counter. Data obtained in this way are shown as the upper curve in Fig. 2.2, where the recoil protons are seen to have a maximum range in aluminum which corresponds to just over 40 cm of air at 15°C and 760-mm pressure. From the known relationship between velocity and range for protons, this maximum corresponds to a proton velocity of 3.3 × 10⁹ cm/sec, or about 5.7 Mev.

The Photon Hypothesis. The maximum energy which can be given to a particle whose rest mass is M, in an elastic (Compton) collision with a photon whose energy is $h\nu$, is

$$E_{max} = \left(\frac{2}{2 + Mc^2/h\nu}\right) h\nu \tag{2.1}$$

Therefore 55-Mev quanta would be required to produce 5.7-Mev recoil protons. Such quanta, if they existed, could impart to a recoil nitrogen nucleus only a kinetic energy of 0.45 Mev. However, the nitrogen recoils were found to have velocities up to 0.47×10^9 cm/sec, or an energy of 1.6 Mev. Recoil atoms having a variety of mass values were then studied by replacing the paraffin converter by films of Li, Be, B, C, and N (as paracyanogen) and also by filling the ionization chamber successively with H_2, He, N_2, O_2, and A. The experimental results showed that, if the recoil atoms were to be explained as arising in collisions with photons, the quantum energy would not be constant but would have to be larger and larger as the mass of the recoil atom increased.

These results showed the quantum hypothesis to be untenable as an explanation of the penetrating radiation from Be + α and B + α.

The Neutron Hypothesis. The concept of a "neutron" (originally as an intimate combination of a proton and an electron) had been discussed by Rutherford (R47) as early as 1920, and many unsuccessful experiments in search of this neutron had been made in the Cavendish Laboratory between 1920 and 1932. Chadwick showed that his observed recoil energies were consistent with the neutron hypothesis. If the penetrating radiation were a stream of uncharged particles, then their great penetrating power would also be understandable.

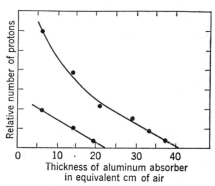

Fig. 2.2   Upper curve, recoil protons from the Be + α reaction in the geometry of Fig. 2.1. Lower curve, recoil protons when the source vessel is rotated 180°, so that the neutrons travel backward with respect to the direction of the α rays. [*From Chadwick* (C12).]

As to the recoil energies, a particle of mass M_1 and velocity V_1 can impart a maximum velocity V_2 to a particle of mass M_2 in a head-on elastic collision, where

$$V_2 = \frac{2M_1}{M_1 + M_2} V_1 \tag{2.2}$$

Then the measured recoil velocities for H and N atoms can be used to determine *both* the mass M_1 and the velocity V_1 of the assumed neutrons. From Eq. (2.2) this gives

$$\frac{M_1 + 14}{M_1 + 1} = \frac{(V_2)_H}{(V_2)_N} = \frac{3.3 \times 10^9 \text{ cm/sec}}{0.47 \times 10^9 \text{ cm/sec}} \tag{2.3}$$

or

$$M_1 = 1.15 \text{ amu} \tag{2.4}$$

with an estimated uncertainty of about 10 per cent.

Further support for this interpretation was obtained by measuring the maximum range and energy of the recoil protons ejected by neutrons which left the Be + α reaction in a direction opposite to that of the incident α rays. These protons are shown in the lower curve of **Fig. 2.2** and have a maximum velocity of about 2.7×10^9 cm/sec, hence an energy of about 3.8 Mev. This energy is consistent with that expected for a neutron of about 1 amu, ejected at an angle of $\vartheta \geq 90°$, if the neutrons at $\vartheta \sim 0°$ are about 5.7 Mev. The penetrating radiation from Be $+ \alpha$ was therefore ascribed to a new type of nuclear reaction, the (α,n) reaction.

Mass of the Neutron. The energetics of the $Be^9(\alpha,n)C^{12}$ reaction could not be used to determine a more accurate mass for the neutron, because the mass of Be^9 had not yet been measured in 1932. Therefore Chadwick determined the Q value for the (α,n) reaction on boron. With incident polonium α rays of 5.3 Mev, the neutron energy in the $\vartheta = 0$ direction was such as to produce recoil protons with a maximum range of about 16 cm in air, hence an energy of about 3.3 Mev. If the neutron has nearly the same mass as the proton, then the neutron energy in the direction $\vartheta = 0$ would also be about 3.3 Mev. The reaction on boron was assumed to be with the B^{11} isotope, because this would lead to a known nuclide N^{14} as the residual nucleus in a $B^{11}(\alpha,n)N^{14}$ reaction. The competing $B^{10}(\alpha,n)N^{13}$ reaction was excluded because N^{13} was unknown. [Artificial radioactivity and the positron were as yet undiscovered, but both were surely present in Chadwick's boron targets. When the normal isotopic mixture of B^{10} and B^{11} is bombarded by polonium α rays, approximately 10 per cent of the neutrons arise from B^{10} and 90 per cent from B^{11} (B98).]

Assuming that the neutrons were from $B^{11}(\alpha,n)N^{14}$, and using the contemporary mass-spectroscopic masses of B^{11}, He^4, and N^{14}, Chadwick's Q-value estimate of the mass of the neutron was

$$1.005 \leq M_n \leq 1.008 \text{ amu}$$

The modern value is 1.008 98 amu. This was a tremendous achievement. In a single paper, Chadwick not only demonstrated convincingly the existence of the neutron but succeeded in determining its mass with an error of less than one-third per cent. Chadwick's original paper is rewarding reading for every student of nuclear physics, as are its companion papers by Feather (F11), showing cloud-chamber photographs of the inverse reaction $N^{14}(n,\alpha)B^{11}$, and by Dee (D17), showing that the neutron does not produce ionization directly and is therefore an "elementary" particle, not a close combination of a proton and an electron.

3. *Discovery of Artificial Radioactivity from* B $+ \alpha$

Every boron and aluminum target which was being subjected to α-ray bombardment by the physicists in Berlin, Paris, Cambridge, and elsewhere was, in fact, intensely radioactive. Even after Chadwick's discovery of the neutron, nearly two more years had to elapse before esoteric nature gave up the secret of induced radioactivity, close to New Year's Day of 1934. The sequence of events between 1932 and 1934 should stand as an object lesson to all young physicists who now seek knowledge of nature's yet unrevealed secrets.

In the Cavendish Laboratory, prior to 1932, induced radioactivity had been repeatedly looked for in light elements subjected to α-ray bombardment. None was found, because the detection instruments were sensitive to delayed proton emission, as in a delayed (α,p) reaction, and were not sensitive to the positron β decay of N^{13} which was actually present in every $B + \alpha$ target.

a. Discovery of the Positron. Carl Anderson was the first to observe and identify the positron when this particle appeared in cloud-chamber photographs of cosmic-ray particles (A28) taken in August, 1932, at the California Institute of Technology. Anderson and Neddermeyer, and other workers elsewhere (A30), promptly showed that positron-negatron pairs were formed when energetic γ rays, particularly the 2.62-Mev γ rays of ThC″, were absorbed by heavy elements, such as Pb. Thus the positron became available to all laboratories for further study.

b. Observation of Positrons from the $B + \alpha$ Reactions. Positrons had also been produced by the absorption in Pb of the radiations from $Be + \alpha$ and $B + \alpha$ neutron sources. At first, and incorrectly, the neutrons were held responsible for producing positrons in Pb. Actually, these neutron sources all emit a component of hard γ rays, which are produced in the (α,n) and (α,p) reactions whenever the final nucleus is produced in an excited level. Curie and Joliot (C60) used a cloud chamber to observe the ejection of positrons from a Pb strip which was being irradiated by the combined radiations from a $Be + \alpha$ source. The yield of positrons was greatly reduced when the $Be + \alpha$ radiations were filtered through a block of Pb before entering the cloud chamber. Curie and Joliot concluded correctly that the positrons were produced by the γ rays and not by the neutrons.

Continuing with various types of cloud-chamber investigations, Curie and Joliot (C61) observed that *boron emits positrons while being bombarded by α rays*. Positrons were also observed from Al while it was being bombarded by α rays. In the case of $Al + \alpha$, the positrons had energies up to about 3 Mev and appeared to be emitted as freely in the backward as in the forward direction. It was tacitly assumed (incorrectly) that there was no time delay between the $B + \alpha$ reaction (or the $Al + \alpha$ reaction) and the emission of the positron. With all thoughts centering on the behavior of the two new particles in physics, the neutron and the positron, a wholly incorrect interpretation of this otherwise crucial experiment was proposed. This was that the well-known reaction

$$_5B^{10} + {_2}He^4 \rightarrow {_1}H^1 + {_6}C^{13} \tag{3.1}$$

was in competition with an alternative mode of disintegration, in which the proton was not emitted but instead a neutron-positron pair was emitted. This incorrect reaction would be written

$$_5B^{10} + {_2}He^4 \rightarrow {_0}n^1 + {_1}e^+ + {_6}C^{13} \tag{3.2}$$

and from its energetics Curie and Joliot proposed a neutron mass of 1.012 amu.

These experiments were not followed up by other workers. It remained, happily, for Curie and Joliot to straighten the matter out themselves some six months later by observing that boron continued to emit positrons even after the α-ray source was removed. Thus, artificial radioactivity was first recognized.

c. Recognition of Radioactivity in N^{13}. Curie and Joliot (C62) found that foils of B, Al, or Mg, after a 10-min exposure to α rays from polonium, continued to emit positrons after the α-ray source was removed. The rate of emission of positrons decreased exponentially with time after removal of the α-ray source. Each of the three cases exhibited a different *half-period* of decay, showing that the effects were not due to some contaminant which was common to all three sources. Also, the maximum *energy* of the positrons, as judged by their range in absorbing foils, was different for the three cases. When Al was irradiated by α rays of reduced energy, the *yield* of positrons was reduced, but their energy and half-period remained unaltered. Finally, the *positrons* were not accompanied by negatrons and were therefore not due to pair production.

These four experimental characteristics showed that the delayed positron emission could be attributed to "a new type of radioactivity." Previously there had been known only the α decay and the negatron β decay of the heavy radionuclides in the Th, U, and Ac series. Now there was added positron β decay, and in the lightest elements. In the case of B + α, the nuclear reactions were interpreted by Curie and Joliot as the formation of the hitherto unknown nuclide N^{13}, according to

$$_5B^{10} + {}_2He^4 \rightarrow {}_0n^1 + {}_7N^{13} \tag{3.3}$$

followed by the radioactive decay of N^{13}, with a half-period of about 14 min (shown later to be 10.0 ± 0.1 min), according to

$$_7N^{13} \rightarrow \beta^+ + {}_6C^{13} \tag{3.4}$$

Analogously, the Al + α and Mg + α reactions were interpreted as

$$_{13}Al^{27} + {}_2He^4 \rightarrow {}_0n^1 + {}_{15}P^{30} \qquad {}_{15}P^{30} \rightarrow \beta^+ + {}_{14}Si^{30} \tag{3.5}$$
$$_{12}Mg^{24} + {}_2He^4 \rightarrow {}_0n^1 + {}_{14}Si^{27} \qquad {}_{14}Si^{27} \rightarrow \beta^+ + {}_{13}Al^{27} \tag{3.6}$$

Radiochemical procedures were invoked to prove beyond doubt the existence of N^{13} and P^{30} (C63). Boron nitride, BN, was irradiated with α rays and then treated with caustic soda in order to produce gaseous ammonia. The induced activity could be separated from the boron and carried away in the ammonia. Therefore the N^{13} was shown to follow the chemistry of ammonia. Analogously, the P^{30} activity was separated from the Al + α targets by forming gaseous phosphorus hydride, PH_3, and subsequently the P^{30} positron activity was shown to follow the chemistry of phosphorus, not aluminum.

The principal physical characteristics of these positron β-ray emitters could be fitted satisfactorily into Fermi's (F34) theory of the negatron β decay of heavy elements, which had been published almost simultaneously with the discovery of "artificial" radioactivity by Curie and Joliot. As a result of this happy coincidence, the theory of β decay and the experimental work on artificial radioactivity gave important support to each other.

Competition between (α,p) *and* (α,n). With positive proof in hand for the reaction $B^{10}(\alpha,n)N^{13}$, Curie and Joliot suggested that Chadwick's experiments had, in fact, involved this reaction primarily, instead of the assumed $B^{11}(\alpha,n)N^{14}$, and on this basis they proposed a neutron mass of 1.010 ± 0.005 amu. The lasting point from all this was the demonstration, for the first time, of *competing nuclear reactions*. In fact, B^{10} and B^{11} both undergo the (α,p) and (α,n) reactions, but of course with different cross sections, Q values, and energetics. In the case of B^{10}, α-ray bombardment leads eventually to C^{13} by way of two competing routes

$$\text{and} \qquad \begin{array}{c} B^{10}(\alpha,p)C^{13} \\ B^{10}(\alpha,n)N^{13} \qquad N^{13} \rightarrow \beta^+ + C^{13} \end{array} \qquad (3.7)$$

while from B^{11} the competition leads to N^{14} by way of

$$\text{and} \qquad \begin{array}{c} B^{11}(\alpha,p)C^{14} \qquad C^{14} \rightarrow \beta^- + N^{14} \\ B^{11}(\alpha,n)N^{14} \end{array} \qquad (3.8)$$

Early Evidence for a Compound Nucleus. It began to be recognized that nuclear reactions may involve the formation of an intermediate, or compound, nucleus, such as (N^{14}) in the case of $B^{10} + \alpha$, and that this compound nucleus can dissociate in any of several ways. The suggestion by Curie and Joliot (C62) that their newly discovered N^{13} could probably be produced by deuteron bombardment of carbon, according to the reaction $C^{12}(d,n)N^{13}$, was quickly verified experimentally in the laboratories at Pasadena (C51) and at Berkeley (H35), where deuteron beams were already available. An excited compound nucleus (N^{14}) could therefore be visualized in the scheme

$$\begin{array}{ccc} B^{10} + \alpha & & n + N^{13} \\ & \searrow \quad \nearrow & \\ & (N^{14}) & \qquad (3.9) \\ & \nearrow \quad \searrow & \\ C^{12} + d & & p + C^{13} \end{array}$$

A period of rapid discovery of new nuclear reactions came into full tide. Within a year, some 140 well-verified nuclear reactions could be systematically catalogued as representing a small number of type reactions (E23), of which (α,p) and (α,n) were simply the "historical firsts." Rapid advances in the theoretical understanding of nuclear reactions followed when in 1936 Bohr (B94) and, independently, Breit and Wigner (B118) developed the concept of the compound nucleus as an intermediate system of relatively long life, in which the excitation energy may be shared by all the nucleons.

d. Production of Negatron β Activity by Neutron Capture. Immediately after the discovery of *positron β* activity, in reactions such as (α,n) which *reduce* the ratio of neutrons to protons, Fermi (F32, F39) and his coworkers irradiated all available elements with neutrons and produced *negatron β* activity in more than 40 elements. The reactions involved were (n,γ), (n,p), and (n,α), all of which *increase* the ratio of neutrons to protons.

In a number of cases, the same radionuclide could be produced by neutron bombardment of three adjacent elements. This circumstance often allowed a unique specification of the particular isotopes which were responsible for the reaction and was thus of special advantage. For example, the 15-hr β^--emitting isotope of Na could be definitely assigned as Na^{24}, produced in the reactions

$$_{11}Na^{23}(n,\gamma)Na^{24}$$
$$_{12}Mg^{24}(n,p)Na^{24} \qquad (3.10)$$
$$_{13}Al^{27}(n,\alpha)Na^{24}$$

When uranium was irradiated by neutrons, a number of β-active nuclides were produced. These were incorrectly classed as *"transuranic elements"* until five years later, when Hahn and Strassmann (H5) proved their identity as middleweight *fission products*, through the skillful utilization of radiochemical techniques.

4. *Resonances in the Formation of the Compound Nucleus*

In order to form a compound nucleus, in reactions such as $B^{10} + \alpha$, the incident particle must penetrate the coulomb barrier and also the nuclear surface. We have noted in Chap. 2 that the probability of transmission through the potential step at the "surface" of the nucleus is usually not a monotonic function of the bombarding energy. Instead, there are particular values of the incident energy for which the probability of formation of the compound nucleus is largest. The excitation energy of the compound nucleus is always determined by the masses of the colliding nuclei, plus the incident kinetic energy in C coordinates. If the excitation energy of the compound nucleus would just equal that of one of its excited (virtual) levels, then we could expect *resonance* formation of the compound nucleus and a large reaction probability (Chap. 14, Sec. 1).

The possibility of resonance in nuclear reactions was first clearly pointed out by Gurney (G49) in 1929, shortly after the introduction of the wave concepts of barrier transmission by Gamow and by Gurney and Condon. Experimental evidence appeared soon thereafter, in the case of the $Al(\alpha,p)Si$ reaction, as observed by Pose (P26) and by Chadwick, Constable, and Pollard (C14). With the attainment of higher resolution, through improvement of experimental techniques, it has been possible to measure both the excitation energy and the total width of many nuclear levels by means of resonances in the formation of the compound nucleus.

Figure 4.1 is an example of resonance-reaction measurements. Here a number of energy levels in the compound nucleus (N^{14}) are formed by bombarding B^{10} with α rays of various energies. In order to eliminate ambiguity due to the presence of B^{11}, measurements were made on two targets, one containing the normal 18.8 per cent B^{10} and the other containing 96 per cent B^{10}. All the resonance peaks in Fig. 4.1 are due to $B^{10} + \alpha$. In order to attain high resolution, very thin targets of boron were prepared by evaporation in vacuum onto copper backing plates. The α rays were He nuclei, accelerated by an electrostatic generator to various energies between 1 and 3 Mev. Relative values of the cross section for formation of the compound nucleus

$$B^{10} + He^4 \rightarrow (N^{14}) \qquad (4.1)$$

were measured as a function of α-ray energy by observing a particular mode of dissociation of (N^{14}). Some (N^{14}) nuclei dissociate, by emission of a low-energy proton, to a 3.9-Mev excited level in C^{13}, which subsequently emits a 3.9-Mev γ ray in its transition to the ground level of C^{13}.

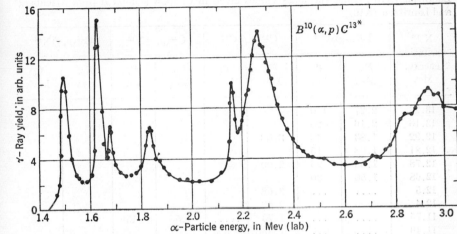

Fig. 4.1 Relative yield of the 3.9-Mev γ rays from C^{13*}, showing resonances in the formation of the compound nucleus (N^{14}) in the reaction $B^{10}(\alpha,p)C^{13*}$. A thin target ($\sim$10-kev stopping power for α rays) of isotopically enriched B^{10} was used. The γ rays were observed with a scintillation spectrometer, at 90° from the α-particle beam. [*From Talbott and Heydenburg* (T2).]

Thus the nuclear reaction which begins as shown in Eq. (4.1) can be completed through the particular exit channel

$$(N^{14}) \rightarrow H^1 + C^{13*} \qquad C^{13*} \rightarrow C^{13} + \gamma \qquad (4.2)$$

Figure 4.1 shows the observed intensity of this 3.9-Mev γ radiation as a function of the incident α-ray energy (T2). Then the peaks of γ-ray intensity in Fig. 4.1 correspond to resonance penetration of the $B^{10} + \alpha$ barrier and formation of N^{14*} in a succession of excited levels.

Excitation Energy of Resonance Levels. Each level has an excitation energy equal to the ground-level mass differences,

$$B^{10} + He^4 - N^{14} = 11.61 \text{ Mev}$$

plus the incident kinetic energy in C coordinates, which is given closely by $(\frac{10}{14})E_\alpha$, where E_α is the kinetic energy of the α ray in L coordinates.

For example, the resonance at $E_\alpha = 1.83$ Mev locates a virtual level N^{14*} at an excitation energy of $11.61 + (\frac{10}{14})1.83 = 12.92$ Mev.

Width of Resonance Levels. From Fig. 4.1 we can also estimate the width Γ of each of the virtual levels. The total width Γ, as defined in Chap. 11, corresponds physically to the full width of the resonance peak, measured at one-half the maximum height of the peak. Table 4.1 lists

TABLE 4.1. EXCITED LEVELS IN N^{14}, AS DETERMINED BY RESONANCES IN THE YIELD CURVES OF (α,p), (d,p), (p,n), AND (p,γ) REACTIONS ON TARGETS WHICH GIVE N^{14} AS THE COMPOUND NUCLEUS

E_α, E_d, E_p signify the bombarding energy, in laboratory coordinates, at the peak of the resonance. The observed full width Γ at half maximum is given in kev, when known. Excitation energies of N^{14*} follow the recalculated values by Ajzenberg and Lauritsen (A10), using the mass values given in Chap. 3 [compiled from Ajzenberg and Lauritsen (A10)].

N^{14*} excitation energy, Mev	$B^{10}(\alpha,p)C^{13}$		$C^{12}(d,p)C^{13}$		$C^{13}(p,n)N^{13}$		$C^{13}(p,\gamma)N^{14}$	
	E_α, Mev	Γ, kev	E_d, Mev	Γ, kev	E_p, Mev	Γ, kev	E_p, Mev	Γ, kev
13.23	2.27	130						
13.16	2.16	20						
12.92	1.83	40	3.08					
12.81	1.68	15						
12.78	1.63	25	2.90					
12.68	1.50	30						
12.5	....	...	2.68					
12.4	....	...	2.49					
11.75	....	...	1.73	.....	4.53	~150		
11.49	....	...	1.435	5.5				
11.42	....	...	....	.....	4.18	35		
11.38	....	...	1.30	80				
11.26	....	...	1.16	200				
11.23	....	...	1.13	30	4.01	22		
11.04	....	...	0.91	200	3.77	~100		
10.43	....	...	......	.....	....	.....	3.11	30
9.49	....	...	......	.....	....	.....	2.10	45
9.18	....	...	....	.....	....	.....	1.76	2
8.70	....	...	....	.....	....	.....	1.25	500
8.62	....	...	....	.....	....	.....	1.16	6
8.06	....	...	....	.....	....	.....	0.55	32

the energies and estimated widths of some N^{14*} levels, as determined from Fig. 4.1.

Alternative Methods for Forming the Compound Nucleus. According to Bohr's postulates, the characteristics of the compound nucleus are independent of its mode of formation, and the same set of levels can be formed in a variety of ways. As an illustration of one of the experimental bases for this concept, we may note that a few of the excited levels in N^{14} have been produced in more than one type of resonance reaction. Table

4.1 summarizes the presently available experimental results. Only a small degree of overlap is provided by the energies used thus far for α, d, and p bombardments. Some of the higher-energy (d,p) cases may be complicated by stripping reactions, operating in competition with formation of a compound nucleus by actual capture of the deuteron.

Energy-level Diagrams for Resonance Reactions. Figure 4.2 illustrates an informative and conventional method (A10) for visualizing the energetics of resonance reactions. Yield curves, such as Fig. 4.1, are rotated

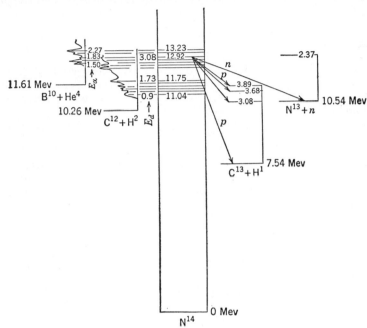

Fig. 4.2 Typical energy-level diagram for the resonance formation of N¹⁴* from B¹⁰ + α and from C¹² + d bombardments. Once formed, each excited level may transform toward the ground level by γ-ray emission, or it may dissociate in any one of a variety of exit channels. As an illustration, the figure shows the dissociation of the 12.92-Mev level in N¹⁴* by proton emission to levels in C¹³ and by neutron emission to levels in N¹³. Note that the energy scales of the yield curves are marked with E_α and E_d in Mev in laboratory coordinates but are plotted to the vertical energy scale in C coordinates, i.e., $\frac{10}{14}E_\alpha$ and $\frac{12}{14}E_d$. In order to emphasize the features shown, numerous additional levels and reactions have been omitted. [*See Ajzenberg and Lauritsen* (A10) *for complete diagrams.*]

and run vertically so that the resonance peaks line up horizontally with their corresponding virtual levels in the compound nucleus.

Resonances in Elastic Scattering. One of the modes of dissociation which is always possible for the compound nucleus is the reemission of the incident particle, or a similar particle, without loss of total kinetic energy in the system. This process is known as *elastic anomalous scattering* and was discussed in Chap. 2. We emphasize here that the resonance energies at which anomalous elastic scattering is pronounced serve to locate excited *levels in the compound nucleus*, not in the target nucleus. Thus resonances (M48) in the elastic scattering "reactions" denoted $C^{13}(p,p)C^{13}$, or $B^{10}(\alpha,\alpha)B^{10}$, identify levels in N^{14} and will occur at the same bombarding energies which bring out resonance peaks in the cross sections for the competing reactions $C^{13}(p,n)N^{13}$ and $B^{10}(\alpha,p)C^{13}$. In energy diagrams such as Fig. 4.2, anomalous elastic scattering can be visualized as a capture and reemission along the same diagonal line, such as the proton line which joins the 12.92-Mev level of N^{14*} and the *ground* level of $C^{13} + p$.

Problem

The reaction $N^{14}(n,p)C^{14}$ is found to exhibit resonances at 499, 640, 993, and 1,415 kev. The reaction $C^{14}(p,n)N^{14}$ also exhibits four resonances, and these are found at proton energies which are about 664 kev greater than the neutron energies for the four $N^{14}(n,p)C^{14}$ resonances.

(a) Show both analytically and in a nuclear energy-level diagram that these correspond to the same set of excited levels in N^{15} and that the $C^{14}(p,n)N^{14}$ resonances should require a greater bombarding energy than the $N^{14}(n,p)C^{14}$ resonances, by just the threshold energy (about 664 kev) for the $C^{14}(p,n)N^{14}$ reaction.

(b) Explain briefly and clearly whether it is ever possible to use neutrons from the reaction $C^{14}(p,n)N^{14}$ to produce the inverse reaction $N^{14}(n,p)C^{14}$ in another target, remembering that Q for the first reaction is exactly $-Q$ for the second reaction.

5. *Energy Loss in Inelastic Scattering*

Inelastic scattering can be characterized by reactions such as

$$N^{14}(p,p')N^{14*}$$

where the asterisk denotes a nucleus in a definite excited level. The emitted particle is experimentally the same as the captured particle, but there is a loss of kinetic energy in the system. This energy is found as excitation energy in the *product* nucleus. Thus, in $N^{14}(p,p')N^{14*}$, the differences in the energies of groups of scattered protons correspond to the energy separations of excited levels in N^{14}.

Inelastic Scattering by N^{14}. Figure 5.1 shows the groups of protons which are scattered at 90°, in laboratory coordinates, when a thin nylon target is bombarded by 6.92-Mev protons (B82). The scattered protons were analyzed in momentum by a 180° magnetic spectrograph. By noting the change in momentum of any group as the bombarding energy is changed, the mass of the nucleus responsible for the scattered group can be determined from the Q equation. Near $B\rho = 353$ kilogauss-cm (5.97 Mev), there are three proton groups, which are due to elastic scattering by C^{12}, N^{14}, and O^{16} in the nylon target. The proton groups at $B\rho = 283$ and 219 kilogauss-cm (3.84 and 2.30 Mev) have been

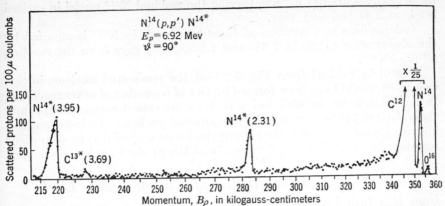

Fig. 5.1 Scattered proton groups, observed at $\vartheta = 90°$ in laboratory coordinates, when a thin nylon film is bombarded by 6.92-Mev protons. The two proton groups marked N^{14*} have Q values of -2.31 Mev and -3.95 Mev. They correspond to the formation of excited levels in N^{14*} at $+2.31$ and $+3.95$ Mev by the inelastic scattering process $N^{14}(p,p')N^{14*}$. [*From Bockelman, Browne, Buechner, and Sperduto* (B82).]

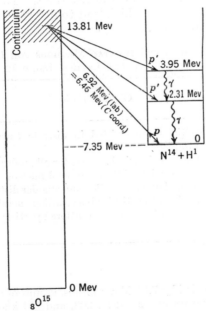

Fig. 5.2 Energetics of inelastic scattering of protons for the data on $N^{14}(p,p')N^{14*}$ shown in Fig. 5.1.

inelastically scattered by N^{14}, leaving the residual N^{14*} nuclei in excited levels at 2.31 and 3.95 Mev.

Independent confirmation of these two levels in N^{14*} is afforded by the observation (T20) of 2.31- and 1.64-Mev γ rays from the reaction $C^{13}(d,n)N^{14*}$.

It will be evident from Fig. 5.2 that the compound nucleus, in this case (O^{15}), could have been formed by any of a number of other reactions. In the dissociation by emission of protons, we expect energy groups, and these correspond to excitation of the product nucleus. Inelastic scattering can therefore be regarded energetically as a special type of nuclear reaction, in which the target nucleus and the product nucleus are alike.

6. *Summary of the Determination of Nuclear Energy Levels from Reaction Energetics*

Nuclear spectroscopy has for its experimental goal the determination of the excitation energy, width, nuclear moments, isobaric spin, and parity of the excited levels in nuclei. The low-lying levels are mostly accessible to study through radioactive decay, as discussed in Chap. 6. Upper levels are evaluated largely through the energetics, cross sections, and angular distributions of nuclear reactions. Table 6.1 summarizes the nuclear-reaction methods which lead to determinations of the excitation energy of nuclear levels.

TABLE 6.1. SUMMARY OF EXPERIMENTAL METHODS FOR DETERMINATION OF THE EXCITATION ENERGY OF NUCLEAR LEVELS, USING REACTION ENERGETICS

Method	Characteristics	Locates excited levels in
"Fine structure" of reaction products	Particles are emitted in discrete energy groups	Final nucleus
Resonance reactions..	Peaks in the yield curves, for all modes of dissociation of the compound nucleus	Compound nucleus
Elastic scattering....	Anomalous cross section and angular distribution at particular bombarding energies	Compound nucleus
Inelastic scattering...	Groups of low-energy scattered particles	Final nucleus (same as target)

√ Problem

When N^{14} is bombarded by 7.56-Mev protons, groups of protons are observed at 90° which have momenta of $B\rho = 245$, 203, and 194 kilogauss-cm, where all quantities are measured in laboratory coordinates. Show that these inelastically scattered proton groups correspond to the formation of N^{14*} in excited levels at 3.95, 4.91, and 5.10 Mev. What would be the energy and momentum of the elastically scattered protons, in the same experimental arrangement? [Data are from Bockelman et al., *Phys. Rev.*, **92**: 665 (1953).]

CHAPTER 14

Energy Dependence of Nuclear-reaction Cross Sections

The cross sections for various nuclear reactions depend on bombarding energy in a highly individualistic manner. No two are alike. Experimental similarities between reactions are usually limited to gross features and to general trends. The detailed dependence of cross section on bombarding energy is often called the "*excitation function*," or the "transmutation function," for the particular reaction. Presently available theories cannot predict the detailed shape of the excitation function for a new reaction. However, the general features of many excitation functions can now be accounted for, and predictions of gross behavior can be made.

Major advances in the quantitative theory of nuclear reactions have been made in recent years and are continuing. But, in the absence of knowledge of the wave functions for the interior of a nucleus, these theories have to be based upon consecutively improved sets of simplifying assumptions concerning the interior of nuclei.

Current theories of the cross section for those nuclear reactions in which a compound nucleus is formed divide into two broad classifications. At low bombarding energies the excited levels of the compound nucleus are discrete and may be widely spaced. Here the reaction cross sections are described by a *resonance theory*. At higher bombarding energies the excited levels in the compound nucleus are more closely spaced, broader, and partially overlapped. In this energy domain, the so-called *continuum theory* undertakes to describe the general variation of cross section with bombarding energy, as averaged over many resonances.

In the earliest theories the geometrical area of the target nucleus πR^2 served as a first approximation for the reaction cross section, provided that the bombarding energy was adequate to surmount the nuclear coulomb barrier. When the concept of barrier transmission became established, the cross section was visualized as proportional to $T_{in}T_{out}$, where T_{in} and T_{out} were Gamow transmission factors for the incoming and outgoing particles. For charged-particle reactions, such as (α,p), the rapid variation of T_{in} with bombarding energy did tend to match the rapid rise of the cross section with bombarding energy, and this dependence on T_{in} remains as a parameter in modern theories. The discovery of resonance energies in excitation functions for $Al(\alpha,p)$ and $Mg(\alpha,p)$ was quickly attributed to a "tunnel effect," or resonance penetration of the nuclear barrier. After a major modification which we shall discuss shortly, the resonance concept has found a permanent place in the theory of nuclear reactions.

Discovery of Slow Neutrons and the 1/V Law. The neutron experiments of 1935, by Fermi and his collaborators in Rome, stimulated far-reaching developments in our knowledge and understanding of nuclear reactions. In the course of their studies of neutron-induced radioactivity, Fermi and his group noticed that the activation of silver, by neutrons from a radon-plus-beryllium source, depended in an irregular way on the geometrical conditions of the experiment. These experimental anomalies were traced to the influence of hydrogenous substances, such as a wooden table top, paraffin, and water. Following up these leads, Fermi and his coworkers showed that fast neutrons can be slowed down (or "moderated") by elastic collisions with hydrogen and that a number of elements possess remarkably large capture cross sections for slow neutrons (A27). Boron, for example, was shown to have a capture cross section for slow neutrons which is about 1,000 times the geometrical cross section of the nucleus. Cadmium was found to have a cross section of about 10^{-20} cm^2 for slow neutrons. On the theoretical side, Fermi and coworkers showed that the capture cross section for slow neutrons should be proportional to $1/V$, where V is the velocity of the neutrons. This well-verified generalization can be interpreted most simply as meaning that the probability of neutron capture is proportional to the time which the neutron spends near the target nucleus, there being no coulomb barrier to be penetrated because the neutron has no charge.

Resonance Capture of Slow Neutrons. Moon and Tillman, followed promptly by many other workers, showed early in 1936 that in many elements there are narrow energy regions of strong selective absorption of slow neutrons. These resonances are generally superimposed upon a $1/V$ variation of capture cross section. Figure Introduction.1 illustrates these two effects, in terms of the total neutron cross sections of B, Cd, and Ag.

In many cases, the strong resonance maxima of neutron capture were found to be *unaccompanied by maxima in the scattering cross section*. This important experimental fact dictated a major revision in the resonance model which had appeared to be satisfactory for the (α,p) resonance reactions. It was necessary to account for strong resonance capture of the slow neutron and, at the same time, to be able to account for a very small probability for reemission of the neutron. Breit and Wigner (B118) first showed in 1936 that this could be accomplished if the compound state has a higher probability of decay by other modes than by reemission of the neutron. The compound nucleus thus corresponds to a damped oscillator, accepting the incident neutron readily at its resonance energy, but dissipating this energy mainly by γ-ray transitions to lower levels of the compound nucleus, as in the (n,γ) reactions. This model is often referred to as the *dispersion theory* of nuclear reactions because of its parallelism with the theory of the dispersion of optical light. The compound nucleus becomes, in this model, an intermediate state in which the

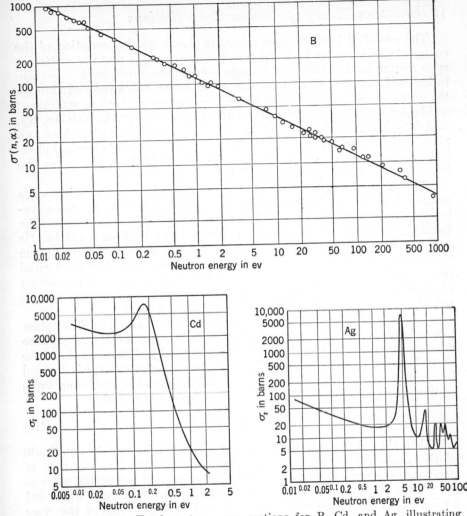

Fig. Introduction.1 Total neutron cross sections for B, Cd, and Ag, illustrating typical combinations of $1/V$ dependence (pure, in the case of boron) and slow-neutron resonances. The resonance in Cd at $E_0 = 0.176$ ev has a total width $\Gamma = 0.115$ ev and a maximum value of $\sigma_0 = 7,200$ barns. The curves are for the normal isotopic mixtures. In Cd, the 0.176-ev resonance is due entirely to Cd^{113} (relative abundance, 12.3 per cent); hence $\sigma_0 \simeq 57,000$ barns for Cd^{113} alone. The complex γ-ray spectrum leading to the ground level of Cd^{114} has been measured by Bartholomew and Kinsey (B16). [*From Goldsmith, Ibser, and Feld (G29) and Hughes (H68)*.]

excitation energy can be shared by several nucleons and from which deexcitation can occur in a variety of competing modes. The dispersion theory, or *resonance theory*, of Breit and Wigner arose independently and simultaneously with Bohr's many-body strong-interaction model, and the two together established the modern concept of the compound nucleus.

1. *Resonance Theory of Nuclear Cross Sections*

The so-called Breit-Wigner formulas give a good description of the energy dependence for both the reaction cross section and the scattering cross section in the vicinity of a single isolated resonance level. As theoretical and experimental knowledge about nuclei has advanced through the years, a number of derivations of these formulas, both in specialized and in generalized forms, have been given by various authors (B118, K5, B52, S38, B112, W51, W49, F45). We shall restrict ourselves here to a plausibility argument (p. 391 of B68) which displays the principal physical concepts of the resonance cross sections. At first, we ignore the intrinsic spins of the colliding particles.

The incident particles are described as a plane wave, with wave number $k = 1/\lambda$, where $\lambda = \hbar/MV$ is the rationalized de Broglie wavelength of relative motion and V is the mutual velocity of approach of the colliding particles whose reduced mass is M and whose total kinetic energy in C coordinates is $E = MV^2/2 = (k\hbar)^2/2M$. This incident plane wave is the sum of elementary spherical partial waves, each characterized by successive integer values of the orbital-angular-momentum quantum number l. Each partial wave is the sum of an incoming wave and an outgoing wave of equal amplitude (Appendix C, Sec. 6).

a. Limiting Values of the Potential-scattering and the Absorption Cross Sections. For *elastic potential scattering*, the maximum possible cross section occurs when the scattering potential just reverses the phase of the incoming partial wave, so that the outgoing partial wave is doubled in amplitude. The corresponding maximum possible scattering cross section emerges at once from Eq. (122) of Appendix C and is

$$(\sigma_{sc})^l_{max} = 4\pi(2l + 1)\lambda^2 \tag{1.1}$$

When there is some absorption of the incoming wave, the amplitude of the scattered outgoing wave is reduced. In the limiting case of maximum absorption, there is no outgoing portion of the partial wave at all. Then the incoming portion has one-half the amplitude which led to Eq. (1.1). Consequently, the maximum possible value of the cross section for formation of the compound nucleus is one-fourth of Eq. (1.1), or

$$(\sigma_{com})^l_{max} = \pi(2l + 1)\lambda^2 \tag{1.2}$$

For the important special case of slow neutrons, which can involve only s-wave collisions ($l = 0$), the maximum possible capture cross section becomes simply $\pi\lambda^2$, and therefore it can be enormously larger than the geometrical cross section πR^2 of the target nucleus.

b. Formation of the Compound Nucleus. The cross section for formation of the compound nucleus, by capture of the incident particle, can be represented as the maximum cross section times the probability for transmission through the nuclear barrier and the nuclear surface by a particle a, with orbital angular momentum l. If the localized effects of resonances are ignored, the over-all transmission coefficient can be represented approximately by

$$T_a \simeq \frac{4k}{K} P_a \qquad (1.3)$$

as given by Eq. (4.7) of Chap. 11. Here P_a is a Gamow-type penetration factor for the coulomb barrier and centrifugal barrier, and $4k/K$ is the probability that the incident particle can pass successfully from outside the nucleus, where its wave number is k, to the region inside the nucleus, where its wave number is K $(\gg k)$.

The effect of the resonance level must now be superimposed upon the smoothly varying barrier transparency represented by Eq. (1.3). At a bombarding energy E, which is in the neighborhood of a resonance E_0, we may, by analogy with optical dispersion theory, represent the shape of the resonance by a function $y(E)$, given by

$$y(E) = \frac{C}{(E - E_0)^2 + (\Gamma/2)^2} \qquad (1.4)$$

where Γ is the full width of the resonance measured at half maximum, i.e.,

$$y(E) = \tfrac{1}{2}y(E_0) \qquad \text{when } E - E_0 = \pm \frac{\Gamma}{2}$$

The normalization constant C is to be evaluated such that the average value of $y(E)$ is unity, when averaged over several resonances whose energy spacing is D_l. This gives

$$\frac{1}{D_l} \int_{-\infty}^{\infty} y(E)\, dE = 1 \qquad \text{when } C = \Gamma \frac{D_l}{2\pi} \qquad (1.5)$$

The average spacing D_l of levels whose angular momentum is l is given in terms of T_a and the partial level width Γ_a for escape (or capture) of the particle a, by Eq. (4.8) of Chap. 11, which is

$$\frac{D_l}{2\pi} \sim \frac{\Gamma_a}{T_a} \qquad (1.6)$$

We can now write the cross section for formation of the compound nucleus with angular momentum l by combining Eqs. (1.2) to (1.6), obtaining

$$\sigma^l_{\text{com}} = \pi(2l + 1)\lambda^2 T_a y(E) \qquad (1.7)$$

$$\sigma^l_{\text{com}} = \pi(2l + 1)\lambda^2 \frac{\Gamma_a \Gamma}{(E - E_0)^2 + (\Gamma/2)^2} \qquad (1.8)$$

where Γ is the total width of the resonance level.

c. Resonance-reaction Cross Section. Once formed, the compound nucleus can transform in any one of a number of permitted modes, each represented by a partial width Γ_i, where

$$\Gamma = \Sigma \Gamma_i = \Gamma_a + \Gamma_b + \Gamma_c + \cdots$$

as in Eq. (4.4) of Chap. 11. The fraction of transitions which follow any particular "channel" or "alternative," say, Γ_b, is simply Γ_b/Γ. Then the cross section for the reaction (a,b), through a single resonance level, becomes

$$\sigma(a,b) = (\sigma_{\text{com}}^l)\left(\frac{\Gamma_b}{\Gamma}\right)$$

$$= \pi(2l + 1)\lambda^2 \frac{\Gamma_a\Gamma_b}{(E - E_0)^2 + (\Gamma/2)^2} \qquad (1.9)$$

If a or b is a charged particle, then the partial widths Γ_a or Γ_b are understood to contain Gamow-type coulomb penetration factors, as in Eq. (4.8) of Chap. 11.

Equation (1.9) applies to all resonance cross sections except for the elastic reemission of the incident particle, $\sigma(a,a)$, that is, elastic resonance scattering, which is discussed later [Eqs. (1.15) to (1.18)] and which requires separate treatment because coherence between the waves which describe elastic resonance scattering and potential scattering may produce interference maxima and minima, as illustrated later in Fig. 1.3. The *elastic-scattering cross section*, Eq. (1.16), σ_{sc} includes all types of elastic scattering, potential and resonance. Equation (1.9) does apply to *inelastic resonance scattering*, i.e., to the reemission of the incident particle, which we can designate as $\sigma(a,a')$.

When all possible resonance "reactions" $(b \neq a)$ are summed, we have the so-called *reaction cross section* σ_r or, synonymously, the *absorption cross section* σ_{abs} (F49). These include all the possible exit channels for Eq. (1.9), except that of elastic resonance scattering $(b = a)$. The relationship between the cross section for formation of the compound nucleus σ_{com}^l and the absorption, or reaction, cross section follows from Eq. (1.9).

$$\sigma_{\text{abs}}^l \equiv \sigma_r^l = \sum_{b \neq a}\sigma(a,b) = (\sigma_{\text{com}}^l)\sum_{b \neq a}\frac{\Gamma_b}{\Gamma}$$

$$= (\sigma_{\text{com}}^l)\left(1 - \frac{\Gamma_a}{\Gamma}\right) = \sigma_{\text{com}}^l - \sigma(a,a) \qquad (1.9a)$$

Instructive experimental examples may be found in the precision measurements of the cross sections for $Li^7(p,\gamma)$, $Li^7(p,p)$, $Li^7(p,p')$, and other reactions by Brown et al. (B130). The so-called *total cross section* σ_t, such as would apply to the attenuation of a collimated beam of incident particles, is then

$$\sigma_t = \sigma_{\text{abs}} + \sigma_{sc} \qquad (1.9b)$$

where the elastic-scattering cross section σ_{sc} includes the elastic resonance scattering which was excluded from σ_{abs}, and where each cross section has been summed over all effective l values.

In the very important special case of the resonance capture of thermal neutrons $(l = 0)$, followed by radiative deexcitation of the compound nucleus, the shape of the so-called *radiative-capture* cross section σ_{cap} for a single level becomes

$$\sigma_{cap} \equiv \sigma(n,\gamma) = \pi\lambda^2 \frac{\Gamma_n\Gamma_\gamma}{(E - E_0)^2 + (\Gamma/2)^2} \tag{1.10}$$

which is a common form of the *Breit-Wigner single-level formula*, when the target nucleus has zero intrinsic angular momentum and the compound nucleus has a neutron width Γ_n, radiation width Γ_γ, and total width $\Gamma = \Gamma_n + \Gamma_\gamma + \cdots$. Usually, when E is small, it is found experimentally that $\Gamma_\gamma \gg \Gamma_n$, that is, the compound nucleus has a large damping and the relative probability of reemission of the neutron (n,n) is very small.

It is often useful to express Eq. (1.10) in terms of σ_0, the maximum value of the radiative-capture cross section, which is reached at $E = E_0$. We take the total width Γ as constant but recall from Eq. (4.8) of Chap. 11 that the neutron width Γ_n is proportional to k, hence to $1/\lambda$, and to $\sqrt{E}$. Then Eq. (1.10) becomes

$$\sigma(n,\gamma) = \sigma_0 \sqrt{\frac{E_0}{E}} \left\{ \frac{1}{[(E - E_0)/(\Gamma/2)]^2 + 1} \right\} \tag{1.11}$$

When analyzed in this conventional fashion, the resonance in $Cd(n,\gamma)$ seen in Fig. Introduction.1 has the values $\sigma_0 = 7,200$ barns, $\Gamma = 0.115$ ev, $E_0 = 0.176$ ev.

The $1/V$ law for neutron absorption is also contained in Eq. (1.11). For a broad resonance, $\Gamma \gg (E - E_0)$, or, when $E \ll E_0$, the expression in the curly braces in Eq. (1.11) becomes essentially independent of E. Then the reaction cross section becomes proportional to $1/\sqrt{E}$, that is, to $1/V$, where V is the velocity of the incident neutron.

The effects of the intrinsic angular momentum of the target nucleus can be very complicated when applied to the total (reaction plus scattering) cross section. For the case of neutron-reaction cross sections, the angular momentum I_t of the target nucleus can be shown (A2) to introduce a multiplicative statistical factor

$$\frac{(2I_c + 1)}{(2I_t + 1)(2I_a + 1)(2l + 1)} \tag{1.12}$$

into Eq. (1.9), where $I_a = I_n = $ "spin" of the projectile and $I_c = $ angular-momentum quantum number of the compound nucleus. Introduction of this factor leads to a statistical coefficient of

$$\frac{(2I_c + 1)}{(2I_n + 1)(2I_t + 1)} \tag{1.13}$$

on the right-hand side of Eqs. (1.10) and (1.11), in agreement with Eq. (4.13) of Chap. 11. In the literature, this statistical factor has often been absorbed into Γ_n or into σ_0 of Eqs. (1.10) and (1.11) instead of being represented explicitly.

In some cases the elementary model which we have discussed gives a good representation of the more accurate theoretical results. In general, the barrier can influence the cross section in a more complicated manner than is representable as a factor (F67). Factorization of the cross section into barrier terms and specifically nuclear terms, as in Eq. (1.7), is only an approximate treatment but has the merits of mathematical simplicity and ease of visualization.

A more detailed mathematical analysis shows that the resonance energy E_0 is constant and independent of E only in the special case of s-wave neutron resonances. For charged-particle resonances, and for any $l \neq 0$ case, the variation of E_0 and Γ with E may become significant, especially for broad resonances (T18). When the Breit-Wigner formula is fitted to experimental resonance curves, it is common to treat E_0 and Γ as constants of the level and to neglect any theoretical variations with bombarding energy E.

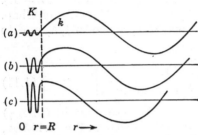

Fig. 1.1 Schematic representation of the modified radial partial wave function φ for a neutron whose wave number is k outside the nucleus and $K(K \gg k)$ inside the nuclear surface at $r = R$. The usual case of potential scattering is shown at a, where the internal amplitude is $\sim k/K$ times the external amplitude. At a resonance energy, where k corresponds to E_0, the logarithmic derivative of φ is zero, and the inner and outer waves join at full amplitude, illustrated at c. An intermediate case, near resonance, is illustrated at b. [*From Feshbach, Peaslee, and Weisskopf* (F45).]

d. Elastic-scattering Cross Section. The characteristic shape for the resonance absorption peak, as given by the denominator of Eq. (1.4), as well as the form of Eq. (1.8), has been developed from general considerations by Feshbach, Peaslee, and Weisskopf (F45). In this treatment the incident particles (in particular, s-wave neutrons) are represented by a plane wave of wave number k outside the nucleus. Inside the nucleus, a captured neutron will have a very large kinetic energy (~ 20 Mev) and a correspondingly large wave number K ($\sim 1 \times 10^{+13}$ cm^{-1}). The nuclear radius is then defined as the distance $r = R$ at which the wave number of the incident neutron changes from k to K. At the nuclear surface, the outside wave function must join the inside wave function smoothly, and with equal derivative. Thus if $\varphi = r\psi$ is the modified radial wave function for the partial wave l, both φ and $d\varphi/dr$ must be continuous across the nuclear surface at $r = R$. Then a useful function $f(E)$ of the bombarding energy E can be defined as R times the value at $r = R$ of the logarithmic derivative of φ, that is,

$$f(E) \equiv R \left(\frac{d\varphi/dr}{\varphi} \right)_{r=R} \tag{1.14}$$

It is then possible to express the particle width Γ_a, the total width Γ, and the general form of Eqs. (1.8) and (1.9) in terms of the level spacing and certain general properties of $f(E)$. It is found that resonance occurs always when the real part of $f(E)$ is zero.

Figure 1.1 is an instructive schematic representation of the wave function φ, inside and outside the nucleus (compare Fig. 11 of Appendix C). In order to join φ at the nuclear surface $r = R$, the amplitude inside the nucleus must be generally of the order of k/K ($\ll 1$) times the amplitude outside the nucleus (Fig. 1.1a). Transmission through the nuclear surface is correspondingly small ($\sim k/K$), and the effect on the incident wave is mainly elastic *"potential scattering,"* in which the incident particles do not enter the target nucleus. In the limiting case of no transmission, the scattering would be similar to that from an impenetrable sphere, for which $\varphi = 0$ at $r = R$.

In contrast with this "normal" situation between resonances, Fig. 1.1c illustrates the behavior of φ at a resonance level. The resonance levels correspond to certain exceptional values of K, such that the inside wave function has nearly a zero derivative at the edge of the nucleus. Then the internal wave function can join the external wave function at substantially full amplitude. The incident neutron has a large probability of entering the nucleus at the resonance energy E_0.

Reemission of the captured neutron might be expected from the fraction Γ_n/Γ of the compound nuclei. If this elastic *"resonance scattering"* were the only effective mechanism for elastic scattering, then its cross section could be written at once from Eq. (1.8) and would be

$$\sigma(n,n) = (\sigma_{\text{com}}^l)\left(\frac{\Gamma_n}{\Gamma}\right)$$

$$= \pi(2l + 1)\lambda^2 \frac{\Gamma_n\Gamma_n}{(E - E_0)^2 + (\Gamma/2)^2} \tag{1.15}$$

So long as the compound nucleus is highly damped, that is $\Gamma_n \ll \Gamma_\gamma + \cdots$, this elastic resonance scattering will be small compared with the competing reaction cross section $\sigma(n,\gamma)$, etc., of Eq. (1.9).

Equation (1.15) is meaningful only if the elastic potential scattering is zero. In the general case, the amplitudes of the resonance scattering and of the potential scattering will add coherently, in order to produce the total scattering. From the characteristics of $f(E)$, it can be shown (F45) that the elastic-scattering cross section σ_{sc}, for s-wave neutrons on a spinless target, is given by the absolute value of

$$\sigma_{sc} = 4\pi\lambda^2 \left| \frac{\Gamma_n/2}{(E - E_0) + i(\Gamma/2)} + e^{ikR}\sin kR \right|^2 \tag{1.16}$$

Here the coefficient $4\pi\lambda^2$ is the maximum possible s-wave scattering cross section as given by Eq. (1.1), while within the bars the first term is the resonance-scattering amplitude, which if present alone would lead to Eq. (1.15). The final term is the potential-scattering amplitude, which if present alone would lead to

$$\sigma_{sc} = 4\pi\lambda^2 \sin^2 kR \tag{1.17}$$

For small energies, $kR \ll 1$ as $E \to 0$, and Eq. (1.17) reduces to

$$\sigma_{sc} \simeq 4\pi R^2 \tag{1.18}$$

which is the potential-scattering cross section for an impenetrable sphere when $R \ll \lambda$.

The general expressions (W51, B68, M69, F45, T18) for total elastic scattering are vastly more involved than Eq. (1.16). Even for neutron scattering, introduction of $l > 0$ and of finite angular momentum in the target nucleus gives rise to complications due to the dependence of E_0 and Γ on E. For charged particles, the resonance scattering involves coherence between coulomb potential scattering, nuclear potential scattering, and resonance scattering, as depicted schematically in Fig. 7.1 of Chap. 2.

e. Experimental Determination of the Shape of Resonance Excitation Functions. Experimentally, the total width Γ of a resonance-capture level is the difference of bombarding energy at half the maximum cross section, for an infinitely thin target and for monoenergetic incident beams. The perennial experimental compromise between resolution and intensity dictates a finite target thickness and a slightly inhomogeneous incident energy. Both must, of course, be narrower than the natural width Γ of the level being studied.

For slow-neutron resonance studies, bombarding energies between about 10^{-3} ev and 10^{+3} ev can be obtained, with an energy spread of about 5 to 25 per cent, through the use of crystal spectrometers, mechanical velocity selectors, or modulated ion sources. Techniques, results, and interpretations are summarized from time to time, as in the valuable compilations of neutron-cross-section data by Goldsmith, Ibser, and Feld (G29), by Adair (A2), and others. Figure Introduction.1 showed illustrative results.

For charged particles, such as protons and α particles, energies from a few kev up to several Mev, with an inhomogeneity of $\sim$0.1 per cent, are obtainable from electrostatic generators fitted with auxiliary magnetic or electrostatic filters. Illustrative results are shown in Figs. 1.2 to 1.4. These three figures deal with the spectacular resonances in Si^{28}, which are observed when Al is bombarded with protons. The original experimental papers should be consulted for an insight into the experimental limitations and techniques.

Aluminum has but one stable isotope, and so there is no ambiguity concerning mass numbers. Figure 1.2 shows some 31 prominent resonance peaks in the $Al^{27}(p,\gamma)Si^{28}$ reaction, between $E_p = 0.5$- and 1.4-Mev bombarding proton energy. Thus the mean distance between these levels is about 30 kev. The proton width Γ_p is expected to rise from $\sim$1 ev at $E_p \sim 0.6$ Mev to $\sim$1 kev at $E_p \sim 1.4$ Mev, as estimated from barrier transmission for s-wave protons. From the absolute yield of γ rays, the radiation width Γ_γ was found to be of the order of 1 ev for all E_p. Thus the $Al^{27}(p,\gamma)Si^{28}$ widths shown in Fig. 1.2 are mainly of instrumental origin, as the experimental energy resolution was $\sim$4 kev. Shoemaker et al. (S35) have improved the experimental resolution and have measured the reaction products (γ rays, α rays, and protons) from Al + p in the region of 1.4 to 4 Mev. These results are extremely complicated, partly because of the high nuclear angular momentum

$I = \frac{5}{2}$ of Al^{27}, and have thus far defied exact theoretical analysis in terms of the angular momenta and widths of the excited levels of the compound nucleus Si^{28}.

One of the strong resonances in the $Al(p,\gamma)Si$ reaction is of special experimental importance, because it serves as an interlaboratory reference standard for the voltage calibration of proton generators. Prior to 1949 this particular resonance was taken as 985 kev, as it is shown in Figs. 1.2 and 1.3. Herb et al. (H38) then remeasured the proton energy

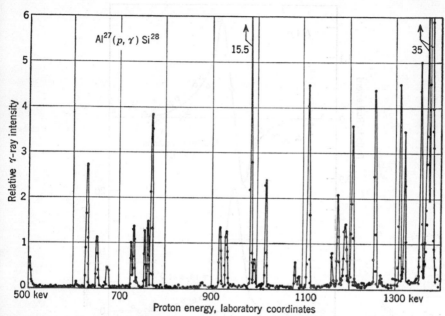

Fig. 1.2 The yield of high-energy γ rays, indicating resonance capture, in the reaction $Al^{27}(p,\gamma)Si^{28}$. The Al targets used in these measurements had a thickness of only about 1-kev stopping power for protons and were prepared by vacuum evaporation onto Cu or Ag disks. The incident proton energy was controlled to about ± 1.5 kev, so that the over-all experimental resolution is about 4 kev. Each of these 31 resonances is thought to have a natural width $\Gamma = \Gamma_p + \Gamma_\gamma$ of about 1 kev or less; hence the widths shown here are primarily of experimental origin. [*From Bröstrom, Huus, and Tangen* (B129).]

required to produce this resonance, using a large 90° electrostatic analyzer, in which the deflecting potential was supplied by dry-cell battery stacks. These measurements gave 993.3 $\pm$ 1 kev (laboratory coordinates) which has been used as a reference standard for many subsequent proton-energy measurements in a number of laboratories.

The structure of this 993-kev resonance is shown in Fig. 1.3. The $Al^{27}(p,\gamma)Si^{28}$ reaction is in competition with elastic resonance scattering $Al(p,p)Al$ at the same energies. This elastic scattering is the coherent combination of coulomb scattering, potential scattering, and resonance scattering. Destructive interference at proton energies just below resonance produces the characteristic shape of the scattering cross section which is shown in the upper part of Fig. 1.3. Analysis suggests (B31) that this 993-kev resonance is produced by s-wave protons; hence the compound nucleus Si^{28} has an angular momentum of $\frac{5}{2} \pm \frac{1}{2}$, i.e., either 2 or 3. The total natural width $\Gamma = \Gamma_p + \Gamma_\gamma$ is about 100 ev, and it seems proper to assume that at the excitation energy involved $\Gamma_p \gg \Gamma_\gamma$.

The reaction $Al^{27}(p,\alpha)Mg^{24}$ is another consequence of proton bombardment of Al. Its excitation function reveals a number of sharp

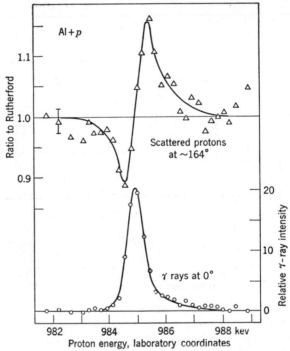

Fig. 1.3 Below, the shape of the $Al^{27}(p,\gamma)Si^{28}$ resonance at 985 kev (pre-1949 energy scale) or 993 kev on the post-1949 energy scale (H38). Above, the elastic-scattering cross section for protons on Al, at the same energies, referred to the Rutherford (coulomb) scattering as unity. The scattering cross section is characteristic of the destructive interference between the coherent coulomb scattering, potential scattering, and resonance scattering. [*From Bender, Shoemaker, Kaufmann, and Bouricius* (B31).]

resonances (S35) which correspond to excited levels in the compound nucleus Si^{28}. Using the same experimental equipment, Kaufmann et al. (K8) have studied the *inverse reaction* $Mg^{24}(\alpha,p)Al^{27}$ by bombarding the separated Mg^{24} isotope with electrostatically accelerated α particles. The Si^{28} resonances which are observed in the excitation functions for these two inverse reactions are compared in Fig. 1.4. The good agreement between the level structure and the relative intensities for these inverse reactions constitutes very strong experimental support for the compound-nucleus hypothesis in these resonance reactions.

Note that the energy scales in Fig. 1.4 are in C coordinates and that the proton energy scale is 1.613 Mev less than the α-particle energy scale. This energy difference of 1.613 Mev is the Q value of the $\text{Al}^{27}(p,\alpha)\text{Mg}^{24}$ reaction. Recall the reciprocity relationships between the cross sections for inverse processes, discussed in Chap. 10, Sec. 4. In the reaction $\text{Al}^{27}(p,\alpha)\text{Mg}^{24}$ the products are both even-even nuclides and have zero intrinsic nuclear angular momentum, whereas Al^{27} has $I_{\text{Al}} = \frac{5}{2}$ and the proton has $I_p = \frac{1}{2}$. From Eq. (4.15) of Chap. 10, we can write the

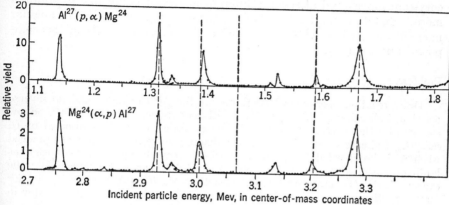

Fig. 1.4 Resonance yields of the inverse reactions $\text{Al}^{27}(p,\alpha)\text{Mg}^{24}$ and $\text{Mg}^{24}(\alpha,p)\text{Al}^{27}$, observed at a laboratory angle of $164 \pm 5°$. The α-particle energies exceed the corresponding proton energies by 1.613 Mev, which is the Q value of the $\text{Al}^{27}(p,\alpha)\text{Mg}^{24}$ reaction. The target thicknesses were ~13 kev, and the inhomogeneity of the bombarding beam was about 0.1 per cent. [*From Kaufmann, Goldberg, Koester, and Mooring* (K8).]

expected ratio of the cross sections for the (α,p) reaction and the inverse (p,α) reaction. This ratio is

$$\frac{\sigma_{\alpha,p}}{\sigma_{p,\alpha}} = \frac{(2I_{\text{Al}} + 1)(2I_p + 1)(MV)_p^2}{(MV)_\alpha^2} = 12\,\frac{(MV)_p^2}{(MV)_\alpha^2} \qquad (1.19)$$

where $(MV)_\alpha = h/\lambda_\alpha$ is the C-coordinate momentum in the $\text{Mg}^{24} + \alpha$-particle channel and $(MV)_p = h/\lambda_p$ is the momentum in the associated $\text{Al}^{27} + p$ channel. Note that the general reciprocity relationship, of which Eq. (1.19) is a special case, emerges also from the Breit-Wigner reaction cross sections of Eq. (1.9) when they are combined with the statistical weighting factors given by Eq. (1.12). Qualitatively, the relative cross sections shown in Fig. 1.4 agree with Eq. (1.19); quantitatively, a discrepancy of the order of a factor of 3 is probably due to difficulties in measuring the effective thicknesses of the Al and Mg targets (K8).

Elastic scattering resonances in the energy domain covered by Fig. 1.4 have also been studied by Kaufmann et al. (K8, S35). Experimental results and tentative interpretations will be found in the original papers. In general, some $\text{Mg}^{24}(\alpha,\alpha)\text{Mg}^{24}$ elastic scattering resonances are associated with $Al^{27}(p,p)Al^{27}$ scattering resonances and with $Mg^{24}(\alpha,p)Al^{27}$ and $Al^{27}(p,\alpha)Mg^{24}$ reaction resonances. Some other scattering resonances are not associated with reaction resonances at the same bombarding energy. Interpretations in terms of the angular momentum of the compound level in Si^{28}, and the partial level widths, are obtainable for some but not yet for all the observed resonance levels.

When the target nucleus has zero angular momentum, as in the case of $C^{12}(p,p)C^{12}$, and when the shape of the elastic-resonance-scattering curves are measured at several different angles, it is possible to obtain a more complete theoretical analysis of the data and to specify the angular momentum, parity, width, and excitation energy of levels in the compound nucleus (J1).

Problem

Draw reaction energy-level diagrams for the $Al^{27}(p,\alpha)Mg^{24}$ and its inverse reaction, indicating qualitatively the position of resonance levels in Si^{28}. Show clearly why the proton and α-particle energy scales in Fig. 1.4 are offset by Q, not $2Q$. Indicate schematically on your diagram some of the reactions produced when Al is bombarded by protons, especially (p,γ), (p,p), (p,α), and reactions leading to excited levels in Al^{27}, Si^{28}, and Mg^{24}. Determine numerically the expected ratio of the cross sections of the reactions $Mg^{24}(\alpha,p)Al^{27}$ and $Al^{27}(p,\alpha)Mg^{24}$ for the particular resonance which occurs at an α-particle energy of 3.28 Mev in C coordinates.

2. *Continuum Theory of Nuclear Cross Sections*

At higher bombarding energies, say, of the order of 1 to 30 Mev, the individual levels of the compound nucleus become broader and also more closely spaced. Then the energy levels can best be visualized as a continuum of possible energy states. The so-called *continuum theory* of nuclear cross sections, which is applicable in this energy domain, is an average over many resonances.

Figure 2.1 illustrates the disappearance of resolvable resonances, as the bombarding energy is increased, in a representative element of moderate atomic weight. In heavier elements, the "continuum" begins at even smaller bombarding energies.

The earlier continuum theories, by Konopinski and Bethe (K38) and by Weisskopf and Ewing (W25), were characterized by a *sticking probability* ξ, which denoted the probability that an incident particle would combine with the target nucleus to form a compound nucleus. These theories can be represented by the expression

$$\sigma_{\text{com}} = \pi \lambdabar^2 \sum_{l=0}^{\infty} (2l + 1)P_l\xi_l \tag{2.1}$$

where P_l denotes the probability that an incident particle whose angular momentum is l will reach the nuclear surface and ξ_l denotes the probability that the particle will enter and remain in the nucleus. In the continuum theories internal elastic scattering is explicitly excluded. Elastic scattering here is proportional to $(1 - \xi_l)$ and is visualized in terms of an incident particle which never merges with the target nucleus. Comparison with Eqs. (1.3) and (1.7) shows that, in these early continuum theories, P_l is physically similar to a Gamow-type penetration probability, while the sticking probability ξ_l can be identified with the probability $4kK/(k + K)^2$ of transmission through the potential discontinuity at the nuclear surface.

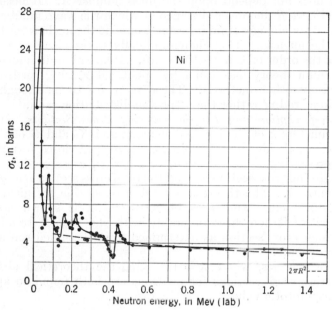

Fig. 2.1 The total cross section (absorption plus scattering) of nickel for neutrons from 0.01 to 1.5 Mev.   Approximately monoenergetic neutrons (± 20 kev below 0.5 Mev; ± 150 kev above 0.5 Mev) were produced by bombarding a thin Li target with protons accelerated by an electrostatic generator.   The dotted line is from the continuum theory of Feshbach and Weisskopf (F49), assuming a nuclear radius of 4.6 $\times$ 10^{-13} cm.   [*The experimental data are from Barschall, Bockelman, and Seagondollar* (B15).]

a. Neutron Cross Sections.   At the beginning of 1954, the continuum theories of nuclear-reaction cross sections were undergoing major revisions (F46), in order to match systematic trends which had been found in neutron cross sections.   The physical significance of these revisions may be best understood by comparison with the schematic continuum theory developed in 1949 by Feshbach and Weisskopf (F49).   That theory deals explicitly with neutron-induced reactions only.   The energy dependence of nuclear cross sections, averaged over individual fluctuations and resonances, is expressed in terms of two parameters of the inner nuclear structure.   These are the nuclear radius R and the wave number K of the incident neutron after it is in the interior of the compound nucleus. Both R and K have definitions which are analogous to those used in the resonance theory by Feshbach, Peaslee, and Weisskopf discussed in Sec. 1 of this chapter. The wave number K for the neutron within the nucleus becomes $K^2 = K_0^2 + k^2$, where k is the wave number of the incident neutron as it approaches the nucleus and K_0 is the interior wave number K if the bombarding energy is zero. It is estimated that $K_0 \simeq 1 \times 10^{+13}$ cm^{-1}, which corresponds to a neutron of the order of 20-Mev kinetic energy. Under the assumption of constant density in nuclei, K_0 does not depend upon the mass number A. It needs to be emphasized that R denotes a distance at which the wave number of the incident neutron changes from its value k outside the nucleus to the value K inside the nucleus. This change actually takes place over a finite distance of the order of $1/K$ ($\sim 10^{-13}$ cm). Hence all radii inferred from this continuum theory may differ by about $\pm 1 \times 10^{-13}$ cm from radii determined by other methods. These radii are to be thought of as "nuclear-force radii" rather than "proton-distribution radii."

Neutron-absorption and Elastic-scattering Cross Sections. In terms of the parameters k of the incident neutron and K_0 and R of the compound nucleus, Feshbach and Weisskopf developed closed formulas and graphs representing the absorption, or reaction, cross section σ_{abs}, the elastic-scattering cross section σ_{sc}, and the total cross section $\sigma_t = \sigma_{abs} + \sigma_{sc}$ for fast neutrons. The theoretical total cross section for nickel, using $K_0 = 1 \times 10^{+13}$ cm^{-1} and $R = 4.6 \times 10^{-13}$ cm, is shown dotted in Fig. 2.1, where it compares favorably with the general trend of the observed total cross section as determined from these neutron attenuation measurements.

At large energies, where $\lambda \equiv 1/k \ll R$, the theoretical absorption and scattering cross sections for neutrons are both found to approach the same asymptotic value

$$\sigma_{abs} = \sigma_{sc} = \pi(R + \lambda)^2 \qquad (2.2)$$

Therefore the total cross section, for high-energy neutrons, becomes

$$\sigma_t = \sigma_{abs} + \sigma_{sc} = 2\pi(R + \lambda)^2 \qquad (2.3)$$

The elastic scattering referred to here is purely potential scattering, as internal or resonance elastic scattering is usually explicitly excluded in continuum theories of nuclear cross sections. For neutrons whose laboratory kinetic energy is E Mev, the rationalized de Broglie wavelength λ and the wave number k are given closely by

$$\lambda = \frac{1}{k} = \frac{4.55 \times 10^{-13}}{[E(\text{Mev})]^{\frac{1}{2}}} \qquad \text{cm} \qquad (2.4)$$

if the reduced mass is assumed equal to the neutron mass. Although the total cross section σ_t for extremely fast neutrons has the asymptotic value $\sigma_t \to 2\pi R^2$, as given by older theories, Eqs. (2.3) and (2.4) show that for most practical cases (say, $E \sim 10$ to 25 Mev) λ should not be neglected in comparison with R. For example, if $R \simeq 1.4 \times 10^{-13}$ $A^{\frac{1}{3}}$

cm, then for 20-Mev neutrons on Pb, $R/\lambda \simeq 8.1$.   In Eq. (2.2), λ can be interpreted as the "size" of the incident neutron.   Then the collision area presented by a target nucleus is just $\pi(R + \lambda)^2$.

Experimental determinations of the total cross section for fast neutrons on a wide variety of elements have been made by many workers. [See (C40) and (D14) for measurements using monoenergetic neutrons and for references to the earlier work.]   In general, the total cross section is found to vary approximately with $A^{\frac{2}{3}}$, as would be expected from Eq. (2.3).   Figure 2.2 is a plot of the measurements (D14) of σ_t for 13 elements, using monoenergetic 19.0 $\pm$ 0.2-Mev neutrons, obtained from the $H^3(d,n)He^4$ reaction.   These cross sections were measured with an

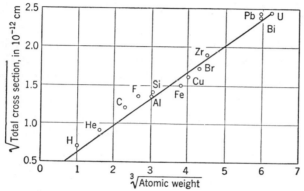

Fig. 2.2   Total cross section σ_t for 19-Mev neutrons on 13 representative elements. The straight line is the function $(\sigma_t)^{\frac{1}{2}} = (2\pi)^{\frac{1}{2}}(R_0 A^{\frac{1}{3}} + \lambda)$, with $R_0 = 1.4 \times 10^{-13}$ cm and $\lambda = 1.04 \times 10^{-13}$ cm, no correction being made on λ for reduced mass.   [*From Day and Henkel* (D14).]

accuracy of ± 3 per cent.   Deviations from the straight line in Fig. 2.2, which represents Eq. (2.3), with

$$R = 1.4 \times 10^{-13}A^{\frac{1}{3}}   \text{cm} \qquad (2.5)$$

are therefore indicative of the approximate character of Eqs. (2.3) and (2.5) and the inadequacy of their underlying assumptions.   It is expected that a more refined continuum theory (F46, F47) may give a better match with the total-cross-section data for fast neutrons and a reappraisal of the "nuclear-force radii."

"Transparency" of Nuclei.   At neutron energies well above 25 Mev, the total cross sections for all elements are found experimentally to decrease with increasing neutron energy.   Typical observations are shown in Fig. 2.3.   These measurements suggest that nuclei are, in fact, not "opaque" to incident high-energy neutrons.   The measurements can be unified by assuming that heavy nuclei have an absorption coefficient for fast neutrons which is less than infinite.   For 90-Mev neutrons, for example, an absorption coefficient of 2.2×10^{12} cm^{-1}, which corresponds to a mean path length of 4.5×10^{-13} cm in nuclear matter, gives a reasonable account (F42) of the experimental data.   The nucleus is

thus not "opaque," but slightly "translucent" to incident high-energy neutrons.

Shadow Scattering of Fast Neutrons. The angular distribution of elastically scattered very fast neutrons is of special interest. There is a pronounced maximum in the forward direction, followed at moderate angles by successive minima and maxima, as in an optical diffraction pattern. Representative experimental results are shown in Fig. 2.4 for 84-Mev neutrons ($\lambda = 0.49 \times 10^{-13}$ cm) on Al, Cu, and Pb (B110). The total-elastic-scattering cross section is approximately

$$\sigma_{sc} = \pi(R + \lambda)^2$$

as given by Eq. (2.2).

The principal physical features of this "shadow scattering" can be understood from a simplified qualitative argument. We assume at first that $\lambda \ll R$ and that any neutron which strikes the nucleus will be absorbed. The absorption cross section is then simply $\sigma_{abs} = \pi R^2$. In the language of wave optics, the nucleus is like a black sphere which casts a shadow, as indicated schematically in Fig. 2.5. As in the Fraunhofer diffraction of a plane wave by an opaque circular disk, this shadow is produced by interference between the incident wave and a scattered wave, and the edges of the shadow cannot be perfectly sharp. Immediately behind the obstacle, the shadow could be produced by replacing the nucleus by a disk of area πR^2 which emits, in the direction of the shadow, neutron waves of the same intensity and wavelength as the incident neutrons, but of opposite phase. The total scattering required to produce the shadow is thus just equal to the total energy absorbed by the opaque nucleus. Therefore the scattering cross section is just equal to the absorption cross section, if the nucleus absorbs all neutrons which are incident upon it. Thus $\sigma_{sc} = \sigma_{abs}$, as in Eq. (2.2). In order to produce complete destructive interference, this shadow scattering must have the same wavelength as the incident neutrons; hence it is elastic scattering.

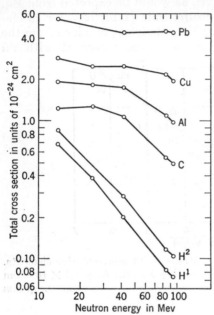

Fig. 2.3 Total neutron cross sections σ_t of five elements for neutrons of 14, 25, 42, 84, and 95 Mev. The decrease in σ_t at the higher neutron energies suggests that all neutrons which strike the target area $\pi(R + \lambda)^2$ are not captured and that nuclear matter is slightly transparent to swift neutrons. [*From Hildebrand and Leith* (H51).]

According to ordinary wave optics, the scattering angles for shadow scattering are of the order of λ/R. In ordinary optical situations, where usually $\lambda/R \ll 1$, the shadow may extend practically to infinity, and the shadow scattering may not be easily measurable. For nuclei, however, the angle λ/R may be of the order of 0.1 radian, or 6°. Then the complete shadow behind the nucleus becomes blurred or dissolved in a distance of the order of $R/(\lambda/R) = R^2/\lambda$, which may only be a few times the nuclear radius. At the distance of the measuring equipment, the

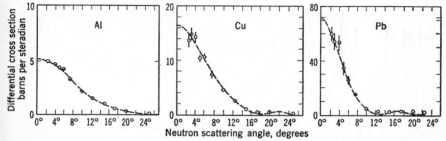

Fig. 2.4   Angular distribution of elastically scattered 84-Mev neutrons on targets of Al, Cu, and Pb. [*From Bratenahl, Fernbach, Hildebrand, Leith, and Moyer* (B110).]

shadow scattering is then manifest as a small-angle $(\sim\lambda/R)$ elastic scattering.

Relatively simple quantitative theories (F42, P7, T11), taking into account the fact that the target nucleus is surely not perfectly opaque to very-high-energy neutrons, and that only neutrons with angular momenta $l < R/\lambda$ may strike the nucleus, give a good representation of

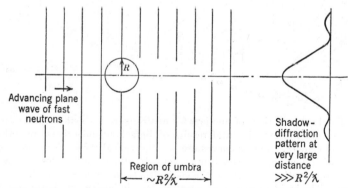

Fig. 2.5   Schematic representation of fast-neutron "shadow scattering," or diffraction scattering. If the nucleus absorbs all incident neutrons, then $\sigma_{sc} = \sigma_{\text{abs}}$. The major portion of the scattering occurs within an angle of the order of λ/R.

experimental data, such as Fig. 2.4. Much work remains to be done before the agreement can be said to be exact.

Total Neutron Cross Sections at 0 to 3 Mev.   Over the neutron energy domain from about 0.05 Mev to 3 Mev, Barschall and collaborators (B14, M45, W6a, O1a) have measured the total cross section of a number of elements. Figure 2.1 illustrates these experimental results for the

case of nickel.   When the cross sections for each element are averaged
over the individual resonance peaks, and the resulting smooth curves for
a number of elements are compared, a systematic pattern emerges (B14).
These smoothed total cross sections are shown in the upper part of Fig.

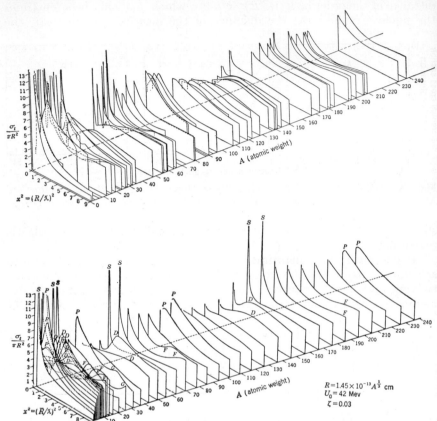

Fig. 2.6   Total cross sections of nuclides for neutrons from about 0.05 Mev to 3 Mev.
Upper curves are the experimental results of Barschall and others, smoothed over
individual resonances.   Lower curves are the theoretical results for a single-particle
interaction with a nonopaque nuclear model.   In all curves, the vertical coordinate
is the total cross section in units of the geometric target area πR^2, with $R = 1.45 \times$
$10^{-13}A^{\frac{1}{3}}$ cm.   The incident neutron energy E_n Mev in laboratory coordinates is given
in terms of the parameter $x^2 = (R/\lambda)^2 = E_n(A^{\frac{3}{3}}/10) [A/(A + 1)]$.   Then for 1 Mev,
$x^2 = 1.14$ for $A = 40$, $x^2 = 2.7$ for $A = 140$, and $x^2 = 3.4$ for $A = 200$.   Letters
S, P, D, F, G on the theoretical curves denote the character of the large-scale resonance which is responsible for the maxima shown.   [*From Feshbach, Porter, and
Weisskopf* (F47).]

2.6.   Note, for example, the broad *maxima* in the total cross section for
neutron energies of ~1.5 Mev ($x^2 \simeq 4$) in middleweight elements $A \sim 140$
(I, Ba, La, Ce, etc.) and the broad *minima* at the same neutron energies
($x^2 \simeq 6$) in heavy elements $A \sim 200$ (Pb, Bi, etc.).

In its original form, the continuum theory of Feshbach and Weisskopf does not account for these systematic features. The predicted absorption cross section at high energies, as given by Eq. (2.2), becomes, for small energies, very roughly

$$\sigma_{abs} \simeq \pi(R + \lambda)^2 \left[\frac{4kK}{(k + K)^2} \right] \tag{2.6}$$

where the quantity in the square brackets is the usual expression for the transparency of the potential step at the surface of the nucleus. For very small bombarding energies, $k \ll K$ and $R \ll \lambda = 1/k$, so that the predicted absorption cross section would be approximately

$$\sigma_{abs} \simeq \frac{4\pi}{kK} \qquad \text{for } \lambda \gg R \tag{2.7}$$

which contains the familiar $1/V$ law of slow-neutron absorption and is large compared with σ_{sc} of Eq. (1.18). These too-simple relationships imply a monotonic variation of total cross section between

$$\sigma_t \simeq 2\pi(R + \lambda)^2 \qquad \text{for large energies}$$

and

$$\sigma_t \simeq \frac{4\pi}{kK} \qquad \text{for very small neutron energies}$$

The systematic maxima and minima seen in the experimental cross sections suggest an interference phenomenon between the incident neutron wave and some outgoing wave. The outgoing wave may be the residue from incomplete absorption of the incident neutron wave. To test such a model, Feshbach, Porter, and Weisskopf (F46, F47) have revised the continuum theory of Feshbach and Weisskopf by allowing for partial nuclear transparency. This is done by introducing a complex potential $U(r)$ for the nuclear potential well, such that

$$\begin{align}
U(r) &= -U_0(1 + i\zeta) & \text{for } r < R \\
U(r) &= 0 & \text{for } r > R
\end{align} \tag{2.8}$$

The real number U_0 gives the depth of the potential well and is to be identified with $K_0^2(\hbar^2/2M)$ of the original theory. The parameter ζ introduces a finite absorption coefficient ζK for neutrons passing into nuclear matter. Then the mean path length, or distance within which the neutron intensity is reduced by the factor $1/e$, is $(\zeta K)^{-1}$. Neutron absorption is essentially complete if $R \gg (\zeta K)^{-1}$, when the original continuum theory of Eqs. (2.2) and (2.7) would be valid.

Calculations of the resulting total cross sections and the differential scattering cross sections are straightforward but laborious. Figure 2.6 shows the results of these calculations (F47), insofar as they apply to the total neutron cross sections in the energy domain up to 3 Mev. For these calculations the choice of parameters was

$$U_0 = 42 \text{ Mev}$$
$$R = 1.45 \times 10^{-13} A^{\frac{1}{3}}$$
$$\zeta = 0.03$$

It is seen that many of the experimentally observed broad maxima and minima are well represented. Insofar as the gross features of the total cross section σ_t are concerned, the parameters $U_0 = 42$ Mev and $\zeta = 0.03$ were found (F47) to be clearly better than $U_0 = 19$ Mev and $\zeta = 0.05$, especially for $A < 60$ and for neutron energies below 1 Mev. Adair (A5) has pointed out that a well depth of about 42 Mev is also in better agreement with interpretations of the spacing of bound levels in heavy nuclei (B89) and of the variation of the thermal neutron scattering length, a, with nuclear size (F58). The theory also reproduces some of the main features of the observed angular distribution of elastically scattered 1-Mev neutrons (W6b), but these theoretical results are much less sensitive to the choice of U_0 and ζ. Finally, the theory provides estimates of the variation with mass number A of the cross section for compound-nucleus formation. These estimates are qualitatively similar to present experimental results (F47) and provide clues for the future refinement of the theory.

In the 0- to 3-Mev domain, with the parameters as chosen above, the "absorption coefficient" for neutrons in nuclear matter has the value $\zeta K \simeq 0.042 \times 10^{+13}$ cm^{-1}. This corresponds to a probability $1/e(\simeq 0.37)$ of *not* being absorbed while traveling a distance $(\zeta K)^{-1} \simeq 24 \times 10^{-13}$ cm in nuclear matter. This distance is about 1.5 times the diameter of a nucleus whose atomic weight is ~ 100. To the extent that the theory is valid in its present form, it implies that nuclear matter is far from opaque to incident neutrons, a conclusion which had been drawn earlier from the high-energy-neutron cross sections shown in Fig. 2.3. This implies that the interactions between nucleons within a nucleus may not be as strong as was once thought and is in consonance with the ideas of an independent particle moving in a potential well, which characterizes the shell model of nuclear structure.

b. Nuclear Cross Sections for Charged Particles. Excitation functions for nuclear reactions produced by the absorption of charged particles are more complicated than the neutron cross sections, because the incident particle has to cope with the coulomb barrier, in addition to all the effects which are present for incident neutrons. For the large group of reactions in which a compound nucleus is formed, the cross section is clearly the product of the probability of formation of the compound nucleus σ_{com}, as in Eq. (2.1), times the fraction of these compound nuclei which traverse the particular exit channel of interest. No simple analytical expressions can be written down to represent the combined coulomb-barrier penetration P_l and the sticking probability ξ_l although these parameters can serve us as useful conceptual guides.

When averaged over any individual narrow resonances, σ_{com} can be expected to increase rapidly with bombarding energy E, more or less in proportion to the increased probability of penetrating the coulomb barrier. If we confine our attention to compound nuclei whose excitation energy is, say, 1 Mev or more above the dissociation energy, then deexcitation may take place through a number of competing channels. The absolute probability, or partial width, for any particular mode of decay depends on the energy available for that emitted particle. This in turn depends on the Q value of the particular reaction (α,n), (α,p), etc.

Relative Probability of n, p, α, γ Emission from the Compound Nucleus. For the *same* available energy of the *emitted* particle, neutron emission is always much more probable than proton emission, because of the emergent coulomb barrier against the emission of charged particles. Similarly, proton emission is more likely than α-particle emission, for the same kinetic energy of emission. The probability of γ-ray emission is

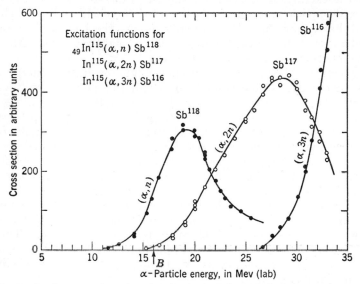

Fig. 2.7 Excitation functions for the (α,n), $(\alpha,2n)$, and $(\alpha,3n)$ reactions on In^{115}, leading to the radioactive isotopes of antimony as marked on each curve. The three excitation curves each have their own arbitrary vertical scale and cannot be referred to one another on an absolute scale. The smoothly rising front face of the $In^{115}(\alpha,n)Sb^{118}$ excitation function represents the cross section for formation of the compound nucleus $_{51}Sb^{119}$ and should continue to rise monotonically with increasing bombarding energy if all products of the dissociation of $_{51}Sb^{119}$ could be added on an absolute scale. The approximate height of the coulomb barrier is marked B. [*From Temmer* (T12).]

always very small compared with that of neutron emission, if the neutron and γ ray would have the same energy after emission. Deexcitation by γ-ray emission is significant only when the excitation energy of the compound nucleus is small, so that only very little kinetic energy would be available for an emitted neutron. Because the separation energy of a neutron or proton is of the order of 5 to 8 Mev, the energy available for γ-ray emission always exceeds that available for neutron or proton emission. This accounts, of course, for the prevalence of (n,γ) reactions with thermal neutrons.

Competition in Charged-particle Reactions. Figure 2.7 illustrates several important characteristics of charged-particle reactions in the higher-energy and mass domain, where prominent resonance peaks are no longer seen. Indium, whose principal stable isotope $_{49}In^{115}$ has a 95.8 per cent abundance, is bombarded by 37-Mev α particles from a cyclotron. By using as the target a stack of 0.000 25-in. aluminum foils, on each of which had been evaporated a 5-mg/cm^2 layer of indium, complete excitation functions were obtained from 37-Mev α particles down to about 12-Mev α particles, in steps of about 1 Mev.

At the lower bombarding energy, only the (α,n) reaction takes place, leading to radioactive Sb^{118} (half-period 5.1 hr). The steeply rising front face of the excitation function for the $In^{115}(\alpha,n)Sb^{118}$ reaction is typical of charged-particle reactions just above the threshold and well below the coulomb-barrier height. It represents mainly the increased probability of penetration of the coulomb barrier, whose height is about 16 Mev if the effective nuclear radius is 7.3×10^{-13} cm.

At about 15-Mev bombarding energy, the excitation energy of the compound nucleus is high enough to permit the emission, or "evaporation," of two neutrons. Then the $In^{115}(\alpha,2n)Sb^{117}$ reaction begins to appear. This reaction operates in competition with the (α,n) reaction. As the bombarding energy is raised well above the threshold for the $(\alpha,2n)$ reaction, this mode of deexcitation becomes favored over the (α,n) reaction. The (α,n) cross section passes through a maximum at about 19 Mev and declines at higher energies as it loses out to competition from the $(\alpha,2n)$ reaction. At bombarding energies above about 26 Mev, the compound nucleus, after losing two neutrons, may still have enough excitation energy to emit one more neutron, instead of transforming toward the ground level of Sb^{117} by γ-ray emission. Then the $In^{115}(\alpha,3n)Sb^{116}$ reaction puts in an appearance. At still higher energies, $(\alpha,3n)$ predominates competitively, forcing $(\alpha,2n)$ into a decline, as shown in Fig. 2.7.

In these experiments, the yields of Sb^{118}, Sb^{117}, and Sb^{116}, at each bombarding energy (i.e., on each of the stacked foils), were determined by radioactive assay on a basis of their half-periods (5.1 hr, 2.8 hr, and 1.0 hr) and their distinctive positron and conversion electron spectra. Also, all three were identified chemically as antimony and as masses 118, 117, and 116 by mass-spectroscopic (calutron) analysis. An energetically possible (α,p) reaction could not be observed by these methods, because it leads to stable Sn^{118} rather than to a radioactive product.

If all possible reaction products could be measured, and each on an absolute scale, then their sum would be expected to form a smoothly rising total cross section, corresponding to σ_{com}.

Compound Nucleus in Charged-particle Reactions. Some instructive experimental results which depict clearly the course of many charged-particle reactions are shown in Fig. 2.8. Using the usual stacked-foil techniques, excitation functions were measured by Ghoshal (G21) for the production of radioactive Zn^{63}, Zn^{62}, and Cu^{62}, as consequences of the bombardment of enriched Ni^{60} (85 per cent isotopic abundance) with α particles and the bombardment of normal Cu^{63} (69 per cent) with protons. This family of reactions all go through the one compound nucleus $_{30}Zn^{64}$, in accord with the following scheme

$$\begin{array}{ccc}
{}_{28}Ni^{60} + \alpha & & n + {}_{30}Zn^{63} \\
\searrow & \nearrow & \\
& ({}_{30}Zn^{64}) \rightarrow 2n + {}_{30}Zn^{62} & \quad (2.9) \\
\nearrow & \searrow & \\
{}_{29}Cu^{63} + p & & n + p + {}_{29}Cu^{62}
\end{array}$$

Absolute cross sections could be estimated because the decay schemes of Zn^{63}, Zn^{62}, and Cu^{62} are fairly well known. The activities produced by proton bombardment of the unwanted Cu^{65} (31 per cent) in the copper targets were excluded from the radioactivity measurements by selective absorption of their β rays.

The mass of the reactants $Cu^{63} + H^1$ is about 7 Mev greater than the mass of $Ni^{60} + He^4$. Consequently, the same excitation in the compound nucleus Zn^{64} is produced by protons whose energy is E_p as by α particles whose energy is $E_\alpha = E_p + 7$ Mev. In Fig. 2.8, the two sets of yield curves are superimposed by translating the E_α scale by 7 Mev with respect to the E_p scale. Then the horizontal scale is a linear measure of the excitation energy of the compound nucleus for all six curves. For any given excitation energy, Fig. 2.8 shows clearly that the competitive *ratio of yields is independent of the mode of formation of the compound nucleus*, i.e., the ratio of $(p,n):(p,2n):(p,np)$ is the same as the ratio of $(\alpha,n):(\alpha,2n):(\alpha,np)$.

The rising front of the (α,n) excitation function represents the total cross section σ_{com} in the lower-energy region, because there are no effective competing modes for deexcitation or dissociation of the compound nucleus. Similarly, the rising front of the (p,n) excitation curve represents σ_{com} for the $Cu^{63} + H^1$ collision and is only slightly less than σ_{com} for the $Ni^{60} + He^4$ collision. The close similarity between the absolute cross sections for (p,n) at E_p and for (α,n) at $E_\alpha = E_p + 7$ Mev is mostly accidental.

The yield curves for $_{29}Cu^{62}$ exceed those for $_{30}Zn^{62}$ by about a factor of 4. At first sight, this is a remarkable result, because it implies that, after the first neutron is evaporated off from the compound nucleus, proton emission is favored over the emission of a second neutron. Several physical factors may combine to produce this favoritism of (α,np) over $(\alpha,2n)$: (a) The reaction energy, or Q value, for (α,np) is approximately 3 Mev greater than for $(\alpha,2n)$; (b) the residual nucleus $_{29}Cu^{62}$ is odd-Z odd-N and will be expected to have a greater density of excited levels into which to receive the (α,np) transitions than is the case for $(\alpha,2n)$ transitions into the even-Z even-N nucleus $_{30}Zn^{62}$; and (c) some of the so-called (α,np) transitions may actually be (α,d), which would be indistinguishable in these observations and which would have about 5 Mev more reaction energy available than the $(\alpha,2n)$ reaction. Completely similar considerations apply to the competition between (p,np) and $(p,2n)$.

In Fig. 2.9, the sum of the cross sections for (α,n), $(\alpha,2n)$, and (α,np) is plotted against E_α. If these three reactions represented all the effective exit channels for dissociation of the compound nucleus, then their sum should represent σ_{com}, the total cross section for formation of the compound nucleus. It will be noted that there is an inflection in the total-cross-section curve, at about 20 Mev. This is thought to be due to competition from the unobserved (α,p) reaction, which leads to stable $_{29}Cu^{63}$ and is effective only over a limited domain of E_α. In a plot of the

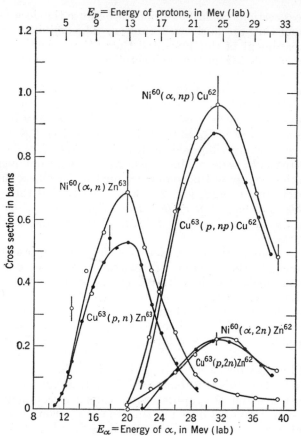

Fig. 2.8 Experimental cross sections for the production of Zn^{63}, Zn^{62}, and Cu^{62} from $Ni^{60} + \alpha$ and from $Cu^{63} + p$. Note that the energy axes are translated so that $E_\alpha = E_p + 7$ Mev. [*From Ghoshal* (G21).]

total proton cross section, $(p,n) + (p,2n) + (p,np)$, a similar inflection is found at $E_p \sim 13$ Mev and would correspond there to inelastic scattering (p,p'). Also, some additional unobserved reaction or reactions, such as $(\alpha,3n)$, is becoming effective above $E_\alpha \sim 32$ Mev. The two dashed curves in Fig. 2.9 correspond to theoretical values of σ_{com}, as discussed in the following paragraphs.

Continuum Theory of Charged-particle Reactions. The continuum theory undertakes primarily to give a quantitative evaluation of the cross section σ_{com}, Eq. (2.1), for the formation of the compound nucleus. Because σ_{com} cannot be expressed in a simple analytical form, the theoretical results are usually presented as tables or graphs. Those which have been most used are the successively improved sets of tables for σ_{com} developed by Weisskopf and his collaborators (W21, B68, S30), the most recent of which are the tables by Shapiro (S30) covering explicitly $10 \le Z \le 90$, for p, d, or α bombardment at energies from 0.2 to 1.8 times the s-wave barrier height.

In its present form, this continuum theory assumes that: (*a*) The bombarding energy is sufficiently large to produce the compound nucleus

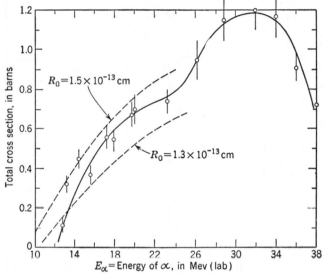

Fig. 2.9   The sum of the $(\alpha,n) + (\alpha,2n) + (\alpha,np)$ cross sections of Fig. 2.8, as here plotted, is an approximation to the total cross section σ_{com} for formation of the compound nucleus $Ni^{60} + He^4 \rightarrow (Zn^{64})$. Theoretical values for σ_{com}, computed from Shapiro's (S30) tables, are shown by the dashed curves for two values of the nuclear unit radius R_0. In the theoretical curves, the effective value of the coulomb-barrier height is taken as $B = Zze^2/R$, where $R = (R_0 A^{\frac{1}{3}} + \rho_\alpha)$ and $\rho_\alpha = 1.21 \times 10^{-13}$ cm is a correction for the finite radius of the α particle (compare Fig. 6.3 of Chap. 2).

in a state whose excitation energy is high, say, ~ 1 Mev above the threshold for neutron emission, so that dissociation through a number of competing channels is energetically possible and (*b*) the probability of elastic reemission of the incident particle is negligible compared with the probability of inelastic scattering, neutron emission, or γ-ray emission. This second assumption implies a strong interaction between the entering particle and the other nucleons and is valid only to the extent that the target nucleus can be regarded as opaque. Corrections for a noninfinite absorption coefficient of the entering particle, such as those already applied to the neutron for Fig. 2.6, may be expected and will be **more** complicated because of the coulomb barrier.

Representative values for the cross section σ_{com} for formation of the compound nucleus are plotted in Fig. 2.10. Three principal physical features should be noted. First, at bombarding energies E_p of less than about half the barrier height $(B = Zze^2/R)$, the change of σ_{com} with bombarding energy is very rapid. Second, σ_{com} approaches an asymptotic

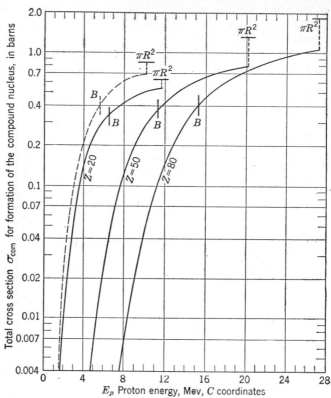

Fig. 2.10 Theoretical predictions of the total cross section σ_{com} for formation of a compound nucleus by protons whose kinetic energy in center-of-mass coordinates is E_p, for target nuclides having $Z = 20$, 50, or 80. The bars marked B indicate the coulomb-barrier height $B = Zze^2/R$. In the three solid curves, the nuclear radius is assumed to be $R = 1.3 \times 10^{-13} A^{\frac{1}{3}}$ cm. The dotted curve shows the effect on the $Z = 20$ cross section if the radius is taken as $R = 1.5 \times 10^{-13} A^{\frac{1}{3}}$ cm. For each of the four curves, the asymptotic limit of σ_{com}, which is πR^2, is shown as a horizontal bar above the maximum bombarding energy $E_p = 1.8B$ as tabulated by Shapiro. [*The curves are drawn from the tables prepared by Shapiro* (S30).]

limit of πR^2 but falls considerably short of this limit even at $E_p \sim 2B$, and especially so for large Z. Third, transmission through the barrier is distinctly incomplete when the bombarding energy E_p equals the barrier height B. The cross sections at $E_p = B$ are of the order of one-half to one-fourth the nuclear geometric area πR^2. This is because the total-reaction cross section represents a summation over all orbital-angular-momentum values l of the colliding particles, as set forth in Eq. (2.1).

The so-called barrier height $B = Zze^2/R$ refers, however, only to the coulomb barrier and does not include the effective increase due to the centrifugal barrier (Appendix C, Fig. 10) for partial waves having $l > 0$.

At energies well above the barrier height B for s waves, the exact calculations give values for σ_{com} which agree surprisingly well with the simple semiclassical formula (Chap. 2, Sec. 8)

$$\sigma_{com} \simeq \pi(R + \lambda)^2 \left(1 - \frac{U}{E}\right) \tag{2.10}$$

where $U \equiv Zze^2/(R + \lambda) = B[R/(R + \lambda)]$ is the coulomb potential at a separation $R + \lambda$ and $E = \hbar^2/2M\lambda^2$ is the incident kinetic energy in center-of-mass coordinates. Equation (2.10) is only about 15 per cent larger than the quantum-mechanical values when $E/B = 1.2$ and represents the exact calculations quite well for $E/B > 2$.

Effect of Nuclear Radius on the Reaction Cross Section σ_{com} for Charged Particles. In Fig. 2.10 the dotted curve shows the theoretical reaction cross section σ_{com} when the nuclear unit radius is assumed to be

$$R_0 = 1.5 \times 10^{-13} \text{ cm}$$

The solid curves are for $R_0 = 1.3 \times 10^{-13}$ cm. Notice that σ_{com} is increased, for all values of E_p, by an increase in R_0. This increase is attributable primarily to two physical factors, both of which operate in the same direction. First, a larger radius, $R = R_0 A^{\frac{1}{3}}$, increases the geometrical size of the target πR^2, which is the asymptotic limit of σ_{com}. Second, a larger radius lowers both the coulomb barrier and the centrifugal barrier and thus facilitates barrier penetration at all energies.

In Fig. 2.9, the theoretical values of σ_{com} for the case of $_{28}Ni^{60} + He^4$ are shown for two values of the nuclear unit radius, $R_0 = 1.3 \times 10^{-13}$ cm and $R_0 = 1.5 \times 10^{-13}$ cm. It is seen that these particular experimental data are well represented by a nuclear unit radius in the domain of 1.3×10^{-13} to 1.5×10^{-13} cm. Shapiro (S30) has made a number of similar comparisons, especially for reactions induced by protons. Within the accuracy of present experimental data and of present theory (opaque nucleus), the results are in agreement with a nuclear unit radius in the vicinity of $R_0 = (1.4 \pm 0.1) \times 10^{-13}$ cm.

CHAPTER 15

Radioactive-series Decay

The exponential laws which govern the decay and growth of radioactive substances were first formulated by Rutherford and Soddy in 1902 (R52) in order to explain their experiments on the thorium series of radioactive substances. Useful mathematical generalizations were made in 1910 by Bateman (B20). The more general forms of the decay and growth equations are therefore often referred to as "the Bateman equations." For three decades the applicability of the equations governing series decay was confined to the uranium, actinium, and thorium series of naturally occurring radioactive substances. With the discovery of nuclear fission a vast number of cases of radioactive-series decay appeared among the fission products. The behavior of all these can be understood with the help of the original Bateman equations.

1. Decay of a Single Radioactive Nuclide

a. Radioactive Decay Constant λ. Consider a group containing a large number A of identical radioactive atoms. Let the probability that any particular atom will disintegrate in unit time be λ, the *total radioactive decay constant*. Then the *activity* of these atoms, i.e., the total number of disintegrations per unit time (in a time which is short compared with $1/\lambda$), will be simply $A\lambda$. The rate of depletion, dA/dt, of the group of atoms is equal to the activity, so long as we do not provide any new supply of radioactive atoms. Because A decreases as time increases, we insert a minus sign and write

$$\frac{dA}{dt} = -A\lambda \tag{1.1}$$

Rewriting this fundamental relationship in integral form, with the variables separated, we have

$$\int \frac{dA}{A} = -\int \lambda \, dt \tag{1.2}$$

We now make the fundamental assumption that *the probability of decay of an atom is independent of the age of that atom.* Then if λ is independent of t and is constant, we can integrate Eq. (1.2) simply. If

470

there were A_0 atoms at $t = 0$, while A atoms remain at time $t = t$, then Eq. (1.2) becomes

$$\ln\left(\frac{A}{A_0}\right) = -\lambda t \tag{1.3}$$

or, in the usual exponential form,

$$A = A_0 e^{-\lambda t} \tag{1.4}$$

Recalling that $A_0\lambda$ is the activity at $t = 0$, Eq. (1.4) can be written in terms of the ratio of the activities at t and at $t = 0$. Because λ is independent of t, we can write

$$\frac{A\lambda}{A_0\lambda} = e^{-\lambda t} \tag{1.5}$$

in agreement with the empirical law of radioactive decay and the associated disintegration hypothesis of Rutherford and Soddy (R52).

The exponential law, Eq. (1.4), of radioactive decay can also be derived from the laws of chance† without any knowledge of the mechanism of disintegration. The only assumptions needed are that:

1. The probability of decay λ is the same for all atoms of the species.

2. The probability of decay λ is independent of the age of the particular atom.

These conditions are mathematically "sufficient," as was first shown by von Schweidler (S20). They are also mathematically "necessary" conditions, as is most readily seen from the experimental fact that the statistical fluctuations in α-ray emission obey the Poisson distribution (Chap. 26), for the derivation of which assumptions analogous to those given above are both necessary and sufficient. Ruark (R38) has developed an analytical proof that these conditions are mathematically necessary. The point is of importance because the wave-mechanical theories of α ray and β-ray radioactive decay involve the basic assumption that the probability λ of decay in unit time is independent of the age of the particular atom in question.

The most direct experimental proof that the decay constants of a number of naturally occurring radioactive substances have not changed in the last 10^9 yr comes from the sharpness of individual rings in uranium and thorium pleochroic halos in mica (H32, H33, H34).

The disintegration law of Eq. (1.4) applies universally to all radio-

---

† If ϑ is a time interval which is very small compared with $1/\lambda$, then $\lambda\vartheta$ is the chance that a particular atom will decay in the time ϑ. Its chance of survival for a time ϑ is then $(1 - \lambda\vartheta)$, for a time 2ϑ is $(1 - \lambda\vartheta)^2$, . . . , and for any arbitrary time $t = n\vartheta$ is $(1 - \lambda\vartheta)^n = (1 - \lambda\vartheta)^{t/\vartheta}$. It can be verified easily by series expansion that, if the arbitrary time interval ϑ is taken as very small, then in the limit of $\vartheta/t \to 0$

$$\lim_{\vartheta/t \to 0} (1 - \lambda\vartheta)^{t/\vartheta} = e^{-\lambda t}$$

Thus the chance of survival is $e^{-\lambda t}$ *for each atom.* Hence the *average fraction* which survives a time t is also $e^{-\lambda t}$. We must expect statistical fluctuations in the *actual fraction* which survives, such that the average value is $e^{-\lambda t}$.

active nuclides, but the constant λ is different for each nuclide. The known radioactive nuclides extend between $\lambda = 3 \times 10^6$ sec^{-1} (for ThC′) and $\lambda = 1.58 \times 10^{-18}$ sec^{-1} (for Th), a range of over 10^{24}. The decay constant λ is one of the most important characteristics of each radioactive nuclide; it is essentially independent of all physical and chemical conditions such as temperature, pressure, concentration, or age of the radioactive atoms. Among the more than 800 known radioactive nuclides, no two have exactly the same decay constant. The identification of some radioactive samples can be made simply by measuring λ, which can serve as a type of qualitative chemical analysis.

b. Partial Decay Constants. Many nuclides have at risk several alternative modes of decay. For example, Cu^{64} can decay by electron capture or by positron β-ray emission or by negatron β-ray emission. If the competing modes of decay of any nuclide have probabilities λ_1, λ_2, λ_3, . . . per unit time, then the total probability of decay is represented by the total decay constant λ, where

$$\lambda = \lambda_1 + \lambda_2 + \lambda_3 + \cdots \tag{1.6}$$

The "partial activity" of a sample of A nuclei, if measured by a particular mode of decay characterized by λ_i, is then

$$\frac{dA_i}{dt} = \lambda_i A = \lambda_i A_0 e^{-\lambda t} \tag{1.7}$$

and the total activity is

$$\frac{dA}{dt} = \sum_i \frac{dA_i}{dt} = A \sum_i \lambda_i = \lambda A_0 e^{-\lambda t} \tag{1.8}$$

Note that partial activities, such as positron β rays from Cu^{64}, are proportional to total activities at all times. Each partial activity falls off with time as $e^{-\lambda t}$, not as $e^{-\lambda_i t}$. Physically, this is because the decrease of activity with time is due to the depletion of the stock of atoms A, and this depletion is accomplished by the combined action of all the competing modes of decay.

c. Units of Radioactivity. The curie unit was redefined in 1950 by action of the international Joint Commission on Standards, Units, and Constants of Radioactivity (P3) in such a way that it applies to all radioactive nuclides and is no longer tied to the presumed activity of 1 g of radium. This definition is *"The curie is a unit of radioactivity defined as the quantity of any radioactive nuclide in which the number of disintegrations per second is* 3.700 $\times$ 10^{10}.*"* The "number of disintegrations" is the sum of all competing modes of disintegration. Therefore the full decay scheme of a nuclide has to be known, including the electron-capture branching, before the quantity of any sample can be expressed in curies as a result of measurements on any particular mode of disintegration, such as β rays or α rays. In practical use, the "quantity of" any radionuclide is usually nearly synonymous with the "total activity of" the nuclide.

d. Half-period T.   The half-period T is the time interval over which the chance of survival of a particular radioactive atom is exactly one-half.   Then, if λ is the total decay constant, Eq. (1.3) gives

$$T = \frac{\ln 2}{\lambda} = \frac{0.693}{\lambda} \tag{1.9}$$

In a large initial stock of A_0 atoms, with initial activity $A_0\lambda$, the expectation value of the activity $A\lambda$, one half-period later, is $A\lambda = A_0\lambda/2$.

For mnemonic reasons, the half-period T (or $T_{\frac{1}{2}}$ whenever there is any ambiguity about symbols) is much more frequently employed than the decay constant λ.   The *half-period* is sometimes also called the *half-value time* or, with less justification, the *half-life*.

Two related periods which are useful in the laboratory are the nine-tenths period and the one-tenth period.   Nine-tenths of the atoms survive longer than the *nine-tenths period* $T_{\frac{9}{10}}$ whose value is

$$T_{\frac{9}{10}} = \frac{\ln\left(\frac{10}{9}\right)}{\lambda} = 0.1520 T_{\frac{1}{2}} \simeq \frac{3}{20} T_{\frac{1}{2}} \tag{1.10}$$

One-tenth of the atoms survive longer than the *one-tenth period*, given by

$$T_{\frac{1}{10}} = \frac{\ln 10}{\lambda} = 3.322 T_{\frac{1}{2}} \simeq \frac{10}{3} T_{\frac{1}{2}} \tag{1.11}$$

Cruder but handier approximations are $T_{\frac{9}{10}} < \frac{1}{6} T_{\frac{1}{2}}$ and $T_{\frac{1}{10}} > 3 T_{\frac{1}{2}}$.

e. Mean Life τ.   The actual life of any particular atom can have any value between 0 and ∞.   The average life of a large number of atoms is, however, a definite and important quantity.

If there are A_0 atoms present initially, then the number remaining undecayed at a subsequent time t is $A = A_0 e^{-\lambda t}$.   Each of these atoms has a life longer than t.   Those which decay between t and $t + dt$ each have a life span t.   The absolute number of atoms having a life t is therefore $A\lambda\, dt = A_0\lambda e^{-\lambda t}\, dt$.   The total lifetime L of all the atoms is therefore

$$L = \int_0^\infty tA\lambda\, dt = \int_0^\infty tA_0\lambda e^{-\lambda t}\, dt = \frac{A_0}{\lambda} \tag{1.12}$$

Then the average lifetime L/A_0, which is called the *mean life* τ, is simply

$$\tau = \frac{1}{\lambda} \tag{1.13}$$

Thus the mean life exceeds the half-period and is always given by

$$\tau = \frac{T}{0.693} = 1.44 T \tag{1.14}$$

Substitution in Eq. (1.4) shows that the mean life is the time required for the number of atoms, or their activity, to fall to $e^{-1} = 0.368$ of any initial value.

f. Total Number of Radioactive Atoms. The total *number of radio-active atoms* A present at any time is simply the product of the total activity $A\lambda$ and the mean life, because

$$(A\lambda)\tau = \frac{A\lambda}{\lambda} = A \tag{1.15}$$

The relationships of A_0, A, t, λ, T, and τ are illustrated graphically in Fig. 1.1. It will be noted that the area under the *decay curve* of activity

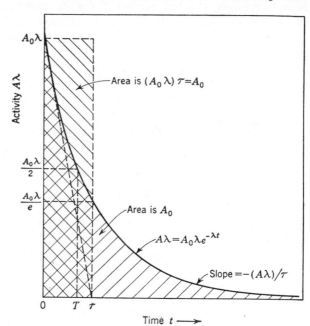

Fig. 1.1 Graphical relationships in the decay of a single radioactive nuclide. $T = 0.693/\lambda = 0.693\tau$; $\tau = 1.44T$; $\tau = 1/\lambda$. $T =$ half-period; $\tau =$ mean life; $\lambda =$ decay constant; $A_0 =$ number of atoms at time $t = 0$; $A =$ number of atoms at t. The slope of the activity curve at any time t is $d(A\lambda)/dt = -(A_0\lambda)\lambda e^{-\lambda t} = -\lambda(A\lambda) = -(A\lambda)/\tau$. The initial slope, at $t = 0$, is $-\lambda(A_0\lambda) = -(A_0\lambda)/\tau$. If the initial slope is extrapolated (dotted line), it intersects the time axis at the mean life τ.

vs. time equals the total number of atoms which were present initially; thus,

$$\text{Area} = \int_0^\infty A\lambda \, dt = \int_0^\infty \lambda A_0 e^{-\lambda t} \, dt = A_0 \tag{1.16}$$

This area is the same as that within the rectangle $A_0\lambda\tau$. Thus, if the initial activity $A_0\lambda$ could remain constant for a mean life τ, all the atoms would have been transformed.

g. Aids in the Computation of Radioactive Decay. Computations of $e^{-\lambda t}$ can be tedious if a few simple aids are ignored. Some of the most useful elementary techniques (K24) follow.

Semilogarithmic Graph Paper. If relative activities $A\lambda/A_0\lambda$ or relative amounts A/A_0 are plotted on the logarithmic axis, against time t on the linear axis, then $e^{-\lambda t}$ is a straight line passing through the points $A/A_0 = 1$ at $t = 0$ and $A/A_0 = 0.5$ at $t = T$. Depending on the scale of the graph paper, two- or three-place accuracy is obtainable, as illustrated in Fig. 12.1*b*.

Common (Base 10) Logarithm Tables, or Slide Rules. It may be noted that Eq. (1.3) or (1.4) can be expressed equally well using the base 10, instead of the base e. Thus

$$\frac{A_0}{A} = e^{\lambda t} = e^{\lambda T(t/T)} = 2^{(t/T)} \tag{1.17}$$

$$\ln\left(\frac{A_0}{A}\right) = \left(\frac{t}{T}\right)\ln 2 = \frac{0.693t}{T} \tag{1.18}$$

$$\log_{10}\left(\frac{A_0}{A}\right) = \left(\frac{t}{T}\right)\log_{10} 2 = \frac{0.301t}{T} \tag{1.19}$$

or $$\frac{A}{A_0} = e^{-\lambda t} = \left(\tfrac{1}{2}\right)^{t/T} = e^{-0.693(t/T)} = 10^{-0.301(t/T)} \tag{1.20}$$

Thus, on slide rules, the value of the mantissa of $0.301(t/T)$ can be set on the L scale, and A_0/A can be read on the C scale, or A/A_0 read directly on the CI scale.

Log-Log Slide Rules. These rules have scales of e^x and of e^{-x}. At the risk of being gratuitous, it should be said that the student will be amply rewarded by becoming familiar with their range and uses. When 0.5 on the log-log scale is set opposite the half-period T, A/A_0 can be read directly for all other values of t. Analytically, the operation of the exponential scales can be illustrated by the following expressions

$$e^{-\lambda t} = \left(\frac{1}{2}\right)^{t/T} \qquad \log e^{-\lambda t} = \frac{t}{T}\log\left(\frac{1}{2}\right)$$

$$\log\log e^{-\lambda t} = \log\log\left(\frac{1}{2}\right) + \log\left(\frac{t}{T}\right) \tag{1.21}$$

Approximate Forms. For values of t which are small compared with the half-period, use of the exponential expansion

$$e^{-\lambda t} = e^{-(t/\tau)} = 1 - (t/\tau) + \frac{(t/\tau)^2}{2} - \cdots \tag{1.22}$$

is often the most accurate procedure.

Problems

1. The relative intensities of negatron β decay, electron-capture decay, and positron β decay of Cu^{64} are approximately $(\beta^-):(EC):(\beta^+) = 2.0:2.0:1.0$. The half-period of Cu^{64} is 12.8 hr.

(a) Calculate the total decay constant λ and the partial decay constants λ_{β^-}, λ_{EC}, λ_{β^+} in sec^{-1}.

(b) What is the "partial half-period" for negatron β decay, i.e., the half-period for a Cu^{64} nucleus in which the possibility of other modes of decay has been turned off?

(c) Evaluate in millicuries a source of Cu^{64} which emits 3.7×10^7 negatron β rays per second.

Ans.: (b) 32.0 hr; (c) 2.5 mc.

2. Determine the half-period of K^{40}, knowing that ordinary potassium (a) is a mixture of K^{39}, K^{40}, and K^{41} containing 0.0119 atom per cent K^{40}; (b) emits 31 β rays/sec per gram in transitions of $K^{40} \xrightarrow{\beta^-} Ca^{40}$; and (c) emits 3.4 γ rays/sec per gram in electron-capture transitions $K^{40} \xrightarrow{EC} A^{40}$, and every EC transition is accompanied by just one photon. *Ans.:* 1.15×10^9 yr.

3. Compute the number of grams and the number of radioactive atoms contained in 1 mc of (a) radiosodium (Na^{24}, $T = 14.8$ hr); (b) radiophosphorus (P^{32}, $T = 14.5$ days); and (c) radium (Ra^{226}, $T = 1,620$ yr). *Ans.:* mass, 1.1×10^{-10} g of Na^{24}; 3.5×10^{-9} g of P^{32}; 0.0010 g of Ra.

4. (a) A radioactive substance has a mean life τ sec, an activity of a_1 disintegrations per second at time t_1, and an activity of a_2 at time t_2. Show that the number of atoms ($A_1 - A_2$) disintegrating between t_1 and t_2 is

$$A_1 - A_2 = \tau(a_1 - a_2)$$

(b) If the average energy per β ray of 12.6-hr iodine I^{130} is 0.29 Mev, determine the β-ray energy in ergs liberated in 24 hr by an iodine source whose initial strength is 1 mc.

(c) If this iodine is present in 2 g of thyroid tissue, determine the radiation dose absorbed in 24 hr by the tissue, remembering that 1 rep (roentgen equivalent physical) corresponds to the absorption of 94 ergs per gram of tissue. *Ans.:* (b) 8.2×10^5 ergs; (c) 4,400 rep.

5. In 1 g of natural uranium,

(a) What is the activity of U^{238}, UX_1, UX_2, and U^{234}, in μc?

(b) What is the ratio of the activity of U^{235} to that of U^{238}?

(c) What is the number of spontaneous fissions per hour?

DATA: The decay series of U^{238} and U^{235} and half-periods are

$$_{92}U^{238} \xrightarrow[4.51 \times 10^9 \text{ yr}]{\alpha} UX_1 \xrightarrow[24.1 \text{ d}]{\beta} UX_2 \xrightarrow[1.14 \text{ min}]{\beta} U^{234} \xrightarrow[2.35 \times 10^5 \text{ yr}]{\alpha} \text{Io}$$

$$\rightarrow \text{Io} \xrightarrow[8.0 \times 10^4 \text{ yr}]{\alpha} Ra^{226} \xrightarrow[1,620 \text{ yr}]{\alpha} Rn \xrightarrow[3.82 \text{ d}]{\alpha} \cdots$$

$$_{92}U^{235} \xrightarrow[7.1 \times 10^8 \text{ yr}]{\alpha} UY \xrightarrow[25.6 \text{ hr}]{\beta} Pa \xrightarrow[3.43 \times 10^4 \text{ yr}]{\alpha} Ac \xrightarrow[22 \text{ yr}]{\beta} RdAc \xrightarrow[18.9 \text{ d}]{\alpha} AcX^{223} \xrightarrow[11.2 \text{ d}]{\alpha} \cdots$$

In natural uranium, there is 1 atom of U^{235} per 139 atoms of U^{238}. The partial half-periods for spontaneous fission are

U^{238} 8.0×10^{15} yr
U^{235} 1.9×10^{17} yr
U^{234} 2 $\times 10^{16}$ yr

Ans.: (a) 0.33 μc per gram U for each; (b) 0.046; (c) 25 fissions per hour per gram U (these are generally useful numbers, worth memorizing).

6. If an atom is known to exist at $t = 0$, what is its probability of decaying in the time interval Δt between t and $t + \Delta t$, if its decay constant is λ? Under what restrictions does this general relationship reduce to simply $\lambda \Delta t$?

Ans.: $(1 - e^{-\lambda \Delta t})e^{-\lambda t}$; reduces when $\lambda t \ll 1$ and $\lambda \Delta t \ll 1$.

2. *Radioactive-series Decay.   Growth of a Daughter Product*

In a number of cases a radioactive nuclide A decays into a nuclide B which is also radioactive.   Let the initial part of such a series be represented by

$$A \xrightarrow{\lambda_A} B \xrightarrow{\lambda_B} C$$

where λ_A is the decay constant of atoms of type A and λ_B is the decay constant of atoms of type B, and where the symbols A and B represent the number of atoms of each type which are present at any time t. The limiting case in which B is stable is represented then by $\lambda_B = 0$.

a. The General Differential Equation for a Daughter Product.   At any time t, the activity of A is $A\lambda_A$ and the activity of B is $B\lambda_B$.   The rate of change dB/dt, in the number of atoms of type B, is then equal to the supply of new atoms of type B due to the decay of A, diminished by the rate of loss of B through its own decay, or

$$\frac{dB}{dt} = A\lambda_A - B\lambda_B \qquad (2.1)$$

If the only source of atoms of type A is from an initial supply $A = A_0$ at $t = 0$, then

$$A = A_0 e^{-\lambda_A t}$$

and, with these initial conditions on A, Eq. (2.1) becomes

$$\frac{dB}{dt} = A_0 \lambda_A e^{-\lambda_A t} - B\lambda_B \qquad (2.2)$$

From this differential equation, we wish to obtain an explicit solution for B as a function of time.   We proceed, as usual, by a seasoned guess that the general solution will be of the form

$$B = A_0 (h_A e^{-\lambda_A t} + h_B e^{-\lambda_B t}) \qquad (2.3)$$

In order to evaluate the coefficients h_A and h_B, we substitute B and dB/dt from Eq. (2.3) into Eq. (2.2) and collect terms, obtaining

$$e^{-\lambda_A t}(-h_A \lambda_A - \lambda_A + h_A \lambda_B) = 0 \qquad (2.4)$$

If this is to be valid for all values of t, the parentheses must equal zero, and therefore we have

$$h_A = \frac{\lambda_A}{\lambda_B - \lambda_A} \qquad (2.5)$$

The coefficient h_B depends on the value of B at $t = 0$.   For the important special case in which $B = 0$ at $t = 0$, we have at once from Eq. (2.3)

$$h_A + h_B = 0 \qquad (2.6)$$

Hence $h_B = -h_A$, and we have for the *amount* of B

$$B = A_0 \frac{\lambda_A}{\lambda_B - \lambda_A}(e^{-\lambda_A t} - e^{-\lambda_B t}) \qquad (2.7)$$

as the important general solution for the initial conditions $A = A_0$, and $B = 0$, at $t = 0$.

Then the *activity* of B is $B\lambda_B$ [*not* dB/dt; see Eq. (2.1)], where

$$B\lambda_B = A_0\lambda_A \frac{\lambda_B}{\lambda_B - \lambda_A} (e^{-\lambda_A t} - e^{-\lambda_B t}) \qquad (2.8)$$

or, since the activity of A at t is $A\lambda_A = A_0\lambda_A e^{-\lambda_A t}$,

$$B\lambda_B = (A\lambda_A) \frac{\lambda_B}{\lambda_B - \lambda_A} (1 - e^{-(\lambda_B - \lambda_A)t}) \qquad (2.9)$$

Various special cases, depending on the relative magnitudes of λ_A and λ_B, will be discussed and plotted in Sec. 5 below.

3. *Accumulation of Daughter Atoms*

The most fundamental physical concepts underlying the entire mathematical theory of radioactive-series decay are embodied in Eq. (2.1). The same concepts will reappear as Eq. (7.1) and Eq. (8.1) in the more general treatment of a long series of substances. This is the principal justification for having presented here the classical method of deriving Eq. (2.7).

Another viewpoint is highly instructive and also lends itself directly to other problems which are mathematically similar (such as to the secondary radiation produced when γ rays pass through an absorbing barrier).

At time $t = 0$, let $A = A_0$ and $B = 0$. Then at a later time, $t = x$, there will remain $A = A_0 e^{-\lambda_A x}$ atoms of A. In the time interval between x and $x + dx$, the number of new atoms of B formed will be $A\lambda_A\, dx$. The fraction of these atoms of B which survive until a later time $t = t$ is $e^{-\lambda_B(t-x)}$. Then the total stock of B at $t = t$ is given by an integral over all values of the time x between $x = 0$ and $x = t$ and is

$$B = \int_0^t (A\lambda_A\, dx)(e^{-\lambda_B(t-x)}) \qquad (3.1)$$

$$B = \int_0^t A_0\lambda_A e^{-\lambda_A x} e^{-\lambda_B(t-x)}\, dx$$

$$= A_0\lambda_A e^{-\lambda_B t} \int_0^t e^{-(\lambda_A - \lambda_B)x}\, dx$$

$$= A_0\lambda_A e^{-\lambda_B t} \left[\frac{1}{\lambda_B - \lambda_A} (e^{-(\lambda_A - \lambda_B)t} - 1) \right]$$

$$= A_0 \frac{\lambda_A}{\lambda_B - \lambda_A} (e^{-\lambda_A t} - e^{-\lambda_B t}) \qquad (3.2)$$

The result, Eq. (3.2), of this entirely different approach is, of course, the same as Eq. (2.7). The same concept can be successively reapplied in order to derive the expressions for the amounts of C, D, . . . , N, produced in time t from A_0 at $t = 0$. This is left as an exercise. We shall follow the more conventional methods based on analogues of the basic idea, $dB/dt = A\lambda_A - B\lambda_B$, in developing later the general expressions for C, D, . . . , N.

4. *Time of Maximum Activity of Daughter Product. Ideal Equilibrium*

We note at once from Eq. (2.7) that the amount of B is zero both at $t = 0$ and at $t = \infty$, when all the atoms of both A and B have decayed. At some intermediate time t_m the amount of B, and hence its activity $B\lambda_B$, passes through a maximum value. This is the time t_m for which $dB/dt = 0$. The differential of B, Eq. (2.7), with respect to time is zero when

$$\lambda_A e^{-\lambda_A t_m} = \lambda_B e^{-\lambda_B t_m}$$

from which it follows that the time t_m of maximum activity of B is

$$t_m = \frac{\ln (\lambda_B/\lambda_A)}{(\lambda_B - \lambda_A)} \tag{4.1}$$

if, at $t = 0$, $A = A_0$ and $B = 0$.

Equation (4.1) may be easily transformed to read directly in terms of mean life τ and half-period T; thus

$$t_m = \frac{\ln (\tau_A/\tau_B)}{(1/\tau_B) - (1/\tau_A)} = \tau_B \left(\frac{\tau_A}{\tau_A - \tau_B}\right) \ln \frac{\tau_A}{\tau_B}$$

$$= \tau_B \left(\frac{T_A}{T_A - T_B}\right) \ln \left(\frac{T_A}{T_B}\right) \tag{4.2}$$

This important result shows that t_m is positive and real for either $T_A > T_B$ or $T_A < T_B$. No physical cases are known for which $T_A = T_B$. But if the two half-periods are nearly equal, we may write

$$T_A = T_B(1 + \delta) \qquad \text{where } \delta \ll 1$$

Making use of the expansion of the logarithm

$$\ln (1 + \delta) = \delta - \frac{\delta^2}{2} + \frac{\delta^3}{3} - \cdots$$

we have

$$t_m = \tau_B \frac{1 + \delta}{\delta} \left(\delta - \frac{\delta^2}{2} + \cdots\right)$$

$$= \tau_B(1 + \delta) \left(1 - \frac{\delta}{2} + \cdots\right)$$

$$\simeq \tau_B \left(1 + \frac{\delta}{2}\right) \simeq \tau_B \left(\frac{T_A}{T_B}\right)^{\frac{1}{2}}$$

$$= \sqrt{\tau_A \tau_B} \tag{4.3}$$

Thus, in the limiting case where parent A and daughter B have substantially the same half-period, the maximum activity of B occurs about one mean life after the accumulation of B is begun.

At t_m, we have from Eq. (2.1)

$$A\lambda_A = B\lambda_B \tag{4.4}$$

Thus the activity of the residual parent A and of the accumulated daughter B are *equal only at* t_m, at which time each is equal to

$$
\begin{aligned}
A\lambda_A &= A_0\lambda_A e^{-[\lambda_A \ln(\lambda_B/\lambda_A)]/(\lambda_B-\lambda_A)} \\
&= A_0\lambda_A \left(\frac{\lambda_A}{\lambda_B}\right)^{\lambda_A/(\lambda_B-\lambda_A)} \\
&= A_0\lambda_A \left(\frac{T_B}{T_A}\right)^{T_B/(T_A-T_B)}
\end{aligned}
\tag{4.5}
$$

The situation in which the activities of the parent and daughter are equal is called *ideal equilibrium* and exists only at the moment t_m. It is to be emphasized that from $t = 0$ to $t = t_m$ the activity of the parent always exceeds the activity of the daughter, that is, dB/dt is positive. Conversely, *from $t = t_m$ to $t = \infty$ the activity of the daughter continuously exceeds the activity of its parent*, that is, dB/dt is negative.

Problems

1. On a single curve for the decay of parent activity, to a scale such as Fig. 1.1, draw accumulation curves of daughter activity $B\lambda_B$, if (a) $T_B \ll T_A$, (b) $T_B < T_A$, (c) $T_B \simeq T_A$, and (d) $T_B > T_A$.

2. Consider the decay scheme: $A \rightarrow B \rightarrow C$, with $\lambda_A < \lambda_B$. After transient equilibrium is established between A and B, show that the interval of time Δt such that (activity of A at $t - \Delta t$) = (activity of B at t) is given by

$$\Delta t = \tau_A \ln\left(\frac{\lambda_B}{\lambda_B - \lambda_A}\right)$$

and that this approaches $\Delta t = \tau_B$ as τ_B/τ_A approaches zero.

5. *Ratio of Activity of Parent and Daughter. Transient Equilibrium*

The ratio of the activities of the parent and daughter, under the initial conditions $B = 0$ at $t = 0$, is given at once by Eq. (2.9). This activity ratio $B\lambda_B/A\lambda_A$ is zero for $t = 0$, unity for $t = t_m$, and has its maximum value for large values of t. Several distinct cases arise, depending on the relative half-periods of A and B.

a. Daughter Longer-lived Than Parent. If $T_A < T_B$, then the activity ratio $B\lambda_B/A\lambda_A$ increases continuously as t increases. Thus, when $\lambda_A > \lambda_B$, Eq. (2.9) may be written

$$\frac{B\lambda_B}{A\lambda_A} = \frac{\lambda_B}{\lambda_A - \lambda_B}(e^{(\lambda_A - \lambda_B)t} - 1) \tag{5.1}$$

Such a case is illustrated by Fig. 5.1 which represents the well-known series

$$Te^{131} \xrightarrow[T_A = 1.25\,d]{} I^{131} \xrightarrow[T_B = 8.0\,d]{} Xe^{131}$$

In the extreme case when $T_A \ll T_B$, the activity of the daughter substance finally becomes effectively independent of the residual activity of

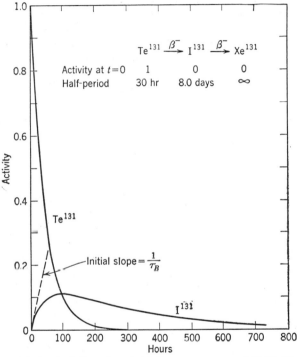

Fig. 5.1 Decay of the activity of an initially pure source of Te[131] ($T = 1.25$ days) and growth of its decay product I[131] ($T = 8.0$ days) produced in the Te[131] source. The maximum activity of I[131] occurs at $t_m = 3.96$ days $= 95.0$ hr, in accord with Eq. (4.1). The ratio of activity of I[131] to that of its parent Te[131] increases continuously with time, Eq. (5.1).

the parent. Thus, for $t \gg T_A$, Eq. (5.1) or Eq. (2.7) becomes

$$B\lambda_B \simeq A_0\lambda_B e^{-\lambda_B t} \tag{5.2}$$

Thus the initial stock of short-lived atoms A_0 has, in effect, quickly become an initial stock of long-lived atoms B_0, with $A_0 \simeq B_0$, which decay exponentially like $e^{-\lambda_B t}$.

b. Daughter and Parent of Nearly Equal Half-period. If T_A and T_B are nearly equal, such that $T_A = T_B(1 + \delta)$, where $\delta \ll 1$, then Eq.

(2.9) for the ratio of activities of daughter to parent becomes

$$\frac{B\lambda_E}{A\lambda_A} = \frac{1+\delta}{\delta}\left(1 - e^{-\frac{\delta}{1+\delta}\frac{t}{\tau_B}}\right)$$

$$= \frac{t}{\tau_B}\left(1 - \frac{\delta}{1+\delta}\frac{t}{2\tau_B} + \cdots\right)$$

$$\simeq \frac{t}{\tau_B} \tag{5.3}$$

Thus the activity ratio would increase approximately linearly with time, so long as $t \ll 2\tau_B/\delta$.

c. Daughter Shorter-lived Than Parent. If $T_A > T_B$, then the ratio of the activities increases with time at first and then approaches a constant value. Thus Eq. (2.9) can be written as

$$\frac{B\lambda_B}{A\lambda_A} = \frac{T_A}{T_A - T_B}\left(1 - e^{-[(T_A-T_B)/T_A]\lambda_B t}\right) \tag{5.4}$$

For all values of t which are large compared with $\tau_B T_A/(T_A - T_B)$, Eq. (5.4) becomes simply

$$\frac{B\lambda_B}{A\lambda_A} = \frac{T_A}{T_A - T_B} \qquad \text{for large } t \tag{5.5}$$

When the ratio of the activities of daughter to parent is constant, a particular type of radioactive equilibrium exists. This is spoken of as *transient equilibrium* when the ratio $T_A/(T_A - T_B)$ is clearly greater than unity. Such cases are very common.

If $A\lambda_A$ is the activity of the parent at some time t, which is long enough so that equilibrium has been established between A and B, then we may ask what additional time Δt must elapse before the activity $B\lambda_B$ of the daughter will fall to the value $A\lambda_A$. It can be shown that the activity $B\lambda_B$ at $t + \Delta t$ is the same as the activity $A\lambda_A$ at t, if

$$\Delta t = \tau_B\left[1 + \frac{1}{2}\left(\frac{T_B}{T_A}\right) + \frac{1}{3}\left(\frac{T_B}{T_A}\right)^2 + \cdots\right]$$

$$\simeq \tau_B \qquad \text{if } T_B \ll T_A \tag{5.6}$$

An important classical example is the transient equilibrium between mesothorium-1 (MsTh₁) and radiothorium (RdTh). Pure MsTh₁ (which is isotopic with radium) can be separated from thorium minerals and has a half-period of 6.7 yr. The decay series can be written

$$_{88}\text{MsTh}_1 \xrightarrow[T_A = 6.7 \text{ yr}]{\beta^-} {}_{89}\text{MsTh}_2 \xrightarrow[T = 6 \text{ hr}]{\beta^-} {}_{90}\text{RdTh} \xrightarrow[T_B = 1.90 \text{ yr}]{\alpha} {}_{88}\text{ThX} \xrightarrow{\alpha}$$

The first decay product MsTh₂ has a half-period of only 6.13 hr and decays promptly into RdTh. The accumulation of RdTh is controlled by its own half-period of 1.90 yr. When viewed on a time scale measured in years, the half-period of the intermediate product MsTh₂ is so short that its activity can be taken as always equal to that of MsTh₁.

Analytically, this corresponds to ignoring the presence of MsTh$_2$ as an intermediate product and can be justified easily from Eq. (8.2a). We see from Eq. (5.5) that the equilibrium activity ratio will be

$$\frac{\text{RdTh}}{\text{MsTh}_1} = \frac{B\lambda_B}{A\lambda_A} = \frac{6.7}{6.7 - 1.9} = 1.39 \tag{5.7}$$

This is clearly a case of transient equilibrium, because the constant-activity ratio is significantly greater than unity. Figure 5.2 shows the decay of an originally pure source of MsTh$_1$ and the growth in it of RdTh.

Its importance lies in the fact that mesothorium is the most refinable, commercially important, long-lived member of the thorium series. Mesothorium is used to replace radium in some self-luminous paints. In the laboratory, mesothorium sources are used primarily as a convenient source of the 2.62-Mev γ rays of ThC''. These γ rays have the highest quantum energy available from any naturally occurring sources. The half-periods of all the decay products of RdTh are relatively short, so that ThC'' is essentially in equilibrium with RdTh. Accordingly, an originally pure MsTh$_1$ source will *increase* in γ-ray activity up to a time $l_m = 4.8$ yr, Eq. (4.1); then the activity will begin to decline with an apparent half-period which varies with time, in accord with Eq. (2.8).

The observation that the rate of emission of disintegration particles

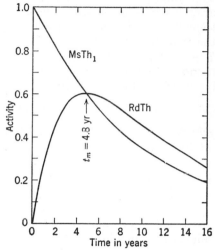

Fig. 5.2 The activity of an originally pure MsTh$_1$ source and of the RdTh produced in it. The maximum activity of the RdTh occurs at 4.8 yr in accord with Eq. (4.1), at which time its activity is the same as its parent. At larger values of the time coordinate, the activity of RdTh approaches its transient equilibrium value of 1.39 times the residual activity of MsTh$_1$, Eq. (5.7).

from a radioactive product permanently exceeds the activity of its parent substance, when the two are in equilibrium, is not the paradox which it may seem at first sight. This condition can be visualized in two ways. First, reference to Eq. (2.1) reminds us that, if the amount of the product B is decreasing with time, then dB must be negative, and hence the rate of its decay $B\lambda_B$ must exceed the rate of its formation by the decay $A\lambda_A$ of its parent. Secondly, the area under a curve such as those in Fig. 5.2 for $t = 0$ to $t = \infty$ represents the total number of disintegrations, hence the total number of radioactive atoms originally available. The area under the two curves must be equal for the two because the same nuclei are involved, only at different stages in their disintegration series. From $t = 0$ to $t = t_m$ the activity of the parent exceeds that of its product. After t_m the activity of the product must therefore exceed that of its parent.

d. Daughter Much Shorter-lived Than Parent. When the half-period of the daughter product is negligible compared with that of its parent, then Eq. (2.9) takes on a particularly simple form. Then $\lambda_A \ll \lambda_B$, and Eq. (2.9) becomes

$$B\lambda_B = A\lambda_A(1 - e^{-\lambda_B t}) \tag{5.8}$$

The daughter activity $B\lambda_B$ increases according to the simple exponential growth curve governed by *its own decay constant* λ_B. This was the historically important case discovered by Rutherford and Soddy (R52) in the growth of ThX ($T = 3.64$ days) from thorium (actually from RdTh, $T = 1.90$ yr). Other important examples include the growth of radon in radium sources, etc. In these cases the equilibrium ratio of activities becomes substantially unity. Note then that

$$B\lambda_B = A\lambda_A \qquad \text{for } t \gg T_B \tag{5.9}$$

only if $T_A \gg T_B$. This condition is spoken of classically as *secular equilibrium*.

6. *Yield of a Radioactive Nuclide Produced by Nuclear Bombardment*

Consider any nuclear reaction which results in the production of a radioactive nuclide, e.g.,

$$_{11}Na^{23} + H^2 \rightarrow H^1 + {}_{11}Na^{24}$$

In this reaction the number of target atoms of Na^{23} which are accessible to the deuteron beam can be called A_0. The probability of transforming one of these atoms into Na^{24} in unit time can be called λ_A. Then $A_0\lambda_A$ is the rate at which new atoms of Na^{24} are produced. We see that the target is to be treated mathematically as though it were a parent source, having an activity $A_0\lambda_A$, and producing a radioactive substance B. Thus the scheme

$$A \xrightarrow{\lambda_A} B \xrightarrow{\lambda_B} C$$

represents the reactions

$$Na^{23} \xrightarrow[\lambda_A]{(d,p)} Na^{24} \xrightarrow[\lambda_B]{\beta^-} Mg^{24}$$

The probability λ_A of producing the (d,p) reaction is very small, but the number of target atoms A_0 is very large. Hence, mathematically,

$$A_0\lambda_A \text{ is finite} \qquad \lambda_A \rightarrow 0 \qquad A_0 \rightarrow \infty$$

Usually, a negligible fraction of the atoms of the target is transformed so that the number of residual target atoms, $A = A_0 e^{-\lambda_A t}$, is effectively equal to A_0. However, in some exceptional instances a measurable fraction of the target may be consumed, such as in the production of plutonium through intense and prolonged neutron irradiation of uranium.

In the $Na^{23}(d,p)Na^{24}$ example, the activity $B\lambda_B$ of Na^{24} produced after a uniform bombardment of duration t will be given by Eq. (5.8) for the growth of activity of a daughter product from an effectively long-lived parent.

The *yield* Y of such a nuclear reaction is the rate of production of activity (*not* atoms) of the radioactive nuclide, under specified bombardment conditions of deuteron energy and current, etc. For example, the yield of Na^{24} from the reaction $Na^{23}(d,p)Na^{24}$ is 11.1 mc/(hr)(μa) of 14-Mev deuterons bombarding a thick target of metallic sodium (C24).

The yield is the rate at which new activity is formed. In the important but special case of a first daughter product, the *yield* is a constant and is equal to *the initial slope of the growth curve of the activity formed*, or

$$Y = \left[\frac{d(B\lambda_B)}{dt}\right]_{\text{at } t=0} \tag{6.1}$$

For $B\lambda_B$ we can take Eq. (5.8) when $\lambda_A \ll \lambda_B$. For greater generality let us use instead the more fundamental expression of Eq. (2.8). Then, in general, the yield of B is

$$
\begin{aligned}
Y &= A_0\lambda_A \frac{\lambda_B}{\lambda_B - \lambda_A} (-\lambda_A e^{-\lambda_A t} + \lambda_B e^{-\lambda_B t})_{t=0} \\
&= A_0\lambda_A\lambda_B
\end{aligned} \tag{6.2}
$$

Thus in the growth equations, Eq. (2.8) or (5.8), the effective activity of the "parent" target, or the rate of production of *atoms* of B, is

$$A_0\lambda_A = Y/\lambda_B = Y\tau_B \tag{6.3}$$

Note that the yield, Y, does not have the dimensions of activity, but of *activity per unit time*. The net activity accumulated during a time t is then written as

$$B\lambda_B = Y\tau_B(1 - e^{-\lambda_B t}) \tag{6.4}$$

The maximum activity which can be produced is then $Y\tau_B$. For example, the maximum Na^{24} ($\tau_B = 1.44T = 1.44 \times 14.8$ hr $= 21.3$ hr) activity under the conditions mentioned above would be, per microampere of deuterons,

$$Y\tau_B = 11.1 \frac{\text{mc}}{\text{hr}} \times 21.3 \text{ hr} = 236 \text{ mc} = 0.236 \text{ curie}$$

and this is the "effective activity," $A_0\lambda_A$, of the parent target while under bombardment, by Eq. (6.3). In one half-period T ($= 14.8$ hr for Na^{24}), one-half this ultimate maximum activity can be accumulated. Figure (6.1) shows that it is evidently inefficient to accumulate activity for much more than one or two half-periods. The activity already accumulated decays almost as rapidly as new activity is produced. The rates of production and of decay become substantially equal after about six half-periods ($e^{-\lambda t} = 0.01$ when $t = 6.6T = 4.6\tau$).

Any particular target, when under nuclear bombardment, may be the source of several radioactive substances. For example, when Al^{27} is bombarded by fast neutrons, the following three reactions occur competitively:

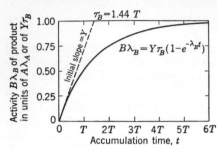

$$Al^{27} \xrightarrow{(n,\gamma)} Al^{28} \qquad T = 2.4 \text{ min}$$

$$Al^{27} \xrightarrow{(n,p)} Mg^{27} \qquad T = 10.2 \text{ min}$$

$$Al^{27} \xrightarrow{(n,\alpha)} Na^{24} \qquad T = 14.8 \text{ hr}$$

Fig. 6.1 Growth of activity in a target irradiated under constant-bombardment conditions. T is the half-period, and τ_B is the mean life of the radioactive nuclide which is being produced. The rate of production of radioactive *atoms* of B is $A_0\lambda_A$, which can be visualized as the "effective activity" of the target under the conditions of bombardment. The rate of production of *activity* of B is then $A_0\lambda_A\lambda_B$ and is called the *yield* Y. The slope of the growth curve at $t = 0$ is the yield Y. If the initial slope is extrapolated (dotted line), it intersects at a time τ_B with the maximum attainable activity of B, which is $1.0\ A_0\lambda_A = 1.0\ Y\tau_B$.

Similarly, the fission of U^{235} leads competitively to many fission chains. Each of these reactions will have its own characteristic yield. In other cases, the same radioactive nuclide may be produced by two different nuclear reactions occurring in the same target. For example, among the reactions when tin is bombarded by deuterons, there are

$$Sn^{118} \xrightarrow{(d,n)} Sb^{119} \qquad T = 39 \text{ hr}$$

$$Sn^{119} \xrightarrow{(d,2n)} Sb^{119} \qquad T = 39 \text{ hr}$$

The yield of each reaction will depend on the conditions of bombardment.

Problem

Under bombardment of sodium by 10 μa of 14-Mev deuterons, the yield of the reaction $_{11}Na^{23}(d,p)_{11}Na^{24}$ is 110 mc per hour. The half-period of Na^{24} is 14.8 hr.

(a) What is the maximum activity of Na^{24} which can be produced under these bombardment conditions?

(b) What activity of Na^{24} will be produced in 8 hr of continuous bombardment?

(c) Eight hours after the conclusion of an 8-hr bombardment, what activity of Na^{24} will remain?

Ans.: (a) 2.34 curies; (b) 734 mc; (c) 504 mc.

7. Growth of a Granddaughter Product

We can write the expressions for the amount and activity of C, accumulated in time t, from an initial supply of A_0 atoms of type A. In the series

$$A \xrightarrow[\lambda_A]{} B \xrightarrow[\lambda_B]{} C \xrightarrow[\lambda_C]{}$$

let there be B atoms of type B and C atoms of type C present at time t. Then the rate of increase in C is, by analogy with Eq. (2.1),

$$\frac{dC}{dt} = B\lambda_B - C\lambda_C \tag{7.1}$$

The solution for C will have the form

$$C = A_0(h_A e^{-\lambda_A t} + h_B e^{-\lambda_B t} + h_C e^{-\lambda_C t}) \tag{7.2}$$

where the coefficients h_A, h_B, h_C depend on the initial conditions. The most important case is for the initial conditions $A = A_0$, $B = 0$, $C = 0$, at $t = 0$. Then Eq. (2.7) gives B as a function of time, and the solution for C can be obtained by substituting Eq. (7.2) into Eq. (7.1) and evaluating the coefficients. In this way it is found that if, at $t = 0$, $A = A_0$, and $B = 0$, then

$$h_A = \frac{\lambda_A}{\lambda_C - \lambda_A}\frac{\lambda_B}{\lambda_B - \lambda_A} \tag{7.3a}$$

$$h_B = \frac{\lambda_A}{\lambda_A - \lambda_B}\frac{\lambda_B}{\lambda_C - \lambda_B} \tag{7.3b}$$

If also $C = 0$, at $t = 0$, then

$$h_A + h_B + h_C = 0$$

and it follows that

$$h_C = \frac{\lambda_A}{\lambda_A - \lambda_C}\frac{\lambda_B}{\lambda_B - \lambda_C} \tag{7.3c}$$

Then the activity $C\lambda_C$ under the initial conditions $A = A_0$, $B = 0$, $C = 0$, at $t = 0$, is

$$C\lambda_C = A_0\lambda_A\left(\frac{\lambda_B}{\lambda_B - \lambda_A}\frac{\lambda_C}{\lambda_C - \lambda_A}e^{-\lambda_A t} + \frac{\lambda_B}{\lambda_A - \lambda_B}\frac{\lambda_C}{\lambda_C - \lambda_B}e^{-\lambda_B t}\right.$$
$$\left. + \frac{\lambda_B}{\lambda_B - \lambda_C}\frac{\lambda_C}{\lambda_A - \lambda_C}e^{-\lambda_C t}\right) \tag{7.4}$$

For numerical work it is often convenient to use the identity

$$\frac{\lambda_1}{\lambda_1 - \lambda_2} = \frac{T_2}{T_2 - T_1} \tag{7.5}$$

The residual activity of the parent radioactive substance is

$$A\lambda_A = A_0\lambda_A e^{-\lambda_A t}$$

which can be factored out of the right-hand side of this equation if desired.

For large values of t, the ratio of the activity $C\lambda_C$ to the residual activity of the parent depends on the relative half-periods of all three substances. If the parent is longer-lived than both B and C, then Eq. (7.4) becomes

$$\frac{C\lambda_C}{A\lambda_A} = \frac{\lambda_B}{\lambda_B - \lambda_A} \frac{\lambda_C}{\lambda_C - \lambda_A} = \frac{T_A}{T_A - T_B} \frac{T_A}{T_A - T_C} \tag{7.6}$$

for $\lambda_A < \lambda_B$ and $\lambda_A < \lambda_C$ and $t \gg \tau_B$ or τ_C. Equation (7.6) then gives the activity ratio corresponding to *transient equilibrium*, or to *secular equilibrium* (unity) if $\lambda_A \ll \lambda_B$ and $\lambda_A \ll \lambda_C$.

The well-known $Te^{131} \to I^{131}$ series will serve as a practical illustration of the behavior of Eq. (7.6). One method of producing these radioactive nuclides is by bombardment of stable Te^{130} with deuterons. The reaction $Te^{130}(d,p)Te^{131}$ is then the effective long-lived parent of Te^{131}. Then in the scheme

$$Te^{130} \xrightarrow[\lambda_A]{(d,p)} Te^{131} \xrightarrow[\lambda_B]{\beta^-} I^{131} \xrightarrow[\lambda_C]{\beta^-} Xe^{131} \text{ (stable)}$$

the activity $C\lambda_C$ of I^{131} accumulated after an irradiation of duration t will be given by Eq. (7.4). Recalling from our discussion of the $Na^{23}(d,p)$ reaction that we can put $\lambda_A \to 0$, while $A\lambda_A$ remains finite and constant, Eq. (7.4) becomes

$$C\lambda_C = A\lambda_A \left[1 - \frac{\lambda_C}{\lambda_C - \lambda_B} \left(e^{-\lambda_B t} - \frac{\lambda_B}{\lambda_C} e^{-\lambda_C t} \right) \right] \tag{7.7}$$

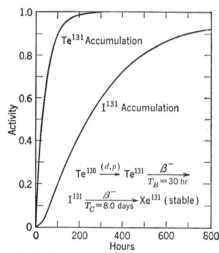

for any finite values of λ_B, λ_C, and t.

The growth of Te^{131} activity, $B\lambda_B$, and of I^{131} activity, $C\lambda_C$, as a function of irradiation time is shown in Fig. 7.1. It will be noted that *the initial slope of the growth curve for the activity $C\lambda_C$ is zero.* Physically, this is because at $t = 0$ there has been no B produced, and so there is no initial production of C by decay of B. Mathematically, we note the same result from Eq. (7.1) in which both terms on the right-hand side are zero at $t = 0$. Similarly, differentiation of Eq. (7.7) gives also $d(C\lambda_C)/dt = 0$ when $t = 0$. We shall return to this concept and to Fig. 7.1 in another connection in Sec. 10.

Fig. 7.1 Accumulation of Te^{131} activity [$B\lambda_B$ of Eq. (6.4)] and of I^{131} activity [$C\lambda_C$ of Eq. (7.7)] in terms of the effective activity $A\lambda_A$ of the reaction $Te^{130}(d,p)Te^{131}$ taken as unity.

a. General Initial Conditions. If at $t = 0$ there was an amount B_0 of substance B present, then at any later time there will be an additional activity of C, due to the C produced by decay of B_0. This *additional* activity of C can be written at once from Eq. (2.8) by appropriate *upgrading of all subscripts* and is

$$C\lambda_C = B_0\lambda_B \frac{\lambda_C}{\lambda_C - \lambda_B} (e^{-\lambda_B t} - e^{-\lambda_C t}) \tag{7.8}$$

for the activity of C at time t due to B_0 at $t = 0$. This activity is, of course, additional to the activity of Eq. (7.4), which represents the activity of C grown only from A_0.

If, at $t = 0$, there was also an amount C_0 of substance C present, then at any later time the *additional* activity due to the residue of this initial stock will be

$$C\lambda_C = C_0\lambda_C e^{-\lambda_C t} \tag{7.9}$$

Problems

1. On a single schematic diagram, show the basic relationships between $A\lambda_A$, $B\lambda_B$, and $C\lambda_C$ as functions of time, if A experiences appreciable decay, for example, $T_A = 5T_B = 3T_C$. Does the $C\lambda_C$ curve cross over $B\lambda_B$ as well as over $A\lambda_A$? Where does the $C\lambda_C$ curve have zero slope? Does the ultimate transient-equilibrium activity ratio $C\lambda_C/B\lambda_B$ depend on T_B?

2. Derive the general expression for the activity $C\lambda_C$ in the series $A \rightarrow B \rightarrow C \rightarrow$, with initial conditions $A = A_0$, $B = C = 0$ at $t = 0$. Use the method based on the production of $B\lambda_B\,dx$ atoms of C during the time interval between x and $x + dx$ and their subsequent decay for the remaining time $(t - x)$.

3. Consider the isomeric transition:

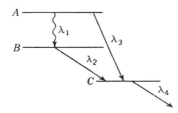

(a) Derive expressions for the *activity* of B and of C, if at $t = 0$: $A = A_0$, $B = C = 0$.

(b) Show that these expressions collapse into the simpler standard form, Eqs. (2.8) and (7.4), when the crossover transition λ_3 is absent.

4. A thorium mineral contains the entire Th series of radioactive nuclides, in secular equilibrium with Th. The series begins as follows:

$$_{90}\text{Th}^{232} \xrightarrow[1.39 \times 10^{10}\,\text{yr}]{\alpha} \text{MsTh}_1 \xrightarrow[6.7\,\text{yr}]{\beta^-} \text{MsTh}_2 \xrightarrow[6.1\,\text{hr}]{\beta^-} {_{90}}\text{RdTh}^{228} \xrightarrow[1.9\,\text{yr}]{\alpha} \text{ThX} \xrightarrow[3.6\,\text{d}]{\alpha}$$

RdTh is seen to be an isotope of Th. When Th is separated chemically from a mineral, it is accompanied by the equilibrium activity of RdTh, but by no MsTh$_1$.

(a) Derive an expression for the activity of RdTh in a thorium salt, as a function of time elapsed after separation of Th, and hence also RdTh, from the mineral. Show graphically the character of the variation with time of the activity of both RdTh and MsTh$_1$ in the Th fraction.

(b) Show that the activity of RdTh passes through a *minimum* value several years after the separation. Find the time of this minimum and the minimum activity of RdTh relative to its equilibrium value. *Ans.*: 4.8 yr; 0.392.

5. From an old and unaltered uranium mineral, the entire ionium and radium content are quantitatively separated into two residues by chemical methods. The radium produced per year in the ionium separate ($\Delta\text{Ra}/\Delta t$) is then compared with the quantity of radium (Ra) originally in the mineral and hence in equilibrium with this amount of ionium. Show that the mean life τ of radium is given directly by a measurement of the ratio of the two radium samples, $Ra/\Delta Ra$, and observation of a calendar for Δt, that is, $\tau = (Ra/\Delta Ra) \, \Delta t$. [Gleditsch and Foyn, *Am. J. Sci.*, **24**: 387 (1932)].

8. *General Equations of Radioactive-series Growth and Decay*

Equations (1.4), (2.7), and (7.4), which refer to one, two, or three radioactive substances, have been generalized and put into a symmetrical form for any number of products by Bateman (B20).

a. Accumulation of Decay Products. Suppose that, at time $t = 0$, there are A_0 atoms of A present and no atoms of its series of decay products $B, C, \ldots, M, N$. Let the decay constants of A and its products be $\lambda_A, \lambda_B, \lambda_C, \ldots, \lambda_M, \lambda_N$. Then, at any time t, the number of atoms of N present will be given by the integral of

$$\frac{dN}{dt} = M\lambda_M - N\lambda_N \qquad (8.1)$$

where M is evaluated from a series of equations similar to Eq. (8.1) for the amounts of the preceding products. The result of this integration is

$$N = A_0(h_A e^{-\lambda_A t} + h_B e^{-\lambda_B t} + \cdots + h_M e^{-\lambda_M t} + h_N e^{-\lambda_N t}) \qquad (8.2a)$$

in which the coefficients are dimensionless functions of the decay constants and have the following systematic values

$$
\begin{aligned}
h_A &= \frac{\lambda_A}{\lambda_N - \lambda_A} \frac{\lambda_B}{\lambda_B - \lambda_A} \frac{\lambda_C}{\lambda_C - \lambda_A} \cdots \frac{\lambda_M}{\lambda_M - \lambda_A} \\[4pt]
h_B &= \frac{\lambda_A}{\lambda_A - \lambda_B} \frac{\lambda_B}{\lambda_N - \lambda_B} \frac{\lambda_C}{\lambda_C - \lambda_B} \cdots \frac{\lambda_M}{\lambda_M - \lambda_B} \\[4pt]
h_M &= \frac{\lambda_A}{\lambda_A - \lambda_M} \frac{\lambda_B}{\lambda_B - \lambda_M} \frac{\lambda_C}{\lambda_C - \lambda_M} \cdots \frac{\lambda_M}{\lambda_N - \lambda_M} \\[4pt]
h_N &= \frac{\lambda_A}{\lambda_A - \lambda_N} \frac{\lambda_B}{\lambda_B - \lambda_N} \frac{\lambda_C}{\lambda_C - \lambda_N} \cdots \frac{\lambda_M}{\lambda_M - \lambda_N}
\end{aligned}
\qquad (8.2b)
$$

The initial condition, that $N = 0$ at $t = 0$, requires that the sum of the coefficients be zero, and these coefficients do satisfy the condition that

$$h_A + h_B + h_C + \cdots + h_M + h_N = 0 \qquad (8.2c)$$

Although the solutions for A, B, C are contained as special cases in the general *Bateman equation*, Eqs. (8.2), it is usually simpler to use the explicit formulations of Eqs. (1.4), (2.7), and (7.4) for these three simplest cases.

The activity of the product N is, of course, $N\lambda_N$, and the values $A_0, A, \ldots, N$ refer to the number of atoms present. To obtain relative weights of the substances, each of these values must be multiplied by the atomic weight of the substance in question.

An important example of the application of Eqs. (8.2) is the equilibrium activity of the short-lived decay products of radon when at $t = 0$ only radon is present. Then in Eqs. (8.2) the symbols A, B, . . . and λ_A, λ_B, . . . represent the radioactive substances and their decay constants as given in Table 8.1. For $t > 4$ hr, equilibrium exists as is

TABLE 8.1. THE SHORT-LIVED DECAY PRODUCTS OF RN

The type of radioactive transition is indicated for each substance. The last row gives the per cent by which the activity of the product exceeds the activity of the parent Rn, when transient equilibrium exists.

Substances:	$_{86}\text{Rn}^{222} \xrightarrow{\alpha}$	RaA $\xrightarrow{\alpha}$	RaB $\xrightarrow{\beta}$	RaC $\xrightarrow[0.0004\alpha]{0.9996\beta}$	RaC' $\xrightarrow{\alpha}$
T:	3.82 days	3 min	26.8 min	19.7 min	150 μsec
Symbols:	$A \longrightarrow$	$B \longrightarrow$	$C \longrightarrow$	$D \longrightarrow$	E
λ in 10^{-4} sec^{-1}:	$\lambda_A = 0.021$	$\lambda_B = 37.9$	$\lambda_C = 4.31$	$\lambda_D = 5.86$	$\lambda_E = 4 \times 10^{11}$
Per cent excess activity:		0.054	0.54	0.89	0.85

shown by the fact that in the expressions from Eqs. (8.2) for A, B, . . . all the exponentials reach values which are negligible compared with the term in $e^{-\lambda_A t}$. Thus the number of atoms of D (that is, RaC) present is

$$D = \frac{\lambda_A}{\lambda_D - \lambda_A} \frac{\lambda_B}{\lambda_B - \lambda_A} \frac{\lambda_C}{\lambda_C - \lambda_A} (A_0 e^{-\lambda_A t}) \qquad (8.3)$$

the term in parentheses being equal to A. Then the activity of D is $D\lambda_D$ and of A is $A\lambda_A$, and rearranging Eq. (8.3) we have the ratio of these activities

$$\frac{D\lambda_D}{A\lambda_A} = \frac{\lambda_B}{\lambda_B - \lambda_A} \frac{\lambda_C}{\lambda_C - \lambda_A} \frac{\lambda_D}{\lambda_D - \lambda_A}$$

$$= \frac{T_A}{T_A - T_B} \frac{T_A}{T_A - T_C} \frac{T_A}{T_A - T_D} = 1.0089 \qquad (8.4)$$

The activity of RaC is therefore 0.89 per cent greater than its parent Rn, and transient equilibrium exists. Similarly the excess activity of the other products in this series is as shown in Table 8.1. The activity of RaC', because of its almost immeasurably short life, is the same as that of its parent RaC, except for a deficiency of 0.04 per cent of the RaC disintegrations which skip the RaC' step by traversing an alternative, or branch, disintegration through RaC'' to RaD.

The solution of Eqs. (8.2) for the α-ray decay products Rn, RaA, and RaC' is shown in Fig. 8.1 as a function of t for 0 to 4 hr, when equilibrium becomes essentially established. Note that the curve for RaC' is appreciably different from a simple accumulation curve, because of the effects of the intermediate products.

b. Decay of a Series of Products. The amount and activity of each radioactive product, due to a nuclear bombardment or a radioactive accumulation of any duration t, have been obtained through Eqs. (8.2). If now the primary source of radioactivity is removed, the amount and activity of each product at any subsequent time can also be calculated with the aid of a group of equations, each having the form of Eqs. (8.2). It is only necessary to remember that the amount of N, for example, remaining at any later time is made up of (1) supply from A, B, . . . , each acting independently as an originally pure source of A, B, . . . , and producing the substance N in accord with Eqs. (8.2); and (2) the residual of the original amount of N present, which decays exponentially. Analytically,

$$N\lambda_N \equiv (\text{activity of } N) = (\text{growth from } A_0) + (\text{growth from } B_0)$$
$$+ \cdots + (\text{growth from } M_0) + (\text{residue of } N_0) \quad (8.5)$$

Thus, no matter how complicated the conditions of bombardment, accumulation, and decay, Eqs. (8.2) may be successfully applied because

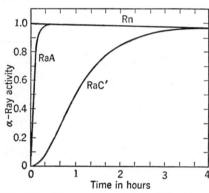

Fig. 8.1   The α-ray activity of Rn $(A\lambda_A)$ and its accumulating decay products RaA $(B\lambda_B)$ and RaC$'$ $(E\lambda_E)$, in terms of the α-ray activity of Rn at $t = 0$.

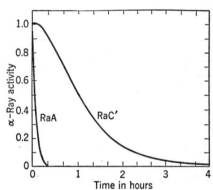

Fig. 8.2   Activity of the α-ray-emitting decay products of Rn, as they decay after having been in transient equilibrium at $t = 0$ with a Rn source having unit activity.

Eq. (8.1) is always the governing basic principle in all radioactive disintegrations.   The decay of the series of products accumulated in Fig. 8.1, when the parent Rn is removed, is shown in Fig. 8.2.

Problems

1. In the production of a radioactive substance B by nuclear bombardment, as in a cyclotron or reactor, according to the scheme $A \xrightarrow{\lambda_A} B \xrightarrow{\lambda_B} C \xrightarrow{\lambda_C}$, show that a continuous and uniform bombardment of duration t produces an activity of B and C equal to

$$I_B = \lambda_B B = I_A(1 - e^{-\lambda_B t})$$

$$I_C = \lambda_C C = I_A \left(1 + \frac{\lambda_C}{\lambda_B - \lambda_C} e^{-\lambda_B t} - \frac{\lambda_B}{\lambda_B - \lambda_C} e^{-\lambda_C t} \right)$$

where $I_A \equiv A\lambda_A$ is the constant rate of production of B by the nuclear bombardment.   Show that for relatively short bombardments, where $\lambda_B t$ and $\lambda_C t$ may be neglected in comparison with unity, these expressions reduce after series expansion to

$$I_B = I_A(\lambda_B t)$$

$$I_C = \frac{I_A}{2}\,(\lambda_B t)(\lambda_C t)$$

2. After a bombardment of duration x, producing radioactive substance B, which decays into the radioactive substance C, the target is allowed to stand for a time t. Show that the activities of B and C are then

$$I_B = \lambda_B B = I_A(1 - e^{-\lambda_B x})e^{-\lambda_B t}$$

$$I_C = \lambda_C C = I_A \frac{\lambda_C}{\lambda_C - \lambda_B}\left[e^{-\lambda_B t}(1 - e^{-\lambda_B x}) - \frac{\lambda_B}{\lambda_C}e^{-\lambda_C t}(1 - e^{-\lambda_C x})\right]$$

3. Show that the maximum activity of C in the undisturbed target of the previous problem will occur at a time ϑ after the bombardment of duration x, where

$$\vartheta = \frac{1}{\lambda_C - \lambda_B}\,\ln\frac{(1 - e^{-\lambda_C x})}{(1 - e^{-\lambda_B x})}$$

and the maximum activity has the value

$$I_C = I_A e^{-\lambda_B \vartheta}(1 - e^{-\lambda_B x})$$

$$= I_A \frac{(1 - e^{-\lambda_B x})\lambda_C/(\lambda_C-\lambda_B)}{(1 - e^{-\lambda_C x})\lambda_B/(\lambda_C-\lambda_B)}$$

4. If the bombardment in Prob. 2 was long enough to produce equilibrium activities in $B\lambda_B$ and $C\lambda_C$,

(*a*) Show that at any time t after cessation of the bombardment the activity of C is

$$C\lambda_C = A\lambda_A \frac{\lambda_C}{\lambda_C - \lambda_B}\left(e^{-\lambda_B t} - \frac{\lambda_B}{\lambda_C}e^{-\lambda_C t}\right)$$

(*b*) On a basis of a careful examination of this expression and its time derivatives or its expansions for small t, construct a schematic graph of $C\lambda_C$ vs. t. Pay particular attention to the shape of this curve for the values of t which are very small and very large compared with the half-period of the substance B. Give approximate analytical expressions for the activity $C\lambda_C$ at these two extremes of time.

5. Actinon, from a 1-mc source of Ac which is in equilibrium with AcX, is passed through a collecting device in which the AcB produced by the decay of the An is accumulated. Assume that 27 per cent of the available AcB atoms are actually collected and that the accumulation time is x. Three separate accumulation experiments are then performed, with $x = 30$ sec, 36 min, and 24 hr. Calculate and plot the activity of AcC as a function of time for $t = 0$ to 3 hr after the end of the accumulation time, x, for the three values of x.
    Ans.:

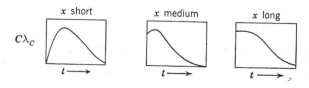

x short   x medium   x long

NOTE: The characteristic and markedly different shape of these three activity curves accounted for the discovery of AcB ($_{82}Pb^{211}$) by Brooks [*Phil. Mag.*, **8**: 373 (1904)] and Bronson [*Am. J. Sci.*, **19**: 185 (1905)]. The important general method of varying the accumulation or irradiation time, in order to disclose and evaluate an intermediate activity λ_B, is now standard procedure, especially for evaluating isomeric levels and for studying fission-product decay chains.

6. From the half-periods and atomic weights involved, determine the equilibrium *weight ratio* between radium and uranium, as in an ancient ore. *Ans.:* 0.34 μg Ra per gram U.

7. Calculate the ratio of the number of grams of protoactinium to the number of grams of radium in an old uranium mineral. Use the nuclear constants given in Prob. 5, Chap. 15, Sec. 1. *Ans.:* 1.0 g Pa per gram Ra.

9. *Accumulation of Stable End Products*

The general theory of the accumulation of a radioactive product applies also to the accumulation of a stable end product. For any stable nuclide, $\lambda = 0$.

Then if A is radioactive and decays into B which is stable, we apply Eq. (2.7)

$$B = A_0 \frac{\lambda_A}{\lambda_B - \lambda_A} (e^{-\lambda_A t} - e^{-\lambda_B t})$$

which, with $\lambda_B = 0$, becomes

$$B = A_0(1 - e^{-\lambda_A t}) \tag{9.1}$$

$$B = A_0 - A \tag{9.2}$$

$$B = A(e^{\lambda_A t} - 1) \tag{9.3}$$

The first two equations for B express the obvious fact that $A_0 = A + B$, that is, the original A_0 atoms are at time t either still untransformed ($= A$) or have transformed into B. The third expression is useful where, for example, t is to be computed from measurements of the residual amount of A and of the amount of its decay product B which has accumulated. This is the principle of those *geological-age measurements* which are based on the accumulation of lead in ancient uranium or thorium minerals.

The accumulation of a stable granddaughter product C follows from Eq. (7.2), which with $\lambda_C = 0$ in Eqs. (7.3) becomes

$$C = A_0 \left(-\frac{\lambda_B}{\lambda_B - \lambda_A} e^{-\lambda_A t} - \frac{\lambda_A}{\lambda_A - \lambda_B} e^{-\lambda_B t} + 1 \right) \tag{9.4}$$

$$C = A_0 \left[1 - e^{-\lambda_A t} - \frac{\lambda_A}{\lambda_B - \lambda_A} (e^{-\lambda_A t} - e^{-\lambda_B t}) \right] \tag{9.5}$$

$$C = A_0 - A - B \tag{9.6}$$

Thus, at time t, the original A_0 atoms are divided between residual A, "holdup" as B, and stable end product C, as required by elementary conservation.

When the supply of active material is from a nuclear reaction, e.g., from

$$\text{Na}^{23} \xrightarrow[\lambda_A]{(d,p)} \text{Na}^{24} \xrightarrow[\lambda_B]{\beta^-} \text{Mg}^{24} \xrightarrow[\lambda_C = 0]{\text{stable}}$$

then we want an expression for C in terms of the target activity $A_0\lambda_A$. In dealing with λ_C ($= 0$), and with λ_A ($\to 0$), mathematical caution is required! It must be recognized that $e^{-\lambda_A t}$ is not *exactly* equal to unity, because λ_A is not zero but only very small. The significant terms in the correct expression for C will arise as the difference between two very large terms. In either Eq. (9.4) or (9.5), the substitution

$$e^{-\lambda_A t} = 1 - \lambda_A t$$

is justified because λ_A is *nearly* zero. After collecting terms and neglecting λ_A in comparison with λ_B, we obtain the result

$$C = A_0\lambda_A \left[t - \frac{1}{\lambda_B} (1 - e^{-\lambda_B t}) \right] \tag{9.7}$$

On comparison with Eq. (5.8), for B, this is seen to be equal to

$$C = A_0\lambda_A t - B \tag{9.8}$$

Thus the steady production rate $A_0\lambda_A$, continued for a time t, produces B radioactive atoms and C stable atoms. If t is large, B may become negligible compared with $A_0\lambda_A t$.

In dealing with the accumulation of the stable end products of longer series, such as the fission chains, the same mathematical precautions are necessary. It is rigorously correct to set the decay constant λ of the final stable product equal to zero; however, the difference between unity and $e^{-\lambda_A t}$ must be preserved as $\lambda_A t$, even though λ_A is nearly zero.

Problems

1. In the series disintegration

$$A \xrightarrow{\lambda_A} B \xrightarrow{\lambda_B} C \xrightarrow{\lambda_C} D \text{ (stable)}$$

show that, if $A\lambda_A$ is the constant activity of a very long-lived source, the number of atoms of D collected in a time t is given by

$$D = A\lambda_A \left[t - \frac{1}{\lambda_B} - \frac{1}{\lambda_C} - \frac{\lambda_C}{\lambda_B(\lambda_B - \lambda_C)} e^{-\lambda_B t} + \frac{\lambda_B}{\lambda_C(\lambda_B - \lambda_C)} e^{-\lambda_C t} \right]$$

$$= A\lambda_A t - B - C$$

2. Tellurium is bombarded by deuterons in a cyclotron, forming

$$_{52}\text{Te}^{130}(d,p)\text{Te}^{131} \xrightarrow[T = 30 \text{ hr}]{\beta^-} \text{I}^{131} \xrightarrow[T = 8.0 \text{ d}]{\beta^-} \text{Xe}^{131} \text{ (stable)}$$

The bombardment conditions are such that the (d,p) reaction is equivalent to a source strength of 2 mc (i.e., 74×10^6 disintegrations per second).

(a) What is the initial rate of production of I^{131}, in microcuries per hour?

(b) How many atoms of Xe^{131} would be produced *during* a single 6-hr bombardment?

(c) What would be the *total* number of atoms of Xe^{131} obtained eventually, if this target were allowed to stand undisturbed for several months following a single 6-hr bombardment?

Ans.: (a) zero; (b) 8×10^8 atoms; (c) 1.60×10^{12} atoms.

3. One gram of natural uranium is carefully purified from ionium and radium and then allowed to stand for about 1 to 10 yr.

(a) What will be the activity of radium, in curies, which will grow in the sample in t yr?

(b) How many cubic centimeters (normal temperature and pressure) of He will grow in the sample in t yr?

Note: As both answers are to be compared with experimental results, a precision of 1 or 2 per cent is entirely adequate for computing (a) and (b).

Ans.: (a) $6 \times 10^{-16}t^2$ curie $Ra/(yr^2)(g\ U)$; (b) $3 \times 10^{-8}t$ cm^3 $He/(yr)(g\ U)$.

4. The half-period of U^{235} was first determined accurately by mass-spectroscopic measurements of the relative isotopic abundance of Pb^{207} and Pb^{206} which are the end products of the decay of U^{235} and U^{238}, accumulated in ancient uranium minerals [A. O. Nier, *Phys. Rev.*, **55**: 153 (1939); **60**: 112 (1941)]. The age t was determined in the same minerals from measurements of U^{238} and Pb^{206}, and the ratio of $U^{238}/U^{235} = 139 \pm 1$ was found to be independent of t. Show that the ratio of the lead isotopes Pb^{207}/Pb^{206} depends on t and on the decay constants λ_A of U^{235}, and λ_U of U^{238}, in the following way

$$\frac{Pb^{207}}{Pb^{206}} = \frac{1}{139} \frac{(e^{\lambda_A t} - 1)}{(e^{\lambda_U t} - 1)}$$

where $\lambda_A = 139\,R\lambda_U$ and R is the activity ratio of U^{235}/U^{238} in natural uranium. Plot the Pb^{207}/Pb^{206} ratio expected in the radiogenic lead, if $R = 0.04$ and if $R = 0.05$, against an age scale from 0 to 2×10^9 yr, and compare with Nier's measurements. Determine the half-period of U^{235}, if the data fit an activity ratio $R = 0.046$. *Ans.:* 7.1×10^8 yr.

5. (a) If a certain mineral contains 1 g of potassium and is known to be 2.0×10^9 yr old, what is the maximum number of milliliters of argon (measured at $0°C$, 760 mm Hg) which should have accumulated in the mineral? Why is your numerical result a maximum value? Use the radioactive constants of K^{40} given in Prob. 2 of Chap. 15, Sec. 1.

(b) Show that the existence of competing EC transitions of K^{40} to A^{40} influences the accumulation of Ca^{40} from the β decay of K^{40} in such a way that

$$Ca^{40} = K^{40} \left(1 + \frac{\lambda_{EC}}{\lambda_\beta} \right)^{-1} (e^{\lambda_\beta (1 + \lambda_{EC}/\lambda_\beta)t} - 1)$$

(c) Calculate the ratio of the number of atoms of radiogenic Ca^{40} per atom of K^{40} expected in a potassium mica which is 2.0×10^9 yr old.

Ans.: (a) 0.0154 cm^3 A^{40} per gram K; (c) 2.1.

10. Summation Rules

In many practical problems much of the involvement of the brute-force mathematical application of the Bateman equations can be skipped, if physical principles and thought are used instead. We illustrate these fruitful physical approaches by explicit development of "summation rules." These unify the processes of accumulation and decay. They apply to any member of a radioactive decay series. They apply also to any other physical process in which successive steps are linked by exponential functions of time or space, as in the multiple scattering and absorption of γ rays, β rays, and neutrons.

a. Summation of Decay and Accumulation Curves. In Fig. 10.1, the accumulation of daughter activity $B\lambda_B$ from a long-lived parent activity $A_0\lambda_A$ follows the growth curve 1, which is

$$(B\lambda_B)_1 = A_0\lambda_A(1 - e^{-\lambda_B t}) \qquad (10.1)$$

At any arbitrary time, $t = x$, after the beginning of the bombardment, the activity $B\lambda_B$ is

$$(B\lambda_B)_x = A_0\lambda_A(1 - e^{-\lambda_B x}) \qquad (10.2)$$

If we separate this activity out, its subsequent decay will follow curve 2, and the activity remaining at any later time, $t = x + y$, will be

$$\begin{aligned}(B\lambda_B)_2 &= (B\lambda_B)_x e^{-\lambda_B y} \\ &= A_0\lambda_A e^{-\lambda_B y} - A_0\lambda_A e^{-\lambda_B(x+y)} \qquad (10.3)\end{aligned}$$

If, in addition to this, the parent source continues to operate, it will produce new daughter activity along the curve 3, and at time $t = x + y$ this activity will be

$$(B\lambda_B)_3 = A_0\lambda_A(1 - e^{-\lambda_B y}) \qquad (10.4)$$

The total daughter activity at time $t = x + y$ is given by the sum of these two fractions (curves 2 and 3) and is equal to

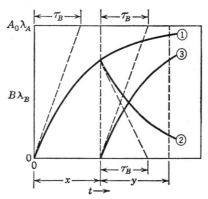

Fig. 10.1 The total accumulated activity, curve 1, is always the sum of a decay curve 2 and a new growth curve 3, where curves 2 and 3 begin at any arbitrary time $t = x$. See Eqs. (10.1) to (10.5). Also, (slope of curve 1) = (slope of curve 3) + (slope of curve 2) at any arbitrary time $t = x + y$.

$$\begin{aligned}(B\lambda_B)_2 + (B\lambda_B)_3 &= A_0\lambda_A(1 - e^{-\lambda_B(x+y)}) \\ &= (B\lambda_B)_1 \qquad (10.5)\end{aligned}$$

which is simply the original uninterrupted growth curve. Physically, this is equivalent to noting that the mere act of separating the activity $(B\lambda_B)_x$ from the parent has no effect whatsoever on its subsequent decay. Once it is produced, *the subsequent behavior of each atom of B is entirely independent of its environment.*

It is also helpful to note that the slope of the accumulation curve 1 is always equal to the sum of the slopes of the decay and growth curves 2 and 3. This generalization can be visualized graphically for the particular time $t = x$. For any value of time t we have

$$\frac{dB}{dt} = A_0\lambda_A - B\lambda_B \qquad (10.6)$$

Multiplying both sides by λ_B gives

$$\frac{d(B\lambda_B)}{dt} = A_0\lambda_A\lambda_B - B\lambda_B\lambda_B = \frac{A_0\lambda_A}{\tau_B} - \frac{B\lambda_B}{\tau_B} \tag{10.7}$$

The term $(A_0\lambda_A/\tau_B)$ is the "yield" or initial slope of the growth curve 3, while $(-B\lambda_B/\tau_B)$ is the initial slope of the decay curve 2. Both slopes are shown dotted on Fig. 10.1.

It can be shown that, under the most general conditions, any growth curve is always the sum of two curves like 2 and 3, one representing the decay of the product and the other representing the immediate growth of new activity. Figure 10.2 expresses this generalization graphically when λ_A is not neglected. Analogous relationships are also valid for all later generations, $C\lambda_C$, $D\lambda_D$, . . . , in a decay series and can be visualized by superimposing Fig. 8.2 on Fig. 8.1. Stated in words, the summation-rule generalization is

$$\begin{bmatrix} \text{Accumulation} \\ \text{at time } t \\ \text{(curve 3 growth)} \end{bmatrix} = \begin{bmatrix} \text{equilibrium amount} \\ \text{at time } t \\ \text{(curve 1 equilibrium)} \end{bmatrix} - \begin{bmatrix} \text{residue of a hypotheti-} \\ \text{cal initial equilibrium} \\ \text{amount, which decays} \\ \text{during the accumula-} \\ \text{tion period} \\ \text{(curve 2 decay)} \end{bmatrix} \tag{10.8}$$

As an elementary illustration, consider the accumulation of $B\lambda_B$ from a decaying parent $A\lambda_A$, with $0 < \lambda_A < \lambda_B$. Then from Eq. (10.8) and Fig. 10.2 with $x = 0$,

$$B\lambda_B \equiv \text{curve 3} = \text{curve 1} - \text{curve 2}$$

$$= \left(A\lambda_A \frac{\lambda_B}{\lambda_B - \lambda_A}\right) - \left(A_0\lambda_A \frac{\lambda_B}{\lambda_B - \lambda_A}\right) e^{-\lambda_B t}$$

$$= A_0\lambda_A \frac{\lambda_B}{\lambda_B - \lambda_A} (e^{-\lambda_A t} - e^{-\lambda_B t}) \tag{10.9}$$

which is the conventional general expression, Eq. (2.8), for the growth of a daughter activity.

The broad significance of the summation rules is that any radioactive parent material (or any nuclear reaction producing a radioactive daughter product) can be considered *to be always in equilibrium with its daughter substance*, if we are willing to overlook consideration of the physical whereabouts of the daughter. Thus 1 g of radium always supports 1 curie of radon, whether or not the radon is confined in the vessel which contains the radium. A hospital which owns 1 g of radium will also always have responsibility for 1 curie of radon. It makes no difference whether the radon is left with the radium or is pumped off the source every 24 hr and distributed in therapeutic applicators throughout the hospital; there will always be a *total* of 1 curie of radon, somewhere in the universe, whose existence is dependent on that 1 g of radium.

b. Transposition of Time Axis. Suppose a neutron source is available which can produce a maximum of 100 mc of Na^{24} through the reaction

$Na^{23}(n,\gamma)Na^{24}$. It is operated for an accumulation time t_a, turned off for a decay time t_d, then operated again for a second accumulation time t_{aa}, as shown in Fig. 10.3. The final Na^{24} activity at time $t_a + t_d + t_{aa}$ can be obtained from a single conventional accumulation curve, by suitable transposition of the coordinates. We have seen that the slope of the accumulation curve is always the yield $(A\lambda_A/\tau_B)$ minus the decay slope $(B\lambda_B/\tau_B)$ and hence depends only on the activity present and not on how or where this activity was produced. At the end of the decay period t_d, call the residual activity $(B\lambda_B)_2$. The subsequent accumulation

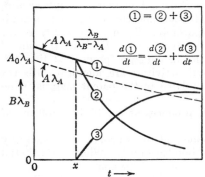

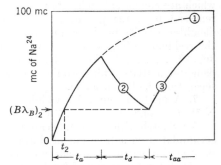

Fig. 10.2 Graphical representation of the summation rules for the activity $B\lambda_B$ of a daughter product, when $0 < \lambda_A < \lambda_B$, and for any x. The dotted curve is the decay of parent activity, $A\lambda_A = A_0\lambda_A e^{-\lambda_A t}$.

Fig. 10.3 Net accumulation from discontinuous bombardments, t_a and t_{aa}, can be read from a single conventional accumulation curve 1 by transposing the time axis.

curve 3 is identical with the original accumulation curve 1 except that it is transposed along the time axis by an amount $(t_a + t_d - t_2)$, where t_2 is the time at which the activity was $(B\lambda_B)_2$ on the original accumulation curve 1.

Problems

A little contemplation saves a lot of calculation.

1. A neutron source is available in your laboratory which produces at equilibrium 100 mc of P^{32} ($T = 14$ days) from $P^{31}(n,\gamma)P^{32}$. For a particular experiment, you need a maximum possible activity of P^{32}. Just as you begin your bombardment, a friend gives you 75 mc of P^{32}. How long should you run your own bombardment so that your total P^{32} on hand will be maximum? What is this maximum activity, in millicuries? What benefit, if any, do you get from the gift? Explain why this is so, using only the exponential growth curve of P^{32} for your neutron source.

2. Show that Eq. (10.5) is also valid for the general case in which the parent activity is not constant but decays as $A\lambda_A = A_0\lambda_A e^{-\lambda_A t}$.

3. In Fig. 10.1 show that, at *any* time $t = x + y$, the

$$(\text{slope of curve 1}) = (\text{slope of curve 2}) + (\text{slope of curve 3})$$

4. (*a*) In any decay series $A \rightarrow B \rightarrow C \rightarrow$, show by comparison of growth and decay equations for $C\lambda_C$ that

$$(C\lambda_C)_{\text{growth}} + (C\lambda_C)_{\text{decay}} = (C\lambda_C)_{\text{equilibrium}}$$

(*b*) Interpret the growth curve for I^{131} in Fig. 7.1 as a decay curve for I^{131} in a mixture of Te^{131} and I^{131} activities which were at equilibrium when a hypothetical nuclear reaction $Te^{130}(d,p)Te^{131}$ was interrupted. Note especially that the initial slope of $(C\lambda_C)_{\text{decay}}$ is zero and give a direct physical reason for this initial constancy of $(C\lambda_C)_{\text{decay}}$.

5. Interpret the two terms of Eq. (10.3) graphically and physically.

6. A long-lived parent radioactive material, whose activity is k mc, produces a short-lived daughter (for example, Ra → Rn). At regular time intervals ϑ, which are comparable with its mean life τ, the accumulated daughter product is removed from the parent and stored separately. Then $k(1 - e^{-\vartheta/\tau})$ is the daughter activity produced in the first time interval, etc. Evaluate the sum of the residual activities of the several samples of daughter product at time 2ϑ, 3ϑ, 4ϑ, . . . , $n\vartheta$. Show that these total activities are identical with the daughter activity which would have accumulated in the parent material if no separations had been made.

7. A neutron source is available which produces at equilibrium 100 mc of Na^{24} ($T = 14.8$ hr) from Na^{23} $(n,\gamma)Na^{24}$.

(*a*) Sketch with reasonable care the exponential growth curve of Na^{24} activity accumulated as a function of duration of bombardment. What is the initial slope of this accumulation curve in millicuries of Na^{24} per hour?

(*b*) A total of 80 mc of Na^{24} is needed for a particular experiment. Twenty mc of Na^{24} is in stock. How long must the source be operated so that at the conclusion of the bombardment a *total* of just 80 mc is available? Correlate an analytical solution with a graphical solution obtained from the curve in (*a*). *Ans.: 2T.*

11. *Approximate Methods for Short Accumulation Times*

For accumulation times t, which are short compared with the mean life of any member of a series

$$A \underset{\lambda_A}{\rightarrow} B \underset{\lambda_B}{\rightarrow} C \underset{\lambda_C}{\rightarrow} D \underset{\lambda_D}{\rightarrow}$$

approximate solutions can be based on series expansions of the exponentials in the general equations, such as Eq. (8.2). A simpler and more instructive approach, which leads, of course, to the same solutions, is the following: We assume that at $t = 0$, $A = A_0$, and $B = C = D = 0$. Then the activity of A is $A_0\lambda_A$, and initially

$$dB = A_0\lambda_A \, dt$$

which, when integrated, gives

$$B = \int_0^B dB = \int_0^t A_0\lambda_A \, dt = A_0\lambda_A t \tag{11.1}$$

This is equivalent to saying that the initial growth of B is linear with time.

The initial rate of accumulation of C is equal to the activity of B, thus

$$dC = B\lambda_B \, dt = A_0\lambda_A t\lambda_B \, dt$$

which, when integrated, leads to

$$C = \int_0^C dC = \int_0^t A_0\lambda_A t\lambda_B \, dt = A_0\lambda_A\lambda_B \left(\frac{t^2}{2}\right) \tag{11.2}$$

This is equivalent to saying that the *average* activity of B is one-half its final activity, that is, $C = (B\lambda_B/2)t = A_0\lambda_A\lambda_B t^2/2$. Similarly, the initial rate of accumulation of D is equal to the activity of C, or

$$dD = C\lambda_C \, dt = A_0\lambda_A\lambda_B \left(\frac{t^2}{2}\right)\lambda_C \, dt$$

which, when integrated, leads to

$$D = \int_0^D dD = \int_0^t A_0\lambda_A\lambda_B \left(\frac{t^2}{2}\right)\lambda_C \, dt = A_0\lambda_A\lambda_B\lambda_C \left(\frac{t^3}{6}\right) \tag{11.3}$$

Note that the decay constant of the product being collected does *not* enter these approximate expressions. This is because in each case $t \ll \tau$, and time for appreciable decay has not elapsed. The end product may be either radioactive or stable (that is, $\lambda = 0$).

In these approximations for B, C, D, etc., it is assumed that t is small compared with any of the mean lives involved. The method is also applicable to radioactive series in which the time t is either large or small compared with any of the mean lives. For example, in the fission-product series

$$\text{U}^{235} \xrightarrow{(n,f)} \text{Xe}^{140} \xrightarrow[T = 16 \text{ sec}]{} \text{Cs} \xrightarrow[40 \text{ sec}]{} \text{Ba} \xrightarrow[300 \text{ hr}]{} \text{La} \xrightarrow[40 \text{ hr}]{} \text{Ce (stable)} \tag{11.4}$$

a time interval of, say, 2 hr is long compared with the mean lives of Xe^{140} and Cs^{140} but short compared with the mean lives of Ba^{140} and La^{140}. Over a period of 2 hr, substantially every fission process will pass through the Xe and Cs steps to at least as far as Ba. The activity of Cs can be taken as equal to that of the fission source $A_0\lambda_A$ without appreciable error. Analytically, the exponentials which contain the large decay constants of Xe and Cs in the general Bateman equation (8.2a) become negligible. Then the accumulation of Ba *activity* in a time t of the order of 2 hr will be

$$(A_0\lambda_A)\lambda_{Ba}t = (A_0\lambda_A)\left(\frac{t}{\tau_{Ba}}\right) \tag{11.5}$$

and the accumulation of La *activity* will be

$$(A_0\lambda_A)\lambda_{Ba}\lambda_{La}\frac{t^2}{2} = \frac{1}{2}(A_0\lambda_A)\left(\frac{t}{\tau_{Ba}}\right)\left(\frac{t}{\tau_{La}}\right) \tag{11.6}$$

Problems

1. What activity of I^{131} is accumulated during a 2-hr bombardment of $Te^{130}(d,p) \rightarrow Te^{131} \rightarrow I^{131}$, if the yield of Te^{131} is 0.92 mc/hr? *Ans.: 6.6 μc.*

2. Assume that one of the primary fission products of U^{235} is $_{54}Xe^{140}$ and that the subsequent series decay to stable $_{58}Ce^{140}$ is

$$U^{235}(n,f) \rightarrow Xe^{140} \xrightarrow[16 \text{ sec}]{} Cs \xrightarrow[40 \text{ sec}]{} Ba \xrightarrow[300 \text{ hr}]{} La \xrightarrow[40 \text{ hr}]{} Ce^{140}$$

A fission source having a yield of 43.3 mc of Xe^{140} per second is operated for 10 hr and then stopped. Using approximate methods (say, ±5 per cent) determine (a) the activity of the Ba^{140} at the end of the bombardment and (b) the activity of the La^{140} at the end of the bombardment. If the radiochemical separations are carried out 40 hr after the end of the bombardment, determine (c) the activity of La^{140} obtained and (d) the activity of Ba^{140} obtained.

If the Ba^{140} in (d) is stored, it will produce an additional amount of La^{140}. (e) How long should the purified Ba^{140} be stored in order to obtain from it a maximum amount of La^{140} in a second radiochemical separation?

Ans.: (a) 23 mc; *(b)* 2.0 mc; *(c)* 12 mc; *(d)* 21 mc; *(e)* 134 hr.

12. *Graphical Methods for Series Growth and Decay*

For any decay series which is to be dealt with repeatedly, graphical solutions of the decay and accumulation equations generally save much time and aid in avoiding errors. With the help of the summation rules, solutions for a wide variety of circumstances can be obtained from graphs representing the growth of all activities from an initial stock of A only, of B only, etc. If the activities are plotted on a logarithmic scale, then the relative accuracy of reading is constant for all values of the activity, and also the ratios of activities of two or more products can be dealt with most simply.

Figures 12.1*a* and 12.1*b* are such semilogarithmic graphs of the growth of Te^{131} and I^{131} activities in a $Te^{130}(d,p)$ target and of the decay of Te^{131} and the growth of its daughter I^{131} in an initially pure source of Te^{131}. The data are, of course, identical with Figs 5.1 and 7.1 which have simple arithmetic coordinates.

To illustrate one type of solution: Suppose we have a $Te^{130}(d,p)$ source whose yield of Te^{131} is 46.2 μc/hr. This source therefore has an effective activity of

$$A\lambda_A = Y\tau_B = (46.2 \text{ μc/hr})(1.44 \times 30 \text{ hr}) = 2{,}000 \text{ μc} = 2 \text{ mc}$$

Suppose this source is operated for 48 hr and then allowed to cool for a time t. How much Te^{131} and I^{131} activity is present at the end of the bombardment? How long should the source cool in order to develop a maximum I^{131} content? From Fig. 12.1*a*, the 48-hr accumulation produces $0.68A\lambda_A = 1.36$ mc of Te^{131} and $0.068A\lambda_A = 0.136$ mc of I^{131}. The activity ratio Te^{131}/I^{131} at this time is $0.68/0.068 = 10$. On Fig. 12.1*b* we note that some hypothetical source of originally pure Te^{131} would have developed an activity ratio $Te^{131}/I^{131} = 10$ if it had stood for about 21 hr. (The activity ratio, of 10 in this case, is most easily transferred from Fig. 12.1a to 12.1b by noting that, on a logarithmic coordinate scale, constant distances correspond to constant ratios of the variables plotted.)   The absolute separation between the Te^{131} and I^{131} curves on Fig. 12.1a can therefore be measured with a pair of dividers or marked along the edge of a card.   Moving then to Fig. 12.1b, the same activity ratio is found at that time when the Te^{131} and I^{131} curves have the same linear separation as was determined on Fig. 12.1a.   Now we note that *the subsequent history of a mixture having any particular activity ratio* (in this case, 10) *is completely independent of how the mixture originated*.   Therefore, Fig. 12.1b gives the variations in Te^{131} and I^{131} activity in the cooling target by taking 21 hr on Fig. 12.1b as the origin of time coordinates during the cooling period.   Also, the activity coordinates are readily normalized to an absolute basis.   At the beginning of the cooling period we found from Fig. 12.1a that there is 1.36 mc of Te^{131} present.   On Fig. 12.1b the relative activity of Te^{131} at 21 hr (i.e., when $Te^{131}/I^{131} = 10$) is 0.60.   Therefore, on Fig. 12.1b for the cooling mixture the activity coordinate is to be normalized for this problem by multiplying the scale by $1.36/0.60 = 2.27$.   The maximum activity of I^{131} occurs on Fig. 12.1b at 95 hr and is 0.11 times the initial activity of the hypothetical source of pure Te^{131} at zero time.   Therefore, the maximum activity of I^{131} in our cooling target occurs $95 - 21 = 74$ hr after the end of the bombardment, and at that time the I^{131} activity is

$$0.11 \times 2.27 = 0.25 \text{ mc}$$

In analogous fashion, the activity of both Te^{131} and I^{131} in the cooling target can be obtained from Fig. 12.1b for any arbitrary time of cooling. If we extend the original problem by introducing a second bombardment of the same target, at a different deuteron current and hence at a different yield, the two graphs still provide quick solutions.   For example, suppose the original bombardment of 48 hr is followed by a cooling period of 24 hr and then by a second bombardment of 72 hr at twice the original yield. The Te^{131} and I^{131} in the target at the conclusion of the second bombardment can be obtained in the following way.   We recognize that the second bombardment produces new activities which can be obtained from Fig. 12.1a.   The residues of the Te^{131} and I^{131} from the first bombardment will be unaffected by the second bombardment and are obtained from Fig. 12.1b by assuming a cooling period which includes the second bombardment, i.e., $24 + 72 = 96$ hr.   Then the total activities at the end of the second bombardment equal the sum of that produced in the second bombardment plus the residues from the first bombardment. After these have been totalized, and their ratio determined, Fig. 12.1b can be reused to obtain the effects of cooling after the second bombardment, if desired.   Evidently, Figs. 12.1a and 12.1b provide easy solutions to very complicated situations and can replace hours of computation based only on the analytical equations.

Figures 12.2a and 12.2b provide the corresponding graphs for the important fission products Ba^{140} and La^{140}.   Figures 12.3a and 12.3b provide the data describing the decay products of actinium.

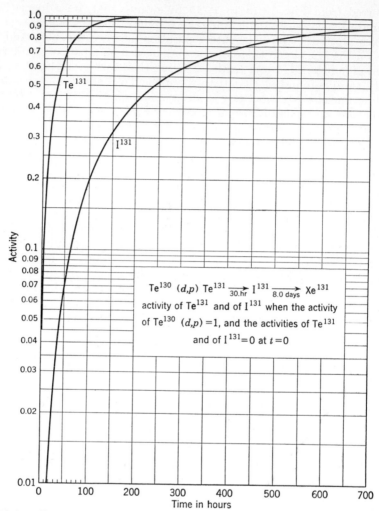

Fig. 12.1a Growth of Te¹³¹ and I¹³¹ activity when atoms of Te¹³¹ are supplied at a constant rate $(A\lambda_A = 1)$, as from the Te¹³⁰(d,p) reaction, if the activity of Te¹³¹ and of I¹³¹ is zero at $t = 0$. (From Fig. 7.1.)

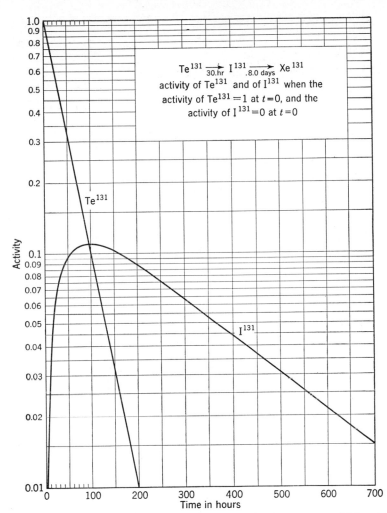

Fig. 12.1b   Decay of Te[131] and growth of I[131] activity in a source which, at $t = 0$, contained unit activity of Te[131] and no I[131].   (From Fig. 5.1.)   The activities of Te[131] and I[131] are equal at $t_m = 95$ hr.   Thereafter the ratio of I[131] to Te[131] activities increases constantly with time.

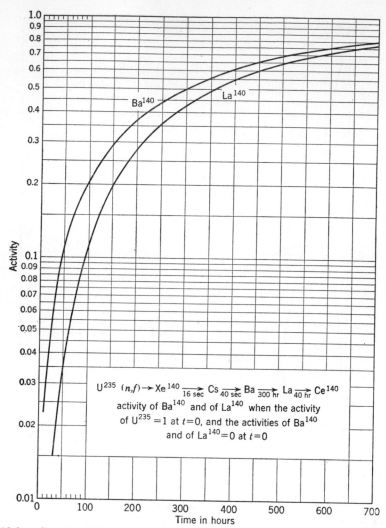

Fig. 12.2a Growth of Ba[140] and La[140] activity when atoms of Ba[140] are supplied at a constant rate $(A\lambda_A = 1)$ from the fission of U[235], if the activity of Ba[140] and of La[140] is zero at $t = 0$.

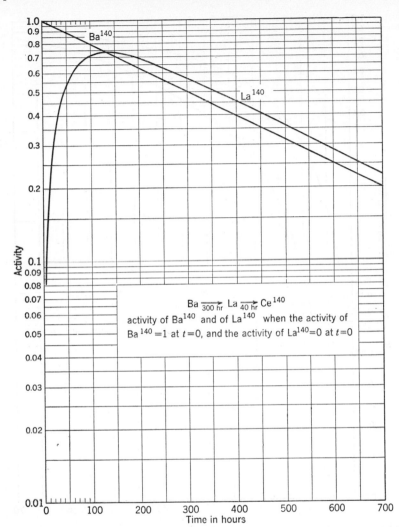

Fig. 12.2b   Decay of Ba¹⁴⁰ and growth of La¹⁴⁰ activity in a source which, at $t = 0$, contained unit activity of Ba¹⁴⁰ and no La¹⁴⁰. The activities of Ba¹⁴⁰ and La¹⁴⁰ are equal at $t_m = 134$ hr.

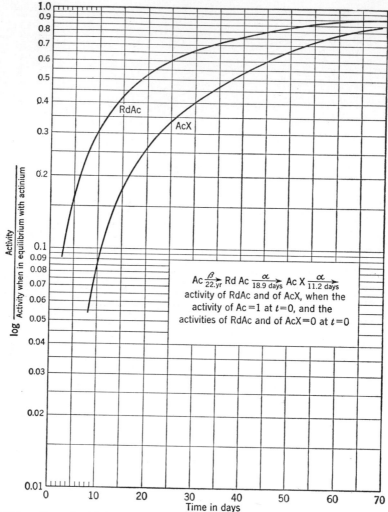

Fig. 12.3a Growth of RdAc ($= {}_{90}Th^{227}$) and of AcX ($= {}_{88}Ra^{223}$) activity from their long-lived parent ${}_{89}Ac^{227}$, when the activity of Ac is unity, if the activity of RdAc and of AcX is zero at $t = 0$.

Problems

1. A slug containing U^{235} is irradiated with thermal neutrons as a fission source of the very potent γ-ray emitter La^{140}, according to

$$U^{235}(n,f) \rightarrow Xe^{140} \rightarrow Cs \rightarrow Ba \rightarrow La^{140} \rightarrow Ce^{140}$$

and is operated at constant power level, such that its equivalent activity as parent of the Ba-La^{140} series is 4 curies. By means of the conventional graphs of the Bateman equations for this series, determine (*a*) the activity of Ba^{140}

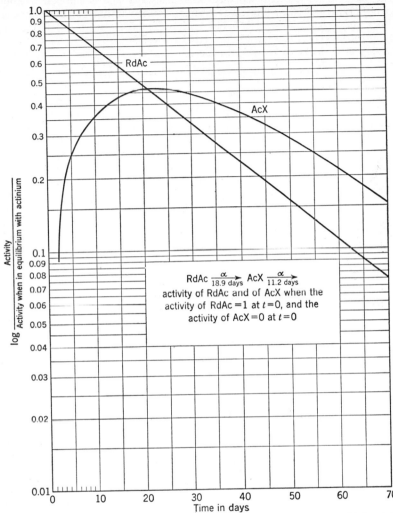

Fig. 12.3b   Decay of RdAc and growth of AcX activity in a source which, at $t = 0$, contained unit activity of RdAc and no AcX.   The activities of RdAc and AcX are equal at $t_m = 20.6$ days.   All the subsequent decay products of AcX are short-lived, for example, An ($T = 3.9$ sec), and are in secular equilibrium with AcX on a time scale measured in days, such as this is.

after 100 hr of continuous operation and (*b*) the activity of La^{140} after 100 hr of continuous operation.

The slug is allowed to stand untreated for 150 hr; determine (*c*) the residual activity of Ba^{140} and (*d*) the residual activity of La^{140}.

The slug is now returned to the neutron source and operated again, at the same power level, for 200 additional hr; determine (*e*) the total activity of Ba^{140} and (*f*) the total activity of La^{140}.

The Ba^{140} in (e) is separated out radiochemically and is shipped to another site, where it arrives 60 hr later. Determine (g) the activity of La^{140} on arrival.

Ans.: (a) 0.820 curie; (b) 0.444 curie; (c) 0.580 curie; (d) 0.635 curie; (e) 1.854 curies; (f) 1.524 curies; (g) 1.104 curies.

2. Actinium decays according to the scheme

$$Ac \xrightarrow[22\ yr]{} RdAc \xrightarrow[18.9\ d]{} AcX \xrightarrow[11.2\ d]{} An \rightarrow$$

A certain sample of pure Ac, free of decay products, has an initial activity of 2 mc. After the Ac has accumulated its decay products for 30 days, the RdAc and AcX are removed by radiochemical separation.

(a) Find the activity of the RdAc and of the AcX at the instant of separation.

(b) In this separated material, find the activity of RdAc and of AcX 20 days after the separation.

(c) A radiochemist mixes 0.5 mc of pure RdAc and 0.5 mc of pure AcX. Find the activity of each 30 days after mixing.

Ans.: For RdAc: (a) 1.33 mc; (b) 0.645 mc; (c) 0.167 mc. For AcX: (a) 0.80 mc; (b) 0.872 mc; (c) 0.301 mc.

3. A Te^{130} target is bombarded for 240 hr, producing a certain mixture of Te^{131} and I^{131} according to the reactions

$$Te^{130}(d,p) \rightarrow Te^{131} \rightarrow I^{131} \rightarrow$$

The unseparated target is allowed to cool for 100 hr. At this time the I^{131} is separated out and its activity is found to be 9.4 mc. Find the yield of Te^{131} in millicuries per hour during the bombardment. *Ans.:* 0.46 mc Te^{131} per hour.

4. A slug containing U^{235} is bombarded at a uniform rate with thermal neutrons for 150 hr and then allowed to cool while in transit to another site. On arrival, 100 hr after the end of the bombardment, the slug is found to contain 20.0 curies of La^{140} activity.

(a) Has the La^{140} activity increased or decreased during transit? By what factor?

(b) Find the yield of Ba^{140}, in millicuries per hour, during the bombardment. *Ans.:* (a) increased 25 per cent, (b) 190 mc Ba^{140} per hour.

5. La^{140} samples resulting from the disintegration $Ba^{140} \xrightarrow[300\ hr]{\beta^-} La^{140}$ are to be used in a series of experiments. Whenever the La activity reaches the maximum attainable value the La is separated from its parent to form a sample for study. The Ba continues to produce La and, when the new La growth reaches its maximum value, it is separated into a second sample. This procedure is continued as long as samples so obtained have an activity greater than 1 mc at separation.

(a) If the initial amount of pure Ba^{140} is 5 mc, how many useful samples of La^{140} can be obtained under the above conditions?

(b) What will be the instantaneous activity of the last sample of La^{140} at the time of its separation?

(c) What will be the total activity of all La samples at that time?

Ans.: (a) 5; (b) 1.07 mc; (c) 1.21 mc.

α-Ray Spectra

Until the discovery of spontaneous fission, α decay was the only known type of radioactive disintegration in which nuclei emit heavy particles. Rutherford showed in 1899 that uranium minerals emit at least two kinds of radiations having widely different penetrating powers, as indicated by the ionization produced by uranium minerals screened by absorbers of various thicknesses. Rutherford named the softer component "α rays" and the harder, or more penetrating, component "β rays." During the subsequent 15 years, Rutherford and his students carried out a series of masterly experiments on the characteristics of the α rays.

By successfully deflecting the α rays from radium and its decay products with both magnetic and electric fields, Rutherford showed that the α rays are positively charged, are emitted with an initial velocity of the order of one-tenth the velocity of light, and have a specific charge ze/M which is about $1/4,000$ of e/m_0 for the electron. The brilliant experiments by Rutherford and Royds in 1909 directly demonstrated that the α ray is an ionized helium atom projected at high speed from the disintegrating atom. By collecting the total charge carried by a counted number of α particles, Rutherford and Geiger showed that the initial charge on the α ray is substantially $2e$. These experiments also provided the most accurate measurement of the electronic charge which was available prior to the oil-drop experiments by Millikan.

Until 1930 it was thought that each α-active substance emits α rays of only one energy (usually in the domain of 4 to 6 Mev), except for the very small proportion of exceptionally high-energy α rays emitted by RaC' and ThC'.

1. Fine Structure of α-Ray Spectra

We have noticed in Chap. 2, Sec. 6 that the probability of transmission of an α particle through a nuclear barrier is a very rapidly varying exponential function of the transition energy. Recall Fig. 6.2 of Chap. 2, in which we see that, for heavy elements, a decrease of only 10 per cent in the α-ray energy reduces the transition probability by a factor of more than 10^3. Therefore most α-ray transitions tend to go predominantly to the ground level of the decay product, because then the transition energy is greatest. Transitions to excited levels in the decay product usually, but not always, represent a very small fraction of the total transitions and are always confined to low-lying excited levels.

a. Short-range α Rays. Prior to 1930 the energy of an α ray was usually specified in terms of the measured range of the α ray, in centimeters of air at 15°C and 760 mm Hg. The actual kinetic energy of α rays had been measured by magnetic deflection only for a few substances (especially Po, ThC, ThC', and RaC') which served as reference standards and provided the experimentalist with an empirical range-energy relationship for α rays. Representative values are given in Table 1.1. Details will be found in Chap. 22, Sec. 3. When α-ray transitions

TABLE 1.1. PRE-1954 SUBSTANDARDS OF α-RAY MEAN RANGE, VELOCITY, AND KINETIC ENERGY, IN LABORATORY COORDINATES (H62)

Emitter	Mean range, cm of air at 15°C, 760 mm ±0.007	Initial velocity, 10^9 cm/sec ±0.0001	Kinetic energy, Mev ±0.001
Po($_{84}$Po^{210})	3.842	1.5967	5.298
RaC'($_{84}$Po^{214})	6.907	1.9215	7.680
ThC'($_{84}$Po^{212})	8.570	2.0535	8.776

to excited levels of the product nucleus were discovered in 1929, these lower-energy α-ray groups were designated *short-range* α rays.

Rosenblum (R35) first analyzed α-ray spectra with a semicircular focusing magnetic spectrograph, using a path diameter of about 25 cm, a field of about 36,000 gauss, and photographic recording. These important experiments showed that the α rays from ThC ($_{83}$Bi^{212}) are not monoenergetic but consist of several closely spaced monoenergetic groups, or "α-ray lines." Out of a total disintegration energy of some 6.2 Mev, the two most energetic groups have an energy separation of only 0.040 Mev, which is less than a 1 per cent difference in energy. Because of the characteristic close spacing found in ThC, and subsequently in a number of other α emitters, the α-ray lines are known as the *fine structure* of α-ray spectra.

Each α-ray line is itself effectively monoenergetic. Taking the maximum α-ray line width as equal to the level width Γ_α of the shortest-lived α-ray emitter (ThC', mean life $\sim 4 \times 10^{-7}$ sec), the uncertainty principle gives [Chap. 11, Eq. (4.3)]

$$\Gamma_\alpha \leq \frac{6.6 \times 10^{-16} \text{ ev-sec}}{4 \times 10^{-7} \text{ sec}} \simeq 10^{-9} \text{ ev} \qquad (1.1)$$

The α-ray energy for ThC' is $E_\alpha = 8.776$ Mev; hence the fractional width of this α-ray line would be expected to be about $\Gamma_\alpha/E_\alpha \sim 10^{-16}$. Clearly, the natural line width is far less than the limit of resolution of any foreseeable α-ray spectrometer.

For the measurement of α-ray spectra, there was constructed at the Cavendish Laboratory a large (40-cm radius) annular magnet (∼5,000 to 10,000 gauss) with electrical detection by means of a pulse counter and linear amplifier (R53). This style of focusing magnetic spectrograph became the prototype for the momentum filters subsequently developed for precision analysis of the energetics of nuclear reactions (B138, C32). With the Cavendish magnetic spectrograph, Lewis and Bowden (L24) determined the velocity of over 50 α-ray groups, relative to the main group of RaC′. Small differences, such as the 40.0-kev separation between the two principal α-ray lines in the ThC $\overset{\alpha}{\rightarrow}$ ThC″ transition, can be determined accurately by electrostatic acceleration or deceleration of either α-ray group in this apparatus. The standard reference value of $B\rho = (3.992\ 77 \pm 0.000\ 16) \times 10^5$ gauss-cm for the main α-ray group of RaC′ was provided by the painstaking magnetic deflection measurements by Briggs (B121) in 1936.

Subsequently, the fine structure of many α-ray spectra has been studied in several laboratories, using a variety of magnetic deflection techniques (R15). In recent years, ionization methods have been refined so that the kinetic energy of an α ray can be measured with reasonable accuracy (∼1 to 2 per cent) in terms of the total ionization which it produces in an argon-filled ionization chamber (R8) or in a scintillator (D16). Spectra are obtained, in terms of the distribution in size of the individual α-ray ionization pulses, by electronic multichannel pulse-height analyzers. The collected results of these measurements will be found in the standard tables of nuclear data (N4, H61). More recently Briggs (B122) has reappraised all available energy measurements on the natural α rays and has recommended "1954 values" of

$$RaC' = 7.6804 \pm 0.0009 \text{ Mev}$$
$$ThC' = 8.7801 \pm 0.004 \text{ Mev}$$
$$Po^{210} = 5.3007 \pm 0.0026 \text{ Mev}$$

These are not in statistically significant disagreement with the pre-1954 values given in Table 1.1, in view of the larger standard errors recommended by Briggs for the new ThC′ and Po²¹⁰ energies.

Figure 1.1 illustrates the general character of α-ray fine-structure spectra, in terms of the momentum and relative abundance of the α-ray lines observed in the ThC $\overset{\alpha}{\rightarrow}$ ThC″ transition. Table 1.2 summarizes the energetics of this α-ray spectrum. The disintegration energy E_0 is given by

$$E_0 = E_\alpha + E_R = E_\alpha \left(1 + \frac{M_\alpha}{M_R}\right) = E_\alpha \left(\frac{M_\alpha}{M_0}\right) \tag{1.2}$$

in which E_α is the measured kinetic energy of the α ray in laboratory coordinates, E_R is the kinetic energy of the recoil atom, and M_0 is the reduced mass of the α particle (M_α) and of the recoil atom (M_R).

In Fig. 1.2, the ThC $\overset{\alpha}{\rightarrow}$ ThC″ α-ray transitions are shown in an energy-level diagram of the product ThC″ ($_{81}Tl^{208}$). Each of the excited

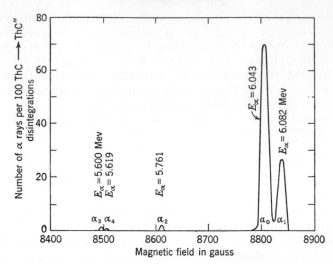

Fig. 1.1 Magnetic analysis of the α-ray spectrum for the transition ThC $\xrightarrow{\alpha}$ ThC'' ($_{83}Bi^{212} \rightarrow {}_{81}Tl^{208} + He^4$) adapted from Rutherford, Wynn-Williams, Lewis, and Bowden (R53). Abscissas give the magnetic field for approximately 40-cm radius of curvature; the corresponding kinetic energies in Mev are also shown for each component of the α-ray fine-structure spectrum. The fine-structure α-ray groups are named α_0, α_1, α_2, . . . , in order of their abundance, following Rosenblum's nomenclature (R35).

levels of ThC'' then decays toward the ground level by γ-ray emission, as was first pointed out by Gamow (G3) in 1930. The γ-ray transitions shown in Fig. 1.2 and their associated internal-conversion electron spectra have been observed directly by Ellis and others. These γ-ray

TABLE 1.2. THE α-RAY GROUPS OF ThC $\xrightarrow{\alpha}$ ThC'' (R53, L24)
Energies have been recalculated, using 1.9215×10^9 cm/sec as the initial velocity of the standard RaC' reference α ray.

Group	Branching ratio	α-Ray energy E_α, Mev	Disintegration energy E_0, Mev	Energy difference from α_1 group, Mev
α_1	0.272	6.082	6.199	0
α_0	0.698	6.043	6.159	0.040
α_2	0.0180	5.761	5.871	0.328
α_4	0.0016	5.619	5.727	0.472
α_3	0.0110	5.600	5.707	0.492

energies are in excellent agreement with the energy differences between the individual α-ray groups. Tentative assignments of the angular momentum of the ThC'' levels, based on the internal-conversion coefficients, are also shown in Fig. 1.2. The relatively small abundance of the ground-level α-ray line (α_1) is characteristic of the fine structure of α-ray transitions from odd-Z nuclides. In even-Z even-N nuclides the ground-level group is always the most abundant. These and other regularities will be discussed in Sec. 4.

b. Long-range α Rays. The shortest-lived radionuclide known in nature is the α emitter ThC' ($_{84}Po^{212}$), whose measured half-period is 0.30 μsec. Experimental work is therefore done on sources of ThC' which are in equilibrium with its radioactive parent ThC ($_{83}Bi^{212}$). As is shown in Fig. 1.3, ThC exhibits dual decay, two-thirds by β decay to

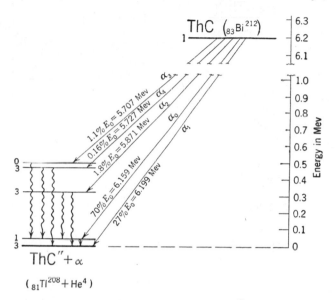

Fig. 1.2 Energy-level diagram for the transition ThC $\xrightarrow{\alpha}$ ThC''. Tentative assignments of angular momentum for each level are shown, according to the analysis by F. Oppenheimer (O2). Note the $\sim$5-Mev discontinuity in the energy scale.

ThC', and one-third by α decay to ThC''. Every source of ThC therefore emits a tremendously complicated group of α, β, and γ radiations.

The main group of α rays from ThC' $\xrightarrow{\alpha}$ ThD has an energy $E_\alpha = 8.776$ Mev, which markedly exceeds the energy of any α rays in the ThC $\xrightarrow{\alpha}$ ThC'' branch. Among the complicated radiations from ThC sources, Rutherford and Wood noted in 1916 a few particles whose range is about 11.6 cm of air, or markedly in excess of the 8.6-cm range of the well-known 8.776-Mev α rays from ThC' $\xrightarrow{\alpha}$ ThD. These long-range particles have a relative abundance of about one per 10^4 α rays of ThC'. Their presence was an annoying and complicating factor in Rutherford's scattering and disintegration experiments, and their true nature was not determined until 1921, when Rutherford showed by magnetic deflection that the long-range particles are primary α rays, emitted by the ThC complex.

It is now well established that these long-range α rays are *emitted from excited levels* of ThC′. Figure 1.3 shows the transitions which are involved. The β decay of ThC is complex and results in the formation of excited levels of ThC′ following about one-fourth the β-ray transitions. Most of these excited nuclei emit γ radiation in ordinary transformations toward the ground level of ThC′. But in this nucleus the lifetime for α decay is comparable with the lifetime for γ decay. Consequently a small fraction of the excited ThC′ nuclei will undergo α decay directly from an excited level. The relative abundance and energies of the three

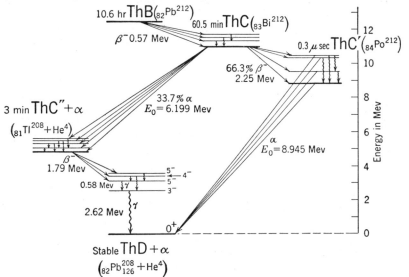

Fig. 1.3 Decay schemes for the principal transitions in the "thorium active deposit" ThB $\xrightarrow{\beta}$ ThC $\xrightarrow{\alpha,\beta}$ · · · · Notice that the short-range α rays of ThC are α transitions *to* excited levels, while the long-range α rays of ThC′ are α transitions *from* excited levels. Notice the origin of the very important and useful 2.62-Mev γ ray, which is in cascade with a preceding 0.58-Mev γ ray and a β transition (E7). When all α-, β-, and γ-ray energies are summed, the total disintegration energy is the same (11.19 Mev) in the two competing branches ThC $\xrightarrow{\beta}$ ThC′ $\xrightarrow{\alpha}$ ThD and ThC $\xrightarrow{\alpha}$ ThC″ $\xrightarrow{\beta}$ ThD. The angular momentum and parity assignments in ThD are as determined by Elliott and coworkers (E7).

known long-range α-ray groups of ThC′ are summarized in Table 1.3. An analogous situation exists in the radium decay series, where RaC′ ($_{84}Po^{214}$) emits some 12 separate energy groups of long-range α rays, whose total abundance is about 30 long-range α rays per 10^6 normal 7.680-Mev α rays. In the RaC′ case also, the physical origin of these rare and exceptionally high-energy α rays lies in an unusually short lifetime for α decay and a partly successful competition between α decay and γ decay of excited levels. In both RaC′ and ThC′ the spectra of γ rays and conversion electrons are in good agreement with the differences in α-ray disintegration energy.

Note that the energy differences are considerably larger than those found in the short-range α-ray fine structure. Both the known examples of long-range α radiation occur in even-Z even-N nuclides ($_{84}Po^{212}$ and $_{84}Po^{214}$) and both decay by α emission to "magic number" nuclei $Z = 82$. Indeed, ThC' ($_{84}Po^{212}$) decays to the "doubly magic" $_{82}Pb^{208}$, in which $Z = 82$ and $N = 126$.

TABLE 1.3. THE LONG-RANGE α-RAY SPECTRUM OF ThC' → ThD
($_{84}Po^{212} \to _{82}Pb^{208}_{126} + He^4$) ACCORDING TO RYTZ (R54)

Group	Relative abundance	α-Ray energy E_α, Mev	Disintegration energy E_0, Mev	Excitation energy in parent ThC', Mev
Normal: α_0	10^6	8.776	8.946	0
Long-range: α_2	35	9.489	9.671	0.725
Long-range: α_3	20	10.417	10.617	1.671
Long-range: α_1	170	10.536	10.739	1.793

Problems

1. From α-decay theory (Chap. 2, Sec. 6), calculate the mean life against α decay for each of the excited levels of ThC' in terms of the mean life of the ground level. The observed *mean life* of the ground level is 4×10^{-7} sec. Experimentally, the ratio of γ rays to α rays from the 1.793-Mev excited level has been estimated to be approximately 100 γ rays per α ray. Estimate the partial mean life of the 1.793-Mev level against γ decay.

2. Using modern values of the fundamental physical constants, convert to Mev Briggs's (B121) measured value of

$$B\rho = (3.992\ 77 \pm 0.000\ 16) \times 10^5 \text{ gauss-cm}$$

for the main α-ray line of RaC'.

2. *Genealogy of Nuclides Which Emit α Rays*

All the α-ray-emitting heavy nuclides can be classified into one of four decay series of radionuclides. For example, ThC is a member of the thorium series, headed by the naturally occurring nuclide Th^{232}.

a. The Thorium ($4n$) Series. The interrelationships of radioactive-series decay for the thorium series can be visualized from Fig. 2.1. Notice that every member of the thorium decay series has a mass number A which is a multiple of four, that is, $A = 4n$. The mass number changes in α decay by $\Delta A = 4$, or $\Delta n = 1$, and in β decay by $\Delta A = 0$, $\Delta n = 0$. The longest-lived member $_{90}Th^{232}$ has a half-period of

$$T_{\frac{1}{2}} = 13.9 \times 10^9 \text{ yr}$$

which is about five times longer than the age of the earth. This long

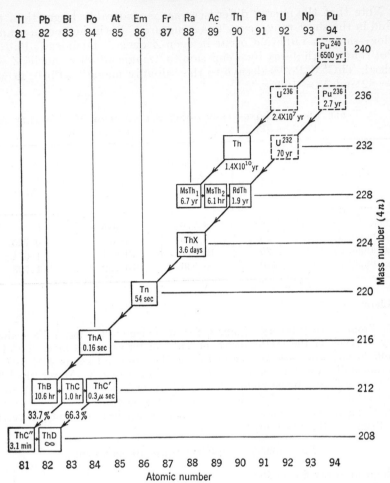

Fig. 2.1 Main line of decay for the thorium series, or 4n series, of heavy radioactive nuclides. Solid boxes denote nuclides which occur in nature. Diagonal arrows denote α decay; horizontal arrows indicate β decay. All artificially produced nuclides with A = 4n and A > 208 will decay into this most stable line of descent. A few artificially produced 4n nuclides are shown in dotted boxes. All possible 4n nuclides probably were present when the universe was very young. Short-lived nuclides, such as thoron, are found in nature today only because of a genealogical accident; they have a long-lived ancestor in Th²³².

lifetime permits the occurrence in nature of Th²³² and all its decay products, which are shown in solid boxes in Fig. 2.1.

The immediate parent of Th²³² is the α emitter U²³⁶, but its half-period is only 2.4 × 10⁷ yr, or about one-hundredth the age of the earth. Consequently U²³⁶ is no longer found in natural sources. Geophysical evidence clearly has indicated that U²³⁶ was one of the ordinary uranium isotopes when the universe was very young. For example, pure uranium minerals, such as the Joachimstal pitchblende, contain traces of thorium which are consistent with the hypothesis that they are the decay product of a U^{236} isotope whose half-period was of the order of 5×10^7 yr (M44a, R19).   Samples of U^{236} are now produced for detailed study by several nuclear reactions, notably $U^{235}(n,\gamma)U^{236}$.

A number of other heavy nuclides having $A = 4n$ have been produced in a variety of nuclear reactions (H61).   A few of these, Pu^{240}, Pu^{236}, U^{236}, and U^{232}, are shown also on Fig. 2.1 but in dotted boxes to indicate their artificial origin.   As there are no stable nuclides heavier than Bi^{209}, all artificially produced heavier nuclides which happen to have a mass number $A = 4n$ can be expected also to join into the thorium series as a consequence of α decay or of β^- decay or electron-capture (EC) transitions.

Dual Names of Heavy Radionuclides.   Each of the 40 or so naturally occurring radionuclides in the Th, U, and Ac series had been identified, named, and studied long before the artificial production of heavy radionuclides.   In order to identify the new artificial nuclides, it was logical and essential to utilize the usual nuclidic notation, for example, $_{83}Bi^{213}$. Now each of the naturally radioactive heavy nuclides has two synonymous names.   Both sets of names are useful, depending on the context. In commerce and in medicine, "radium" is not an ambiguous term and connotes only Ra^{226}.   But if Ra^{228} is wanted, it is asked for commercially as "mesothorium."   Both sets of names will probably remain in use, although the dualism sometimes perturbs both new workers and veterans. In Fig. 2.1, the solid boxes contain the symbols for the established names of each of the naturally occurring members of the Th series; their corresponding nuclidic designations can be read at once from the Z and A coordinate scales.

b. The Neptunium $(4n + 1)$ **Series.**   In nature there is no

$$A = 4n + 1 \text{ series}$$

This is because its longest-lived member $_{93}Np^{237}$ has a half-period of only 2.2×10^6 yr.   The entire series has been produced artificially, and the genealogical interrelationships have been well established (H61).   This series is known as the "neptunium series," in honor of its longest-lived member, or, equally commonly, just the "$4n + 1$ series."   The main line of descent is shown in Fig. 2.2.   Other nearby nuclides which have $A = 4n + 1$ can be expected to join into this most stable line of descent. Notice that the radium isotope in the main line of descent is a β-ray emitter.   The subsequent α-ray cascade is between nuclides of odd-Z, and no "emanation," or radon isotope, lies in the main line.   Notice also that the $4n + 1$ series terminates at stable $_{83}Bi^{209}$.   This is the only series which does not terminate at an isotope of Pb.

c. The Uranium $(4n + 2)$ **Series.**   Figure 2.3 shows the genealogical relationships in the uranium, or uranium-radium, series.   This is the longest-known series.   In nature, it begins with the heaviest naturally occurring nuclide $_{92}U^{238}$ (uranium I) and passes a second time through $Z = 92$ as a consequence of an $\alpha\beta\beta$ decay sequence.   This is followed by a unique cascade of five successive α transitions. At the end of the series, the αββ sequence (which characterizes the 4n and 4n + 2 series) is repeated twice, so that the uranium series terminates on the lightest of the radiogenic isotopes of Pb.

Five of the members of the uranium series are commercially important nuclides (U, Ra, Rn, RaD, and Po).

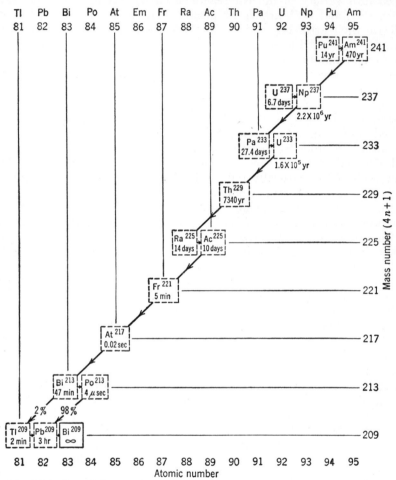

Fig. 2.2 Main line of descent for members of the neptunium (4n + 1) series. Only the stable end product, Bi²⁰⁹, is a naturally occurring nuclide.

An interesting (4n + 2) collateral series, sometimes called the *protoactinium series*, is headed by the artificially produced nuclide ₉₁Pa²³⁰. About 92 per cent of the Pa²³⁰ nuclei undergo EC transitions to Io²³⁰, but the remaining 8 per cent branch by β decay to U²³⁰. In a cascade of four successive α transitions, beginning with U²³⁰, this collateral series joins the main line of descent of the uranium series at RaC'.

An illuminating and compact illustration of the experimental methods which are used for unraveling a new radioactive decay series has been given by Studier and Hyde in their report on the protactinium series (S79).

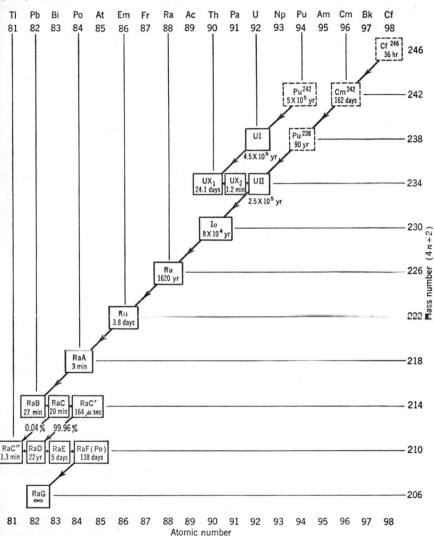

Fig. 2.3 The uranium series $(4n + 2)$, shown here, is the longest-known decay chain. A few artificially produced members are shown in dotted boxes. A collateral series, not found in nature, includes U^{230} and joins the uranium series at RaC' ($_{84}Po^{214}$).

d. The Actinium $(4n + 3)$ Series. The actinium series, Fig. 2.4, has been studied since 1902, when Giesel discovered the "actinium emanation" which we now call actinon, yet the series is still not fully understood. It was not until 1935 that the rare uranium isotope U^{235} was

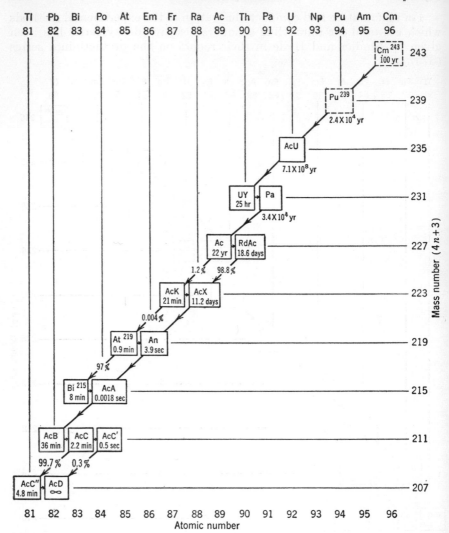

Fig. 2.4 The actinium $(4n + 3)$ series. The nuclides shown in solid boxes occur in nature. Note the weak collateral branch $Ac^{227} \xrightarrow{\alpha} AcK \xrightarrow{\alpha} At^{219} \xrightarrow{\alpha} Bi^{215} \xrightarrow{\beta} AcA$ which contains the only isotopes of francium and astatine which occur in nature. In this branch, the percentages shown refer to the fraction of each nuclide which undergoes α decay. The main line of descent is through actinium X (Ra^{223}) and actinon (Em^{219}).

directly identified mass-spectroscopically (D20) and was shown to be the long-sought parent (actinouranium) of the actinium series. Because it is the only naturally occurring nuclide which undergoes fission by slow neutrons, U^{235} has attained international fame even in lay circles.

Actinium itself (Ac^{227}) can be separated from uranium minerals by coprecipitation with the rare earth lanthanum and long served as the usual laboratory source of the actinium series. Its radiations are extremely soft, and remained undetected until 1935. The β-ray spectrum of actinium has a maximum energy of only 0.04 Mev. A very-low-abundance α-ray branch was not found until 1939 but is of considerable importance because it leads to AcK, which is the only naturally occurring isotope of *francium* ($Z = 87$). AcK transforms mainly by β^- decay into AcX (Ra^{223}) but 0.004 per cent of the AcK nuclei transform by α decay into *astatine* ($Z = 85$). Thus the actinium series contains, in a collateral branch, the only known naturally occurring isotopes of elements 85 and 87. Informative discussions of the varied types of experimental evidence which have helped to unravel the actinium series have been prepared by Rutherford (R44) and by Sargent (S5). Accurate studies of the actinium series are now greatly facilitated through the isolation of strong and pure sources of Ac^{227}, produced artificially by pile-neutron irradiation of Ra^{226}, through the reactions $Ra^{226}(n,\gamma)Ra^{227} \xrightarrow{\beta^-} Ac^{227}$ (H3).

Branching. In every series there is branching, by competition between α decay and β decay of the C body (ThC, Bi^{213}, RaC, AcC). The relative abundance of the α-ray branch is always such that the even-A series ($4n$ and $4n + 2$) exhibit the sequence $\alpha\beta\beta\alpha$ in the main branch, whereas the odd-A series ($4n + 1$ and $4n + 3$) show the decay sequence $\alpha\beta\alpha\beta$ in the main branch.

3. *The Nuclear Energy Surface, for Heavy Nuclides*

We now inquire about the physical considerations which determine the systematic sequence of α-decay and β-decay transitions among the heavy nuclides.

It can be shown from the semiempirical mass formula that *all heavy nuclides* (say, $A \geq 150$) *are energetically unstable against α decay.* However, all these nuclides have coulomb-barrier heights $B > 20$ Mev, and if the disintegration energy E_0 is small (say, $E_0 < 0.1B$) the resulting α-decay rate may be too small to be detected.

Some heavy nuclides are energetically completely stable against β decay. In such nuclides, for example, U^{238} and Th^{232}, a half-period of $\sim 10^{10}$ yr for α decay is easily measurable. However, if a nuclide with a similar half-period for α decay were energetically unstable against β decay and had a partial half-period of, say, 1 yr or 1 month for β decay, then the competing α decay would not be measurable. Such a nuclide would be reported as a pure β emitter.

a. Nuclear Energy Surface for $A > 200$. Figure 3.1 is a Z vs. N diagram, similar to Fig. 3.1 of Chap. 8, showing all the known very heavy nuclides, both natural and artificial. Recall that isobars occur on the diagonal lines of constant $A = Z + N$ and that the diagram may be visualized as three-dimensional, with a mass coordinate emerging normally from the plane of the paper. This three-dimensional diagram represents the nuclear energy surface, and cross sections at constant values of A show the contour of the mass-energy valley. Near or at the bottom of the mass-energy valley for any odd-A there is one value of

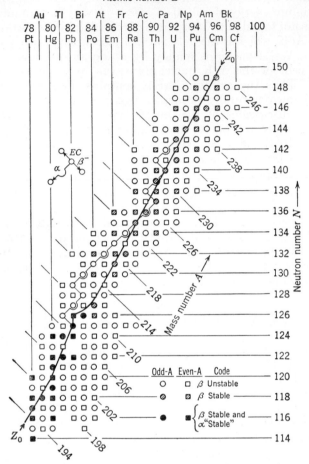

Fig. 3.1 The known stable and radioactive nuclides which have $A > 200$. When a mass or energy scale, such as that of Fig. 3.2, is added normal to the ZN plane, we have the nuclear energy surface. The line of β stability is marked Z_0. Lines connecting $_{92}U^{235}_{143}$ with its decay products show the main line of descent of the actinium $(4n + 3)$ series. Natural or artificial occurrence of a nuclide is not distinguished on this diagram, because natural occurrence is merely a genealogical accident. Only three radionuclides have α-decay half-periods comparable with the age of the universe (Th^{232}, U^{238}, and U^{235}) and are also β-stable. These and their decay products are the naturally occurring heavy radionuclides.

Z which corresponds to a β-stable nuclide, but the actual bottom of the valley is usually at some nearby noninteger value Z_0. For even-A, the influence of pairing energy δ causes the mass-energy valley to be double-valued, with even-Z nuclides occupying the lower of two mass parabolas (Fig. 3.2 of Chap. 11), and with the possibility of two or even three β-stable isobars, all with even-Z, and in the vicinity of Z_0.

In Fig. 3.1 the empirical locus of Z_0, the bottom of the mass-energy valley, or the "*line of β stability*," is shown as given by Kohman (K33, S80). Note especially that, in this region, the slope of the line of β stability is about $\Delta N / \Delta Z_0 \simeq 1.8$. Thus the addition of two protons requires the addition of nearly four neutrons if the same degree of β stability is to be maintained.

The closed-shell effect of 126 neutrons, in depressing the mass of a nuclide in comparison with its isobars, is evident in Fig. 3.1, where the Z_0 line turns abruptly at $N = 126$ and passes very close to the doubly magic $_{82}Pb_{126}^{208}$.

Nuclides which are energetically stable against β decay are shown by shaded and solid symbols in Fig. 3.1. These are the *pure α emitters*. The occurrence of pure α emitters is identical with the occurrence of stable isobars at smaller values of A. Note that for odd-A (circles) there is but one β-stable nuclide for each A, and that for even-A (squares) there are usually two β-stable nuclides for each A. All other nuclides transform by competition between α decay and $β^-$ decay if $Z < Z_0$, and by competition between α decay and EC transitions if $Z > Z_0$. Above $A \sim 200$, the relative probability of $β^+$ decay is very much smaller than electron capture, and although positron β decay is energetically possible in many of the neutron-deficient nuclides ($Z > Z_0$), $β^+$ decay has not been observed for $A \geq 200$.

Figure 3.1 also shows the sequence of the main line of decay in the actinium ($4n + 3$) series. Note how α decay ($\Delta Z = \Delta N = -2$) invariably moves the nuclide over toward the left side of the mass-energy valley and occasionally causes a crossing of the bottom of the valley, from right toward left, for example, at $_{90}RdAc_{137}^{227} \xrightarrow{\alpha} {}_{88}AcX_{135}^{223}$. The general result of α decay is then to increase β instability, because it causes a decrease in Z which is greater than the corresponding decrease in Z_0. Eventually $β^-$ decay achieves a high enough probability to return the decay sequence toward Z_0. The reader may gain a closer feeling for this important crisscrossing of the mass-energy valley by drawing the $4n$, $4n + 1$, and $4n + 2$ series onto Fig. 3.1.

b. Mass-energy Parabolas for α Decay and β Decay. The energetics and competition between α decay and $β^-$ decay can be visualized as in Fig. 3.2. Here the cross sections of Fig. 3.1 at $A = 219, 223, 227$, and 231 are presented on a single scale as the corresponding mass-energy parabolas, similar to Fig. 3.1 of Chap. 11. The vertical energy scale corresponds to the measured disintegration energies between the nuclides shown. This energy scale is also linear in total atomic mass, in the vicinity of total mass number 231, if the mass of He⁴ is added to the nuclides on the $A = 227$ parabola, while 2He⁴ is added to the $A = 223$ parabola, and 3He⁴ to the $A = 219$ isobars.

Recall that every nuclide on Fig. 3.2 is energetically unstable against α decay. In every case, the ratio of α/β branching depends on the energies available and on angular-momentum and parity differences. The main line of descent in the actinium series is plotted through the successive parabolas of Fig. 3.2. Three of the nuclides shown are β-stable (solid circles) and therefore are pure α emitters. The position of actinium

($_{89}$Ac^{227}) should be noted, and its weak but definite $\alpha\alpha$ branch through
AcK ($_{87}$Fr^{223}) and $_{85}$At^{219} may be followed along the dotted lines on Fig.
3.2. Notice that actinon ($_{86}$Em^{219}) is β-unstable by some 0.26 Mev, but
this energetically possible β transition does not compete detectably with

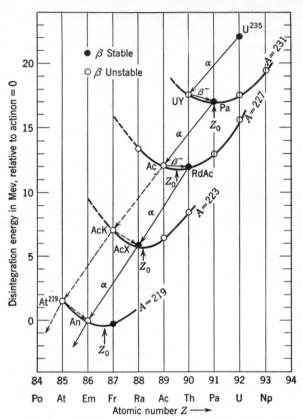

Fig. 3.2 Mass-energy parabolas which are cross sections of the nuclear energy surface of Fig. 3.1 taken at the successive $(4n + 3)$ mass numbers 231, 227, 223, and 219.
The main line of decay of the actinium series is shown by the solid arrows, while the
dotted arrows trace the weak collateral branch, which contains the only naturally
occurring isotopes of francium and astatine. Every nuclide shown is α-unstable.
Those marked by solid circles are pure α emitters because they are β-stable. All
others may exhibit competitive branching between α decay and β decay. Note that
the shift in Z_0 between successive parabolas is about 1.5, whereas $\Delta Z = 2$ for α decay.
This causes β decay to be interspersed occasionally in the $\alpha\alpha$ cascades, e.g., at $_{89}$Ac^{227}.

the observed α decay ($E_0 = 6.95$ Mev, $T_{\frac{1}{2}} = 3.92$ sec) of this nuclide,
which at present is regarded as a pure α emitter.

The principles depicted in Fig. 3.2 can be extended at once to the
even-A series. Then each value of A must be represented by two
parabolas, one for even-Z and one for odd-Z (as in Fig. 3.2 of Chap. 11).
The decay sequence $\alpha\beta\beta\alpha$ which characterizes the $4n$ and $4n + 2$ series

will be found to have its origin in these double parabolas. The first β decay is of an even-Z nuclide and leads to a second β decay of the odd-Z nuclide thus produced. As would be expected from the separation 2δ of the dual mass-energy parabolas, the second β decay is always more energetic and has a shorter half-period than the first β decay in the $\alpha\beta\beta\alpha$ sequence.

Problems

1. Note from Fig. 3.1 that uranium has seven isotopes which are β-stable. Explain from qualitative physical considerations why this is possible. Show especially why U^{238} emits no β rays at all, even though the most stable value of the nuclear charge Z_0 for $A = 238$ would be about 93.4.

2. Plot, approximately to scale, the dual mass-energy parabolas for $A = 232$, 228, and 224, in a diagram analogous to Fig. 3.2. Trace on this diagram the decay sequence of the higher members of the Th series

$$_{90}Th^{232} \xrightarrow{\alpha} MsTh_1 \xrightarrow{\beta} MsTh_2 \xrightarrow{\beta} RdTh \xrightarrow{\alpha}$$

and show clearly why this series involves an $\alpha\beta\beta\alpha$ decay sequence.

3. $_{92}U^{236}$ and $_{94}Pu^{236}$ are both β-stable, while Np^{236} undergoes dual decay according to

$$_{93}Np^{236} \quad \begin{array}{c} \nearrow EC(67 \text{ per cent})_{92}U^{236} \\ \\ \searrow \beta^-(33 \text{ per cent})_{94}Pu^{236} \end{array}$$

Show these on a mass-energy parabola diagram. Show clearly why *both* U^{236} and Pu^{236} are β-stable. What prevents $_{92}U^{236} \xrightarrow{\beta^-} Np \xrightarrow{\beta^-} {}_{94}Pu^{236}$?

4. Look up the properties of the "protactinium series," headed by $_{91}Pa^{230}$, and plot their radioactive decay series on a Z vs. A diagram (like Fig. 2.3) and on a Z vs. N diagram (like Fig. 3.1).

5. Note the position of actinium (Ac^{227}) in Fig. 3.2, and discuss qualitatively the physical reasons for its small β decay energy, its long half-period, and its small α/β branching ratio (1.2 per cent).

4. *Systematics of α Decay Energies*

Empirical regularities in the variation of total α-disintegration energy, $E_0 = E_\alpha + E_{recoil}$, with mass number, atomic number, and half-period have furnished many guides for the development of theories of nuclear structure (P15). We give here only a few samples, which illustrate some of these systematic correlations, and which have rather immediate interpretations in terms of nuclear structure and nuclear transitions.

a. Energy vs. Mass Number. In Fig. 4.1 some of the available measurements (H61) on α decay energies E_0 are plotted as a function of mass number A. For ease of visualization, points of equal Z have been connected by straight lines. The resulting curves exhibit a systematic decrease of E_0 with increasing A among each set of isotopes.

Shell Effects. An abrupt alteration of this behavior is evident in Fig. 4.1 in the region of $A \sim 210$ and is clearly due to the closing of a neutron shell at $N = 126$. The shell effect is sufficiently strong to reduce the energy available for α decay of $_{83}\text{Bi}^{209}_{126}$ to an estimated $E_0 \simeq 3.2$ Mev (H61), which is too small to produce detectable α emission. Hence Bi^{209} is a "stable" nuclide ($T_{\frac{1}{2}} \gg 10^{17}$ yr).

A number of α-emitting radionuclides have been produced among the rare-earth elements, in the vicinity of $N = 82$. Although the data are

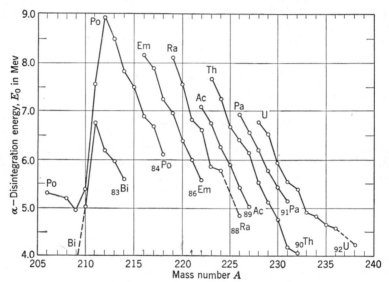

Fig. 4.1 Systematics of the α decay energy E_0 (for ground-to-ground transitions) as a function of mass number A and nuclear charge Z. Points of equal Z have been joined to give curves for the isotopes of several heavy elements. In order to simplify the figure, the available experimental data have been plotted for only a few values of Z, mostly even-Z. Representative odd-Z data are given to illustrate the generalization that the curves for odd-Z do not differ in character from those for even-Z. [*The data are from the tables by Hollander, Perlman, and Seaborg* (H61); *the general character of the plot follows those of Perlman, Ghiorso, and Seaborg* (P15).]

much less extensive, analogous effects due to the closing of the $N = 82$ shell have been found (R8).

Semiempirical Mass Formula. Figure 4.1 shows that, when shell effects are excluded, each series of isotopes exhibits an approximately linear decrease of E_0 with increasing A. In understanding the physical origins of this variation we can obtain sound qualitative guidance from the semiempirical mass formula. The general features are easily accessible from Eq. (3.15) of Chap. 11. In that notation, the total energy of α decay becomes

$$E_0 = M(Z,A) - M(Z - 2, A - 4) - M(\text{He}^4) \qquad (4.1)$$

Because the total number of neutrons and the total number of protons do not change in α decay, Eq. (4.1) can be rewritten directly in terms of the binding energies as

$$E_0 = B(\text{He}^4) + B(Z - 2, A - 4) - B(Z,A) \qquad (4.2)$$

where $\qquad B(Z,A) = a_v A - a_s A^{\frac{2}{3}} - a_c \dfrac{Z^2}{A^{\frac{1}{3}}} - \dfrac{a_a (A - 2Z)^2}{A} \pm \delta \qquad (4.3)$

In α decay, $(A - 2Z)$ is constant, and the slight variation of δ between parent and product nuclei is negligible. The binding energy $B(\text{He}^4)$ of the α particle is 28.3 Mev, and the finite difference $B(Z - 2, A - 4) - B(Z,A)$ in Eq. (4.2) can be well approximated by the corresponding derivatives, with $dZ = -2, dA = -4$. Then Eq. (4.2) can be expressed as

$$E_0 \simeq 28.3 \text{ Mev} - 2\frac{\partial B}{\partial Z} - 4\frac{\partial B}{\partial A} \qquad (4.4)$$

$$E_0 = 28.3 - 4a_v + \frac{8}{3} a_s \frac{1}{A^{\frac{1}{3}}} + 4a_c \frac{Z}{A^{\frac{1}{3}}}\left(1 - \frac{Z}{3A}\right) - 4a_a\left(1 - \frac{2Z}{A}\right)^2 \qquad (4.5)$$

in which Z and A represent mean values between the parent and product nuclei, and the a's are the usual coefficients of the semiempirical mass formula (Table 3.3 of Chap. 11).

Substitution of typical numerical values into Eq. (4.5) indicates that E_0 is positive for all nuclides which are heavier than $A \sim 150$, the exact value depending slightly on the choice of constants. This is the basis for the general statement that all heavy nuclei are energetically unstable against α decay.

In Fig. 4.1, the slope of the isotope lines is the partial derivative of E_0 with respect to A. From Eq. (4.5) this slope is given by

$$\frac{\partial E_0}{\partial A} = -\frac{8}{9} a_s \frac{1}{A^{\frac{4}{3}}} - \frac{4}{3} a_c \frac{Z}{A^{\frac{4}{3}}}\left(1 - \frac{4Z}{3A}\right) - 16a_a \frac{Z}{A^2}\left(1 - \frac{2Z}{A}\right) \qquad (4.6)$$

Qualitatively, Eq. (4.6) clearly predicts a negative slope because every term is negative. Physically, these three terms represent the differential changes in surface energy, coulomb energy, and asymmetry energy, all of which operate in the *same* direction. In Fig. 4.1, the average slope of the line for the thorium isotopes is about 0.4 Mev/amu. Equation (4.6) gives numerical results which are smaller than this by a factor of 2 or 3, because the coefficients of Table 3.3, Chap. 11, are not suitable for such large values of A. When more accurate numerical values are wanted (K34), the parabolic formulation of the semiempirical mass formula [Eq. (3.28) of Chap. 11] gives good results when used with local values of Z_0 and γ.

By comparing points of equal mass number, we also find from Fig. 4.1 an approximately linear increase of E_0 with increasing Z among isobars. The origin of this variation can also be developed from the semiempirical mass formula, or it can be visualized directly by inspection of the mass parabolas in Fig. 3.2.

b. Energy vs. Half-period. Rutherford pointed out as early as 1907 that some systematic relationship seems to exist between the half-period and the range of the emitted α ray. It appeared that the velocity of the α rays was greater, the shorter the half-period of the α-ray emitter. After systematic experimental verification, this basic relationship became known as the *Geiger-Nuttall rule*.

Geiger-Nuttall Diagram. Geiger and Nuttall (G15) made the first extensive determinations of the range of the α rays from a large number of radioactive substances, and they found a simple empirical relationship between the α-ray range R and the radioactive decay constant $\lambda = 0.693/T_{\frac{1}{2}}$ of the substance. Members of the three naturally occurring radioactive series were found to fall along three straight lines, one for each family, when $\log \lambda$ is plotted against $\log R$, as shown in Fig. 4.2.

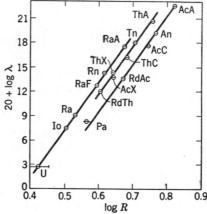

Fig. 4.2 Original form of the Geiger-Nuttall relationship between α-ray disintegration energy (as range R of the α rays) and half-period (as decay constant λ). [*From Geiger* (G12).]

Geiger also showed that the range R of an α ray is roughly proportional to the cube of its initial velocity V, and the approximate relationship

$$R = \text{const } V^3 \tag{4.7}$$

is known as *Geiger's rule*. The Geiger-Nuttall diagram of Fig. 4.2 is therefore equivalent to an empirical relationship between λ and V. Several empirical formulations of the relationship between λ and V were proposed. Swinne (S82) showed that most of the data could be well represented by

$$\log \lambda = a + bV^n \tag{4.8}$$

where a and b are constants and n is the order of 1 or 2.

A number of ultimately unsuccessful theoretical explanations of this formulation of the Geiger-Nuttall rule were proposed (R50) prior to the development of the wave mechanics. In 1928, the barrier-transmission hypothesis of Gamow and of Gurney and Condon gave the most satisfactory account of the data, and it has been altered subsequently only in details [Chap. 2, Eqs. (5.86), (5.87), and (6.2)]. The form of the barrier-penetration equations is such that correlation plots of log λ against $1/\sqrt{E_\alpha}$ give nearly straight lines, as was shown by Kurie and Knopf (K49).

For the systematic study of nuclear properties as revealed by α decay, Perlman, Ghiorso, Seaborg (P15), and their colleagues have made excellent use of "Geiger-Nuttall" diagrams in which the measured half-period $T_{\frac{1}{2}}$ and the disintegration energy E_0 are directly apparent. Figure 6.2 of Chap. 2 and Fig. 4.3 here are representative of this system of presentation. It is to be emphasized that the half-period $T_{\frac{1}{2}}$ used here is in every case the *partial half-period* for the particular mode of decay. When α-β branching or α-ray fine structure is involved in a decay scheme, the partial half-period, say, $(T_{\frac{1}{2}})_1$, for a particular mode of transformation *exceeds* the observed half-period $(T_{\frac{1}{2}})_{\text{total}}$ of the radionuclide and is given by

$$(T_{\frac{1}{2}})_1 \equiv \frac{0.693}{\lambda_1} = (T_{\frac{1}{2}})_{\text{total}} \left(\frac{1}{f}\right) \qquad (4.9)$$

where

$$f \equiv \frac{\lambda_1}{\lambda_1 + \lambda_2 + \lambda_3 + \cdots} \qquad (4.10)$$

is the fraction of all the disintegrations which traverse the branch whose partial half-period is $(T_{\frac{1}{2}})_1$, or simply $T_{\frac{1}{2}}$ when the subscript is dropped. The disintegration energy E_0 includes the correction for recoil, as given by Eq. (1.2).

Even-Z Even-N α Transitions. In α decay the even-odd character of the parent and product is necessarily the same. Because the nuclear angular momentum is $I = 0$ for all measured even-Z even-N nuclides, it can be safely assumed that the ground-to-ground α transitions between even-Z even-N nuclides involve no change in angular momentum or parity and are $0^+ \rightarrow 0^+$ s-wave emissions. The one-body theory of α decay, as discussed in Chap. 2, supplies an excellent correlation of all known cases of even-Z even-N α decay, provided that neither Z nor N is a magic number in the parent or product. The systematics of even-Z even-N α decay, as developed by Perlman and Ypsilantis (P16), is illustrated for ground-to-ground transitions in Fig. 6.2 of Chap. 2. These curves serve as base lines for the systematic comparison of $T_{\frac{1}{2}}$ with E_0 in other families of α emitters.

Transitions to the first excited level of the product, which probably has $I = 2$ and even parity, also fall upon these same curves. For example, the two most energetic α-ray groups of $Ra(Ra^{226})$, $Io(Th^{230})$, and $RdTh(Th^{228})$ all fall on the curves for their Z values. However, transitions to the *second* and higher excited levels of the product nucleus appear to have a longer partial half-period than would be expected for their decay energy (A34).

Figure 4.3 reproduces a portion of the uranium curve ($Z = 92$) from **Fig. 6.2** of Chap. 2 and also shows the position which would be occupied by the protactinium isotopes ($Z = 91$) and by the bismuth isotopes ($Z = 83$) if they were interpolated into the even-Z even-N diagram. We shall use these curves as base lines representing the relationship between E_0 and $T_{\frac{1}{2}}$ for "allowed" or "unhindered" α decay, as defined by ground-to-ground transitions in even-Z even-N radionuclides. It will be found that the experimental points representing E_0 and $T_{\frac{1}{2}}$ for other types of α transitions often lie above these curves, as was clearly shown by Perlman, Ghiorso, and Seaborg (P15). Such transitions therefore have a longer

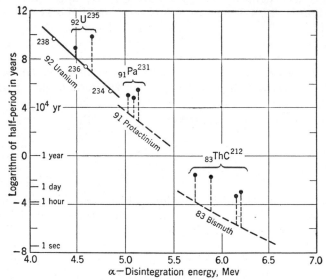

Fig. 4.3 Examples of the systematics of α decay in odd-nucleon nuclei. The curves are base lines derived from the empirical relationship between disintegration energy E_0 and partial half-period $T_{\frac{1}{2}}$ for ground-to-ground transitions in even-Z even-N nuclides (Fig. 6.2 of Chap. 2). Representative measured values for nuclides which contain one or two odd nucleons are shown by solid circles, and the length of the dotted line which joins these points to their base line is a direct measure of the hindrance factor for the transition. Note that for odd-nucleon nuclei the ground-to-ground transition is the most highly hindered.

partial half-period than expected for their decay energy and may be conveniently referred to as "forbidden," "unfavored," or "*hindered*" *transitions.*

Even-Z Odd-N α Transitions. The α decay of $_{92}U^{235}_{143}$ is typical of the behavior of even-Z odd-N nuclides. Transitions from ground to ground are found to be greatly hindered. In U^{235} only about 10 per cent of the α transitions go to the ground level of its decay product, even though this affords the largest energy. The partial half-period for the ground-to-ground transition is found to be about 1,000-fold longer than for an even-Z even-N α transition having the same energy, as is shown by the experimental point at $E_0 = 4.66$ Mev on Fig. 4.3. This transition may therefore be described as 1,000-*fold hindered.*

About 83 per cent of the α transitions of U^{235} go to an 0.18-Mev excited level in the decay product. For these transitions, the partial half-period is about 8.5×10^8 yr, as shown by the experimental point at $E_0 = 4.48$ Mev on Fig. 4.3. Comparison with the uranium curve as a base line shows that this transition, to an excited level, is only about 14-fold hindered.

The important physical fact is not that this lower-energy transition is merely more abundant on an absolute basis than the ground-to-ground transition (by a ratio of about $\frac{83}{10} \simeq 8$) but that, when the energies of disintegration are considered, the lower-energy transition is much less hindered than the ground-to-ground transition (by a ratio of about $1,000/14 \simeq 70$). Thus the transition to the ground level is about 70 times more hindered, *for its energy E_0*, than is the transition to an excited level.

Odd-Z Even-N α Transitions. Qualitatively, the odd-Z even-N nuclides have the same general behavior as the even-Z odd-N nuclides. Transitions to the ground level of the product are hindered, in comparison with similar transitions in even-Z even-N nuclides. Fine-structure studies in a few odd-Z even-N nuclides have shown that transitions to excited levels are less hindered than transitions to the ground level. This family of nuclides can be illustrated by $_{91}Pa^{231}_{140}$, whose three major α-ray groups are plotted on Fig. 4.3. Ground-to-ground transitions occur in only about 11 per cent of the disintegrations and are shown by the point at $E_0 = 5.13$ Mev in Fig. 4.3. However, an excited level at 0.04 Mev receives some 47 per cent of the transitions, and another excited level at 0.10 Mev receives about 25 per cent of the transitions. In Fig. 4.3 the length of the dotted line connecting these three transitions with the $Z = 91$ base line shows that the ground-to-ground transition is about 300-fold hindered, while transitions to the excited levels are somewhat less hindered.

Odd-Z Odd-N α Transitions. All the odd-Z odd-N nuclides are unstable against β decay. In the competing α decay, the fine structure of the α spectrum has been measured in only a few cases. The best-studied example is $ThC(_{83}Bi^{212}_{129})$ whose α spectrum, as shown in Fig. 1.1, again exhibits a low abundance for the ground-to-ground transition. In Fig. 4.3 the ground-to-ground component of the ThC α spectrum is seen to be approximately 1,000-fold hindered, while the transition to the first excited level is about 600-fold hindered.

Effects of an Odd Nucleon on the Half-period. If the hindrance of the ground-level transition in U^{235} were to be attributed to angular momentum, then a change of $\Delta I \simeq 10$ would be required (P15). That this is unreasonable is indicated by the measured angular momenta $I = \frac{5}{2}$ for $_{92}U^{235}$ and $I = \frac{3}{2}$ for $_{91}Pa^{231}$. The intervening β transition of $_{90}UY^{231} \rightarrow {_{91}Pa^{231}}$ (Fig. 2.4) is at most $\Delta I = 1$, and so the ground-to-ground α transition of U^{235} probably involves $\Delta I \leq 2$. Some other explanation of the hindrance of ground-to-ground α transitions in even-Z odd-N nuclides must be sought.

It has been suggested (P15) that the effect of the odd nucleon is *to retard the assembly of the α particle* in the parent nucleus, a process which must precede emission of the α particle, and thus *to reduce the hypothetical decay constant without barrier,* λ_0 [Chap. 2, Eq. (6.3)]. Presumably the last odd nucleon is the most loosely bound, and it must become one of the constituents of the α particle if the transition is to be ground-to-ground. On the other hand, if the transition involves less than the maximum energy, the α particle might be assembled from paired nucleons of the "core," leaving the odd nucleon in its higher orbit, and therefore leaving the product nucleus in an excited level. If we make the pictorially plausible assumption that the assembly of an α particle is more probable from paired nucleons than it is from unpaired nucleons, then the transitions to excited levels might well be less hindered than the transitions to ground.

This qualitative explanation, if valid at all, would apply equally to odd-Z even-N and to even-Z odd-N nuclides and is in accord with the measurements on these types. It might be expected that the even-A odd-Z odd-N nuclides are probably even more hindered, but as yet there are insufficient experimental data to furnish a critical test.

Effects of Nucleon Shells on the Half-period. The base-line curves of Fig. 4.3, and of Fig. 6.2 of Chap. 2, correspond to a constant value for the nuclear unit radius R_0. Nuclei in which Z or N represents a closed shell are more tightly bound and appear also to have a slightly smaller unit radius than their neighbors. The closed shell therefore produces two separate effects which are seen in α decay systematics. First, the α decay energy is reduced when the parent contains a closed shell, as shown in Fig. 4.1. Second, the shrinkage of the nuclear radius, at $Z = 82$ or $N = 126$, reduces the effective radius for α decay, thickens the nuclear barrier, and lengthens the half-period in comparison with what it would be if the shell effect only changed the disintegration energy. From the experimental evidence available so far, it appears that the effective radius for α decay may, in fact, depend somewhat upon the parent as well as upon the product nucleus.

Transitions in the vicinity of closed shells may therefore be hindered by both energy and radius effects, in addition to any odd-nucleon effects which may be present. It seems probable that the 1,000-fold hindrance in the α decay of ThC is a combination of all three effects, because this disintegration carries the nuclide across the $Z = 82$ shell boundary $(_{83}Bi^{212} \rightarrow {}_{81}Tl^{208} + He^4)$.

It was noted long ago that ThC′ $(_{84}Po^{212})$ has an actual half-period (0.3 μsec) which is of the order of thirty times longer than would be predicted by extrapolation of any type of Geiger-Nuttall diagram. In this even-Z even-N nuclide, the hindrance to α decay can be explained as a shrinkage of the nuclear unit radius R_0 of the decay-product nucleus (the doubly magic $_{82}Pb^{208}_{126}$) by about 3.6 per cent (P16).

It is of special interest to note that there are as yet no known α-emitting isotopes of lead ($Z = 82$), although α-emitting isotopes of mercury ($Z = 80$) and gold ($Z = 79$) have been produced successfully.

Problems

1. Ra^{226} decays by the emission of three successive α particles

$$_{88}Ra^{226} \xrightarrow{\alpha} _{86}Rn^{222} \xrightarrow{\alpha} _{84}RaA^{218} \xrightarrow{\alpha} _{82}RaB^{214}$$

The disintegration energies E_0 are, respectively, 4.863 Mev, 5.587 Mev, and 6.110 Mev. Energetically, we notice that Ra^{226} could also decay directly to $_{82}RaB^{214}$ by the emission of $_6C^{12}$

$$_{88}Ra^{226} \rightarrow _{82}RaB^{214} + _6C^{12}$$

with the release of an even greater total kinetic energy because the mass of C^{12} is less than the mass of three α particles. Make whatever simplifying assumptions seem reasonable, and estimate the half-period of Ra^{226} for C^{12} emission. Which physical parameters are of predominant importance in suppressing the emission of C^{12}, in favor of α-ray emission from Ra^{226}?

2. Obtain appropriate differentials of the semiempirical mass formulation for the α decay energy E_0 and show that an approximately linear *increase* of E_0 with Z is expected among isobars. Correlate this result with the data of Fig. 4.1.

3. (a) Estimate the value of the mass number A above which α emission is energetically possible, by using the approximate relationship $A - 2Z \simeq 0.006A^{\frac{3}{2}}$ in Eq. (4.5).

(b) What is the predicted α decay energy for ordinary gold?

4. $_{62}Sm^{146}$ is not found in nature and has not been observed in laboratory reactions. It has been said that if artificially produced, "Sm^{146} would almost certainly be β-stable and have an α half life shorter than the age of the earth." What quantitative steps would you want to take before you would personally support the statement?

β-Ray Spectra

Among nuclear spectra, that of the β rays has the unique property of being *continuous*. In each β-ray spectrum, there are electrons of all energies up to a definite maximum value. This maximum value is characteristic of the particular radionuclide.

The first 30 years of β-ray spectroscopy were consumed in establishing the general characteristics of the β-ray continuum, as seen in the naturally occurring negatron β-ray emitters, principally RaE.

A successful theory of the shape of β-ray spectra and the lifetime of β-ray emitters was provided by Fermi in 1934, and in the same year a large number of new negatron and positron β-ray emitters became available through the discovery of artificial radioactivity. Progress has been more rapid since then, and by the early 1950s many of the fundamental problems concerning β-ray spectra had been solved. We shall review here the established characteristics of β-ray spectra, in terms of the original discovery experiment when feasible. Further details, including the many experimental and theoretical pitfalls which have repeatedly brought about temporary setbacks, will be found in an abundance of excellent reviews on β decay and β-ray spectroscopy (K39, S43, C8, P32, S37a).

1. Experimental Characteristics of the β-Ray Continuum

a. Exponential Absorption of the β-Ray Continuum. The absorption curve for β rays displays a characteristic exponential shape. As the absorber thickness is increased, the fractional transmission decreases nearly exponentially but finally drops to zero when the absorber thickness equals the maximum range of the β rays (F12). When these absorption characteristics were first discovered (S13, H4), about 1907, it was known that the absorption curves for γ rays and X rays are exponential. However, the only previously known corpuscular radiation, the α ray, exhibits a definite range and not an exponential absorption curve. Magnetic deflection experiments by W. Wilson, J. A. Gray, and especially by J. Chadwick in 1914 (C10) first showed that the primary spectrum of β rays is continuous and provided a qualitative explanation for the originally puzzling experiments on the absorption and scattering of β rays (R44).

b. Line Spectra of Conversion Electrons. Many β-ray substances emit γ rays also. Therefore their continuous β-ray spectra are accompanied by line spectra of conversion electrons. The relationship between the conversion electrons and γ rays was not recognized until 1922. Prior to that time, the conversion electrons erroneously were thought to be disintegration electrons and possibly to represent the primary spectrum. The line spectrum of conversion electrons was originally called the "line spectrum of β rays," or the "natural β-ray spectrum" (R50). We shall reserve the term β ray for the continuous spectrum of negatrons, or of positrons, emitted by the nucleus.

The conversion electrons are truly associated only with γ decay and can therefore occur whenever γ decay accompanies α decay, β decay, EC transitions, or isomeric transitions. Experimentally, their prominent intrusion in negatron β-ray spectra is an annoying but accidental consequence of the physical identity of atomic electrons and the negatively charged β-ray electrons.

c. Typical β-Ray Spectra. A remarkably wide variety of magnetic focusing β-ray spectrometers has been developed for the accurate measurement of the shape of β-ray spectra. Descriptions of these instruments will be found in a number of review articles (C8, P18) and in the current periodical literature. Because a magnetic filter is a momentum sorting instrument, the experimental results usually are reported as a momentum spectrum, rather than as an energy spectrum. For orientation, Figs. 1.1 to 1.6 show the β-ray spectra of representative, carefully studied nuclides, on both momentum and energy scales.

Note in Fig. 1.1 the asymmetry of the momentum $(B\rho)$ distribution of β rays from RaE. This overabundance of low-momentum β rays is characteristic of the spectral shape for many, but not all, *forbidden* transitions. When the spectrum is translated into an energy distribution, as in Fig. 1.2, the asymmetry is especially marked.

Figure 1.3 shows the momentum distribution for the much-studied *negatron* β-ray spectrum of Cu^{64}. Note the high degree of symmetry, which is characteristic of *allowed* β^- spectra. On Gamow-Teller selection rules, as discussed in Chap. 6, both the negatron and the positron β-ray transitions of Cu^{64} are allowed transitions, $p_{\frac{3}{2}} \rightarrow f_{\frac{5}{2}}$, with $\Delta I = 1$, no, (N23). In Fig. 1.4, the corresponding energy distribution is seen to be asymmetric, greatly favoring β rays of small energy. The average β-ray energy is about $0.3\ E_{max}$ (M11).

Figure 1.5 shows the *positron* β-ray momentum distribution of Cu^{64}. This spectrum is also characteristic of allowed transitions. Note especially how the low-momentum end of the positron spectrum differs from the allowed negatron spectrum, as a consequence of the interaction between the β ray and the coulomb potential of the nucleus. Positrons with very low momentum are scarce in the spectrum, and the most probable momentum is slightly greater than one-half the maximum momentum. In the corresponding positron energy distribution, Fig. 1.6, the usual asymmetry is seen. The average β-ray energy is about $0.4\ E_{max}$ (M11). In common with all β-ray energy distributions, there is a definite

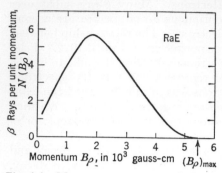

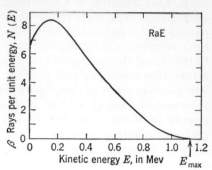

Fig. 1.1 Momentum spectrum of the β rays from RaE, a forbidden transition. [*From Neary* (N7).]

Fig. 1.2 Energy spectrum of the β rays from RaE. [*From Neary* (N7).]

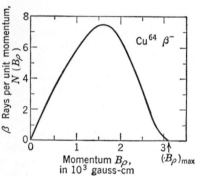

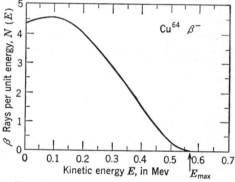

Fig. 1.3 Momentum spectrum of the negatron β rays from Cu^{64}, an allowed transition. [*From Reitz* (R14).]

Fig. 1.4 Energy spectrum of the negatron β rays from Cu^{64}. (Calculated from Fig. 1.3.)

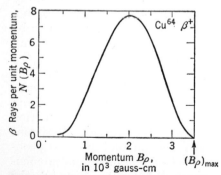

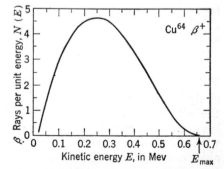

Fig. 1.5 Momentum spectrum of the positron β rays from Cu^{64}, an allowed transition. [*From Reitz* (R14).]

Fig. 1.6 Energy spectrum of the positron β rays from Cu^{64}. (Calculated from Fig. 1.5.)

upper limit, at an energy E_{max}. Near this upper limit, the number-energy distribution approaches the energy axis as a "second-order contact," i.e., the number of β rays in successive energy intervals, E to $E + dE$, decreases approximately as the square of $(E_{max} - E)$.

d. Change in Nuclear Charge Accompanying β Decay. The very early radiochemical work by Soddy, Boltwood, and others showed that β decay is accompanied by a shift in chemical properties and corresponds to a change of one unit in atomic number. This principle became part of Soddy's displacement law (Chap. 1, Sec. 5) and was easily demonstrated among the β emitters of the naturally occurring radioactive series because both parent and product are often radioactive, as in the case of $_{83}\text{RaE}^{210} \xrightarrow{\beta^-}$ $_{84}\text{Po}^{210} \xrightarrow{\alpha} _{82}\text{Pb}^{206}$. For positron β-ray emitters, such as $_{11}\text{Na}^{22} \xrightarrow{\beta^+} _{10}\text{Ne}^{22}$, the stable decay product has not been accumulated in chemically manageable quantities. Nevertheless, the atomic number of the decay product can be determined unambiguously by means of the energy separation of the conversion electrons. It is therefore certain that the disintegration β rays comprise a *primary* spectrum. In particular, the continuous negatron β-ray spectrum is not a secondary spectrum of accelerated atomic electrons, produced by some as yet undiscovered process.

e. Number of β Rays per Disintegration. Direct physical measurements of the total number of negatrons emitted by β-ray bodies which are in radioactive equilibrium with an α-ray substance whose disintegrations can be counted readily, such as $\text{RaE} \xrightarrow{\beta^-} \text{Po} \xrightarrow{\alpha} \text{Pb}$ (E13), invariably show that *one β ray is emitted by each disintegrating atom*. Conversion electrons, if present, will, of course, augment the total number of negatrons emitted. Thus ThB emits a total of about 1.4 electrons per disintegration (R.50), but 0.4 of these are atomic electrons ejected by internal conversion of the excited product nucleus.

f. Average Energy of β Rays. We have seen that α rays are emitted from nuclei as monoenergetic groups. Thus the energy difference between parent and product is the same for all nuclei in the group, and all nuclei of a given type are energetically identical. If all RaE nuclei are identical, and all their decay product nuclei (polonium) are identical, the law of conservation of energy requires that the same amount of energy be emitted in every β-ray disintegration of RaE. It was therefore proposed that all β rays are ejected from the nucleus with the same energy, corresponding to the maximum energy of continuous spectrum, but that while emerging through the cloud of atomic electrons some absorption or other degradation process intervened to produce a continuous spectrum. If this were the case, the average energy of disintegration as measured in a calorimeter would equal E_{max}, because any kinetic energy imparted to the atomic electrons must eventually appear as heat.

In order to determine whether or not the observed continuous spectrum is the primary spectrum, microcalorimeter measurements were first made on RaE in 1927. The number of disintegrations involved and the calibration constant of the calorimeter can be obtained by subsequent observations on the α rays from polonium, the decay product of RaE.

For RaE, $E_{max} = 1.17$ Mev. Microcalorimeter observations by Ellis and Wooster (E11) gave 0.35 ± 0.04 Mev for the average energy of disintegration. The experiment was improved and repeated by Meitner and Orthmann (M40) who obtained 0.34 ± 0.02 Mev and by Zlotowski (Z2) who found 0.320 ± 0.005 Mev. These measurements provide complete confirmation of the results of this fundamental experiment and show that for RaE the average energy of the disintegration β rays is only (0.28 ± 0.01) E_{max}. This value is in agreement with the mean energy deduced from the observed β-ray spectrum, seen in Fig. 1.2. These findings have been amply confirmed by microcalorimeter measurements on simple β-ray emitters (M76) such as $P^{32}(E_{max} = 1.70$ Mev) which emits 4.15 μw/mc (Z4) and thus has an average energy of 0.70 Mev, or 0.41 E_{max}, in agreement with its measured β-ray spectral distribution. It must be concluded that *the observed continuous spectrum portrays the primary distribution of β-ray energies as emitted by the disintegrating nucleus.*

g. Decay Constant in Various Portions of the β-Ray Spectrum. Many observations have been made on the radioactive decay constant of β rays in various portions of the continuous spectrum. Invariably, *the rate of decay is independent of the portion of the β-ray spectrum which is chosen.* This is equivalent to saying that the shape of the β-ray spectrum does not vary with the age of a given sample of a radionuclide. (Routine tests for contamination in β-ray sources are based on this well-established principle.) Physically, this observation means that all the nuclei in a given radionuclide are identical and that each nucleus has a partial decay constant, say, λ_E, for disintegrating with a β-ray energy between E and $E + dE$. The sum of these partial decay constants, from $E = 0$ to $E = E_{max}$, is the total probability of decay λ for each nucleus. The residual stock of untransformed nuclei then decreases as $e^{-\lambda t}$, and the activity in any energy band E to $E + dE$ decreases at the same rate.

h. Decay Energy Equals the Maximum Energy of the β-Ray Spectrum. Sargent showed in 1933 that nuclides which have large values of the upper limit of their β spectrum also have large decay constants (Fig. 3.1, Chap. 6). With this and other evidence in view, Ellis and Mott (E10) proposed that the energy difference between the parent and product nuclei equals the upper limit E_{max} of the β spectrum. This interpretation has proved to be entirely correct (Chap. 3, Sec. 4) but in 1933 it was a bold assumption, concerning which Ellis and Mott remarked:

We do not wish in this paper to dwell on what happens to the excess energy in those disintegrations in which the electron is emitted with less than the maximum energy. We may, however, point out that if the energy merely disappears, then in a β-ray decay energy is not even statistically conserved. Our hypothesis is, of course, also consistent with the suggestion of Pauli that the excess energy is carried off by particles of great penetrating power such as neutrons of electronic mass.

The first good experimental proof that E_{max} equals the disintegration energy in β^- decay was the observation by W. J. Henderson (H36) that the total energy of the branch disintegration of ThC into ThD is the same for the two branches $_{83}$ThC $\overset{\beta}{\to}$ $_{84}$ThC' $\overset{\alpha}{\to}$ $_{82}$ThD, and $_{83}$ThC $\overset{\alpha}{\to}$ $_{81}$ThC'' $\overset{\beta}{\to}$ $_{82}$ThD, provided that the two β transformations are represented by the maximum energy of their respective β-ray spectra. The decay schemes and the energetics of these branch transformations are shown in Fig. 1.3 of Chap. 16. This proof involves the difference between two β-ray spectra, and the later measurements on individual artificially radioactive nuclides are even more compelling (e.g., Chap. 3, Sec. 4, Prob. 8).

2. *The Neutrino*

The neutral particle of great penetrating power which Pauli (P8) proposed informally about 1931 is now well established as a consequence of extensive experimental and theoretical work. Fermi's theory of β decay, in 1934, developed for the first time a set of measurable consequences of the existence of a neutrino, and these have now been completely verified experimentally. Before discussing the details of Fermi's theory of β decay, we may survey briefly the principal experimental evidence concerning the neutrino.

a. Conservation Laws. In the beginning, we may regard the neutrino as a particle whose properties are selected in such a way that β decay can take place without violating any of the conservation laws. Each β disintegration is to involve the simultaneous emission of one β-ray electron and one neutrino.

Charge is already conserved by the disintegration electron in β decay; hence the neutrino has *zero charge*. The energetics of light-element reactions (L27) shows that the mass-energy balance in β decay is exact, within an experimental uncertainty of about 4 kev, when the kinetic energy of the residual atom and of the β rays of maximum energy E_{max} is considered. Therefore the neutrinos which accompany these β rays can have a rest mass which is at most 1 per cent that of an electron and is probably identically zero. We shall see later that the rest mass of the neutrino also influences the shape of the β-ray spectrum near E_{max}, and that theory and experiment are in accord with *zero rest mass* for the neutrino.

In β decay, the parent and product nuclei always have the same mass number. This requires (Chap. 4, Sec. 7) that both have the same statistics and that their nuclear angular momenta may differ only by zero or an integer multiple of $\hbar$. But the β-ray electron has Fermi-Dirac statistics and a spin of $\hbar/2$. In order to conserve statistics and angular momentum, the neutrino must also have *Fermi-Dirac statistics* and an *intrinsic spin of $\hbar/2$*.

A neutrino of zero charge and zero rest mass could be expected (B40) to ionize air only to the minute extent of $10^{-3} \mu^2$ ion pairs per centimeter of path, where μ is its magnetic dipole moment in Bohr magnetons. The neutrinos are not absorbed by small thicknesses of material, as is shown by the fact that they produce no effect in a β-ray calorimeter. Nahmias (N2) filtered the α, β, and γ rays emitted by 5 g of radium, with up to 91 cm of Pb, and showed that residual ionization by neutrinos was not detectable. This corresponds to an ionization mean free path which exceeds 10^6 g/cm², and it also places an upper limit of about 1/4,000 Bohr magneton, or one-half nuclear magneton, on the *magnetic moment*, if any, of the neutrino. Nahmias's negative result shows that the cross section for interaction of a neutrino with an electron is smaller than 10^{-31} cm² (10^{-7} barn) per electron. Cowan et al. (C47a) deduce an upper limit of 10^{-7} Bohr magneton for the magnetic moment of the neutrino, based on observations of a liquid scintillator irradiated by neutrinos from a fission reactor. Wollan (W68) showed that the cross section for interaction of a neutrino with a proton is smaller than 2×10^{-30} cm² because the intense flux of neutrinos outside the shield of a uranium reactor produces no detectable ionization in a hydrogen-filled chamber. The neutrino indeed fulfills Pauli's specification of great penetrating power.

b. Neutrino Recoil Measurements. Any β ray whose kinetic energy is E must be accompanied by a neutrino whose kinetic energy is

$$E_\nu = (E_{\max} - E)$$

From relativistic dynamics (Appendix D), any particle with zero rest mass can carry kinetic energy only if it has the *velocity of light c*. The *momentum* p_ν of the neutrino is then $p_\nu = E_\nu/c = (E_{\max} - E)/c$. For kinetic energies which are appreciably greater than $m_0c^2 = 0.51$ Mev, neutrinos and β rays will have comparable momenta. It is therefore feasible to study experimentally the momentum relationships in β decay. A number of such experiments have been conducted successfully, and the methods and results up to 1948 were admirably reviewed by Crane (C50), by Allen (A15), and by Gamow (G6).

The experimental approach involves a measurement of the momentum relationships between the β ray and the recoil atom. This can be performed in many ways, the simplest being a measurement of the momentum of the recoil atoms. In the more complete types of experiment, individual disintegrations are studied by coincidence methods and evaluations are obtained for at least two of the three measurable parameters: (1) the momentum of the β ray, (2) the momentum of its own recoil atom, and (3) the angle between the direction of emission of the β ray and the direction of the recoil atom.

In all cases, it is found that linear momentum is not conserved between the β ray and the recoil atom alone. The magnitude and direction of the "missing" momentum are just what would be expected if a neutrino of zero rest mass and energy ($E_{\max} - E$) were involved as a third particle in the disintegration. For example, Sherwin (S34) has measured the momentum of β rays from P^{32} by magnetic deflection, while simultaneously observing the velocity of the recoil atom in a predetermined direction by means of a time-of-flight measurement. In the individual disintegrations, it is found that the missing energy ($E_{\max} - E$) and the missing momentum have the ratio c (± 20 per cent), as is predicted by the conservation laws if the unobserved energy and momentum are to be ascribed to a single "package," the zero-mass neutrino.

Angular Correlation between Neutrino and Electron in β Decay.   Analogous measurements have been carried out by Allen and others (A16, R41) on the β rays and the recoil Li^6 atoms produced in the β decay of He^6 ($E_{max} = 3.5$ Mev).   Beyond merely confirming the neutrino hypothesis, these experiments begin to furnish good data on the angular correlation between the direction of emission of the neutrino and the β ray.

It can be shown theoretically that the angle ϑ between the direction of emission of the neutrino and the β ray is very sensitive to the fundamental interaction assumed between the transforming nucleon and the electron-neutrino field.   For allowed transitions, in nuclides having low atomic number and high-energy β rays, Hamilton (H13) has shown that the neutrino-electron angular correlation function $w(\vartheta)$ has the values given in Table 2.1 for the five possible invariant forms of β interaction, where $\beta \equiv V/c$ is the velocity of the β ray in terms of the velocity of light and $w(\vartheta)$ is the relative probability per unit solid angle that the neutrino will be emitted at an angle between ϑ and $\vartheta + d\vartheta$ with respect to the direction of the β-ray electron.

TABLE 2.1. NEUTRINO-β ANGULAR CORRELATION

ν-β angular correlation function	Form of β interaction	Selection rules
$w(\vartheta) = 1 + (\beta/3) \cos \vartheta$	Tensor	$\Delta I = 0, \pm 1,$ no; not $0 \to 0$
$w(\vartheta) = 1 - (\beta/3) \cos \vartheta$	Axial vector	(Gamow-Teller)
$w(\vartheta) = 1 - \beta \cos \vartheta$	Scalar	$\Delta I = 0$, no (Fermi)
$w(\vartheta) = 1 + \beta \cos \vartheta$	Polar vector	
$w(\vartheta) = 1 - \beta \cos \vartheta$	Pseudoscalar	$\Delta I = 0$, yes

The shape of the β spectrum for allowed transitions is the same for all five possible forms of interaction, but the correct form of interaction can be selected eventually on a basis of ν-β angular-correlation measurements.   These experiments are difficult and will require further work before the results become unequivocal.   For the interesting He^6 β-ray spectrum ($E_{max} = 3.5$ Mev; $T_{\frac{1}{2}} = 0.8$ sec; $\Delta I = 1$, no; G-T allowed) the ν-β angular-correlation measurements of Rustad and Ruby (R41) are in good agreement with the $1 + (\beta/3) \cos \vartheta$ distribution which characterizes the tensor interaction.   Recoil measurements on Ne^{19} suggest that the Fermi part of the β interaction may be entirely scalar (A12a, M22a).

ν-β Angular Correlation in Forbidden Transitions.   In forbidden β transitions, the orbital angular momentum of the transforming nucleon usually changes by one or more units of $\hbar$.   This angular momentum must be provided by the emitted neutrino and β ray.   Near the middle of the β-ray energy distribution the electron and neutrino have comparable linear momenta, and they tend to be emitted in the same direction (small ϑ), thus utilizing their combined linear momenta to provide the needed nuclear-angular-momentum change.   Near the upper energy limit of the β-ray spectrum the neutrino has a small momentum, while near the lower limit the electron has a small momentum. Parallelism of the neutrino and electron is therefore less important near the two ends of the β-ray energy distribution. But near the middle of the spectrum, *the neutrino and electron tend to be emitted in the same direction in forbidden β-ray transitions.* These qualitative inferences are in agreement with the somewhat complicated analytical expressions of $w(\vartheta)$ for forbidden transitions (H13).

Neutrino Momentum in Electron-capture Transitions. Electron-capture transitions provide the simplest demonstration of neutrino momentum. Following capture by the nucleus of one of its own atomic electrons, the energy of the transition is presumed to be shared between only two bodies, the emitted neutrino and the residual recoil atom. Therefore the spectra of neutrino and of recoil energies should both be monoenergetic, rather than being continuous as in the three-body, β-decay system.

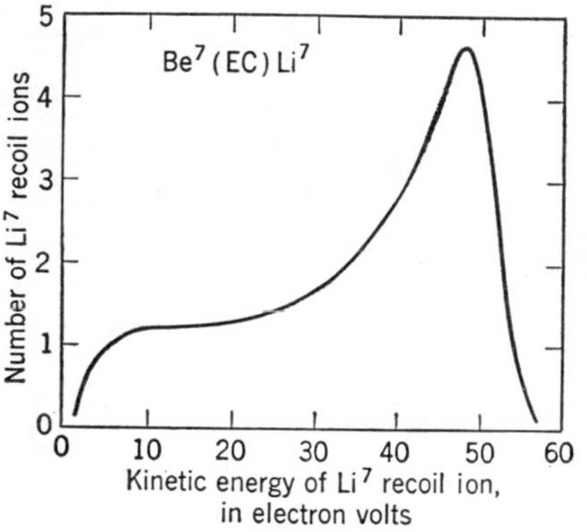

When the electron-capture transition goes to the ground level of the decay product there is no complication introduced by recoil from γ-ray emission. Then, from conservation of energy and linear momentum, a recoil atom of mass M should acquire a recoil kinetic energy E_R, from a zero-mass neutrino, given by

$$E_R = \frac{Q^2}{2Mc^2} \qquad (2.1)$$

Fig. 2.1 Spectrum of Li[7] recoil energies following electron-capture transitions in Be[7]. [*From Davis* (D10).]

where Q is the total disintegration energy shared by the neutrino and the recoil atom. In selecting radionuclides for an experimental test of Eq. (2.1), one seeks, among other properties, a large Q and a small mass in order to maximize the available recoil energy. At the same time, Q must be less than 1.02 Mev, in order to exclude positron emission in competition with electron capture.

Two radionuclides which are reasonably satisfactory are Be[7] and A[37]. The decay scheme of Be[7] is shown in Fig. 4.4 of Chap. 3. About 89 per cent of the EC transitions go to the ground level of Li[7], with $Q = 0.86$ Mev. From Eq. (2.1) these should produce monoenergetic Li[7] recoil atoms having $E_R = 57$ ev, if only one neutrino is emitted per disintegration. Figure 2.1 shows the recoil-energy spectrum as measured by Davis (D10), using a 90° electrostatic analyzer to determine the kinetic energy of singly charged Li[7] ions, which were projected by neutrino recoil from an approximate monolayer of Be[7] deposited on a hot tungsten ribbon. The high-energy peak in Fig. 2.1 has a measured maximum energy of 56 ± 1 ev. The low-energy tail arises in part from the unknown binding energy of Li ions to the tungsten surface and in part from the continuum of recoil energies which are produced in about 11 per cent of the disintegrations of Be[7], where a 0.38-Mev neutrino emission leads to an excited level in Li[7]. This level has a mean life of about 0.8×10^{-13} sec (E6) and a 0.48-Mev γ ray is emitted. Vectorial combination of the momentum from the 0.38-Mev neutrino and the 0.48-Mev γ ray gives a continuous distribution of recoil energies, up to 57 ev. The observed recoil spectrum is consistent with the assumption that one neutrino, having small or zero rest mass, is emitted in each electron-capture disintegration of Be[7].

Although its recoil ions are much heavier, A[37] has the advantage of being a gaseous source and thus of eliminating uncertainties due to surface work functions. Also, all A[37] transitions go directly to the ground

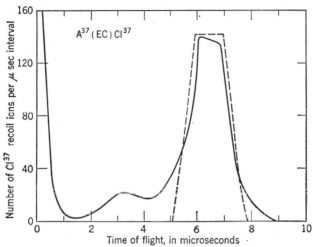

Fig. 2.2 Spectrum of Cl[37] recoil velocities, as time of flight for a 6-cm path, following electron-capture transitions in A[37]. The dashed curve is the distribution expected for 9.7-ev monoenergetic recoil ions. [*From Rodeback and Allen* (R23).]

level of its decay product Cl[37]. There is no interference from γ rays nor β^+ decay. The disintegration energy is $Q = 0.82$ Mev, so that the Cl[37] recoil energy should be 9.7 ev. Auger electrons are emitted following about 82 per cent of the EC transitions (93 per cent K capture, 7 per cent L capture), but these have energies of about 2.4 kv and do not change the momentum of the recoil atom by more than about 0.2 per cent. Figure 2.2 shows the spectrum of Cl[37] recoil energies, observed by Rodeback and Allen (R23) using a time-of-flight measurement, the 20-channel timing circuits being triggered by detection of the Auger electron. The maximum distance traveled by the recoil ions is 6.0 cm, and so the time-of-flight measurements correspond to a recoil velocity of (0.71 ± 0.06) cm/μsec, or an energy of 9.7 ± 0.8 ev. In Fig. 2.2, the counts below about 4 μsec are fictitious coincidences caused mostly by scattered Auger electrons. The over-all results are again consistent with the hypothesis that one neutrino, of zero rest mass, is emitted in each electron-capture transition.

c. Capture of Neutrinos. For all fundamental particles except the neutrino, good experimental data are available on both the "birth" and "death" of the particle, i.e., on its production and on its interactions with matter. The birth and the existence of neutrinos are clear, from the β-ray and electron-capture recoil experiments. Detection of the interactions of free neutrinos with matter has presented a more formidable experimental obstacle.

The only interaction which can be confidently expected is *inverse electron capture.* Here the neutrino would be captured by a nuclear proton or neutron, and a positive or negative electron would be emitted, thus providing for conservation of charge, mass energy, spin, and statistics. These inverse-electron-capture processes can be written

$$p + \bar{\nu} \rightarrow e^+ + n \tag{2.2}$$

and

$$n + \nu \rightarrow e^- + p \tag{2.3}$$

If a distinction exists between neutrinos, ν, and antineutrinos, $\bar{\nu}$, as in Eq. (3.3) of Chap. 8, then Eq. (2.2) represents antineutrino capture and Eq. (2.3) represents neutrino capture.

To test the $n(\nu,e^-)p$ reaction it would be necessary to use neutrons which are bound in nuclei. For an experimental test of the $p(\bar{\nu},e^+)n$ reaction, Crane (C49) chose the reaction

$$_{17}\text{Cl}^{35} + \bar{\nu} \rightarrow e^+ + {}_{16}\text{S}^{35} \tag{2.4}$$

for study because any S^{35} produced could be isolated chemically and detected by its subsequent β disintegration

$$\text{S}^{35} \rightarrow \beta^- + \bar{\nu} + \text{Cl}^{35} \tag{2.5}$$

The reactions, Eqs. (2.4) and (2.5), form a cycle in which nothing is accomplished except that the energy of the incident neutrino produces a positron-negatron pair. The threshold energy for the incident neutrino is therefore $E_{\max}$ of the β spectrum (0.167 Mev for S^{35}) plus $2m_0c^2$, or ~ 1.2 Mev. To test the reaction $\text{Cl}^{35}(\bar{\nu},e^+)\text{S}^{35}$, Crane left a 1-mc source of mesothorium, in equilibrium with its decay products, in the center of a 3-lb bag of NaCl for 90 days (about one half-period for S^{35}). The salt was then dissolved and the sulfur extracted. The absence of detectable β activity in this sulfur fixed the cross section of the $\text{Cl}^{35}(\bar{\nu},e^+)\text{S}^{35}$ as less than 10^{-30} cm^2, that is, $\sigma < 10^{-6}$ barn.

Theoretical estimates (B48, B43, R13, F41) of σ for the $(\bar{\nu},e^+)$ and (ν,e^-) reactions, with 1- to 2-Mev neutrinos, lead to values of the order of 10^{-42} to 10^{-44} cm^2. These estimates should be reasonably accurate because their basis is essentially the product of the geometrical area $\sim 10^{-24}$ cm^2 of the nucleus and an intrinsic probability of $\sim 10^{-20}$ which is based in principle on the measured half-periods of known electron-capture disintegrations. The physical significance of a nuclear cross section of only 10^{-43} cm² is fantastic. Such particles would pass through the sun with very little chance of collision. The thickness of Pb required to attenuate neutrinos by the factor $1/e \simeq 0.37$ is about 10^{20} cm, or 100 light-years of Pb!

A determined and ambitious effort to detect the $(\bar{\nu}, e^+)$ capture reaction has been in progress for some time at the Los Alamos Scientific Laboratory and the Hanford Engineering Works. This experiment seems to be succeeding. It undertakes to observe the $(\bar{\nu}, e^+)$ reaction on hydrogen, i.e.,

$$H^1 + \bar{\nu} \rightarrow e^+ + n \tag{2.6}$$

by utilizing the intense neutrino flux near the face of a Hanford reactor operating at full power. The hydrogen-containing target consists of about 10 ft³ of a liquid scintillator material. This large scintillator is viewed by 90 photomultiplier tubes, whose outputs feed an 18-channel time-delay analyzer, with 0.5-μsec channel widths. A time-delayed coincidence is initiated by the appearance and annihilation of a positron in the scintillator. The neutron which is produced at this time undergoes several elastic collisions while being reduced in energy until it is captured in an (n,γ) reaction on Cd ($E_0 = 0.176$ ev, Fig. Introduction.1, Chap. 14) which is present as a salt dissolved in the scintillator. The time-delayed coincidence is terminated by detection of a secondary electron produced by absorption of this capture γ ray in the scintillator.

The energy spectrum of neutrinos emitted in the β decay of fission fragments has been estimated by Alvarez, and from this an effective cross section of about 6×10^{-20} barn is expected for the $H^1(\bar{\nu}, e^+)n$ reaction, which has a threshold energy of 1.80 Mev. With this cross section, the available neutrino flux should give a counting rate of about 0.2 count per minute in the scintillator used in 1953. The observed counting rate (R13) was 0.41 ± 0.20 delayed coincidence count per minute. Further work is in progress to improve this measurement. In the meantime, it appears probable that an interaction between free neutrinos and matter has at last been observed.

Problems

1. $_{36}$Kr^{88} has a half-period of about 3 hr and decays to $_{37}$Rb^{88} with the emission of β rays having a maximum energy of 2.4 Mev. No important γ rays have been reported. A particular β ray from Kr^{88} is observed to have a radius of curvature of 6.10 cm in a magnetic field of 1,000 gauss.

(a) What is the energy, in Mev, of this β ray and of its associated neutrino?

(b) What is the kinetic energy of the recoil Rb^{88}, if the angle ϑ between the directions of emission of the β ray and of the neutrino is zero?

(c) What is the maximum possible kinetic energy in ev of the recoil from this β-ray disintegration? (Jacobsen observed 51.5 ± 2 ev.)

2. What is the most probable angle ϑ between the electron and neutrino directions in an allowed β-ray transition (a) if the β interaction is tensor with Gamow-Teller selection rules, and (b) if the β interaction is scalar, with Fermi selection rules? *Ans.:* (a) $\vartheta \simeq 74°$ for $\beta \rightarrow 1$; (b) $\vartheta \simeq 120°$ for $\beta \rightarrow 1$.

3. *Fermi Theory of β Decay*

After the discovery of the neutron in 1932 it became clear that the then known instances of β^- decay were essentially processes in which one neutron in the nucleus transforms into a proton. In 1934 Fermi utilized Pauli's neutrino hypothesis in the first successful quantitative theory of the shape of β^- spectra and of the lifetime of β^--ray emitters. The subsequent discovery of artificial radioactivity brought to light a number of positron emitters. Their β^+ spectra are correctly described by Fermi's original formulation for β^- decay, provided that the nuclear charge Z of the decay product is taken as negative $(-Z)$ for the case of β^+ decay, while remaining positive for β^- decay.

Negatron and positron β decay can then be represented as the transformation of one nucleon in the nucleus, according to

$$n \rightarrow p + \beta^- + \bar{\nu} \tag{3.1}$$

$$p \rightarrow n + \beta^+ + \nu \tag{3.2}$$

where β^- is the ordinary negative electron β ray and β^+ is a positron β ray or, on Dirac's electron theory, a "hole" in the otherwise filled sea of negative energy states for electrons. In a similar way, ν represents the neutrino and $\bar{\nu}$ is the Dirac antineutrino, or "hole" in the negative energy states of neutrinos. The possible distinction between neutrinos and antineutrinos is significant only for the case of double β decay (Chap. 8). For ordinary β decay, as represented by Eqs. (3.1) and (3.2), there is no physical distinction between $\bar{\nu}$ and ν, and we shall refer to either as a neutrino.

The detailed mechanism which underlies Eqs. (3.1) and (3.2) awaits experimental and theoretical clarification. Meson theories of β decay presume that these are two-step processes, involving the formation of a meson which decays into the electron and neutrino pair, but so far these theories have not been successful quantitatively. At present no connection between β decay and the specifically nuclear forces between nucleons has been established.

a. Shape of the Allowed β-Ray Spectrum. In Fermi's theory of β decay (F34, F41, K37, B68, W73) the probability $N(p)\,dp$ that a β ray with momentum between p and $p + dp$ will be emitted in unit time can be written as

$$N(p)\,dp = \frac{2\pi}{\hbar}\left[|\psi_e(0)|\,|\psi_\nu(0)|\,|P|g\right]^2 \frac{dn}{dE_0} \qquad \text{sec}^{-1} \tag{3.3}$$

Here the electron and neutrino, which are created at the moment of emission, are represented as plane waves and have expectation values $|\psi_e(0)|^2$ and $|\psi_\nu(0)|^2$ at the position of the nucleus. The behavior of the transforming nucleon is represented by the transition matrix element $P = \int \psi^*_{\text{initial}} O \psi_{\text{final}}\,d\tau$, where O represents an operator which is appropriate to one of the five possible forms of interaction: scalar, polar vector, tensor, axial vector, or pseudoscalar (K41). The squared modulus $|P|^2$ of the transition matrix element can be interpreted physically as the degree of overlap of the nucleon wave functions for the initial and final states. For allowed transitions, $|P|^2$ is then of the order of unity. In Eq. (3.3), g is a new natural constant, the so-called *Fermi constant*, whose numerical value is determined empirically and is $g \sim 10^{-49}$ cm³ erg, Eq. (3.34a). The characteristic bell shape of the β-ray momentum spectrum is determined primarily by the so-called *statistical factor dn/dE_0*. We shall examine in more detail the statistical factor and the influence of the nuclear charge on the electron function $|\psi_e(0)|^2$.

Statistical Factor. Because of its very large mass, the residual atom receives only a negligible fraction of the kinetic energy in the β disintegration, and so, to a good approximation, kinetic energy is essentially conserved between the neutrino and the β ray. Then if E is the kinetic energy of the β ray and E_0 is the total energy of transformation (the same as E_{max}), the kinetic energy of the neutrino can be written as $(E_0 - E)$ and the momentum of the neutrino as $(E_0 - E)/c$ if its rest mass is zero.

In the β disintegration, momentum is conserved in the three-body system of residual atom, neutrino, and β ray. Because of the presence of the nucleus, momentum need not be conserved between the neutrino and the β ray. Then a β ray whose momentum is p will be associated with a neutrino whose magnitude of momentum q is determined by energy conservation, not momentum conservation, thus

$$ p = \frac{1}{c} \sqrt{E(E + 2m_0 c^2)} \qquad q = \frac{1}{c}(E_0 - E) \qquad (3.4) $$

The statistical distribution of electron momenta in the β-ray spectrum is obtained by considering the volume in phase space which is accessible to an electron whose momentum is between p and $p + dp$ and to an associated neutrino whose momentum is between q and $q + dq$.

The number of electron states in the volume element $4\pi p^2\, dp$ of phase space is

$$ \frac{4\pi p^2\, dp}{h^3} \qquad (3.5) $$

and the number of neutrino states, with neutrino momentum between q and $q + dq$, is

$$ \frac{4\pi q^2\, dq}{h^3} \qquad (3.6) $$

The momenta p and q are related only through conservation of energy, that is, $q = (E_0 - E)/c$. Then the neutrino momentum interval dq is to be taken per unit range of total energy, while the β-ray energy and momentum are held constant (B68); thus $dq = dE_0/c$. Assembling these factors, we find that the number of accessible final states dn/dE_0 per unit range of total energy release is

$$\frac{dn}{dE_0} = \frac{4\pi p^2\,dp}{h^3}\frac{4\pi q^2\,dq}{h^3}\frac{1}{dE_0} = \frac{4\pi p^2\,dp}{h^3}\frac{4\pi}{h^3}\frac{(E_0 - E)^2}{c^3}$$

$$= \frac{16\pi^2}{h^6 c^3}\,p^2(E_0 - E)^2\,dp \tag{3.7}$$

which is the relative probability that the β-ray momentum will be between p and $p + dp$.

It is convenient to express β-ray momenta and energies as the dimensionless quantities η and W, where

$$\eta \equiv \frac{p}{m_0 c} = \frac{mV}{m_0 c} = \frac{B\rho(\text{gauss-cm})}{1,704} \tag{3.8}$$

$$W \equiv \frac{m}{m_0} = \frac{E + m_0 c^2}{m_0 c^2} = \frac{E(\text{Mev})}{0.51} + 1 \tag{3.9}$$

The relativistic relationship between the momentum η and the *total* energy W (including the rest energy $m_0 c^2$) then becomes (see Appendix D for details)

$$W^2 = \eta^2 + 1 \tag{3.10}$$

and the electron's velocity V, in terms of the velocity of light c, is simply

$$\beta \equiv \frac{V}{c} = \frac{\eta}{W} \tag{3.11}$$

In terms of η and W, Eq. (3.7) takes on its common form

$$\frac{dn}{dE_0} = \left(\frac{16\pi^2 m_0^5 c^4}{h^6}\right)\eta^2(W_0 - W)^2\,d\eta \tag{3.12}$$

The statistical factor $\eta^2(W_0 - W)^2\,d\eta$ gives an excellent representation of the shape of allowed β-ray spectra in low-Z nuclides, as represented by the $Z = 0$ curve in Fig. 3.1. For small η, the number of β rays $N(\eta)$ per momentum interval varies approximately as η^2. This parabolic variation is mirrored at the high-energy end of the momentum spectrum, where $N(\eta)$ varies about as $(W_0 - W)^2$, which can be shown to be approximately proportional to $(\eta_0 - \eta)^2$ near the high-energy limit.

Nuclear Coulomb Factor. The emitted β ray experiences a coulomb force while it is in the vicinity of the nucleus. Classically, a negatron β ray would be decelerated by the positively charged nucleus, so that the final spectrum should contain more very slow β^- rays than is given by the statistical factor alone. Conversely, positron β rays would be accelerated, and the final β^+ spectrum should be impoverished in very slow β^+ rays. Qualitatively, β^- and β^+ spectra do differ in just this fashion, as is evident in Figs. 1.3 and 1.5.

Quantitatively, the effect of the nuclear coulomb potential can be evaluated as a perturbation on the electron wave function ψ_e, in Eq. (3.3). The resulting changes in spectral shape are most important in the low-energy end of the β spectrum. A nonrelativistic calculation shows that the probability $N(\eta)$ of emission of a β ray with momentum between η and $\eta + d\eta$ is altered by the factor

$$F_N(Z,\eta) \simeq \frac{2\pi y}{1 - e^{-2\pi y}} \qquad \text{nonrelativistic} \qquad (3.13)$$

where $\qquad y \equiv \dfrac{\pm Z}{137\beta} = \pm Z\alpha \dfrac{W}{\eta} \qquad \begin{cases} +Z \text{ for } \beta^- \text{ decay} \\ -Z \text{ for } \beta^+ \text{ decay} \end{cases} \qquad (3.14)$

where $\alpha = e^2/\hbar c \simeq \frac{1}{137}$ is the fine-structure constant and $|Z|$ is the nuclear charge of the *decay product*.

For *negatrons* at the low-energy end of the spectrum, $\beta \ll 1$, and $F_N(Z,\eta) \to 2\pi y \propto \dfrac{1}{\eta}$. When the statistical factor $\eta^2(E_0 - E)^2 d\eta$ is multiplied by $F_N(Z,\eta)$, the resulting momentum distribution of low-energy negatrons is approximately linear with momentum η, as shown by the curve marked β^- in Fig. 3.1, and also by the Cu^{64} β^- spectrum in Fig. 1.3.

For *positrons* at the low-energy end of the spectrum, $F_N(Z,\eta) \to 2\pi|y|e^{-2\pi|y|}$. Thus there is a very severe exponential reduction in the number of very-low-energy positrons in β^+ spectra. At first sight, it may be surprising that the coulomb effect hampers β^+ emission in comparison with β^- emission. The effect is not classical. Quantum-mechanically, there is a mutual potential barrier between the positron and the positively charged nucleus. In order to be emitted, the positron must penetrate this potential barrier. We see that for low-energy positrons $F_N(Z,\eta)$ contains the typical barrier transmission factor $e^{-2\pi|Z|/137\beta}$, in close analogy with the Gamow factor for α rays. The effect on the momentum distribution is shown by the curve marked β^+ in Fig. 3.1.

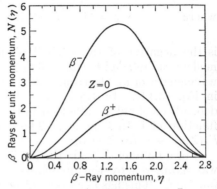

Fig. 3.1 Nuclear coulomb effects on the momentum distribution in allowed β-ray spectra. The curve marked $Z = 0$ contains only the effect of the statistical factor. The other two curves show the modifications of this spectrum ($\eta_0 = 2.8$; $E_{max} = 1.0$ Mev) produced by the nuclear coulomb factor, as evaluated (N5) for negatron or positron decay of calcium ($Z - 20$). Note the enhancement of the β^--decay probability in all portions of the spectrum. Conversely, the coulomb barrier against positron emission suppresses the entire β^+ spectrum and nearly eliminates the emission of low-momentum positrons. All curves are drawn, using Eq. (3.17), for constant $|P|^2$. Coulomb effects on the energy-distribution curves are even more dramatic, because of the velocity factor $dW = \beta\, d\eta$. Compare, for example, Figs. 1.4 and 1.6.

Most of the nuclear coulomb effect is produced in the region within the K shell of atomic electrons. When the binding energy

$$B_K \simeq \left(\frac{Z}{137}\right)^2 \left(\frac{m_0 c^2}{2}\right)$$

of a K electron in the decay product is not $\ll m_0 c^2$, a relativistic form for the coulomb factor should be used. This can be developed in terms of Dirac's electron theory, with the electron wave functions evaluated at the surface of the nucleus R, in order to avoid a singularity which occurs at the origin. To an excellent approximation, the relativistic nuclear coulomb factor (F34, K37) is

$$F(Z,\eta) = \left\{ \frac{4(1 + s/2)}{[\Gamma(3 + 2s)]^2} \left(\frac{2R}{\hbar/m_0 c} \right)^{2s} \right\} \{ \eta^{2s} e^{\pi y} |\Gamma(1 + s + iy)|^2 \} \quad (3.15)$$

where $$s = [1 - (Z/137)^2]^{\frac{1}{2}} - 1 \simeq -\frac{1}{2} \left(\frac{Z}{137} \right)^2 \quad (3.16)$$

is the negative of the K-shell binding energy, in $m_0 c^2$ units; R is the nuclear radius; and $\hbar/m_0 c = 386 \times 10^{-13}$ cm is the rationalized Compton wavelength of an electron. The coulomb parameter y remains as given in Eq. (3.14). In Eq. (3.15) the expression in the first curly braces depends on Z only, while that in the second curly braces is a complicated function of both Z and η. The entire expression reduces to $F(Z,\eta) \rightarrow F_N(Z,\eta) \rightarrow 1$, for $Z \rightarrow 0$.

For a number of years the application of Eq. (3.15) to many β spectra was hampered by the inadequacy of existing tables of the complex Γ function. This has been remedied by the publication in 1952 of "Tables for the Analysis of Beta Spectra," from the National Bureau of Standards (N5), where the expression in the second curly braces of Eq. (3.15), after multiplication by η^2, is called $f(Z,\eta)$ and is tabulated over a wide range of η and for $Z = 1$ to 100. A numerical comparison of these values with those given by several analytical approximations which were used in β-ray spectroscopy prior to 1952 has been given by Feister (F24). The nonrelativistic approximation [Eq. (3.13)] has less than 5 per cent error for $Z \leq 30$, and $0.6 \leq \eta \leq 5$.

Screening by Atomic Electrons. In addition to the nuclear coulomb effect $F(Z,\eta)$, the electrostatic potential of the atomic electrons affects the shape of β-ray spectra. These corrections cannot be expressed in a simple analytical form. Reitz (R14) has tabulated the corrections due to "outer screening," for β^- and β^+ rays from 1.5 kev to 400 kev, in the elements $_{16}$S, $_{29}$Cu, $_{49}$In, $_{84}$Po, and $_{92}$U. The required solutions for the relativistic motion of a Dirac electron in the field of a Thomas-Fermi atom were obtained by electronic integration on the ENIAC computer. As was expected from previous approximate calculations of the screening correction by Rose and by Longmire and Brown, the atomic electrons exert very little influence on negatron β^- spectra but may profoundly affect the low-energy end of positron β^+ spectra, especially in heavy elements.

Screening by atomic electrons *reduces* the probability of β^- emission by about 2 per cent for a 50-kev β^- ray at $Z \sim 50$, and the effect is enhanced as Z increases or as the β^--ray energy decreases. For positron emission, the effects of screening by atomic electrons are much more important, because the potential of the atomic electrons has the effect of reducing the height and thickness of the potential barrier which must be penetrated by the emitted positron. Screening therefore tends to *increase* the probability of positron emission, while reducing the probability of negatron emission. For a 50-kev positron β^+ ray, the probability of emission is increased by about 37 per cent at $Z \sim 50$ and by a factor of 2.9 at $Z \sim 92$.

In general, electron screening can be thought of as having only a small suppressive effect on the low-energy end of β^- spectra, but of enhancing considerably the emission of low-energy β^+ rays, especially below, say, 100 kev in the heavier elements.

Allowed Spectra, β^+/β^- Ratio. We can now substitute analytical expressions into Eq. (3.3) in order to obtain a general formulation of the probability $N(\eta)\, d\eta$ for the emission of a β ray whose momentum lies between η and $\eta + d\eta$, when the total disintegration energy is $W_0 = (E_{max}/m_0c^2) + 1$ and screening by the atomic electrons is neglected. This final expression for the shape of an allowed β-ray spectrum is

$$N(\eta)\, d\eta = \left(\frac{64\pi^4 m_0^5 c^4 g^2}{h^7}\right) |P|^2\, F(Z,\eta)\eta^2(W_0 - W)^2\, d\eta \qquad (3.17)$$

where the nuclear coulomb factor $F(Z,\eta)$ is given by Eq. (3.15).

Experimental tests of Eq. (3.17) have been made, using a variety of radionuclides. A nearly ideal case is Cu^{64}

$$_{29}Cu^{64} \nearrow \beta^- + {}_{30}Zn^{64} \qquad E_{max} = 0.57 \text{ Mev}$$
$$\searrow \beta^+ + {}_{28}Ni^{64} \qquad E_{max} = 0.66 \text{ Mev} \qquad (3.18)$$

which emits allowed β^- and β^+ spectra, of comparable energy, and comparable intensity ($\beta^-/\beta^+ \simeq 2.0$). Instrumental effects due to the scattering of low-energy β rays in sources of finite thickness, as well as changes of detector efficiency with β-ray energy, therefore tend to be nearly equal in the two spectra. A sensitive test of the Fermi theory is obtained by comparing the number of positron and negatron β rays in the *same* momentum interval η to $\eta + d\eta$. From Eq. (3.17), the ratio of positrons $N_+(\eta)$ to negatrons $N_-(\eta)$ should be dominated by the "barrier" term $e^{\pi y}$ in $F(Z,\eta)$, while all other energy-dependent terms nearly cancel. Then

$$\frac{N_+(\eta)}{N_-(\eta)} = \frac{F_+(Z,\eta)}{F_-(Z,\eta)} \frac{|P|_+^2}{|P|_-^2} \frac{(W_0 - W)_+^2}{(W_0 - W)_-^2}$$
$$\simeq \text{const } \frac{e^{-\pi(Z-1)/137\beta}}{e^{\pi(Z+1)/137\beta}} = \text{const } e^{-2\pi Z/137\beta} \qquad (3.19)$$

where $Z = 29$ is the atomic number of the common parent Cu.

Figure 3.2 shows the ratio of positron to negatron β rays N_+/N_-, for various values of η, as observed by Wu and Albert (W75) using a Cu^{64} source of only ~ 0.1-mg/cm^2 thickness in a solenoidal magnetic β-ray spectrometer. The slight variations between theory and experiment at energies below about 50 kev are possibly of instrumental origin.

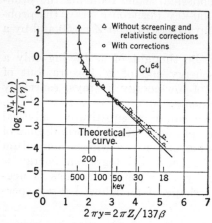

Fig. 3.2 Ratio of positrons to negatrons in the β spectra of Cu⁶⁴. The theoretical curve corresponds to Eq. (3.17), corrected for the effects of screening by atomic electrons. [*Adapted from Wu and Albert* (W75).]

This excellent agreement with the Fermi theory for the detailed shape of β-ray spectra has been confirmed in spectral measurements on even thinner sources of Cu^{64} ($\sim\mu g/cm^2$) prepared in uniform thickness by thermal evaporation onto very thin Zapon or Al source mounts by Langer, Moffat, and Price (L7) and by Owen and Cook (O7).

Kurie Plot. Prior to the development of Fermi's theory, and the subsequent improvement of experimental techniques in β-ray spectroscopy (P18, C8), all efforts to deduce an analytical expression for the shape of β-ray spectra by empirical curve fitting were unsuccessful. However, with Eq. (3.17) in hand it is possible to devise coordinates such that allowed β-ray spectra may be plotted as straight-line graphs, as was first pointed out by Nordsieck and Kurie, Richardson, and Paxton (K50). For allowed transitions, the transition matrix element

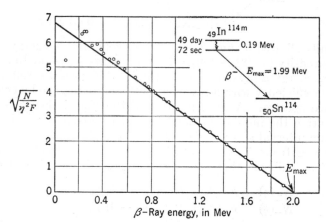

Fig. 3.3 Kurie plot of the β⁻ spectrum of In¹¹⁴. Note especially that N means $N(\eta)$, the number of β rays in a *momentum* interval $\Delta\eta$ of constant size. The horizontal coordinate is the kinetic energy E which corresponds to the mid-point of the momentum interval η to $\eta + \Delta\eta$. When spectral data give a straight line, such as this one, then $N(\eta)$ is in agreement with the Fermi momentum distribution, Eq. (3.17). The intercept of this straight line, on the energy axis, gives the disintegration energy $E_{max}(\equiv E_0)$, if the rest mass of the neutrino is zero. [*From Lawson and Cork* (L17).]

$|P|^2$ is independent of η. Then Eq. (3.17) can be put in the form

$$\left[\frac{N(\eta)}{\eta^2 F(Z,\eta)}\right]^{\frac{1}{2}} = \text{const } (W_0 - W) \tag{3.20}$$

Therefore a straight line results when the quantity $\sqrt{N/\eta^2 F}$ is plotted against a linear scale of β-ray energy, either as W or as E. Such graphs are called *Kurie plots*, or *Fermi plots*. They are especially useful for revealing deviations from the theory and for obtaining the upper energy limit, E_{max}, as the extrapolated intercept of $\sqrt{N/\eta^2 F}$ on the energy axis, at W_0 or E_0. Practically all new results on the shape of β-ray spectra are currently published as Kurie plots, rather than as actual momentum or energy spectra.

As illustrations, Fig. 3.3 and Fig. 3.4 are Kurie plots for two historically important spectra, In[114] and S[35]. From 1935 until about 1939, the so-called Konopinski-Uhlenbeck, or K-U, modification (K40) of the Fermi theory was in vogue because it seemed to fit existing spectral data better than the original Fermi distribution. One predominant consequence of the Konopinski-Uhlenbeck theory (K40, K50, K37) was the replacement in Eq. (3.17) of $(W_0 - W)^2$ by $(W_0 - W)^4$. Kurie plots on the Konopinski-Uhlenbeck theory were therefore of $(N/\eta^2 F)^{\frac{1}{4}}$ against energy. As β-ray spectrometers and radioactive source preparation were improved, the apparent Konopinski-Uhlenbeck shapes were found to be instrumental distortions of Fermi shapes, brought about primarily by

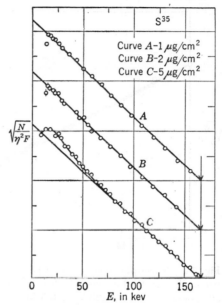

Fig. 3.4 Kurie plots of the β⁻ spectrum of S[35], showing improved agreement with the Fermi distribution as the source is made thinner and internal scattering is reduced. [*From Albert and Wu* (A11).]

internal scattering of soft β rays in the source (T33, L15). The β⁻-ray spectrum of In[114], Fig. 3.3, provided conclusive evidence in favor of the Fermi distribution as given by Eq. (3.17). This radionuclide was well suited because, by good fortune, it combines a long half-period with a high-energy allowed β⁻ spectrum. It does this by virtue of a 49-day 0.19-Mev isomeric level, In[114m], which controls the decay rate and which decays to the 72-sec ground level of In[114] from which an allowed β⁻ spectrum is emitted with $E_{\text{max}} = 1.99$ Mev. With such high-energy β rays, the effects of scattering in the source were minimized, and Lawson and Cork (L17) found a straight-line Kurie plot of $\sqrt{N/\eta^2 F}$ against energy, as shown in Fig. 3.3.

Figure 3.4 shows Kurie plots for the β spectrum of S^{35}. This nuclide has a convenient half-period of 87 days but, as would be expected for a long-lived allowed transition, it emits only a soft β-ray spectrum, with $E_{max} = 0.167$ Mev. Albert and Wu (A11) found that deviations from a linear Kurie plot could be attributed to finite source thickness in the β-ray spectrometer. Figure 3.4 shows clearly that the Kurie plot becomes straight as the experimental technique is improved through the use of thinner sources.

Mass of the Neutrino. It will be qualitatively evident from Eqs. (3.4) and (3.7) that the shape of the β-ray spectrum depends on the rest mass m_ν assumed for the neutrino. The influence of a finite neutrino

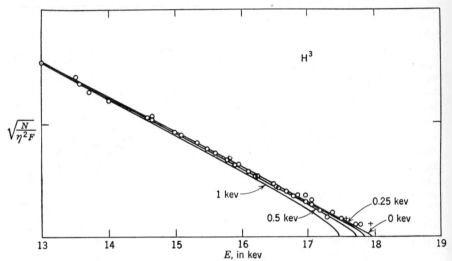

Fig. 3.5 Kurie plot near the end point ($E_{max} = 17.9 \pm 0.1$ kev) of the H^3 β^- spectrum. Theoretical curves which represent the effect of finite neutrino rest mass m_ν are drawn for $m_\nu = 0.25$ kev, 0.5 kev, and 1 kev. The data suggest that $m_\nu < m_0/2,000$. [*From Langer and Moffat* (L6).]

mass would be greatest near the upper energy limit E_0, where the Kurie plot would turn down sharply toward the energy axis, as shown in Fig. 3.5. It can be shown that this intercept should occur at an energy which is $m_\nu/2$ smaller than the extrapolated intercept of a straight-line Kurie plot, if the particle which accompanies β^- rays is a Dirac antineutrino. The corresponding energy difference is m_ν if the antineutrino and neutrino are identical ("Majorana neutrinos," Chap. 8, Sec. 3).

High-resolution measurements of the shape of the S^{35} spectrum (C38) and of the H^3 β^--ray spectrum (L6) near their end points have been made successfully with a large magnetic spectrometer. The experimental results for H^3, which are shown in Fig. 3.5, fix the rest mass of the Dirac antineutrino as less than 250 ev, or

$$m_\nu < \frac{m_0}{2,000} \qquad (3.21)$$

where m_0 is the rest mass of an electron. A confirming result has been obtained in the case of H^3, using a spherical electrostatic integral spectrograph (H15). The assumption that the rest mass of neutrinos is identically zero is well supported by these experiments.

b. Shape of Forbidden β-Ray Spectra. The nuclear transition matrix element $|P|^2$ of Eq. (3.3) is independent of β-ray energy, in the case of allowed transitions, for any of the five theoretically possible forms of interaction between the transforming nucleon and the electron-neutrino field. All allowed transitions, on either Gamow-Teller or Fermi selection rules (Chap. 6, Sec. 3), have the spectral shape given by Eq. (3.17).

Konopinski and Uhlenbeck have calculated the shape factors which would apply to forbidden transitions on each of the five forms of interaction. The results are given in the form of shape correction factors C_n by which the allowed distribution of Eq. (3.17) must be multiplied (K37, K41, S47) in order to obtain the shape of the forbidden spectrum. The corresponding shape factor C_0 for allowed transitions is the constant $(1 + s/2)$ which appears in Eq. (3.15). It is found that many first-forbidden spectra and a few second-forbidden spectra (on a basis of log ft values) can and do have the same shape as allowed spectra. Well-established examples include Au^{198}, Re^{186}, and P^{32} (L8).

The shape correction factor has a simple form for the parity-favored transitions, in which ΔI is one unit greater than the order of forbiddenness. For not too large Z, the theoretical correction factor for those Gamow-Teller first-forbidden transitions which have the selection rule $\Delta I = 2$, yes, is proportional to

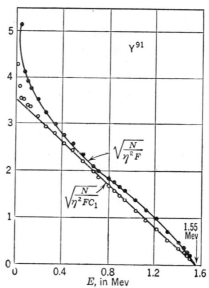

Fig. **3.6** Kurie plot of the Y^{91} first-forbidden ($\Delta I = 2$, yes) β spectrum. Solid points represent the ordinary Kurie plot of an allowed spectrum, Eq. (3.20). Open points, and a reasonably good fit, result when the first-forbidden shape correction factor C_1 of Eq. (3.22) is included. [*Adapted from Wu and Feldman* (W76, W73).]

$$C_1 \simeq p^2 + q^2 \simeq (W^2 - 1) + (W_0 - W)^2 \qquad (3.22)$$

where p and q are the momenta of the associated electron and neutrino. This shape factor provides for the emission of more high-energy β rays, and also more low-energy β rays if $W_0 > 2$ ($E_{max} > 0.51$ Mev), than are found in spectra which have the allowed shape.

Figure 3.6 shows the Kurie plot for the $β^-$ spectrum of Y^{91} for which the shell model predicts (M27) a $p_{\frac{1}{2}} \rightarrow d_{\frac{5}{2}}$ transition, thus $\Delta I = 2$, yes. The ordinary Kurie plot of $\sqrt{N/\eta^2 F}$ shows that there is an excess of low-energy β rays and also of high-energy β rays. Inclusion of the shape factor given by Eq. (3.22) produces a straight-line Kurie plot and therefore represents agreement between theory and experiment. A number of other radionuclides have been found to have the unique first-forbidden shape factor given by Eq. (3.22), including (W73, S37, L8) Cl^{38}, A^{41}, K^{42}, Br^{84}, Rb^{86}, Sr^{89}, Sr^{90}, Sr^{91}, Y^{90}, Y^{91}, Sb^{125}, and the 92 per cent low-energy branch in Cs^{137}. These are sometimes called "*α-type forbidden spectra.*"

For parity-favored second-forbidden transitions ($\Delta I = 3$, no), such as Be^{10}, the shape correction factor is

$$C_2 \simeq p^4 + \tfrac{10}{3}p^2q^2 + q^4 \tag{3.23}$$

while for parity-favored third-forbidden transitions ($\Delta I = 4$, yes), such as K^{40}, the shape correction factor becomes (K39, W74)

$$C_3 \simeq p^6 + 7p^2q^2(p^2 + q^2) + q^6 \tag{3.24}$$

Some second-forbidden ($\Delta I = 2$, no) transitions have been found to have shapes which are also relatively simple. Thus the 8 per cent high-energy branch in Cs^{137} has (L5) a shape factor which is well approximated by $C_{2T} \simeq (W_0 - W)^2 + 0.030(W^2 - 1)$.

Details of the rapid advance of knowledge concerning the shape and half-period of forbidden β spectra will be found in the excellent reviews by Wu (W73, W74) and by Konopinski and Langer (K39).

c. Half-period for β Decay. The probability of β decay per unit time, and into a momentum interval $d\eta$, is given by Eq. (3.17). The total probability of decay per unit time, which is the radioactive decay constant λ, is simply the integral over all possible values of η, that is,

$$\lambda = \frac{\ln 2}{T_{\frac{1}{2}}} = \int_0^{\eta_0} N(\eta)\, d\eta \tag{3.25}$$

where $T_{\frac{1}{2}}$ is the partial half-period for the particular mode of β decay involved.

The results of the integration in Eq. (3.25) are more generally useful if the momentum distribution is first transformed to the corresponding energy distribution. Making use of the relationships $W^2 = \eta^2 + 1$, $W\, dW = \eta\, d\eta$, and $F(Z,\eta) = F(Z,W)$, the energy distribution which is equivalent to Eq. (3.17) is

$$N(W)\, dW = \frac{|P|^2}{\tau_0} F(Z,W)(W^2 - 1)^{\frac{1}{2}}(W_0 - W)^2 W\, dW \tag{3.26}$$

where

$$\tau_0 \equiv \frac{h^7}{64\pi^4 m_0^5 c^4 g^2} \tag{3.27}$$

and $N(W)\, dW$ is the number of β particles in the energy range W to $W + dW$. The universal time constant τ_0 is a new natural constant, which has its origin in the Fermi constant, $g \sim 10^{-49}$ cm³ erg, but is easier to visualize because τ_0 is an ordinary time interval of the order of an hour. A closer experimental estimate of τ_0 will be made in Eq. (3.33). Then the partial decay constant λ and the associated partial half-period

$T_{\frac{1}{2}}$ can be written

$$\lambda = \frac{0.693}{T_{\frac{1}{2}}} = \int_1^{W_0} N(W)\, dW \equiv \frac{|P|^2}{\tau_0} f(Z, W_0) \qquad (3.28)$$

The *Fermi integral function* $f(Z, W_0)$ can be evaluated analytically only for the limiting case of $Z = 0$, when the coulomb factor $F(Z, \eta) = 1$. Then

$$f(0, W_0) = \int_1^{W_0} (W^2 - 1)^{\frac{1}{2}} (W_0 - W)^2 W\, dW$$

$$= (W_0^2 - 1)^{\frac{1}{2}} \left(\frac{W_0^4}{30} - \frac{3W_0^2}{20} - \frac{2}{15} \right)$$

$$+ \frac{W_0}{4} \ln [W_0 + (W_0^2 - 1)^{\frac{1}{2}}] \quad (3.29)$$

The logarithmic term is important at low energies only. Expansion of Eq. (3.29) gives a useful approximation for small energies, which is

$$f(0, W_0) = 0.2155(W_0 - 1)^{\frac{7}{2}} + 0.0898(W_0 - 1)^{\frac{9}{2}} + \cdots \quad (3.30)$$

For intermediate values of W_0, $f(0, W_0)$ has the following values

W_0	1	1.2	1.4	2	3	4	5	6	8	11
$[f(0, W_0)]/W_0^5$	0	0.0003	0.002	0.0098	0.0196	0.0247	0.0274	0.0292	0.0310	0.0320

For large energies, a good approximation is

$$f(0, W_0) \sim 0.030 W_0^5 \qquad (3.31)$$

This important result shows that, other factors being equal, the half-period for β decay follows the so-called "fifth-power law of β decay," that is, $T_{\frac{1}{2}} \propto (E_{max} + m_0 c^2)^{-5}$. [It should be noted in passing that one reason for abandoning the Konopinski-Uhlenbeck modification (K40) of the Fermi theory was that it predicts a variation of $f(0, W_0)$ with W_0^7, in disagreement with experiment.]

Evaluation of $f(Z, W_0)$ for finite Z is laborious but has been carried out by graphical integration and with the use of approximate forms for the coulomb factor $F(Z, \eta)$. The results have been prepared as graphs of $\log_{10} [f(Z, W_0)]$ vs. W_0, for values of Z from 0 to ± 100 in steps of $\Delta Z = 10$, by Feenberg and Trigg (F22), and as graphs of

$$\frac{f(Z, W_0)}{f(0, W_0)}$$

by Moszkowski (M61). Representative values of $f(Z, W_0)$ are plotted in Fig. 3.7.

It will be noted that, for not too large Z/η, a reasonable rough approximation for $f(Z, W_0)$ can be obtained by representing the coulomb factor, Eq. (3.13) or Eq. (3.15), as $e^{\pi \bar{y}}$, where $\bar{y}$ is an average value of

$$y = \frac{\pm Z}{137\beta}$$

for the β spectrum.   Then

$$f(Z,W_0) \simeq e^{\pi\bar{\nu}}f(0,W_0) \qquad \text{small } \frac{Z}{\eta} \qquad (3.32)$$

Universal β-Ray Time Constant.   The squared nuclear transition matrix element $|P|^2$ can be evaluated theoretically for only a few transitions (K39, K30, G17).   Among these is the $\Delta I = 1$, no, transition $({}^1S_0 \rightarrow {}^3S_1)$

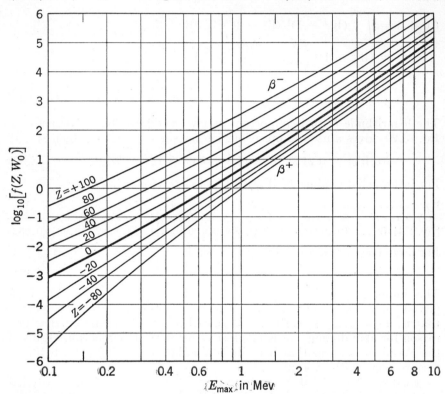

Fig. 3.7   The Fermi integral function $f(Z,W_0)$ of Eq. (3.28). Z is the atomic number of the *decay product* and is positive for negatron β^--ray emitters and negative for positron β^+-ray emitters.   The nuclear disintegration energy $W_0 = [(E_{max}/m_0c^2) + 1]$ is expressed directly as E_{max} in Mev on the abscissas.   The curve for $Z = 0$ is $f(0,W_0)$ of Eq. (3.29).   [*Adapted from Feenberg and Trigg* (F22).]

of He⁶, which is superallowed with $|P|^2 = 6$ on Gamow-Teller selection rules but would be forbidden on Fermi selection rules (Table 3.1, Chap. 6).

For He⁶, $E_{max} = 3.50$ Mev, and $T_{\frac{1}{2}} = 0.823$ sec (H61).   Then $W_0 = 7.86$, $f(3,W_0) \simeq 1,000$, and

$$\tau_0 = \frac{T_{\frac{1}{2}}}{0.693} |P|^2 f(Z,W_0) \simeq 7,000 \text{ sec} \qquad (3.33)$$

Thus τ_0 is in the domain of 7,000 sec.   From Eq. (3.27) the Fermi g

constant becomes

$$g_{GT} \simeq 1.6 \times 10^{-49} \text{ cm}^3 \text{ erg} \qquad (3.34a)$$

for β interactions which follow the Gamow-Teller selection rules (tensor or axial vector interaction).

In contrast with He^6, the β decay of O^{14} appears to follow Fermi selection rules in substantially all its transitions (G17). Within an experimental accuracy of ~ 0.3 per cent, the positron β decay of O^{14} goes entirely to the excited level at 2.31 Mev in N^{14} (Fig. 4.1 of Chap. 11) which is known from other evidence to have $I = 0^+$. Thus the transition is $0^+ \rightarrow 0^+$, that is, $\Delta I = 0$, no, which is allowed on Fermi selection rules and forbidden on Gamow-Teller rules. The β-ray spectrum is found to have an allowed shape and an end point of 1.835 ± 0.008 Mev. For this transition, the Fermi matrix element has the theoretical value $|P|^2 = 2$. Combining these values with the half-period of 72.1 ± 0.4 sec, Gerhart (G17) finds for the Fermi g constant, in a pure Fermi transition,

$$g_F - 1.374 \pm 0.016 \times 10^{-49} \text{ cm}^3 \text{ erg} \qquad (3.34b)$$

Within present experimental accuracy, it appears that $(g_{GT})/(g_F)$ is very close to unity. A number of β transitions may involve mixtures of Fermi and Gamow-Teller selection rules.

Comparative Half-period. As discussed in Chap. 6, the degree of forbiddenness of β-ray transitions can often be estimated from its so-called comparative half-period $ft \equiv [f(Z,W_0)]T_{\frac{1}{2}}$. From Eq. (3.28), the comparative half-period is

$$ft \equiv \lfloor f(Z,\overline{W}_0) \rfloor T_{\frac{1}{2}} = \frac{0.693_{i0}}{|P|^2} = \frac{\text{universal constant}}{|P|^2} \qquad (3.35)$$

For He^6, $ft \simeq 830$ sec, and for H^3, $ft \simeq 1,000$ sec. These are characteristic superallowed transitions, with $\log ft \sim 3$. Values of $\log ft$ for other transitions can be estimated readily from Eq. (3.35) and Fig. 3.7.

The comparative half-periods for forbidden transitions (Fig. 3.2 of Chap. 6) are usually evaluated using the value of $f(Z,W_0)$ which is characteristic of the shape of allowed spectra Eq. (3.28). When the shape of a forbidden spectrum has been evaluated, it is more appropriate to use a value of $f(Z,W_0)$ which actually corresponds to the spectral shape. The group of nuclides for which $\Delta I = 2$, yes, were first treated in this way by Shull and Feenberg (S37), who found that a good approximation for the Fermi function $f_1(Z,W_0)$ of these particular transitions is

$$f_1(Z,W_0) \simeq (W_0^2 - 1)[f(Z,W_0)] \qquad (3.36)$$

When the comparative half-periods of these $\Delta I = 2$, yes, transitions are computed as $\log f_1 t = \log [(W_0^2 - 1)ft]$, a narrow range of values is found, in the domain of $\log [(W_0^2 - 1)ft] \simeq 10.0 \pm 0.5$. The parity-favored transitions $\Delta I = n + 1$, where n is the order of forbiddenness, whose spectral shapes are given by Eqs. (3.22) to (3.24), have been evaluated by Davidson (D7).

Competition with Neutron Emission. Delayed Neutron Emitters. That β decay is an extremely slow nuclear process is well illustrated by the existence of several so-called *delayed neutron emitters*, such as

$$_{35}Br^{87} \ (T_{\frac{1}{2}} = 55.6 \text{ sec})$$

and $_{53}I^{137} \ (T_{\frac{1}{2}} = 22 \text{ sec})$, which occur among the products of uranium or thorium fission.

Figure 3.8 shows the principal transitions in the decay of Br^{87} and its immediate products (S69). The stable isobar of mass number $A = 87$ is $_{38}Sr^{87}_{49}$, whose directly measured nuclear angular momentum is $I = \frac{9}{2}$. From the shell model and comparative half-periods ft, as discussed in Chap. 6, the angular momentum and the state of the odd nucleon have been evaluated for each of the levels, as shown on Fig. 3.8.

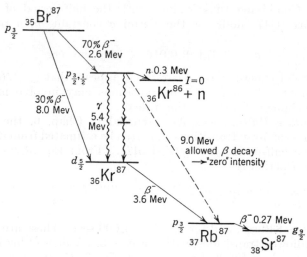

Fig. 3.8 Decay scheme of Br^{87} and its products. The 5.4-Mev excited level in Kr^{87} emits 5.4-Mev γ rays and 0.3-Mev neutrons, but the 9.0-Mev allowed β transition from this level to the ground level of Rb^{87} is too slow to be seen.

Some 70 per cent of the β transitions of Br^{87} go to the 5.4-Mev excited level in Kr^{87}. This is an allowed transition ($\log ft = 4.7$); hence the 5.4-Mev level is a $p_{\frac{3}{2}}$ or a $p_{\frac{1}{2}}$ state. It is the deexcitation of this 5.4-Mev level in Kr^{87} which interests us here.

The 5.4-Mev level in Kr^{87} lies about 0.3 Mev above the combined mass of Kr^{86} plus a neutron. Thus the neutron separation energy for Kr^{87} is $S_n \simeq 5.1$ Mev, and the 5.4-Mev level is a virtual, or unbound, level. Some two-seventieths of the excited Kr^{87} nuclei (or 2 per cent of the original Br^{87} nuclei) emit a neutron in the transition $Kr^{87} \rightarrow n + Kr^{86} + 0.3$ Mev. The mean life of the 5.4-Mev level is too short to be measured by present techniques, and $\frac{68}{70}$ of the time it decays by γ emission toward the ground level of Kr^{87}. The "delayed neutrons" are delayed entirely by the 55-sec half-period of their β-ray parent Br^{87}.

The 5.4-Mev level in Kr^{87} is $5.4 + 3.6 = 9.0$ Mev above the $p_{\frac{3}{2}}$ ground level of Rb^{87}. An allowed β-ray transition ($\Delta I = 0$ or 1, no) could therefore take place with the release of 9.0 Mev. But even such an energetic β transition is much too slow to be seen in competition with deexcitation of the level by γ-ray emission and by neutron emission.

d. Electron-capture Transitions. Whenever it is energetically allowed by the mass difference between neighboring isobars (Chap. 3), a nucleus Z may capture one of its own atomic electrons, transforming to the isobar of atomic number $Z - 1$. Usually the electron-capture (EC) transition involves an electron from the K shell, because these have the greatest probability density of being in the nucleus. The L shell also contains two penetrating electrons, the so-called L_I s electrons with $l = 0$. The ratio of L_I capture to K capture is usually of the order of 10 per cent (R33), unless there is insufficient disintegration energy for K capture, when L_I capture takes place alone. We shall outline here only the theory of allowed EC transitions. The theory of forbidden transitions has been discussed by Marshak (M13), Bouchez (B103), and others.

In EC transitions, a nuclear proton changes to a neutron, and the disintegration energy is carried away by a neutrino; thus,

$$p + e^- \rightarrow n + \nu \tag{3.37}$$

The residual nucleus may be left in either its ground level or an excited level. The companion reaction, positron capture ($n + e^+ \rightarrow p + \bar{\nu}$), is not seen because it is impossible to produce a density of positrons at the nucleus which is comparable with the density of atomic electrons.

The fundamental difference between EC and its competing β^+ emission is that in EC transitions a *bound* electron is absorbed, rather than one from the continuum of negative energy states, in which a hole corresponds to positron emission. The total energy of a bound K electron can be written as

$$m_0 c^2 - B_K \simeq m_0 c^2 (1 + s) = m_0 c^2 \sqrt{1 - \left(\frac{Z}{137}\right)^2}$$

where s is always negative and is defined as in Eq. (3.16). Then if the disintegration energy available for β^+ emission is $W_0 = (E_0/m_0 c^2) + 1$, where as usual $E_0 \equiv E_{max}$ of the β^+ spectrum, the disintegration energy available for EC is

$$W_0 + 1 + s \simeq W_0 + 1 = \frac{E_0}{m_0 c^2} + 2 \tag{3.38}$$

Neglecting the kinetic energy of the recoil atom, Eq. (3.38) gives the kinetic energy of the emitted neutrino.

In contrast with Eq. (3.7), the phase-space volume is determined entirely by the energy of the emitted neutrino, because the electron is in a definite quantum state before its capture. In place of Eq. (3.12), the statistical factor for EC is then simply

$$\frac{4\pi m_0^2 c}{h^3}(W_0 + 1 + s)^2 \tag{3.39}$$

The electron wave function ψ_e in Eq. (3.3) is to be replaced for EC transitions by the relativistic wave function of a bound K electron, and a factor of 2 introduced because either of the two K electrons can be captured. The calculation gives (K37, B68) for the probability λ_K of K capture per unit time

$$\lambda_K = \frac{|P|^2}{\tau_0}f_K \tag{3.40}$$

where the squared transition matrix element $|P|^2$ is the same as for the competing β^+ transition, τ_0 is the universal time constant of β decay [Eqs. (3.27) and (3.33)], and the function $f(Z,W_0)$ of β^+ decay is replaced for allowed K capture by

$$f_K = 2\pi\left(\frac{Z}{137}\right)^{3+2s}\left(\frac{2R}{\hbar/m_0 c}\right)^{2s}$$
$$\left[\frac{2+s}{\Gamma(3+2s)}\right](W_0 + 1 + s)^2 \tag{3.41}$$
$$f_K \simeq 2\pi\left(\frac{Z}{137}\right)^3(W_0 + 1)^2 \tag{3.42}$$

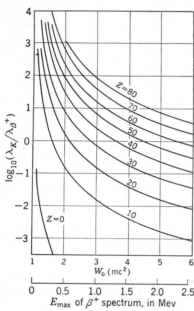

Fig. 3.9 Ratio of K-capture transition probability λ_K to positron β-ray transition probability λ_{β^+} for allowed transitions. Z is the atomic number of the *product nucleus*, as in the theory of β decay. Although positron emission is energetically excluded for $W_0 < 1$, K capture can take place in the energy domain $1 > W_0 > (-1 - s)$, where the ratio $\lambda_K/\lambda_{\beta^+} = \infty$. In terms of the masses of the initial and final atoms, $E_{max} = {}_{z+1}M - {}_zM - 2m_0c^2$ and $W_0 = [(E_{max}/m_0c^2) + 1]$. [*From Feenberg and Trigg* (F22).]

where the symbols have the same meaning as in Eq. (3.15), except that for K capture Z is the atomic number of the *parent nucleus*.

Ratio of Electron Capture to Positron β Decay. The same selection rules apply to EC transitions as to the competing β^+ transition. Then, in allowed transitions to any particular level of the residual nucleus, the ratio of the number of nuclei transforming by K capture to those transforming by β^+ emission is given by the ratio

$$\frac{\lambda_K}{\lambda_{\beta^+}} = \frac{f_K}{f(Z,W_0)} \simeq \frac{2\pi(Z/137)^3(W_0 + 1)^2}{f(Z,W_0)} \tag{3.43}$$

Measurements of the branching ratio between K capture and β^+ emission in a number of nuclei have been summarized by Bouchez (B103). Recalling that the experiments themselves are often quite difficult, the agreement with theory is good.

Figure 3.9 shows graphically how the ratio of K capture to positron β-ray emission depends on Z and the disintegration energy, for allowed transitions. Note that in heavy elements K capture is greatly favored over positron emission. For example, at $Z \sim 80$, a positron β-ray spectrum for which $E_{max} = 0.51$ Mev $(W_0 = 2)$ will operate at a 1,000 to 1 disadvantage in comparison with K capture. The ratio of L_I capture to K capture also increases with Z and is about 0.15 for $Z \sim 80$ (R33). Thus, less than 0.1 per cent of the transitions will be by β^+ emission. This explains the complete absence of observable positron emitters among the heavy elements, which we noted in Chap. 16.

Physically, electron capture is favored in high-Z nuclides for two reasons. The electron orbits are smaller, and so there is a greater probability for an electron to be within the nuclear volume in heavy nuclei, and, secondly, the potential barrier $e^{-\pi|y|}$ of Eq. (3.15) against positron emission increases in effectiveness as Z increases.

Auger Electrons. Following K capture, there is an electron vacancy in the K shell. This is filled by a transition of an L electron into the K shell and the emission of either a K_α X-ray photon (especially in heavy elements) or an Auger electron (especially in light elements). The energy of the K_α photon is $(B_K - B_L)$; that of the competing L-shell Auger electron is $(B_K - 2B_L)$. B_K and B_L are the electron binding energies in the K and L shells of the product nucleus.

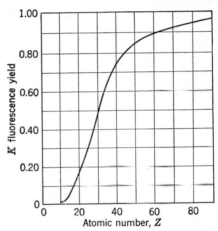

Fig. **3.10** Empirical variation of the K fluorescence yield with Z [*as compiled by Broyles, Thomas, and Haynes* (B135).]

The X-ray and Auger-electron spectra have been measured directly for a number of electron-capture nuclides (B135).

The competition between the emission of a K X ray and the emission of an Auger electron is described by the K *fluorescence yield*, which is defined as the number of K X-ray quanta emitted per vacancy in the K shell. The probability that a K X ray will be emitted is nearly unity in high-Z elements and nearly zero in low-Z elements. Figure 3.10 shows the empirical variation of this probability with Z (B135, B142).

Effect of Chemical Combination on Electron Capture. The density of L_I electrons at the position of the $_4Be^7$ nucleus will depend slightly on the chemical form of the beryllium. The possibility of producing by chemical means a change in the half-period of Be^7, which decays only by electron capture, was first demonstrated by Segrè and by Daudel. The effects are very small but definite. For comparison with the experimental results, no adequate theory of the expected changes in electron density exists. The experimental results have been summarized and extended by Kraushaar, Wilson, and Bainbridge (K46), who find that the decay constant λ of metallic Be^7 is reduced by (0.013 ± 0.005) per cent when the Be^7 is in the form of BeO, and by an additional (0.061 ± 0.005) per cent when the Be^7 is in the form of BeF_2.

Problems

1. Calculate and plot the energy distribution spectra which correspond to the β-ray momentum spectra given in Fig. 3.1.

2. (a) Calculate the shape of the β-ray spectrum expected in the disintegration of the free neutron. Present the results as a momentum spectrum and a Kurie plot.

(b) If $|P|^2 = 3$ for an $s_{\frac{1}{2}} \to s_{\frac{1}{2}}$ transition on Gamow-Teller selection rules, calculate the expected half-period of the free neutron against β decay.

3. If the β transition $H^3 \to He^3 + \beta^-$ is regarded as allowed and corresponding to an $s_{\frac{1}{2}} \to s_{\frac{1}{2}}$ transition with $|P|^2 = 3$, calculate the expected half-period of H^3 if the maximum energy of the β-ray spectrum is 0.018 Mev and $\tau_0 \simeq 7,000$ sec.

4. The following series of mirror nuclides are all positron emitters, and none emits γ rays.

Nuclide	$_6C^{11}$	$_8O^{15}$	$_{10}Ne^{19}$	$_{12}Mg^{23}$	$_{14}Si^{27}$	$_{16}S^{31}$	$_{18}A^{35}$
β^+ E_{max}, Mev ...	0.99	1.68	2.18	2.99	3.48	3.9	4.4
Half-period, sec..	1,230	118	18.2	11.9	4.9	3.2	1.88

(a) Calculate the ft values, and also the matrix elements for these transitions, using the approximation $f(Z, W_0) = e^{\pi \bar{\nu}} f(0, W_0)$.

(b) Why would you expect the matrix elements for these transitions to be so similar?

5. N^{17} decays by β^- to an excited level of O^{17} with a maximum energy of 3.72 Mev. This excited level dissociates by neutron emission. F^{17} decays by positron emission with a maximum energy of 1.72 Mev. No γ rays are present in F^{17} decay. From other experiments the following values are known:

$$(n - H^1) = 0.78 \text{ Mev}$$
$$(N^{17} - O^{17}) = 8.80 \text{ Mev}$$
$$(O^{16}H^1 - F^{17}) = 0.59 \text{ Mev}$$

The known excited levels of O^{16} have excitation energies of 6.05, 6.13, 6.9, 7.1, and higher Mev.

(a) Using only the above data calculate the energy of the emitted neutrons in the laboratory system.

(b) Show all energies involved on an energy-level diagram for mass number 17.

CHAPTER 18

Ionization of Matter by Charged Particles

In the experimental study of the energy levels and transitions of nuclei, there are many cases which require the measurement of the kinetic energy of a swift charged particle by methods which depend upon absorption and scattering phenomena. Additionally, the response characteristics of every type of radiation-detection instrument depend upon the interaction of charged particles with the sensitive elements of the detector. In order to perform measurements, and to interpret them correctly, it is of fundamental importance to understand the various types of interaction between swift charged particles and matter. The term "swift particles," as used here, refers to particles whose velocities are very much higher than the velocities of thermal agitation.

The interactions which we shall consider here are those which are due primarily to *coulomb forces.* These include ionization, scattering, and various types of radiative losses. Interactions which involve the specifically nuclear short-range forces between nucleons have been discussed in detail in Chaps. 10 and 14.

In the following chapters we shall examine each mode of interaction, on a generalized basis, for swift particles of any mass and charge. Each of these general relationships will then be particularized for the case of "light" particles (electrons) and "heavy" particles (mesons, protons, α rays, . . .).

a. Interactions between Swift Charged Particles and Matter. The mechanisms by which a charged particle loses its kinetic energy, or is deflected from its original path, involve four principal types of interaction. These may be classified as follows:

1. *Inelastic Collision with Atomic Electrons.* Inelastic collisions with bound atomic electrons are usually the predominant mechanism by which a swift charged particle loses kinetic energy in an absorber. As a result of each such collision, one or more atomic electrons experience a transition to an excited state (excitation) or to an unbound state (ionization). These collisions are discussed in this chapter from the standpoint of energy transfer. The deflections experienced by the incident particle are treated in Chap. 19.

2. *Inelastic Collision with a Nucleus.* In a close, noncapture encounter with a nucleus, the incident charged particle invariably experiences a

deflection. In some, but not all, such deflections a quantum of radiation is emitted (bremsstrahlung), and a corresponding amount of kinetic energy is lost by the colliding particles. This radiative type of inelastic nuclear collision is considered in Chap. 20. The probability of nuclear excitation in a noncapture collision also exists, but it is generally much smaller than the radiative probability.

3. *Elastic Collision with a Nucleus.* In elastic nuclear scattering the incident particle is deflected but does not radiate, nor does it excite the nucleus. The incident particle loses only the kinetic energy required for conservation of momentum between the two particles. Incident electrons have a high probability of experiencing nuclear elastic scattering, as discussed in Chap. 19.

4. *Elastic Collision with Atomic Electrons.* An incident charged particle may be elastically deflected in the field of the atomic electrons of a struck atom. Energy and momentum are conserved, and the energy transfer is generally less than the lowest excitation potential of the electrons, so that the interaction is really with the atom as a whole. Such collisions are significant only for the case of very-low-energy (< 100 ev) incident electrons, where they are involved in the Ramsauer effect and related phenomena (B124).

b. Stopping of Swift Charged Particles. In an absorbing material, a moving particle is slowed down and finally brought to rest by the combined action of all four of these elastic and inelastic processes. A particle whose initial kinetic energy is, say, 1 Mev may have more than 10^4 individual collisions before being stopped. In general, each incident particle may experience a number of collisions of each type.

Which type of interaction, if any, will occur when a swift particle passes a particular atom is described only by the laws of chance. From collision theory, one can obtain the probabilities of any particular type of collision, of any particular energy loss, and of any particular change of direction of the motion of the incident particle. After the first collision, these probabilities can be applied to a second collision, then to a third, etc. This method is very complicated; but some reasonable results have been obtained, notably at Los Alamos, using electronic computing devices.

The theory of individual encounters is of great importance for a clear understanding of the behavior of swift particles in matter. However, the statistical average of the effects of all the collisions is invariably obtained by direct experiment. Range-energy relations for swift particles are therefore almost purely empirical (Chaps. 21 and 22).

c. Heavy and Light Incident Particles. It is convenient to distinguish between the behavior of heavy particles and light particles. The "heavy-particle" group includes all those whose rest mass is large compared with that of an atomic electron. Their static properties are summarized in Table 1. The "light-particle" group consists solely of positive and negative electrons.

Nomenclature and Sources of Electrons. Since the discovery of the free positive electron by Anderson in 1932, the nomenclature of the light particles has been in a transition state from which it has not yet emerged. Often the exact meaning of the words "electron" and "electronic" must be judged from the context.

The original meaning of the term "electron" was the *indivisible elementary quantity of electric charge*, $e = 4.80 \times 10^{-10}$ esu, without regard to sign. Thus a proton carries one "electronic charge."

A second, and entirely different, meaning of the term "electron" arose, as the name of a *particle of a particular rest mass*, $m_0 \sim 10^{-27}$ g.

Originally, these two definitions caused no ambiguity, because only the "atomic electrons" of charge $(-e)$ were known. Later the β rays from naturally radioactive nuclides were shown to have the same charge and mass as atomic electrons, and so they are also called electrons. When the new particle of charge $(+e)$ and mass m_0 was discovered in the cosmic radiation, it was consistent with both the mass definition and the charge definition also to call this particle an electron. Soon the same positive particle was found to be emitted in the radioactive β decay of N^{13}, P^{30}, etc., and positively charged β rays were recognized.

TABLE 1. PROPERTIES OF THE PRINCIPAL "HEAVY" CHARGED PARTICLES

Particle	Symbols	Rest mass	Charge	Spin	Statistics
μ meson........	μ^+	$\sim 212 m_0$	$+e$	$\frac{1}{2}$	Fermi
	μ^-	$\sim 212 m_0$	$-e$	$\frac{1}{2}$	Fermi
π meson........	π^+	$\sim 276 m_0$	$+e$	0	Bose
	π^-	$\sim 276 m_0$	$-e$	0	Bose
Proton.........	p; $_1H^1$	$1,836 m_0$	$+e$	$\frac{1}{2}$	Fermi
		1.0076 amu			
Deuteron.......	d; $_1H^2$	2.0142 amu	$+e$	1	Bose
Triton..........	t; $_1H^3$	3.0164 amu	$+e$	$\frac{1}{2}$	Fermi
Helium 3.......	$_2He^3$	3.0159 amu	$+2e$	$\frac{1}{2}$	Fermi
α ray..........	He^4	4.0028 amu	$+2e$	0	Bose

To minimize this ambiguity, Anderson and Millikan (A29) introduced in 1934 the designations *positron* for the "free positive electron" and *negatron* for the "free negative electron." It has since been pointed out that the "*r*" in these words is etymologically dubious. The Sixth General Assembly of the International Union of Pure and Applied Physics (Amsterdam, July 8 to 10, 1948) unanimously recommended the use of the terms *positon* and *negaton* as a means of disinguishing between positive and negative electrons. However, common usage, as seen in the periodical literature, still tends to retain the "*r*." According to the bulk of current usage,

"*An electron*" means a particle of rest mass $m_0 \sim 10^{-27}$ g, without regard to the sign of its charge.

"*A positron*" (or positon) is an electron whose charge is $+e$.

"*A negatron*" (or negaton) is an electron whose charge is $-e$.

The electronic charge means the charge e, without regard to sign or type of particle (electron, proton, ...).

Table 2 lists some of the most common sources of swift electrons and the types of spectrum which they give; note that there are no sources of monoenergetic positrons.

TABLE 2. SOME COMMON SOURCES OF SWIFT ELECTRONS

Mode of production	Type of spectrum	Type of electron
β decay..	Continuous	+ or −
Pair production.................................	Continuous	+ and −
Internal conversion.............................	Monoenergetic	−
Cathode rays, synchrotron, betatron, electrostatic generators......................................	Monoenergetic	−
Compton effect..................................	Continuous	−
Heavy ionizing particles (δ rays)...................	Continuous	−
μ-Meson decay	Continuous	+ and −

1. *Classical Theory of Inelastic Collisions with Atomic Electrons*

When a swift charged particle traverses any absorber, its coulomb interactions with the atomic electrons can be visualized, in a first approximation, as instances of Rutherford scattering. Because of the small mass of the atomic electrons, the transfer of kinetic energy in these coulomb collisions may be large, with the result that the electron is projected out of its atom. The liberated electron and the residual ionized atom then constitute a *primary* ion pair. Often the energy transferred to the struck electron may be of the order of 1 kev or more. Then the ejected electron is itself a swift charged particle (called a δ ray) which produces *secondary* ionization while being brought to rest.

In this chapter we shall center our attention on the mechanism and magnitude of the energy transferred in individual ionizing collisions. The contemporary theory of the ionization and excitation produced by swift charged particles can be understood best by noting how it supplements and modifies the simple classical collision theory. Therefore, we first review the classical, nonrelativistic, collision theory, as it was developed by Bohr.

a. Bohr's Classical Theory of the Stopping of Swift Charged Particles. We begin by assuming, temporarily, that all the electrons in the absorber are free electrons. This assumption is clearly justified for those collisions in which the struck electron receives so much kinetic energy that its initial binding energy can be neglected. Then the collision reduces to the much simpler case of an elastic coulomb collision.

Figure 1.1 gives a schematic representation of the classical coulomb collision between an incident particle (which has charge ze, mass M, velocity V, and kinetic energy $T = \frac{1}{2}MV^2$ in laboratory coordinates) with a free and initially stationary atomic electron (which has charge

$-e$ and mass m_0).   Let x be the impact parameter for a collision in which the energy transfer is Q.   Then, as is shown in Appendix B, Eq. (96), the classical differential cross section per atomic electron, for an energy transfer between Q and $Q + dQ$, is

$$d\sigma = 2\pi x \, dx = \frac{2\pi z^2 e^4}{m_0 V^2} \frac{dQ}{Q^2} \equiv \Phi_0(Q) \, dQ \text{ cm}^2/\text{electron} \qquad (1.1)$$

Here $\Phi_0(Q)$ denotes the particular function which characterizes the classical, nonrelativistic collision theory. Later we shall consider other theories of the interaction and will denote their results by $\Phi_1(Q)$, $\Phi_2(Q)$, ... The symbol $d\sigma$ is employed broadly to represent the differential cross section $\Phi(Q) \, dQ$, regardless of the theory involved.

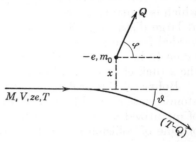

Fig. 1.1   Schematic representation of an ionizing collision, in which there is an energy transfer Q, in laboratory coordinates, from the incident charged particle (ze,M) to an initially stationary atomic electron $(-e,m_0)$.   If the forces between the colliding particles are attractive, instead of repulsive as shown here, then both ϑ and φ will change in sign but not in magnitude.

Note especially from Eq. (1.1) that the probability of a given energy transfer Q varies inversely with the square of that energy loss.   "Soft" collisions, in which the energy loss is small, are therefore strongly favored over "hard" collisions, in which the energy loss is large.

When this incident particle traverses a distance ds in an absorber which contains N atoms/cm³, each with Z electrons/atom, the expectation value for the energy loss per unit path length dT/ds will be

$$\frac{dT}{ds} = NZ \int_{Q_{\min}}^{Q_{\max}} Q \, d\sigma \qquad \text{ergs/cm} \qquad (1.2)$$

If we use for $d\sigma$ the classical cross section given by Eq. (1.1), then Eq. (1.2) becomes

$$\left(\frac{dT}{ds}\right)_{\text{classical}} = \frac{2\pi z^2 e^4}{m_0 V^2} NZ \ln \frac{Q_{\max}}{Q_{\min}} \qquad (1.3)$$

The maximum energy transfer in a head-on collision $Q_{\max}$ is easy to write, but evaluation of the minimum energy transfer $Q_{\min}$ presents a very difficult problem.   Bohr dealt with this problem by basing the classical theory on the concepts of impact parameter x and time of collision $\tau \sim x/V$, rather than on the energy transfer Q.   The analytical relationship between x and Q is (see Appendix B, Sec. 3)

$$Q = \frac{2z^2 e^4}{m_0 V^2} \left[\frac{1}{x^2 + (b/2)^2} \right] \qquad (1.4)$$

$$b \equiv \frac{2ze^2}{m_0 V^2} \left(\frac{M + m_0}{M} \right) \qquad (1.5)$$

where M, V, and ze characterize the incident particle. Then Eq. (1.2), when expressed in terms of the classical impact parameter x, becomes

$$\left(\frac{dT}{ds}\right)_{\text{classical}} = \frac{4\pi z^2 e^4}{m_0 V^2} NZ \int \frac{x\,dx}{x^2 + (b/2)^2} \qquad \text{ergs/cm} \qquad (1.6)$$

Classical Cutoff for Adiabatic Collisions. If the integration of Eq. (1.6) or (1.3) is carried out from head-on collisions $x = 0$ all the way to $x = \infty$, the predicted energy loss will be infinite. This infinite result, which is contrary to reality, arises from the large number of soft collisions at large distances. Therefore some finite maximum, or cutoff, value is needed for the impact parameter x, beyond which the energy transfer is taken to be zero. Physically this cutoff corresponds to recognizing that the struck electron is originally bound to an atom of the absorber.

Bohr met this problem in 1913, before he had developed his theory of atomic spectra, and therefore before the existence of the present concept of quantized atomic energy levels. He based his cutoff on the concept of time of collision τ and its relation to an assumed natural frequency ν of the atomic electron. Bohr assumed that if a bound electron were displaced, as by the coulomb force from a passing particle, then restoring forces within the atom would cause the electron to oscillate with some natural period of vibration $1/\nu$. In those collisions for which the collision time, $\tau \sim x/V$, is much shorter than $1/\nu$, the atomic electron would behave essentially as a free electron. In those collisions for which $\tau \gg 1/\nu$, the interaction should be essentially adiabatic, no net energy would be transferred, and the electron would act as though completely bound. Based on a detailed consideration of the energy transferred to the atomic electron, Bohr (B91) calculated an exact value for the maximum effective collision time τ_ν and for the corresponding maximum effective impact parameter x_ν of

$$x_\nu = \tau_\nu V = \frac{1.123\,V}{2\pi\nu} \qquad (1.7)$$

The integral of Eq. (1.6), evaluated from $x_{\min} = 0$ to $x_{\max} = x_\nu$, with $(x_\nu)^2 \gg (b/2)^2$, then gives a finite energy loss per unit path length equal to

$$\left(\frac{dT}{ds}\right)_{\text{classical}} = \frac{4\pi z^2 e^4}{m_0 V^2} NZ \ln \frac{1.123 m_0 V^3 M}{2\pi \nu z e^2 (M + m_0)} \qquad \text{ergs/cm} \qquad (1.8)$$

if all the electrons have the same characteristic frequency ν. Now if each atom contains Z electrons, having individual characteristic frequencies $\nu_1, \nu_2, \ldots, \nu_i, \ldots, \nu_Z$, then the average energy loss becomes

$$\frac{dT}{ds} = \frac{4\pi z^2 e^4}{m_0 V^2} N \sum_{i=1}^{i=Z} \ln \frac{1.123 m_0 V^3 M}{2\pi \nu_i z e^2 (M + m_0)} \qquad (1.9)$$

It is convenient to introduce a geometric mean value $\bar{\nu}$ defined by

$$Z \ln \bar{\nu} \equiv \sum_{i=1}^{i=Z} \ln \nu_i \qquad (1.10)$$

Then Eq. (1.9) becomes

$$\left(\frac{dT}{ds}\right)_{\text{Bohr}} = \frac{4\pi z^2 e^4}{m_0 V^2} NZ \ln \frac{1.123 m_0 V^3 M}{2\pi \bar{\nu} z e^2 (M + m_0)} \qquad \text{ergs/cm} \qquad (1.11)$$

b. Limitations of the Classical Theory.   Equation (1.11) represents the classical Bohr theory for the energy lost by swift charged particles of mass M, velocity V, and charge ze, as ionization and excitation of the absorbing material.   It contains three fundamental assumptions:

1. For impact parameters from $x = 0$ to $x = x_\nu$, the atomic electrons behave as though they were completely unbound.   For impact parameters greater than $x = x_\nu$, the electrons behave as though they were completely bound and so there is no energy transfer ($Q = 0$).

2. The maximum impact parameter x_ν is much greater than the distance $b/2$ which the struck electron moves during the collision. This is equivalent to permitting energy losses down to Q_ν, where $Q_\nu \ll 2TMm_0/(M + m_0)^2$.

3. Electrons which are displaced only slightly, in cases when the impact parameter is greater than x_ν, return to the original configuration without absorbing any energy.   This is equivalent to saying that the energy transfer Q_ν at the critical limit $x_{\max} = x_\nu$ is much less than the work necessary to remove the electron from the atom (i.e., less than the ionization potential of the particular electron).

c. The Need for Quantum-mechanical Theories.   Later in 1913 Bohr enunciated his theory of quantized energy levels and the origin of simple atomic spectra.   He returned to the problem of the energy losses of swift charged particles in 1915 (B93) to add relativistic terms and to point out the relationship between x_ν and the newer atomic concepts. Bohr showed that the classical theory, Eq. (1.11), is restricted to those impacts in which V greatly exceeds the orbital speed u of the atomic electrons in their Bohr orbits and that x_ν is a distance which must greatly exceed the radius of the Bohr orbit.   Each of these conditions can be shown to be equivalent to the relationship

$$\beta \equiv \frac{V}{c} \gg \frac{Z}{137} \qquad \text{or} \qquad \frac{Z}{137\beta} \ll 1 \qquad (1.12)$$

for ionization in the K shell.   The second, and more serious, difficulty is that the large cutoff value of the impact parameter,

$$x_{\max} = x_\nu \gg \text{Bohr radius}$$

can be shown to correspond to the admission of minimum energy transfers Q_ν, which are far less than the ionization potential and are therefore incompatible with the accepted theory of atomic structure.   For this reason the classical theory predicted too great an energy loss by high-velocity particles.

Significant advances in the theory did not materialize until after the development of the wave mechanics. Then it became possible to dispense with the concept of definite impact parameters and to treat the soft collisions by the method of partial waves and the Born approximation (Appendix C), which is valid for the collision between the incident particle ze and an atomic electron if $2z/137\beta \ll 1$.

Problem

(a) Show that the maximum effective impact parameter $x_\nu = 1.123V/2\pi\nu$ of the classical theory corresponds in elementary quantum theory to an energy transfer of about

$$Q_{\min} \simeq h\nu \left[\frac{zZ}{(137\beta)^2} \right]^2$$

where $h\nu = (Z/137)^2(m_0c^2/2)$ is the ionization energy and Z is the effective nuclear charge for an atom in the absorber.

(b) Estimate $Q_{\min}/h\nu$ for a 1-Mev β ray and for a 5-Mev α ray in air.

2. Quantum-mechanical Theories of Inelastic Collisions with Atomic Electrons

Various aspects of the general theoretical problem of energy losses due to ionization and excitation were solved, using quantum mechanics, between 1930 and 1933, notably by Mott, Bethe, Möller, and Bloch. In blending these special solutions to form the general solution, there are a few minor discrepancies. However, the main results of the theories are self-consistent. Experimental verification is especially good in the cases of α rays of nonrelativistic energy and of electrons and mesons at extreme relativistic energies. The intermediate domain of mildly relativistic particles, such as 1-Mev electrons, is less well covered, and very few experiments bear directly on the theory.

a. Hard and Soft Collisions. For quantum-mechanical treatment, the collisions are generally divided into two classes, hard and soft. Hard collisions are those in which there is such a large energy transfer that the struck electron can be regarded as initially free. In these close collisions, quantum-mechanical spin and exchange effects enter, and the collision cross section per atomic electron will depend on the spin and nature of the incident particle.

Maximum Energy Transfer. From the conservation laws for momentum and energy, it can be shown that the largest possible energy transfer from an incident particle [velocity $V = \beta c$, rest mass M, kinetic energy $T = Mc^2/\sqrt{1 - \beta^2} - Mc^2$] to an initially stationary atomic electron (rest mass m_0) is

$$Q_{\max} = T \left[\frac{1 + (2Mc^2/T)}{1 + (M + m_0)^2 c^2/2m_0T} \right] \qquad (2.1)$$

This general relationship reduces to the following common special cases

$$Q_{max} = \frac{2m_0V^2}{1-\beta^2}\left[\frac{1}{1+(2m_0/M)(T/Mc^2)}\right] \quad \text{if } M \gg m_0, \text{ any } T \quad (2.2)$$

$$Q_{max} = \frac{2m_0V^2}{1-\beta^2} \quad \text{if } M \gg m_0 \text{ and } Mc^2 \geq T \quad (2.3)$$

and
$$Q_{max} = T \quad \text{if } M = m_0 \quad (2.4)$$

Average Energy Loss in Hard Collisions. Hard collisions include those for which the energy transfer extends from $Q = Q_{max}$ down to some arbitrary value $Q = H$, where the only restriction on H is that it be large compared with the binding energy of the electron. Then the average energy loss per unit path length dT_H/ds in hard collisions is represented by

$$\frac{dT_H}{ds} = NZ \int_H^{Q_{max}} Q\Phi_H(Q)\, dQ \quad \text{ergs/cm} \quad (2.5)$$

where the notation is the same as in Eqs. (1.1) and (1.2).

Soft Collisions. In the soft collisions the energy transfer extends from the arbitrary energy $Q = H$ down to the minimum possible energy transfer $Q = Q_{min}$, which is generally of the order of an excitation energy or the ionization energy of one atomic electron. The quantum-mechanical solution for the average energy loss dT_S/ds in soft collisions is obtained from first-order perturbation theory, using the Born first approximation.

Total Energy Loss per Unit Path. The over-all average energy loss dT/ds is then the sum of the losses dT_H/ds in hard collisions and the losses dT_S/ds in soft collisions. It should be pointed out that detailed calculations of dT_H/ds are not always carried out, partly because of uncertainties in $\Phi_H(Q)$ and partly because these hard collisions are so infrequent that they make only a small contribution to the *most probable value* of the energy loss. In many cases, a result of sufficient accuracy for ordinary work is obtained by carrying the integration for soft collisions up to Q_{max}, instead of just to H, and ignoring dT_H/ds. Such an approximation usually differs from the exact expression only by a small additive constant. This procedure accounts for some of the inconsistencies between the theoretical expressions used by various workers.

b. Hard Collisions, Heavy Particles. Bhabha (B55) and others have calculated the cross section per atomic electron for primary particles of spin 0, $\frac{1}{2}$, and 1. The results have been collected in the excellent summary of high-energy collision theory by Rossi and Greisen (R37).

Spin Zero. For incident particles having spin 0 (for example, α rays, π mesons), charge ze, and rest mass $M \gg m_0$, the differential cross section is

$$\Phi_1(Q)\, dQ = \frac{2\pi z^2 e^4}{m_0 V^2}\frac{dQ}{Q^2}\left(1 - \beta^2\frac{Q}{Q_{max}}\right) \quad \text{cm}^2/\text{electron} \quad (2.6)$$

For α rays and π mesons whose kinetic energy is not appreciably greater than their rest energy Mc^2, we can use Eq. (2.3) for Q_{max}. Then

Eq. (2.6) becomes

$$\Phi_2(Q)\,dQ = \frac{2\pi z^2 e^4}{m_0 V^2}\frac{dQ}{Q^2}\left[1 - \frac{Q(1-\beta^2)}{2m_0 c^2}\right] \quad \text{cm}^2/\text{electron} \quad (2.7)$$

For the α rays ordinarily met in the laboratory, $\beta^2 \ll 1$, and Eq. (2.6) reduces to the classical cross section $\Phi_0(Q)\,dQ$ as given by Eq. (1.1).

Spin $\frac{1}{2}$. For heavy particles having spin $\frac{1}{2}$ (e.g., protons, μ mesons), the differential cross section for hard collisions is

$$\Phi_3(Q)\,dQ = \frac{2\pi z^2 e^4}{m_0 V^2}\frac{dQ}{Q^2}\left[1 - \beta^2\frac{Q}{Q_{\max}} + \frac{1}{2}\left(\frac{Q}{T + Mc^2}\right)^2\right] \quad \text{cm}^2/\text{electron}$$

$$(2.8)$$

The final term arises from quantum-mechanical spin effects. These are important only at very high energies and only in a small proportion of the collisions. For energies much less than Mc^2 ($\ll 1{,}000$ Mev for protons; $\ll 100$ Mev for μ mesons), Eq. (2.8) reduces to the classical cross section.

Average Energy Loss. A sufficiently accurate value of dT_H/ds for moderate-energy heavy particles, of any spin, is obtained by using the cross section for zero spin, Eq. (2.6), and integrating. Then Eq. (2.5), if $H \ll Q_{\max}$, becomes

$$\frac{dT_H}{ds} = \frac{2\pi z^2 e^4}{m_0 V^2} NZ\left(\ln\frac{Q_{\max}}{H} - \beta^2\right) \quad \text{ergs/cm} \quad (2.9)$$

c. Hard Collisions, Light Particles. The collision between an incident negatron and an atomic electron requires special treatment, because the two electrons are indistinguishable after the collision.

Maximum Energy Transfer between Identical Particles. Consider the collision of an incident negatron of kinetic energy T with an atomic electron which was initially free and stationary. After the collision one of the electrons will have kinetic energy Q, the other, $(T - Q)$. It cannot be determined which electron was the incident electron. Arbitrarily, *the faster electron after the collision is defined as the incident electron* insofar as future collisions are concerned. This is equivalent to restricting the energy transfer Q to values up to $T/2$. Thus, for incident negatrons

$$Q_{\max} = \frac{T}{2} \quad (2.10)$$

Classical Cross Section for Identical Particles. In order to understand the quantum-mechanical cross sections for collisions between two electrons, it is helpful to evaluate the classical cross section first. The classical differential cross section, Eq. (1.1) with $z = -1$,

$$\Phi_0(Q)\,dQ = \frac{2\pi e^4}{m_0 V^2}\frac{dQ}{Q^2}$$

represents the probability that the incident electron loses energy Q and has kinetic energy $(T - Q)$ after the collision. But we must add to this the classical probability that the incident electron loses energy $(T - Q)$

and has kinetic energy Q after the collision, which is

$$\Phi_0(T - Q)\, dQ = \frac{2\pi e^4}{m_0 V^2} \frac{dQ}{(T - Q)^2}$$

Thus the classical differential cross section for the collision between identical particles, i.e., the probability that one particle will have kinetic energy Q after the collision, is the sum of these two probabilities, or

$$
\begin{aligned}
\Phi_4(Q)\, dQ &= \Phi_0(Q)\, dQ + \Phi_0(T - Q)\, dQ \\
&= \frac{2\pi e^4}{m_0 V^2} \left[\frac{1}{Q^2} + \frac{1}{(T - Q)^2} \right] dQ \\
&= \frac{2\pi e^4}{m_0 V^2} \frac{dQ}{Q^2} \left(\frac{T}{T - Q} \right)^2 \left[1 - 2\left(\frac{Q}{T} \right) + 2\left(\frac{Q}{T} \right)^2 \right] \quad \text{cm}^2/\text{electron}
\end{aligned}
$$

$$(2.11)$$

This cross section applies only for $Q \leq (T - Q)$, that is, for $Q \leq T/2$. For $Q \geq T/2$, the corresponding cross section is zero, because these collisions are already included in $\Phi_4(Q)$.

Quantum-mechanical Cross Section for Identical Particles. In order to introduce into the cross section the effects of quantum-mechanical exchange, and of relativity, Möller (M50) treated the problem of the collision between two free negatrons, using the relativistic Dirac theory of the electron. Möller's equation for the differential cross section, in which the slower electron after the collision has a kinetic energy Q, is

$$
\begin{aligned}
\Phi_5(Q)\, dQ = \frac{2\pi e^4}{m_0 V^2} \frac{dQ}{Q^2} \left(\frac{T}{T - Q} \right)^2 & \left\{ 1 - \left[3 - \left(\frac{T}{T + m_0 c^2} \right)^2 \right] \frac{Q}{T} \left(1 - \frac{Q}{T} \right) \right. \\
& \left. + \left(\frac{Q}{T + m_0 c^2} \right)^2 \left(1 - \frac{Q}{T} \right)^2 \right\} \quad \text{cm}^2/\text{electron} \quad (2.12)
\end{aligned}
$$

Like Eq. (2.11), this cross section is symmetric in Q and $(T - Q)$ and is valid for $Q \leq T/2$. The final term within the curly braces is appreciable only for energetic negatrons ($T > m_0 c^2$) and for close collisions ($Q \sim T/2$). This term and part of the middle term within the curly braces are due to spin (M69).

For nonrelativistic negatrons ($T \ll m_0 c^2$), Eq. (2.12) reduces to

$$\Phi_6(Q)\, dQ = \frac{2\pi e^4}{m_0 V^2} \left[\frac{1}{Q^2} + \frac{1}{(T - Q)^2} - \frac{1}{Q(T - Q)} \right] dQ \quad \text{cm}^2/\text{electron}$$

$$(2.13)$$

which is the Mott-Williams (W56) quantum-mechanical cross section for slow electrons, including exchange, and considering the atomic electrons as free.

The cross section for extremely relativistic negatrons emerges from Eq. (2.12) when $T \gg m_0 c^2$ and is

$$\Phi_7(Q)\, dQ = \frac{2\pi e^4}{m_0 V^2} \frac{dQ}{Q^2} \left(\frac{T}{T - Q} \right)^2 \left[1 - \frac{Q}{T} + \left(\frac{Q}{T} \right)^2 \right]^2 \quad \text{cm}^2/\text{electron}$$

$$(2.14)$$

Note that for soft collisions ($Q \ll T$), Eq. (2.12) reduces to $\Phi_0(Q)\,dQ$ for any value of T, including the relativistic case.

Cross Section for Positrons. The differential cross section for positrons, incident on free stationary atomic electrons, involves different exchange effects, because the positron can be distinguished from the negative electron after the collision. Including these effects for particles of spin $\frac{1}{2}$, as well as the possibility of annihilation of the positron, Bhabha (B54, Eq. 19) has obtained an expression for the differential cross section, in which the struck atomic electron acquires a kinetic energy Q. It can be written in the form

$$\Phi_8(Q)\,dQ = \frac{2\pi e^4}{m_0 V^2}\frac{dQ}{Q^2}\left\{1 - \beta^2\left[2\frac{Q}{T} - 3\frac{Q^2}{\mu^2}\left(\frac{1-\beta^2}{\beta^2}\right)\right.\right.$$
$$\left.\left. - \left(\frac{QT}{\mu^2} - \frac{Q^3 T}{\mu^4}\right)\left(\frac{1-\beta^2}{\beta^2}\right)^2 - \left(\frac{Q^2 T^2}{\mu^4} - \frac{Q^3 T^3}{\mu^6} + \frac{Q^4 T^2}{\mu^6}\right)\left(\frac{1-\beta^2}{\beta^2}\right)^3\right]\right\}$$
$$\text{cm}^2/\text{electron} \quad (2.15)$$

where we have used the abbreviations

$$\mu = m_0 c^2 \qquad \beta = V/c$$

$$\frac{1-\beta^2}{\beta^2} = \frac{1}{(T/\mu)[(T/\mu)+2]} \qquad \text{which approaches} \begin{cases} \mu/2T \text{ for } T \ll \mu \\ (\mu/T)^2 \text{ for } T \gg \mu \end{cases}$$

$$\beta^2 = 1 - \frac{1}{[(T/\mu)+1]^2} \qquad \text{which approaches} \begin{cases} 2T/\mu \text{ for } T \ll \mu \\ 1 \text{ for } T \gg \mu \end{cases}$$

Equation (2.15) applies to all values of Q up to T for the head-on collision.

In the nonrelativistic case ($T \ll m_0 c^2$), the expression in the curly braces approaches unity, and the positron-electron differential cross section approaches the classical value $\Phi_0(Q)\,dQ$ for all values of Q. No exchange effect is exhibited in the nonrelativistic case, in contrast with that found for the electron-electron collision.

In the extremely relativistic case ($T \gg m_0 c^2$), the positron-electron cross section becomes

$$\Phi_9(Q)\,dQ = \frac{2\pi e^4}{m_0 V^2}\frac{dQ}{Q^2}\left[1 - \left(\frac{Q}{T}\right) + \left(\frac{Q}{T}\right)^2\right]^2 \qquad \text{cm}^2/\text{electron} \quad (2.16)$$

In some experimental work the positron and negatron are not distinguished after the collision. Then the differential cross section for a collision in which the slower particle after the collision has kinetic energy Q, where $Q \le T/2$ and $T \gg m_0 c^2$, is

$$\Phi_{10}(Q)\,dQ$$
$$= \Phi_9(Q)\,dQ + \Phi_9(T-Q)\,dQ$$
$$= \frac{2\pi e^4}{m_0 V^2}\frac{dQ}{Q^2}\left(\frac{T}{T-Q}\right)^2\left[1 - 2\frac{Q}{T} + 2\left(\frac{Q}{T}\right)^2\right]\left[1 - \frac{Q}{T} + \left(\frac{Q}{T}\right)^2\right]^2 \quad (2.17)$$

Comparison with Eq. (2.14) shows that the first square brackets in Eq. (2.17) represent the ratio of the exchange effect in the positron-negatron collision to that in the negatron-negatron collision for the extreme relativistic case (F70).

The effects of electron spin and of relativistic velocities upon the cross sections for collisions between electrons are illustrated in Fig. 2.1.

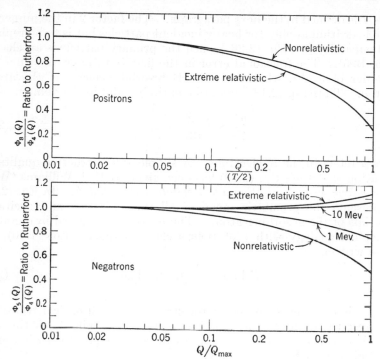

Fig. 2.1 Collision cross sections for incident negatrons [Eq. (2.12) of Möller] and for incident positrons [Eq. (2.15) of Bhabha] relative to the classical Rutherford cross section for identical particles, Eq. (2.11). For ease of comparison, the horizontal scale of energy transfer Q is taken relative to $T/2$ in both diagrams. In the negatron-negatron collision, $T/2 = Q_{max}$.

d. Soft-collision Energy Loss, Nonrelativistic. Bethe (B37) has carried through detailed quantum-mechanical calculations of the energy lost by swift charged particles to bound electrons, using the Born approximation. Beginning with calculations on atomic hydrogen as the absorber, Bethe used as the scattering potential the coulomb potential between the stationary nuclear charge, Ze, ($Z = 1$), and the bound electron e, together with two perturbation terms representing the coulomb energy between the moving particle ze and the nucleus, and between the moving particle and the bound atomic electron. The solution was extended to atoms containing Z electrons by replacing the coulomb field of the nucleus by the field of the nucleus plus $(Z - 1)$ electrons. This nonrelativistic treatment gives a result which is equivalent (W56) to employing an electronic cross section proportional only to dQ/Q^2 and including all energy losses up to that of the head-on collision. The expectation value for the energy loss per unit path length becomes

$$\frac{dT_s}{ds} = \frac{4\pi z^2 e^4}{m_0 V^2} NZ \ln \frac{2m_0 V^2}{I} \tag{2.18}$$

where I is defined in the next paragraph. The factor 2 in the numerator of the logarithm applies for heavy incident particles but is to be replaced by about unity [see Eq. (2.28)] when the primary particle is an electron (W56, B95). The fractional error in the first Born approximation is of the order of u^2/V^2, where u is the Bohr-orbit velocity of the atomic electron. Thus Eq. (2.18) should be entirely valid in the domain

$$\frac{u^2}{V^2} \sim \left(\frac{Z}{137\beta}\right)^2 \ll 1 \tag{2.19}$$

where u refers to the K electrons. A simple and instructive qualitative derivation of Bethe's Eq. (2.18) has been given by E. J. Williams (W59).

Geometric-mean Ionization and Excitation Potential, I. In Eq. (2.18), I represents the geometric mean of all the ionization and excitation potentials of the absorbing atom. The energy I is defined in quantum-mechanical analogy with $\bar{\nu}$ of Bohr's classical theory, Eq. (1.10), and can be written

$$Z \ln I \equiv \sum_{n,l} f_{n,l} \ln A_{n,l} \tag{2.20}$$

Here $f_{n,l}$ is the sum of the oscillator strengths for all optical transitions of the electron in the n,l shell and is close to unity, while $A_{n,l}$ is the mean excitation energy of the n,l shell and can be put equal to the ionization potential with sufficient accuracy.

Theoretical values of I, calculated with hydrogenlike wave functions (B37, W56), are of little practical value. But empirical values of I can be determined, for each value of Z, and when these are used Eq. (2.18) fits the most accurate data on the absorption of α rays remarkably well. For α rays of low velocity, in absorbers of moderate and large Z, the K electrons are somewhat less effective than is implied by Eq. (2.18). Bethe (L32) has shown that this deficiency can be expressed by subtracting an amount C_K from the logarithm in Eq. (2.18). C_K is a function of (u^2/V^2) for the K electrons and varies between 0 and 1.05 (Chap. 22, Fig. 2.1).

Bloch (B70, B71) has evaluated the energy lost by swift particles while traversing heavy atoms whose structure is represented by the Thomas-Fermi model. In this model, I turns out to be closely proportional to Z and can be represented by

$$I \simeq kZ \tag{2.21}$$

where k is an empirical constant whose value is about 11.5 ev (W34) when the correction term C_K is used with Eq. (2.18). If C_K is omitted, then k decreases from about 18 ev for H ($I = 18$ ev) to about 10 ev for Pb

($I = 842$ ev).   Experimental values of I are discussed further in Chap. 22, Sec. 2.

e. Soft-collision Energy Loss, Relativistic.   Bethe (B38) extended his original theory to the case of incident particles having relativistic velocities, $V = \beta c$.   The general result thus obtained is applicable to soft collisions ($Q_{min} \leq Q \leq H$) for any primary particle of charge ze, provided $\beta \gg Z/137$.

$$\left(\frac{dT_s}{ds}\right)_{Bethe} = \frac{2\pi z^2 e^4}{m_0 V^2} NZ \left[\ln \frac{2m_0 V^2 H}{I^2(1 - \beta^2)} - \beta^2 \right] \qquad \text{ergs/cm} \qquad (2.22)$$

Here H is the maximum energy transfer considered.   The factor 2 in the logarithm is applicable to electrons.   Equation (2.22) is the presently preferred solution for swift heavy particles as well as positrons and negatrons.

f. Total Energy Loss for Heavy Particles.   To obtain the total energy loss by ionization, Eq. (2.22) representing the soft collisions must be added to the energy losses due to hard collisions, e.g., Eq. (2.9).   Thus for heavy particles having spin 0, we obtain for the total average energy loss by ionization per unit path length

$$\left(\frac{dT}{ds}\right)_{ion} = \frac{dT_s}{ds} + \frac{dT_H}{ds} = \frac{2\pi z^2 e^4}{m_0 V^2} NZ \left[\ln \frac{2m_0 V^2 Q_{max}}{I^2(1 - \beta^2)} - 2\beta^2 \right] \qquad (2.23)$$

The case of any heavy particle whose kinetic energy is of the order of magnitude or less than its rest mass can be treated, using Eq. (2.3) for Q_{max}, and leads to

$$\left(\frac{dT}{ds}\right)_{ion} = \frac{4\pi z^2 e^4}{m_0 V^2} NZ \left[\ln \frac{2m_0 V^2}{I} - \ln (1 - \beta^2) - \beta^2 \right] \qquad \text{ergs/cm} \qquad (2.24)$$

For small values of β, the two relativistic correction terms in the square brackets of Eq. (2.24) can be approximated as $+\beta^4/2$.   Thus the relativity effect slightly *increases* the energy losses which would be expected on a basis of velocity variation alone.   The reason this increase is small can be visualized by considering the influence of the Lorentz contraction on the effective shape of the electric field of the moving primary particle.   Essentially, the motion of the particle contracts the loci of the equipotential surfaces along the direction of motion and correspondingly broadens them at right angles to the direction of motion, because the total energy of the electrostatic field remains constant.   As a result of contraction along the direction of motion, the field of the moving particle acts on each electron of the absorber for a shorter time. Effectively, the "collision time" is shortened.   On the other hand, the increased lateral extension of the field is equivalent to strengthening the interaction for any particular value of the "impact parameter."   Effectively, the maximum value of the impact parameter is increased.   These two effects, shortening the time of collision but increasing the strength of the interaction, act in opposite directions.   Therefore the net relativistic effect is not great for moderate values of β.

As β increases, the loss dT/ds decreases, mainly because of the $1/V^2$ term outside the square brackets of Eq. (2.24). As V approaches c, the velocity dependence exerts no significant effect, and relativistic effects take over. The ionization losses pass through a minimum when the kinetic energy of the incident particle is in the neighborhood of $3Mc^2$ ($\sim$300 Mev for mesons) and then rises very slowly, approximately logarithmically with increasing primary energy (Fig. 5.1). This minimum has been found experimentally.

g. Total Energy Loss by Light Particles. When the primary particle is a negatron or a positron, the integration of the hard collisions, by means of Eqs. (2.5), (2.12), and (2.15), leads in a straightforward way to manageable but complicated expressions for dT_H/ds. Except in the extreme relativistic domain of cosmic-ray energies, these more exact expressions are seldom used. There are several reasons:

1. The more complicated expressions thus obtained for the total collision loss dT/ds differ by only a few per cent from the values given by simply extending the soft collisions of Eq. (2.22) to $H = Q_{max} = T/2$, or from the values given by neglecting spin and exchange effects and using Eq. (2.23) for electrons as well as for heavy particles.

2. There are uncertainties in all the theories, leading to differences of about a factor of 2 in the logarithm term, and hence there are uncertainties of a few per cent in dT/ds (4 per cent for 1-Mev electrons).

3. Hard collisions are very infrequent and contribute very little to the *most probable* energy loss which is usually the experimentally important quantity. Thus they are of minor experimental importance in determinations of dT/ds. It is, in fact, common when comparing theory and experiment to consider only the soft collisions in which the maximum energy transfer H is of the order of 10^3 to 10^4 ev.

It is important to note that although the hard collisions are infrequent, because of the large energy transfer about one-half the total energy is lost in hard collisions. This means that the *average energy loss* dT/ds will exceed the *most probable energy loss*.

We therefore obtain a result that is quite accurate for positrons and negatrons of all energies from Eq. (2.22) by including energies up to $H = T/2$.

$$\left(\frac{dT}{ds}\right)_{ion} \simeq \frac{dT_s}{ds} = \frac{2\pi e^4}{m_0 V^2}\, NZ \left\{\ln\left[\frac{m_0 V^2 T}{I^2(1 - \beta^2)}\right] - \beta^2\right\} \qquad \text{ergs/cm} \quad (2.25)$$

This will be accurate within experimental error for all cases except extremely relativistic electrons, where spin and sign of the charge of the incident particle produce observable effects.

For simplicity in numerical work, it is convenient to introduce $m_0 V^2 = \beta^2 m_0 c^2$, and $T + m_0 c^2 = m_0 c^2/\sqrt{1 - \beta^2}$, thus obtaining from Eq. (2.25)

$$\left(\frac{dT}{ds}\right)_{ion} = 4\pi r_0^2 \frac{m_0 c^2}{\beta^2}\, NZ \left[\ln \beta \left(\frac{T + m_0 c^2}{I}\right)\left(\frac{T}{m_0 c^2}\right)^{\frac{1}{2}} - \frac{1}{2}\beta^2\right] \qquad \text{Mev/cm}$$

$$(2.26)$$

where $r_0 = e^2/m_0c^2$ = classical electron radius

$4\pi r_0^2 = 1.00 \times 10^{-24}$ cm²/electron = 1.00 barn/electron

$m_0c^2 = 0.51$ Mev

$\beta^2 = (V/c)^2 = 1 - [(T/m_0c^2) + 1]^{-2}$

NZ = electrons/cm³ = 3.88×10^{20} cm⁻³ for air at 0°C, 760 mm

$I \simeq (11 \pm 3)Z$ ev; $I \simeq 86$ ev for air (see Chap. 22, Fig. 2.3)

Substituting in the proper values for a 0.1-Mev electron, one obtains an energy loss of 4.7 kev per centimeter of air. If we assume that this energy loss results in ionization at an average rate of 32.5 ev per ion pair (B56, G45), then the average total specific ionization along the path of the 0.1-Mev electron, in air at 0°C and 760 mm, would be $4,700/32.5 = 145$ ion pairs per centimeter of path.

A very convenient rule of thumb emerges by taking an average value for the square brackets of Eq. (2.26) and neglecting the slow logarithmic increase with T. From this one obtains an approximation for the specific ionization by electrons of energies in the domain of 0 to 10 Mev given by

$$\left(\frac{dT}{ds}\right)_{ion} = \frac{45}{\beta^2} \quad \text{ion pairs/air-cm} \tag{2.27}$$

For nonrelativistic incident electrons $(I \ll T \ll m_0c^2)$, Eq. (2.25) becomes simply

$$\left(\frac{dT}{ds}\right)_{ion} = \frac{4\pi e^4}{m_0V^2} NZ \ln \frac{m_0V^2}{I\sqrt{2}} = \frac{2\pi e^4}{T} NZ \ln \frac{T\sqrt{2}}{I} \quad \text{ergs/cm} \tag{2.28}$$

Comparing Eq. (2.28) with Eq. (2.18), we find that its factor 2, which is applicable to heavy particles, becomes $(1/\sqrt{2})$ if we include as soft collisions all energy losses for nonrelativistic incident electrons.

Problems

1. In an experimental arrangement which cannot distinguish a swift positron from a swift negatron, show that the average value of the energy losses by high-energy positrons $(T \gg m_0c^2)$ in hard collisions $(T \gg H \gg I)$ becomes

$$NZ \int_H^{T/2} Q\Phi_9(Q)\, dQ = \frac{2\pi e^4}{m_0c^2} NZ \left(\ln \frac{T}{H} - 1.388 \right) \tag{1}$$

$$NZ \int_{T/2}^T (T - Q)\Phi_9(Q)\, dQ = \frac{2\pi e^4}{m_0c^2} NZ(0.185) \tag{2}$$

and hence that

$$\frac{dT}{ds} = \frac{dT_H}{ds} + \frac{dT_S}{ds} = \frac{2\pi e^4}{m_0c^2} NZ \left(\ln \frac{T^3}{m_0c^2 I^2} - 1.51 \right) \tag{3}$$

Equation (3) neglects the fact that, after one collision in which $Q > T/2$, the "primary" particle is no longer a positron. Is this justified?

2. (a) Show that for extremely relativistic negatrons, integration over Eq. (2.14) leads to

$$\frac{dT_H}{ds} = \frac{2\pi e^4}{m_0V^2} NZ \left[\left(\ln \frac{T}{H} \right) - 0.261 \right] \quad \text{ergs/cm}$$

and that when the soft collisions of Eq. (2.22) are added

$$\frac{dT}{ds} = \frac{dT_H}{ds} + \frac{dT_S}{ds} = \frac{2\pi e^4}{m_0 V^2} NZ \left[\ln \frac{2m_0 c^2 T}{(1 - \beta^2) I^2} - \beta^2 - 0.261 \right]$$

$$\simeq \frac{2\pi e^4}{m_0 c^2} NZ \left[\left(\ln \frac{T^3}{m_0 c^2 I^2} \right) - 0.568 \right] \qquad \text{ergs/cm}$$

(*b*) Extend Eq. (2.22) to $H = T/2$ for $T \gg m_0 c^2$, and show that this leads to

$$\frac{dT}{ds} \simeq \frac{2\pi e^4}{m_0 c^2} NZ \left[\left(\ln \frac{T^3}{m_0 c^2 I^2} \right) - 1 \right] \qquad \text{ergs/cm}$$

(*c*) Evaluate the per cent difference between the results in (*a*) and (*b*) for 5-, 25-, and 100-Mev electrons in air.

3. A 100-Mev positron impinges at normal incidence on a lead plate 1 mm thick. Compute the probability that this positron will have a sufficiently close encounter with an atomic electron in the lead plate to eject a negatron of greater than, say, 80 Mev. Make any reasonable simplifying assumptions, e.g., neglect radiative losses and low-energy ionization losses.

3. *Comparison of Classical and Quantum-mechanical Theories*

It is now of special interest to compare the classical theory of Bohr, Eq. (1.11), with the Bethe quantum-mechanical theory, Eq. (2.18). The classical visualization of definite impact parameters is valid (see Appendix C, Sec. 4) when $2z/137\beta \gg 1$, whereas the use of the Born approximation makes Bethe's theory valid when $2z/137\beta \ll 1$. It will be further noted that the two theories coincide when the arguments of the logarithm terms are equal. This leads to the condition

$$\frac{1.123 m_0 V^3 M}{2\pi \bar{\nu} z e^2 (M + m_0)} = \frac{2 m_0 V^2}{I} \tag{3.1}$$

for the case of heavy particles, $M \gg m_0$. If we set $I \simeq h\bar{\nu}$ and $1.123 \simeq 1$, Eq. (3.1) becomes

$$\frac{2z}{137\beta} = 1 \tag{3.2}$$

Thus, in the domain where neither limiting theory is rigorously valid, both fortunately converge to the same value. Williams (W59), in discussing a similar situation in the theory of nuclear scattering, has pointed out that both theories will be in error in the same direction (of too much scattering) in this intermediate region. The more nearly correct theory is therefore the one which gives the least scattering, i.e., the least energy losses. As would be expected intuitively, this turns out to be Bohr's theory for $2z/137\beta > 1$ and Bethe's for $2z/137\beta < 1$. It is noteworthy that the classical theory now has acquired renewed interest and significance, especially for the study of the passage through matter of the highly charged fission fragments, for which $2z/137\beta$ is very large.

Bloch (B70, B71) has developed a quantum-mechanical theory of the average energy loss for swift particles which has general validity for all

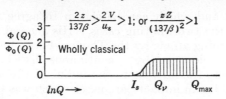

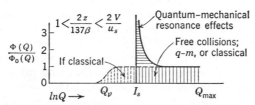

Fig. 3.1 For low-velocity ($V = \beta c$) particles, which have the characteristics given on the diagram, the energy losses are essentially as given by the classical theory and are indicated by vertical shading. The term u_s is the Bohr orbital velocity of the atomic electron whose minimum excitation potential is I_s.

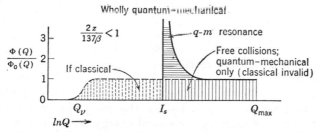

Fig. 3.2 For particles of intermediate velocity, the actual minimum energy loss I_s is about equal to the ionization potential for the particular electron involved. The average energy losses predicted by classical and quantum-mechanical theories are substantially equal. The dotted losses between the classical adiabatic limit Q_ν and I_s are replaced in the quantum-mechanical theory by an abundance of losses of the order of I_s and ascribable to resonance effects.

Fig. 3.3 For high-velocity particles the classical theory would predict too great an energy loss (dotted), because the adiabatic limit Q_ν becomes much smaller than I_s as β increases. The quantum-mechanical resonance effects now amount to a smaller energy transfer (horizontal shading above unity) than those predicted by classical theory for $Q < I_s$. The classical pictures are invalid even above I_s and only the quantum-mechanical theory can be used. The resonance losses (horizontal shading) are substantially equal to the losses in free collisions [vertical shading, below $\Phi(Q)/\Phi_0(Q) = 1$]. This circumstance is evident on comparison of the classical Eq. (1.3) with $Q_{min} = I_s$ and $Q_{max} = 2m_0 V^2$, which is just one-half the quantum-mechanical losses given by Eq. (2.18).

values of $2z/137\beta$ and which can be shown to agree with Bohr's and Bethe's results in the two limiting cases. His general approach was to represent the absorbing atoms by the Thomas-Fermi model, thus replacing discrete atomic electrons by a continuous distribution of electron density varying from the nucleus to the radius of the atom. Collisions were then specified by an impact parameter which was the distance from the nucleus to the path of the incident particle. An important general result from Bloch's calculations was the prediction of the linear dependence of I on Z [Eq. (2.21)].

In any quantum-mechanical theory the energy losses in soft collisions correspond to a type of resonance phenomenon. The swift incident particle, passing near an atom in the absorber, has a finite probability of transferring energy to that particular atom. Actually, however, either no energy at all is transferred or else an energy approximately equal to an excitation or ionization energy of the atom is transferred. In the domain of $2z/137\beta \sim 1$, the classical theory implies a small energy loss to *each* atom, even though this energy loss is less than the minimum excitation potential, and hence physically incorrect. The quantum-mechanical theory replaces this multitude of small losses to each of the atoms by larger losses to only a few of the atoms.

Niels Bohr has written a masterly summary and critique on the penetration of atomic particles through matter, which should be studied by every serious student of the subject. Bohr presents (p. 87 of B95) a series of diagrams illustrating the comparison between the classical and quantum-mechanical theories of energy loss by inelastic collisions with atomic electrons. Figures 3.1 to 3.3 adapt Bohr's instructive diagrams to the coordinates originally introduced by Williams (W55). The effective cross section $\Phi(Q)$ is plotted vertically in terms of its ratio to the classical value $\Phi_0(Q)$. Energy losses Q are plotted horizontally, on a logarithmic scale. Then the area below the curve, between any two values of Q, is proportional to the average energy transfers in the specified energy domain. I_s represents the effective minimum excitation potential of the sth electron and, for simplicity, is not distinguished from other excitation potentials and the nearby ionization potential. Q_ν is the adiabatic limit of minimum classical energy transfer to the sth electron, when the impact parameter has its maximum effective value x_ν of Eq. (1.7).

4. *Energy Loss per Ion Pair by Primary and Secondary Ionization*

The theory of the stopping of charged particles by matter deals with the *kinetic energy* lost by the moving charge. It is not a theory of the *ionization* produced in the absorbing medium. The actual number of ion pairs produced by a given transfer of kinetic energy depends in a complicated way upon the nature and purity of the absorber. Present knowledge in this area is almost entirely empirical (Chap. 22).

In the relatively infrequent hard collisions the struck electron will be given a large kinetic energy.   Such a swift secondary electron, produced from the collision of a charged particle, is known as a δ ray.   An appreciable fraction, roughly one-half, of the energy lost by primary particles appears as δ rays.   These δ rays lose their energy just as any negatron of this energy would.   Thus we see that the total ionization in the absorber will be the sum of the *primary ionization* produced by collisions of the primary particle with atomic electrons and the *secondary ionization* produced by δ rays.   For example, in hydrogen the primary ionization is expected to be about one-half the total, in air about one-third the total, and in heavier elements an even smaller fraction (B37).   Measurements of the primary ionization by 0.2-Mev to 1.6-Mev electrons in H_2, He, Ne, and A have been made by McClure (M31).   Detailed calculations of the number and energy of δ rays produced by swift electrons, protons, and α rays have been tabulated by Lea (p. 28 of L18).

The average energy loss per ion pair varies widely for different absorbers.   For electrons in air it is about 32.5 ev per ion pair (G45, B56), 42.3 ev for helium (J14a), but only 7.6 ev for AgBr in photographic emulsions (W14).   As one would expect, very slow particles lose more energy in excitation than in ionization, and the average energy loss per ion pair generally is greater for very slow particles than for faster particles. This variation is slight and need not be considered for work of ordinary accuracy in the range of particle energies from 0.1 to 5 Mev.   Carefully measured values of the energy loss per ion pair for β rays and α rays in a number of highly purified gases have been reported by Jesse and Sadauskis (J14a).

Problem

The path of a certain homogeneous group of negative electrons passing, in vacuum, at right angles to a magnetic field of 500 gauss has a radius of curvature of 6 cm.

(a) What is the *kinetic* energy of the electrons, in Mev?

(b) What is the velocity, $\beta(= V/c)$, of these electrons?

(c) If these electrons were to pass into *air*, at 1-atm pressure and 20°C, approximately what would be the *specific ionization*, in ion pairs per centimeter, along their paths before they were slowed down appreciably?

(d) If, instead of air, these electrons were to pass into *helium*, at 3-atm pressure and 20°C, approximately what would be their initial relative *energy loss* per centimeter of travel, in terms of their energy loss per centimeter of air at 1 atm and 20°C?

(e) Approximately what initial *specific ionization*, in ion pairs per centimeter, would be expected in *helium*, at 3 atm at 20°C?

5. *Dependence of Collision Losses on the Physical and Chemical State of the Absorber*

a. Effects of Physical State.   The ionization loss of a fast charged particle is greater in a substance in the gaseous state than for an equal mass of the same substance in a condensed state.

The theory of collision losses which we have discussed so far is based on the assumption that each atom is independent of all others. This assumption is true for gases at moderate pressures; however, in condensed substances new phenomena appear. These arise primarily as the result of coupling between different collisions and are due mainly to the conductivity of the medium and to polarization of the medium by the moving charge. These phenomena are negligible if $\beta \ll 1$; however, they may become significant as β approaches 1.

Associated with the concept of retarded potentials, the effective field of a very swift charged particle is greater behind the particle than ahead of it along its direction of motion. The moving particle polarizes nearby atoms in proportion to its effective field. Thus, there is an asymmetric polarization with respect to a plane through the particle and at right angles to its direction of motion (B95, Fig. 6). This polarization field may be regarded as reducing the effective field of the moving particle and thus screening the remote atoms which otherwise would experience energy transfers. This polarization is significant only when the atoms are closer together than the impact parameter for the soft collisions, hence only in condensed materials or gases at very high pressures. The effect reduces the energy losses in distant encounters, i.e., it reduces soft collision losses for very fast particles.

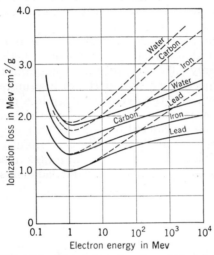

Fig. 5.1 The energy loss by electronic collisions in several substances, according to Halpern and Hall (H10). The dotted curves correspond to the losses expected for independent atoms. The solid curves include the effects of polarization and conductivity in the actual condensed materials.

The magnitude of this effect was first calculated by Fermi (F36, F37), using a macroscopic model containing only one dispersion frequency for the electrons of the absorber. Quite large effects were predicted for very fast particles. Recently, however, Halpern and Hall (H9, H10) and also Wick (W46), using a multifrequency model, have predicted a substantially smaller effect. The effect of conduction electrons, as in metals, was emphasized by Kramers (K44) and has been included as a damping term in the treatment by Halpern and Hall. Aage Bohr (B88) has succeeded in dealing with the problem on a microscopic model, has obtained a result in agreement with that of Wick and of Halpern and Hall, and has admirably collated and summarized the field.

Some results of the multifrequency treatment (H10) are shown in Fig. 5.1. These values have been checked by Hereford (H39) with water and carbon for electrons from 1.4 to 9 Mev, who finds essential agreement between experiment and theory, and by Goldwasser, Mills and Hanson (G30) for 9.6-Mev and 15.7-Mev electrons in polystyrene, Be, Al, Cu, and Au.   For 5.3-Mev α rays, the stopping power of acetylene (C_2H_2) does not exceed that of polystyrene (C_nH_n) by as much as 1 per cent, according to measurements by Ellis, Rossi, and Failla (E12).

   b. Effects of Chemical Bonds.   One might expect changes in stopping power of materials in molecular form as compared to the same material in an atomic form, because the molecular binding causes slight changes in the mean excitation and ionization potential I.   However, L. H. Gray (G45) has pointed out that the changes to be expected in the mean ionization potential I as a result of even vigorous chemical reactions, such as the combination of hydrogen and oxygen to form water vapor, will not affect the stopping power of the mixture by as much as 1 per cent.   This is in agreement with direct observations on α rays, where a summary (G45) of the experimental evidence shows that the stopping power dT/ds of various chemical compounds is simply the sum of the stopping powers of their atomic constituents.

   For protons in the energy domain between 200 Mev and 340 Mev, Thompson (T21) has found that the stopping powers of compounds of H, C, N, O, and Cl are very nearly strictly additive functions of the elements in the compound.   An increase in molal stopping power of about 1 to 2 per cent, corresponding to a reduction in the mean ionization potential, is detectable in compounds containing hydrogen and to a lesser extent for carbon.   Deviations from strict additivity diminish as Z increases and are not detectable for chlorine.

6. Čerenkov Radiation

   Electromagnetic radiation is emitted whenever a charged particle passes through any medium in which the phase velocity of light is less than the particle velocity $V = \beta c$.   This remarkable effect was discovered by Čerenkov (C9), and the theoretical explanation given by Frank and Tamm (F64, M72) has been confirmed experimentally by Collins and Reiling (C33) and by others (H17, M18).

   When high-speed charged particles having nearly the velocity of light pass into a transparent dielectric, the velocity of the particle is unaltered, except for the subsequent ionization and radiative losses.   However, the electric field associated with the particle's charge and the magnetic field associated with the motion of this charge are propagated with a phase velocity of only c/n, where n is the index of refraction of the medium. The resulting electromagnetic radiation is canceled by destructive interference in all directions if $\beta n < 1$; however, if $\beta n > 1$ there will be one direction ϑ in which constructive interference takes place.   If the velocity βc of the particle exceeds the velocity of light c/n in the medium, the particle "runs away" from a slower-moving portion of its own electromagnetic field; consequently all frequencies for which $\beta n > 1$ can be emitted.   The resulting "Čerenkov radiation" is emitted in a conical surface CBE of half angle φ, as shown in Fig. 6.1, provided that

$$\sin \varphi = \cos \vartheta = \frac{(c/n)t}{Vt} = \frac{1}{\beta n} \qquad (6.1)$$

The electric vector of this electromagnetic wave lies in the plane of the conical surface and is radially directed. The conic distribution of the Čerenkov radiation has a natural half breadth of the order of a few degrees; this natural breadth is thought to be due to the succession of discrete changes in electron velocity when photons are emitted (L28).

Fermi (F37) first showed that Čerenkov radiation originates in small energy transfers from swift charged particles to distant atoms, which is subsequently emitted as coherent radiation. Thus Čerenkov radiation

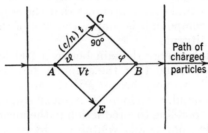

Fig. 6.1 The charged particle moves from A to B in a time t. During this time, electromagnetic radiation which was emitted when the particle passed A has gone a distance $AC = (c/n)t$. Constructive interference of the wavelets takes place on the conical surface CBE, of half angle φ.

is a particular form of energy loss in *very soft collisions*, and not an added amount of energy loss.

Frank and Tamm (F64) have shown from classical theory [and the same result is obtainable from quantum theory (F37, B88)] that the total energy $dT_{\text{Čer}}$ radiated in a short element of the particle's path ds is

$$\left(\frac{dT}{ds}\right)_{\text{Čer}} = \frac{4\pi^2 z^2 e^2}{c^2} \int \left(1 - \frac{1}{\beta^2 n^2}\right) \nu \, d\nu \qquad \text{ergs/cm} \qquad (6.2)$$

where ze is the charge on the moving particle and ν is the frequency of the emitted radiation. The integration is to be carried out over all frequencies for which $\beta n > 1$. The energy lost in Čerenkov radiation is only of the order of 10^3 ev per centimeter of glass or lucite and is generally negligible compared to the ionization losses. Nevertheless, this small energy is readily detectable because a relatively large number of low-energy quanta of visible light are emitted.

Consider the Čerenkov radiation emitted between two frequencies ν_1 and ν_2, as composed of quanta whose average energy is

$$h\bar{\nu} = \frac{h(\nu_1 + \nu_2)}{2}$$

Then from Eq. (6.2) the average number of quanta emitted per centimeter is

$$\frac{1}{h\bar{\nu}}\left(\frac{dT}{ds}\right)_{\text{Čer}} = \frac{4\pi^2 z^2 e^2}{hc^2}(\nu_2 - \nu_1)\left(1 - \frac{1}{\beta^2 n^2}\right)$$

$$= \frac{2\pi z^2}{137}\left(\frac{1}{\lambda_2} - \frac{1}{\lambda_1}\right)\left(1 - \frac{1}{\beta^2 n^2}\right) \quad \text{quanta/cm} \quad (6.3)$$

where $\lambda = c/\nu$ is the vacuum wavelength and n is the average index of refraction over the wavelength interval from λ_2 to λ_1.

Numerical substitution will show that in the visible domain, say, from 4,000 to 8,000 A, about 200 quanta per centimeter will be emitted by an electron ($z = -1$) having $\beta n = 1.5$, e.g., by electrons of a few Mev or more ($\beta \sim 1$), in glass, lucite, or mica ($n \sim 1.5$). This visible radiation will be emitted at an angle ϑ of about 48°. Equation (6.2) shows, through the term $\nu\, d\nu$ which is proportional to $d\lambda/\lambda^3$, that the energy per wavelength interval $d\lambda$ will be proportional to $1/\lambda^3$, while the number of quanta per wavelength interval will be proportional to $1/\lambda^2$. The short wavelengths are therefore preferred, and when observed visually, the Čerenkov radiation appears *bluish-white*.

It is to be noted from Eq. (6.2) that the Čerenkov radiation is *independent of the rest mass* of the moving particle and depends only on the particle's charge and velocity. Getting (G19) first proposed the construction of individual-particle detectors for very fast mesons and electrons by focusing the Čerenkov radiation onto a photomultiplier tube, and "Čerenkov counters" have now become a standard type of detection instrument for very fast charged particles (M16). Mather (M18) has developed a Čerenkov detector for swift protons (340 Mev, $\beta = 0.68$) in which the angular distribution of the Čerenkov radiation provides an absolute measure of the velocity of the proton, with an estimated uncertainty of only ± 0.8 Mev.

CHAPTER 19

Elastic Scattering of Electrons and Positrons

1. Scattering of Electrons by Nuclei

a. Classical Scattering Law of Rutherford. When a swift electron passes near an atomic nucleus of charge Ze and mass M_2, the coulomb forces produce a net deflection ϑ, in the laboratory system. Using the classical collision theory with discrete values of the impact parameter, the Rutherford scattering law emerges in the usual way.† The expression for the differential cross section for a deflection between ϑ and $\vartheta + d\vartheta$, assuming $M_1 \ll M_2$, and $\vartheta = \Theta$ [App. B, Eq. (25)], is

$$d\sigma = 2\pi x \, dx = \frac{\pi}{4} b^2 \cot \frac{\vartheta}{2} \csc^2 \frac{\vartheta}{2} \, d\vartheta \qquad (1.1)$$

where the length b is the *collision diameter*, or the *distance of closest possible approach*, and is defined as

$$b \equiv \frac{z_1 Z e^2}{\frac{1}{2} M_1 V_1^2} \qquad (1.2)$$

and the subscripts 1 refer to the incident particle.

The cross section for scattering through an angle ϑ or greater is

$$\sigma(\geq \vartheta) = \int_\pi^\vartheta d\sigma = 2\pi \int_0^x x \, dx = \pi x^2 = \frac{\pi}{4} b^2 \cot^2 \frac{\vartheta}{2} \qquad (1.3)$$

For example, backward scattering corresponds to $\vartheta \geq \pi/2$. Then $\vartheta = \pi/2$, and $\cot^2 \vartheta/2 = 1$, and the cross section for backward scattering is

$$\sigma\left(\vartheta \geq \frac{\pi}{2}\right) = \left(\frac{\pi}{4}\right) b^2 \qquad (1.4)$$

In case the scattering center is a nucleus of charge Ze, and the incident particle is an electron of velocity $V_1 = \beta c$, mass $M_1 = m_0/\sqrt{1 - \beta^2}$, and charge $z_1 e = \pm e$, the cross section for backscattering becomes

$$\sigma\left(\vartheta \geq \frac{\pi}{2}\right) = \pi Z^2 \left(\frac{e^2}{m_0 c^2}\right)^2 \left(\frac{1 - \beta^2}{\beta^4}\right) \quad \text{cm}^2/\text{nucleus} \qquad (1.5)$$

† For a complete development of the Rutherford law from classical theory, see Appendix B.

The coefficient $\pi(e^2/m_0c^2)^2 \simeq \frac{1}{4}$ barn. Thus, to an electron whose kinetic energy is $m_0c^2 = 0.51$ Mev, for which $\beta^2 = \frac{3}{4}$, nuclei present a back-scattering cross section of $Z^2/9$ barns per nucleus.

The differential scattering cross section is, from Eq. (1.1),

$$d\sigma = \pi Z^2 \left(\frac{e^2}{m_0c^2}\right)^2 \left(\frac{1-\beta^2}{\beta^4}\right) \frac{\cos(\vartheta/2)}{\sin^3(\vartheta/2)} d\vartheta \qquad (1.6)$$

These electrons are scattered into an element of solid angle given by

$$d\omega = 2\pi \sin \vartheta \, d\vartheta = 4\pi \sin \frac{\vartheta}{2} \cos \frac{\vartheta}{2} d\vartheta \qquad (1.7)$$

Therefore the classical differential cross section, $\xi_0(\vartheta) \, d\omega$ for elastic nuclear scattering of electrons into a solid angle $d\omega$, at a mean angle of ϑ in the laboratory system, is

$$d\sigma = \xi_0(\vartheta) \, d\omega = \frac{Z^2}{4} \left(\frac{e^2}{m_0c^2}\right)^2 \left(\frac{1-\beta^2}{\beta^4}\right) \frac{1}{\sin^4(\vartheta/2)} d\omega \qquad \text{cm}^2/\text{nucleus}$$

$$(1.8)$$

b. Quantum-mechanical Scattering. We have already noted that the definite impact parameters of classical theory are limited by the Heisenberg uncertainty principle to the domain where $2Zz/137\beta \gg 1$. Thus the classical treatment is valid for the scattering of slow particles by heavy nuclei. Most of the interesting cases of the scattering of electrons by nuclei lie well outside the domain of classical validity and therefore require a quantum-mechanical treatment. Fortunately, in most normal cases the electron is in the region where $2Z/137\beta \ll 1$ and so is in the domain of the validity of the Born approximation (see Appendix C).

Mott (M67, M64) first applied the relativistic Dirac theory of the electron to the problem of nuclear scattering, using the Born approximation. He obtained a general result for the differential cross section $\xi(\vartheta) \, d\omega$ in terms of a conditionally convergent infinite series. Mott and others have also derived various approximate formulas, among which the one by McKinley and Feshbach (M36), based on an expansion of Mott's exact formula as a power series in $Z/137$, seems most nearly correct. It is†

$$\xi(\vartheta) \, d\omega = \xi_0(\vartheta) \left[1 - \beta^2 \sin^2 \frac{\vartheta}{2} + \pi\beta \frac{Z}{137} \left(1 - \sin \frac{\vartheta}{2}\right) \sin \frac{\vartheta}{2}\right] d\omega \qquad (1.9)$$

and is valid for $\beta \simeq 1$ if $Z/137 \leq 0.2$. Thus the classical differential cross section, $\xi_0(\vartheta) \, d\omega$, is substantially correct when the deflections are small. For the larger values of deflection ϑ, and hence of $\sin(\vartheta/2)$, the quantum-mechanical theory gives a smaller cross section than the classical theory for all light elements.

† Mott's approximation has $\cos^2(\vartheta/2)$ in place of the $(1 - \sin \vartheta/2)$ term and is widely used.

c. Comparison of Quantum-mechanical and Classical Scattering.
Figure 1.1 gives the ratio of the scattering cross section $\xi(\vartheta) \, d\omega$ to the Rutherford cross section $\xi_0(\vartheta) \, d\omega$ for negatrons of 1 Mev and 4 Mev or more, based on exact calculations (M36). The approximate formula, Eq. (1.9), corresponds to the straight-line portions of these curves, starting at $Z/137 = 0$. It will be noted that for very heavy elements, and intermediate scattering angles, the expected scattering exceeds the classical by as much as a factor of 2, while for large-angle scattering the expected scattering may be as little as one-tenth of the classical.

In the limiting case of very slow particles, or for small deflections, we see from Eq. (1.9) that the quantum-mechanical and Rutherford scattering cross sections are equal. Williams (W59) has shown by a dimensional argument that *only an inverse-square interaction*, such as the

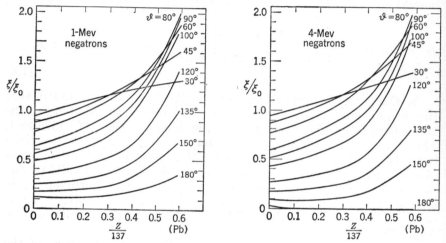

Fig. 1.1 Ratio of quantum-mechanical cross sections $\xi \, d\omega$ to classical (Rutherford) cross sections $\xi_0 \, d\omega$ for elastic single scattering of 1-Mev and 4-Mev negatrons by atomic nuclei. [*From McKinley and Feshbach* (M36).]

coulomb field, can lead to quantum-mechanical cross sections whose limiting forms do not contain h, and which can therefore be identical with the cross sections obtained from classical mechanics. Although the probability of scattering through a small angle ϑ is formally the same in the two theories, the parts of the nuclear field responsible for scattering are not the same (W59). In the classical collision theory, deflection through a small angle ϑ occurs for impact parameters x of the order of $Zze^2/m_0V^2\vartheta$. In the quantum mechanics, deflection through ϑ is mainly due to the coulomb potential at distances of the order of $h/2\pi m_0 V\vartheta$ from the nucleus. The ratio of the classical impact parameter to the equivalent wave-mechanical quantity is $Zz(2\pi e^2/hV) = Zz/137\beta$ for the same deflection. *The wave interaction*, in effect, *takes place much farther from the nucleus*, for the same deflection, if $Zz/137\beta \ll 1$.

Positrons. In Eq. (1.9), the expression in the square brackets represents the effect of electron spin and is purely quantum-mechanical. The manner in which the spin-orbit interaction enters the scattering cross section is seen to give rise to one correction term which is linear in Z. As would be expected, this linear term implies that the scattering is partly dependent upon the sign of the charges of the interacting particles. Equation (1.9) as written applies to the nuclear scattering of negatrons, for which Z is taken as a positive quantity. Conversely, the nuclear scattering of positrons is obtained from Eq. (1.9) when Z is replaced by $-Z$. We see that, for positrons, the final term in the square brackets is always negative. Consequently, the cross section for positron scatter-

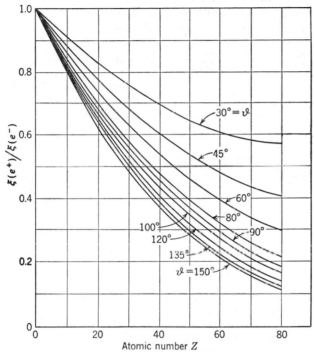

Fig. 1.2 Ratio of the differential nuclear scattering cross sections of positrons $\xi(e^+)$ to that of negatrons $\xi(e^-)$, as a function of Z and the laboratory scattering angle ϑ. These curves are for $\beta \simeq 1$ and apply to electrons of about 4 Mev or greater. [*From Feshbach* (F44).]

ing is always less than that for negatron scattering, at the same energy, angle, and Z. This effect has been demonstrated experimentally by Fowler and Oppenheimer (F63), Lipkin and White (L31), and others.

Theoretical evaluations of the cross sections for positron scattering have been made by Mott, Massey, Feshbach (F44), and others. For small values of Z, Eq. (1.9) is satisfactory, but for elements heavier than Fe ($Z = 26$) numerical summation of Mott's series is required. Such values have been tabulated by Feshbach and are illustrated in Fig. 1.2. Note that $\xi(e^+)/\xi(e^-)$ is always less than unity and decreases as either ϑ or Z increases.

d. Comparison of Theory and Experiment. Experimental studies of single elastic scattering of electrons by nuclei are difficult and have led to many results which are in apparent contradiction with the theory (C16). The bulk of the disagreement has shown no systematic trend (R5) and probably can be ascribed to experimental difficulties in separating the effects of elastic nuclear scattering from other effects such as inelastic scattering by atomic electrons, radiative collisions with nuclei, plural scattering, etc.

Careful studies by Randels, Chao, and Crane (R5) on the single scattering of 0.9- to 12-Mev electrons through angles of 15° and 90° by noble gases and air give agreement with Mott's theory. Experiments with 0.080-Mev electrons (C48) in which precautions were taken to measure only the single scattering by gold nuclei also give agreement with the Mott theory.

Results of detailed observations by Van de Graaff, Buechner, and coworkers (V1, B140) on single scattering of 1.27- to 2.27-Mev negatrons by various metals ($Z = 4$ to 79) are also in agreement with the exact form of the Mott theory. In these experiments the distance of closest approach of the electrons to the scattering nuclei varied between about 7×10^{-13} cm, in the case of Al, to about 100×10^{-13} cm for Au. Thus all the deflections studied occurred in the region between the radius of the nucleus and the radius of the K shell ($\sim 700 \times 10^{-13}$ cm for Au), where a substantially pure coulomb field would be expected. Typical results are shown in Fig. 1.3 which illustrates a case in which the ratio ξ/ξ_0 of quantum-mechanical to classical cross sections changes from less than unity to more than unity as Z increases.

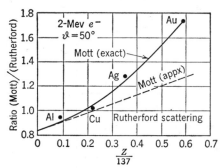

Fig. 1.3 Nuclear single scattering of 2-Mev negatrons at $\vartheta = 50°$. The solid line is the exact Mott theory, while the dotted line represents the approximation, Eq. (1.9). The experimental points are those of Van de Graaff, Buechner, and coworkers (V1, B140) as recalculated by McKinley and Feshbach (M36).

e. Effects of Screening and the Finite Size of the Nucleus. For very high-energy electrons (~ 15 Mev) some reduction in both the large- and small-angle scattering is to be expected (W59, W57, F43).

Electrons which pass the nucleus at a distance equal to or greater than the radius of the K shell will not experience the full coulomb interaction with the nucleus because of *screening* of the nuclear charge by the atomic electrons. Consequently, the very small deflections will be further reduced (and indeed cut off) by this screening.

Conversely, those very-high-energy electrons which have substantially head-on collisions may be thought of as having trajectories which pass through part of the nucleus. The coulomb forces on such an electron are again reduced, and the actual deflection will be less than that computed for a point charge. Important inferences concerning the *electromagnetic radius* of nuclei emerge from studies of these collisions (Chap. 2, Sec. 3).

Thus the effects of screening by atomic electrons and the finite size of the nucleus will decrease the observed scattering in the two extreme cases of small-angle and large-angle scattering, respectively. However, these effects are not noticeable at ordinary β-ray energies.

f. Plural and Multiple Scattering. It should be emphasized that all the preceding relations are for *single scattering* only, i.e., the path length ds in the absorber is taken to be small enough so that the probability of a scattering collision is very small. The probability that the same electron will be scattered twice in this distance is then negligible.

When thicker layers of absorbing material are used, so that one incident particle may suffer *a small number* of scattering collisions, the resulting phenomena are called *plural scattering*. The theory of plural scattering is very complicated.

If the thickness is such that a single particle can suffer *a large number* of scattering collisions, then statistical methods become applicable for the estimation of mean deflections. These phenomena are called *multiple scattering*. The detailed theory of multiple scattering has been worked out by Williams (W58) and Bethe (B42) and is in good agreement with observation on the "false curvature" of electron tracks in a cloud chamber, when no magnetic field is applied (S51).

An understanding of the effects of multiple scattering is imperative in interpreting cloud-chamber data. The statistical cumulative effect of a large number of small deflections along the path of a particle can make some such tracks imitate very well the curvature which a magnetic field would produce. When a magnetic field is also present, it is possible for the true magnetic curvature of the particle's path to be increased, decreased, or even reversed (B42) by the effects of multiple scattering.

Because the nuclear scattering cross section varies with Z^2, the scattering in air or argon will be 50 to 150 times as severe as the scattering in hydrogen. For this reason, cloud chambers in which the magnetic curvature of electron tracks is to be observed should be filled with the lowest-Z gas which will give enough specific ionization along the electron's track to make good pictures.

Multiple scattering of swift charged particles is often appreciable even in thin foils, where the statistical effects lead to a normal law distribution (Chap. 26) of the net small-angle scattering (S56).

2. *Scattering of Swift Electrons by Electrons*

Scattering of swift electrons occurs in an absorber not only by nuclear deflections but also in all the inelastic collisions with atomic electrons. If we assume that the energy transfer is much greater than the binding energy of the struck electron, we may neglect the binding energy and treat the problem as a collision between free particles.

The nonrelativistic cross section for scattering at a laboratory angle of ϑ or greater, for particles of equal mass m_0 and equal charge $\pm e$, can be obtained from Eq. (91) of Appendix B and is

$$\sigma(\geq \vartheta) = 4\pi \left(\frac{e^2}{m_0 V^2}\right)^2 \cot^2 \vartheta \qquad \text{cm}^2/\text{electron} \qquad (2.1)$$

Because the particles have equal mass, there is no backscattering in the laboratory system, and so the maximum value of ϑ is $\pi/2$.

After a nonrelativistic collision between particles of equal mass, the angle between the paths of the particles is always 90° [Appendix B, Eqs. (22) and (26)]. Each primary electron scattered at an angle ϑ is therefore accompanied by a recoil electron at an angle $(\pi/2) - \vartheta$. Experimentally, these electrons are indistinguishable. Thus the *total* number of electrons scattered at a laboratory angle greater than ϑ will be given classically by

$$\sigma(\geq \vartheta) = 4\pi \left(\frac{e^2}{m_0 V^2}\right)^2 (\cot^2 \vartheta + \tan^2 \vartheta) \qquad \text{cm}^2/\text{electron} \qquad (2.2)$$

where the $\tan^2 \vartheta$ really represents recoil electrons produced when the primary electron is scattered through the angle $(\pi/2) - \vartheta$.

Differentiation of Eq. (2.2) leads directly to the classical, or Rutherford, nonrelativistic cross section $\xi_R(\vartheta)\, d\omega$ for the scattering of either electron into a solid angle $d\omega = 2\pi \sin \vartheta\, d\vartheta$ at a mean angle ϑ.

$$d\sigma = \xi_R(\vartheta)\, d\omega = \left(\frac{e^2}{m_0 V^2}\right)^2 \left(\frac{1}{\sin^4 \vartheta} + \frac{1}{\cos^4 \vartheta}\right) 4 \cos \vartheta\, d\omega \qquad (2.3)$$

The factor $4 \cos \vartheta$ can be visualized as representing the ratio of the solid angle in laboratory coordinates and in center-of-mass coordinates, as shown in Appendix B, Eq. (90).

Mott (M65, M69) has developed a quantum-mechanical expression for this cross section, using the symmetry properties (B87) required of the wave function because of the identity of the particles. The resulting cross section for "*Mott scattering*" between identical particles is

$$\xi_M(\vartheta)\, d\omega = \left(\frac{e^2}{m_0 V^2}\right)^2 \left\{ \frac{1}{\sin^4 \vartheta} + \frac{1}{\cos^4 \vartheta} \right.$$
$$\left. + \binom{+2}{-1} \frac{\cos\left[(4\pi e^2/hV) \ln \tan \vartheta\right]}{\sin^2 \vartheta \cos^2 \vartheta} \right\} 4 \cos \vartheta\, d\omega \qquad (2.4)$$

The $+2$ factor in the third term in the curly braces is for particles of spin 0, the -1 for particles of spin $\frac{1}{2}$. This third term results from interference between the two parts of the wave function describing the two-particle system [compare Chap. 10, Eq. (5.1)]. For particles which are not identical quantum-mechanically the third term vanishes. A good approximation for electrons of energy greater than 1 kev is

$$\xi_M(\vartheta)\, d\omega = \left(\frac{e^2}{m_0 V^2}\right)^2 \left(\frac{1}{\sin^4 \vartheta} + \frac{1}{\cos^4 \vartheta} - \frac{1}{\sin^2 \vartheta \cos^2 \vartheta}\right) 4 \cos \vartheta\, d\omega \qquad (2.5)$$

Thus if n nonrelativistic electrons are incident normally on an absorber of thickness ds, which has NZ electrons/cm³, the fraction dn/n of electrons scattered into a solid angle $d\omega$ by electronic scattering will be

$$\frac{dn}{n} = (NZ\ ds)\ \xi_M(\vartheta)\ d\omega \qquad (2.6)$$

The corresponding relativistic expression has been obtained by Möller (M50, Eq. 74; p. 270 of M69), and its integration leads to Eq. (2.12) of Chap. 18 for the energy losses in high-energy electronic collisions.

It is now important to compare the nuclear and electronic scattering of incident electrons. Both cross sections are of the order of $(e^2/m_0V^2)^2$ for $Z = 1$. The nuclear scattering increases with Z^2 while the electronic scattering increases only with Z, the number of electrons per atom. In hydrogen the cross sections for scattering by the two different processes are about equal. In higher-Z elements the nuclear scattering predominates over the scattering by electrons by roughly a factor of Z.

In the theory of multiple scattering, where the statistical average of many collisions is to be evaluated, the effect of the electronic scattering can usually be included, to a satisfactory approximation (W58), by using only the expression for nuclear single scattering, but with

$$(Z^2 + Z) = Z(Z + 1)$$

in place of Z^2.

CHAPTER 20

Radiative Collisions of Electrons with Atomic Nuclei

The discovery of a continuous X-ray spectrum, or bremsstrahlung, which results from the *inelastic* collision of electrons with nuclei was the first step in the beginning of a new era in physics. Röntgen in 1895 first reported these mysterious rays, whose investigation was to lead into the field known today as "modern physics."

X rays are divided into two main types: (1) the line spectra, or *characteristic spectra*, which are electromagnetic radiations given off by an atom as it fills vacancies in a K, L, M, . . . shell; and (2) the *continuous spectra*, or bremsstrahlung, which are associated with the deflection of incident charged particles by the coulomb fields of nuclei.

1. *Theory of Bremsstrahlung*

a. Classical Considerations. According to classical theory, whenever a charge experiences an acceleration it will radiate. Therefore, whenever an incident charged particle is deflected from its path or has its velocity changed, it should emit electromagnetic radiation whose amplitude is proportional to the acceleration. The acceleration produced by a nucleus of charge Ze on a particle of charge ze and mass M is proportional to Zze^2/M. Thus the intensity, which is proportional to the square of the amplitude, will vary as Z^2z^2/M^2.

Thus the total bremsstrahlung per atom varies as the *square of the atomic number* of the absorbing material—a fact that is well confirmed by experiment. We also see that the total bremsstrahlung varies inversely with the *square of the mass of the incident particle*. Therefore protons and α particles will produce about one-millionth the bremsstrahlung of an electron of the same velocity. The μ meson, at first thought to be an electron in cosmic-ray studies, owes its discovery to the fact that its radiative losses were far too small for an electron. It was later found to have a rest mass about $212m_0$, which would mean its radiative losses are about 40,000 times smaller than the losses of an electron of the same velocity. Because of this strong mass dependence, bremsstrahlung is almost completely negligible for all swift particles other than electrons.

In an individual deflection by a nucleus, the incident particle can radiate any amount of energy from zero up to its total kinetic energy T.

Thus the maximum quantum energy $(h\nu)_{\text{max}}$ at the short wavelength limit of the continuous X-ray spectrum is

$$(h\nu)_{\text{max}} = T \tag{1.1}$$

This relationship was established experimentally by Duane and Hunt (D40) in 1915 and is known as Duane and Hunt's law.

b. Quantum-mechanical Theory of Bremsstrahlung. The deflection of a swift electron of velocity $V = \beta c$, rest mass m_0, by a nucleus of charge Ze falls in the domain of $Z/137\beta \ll 1$, if Z is not too large. This puts the interaction into the familiar "blackout" domain, where the true character of the interaction may differ from that which would be deduced from classical mechanics. In a quantum-mechanical treatment we have seen that the first approximation of Born's method calls for neglecting $Z/137\beta$ compared with unity. Born's first approximation is therefore applicable to the problem of bremsstrahlung, except for initial or final electrons of very low velocity.

The quantum-mechanical theory for the bremsstrahlung of relativistic electrons has been developed by Bethe and Heitler (B49, B39, H29) and others, using Dirac's relativistic theory of the electron and the first approximation of Born. Bethe and Maximon (B51) have derived the differential cross section without use of the Born approximation but under the analogous limitations of $T \gg m_0c^2$ and $(T - h\nu) \gg m_0c^2$. The nonrelativistic theory has been developed by Sommerfeld (S61), using exact wave functions, and his equations have been integrated over all angles by Weinstock (W18), for comparison with experiment (H23).

In quantum-mechanical theory, a plane wave representing the electron enters the nuclear field, is scattered, and has a small but finite chance of emitting a photon. The electron is acted on by the electromagnetic field of the emitted photon, as well as by the coulomb field of the nucleus. The intermediate states of the system involve the negative energy states which characterize the Dirac electron theory. The theory of bremsstrahlung is intimately related to the theory of electron pair production (Chap. 24, Sec. 2) by energetic photons in the field of a nucleus.

Because the radiative process involves the coupling of the electron with the electromagnetic field of the emitted photon, the cross sections for radiation are of the order of $\frac{1}{137}$ times the cross sections for elastic scattering. Most of the individual deflections of incident electrons by atomic nuclei are elastic. In only a small number of instances is a photon emitted.

Recall that radiative forces were not taken into account in Mott's theory of the elastic scattering of electrons by nuclei (Chap. 19). In that theory, the influence of energy losses by radiation cannot be taken into account, because the probability that the deflected electron will radiate is of the order of $2\pi e^2/hc = \frac{1}{137}$, and such terms are neglected in comparison with unity in the first-order perturbation theory (Born approximation) used to develop the theory of elastic scattering. The influence of radiative losses on elastic collisions is estimated to be less than 2 or 3 per cent (M66).

Comparison with Classical Theory. The classical theory of bremsstrahlung incorrectly predicted the emission of radiation in *every* collision in which an electron is deflected. Yet for the averages over all collisions, the classical (p. 176 of H29) and the quantum-mechanical cross sections are of the same order of magnitude, namely,

$$\sigma_{\text{rad}} \sim \frac{Z^2}{137} \left(\frac{e^2}{m_0 c^2} \right)^2 \quad \text{cm}^2/\text{nucleus} \tag{1.2}$$

In the quantum-mechanical model there is a small but finite probability that a photon will be emitted each time a particle suffers a deflection; however, this probability is so small that usually no photon is emitted. In the few collisions which are accompanied by photon emission, a relatively large amount of energy is radiated. In this way the quantum theory replaces the multitude of small classical energy losses by a much smaller number of larger energy losses, the averages being about the same in the two theories. Of course, the spectral distributions are very different in the two models. All experimental results are in agreement with the quantum-mechanical model.

Angular Distribution. In the radiative collision, the initial momentum of the incident electron becomes shared between the momenta of three bodies: the residual electron, the atomic nucleus, and the emitted photon. Therefore the photon can have any momentum and the corresponding energy up to $h\nu_{\max} = T$. The momentum $h\nu/c$ of a photon is generally very small compared with the momentum of an electron having the same energy. Only at extreme relativistic energies do these momenta become equal. For the radiative collisions of moderate-energy electrons, momentum is substantially conserved between the nucleus and the deflected electron. The photon carries relatively only a very small momentum and can be emitted in any direction. At extreme relativistic energies, however, *both* the photon and the residual electron tend to proceed in the same direction as the incident electron. The average angle between the direction of the incident electron and the emitted quantum is then of the order of $m_0 c^2/T$ (B39, S10). The large-angle distribution of the bremsstrahlung from very-high-energy electrons is available from the calculations by Hough (H64).

Effects of Nuclear Radius and of Screening. In general, the bulk of the radiation losses of electrons occurs at relatively large distances from the nucleus. As in the case of elastic scattering, the major contributions arise from a region which is much farther from the nucleus than would be given by classical considerations. The dominant contributions to the radiative cross section come from distances of the order of the rationalized Compton wavelength $\hbar/m_0 c$ ($= 385 \times 10^{-13}$ cm) and larger (B49). For much smaller distances, the corresponding scattering volume is small; at much larger distances, the scattering is reduced by interference. At extreme relativistic energies, say, > 10-Mev electrons and in heavy atoms, the radiative losses at very large distances from the nucleus are reduced by screening (B39), while the losses in very close collisions are further reduced by the effects of the finite size of the nucleus (H64).

Differential Radiative Cross Section. The principal quantitative results of the quantum-mechanical theory of radiative collisions may be stated in the following way. For nuclei of charge Ze, the differential cross section $d\sigma_{\mathrm{rad}}$ for the emission of a photon in the energy range between $h\nu$ and $h\nu + d(h\nu)$, by incident electrons of kinetic energy T and total energy $T + m_0c^2$, can be written

$$d\sigma_{\mathrm{rad}} = \sigma_0 B Z^2 \frac{T + m_0c^2}{T} \frac{d(h\nu)}{h\nu} \qquad \mathrm{cm^2/nucleus} \qquad (1.3)$$

where
$$\sigma_0 = \frac{1}{137}\left(\frac{e^2}{m_0c^2}\right)^2 = 0.580 \text{ millibarn/nucleus} \qquad (1.4)$$

and B is a very slowly varying function of Z and T, of the order of magnitude of 10. Figure 1.1 shows the theoretical values of B, which vary by only about a factor of 5 for all values of $h\nu$, T, and Z. Of course, $h\nu \leq h\nu_{\max} = T$. The electron energy T is marked in Mev on each curve. The high-energy curves (≥ 10 Mev) include screening corrections for Pb. The lower curve is for 60-kev electrons in Al, according to Sommerfeld's non-relativistic quantum-mechanical theory (p. 170 of H29). Comparison with Eq. (1.3) shows that, for each value of T, the parameter B is proportional to the *intensity per frequency interval.* The general constancy of B, for all values of $h\nu$, as found experimentally (Fig. 1.3a), for $T \ll m_0c^2$, is fairly well predicted by these theoretical curves.

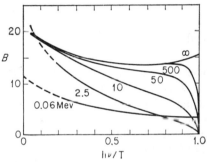

Fig. 1.1 The coefficient B of the differential cross section for bremsstrahlung, Eq. (1.3), according to the numerical evaluations by Heitler (B29).

Experimental studies using 19.5-Mev electrons (K26) suggest that the true bremsstrahlung spectrum is more nearly independent of $h\nu/T$ and is about 10 per cent more intense than the theoretical spectrum; that is, B is more nearly constant and its *average* value is about 10 per cent larger than shown here.

Bremsstrahlung from Heavy Particles. If the incident particle is not an electron but is some particle having charge ze and rest mass M, then the total energy of the particle becomes $(T + Mc^2)$ in the numerator of Eq. (1.3), while the principal effect of the larger rest mass is found in σ_0 which becomes $\frac{1}{137}(ze^2/Mc^2)^2$. As would be expected, the bremsstrahlung from $\sim$2-Mev protons is not significant in comparison with the characteristic K and L X rays produced by ionization in the target (L33, B36).

Total Radiative Loss. Integration of Eq. (1.3) gives the total energy loss per unit path length, due to bremsstrahlung, and is

$$\left(\frac{dT}{ds}\right)_{\text{rad}} = N \int_0^T h\nu \, d\sigma_{\text{rad}} \qquad \text{ergs/cm} \tag{1.5}$$

$$= N\sigma_0 Z^2 (T + m_0 c^2) \int_0^1 B \, d\left(\frac{h\nu}{T}\right) \qquad \text{ergs/cm} \tag{1.6}$$

where N is the number of atoms per cubic centimeter.

Total Radiative Cross Section. The total bremsstrahlung cross section σ_{rad} is defined as the fraction of the *total* energy $(T + m_0 c^2)$ of the electron which is radiated as the electron traverses an absorber of such thickness that it contains 1 atom/cm². Then

$$\sigma_{\text{rad}} \equiv \frac{dT}{T + m_0 c^2} \frac{1}{N \, ds} \tag{1.7}$$

$$\sigma_{\text{rad}} = \sigma_0 Z^2 \int_0^1 B \, d\left(\frac{h\nu}{T}\right)$$

$$\equiv \sigma_0 Z^2 \bar{B} \qquad \text{cm}^2/\text{nucleus} \tag{1.8}$$

and

$$\left(\frac{dT}{ds}\right)_{\text{rad}} = N(T + m_0 c^2)\sigma_{\text{rad}} \qquad \text{ergs/cm} \tag{1.9}$$

Here $\bar{B}$ is the average value of B over the domain $h\nu = 0$ to $h\nu_{\max} = T$.

The theoretical values of B shown in Fig. 1.1, and the corresponding values of $\bar{B}$ which are plotted in Fig. 1.2, are undoubtedly too low near the high-energy limit, $h\nu/T = 1$, of the spectrum. This inaccuracy arises from the use of the Born approximation, which is not applicable to very slow electrons such as those of energy $(T - h\nu)$ near $h\nu = T$.

The following approximate expressions for the bremsstrahlung cross section σ_{rad} of Eq. (1.8) arise from the detailed quantum-mechanical theories (B49):

1. For the nonrelativistic case,

$$T \ll m_0 c^2 \qquad \sigma_{\text{rad}} = \tfrac{16}{3}\sigma_0 Z^2 \qquad \text{cm}^2/\text{nucleus} \tag{1.10}$$

2. For the moderately relativistic case with no screening corrections, $T \sim m_0 c^2$; no analytical expression.

3. For the highly relativistic case, but without screening corrections, $m_0 c^2 \ll T \ll 137 m_0 c^2 Z^{-\frac{1}{3}}$ (for example, for Pb, 0.5 Mev $\ll T \ll$ 16 Mev),

$$\sigma_{\text{rad}} = 4 \left[\ln\left(2\frac{T + m_0 c^2}{m_0 c^2}\right) - \frac{1}{3}\right] \sigma_0 Z^2 \tag{1.11}$$

4. For the extremely relativistic case, with complete screening corrections, $T \gg 137 m_0 c^2 Z^{-\frac{1}{3}}$,

$$\sigma_{\text{rad}} = 4[\ln (183 Z^{-\frac{1}{3}}) + \tfrac{1}{18}]\sigma_0 Z^2 \tag{1.12}$$

Numerical values of the total bremsstrahlung cross section σ_{rad} are plotted in Fig. 1.2.   The values will be a little too small because of the effect of the Born approximation near $h\nu = T$.

c. **Thin-target Bremsstrahlung.**   The long succession of gradually improving theories of bremsstrahlung (C37) has dealt almost exclusively with the thin-target case.   Here one calculates the radiation expected from a collimated beam of monoener-getic electrons, while passing through a target which is so thin that the electrons lose no appreciable energy by ionization, suffer no significant elastic deflections, and have no second radiative collisions.   These are, indeed, rigorous conditions to impose on experiments designed to test the theory.   As a result, only a very few acceptable experiments have been done in the thin-target field.

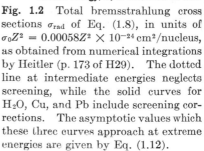

The more prominent features of the thin-target spectrum were inferred from thick-target data as early as 1917 by Webster (W15) and have since been confirmed by various workers (C37).   They are:

1. The radiation from electrons of a given energy T, in any particular direction, has an *intensity* [(energy per photon) × (number of photons)]

Fig. 1.2   Total bremsstrahlung cross sections σ_{rad} of Eq. (1.8), in units of $\sigma_0 Z^2 = 0.00058 Z^2 \times 10^{-24}\,cm^2/nucleus$, as obtained from numerical integrations by Heitler (p. 173 of H29).   The dotted line at intermediate energies neglects screening, while the solid curves for H_2O, Cu, and Pb include screening corrections.   The asymptotic values which these three curves approach at extreme energies are given by Eq. (1.12).

which is constant for all photon energies and cuts off abruptly at $h\nu_{max}$. See Fig. 1.3a.

2. For electrons of various nonrelativistic energies the radiation intensity in a particular direction, and within a particular energy interval,

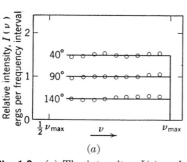

(a)

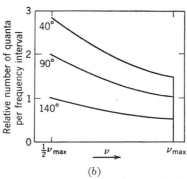

(b)

Fig. 1.3   (a) The intensity, $I(\nu) \propto h\nu\,d\sigma_{rad}$, per frequency interval is independent of the frequency, cuts off sharply at $h\nu_{max}$, and is minimal in the backward direction. Data are for 45-kev electrons on a thin Au target, at 40°, 90°, and 140° from the direction of the incident electrons. [*From Nicholas* (N11).]   (b) The number of quanta per frequency interval varies as $1/h\nu$.   These curves are derived from (a).

varies as $1/T$; that is, the radiation intensity between $h\nu$ and $h\nu + d(h\nu)$ *decreases* with increasing electron energy (H23).

3. The *shape* of the spectral distribution of bremsstrahlung is independent of Z.

4. At very low electron energies the radiation intensity is maximum at right angles to the incident beam. As the electron energy increases, the maximum of the radiation intensity moves forward. At very high electron energies the photon intensity is predominantly in the forward direction.

5. The bremsstrahlung is partially polarized. The direction of its electric vector tends to be parallel to the direction of the incident electron, and the maximum intensity is radiated normal to the plane of motion

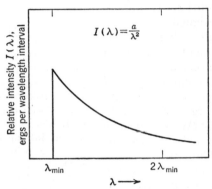

Fig. 1.4 The intensity distribution from a thin target, in terms of the wavelength of the emitted bremsstrahlung. If $I(\nu) = $ const is the intensity per frequency interval, and $I(\lambda)$ is the corresponding intensity distribution per wavelength interval, then $I(\nu)$ $d\nu = I(\lambda)\ d\lambda$, or $I(\lambda) = I(\nu)\ d\nu/d\lambda = $ const $(1/\lambda^2)$. The short wavelength limit $\lambda_{\min}$ corresponds to $\nu_{\max}$, that is, $\lambda_{\min} = c/\nu_{\max}$.

of the electron. In the mixture of unpolarized and linearly polarized radiation, the polarized component predominates near both the low-energy and the high-energy ends of the bremsstrahlung energy spectrum (K47, S61, G24, G23).

Figures 1.3a and b and 1.4 summarize the general character of the experimental findings regarding the spectral distribution and spatial distribution of the thin-target bremsstrahlung for homogeneous electrons.

2. *Comparison of Various Interactions Between Swift Electrons and Atoms*

We may now compare the results of previous sections, in order to appraise the relative importance of several types of collision between incident electrons and the atoms in an absorbing medium.

a. Comparison of Atomic Cross Sections. In order to put all interactions on a common basis, we can develop expressions for the equivalent cross section per atom, for each type of collision. For the sake of brevity, we shall consider only the case of nonrelativistic electrons, $T \le 0.1$ Mev, $\beta \le 0.5$. Each cross section can be expressed in barns per atom with the help of the convenient relationship

$$4\pi \left(\frac{e^2}{m_0 c^2} \right)^2 = 1.00 \times 10^{-24} \text{ cm}^2 = 1.00 \text{ barn} \tag{2.1}$$

Ionization. From Eq. (2.28) of Chap. 18, the cross section per atom for a fractional energy loss dT/T due to an ionizing collision is

$$\sigma_{\text{ion}} \equiv \frac{1}{N} \frac{1}{T} \left(\frac{dT}{ds} \right)_{\text{ion}} = 8\pi \left(\frac{e^2}{m_0 c^2} \right)^2 \frac{Z}{\beta^4} \ln \frac{T \sqrt{2}}{I} \qquad \text{cm}^2/\text{atom}$$

$$= 2 \frac{Z}{\beta^4} \ln \frac{T \sqrt{2}}{I} \qquad \text{barns/atom} \tag{2.2}$$

Backscattering by Nuclei. From Eq. (1.5) of Chap. 19, the cross section per atom for nuclear backscattering of low-energy electrons is

$$\sigma_{\text{nuc}} \left(\vartheta \ge \frac{\pi}{2} \right) \simeq \pi \left(\frac{e^2}{m_0 c^2} \right)^2 Z^2 \left(\frac{1 - \beta^2}{\beta^4} \right) \qquad \text{cm}^2/\text{atom}$$

$$= \frac{1}{4} \frac{Z^2}{\beta^4} \qquad \text{barns/atom} \tag{2.3}$$

Scattering by Atomic Electrons. Because there is no backscattering of electrons by electrons, we may take as "significant" scattering some arbitrary scattering angle, such as 45°. Then for low-energy electrons Eq. (2.2) of Chap. 19 leads to

$$\sigma_{\text{eln}} \left(\vartheta \ge \frac{\pi}{4} \right) \simeq 8\pi \left(\frac{e^2}{m_0 c^2} \right)^2 \frac{Z}{\beta^4} \qquad \text{cm}^2/\text{atom}$$

$$= 2 \frac{Z}{\beta^4} \qquad \text{barns/atom} \tag{2.4}$$

Bremsstrahlung. The cross section for nuclear scattering accompanied by a radiative loss of the fraction $dT/(T + m_0 c^2)$ of the electron's total energy is given directly by Eq. (1.10) of this chapter,

$$\sigma_{\text{rad}} \equiv \frac{1}{N} \frac{1}{(T + m_0 c^2)} \left(\frac{dT}{ds} \right)_{\text{rad}} = \frac{16}{3} \left(\frac{e^2}{m_0 c^2} \right)^2 \frac{Z^2}{137} \qquad \text{cm}^2/\text{atom}$$

$$= \frac{4}{3\pi} \frac{Z^2}{137} \qquad \text{barns/atom} \tag{2.5}$$

A more equitable comparison with the other cross sections would be given by a radiative cross section σ'_{rad} in terms of the fractional loss of *kinetic energy* dT/T, rather than of *total energy* $dT/(T + m_0 c^2)$. This would be

$$\sigma'_{\text{rad}} \equiv \frac{1}{N} \frac{1}{T} \left(\frac{dT}{ds} \right)_{\text{rad}} = \left(\frac{T + m_0 c^2}{T} \right) \sigma_{\text{rad}} \simeq \left(\frac{2}{\beta^2} \right) \sigma_{\text{rad}}$$

$$= \frac{8}{3\pi} \frac{1}{137} \frac{Z^2}{\beta^2} \qquad \text{barns/atom} \tag{2.6}$$

Note how this cross section differs from the analogous cross section for ionization, especially with respect to their dependence on Z and β. Table 2.1 collects the numerical values for each of these five approximate cross sections, evaluated for the specific case of 0.1-Mev electrons in air ($Z = 7.22$; $I \simeq 100$ ev) and in Pb ($Z = 82$; $I \simeq 800$ ev). Note that in light elements the ionization interaction predominates. In heavy elements, ionization and nuclear elastic scattering are of comparable importance in this energy domain.

TABLE 2.1. APPROXIMATE CROSS SECTIONS IN BARNS PER ATOM OF Pb, AND OF AIR, FOR INCIDENT 0.1-MEV ELECTRONS, EQS. (2.2) TO (2.6)

	Ionization	Nuclear elastic backward scattering $\vartheta \geq 90°$	Electronic (inelastic) scattering $\vartheta \geq 45°$	Bremsstrahlung	
				σ_{rad}	σ'_{rad}
Approximate variation with Z and β	Z/β^4	Z^2/β^4	Z/β^4	Z^2	Z^2/β^2
Air......................	1,200	150	160	0.16	1.0
Pb......................	9,400	19,000	1,800	21	130

b. Mass Absorption. Ionization losses per unit distance along the path of a primary particle are proportional to the number of atomic electrons per cubic centimeter of the absorber, NZ. If ρ g/cm³ is the density of the absorber, A its atomic weight, N Avogadro's number, and N the number of atoms per cubic centimeter, then

$$NZ = \left(\frac{\rho N}{A}\right) Z = \rho N \left(\frac{Z}{A}\right) \tag{2.7}$$

The ratio of Z/A is nearly a constant for all elements. Therefore NZ/ρ is approximately constant for all elements (except hydrogen which has twice as many electrons per gram as any other element). Consequently, if distances *along the path* of the particle are measured in units of $\rho\,ds \equiv dw$ g/cm², the ionization losses dT/dw in ergs/(g/cm²) become approximately independent of the material.

Figure 2.1 shows the theoretical ionization and radiative losses in kev/(mg/cm²) for several absorbing materials. Notice that the ionization curves for air, Al, and Pb [which are based on Eq. (2.26) of Chap. 18] do not quite overlap. The actual ionization losses dT/dw decrease slightly as Z increases. This is because (1) Z/A decreases slightly as Z increases, thus *there are fewer electrons per gram in high Z materials*, and (2) the mean ionization potential, $I \simeq kZ$, increases with Z, thus *the electrons are more tightly bound in high Z materials*. The effects of Z/A and of I act in the same direction, to decrease dT/dw as measured along the path of the particle.

The actual path of an electron while passing through an absorbing foil is not straight. Because of the effects of multiple scattering, the actual path length is always greater than the foil thickness traversed. The ratio of the actual path length to the superficial thickness of absorber traversed increases with Z (Chap. 21, Sec. 1).   In the case of electrons (but not heavy particles), the effect of scattering almost exactly balances the decrease of dT/dw with increasing Z. Therefore, if distance is measured in terms of superficial thickness of absorber traversed, say, in milligrams per square centimeter, the ionization losses for positrons and

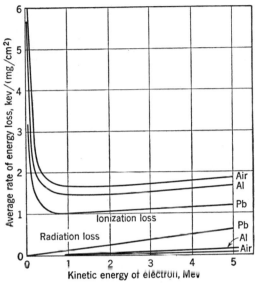

Fig. 2.1 Mass-absorption energy losses for electrons in air, Al, and Pb. The upper three curves are $(dT/dw)_{ion}$, based on Eq. (2.26) of Chap. 18, with $dw = \rho \, ds$, and $I_{air} = 86$ ev, $I_{Al} = 165$ ev, $I_{Pb} = 750$ ev.   The three lower curves show, on the same scales, the average energy loss due to bremsstrahlung $(dT/dw)_{rad}$ as obtained from Eq. (1.9), with $dw = \rho \, ds$. All curves refer to energy losses along the actual path traversed by the electron.

negatrons become nearly independent of the nature of the absorbing material.   It is therefore common in reporting experimental work to use milligrams per square centimeter, or a similar unit, as the measure of absorber thickness.

c. Ratio of Radiative and Ionization Losses. Ionization losses per unit path length vary roughly as $1/\beta^2$ and so are largest for slow particles. On the other hand, radiative losses increase with increasing energy, Eq. (1.9).   At high energies, $T \gg Mc^2$ in general, or $T \gg m_0 c^2$ for electrons, the radiative losses become comparable with the ionization losses.

The ratio of the radiative to the ionization losses, for any particle of rest mass M_0, and high velocity $\beta \simeq 1$, is obtainable from the quotient of Eq. (1.9) and Eq. (2.26) of Chap. 18.   With $137\sigma_0$ generalized to

$(e^2/M_0c^2)^2$, the ratio becomes approximately (B55)

$$\frac{(dT/ds)_{\text{rad}}}{(dT/ds)_{\text{ion}}} \simeq Z \left(\frac{m_0}{M_0}\right)^2 \left(\frac{T}{1,400m_0c^2}\right) \tag{2.8}$$

The factor 1,600 holds for electrons ($M_0 = m_0$) but should be reduced to about 1,000 for mesons ($M_0 \sim 200m_0$). Thus we see that, for electrons, the radiative and ionization losses are equal for $T = 18m_0c^2 = 9$ Mev in Pb (and for $T \sim 100$ Mev in water or air).

The numerical values of σ_{rad} are such that *for electrons at 9 Mev the radiative and ionization losses are each equal to about* 1.45 *Mev per millimeter of* Pb, *or a total of* 2.9 *Mev per millimeter of Pb for both.* This makes a very convenient rule of thumb for estimating high-energy radiative losses (which increase approximately with NZ^2 and T) and ionization losses (which increase with NZ but are nearly independent of T).

CHAPTER 21

Stopping of Electrons by Thick Absorbers

In previous chapters we have considered the individual types of interactions which electrons experience as they pass through matter. We
have developed relationships for the energy losses due to each of these
processes, per unit path length of the electron. New difficulties arise,
however, when one undertakes to apply these results to the usual laboratory situation. This is partly because all these results are based on the
path length of the electron, a quantity which is measurable in only a few
special cases, namely, in cloud chambers and photographic emulsions.
In most β-ray-absorption studies, where the absorber is thick enough
for many collisions to occur, the concept of path length is of little value
and one must turn to the concept of range.

1. *Path Length and Range of Electrons*

As the electron passes through matter it loses its energy in ionizing
and radiative collisions. In each of these it may suffer significant deflections. In addition, there is a large number of deflections due to elastic
scattering. The net result is that the electron's path as it passes through
the absorber is very tortuous. In practice, one finds the path length to
be from 1.2 to 4 times the thickness of the absorber traversed, the ratio
being largest for slow electrons in high Z material (W62, W54, T30, C45,
Y2).

The *range R* of a particle is an experimental concept, relating to the
thickness of an absorber which the particle can just penetrate. Several
distinct definitions of range, which depend upon the method employed
to determine them, are in common usage. They all relate, however, to
roughly the same quantity. Here we wish only to recognize that the
electron's total path length is a quantity which is completely different
from its range. The distinction can be visualized from Fig. 1.1, where
R is the range.

The total path length has been observed in a few experiments, using
cloud chambers or photographic emulsions. Among these, one by E. J.
Williams (W54) provides a direct comparison of total path length S to
range R. In this experiment, monoenergetic electrons were produced in a
cloud chamber by the photoelectric absorption of monochromatic X rays.

The total path length and the maximum distance reached in the initial direction were then measured.

Figure 1.2 presents Williams's (W54) observations on the distribution of path length S and range R in oxygen for 145 individual electrons whose initial kinetic energy was 19.6 kev. Several fundamental features of the interaction of electrons with matter can be visualized from a study of these curves. In this energy domain, radiative losses are negligible and the curves represent the effects of ionization losses, elastic scattering, and straggling of energy losses.

The curve S shows the fraction f of the electrons whose path length exceeds the distance D cm. The slope of the curve dS/dD is the fraction of electrons whose path lengths lie between D and $D + dD$. These

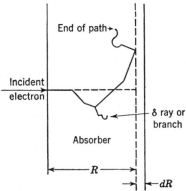

Fig. 1.1 Schematic diagram of the path of an electron which is multiply scattered while traversing an absorber of thickness $R + dR$ and which does not emerge from the absorber. If the absorber had been of thickness R, the electron would have just penetrated it and would be said to have a *range R*. The total *path length S* is measured along the actual path of the electron and is always considerably greater than R.

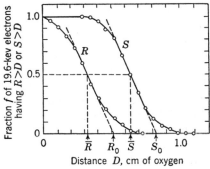

Fig. 1.2 The distribution of path lengths (S) and of range (R) (Fig. 1.1) for 19.6-kev electrons in oxygen at 0°C and 1-atm pressure:

$\bar{R}$ = 0.32 cm = mean range
R_0 = 0.52 cm = extrapolated range
$\bar{S}$ = 0.64 cm = mean path length
S_0 = 0.82 cm = extrapolated path length
$\sqrt{2/\pi}(S_0 - \bar{S})$ = 0.14 cm = $0.22\bar{S}$
  = standard deviation of S about $\bar{S}$

The mean path length is 1.24 times the extrapolated range, under these conditions. [*From Williams* (W54).]

slopes are sufficiently symmetric about $f = 0.5$ so that the mean path length $\bar{S}$ can be taken as the path length at $f = 0.5$, when one-half the electrons have been stopped.

The broad distribution of path lengths is noteworthy and is due to the statistical distribution of energy losses, or *straggling*, for each electron. Some have large losses, including one or more "branches" due to hard collisions, and have short path lengths. Others suffer smaller and fewer losses per millimeter of path and have much longer path lengths. The theoretical value of $(dT/ds)_{ion}$ relates to the average energy losses, and thus its integral is $\bar{S}$, corresponding to the average path length, or *mean path length*.

The profound effects of scattering are shown by a comparison of the R and S curves of Fig. 1.2. We notice that only about 3 per cent of the electrons have sufficiently straight paths to penetrate an absorber whose thickness is equal to the mean path length $\bar{S}$. Indeed, the average range $\bar{R}$ which one-half the electrons will penetrate is just $0.32/0.64 = \frac{1}{2}$ of the average path length. It is important to keep this distinction in mind when we return later to the body of empirical data on the range-energy relationships.

Numerical data on the path length of electrons in argon, oxygen, and hydrogen, as measured by Williams (W54), are given in Table 1.1.

TABLE 1.1. THE AVERAGE PATH LENGTH $\bar{S}$ FOR ELECTRONS IN GASES AT 0°C AND 760 MM Hg (W54)

Gas	Initial energy, kev	Average path length, cm	Number of tracks measured
Argon................	20.44	0.67	
Oxygen..............	7.56 (a)	0.117	114
Oxygen..............	19.59 (b)	0.644	209
Oxygen..............	22.13 (c)	0.847	87
Oxygen..............	av: 20.44 (d)	0.709	
Oxygen..............	20.44 − 7.56 (e)	0.592	
Hydrogen............	4.80	0.35	
Hydrogen............	7.56	0.72	

NOTE: (d) is the average of (b) and (c). (e) is the difference between (d) and (a) and is most useful because, experimentally, it eliminates uncertainties in determining the exact end of the cloud-chamber track in terms of the last blob of ionization, while theoretically it permits integration of $(dT/ds)_{ion}$ over a velocity domain in which the theory should be valid.

These values are in satisfactory agreement (W59, W56) with the quantum theory of energy losses but are in decided disagreement (W55, W54) with the classical theory. These data can be extrapolated to other energies and to other elements, by means of Bethe's result for $(dT/ds)_{ion}$ [Chap. 18, Eq. (2.22)] and its integrals. Transformations which are useful in this integration are discussed in Chap. 22 on heavy particles.

In theory, it is possible to calculate the path length of an electron with the aid of previously developed relations. The average path length of an electron of kinetic energy T will be

$$\bar{S} = \int ds = \int_{T_1}^{T} \frac{dT}{(dT/ds)} \tag{1.1}$$

where

$$\left(\frac{dT}{ds}\right) = \left(\frac{dT}{ds}\right)_{ion} + \left(\frac{dT}{ds}\right)_{rad} \tag{1.2}$$

Because our relations for dT/ds were developed with the aid of the Born approximation, Eq. (1.1) will not be valid as the lower limit of T approaches zero ($T_1 \to 0$). The expression can be used for absorbers that do not stop the electrons. In most cases, however, one finds little useful information from such a calculation since only the average path length $\bar{S}$ can be calculated. Because of the very large straggling effects for electrons, the actual paths will show large variations about this mean value.

2. Thick-target Bremsstrahlung

a. Thick-target Bremsstrahlung from Monoenergetic Electrons. In Chap. 20 we saw that the thin-target bremsstrahlung is a highly idealized case, rarely met in practice. The thick-target case, although far less adequately covered by theory because of its complexity, is none the less the usual laboratory situation. It is met in X-ray tubes, solutions of radioactive substances, and in all other cases where swift electrons are absorbed.

The average bremsstrahlung energy emitted in an element of path length ds is

$$(dT)_{\text{rad}} = \left(\frac{dT}{ds}\right)_{\text{rad}} ds = \frac{(dT/ds)_{\text{rad}}}{(dT/ds)_{\text{ion}} + (dT/ds)_{\text{rad}}} dT \qquad \text{ergs} \quad (2.1)$$

The average energy I radiated by an electron of initial energy T in being stopped is

$$I = \int (dT)_{\text{rad}} = \int_0^T \frac{(dT/ds)_{\text{rad}}}{(dT/ds)_{\text{ion}} + (dT/ds)_{\text{rad}}} dT \qquad (2.2)$$

Integration using the theoretical values of radiative and ionization losses is valid only over the portion of the path for which the electron's velocity is large compared with the velocity of the atomic electrons. In most cases, the integration must be performed graphically, because of the complicated analytical form of $(dT/ds)_{\text{ion}}$ and $(dT/ds)_{\text{rad}}$.

For moderate-energy electrons, radiative losses are very small compared with ionization losses so that Eq. (2.2) is well approximated by

$$I \simeq \int_0^T \frac{(dT/ds)_{\text{rad}}}{(dT/ds)_{\text{ion}}} dT \qquad (2.3)$$

The radiative losses for nonrelativistic electrons, Eqs. (1.9) and (1.10) of Chap. 20, are

$$\left(\frac{dT}{ds}\right)_{\text{rad}} = \tfrac{16}{3} NZ^2 \sigma_0 (T + m_0 c^2) \qquad \text{ergs/cm} \quad (2.4)$$

where $\sigma_0 = \frac{1}{137}(e^2/m_0 c^2)^2 = 5.80 \times 10^{-28}$ cm^2/atom. In this case, $T \ll m_0 c^2$, and so the radiative losses are independent of the energy of the electron and $(dT/ds)_{\text{rad}}$ may be taken outside the integral sign. The remaining integral is then simply the mean path length $\bar{S}$; hence the average energy radiated is

$$I = \text{const } NZ^2 \bar{S} \qquad (2.5)$$

Because $(dT/ds)_{\text{ion}}$ is proportional to NZ, the path length $\bar{S}$ will vary about as $1/NZ$, if we neglect the logarithmic variation of $(dT/ds)_{ion}$ with the geometric-mean ionization potential.   Thus we have

$$I = Zf(T,Z) \qquad (2.6)$$

where $f(T,Z)$ is a function of T and Z, which depends only slightly on Z. We therefore expect the thick-target bremsstrahlung to be independent of N and proportional to the *first power of the atomic number* of the absorber.   This rule will fail only when T and Z are large enough that the radiative losses can no longer be neglected in comparison with the ionization losses.

Spectral Distribution.   The spectral distribution of thick-target bremsstrahlung can be thought of as the sum of the contributions from a number of thin-target cases of various electron energies.   This is illustrated in Fig. 2.1 where a number of thin-target cases (each like Fig. 1.3a, Chap. 20) are superimposed.   To obtain numerical results it is necessary to integrate Eq. (2.1).   This has been done graphically (K20), using the Sommerfeld nonrelativistic theory for $(dT/ds)_{rad}$ and semiempirical values of $(dT/ds)_{ion}$, giving a spectral distribution from thick targets of

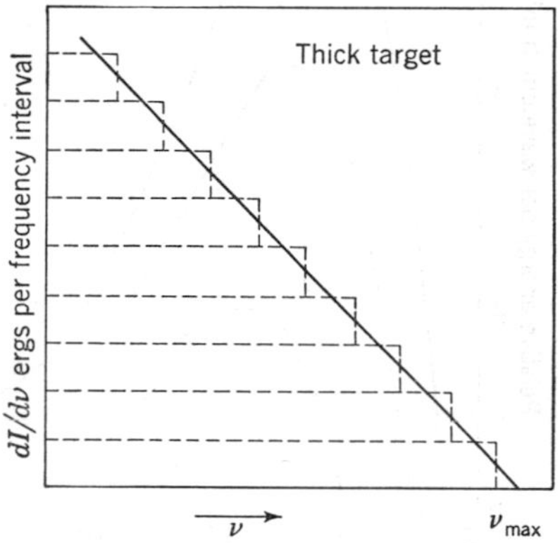

Fig. 2.1   The bremsstrahlung intensity per frequency interval from a thick target can be regarded as composed of a superposition of thin-target curves, having diminishing values of $h\nu_{max}$, as a result of the slowing down of the incident electrons by ionizing collisions in the upper layers of the target.   The total energy per frequency interval $dI/d\nu$ is proportional to $Z(\nu_{max} - \nu)$, from empirical studies on thick targets at nonrelativistic energies, $h\nu_{max} \ll m_0c^2$.

$$dI = \text{const } Z(\nu_{max} - \nu) \, d\nu \qquad (2.7)$$

This result is in agreement with direct experiments (W2).

Total Bremsstrahlung Energy.   When Eq. (2.7) is integrated over all frequencies from $\nu = 0$ to $\nu_{max} = T/h$, we find for the total bremsstrahlung energy I, in Mev per incident electron,

$$I = kZE^2 \qquad (2.8)$$

where $E = 0.51(T/m_0c^2)$ is the initial kinetic energy of the electron in Mev and k is a constant whose dimensions are (1/Mev).   It was Röntgen himself who first demonstrated this increased yield of X rays with increasing Z and E.

Figure 2.2 shows typical thick-target bremsstrahlung "intensity" (total energy integrated over all angles) distributions on a wavelength scale as is conventional in the X-ray field.   The area under each curve is proportional to the square of the kinetic energy of the electrons in agreement with Eq. (2.8).

Experimentally, the angular distribution and total intensity of thick-target bremsstrahlung from homogeneous electrons of 1.25 to 2.35 Mev in Be, Al, Cu, Ag, W, and Au have been studied by Buechner and coworkers (B139). No simple dependence of the X-ray intensity, in any given direction, on Z and E is found. The total bremsstrahlung, integrated over all angles, is found to be proportional to Z, within the accuracy of measurement, and also to be proportional to E^2 within ± 10 per cent, in agreement with Eq. (2.8). The absolute value of the integrated intensity is much more difficult to evaluate experimentally, because of the effects of self-absorption of soft quanta within the target itself, attenuation by the walls and shields of the ion chamber, dependence of the sensitivity of the ion chamber on quantum energy, etc. The absolute intensity estimated by Buechner et al. corresponds to $k = 0.4 \times 10^{-3}$ Mev^{-1} in Eq. (2.8).

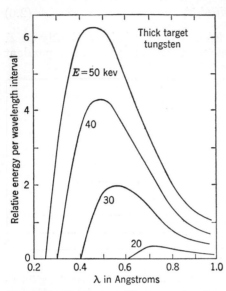

Fig. 2.2 Continuous X-ray spectra for homogeneous electrons, of kinetic energy E, incident on a thick tungsten target. The total bremsstrahlung energy (area under each curve) is empirically proportional to E^2, for $E \ll m_0 c^2$. The short wavelength limit, λ_{min}, of each curve corresponds to $E = h\nu_{max} = h(c/\lambda_{min})$. [*From Ulrey* (U1).]

The numerical value of the constant k is known only approximately. Table 2.1 collects a number of experimental and theoretical evaluations of the constant. These values all lie in the domain (0.4 to

TABLE 2.1. SUMMARY OF THEORETICAL AND EXPERIMENTAL EVALUATIONS OF k, IN EQ. (2.8)

Reference	Date	Electron energy	Method	k, Mev^{-1}
Compton and Allison (C37).	Before 1934	$\ll 0.5$ Mev	Exp.	1.1×10^{-3}
Buechner et al. (B139).......	1948	1.3 to 2.3 Mev	Exp.	0.4×10^{-3}
Ivanov et al. (I7).........	1941	0.5 to 4.6 Mev	Theo.	0.5×10^{-3}
Kirkpatrick (K20).......	1946	$\ll 0.5$ Mev	Theo.	0.7×10^{-3}
Wu (W72).....	1941	~ 1 Mev	Theo.	$0.3 \times 10^{-3} \left(1 + \dfrac{1.02}{E}\right)$
Parker (P6)....	1947	~ 1 Mev	Theo.	0.5×10^{-3}

1.1) $\times 10^{-3}$ Mev^{-1}. Miss Wu's theoretical results did not give the well-established dependence of I on E^2 in the low-energy domain.   Clearly, more work is needed before we can consider the evaluation of Eq. (2.2) as known.   In the meantime, it appears that approximately

$$I \simeq (0.7 \pm 0.2) \times 10^{-3} Z E^2 \qquad I \text{ and } E \text{ in Mev} \qquad (2.9)$$

for thick-target bremsstrahlung, in the energy domain up to about $E = 2.5$ Mev.   Thus the *fraction* of the incident electron energy which is converted into bremsstrahlung in a thick target is approximately

$$\frac{I}{E} \simeq 0.0007 Z E \qquad (2.10)$$

or about 1 per cent for 0.5-Mev electrons absorbed in copper ($Z = 29$).

b. Thick-target Bremsstrahlung from Continuous β-Ray Spectra.
Every β ray emitted by a radioactive substance is a potential producer of continuous X rays.   Such radionuclides as C^{14}, S^{35}, P^{32}, Sr^{90}, and RaE, which emit no γ rays, and are therefore referred to as "pure β-ray emitters," are actually always sources of some electromagnetic radiation.

At least four separate physical processes contribute to the X-ray spectrum of any β-ray emitter.   Two are "external" effects and are produced in those atoms which eventually absorb the β rays.   Two are "internal" effects and originate within the emitting atom, but external to its transforming nucleus.

1. The predominant X radiation is usually the continuous spectrum produced in radiative collisions between β rays and the atoms of the absorber.   This *external bremsstrahlung* has a maximum photon energy equal to the maximum energy of the β rays and an intensity proportional to Z of the absorbing material.

2. *Characteristic X rays* are also produced in the absorber, as a consequence of those ionizing collisions which result in the removal of K, L, M, . . . electrons from atoms of the absorber.   No fully adequate theory has been developed for primary ionization phenomena, hence for the efficiency of production of characteristic X rays.   The characteristic X rays produced by the absorption of the β rays from P^{32} in a number of elements have been photographed with an X-ray crystal spectrometer by Edwards and Pool (E2), but absolute intensity measurements were not made.

3. A continuous spectrum of *internal bremsstrahlung* originates within the transforming atoms and can be attributed to the sudden change of nuclear charge which occurs when a β ray is emitted, or when an orbital electron is captured.   Roughly, there is of the order of $\frac{1}{137}$ quantum of internal bremsstrahlung per β ray.   The theory of internal bremsstrahlung has been developed and compares favorably with experimental findings on the shape and absolute intensity of this continuous spectrum (K25, B72, M58, C17, M2, B84, G32, M3).

4. The sudden change of nuclear charge and the passage of the emitted β ray out through the electronic cloud of its own atom have a

probability of the order of 10^{-4} of producing "internal ionization" of the $K, L, \ldots$ shell of the emitting atom (L20, B84, W29). Subsequently, Auger electrons or *internal characteristic* X *rays* are emitted.

In the following paragraphs we shall examine the characteristics of the usually predominant source of X rays from β-ray sources, the *external bremsstrahlung*.

Average External Bremsstrahlung per β Ray. We can utilize Eq. (2.8), which describes the total thick-target bremsstrahlung for monoenergetic electrons, in order to predict the total external bremsstrahlung produced by the absorption of any continuous β-ray spectrum. Let the total energy of a particular β ray, in m_0c^2 units, be W, where

$$W = \frac{T}{m_0c^2} + 1 = \frac{E}{0.51} + 1 \qquad (2.11)$$

and let $N(W)\, dW$ represent the probability that a given β-active substance will emit an electron having a total energy between W and $W + dW$. The expectation value of the total bremsstrahlung energy which is produced by absorption of the entire β-ray spectrum in a material of atomic number Z will be proportional to

$$kZ \int_1^{W_0} (W - 1)^2 N(W)\, dW$$

where W_0 corresponds to the maximum energy, E_0 Mev, of the continuous β-ray spectrum. The total number of β rays emitted by this source is proportional to

$$\int_1^{W_0} N(W)\, dW$$

Consequently the average total energy I of the bremsstrahlung per β-ray disintegration is

$$I = kZ(0.51)^2 \frac{\int_1^{W_0} (W - 1)^2 N(W)\, dW}{\int_1^{W_0} N(W)\, dW} \qquad (2.12)$$

$$I = kZ(E_{\text{rms}})^2 \qquad \text{Mev}/\beta \text{ disintegration} \qquad (2.13)$$

where E_{rms} is the root-mean-square value of the kinetic energy of the continuous β-ray spectrum in Mev.

In order to express the bremsstrahlung as a fraction of the total kinetic energy of the β rays, we require the *average β-ray energy* E_{av} which is

$$E_{\text{av}} \equiv (0.51) \frac{\int_1^{W_0} (W - 1) N(W)\, dW}{\int_1^{W_0} N(W)\, dW} \qquad \text{Mev}/\beta \text{ disintegration} \qquad (2.14)$$

Then the *fraction* of the β-ray energy dissipated as external bremsstrahlung is given by

$$\frac{I}{E_{\text{av}}} = kZ \frac{(E_{\text{rms}})^2}{E_{\text{av}}} \qquad (2.15)$$

In conventional tables of the radionuclides, each β-ray spectrum is characterized only by its maximum energy, $E_{\max}$ ($= E_0$). In order to evaluate Eq. (2.15) we therefore require the relationships between E_{rms}, E_{av}, and E_0. These can be obtained analytically for β-ray spectra which have the allowed shape and small Z. Then, by Eq. (3.26) of Chap. 17, the shape of the β-ray distribution can be represented, for $Z = 0$, by

$$N(W)\,dW = \text{const}\,(W^2 - 1)^{\frac{1}{2}}$$
$$(W_0 - W)^2 W\,dW \quad (2.16)$$

Substitution of Eq. (2.16) into Eqs. (2.12) and (2.14) permits numerical evaluations of E_{rms} and E_{av}, as functions of E_0. These results are shown in Fig. 2.3. In this $Z = 0$ approximation, we can write

$$E_{\mathrm{rms}} \simeq (0.45 \pm 0.05)E_0 \quad (2.17)$$
$$E_{\mathrm{av}} \simeq (0.40 \pm 0.05)E_0 \quad (2.18)$$

Then the average bremsstrahlung per β ray, Eq. (2.13), becomes

$$I \simeq kZ(0.45)^2 E_0^2 \quad (2.19)$$

or, taking $k \simeq 0.7 \times 10^{-3}$ Mev^{-1},

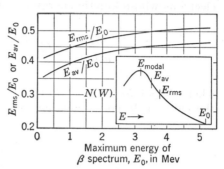

Fig. 2.3 Ratio of root-mean-square β-ray kinetic energy E_{rms}, and of average β-ray energy E_{av}, to the maximum β-ray energy E_0. The two curves apply to allowed spectra, without coulomb corrections, as evaluated from Eqs. (2.12), (2.14), and (2.16). The inset illustrates the qualitative relationships between E_0, E_{av}, E_{rms} and the most probable, or modal, energy of any β-ray spectrum.

$$I \simeq \frac{Z}{7,000} E_0^2 \qquad \text{Mev}/\beta \text{ disintegration} \qquad (2.20)$$

Similarly, the *fraction* of the β-ray energy which appears as external bremsstrahlung, Eq. (2.15), becomes

$$\frac{I}{E_{\mathrm{av}}} = kZE_0 \frac{(E_{\mathrm{rms}}/E_0)^2}{(E_{\mathrm{av}}/E_0)} \simeq kZE_0 \frac{(0.45 \pm 0.05)^2}{(0.40 \pm 0.05)}$$

$$\simeq \frac{Z}{3,000} E_0 \qquad\qquad (2.21)$$

This is about 1.8 per cent for the case of P^{32} β rays in Cu ($E_0 = 1.7$ Mev, $Z = 29$). More exact results may be obtained, where needed, by introducing the coulomb correction $F(Z,W)$ of Chap. 17 into Eq. (2.16) and then performing the subsequent integrations graphically or numerically. This has been done for E_{av} (M11) but not for E_{rms}. Inclusion of the coulomb corrections will increase both E_{av} and E_{rms} for positron β-ray emitters and will decrease both for negatron β-ray emitters.

Spectral Distribution of External Bremsstrahlung from β Rays. The spectrum of bremsstrahlung from the absorption of continuous β rays can be obtained from that of the monoenergetic case, Eq. (2.7). Rewriting Eq. (2.7) in terms of E, $h\nu$, and k, we have

$$dI = 2kZ(E - h\nu)\ d(h\nu) \qquad (2.22)$$

The "intensity" dI [(number of quanta) $\times$ (energy of quantum)] in the energy band $d(h\nu)$ at $h\nu$ is then given by Eq. (2.22), summed over all electrons whose kinetic energy exceeds E. This is

$$\frac{dI}{d(h\nu)} = 2kZ \frac{\int_{W_1}^{W_0} (E - h\nu)N(W)\ dW}{\int_{1}^{W_0} N(W)\ dW} \qquad (2.23)$$

where $E = 0.51(W - 1)$ Mev and the lower limit of the integration is the value of W corresponding to $h\nu$ Mev, or

$$W_1 = \frac{h\nu}{0.51} + 1 \qquad (2.24)$$

Substituting the values of E and $h\nu$ in terms of W and W_1, Eq. (2.23) becomes

$$\frac{dI}{d(h\nu)} = 1.02kZ \frac{\int_{W_1}^{W_0} (W - W_1)N(W)\ dW}{\int_{1}^{W_0} N(W)\ dW} \qquad \text{per } \beta \text{ ray} \qquad (2.25)$$

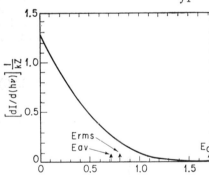

Photon Energy, $h\nu$ in Mev

Fig. 2.4 The external bremsstrahlung spectrum predicted for a typical β-ray emitter, calculated from Eq. (2.25) for the case of P^{32} without coulomb corrections. The total bremsstrahlung energy is the area under this curve and is proportional to the atomic number of the absorber. The maximum photon energy equals the maximum β-ray energy, E_0.

If we neglect the coulomb correction terms, Eq. (2.25) can be evaluated analytically, using Eq. (2.16). A typical result is shown in Fig. 2.4.

It will be noted that the energy distribution of bremsstrahlung from a continuous β-ray source is quite different from the simple straight line which characterizes the monoenergetic case, Fig. 2.1. The large proportion of soft radiation is evident. The intensity of bremsstrahlung depends on Z of the absorber. However, the *shape* of the bremsstrahlung spectrum is independent of Z of the absorber. Hence each β-ray emitter has its own characteristic external bremsstrahlung spectrum.

The external bremsstrahlung from several β-ray emitters has been studied experimentally, especially RaE (A38, D39, S66, S65), UX_2 (S66), P^{32} (E2, M37, S42, W72), and H^3 (G40). It has been verified that the total external bremsstrahlung energy is proportional to the atomic number of the absorber (M37, S66, W72). Reliable measurements of the absolute intensity in any particular case are still lacking, although it is known that the total intensity is of the expected order of magnitude (W72). Absolute measurements could be made (1) if the self-absorption of the bremsstrahlung before it leaves the absorber is evaluated accurately; (2) if the spectral sensitivity of the photon detector is simple and is known (e.g., an "air-wall" roentgen thimble chamber); (3) if internal bremsstrahlung is eliminated from the measurements, e.g., by shielding the photon detector from the β-ray source (E2); and (4) if the characteristic X rays produced in the absorber are evaluated quantitatively.

The net bremsstrahlung from P^{32}, in an aqueous solution contained in a 1-oz glass bottle (as shipped routinely from the Oak Ridge National Laboratory), has a measured value of about 3 mr/hr, at a distance of 1 m, per curie of P^{32}.

When large amounts of the β-ray-emitting fission products are stored in aqueous solution, the bremsstrahlung from the solution (and to a lesser extent from the walls of the tank) can constitute an important source of hard X rays. Lead or other shielding may be required to reduce the radiation hazards, even where only "pure β emitters" are involved, if the quantities stored are large (P6). For $E_0 \sim 2$ Mev, in water, roughly $\frac{1}{2}$ per cent of the β-ray energy will be converted to hard bremsstrahlung, in accord with Eq. (2.21).

No measurements of the shape of the external bremsstrahlung spectrum excited by continuous β rays have been made, and thus there are no data to compare with the predicted shape shown in Fig. 2.4. However, measurements (E2) of the transmission through Pb of the external bremsstrahlung produced by P^{32} β rays in Al, Cu, Ag, Sn, and Pb have shown that the spectra (1) are independent of Z, (2) have a large intensity of low-energy quanta, and (3) have a high-energy component whose effective absorption coefficient in Pb is equivalent to that of photons whose average energy is about $E_0/2$.

3. Range-Energy Relations for Electrons

a. Effects of Straggling. We have noted that the effects of multiple scattering preclude exact calculations of the range of electrons (Fig. 1.1). Such calculations are further complicated by the statistical fluctuations, or "straggling," of energy losses. Straggling, like scattering, is much more pronounced in the case of electrons than for heavy particles. This is because heavy particles lose most of their energy in ionizing collisions with atomic electrons, where conservation of momentum permits fractional energy transfers of the order of the ratio of the masses ($\sim m_0/M$). Therefore each collision results in the transfer of only a small fraction of the energy of a heavy particle. On the other hand, electrons can lose up to one-half (see Chap. 18) their energy in an ionizing collision. In addition to this, the electron may also lose any fraction of its energy in a radiative collision.

Among the most instructive observations on electron absorption are the classic straggling and absorption measurements, made by White and

Millington (W41) with the aid of a β-ray magnetic spectrograph, on seven conversion electron groups from Ra(B + C), covering an energy range from 0.155 to 1.33 Mev. Figure 3.1 illustrates the effect on an originally homogeneous number-energy distribution of 0.2065-Mev electrons, after passing through thin mica foils of varying thickness. Each successive increase in absorber thickness shifts the number maximum toward a lower energy but at the same time very greatly broadens the number-energy distribution. This illustrates the severe straggling encountered in all electron-absorption measurements, which definitely limits range measurements to comparisons with known spectra under identical geometrical conditions.

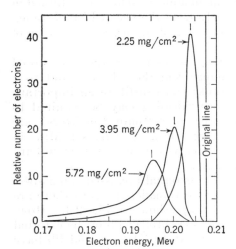

Fig. 3.1 Transmission through mica of the monoenergetic electrons from the 0.2065-Mev conversion line of RaB. The position of the shifted peaks gives the most probable energy loss. Note that it is obviously different from the average energy loss, because the peaks are asymmetric. The data for this figure are computed by transforming the experimental results of White and Millington (W41) from momentum intervals to energy intervals.

Theories relating to the straggling of ionization losses by electrons in thin absorbing foils have been successively improved, especially by Williams (W53), Landau (L4), and Blunck and Leisegang (B81). Accurate measurements by Hungerford and Birkhoff (H77) of the number-energy distribution of the 0.624-Mev conversion electrons from Cs^{137}, after passing through thin foils ($\sim$ 10 to 30 mg/cm²) of Al, Cu, Ag, and Au, are in acceptable agreement with theory, provided that electrons which have been scattered through a large angle are excluded from the measurements.

It must be emphasized that, in contrast with ionization processes, the energy losses by radiation occur in a small number of collisions, in each of which a relatively large proportion of the electron's kinetic energy is lost. Therefore, the radiative loss for an individual electron traversing a thin metal plate may be much less or much more than the average loss for the distance traversed. This is equivalent to saying that the straggling of radiative energy losses is very great (B9, H29). The observed straggling will, of course, be due to the joint action (C43) of the radiative and ionization losses.

b. Range-Energy Relations for Monoenergetic Electrons. Clearly, our previously derived mean values for $(dT/ds)_{ion}$ and $(dT/ds)_{rad}$ can serve only as guides in the estimation of theoretical ranges for electrons. In most practical situations, we must use completely empirical range-energy relationships.

Figure 3.2 is a representative transmission curve for initially mono-energetic electrons. The final portion of the transmission curve is a long tail, because of straggling. Even the qualitative shape of the trans-mission curve depends on the experimental arrangement (E1, V4). Initially, the curve is usually concave toward the origin if (1) detection is by electron counting, (2) low-Z elements are used as absorbers, and (3) the collimating slit system allows electrons which have been deflected by about 30° or less to be counted. Conversely, the curve tends to be initially convex toward the origin when (1) detection is by an ioniza-tion chamber, (2) high-Z absorbers are used, and (3) narrow collima-tion is employed.

In spite of variations in the form of the transmission curves, the thickness of material required to reduce the ionization or counting to nearly zero is a fairly definite ob-servable quantity. Reproducible results are obtained by extrapolat-ing the approximately linear middle portion of the absorption curve, until it cuts the value assigned to background effects. This *extrapo-lated range R_0* (sometimes called the "practical range") is illustrated in Fig. 3.2.

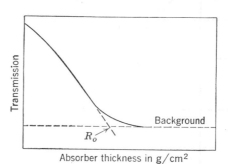

Fig. **3.2**   The extrapolated range R_0, for originally *monoenergetic electrons*, is at the intersection of the extrapolated ionization or counting curve with the estimated con-tribution of background due to γ rays, bremsstrahlung in the absorber, and other causes.

Figure 3.3 collects representative measurements of R_0 in aluminum for electrons having initial kinetic energy E. Notice that in the low-energy domain, R_0 varies with E^2, while in the high-energy domain R_0 is nearly proportional to E. This behavior, and the transition region at intermediate energies, are a consequence of the dependence of $(dT/ds)_{\text{ion}}$ on $1/\beta^2$, hence on $1/T$ (erg) $= 1/E$ (Mev), for $E \leq 0.1$ Mev (Chap. 18). For small energies, the mean path length in an absorber is therefore given approximately by

$$\bar{S} \simeq \text{const} \left(\frac{E^2}{NZ} \right) \tag{3.1}$$

and the range is roughly proportional to the path length. This is equiva-lent to the so-called *Thomson-Whiddington law* (W36, W54), which has long been used in the X-ray literature and according to which the range of soft electrons is proportional to the fourth power of their initial velocity. At larger energies, when $\beta \sim 1$, the range tends to become substantially linear with E, as would be expected qualitatively from the general form of $(dT/ds)_{\text{ion}}$ and $(dT/ds)_{\text{rad}}$.

Empirical relationships between R_0 and E have been proposed by many workers. From 0.5 to 3 Mev, the data are represented within

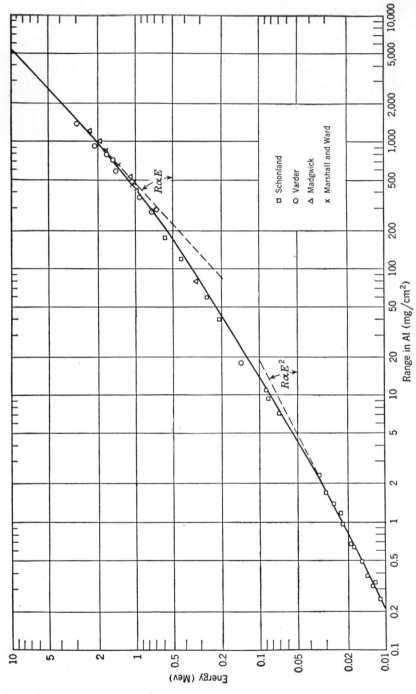

Fig. 3.3 Empirical range-energy relationship for electrons absorbed in aluminum. Experimental values by several observers (S16, V4, M4, M17) on *monoenergetic* electrons are shown. For *monoenergetic electrons*, the range coordinate refers to the *extrapolated range R_0* of Fig. 3.2. For *continuous β-ray spectra* the energy coordinate refers to the end-point energy E_{max}, and the range coordinate becomes the *maximum range R_m* of Fig. 3.4. The smooth curve represents the empirical relationship, Eqs. (3.3) and (3.4), developed by Katz and Penfold (K7).

±5 per cent by the linear relationship

$$R_0(\text{g/cm}^2) = 0.52E(\text{Mev}) - 0.09 \qquad (3.2)$$

An excellent review of all electron range-energy work up to 1951 has been given by Katz and Penfold (K7). Based on a compilation of all available data, these authors propose the following empirical relationships, where E is in Mev. For energies from 0.01 Mev to $\sim$3 Mev

$$R_0(\text{mg/cm}^2) = 412E^n \qquad (3.3)$$
$$n = 1.265 - 0.0954 \ln E$$

For energies from $\sim$1 Mev to $\sim$20 Mev

$$R_0(\text{mg/cm}^2) = 530E - 106 \qquad (3.4)$$

The solid line in Fig. 3.3 is based on these empirical analytical forms. The agreement is excellent.

c. Absorption of Continuous β-Ray Spectra. The typical transmission curve for continuous β-ray spectra shown in Fig. 3.4 differs greatly from that for monoenergetic electrons. It resembles very closely a pure exponential attenuation curve, except that for very small transmission ($\leq$ 1 per cent) a finite upper limit can be identified. The approximately exponential character of the major portion of the transmission curve is an accidental consequence of the shape of β-ray spectra and of the differences between the scattering and absorption of electrons which have various initial energies.

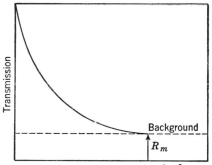

Fig. **3.4** A typical plot of the approximately exponential transmission of a continuous β-ray spectrum through absorbers of various thicknesses. R_m is called the *maximum range.*

Because the shape of the transmission curve depends somewhat on geometrical conditions, more reproducible results are obtained by observing the thickness of absorber required to stop the β rays of highest energy. This maximum thickness is called the *maximum range* R_m, as indicated in Fig. 3.4. R_m is not easy to determine experimentally, because it corresponds to a point of zero intensity. A number of methods for determining R_m have been developed; these have been reviewed and compared most recently by Katz and Penfold (K7).

Feather's Method for Evaluating the Maximum Range. Probably the most widely used experimental method for determining R_m is that developed by Feather (F12). Here, one compares the absorption curve whose end point R_m is to be determined with that of a well-established standard (Feather used RaE). The two curves are normalized to the same initial value on a plot of logarithmic transmission against absorber thickness (see Fig. 3.5). The range of the standard curve is now divided into N equal parts (Feather used $N = 10$, as does Fig. 3.5). These parts are designated R_n^0 in Fig. 3.5, and the end point which has been well established is marked R_m^0. The fractional transmission corresponding to these absorber thicknesses is marked on the standard curve. Points corresponding to the same relative transmission are now marked on the unknown curve; in Fig. 3.5 these are the intersections of horizontal lines and the unknown curve. The absorber thickness corresponding to these transmission values is now marked on the scale of absorber thickness for the unknown (upper abscissa) and is designated R_n^x. The maximum range R_m of the unknown is now the limiting value of $(N/n)R_n^x$ as $n \to N$, in our case as $n \to 10$. This maximum range can easily be obtained

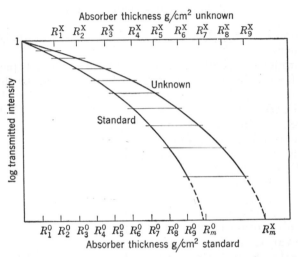

Fig. 3.5 Typical logarithmic-transmission curves for comparing a standard β-ray spectrum with an unknown spectrum, in order to determine the maximum range R_m, by the Feather method.

graphically by plotting $(N/n)R_n^x$ as a function of n, connecting the points by a smooth curve, and reading the value of R_m^x from the extrapolated intercept of the curve with the $n = N$ axis, as shown in Fig. 3.6.

Feather's method has the advantage of being easy to use. It gives results which are usually good to 5 per cent or better. It should be noted that Feather's standard RaE ($E_{max} = 1.17$ Mev; $R_m = 508$ mg Al/cm^2) has a forbidden β-ray spectrum and so is probably not the optimum choice, although it was the best available when the method was developed. The standard might preferably be some pure β-ray emitter (no γ rays) whose spectrum has the allowed shape, such as P^{32}. More complicated methods, which must be used in cases of complex β spectra, have been reviewed by Katz and Penfold (K7).

Range-Energy Relationship for β-Ray Spectra. Having determined R_m for the β-ray spectrum, the corresponding value of E_{max} is read from a plot of the empirical relationship between E_{max}, as measured with β-ray spectrometers, and R_m as determined for the same radionuclides.   Values of $E_{\max}$ and R_m have been determined for some two dozen radionuclides.

A complete compilation of the data available up to 1951 shows (K7) that R_m for continuous β-ray spectra is indistinguishable from the extrapolated range R_0 of monoenergetic electrons whose energy E is the same as $E_{\max}$ of the β-ray spectrum.   This somewhat amazing conclusion is based on the findings of many different laboratories, using a variety of experimental methods.   The equivalence may be attributed (K7) to the fact that all the various methods for measuring range rely mainly on the last half of the absorption curve for their result.   In this portion of the absorption curve the scattering has reached equilibrium (B134), i.e., the effects of multiple scattering have been so great that the angular distribution of electrons has become isotropic.   The further progress of the electrons through the absorber can be described by diffusion theory. The results of the measurements then become independent of many of the

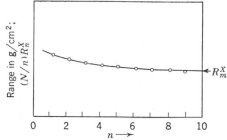

Fig. 3.6   A plot of $(N/n)R_n^X$ as a function of n to obtain the maximum range from the data in Fig. 3.5.

experimental factors such as counter sensitivity, geometry, etc.   Therefore Fig. 3.3 and Eqs. (3.3) and (3.4) represent not only the relationship between R_0 and E for a line spectrum of electrons but also the relationship between R_m and $E_{\max}$ for β-ray spectra.

Mass-absorption Coefficient for Continuous β-Ray Spectra.   For continuous β-ray spectra, a plot of logarithmic transmission against absorber thickness generally has about the same shape as the linear transmission curve for monoenergetic electrons, as shown in Fig. 3.2.   Especially when detection is by an ionization chamber, the transmission curve is often nearly exponential over the majority of its length and can be represented by

$$\frac{I}{I_0} = e^{-\mu x} \tag{3.5}$$

where I/I_0 is the fraction of the initial ionization measured after the β rays have passed through x cm of absorbing material and μ cm^{-1} is the apparent absorption coefficient for the particular spectrum.   If ρ g/cm^3 is the density of the absorber, it is found experimentally that the *mass-absorption coefficient μ/ρ is nearly independent of the atomic weight of the absorber*, rising only slightly with increasing Z.   Particularly in the earlier years, many β-ray spectra were reported (C64) in terms of their apparent mass-absorption coefficients μ/ρ in Al.

Figure 3.7 is a plot of reported values of μ/ρ for several natural radio-nuclides (C64). These data are represented moderately well by the empirical relation

$$\frac{\mu}{\rho} = \frac{17}{E_m^{1.14}} \qquad (3.6)$$

where E_m is in Mev and μ/ρ is in square centimeters per gram of Al. Alternative numerical values of the constant and the exponent have been reviewed by Katz and Penfold (K7). Using Eq. (3.6), the absorber thickness required to reduce the β-ray intensity to one-half its original value is given by

$$D_{\frac{1}{2}} = \frac{0.693}{(\mu/\rho)} = 0.04E^{1.14} \qquad \text{g Al/cm}^2 \qquad (3.7)$$

This is sometimes a convenient rule of thumb for the rapid identification of β-active radionuclides.

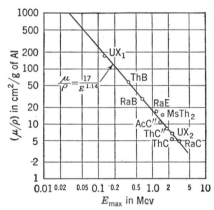

Fig. 3.7　Mass-absorption coefficient in aluminum vs. maximum energy of the β-ray spectrum.

The remarkable fact about the exponential attenuation of β-ray spectra is that the mass-absorption coefficient seems to be determined uniquely by $E_{\max}$. If we begin with a spectrum for which $E_{\max} = 1$ Mev and absorb half the radiation, the remaining radiation retains the absorption coefficient characteristic of the parent β-ray spectrum. It does not shift to a μ/ρ characteristic of, say, 0.5-Mev β rays.

It is possible to imagine various sets of coincidental mechanisms of absorption which would account for this remarkable behavior. Dudley (D42) points out that the mechanisms which appear to be the most nearly correct experimentally are: (1) *The shape of the energy spectrum remains nearly constant throughout the absorption and* (2) *the angular distribution pattern of β rays remains substantially constant during absorption.* Brownell (B134) has shown experimentally that both these assumptions are essentially correct.   After passing through any thickness x of absorber, a certain amount of energy [(number of β rays) $\times$ (average β-ray energy)] enters the thickness dx.   If condition 1 above is true, then the incident energy which is absorbed in the thickness dx, per unit path length of the β rays, is independent of the distance x.   The total fraction of energy absorbed in dx is then proportional to the total path length in the gap.   This total path length in dx is independent of x only if condition 2 above is correct.   Therefore if conditions 1 and 2 are true, the fraction of the energy incident on dx that is absorbed in dx is independent of x.   This is an exponential absorption.   Since conditions 1 and 2 are not rigorously valid, the absorption is only approximately exponential.

4. *Annihilation Radiation*

Thus far, with a few exceptions which have been pointed out, all the results are applicable to either positive or negative electrons.   The positron, however, has the unique property of combining with a negative electron, in an interaction in which the rest mass of both positron and negatron ultimately is given up in the form of electromagnetic radiation. That is, the positron is annihilated, and the subsequent radiation is called annihilation radiation.   Every positron ultimately dies in an encounter with a negatron, in which about $2m_0c^2$ of electromagnetic radiation is emitted.

a. Positronium.   In the Dirac electron theory, a positron passing through matter may be thought of as roughly analogous to a hydrogen ion.   This positron may pick up a negatron and hence form "positronium" (a hydrogenlike atom whose "nucleus" is a positron instead of a proton).   Quantum-mechanically, one can assign to positronium all the various quantum numbers used to describe the hydrogen atom.   It is thought that states of high orbital angular momentum undergo successive radiative transitions until the state of zero orbital angular momentum is reached.   This corresponds to the ground state of the hydrogen atom and, in the case of positronium, has a calculated binding energy of 6.7 ev (W31).   In this S state ($L = 0$) there are two possibilities, the singlet in which the spins of the positron and negatron are antiparallel and the triplet in which the spins are parallel.   The theory predicts a mean life of about 10^{-10} sec for two-quantum annihilation of the singlet state. Annihilation from the triplet configuration requires three-quantum annihilation and is a forbidden transition with a mean life of about 10^{-7} sec.

b. Two-quantum Annihilation.   Nearly all annihilation radiation comes from the singlet state.   Upon annihilation, two quanta, with energy totaling $2m_0c^2$, are emitted.   If the momentum of the center of mass of the two-body system is zero (in the laboratory system), the two quanta will appear exactly back to back, each having an energy of 0.51 Mev.   Experimentally, however, it has been shown by De Benedetti et al. (D15) that, because of thermal agitation, the average momentum of the center of mass is about $0.009m_0c$.   This leads to a finite breadth of the order of 0.5° in the angular distribution, about a mean angle of 180°

between the two annihilation quanta. Because the annihilation takes place from the singlet state of zero total angular momentum, there can be no angular momentum in the electromagnetic field. The theory predicts that, if one photon is linearly polarized, the other must be linearly polarized in a plane at right angles to that of the first. This prediction has been verified in a number of experiments (H40, W77).

In addition to this normal case the theory (H29) also predicts the annihilation of swift positrons in the order of 2 per cent of the interactions. In these cases the initial momentum of the center of mass may be quite large, and roughly half the resulting photons will have energies in excess of 0.51 Mev. Annihilation of swift positrons has been observed experimentally by Deutsch (D26), using positrons from Cu^{64} and Na^{22}.

c. Three-quantum Annihilation in Orthopositronium. The triplet state, or orthopositronium, has a mean life which is long enough to permit laboratory study. Deutsch and coworkers (D28, D27, D30, D31) have measured the decay constant λ and the fine structure and Zeeman splitting of orthopositronium. The measured value of λ agrees quite well with theory and leads to a mean life of about 0.15 μsec for orthopositronium.

Problems

1. (a) Compute the energy loss and the approximate number of quanta of visible light emitted as Čerenkov radiation in the frequency range corresponding to wavelengths in vacuum of $\lambda = 4,000$ to 7,000 A, given off by a 20-Mev electron traversing 1 cm of lucite.

(b) What are the approximate energy losses in 1 cm of lucite due to ionization and due to bremsstrahlung? Lucite has a density of 1.18 g/cm^3, a substantially constant index of refraction of 1.49, and a chemical composition approximately like $(C_5H_8O_2)_x$.

Ans.: (a) 660 ev/cm, 270 quanta/cm; (b) 2.8 Mev/cm, 0.3 Mev/cm.

2. Estimate the rate of loss of kinetic energy, due to *radiation*, by a 2-Mev electron passing through silver. Express the result in both Mev per millimeter of silver and Mev per gram per square centimeter. *Ans.:* ~0.15 Mev/mm, 0.15 Mev per g/cm^2.

3. What is the order of magnitude of the ratio of the rate of loss of kinetic energy by *radiation* for a 10-Mev deuteron and a 10-Mev electron passing through lead? *Ans.:* 10^{-5}.

4. When thin-target radiative losses are expressed in terms of ergs per gram per square centimeter, show that the losses in equivalent superficial thicknesses of material (e.g., same number of milligrams per square centimeter of target) are approximately proportional to Z, rather than Z^2, and are independent of the density as expressed by ρ or by N.

$$\left(\frac{dT}{ds}\right)_{\text{rad}} \propto NZ^2 \qquad \left(\frac{dT}{dw}\right)_{\text{rad}} \propto Z \qquad \text{where } dw = \rho \, ds$$

5. An electron having initial kinetic energy E is totally absorbed in a medium which is a mixture of N_1, N_2, N_3, . . . atoms/cm^3 of substances having atomic numbers Z_1, Z_2, Z_3, ...

Show that, in the expression $I = kZE^2$ for the total external bremsstrahlung, the effective value of Z is

$$Z_{eff} \simeq \frac{N_1 Z_1^2 + N_2 Z_2^2 + N_3 Z_3^2 + \cdots}{N_1 Z_1 + N_2 Z_2 + N_3 Z_3 + \cdots}$$

6. (a) Compute the total external bremsstrahlung in kev per average disintegration of P^{32}, when β rays are absorbed in water.

(b) What fraction of the *average* β-ray energy is radiated as continuous X rays under these conditions?

7. In the following considerations, make use of the general relationship, $W^2 = \eta^2 + 1$, between energy and momentum (and magnetic rigidity $B\rho$) for particles of any rest mass. In a cloud chamber supplied with a magnetic field B, the path of a certain charged particle is seen to have a radius of curvature ρ such that $B\rho = 160,000$ gauss-cm.

(a) What is the kinetic energy of the particle in Mev, and its velocity β in terms of the velocity of light, if the rest mass of the particle is (1) m_0 (an electron), (2) $212\ m_0$ (a μ meson), and (3) $1,836m_0$ (a proton)?

(b) Estimate the specific ionization which would be produced by each of these three types of particle in air at 15°C, 760 mm Hg.

(c) Estimate the rate of energy loss per millimeter of lead for each type of particle, for ionization losses alone.

(d) Estimate the rate of energy loss by radiation per millimeter of lead for each type of particle.

8. The most energetic β rays from the 12.4-hr isotope of potassium are found to have a radius of curvature of 10.8 cm in a magnetic field of 1,250 gauss.

(a) What is the maximum energy of the β-ray spectrum?

(b) How many millimeters of aluminum absorber would be required to stop all the β rays from this isotope?

Ans.: (a) 3.57 Mev; (b) 6.6 mm.

9. Assume that 0.52-Mev electrons pass into a large reservoir of *helium at 3-atm* pressure, 20°C, in which they are totally absorbed.

(a) What will be the approximate extrapolated *range* of the group of electrons?

(b) What is the approximate average *total radiative loss*, in ev. per electron?

(c) What is the approximate *total ionization* produced in helium, in ion pairs per electron?

10. Estimate the rate of loss of kinetic energy, due to *ionization*, by a 2-Mev electron passing through silver. Express the result in both Mev per millimeter of silver and in Mev per gram per square centimeter.

CHAPTER 22

Passage of Heavy Charged Particles through Matter

The interactions of swift "heavy" ($M \gg m_0$) charged particles with matter usually are much less complicated than the interactions of "light" particles (electrons) with matter. Protons, α particles, and their near relatives (H^2, H^3, He^3) lose most of their energy through ionization and excitation of the atoms in the absorber. Elastic nuclear scattering and bremsstrahlung are generally negligible in comparison with ionization. The paths of these heavy particles tend to be straight; hence intervals of path length ds and of range dr are substantially equivalent. Nuclear elastic scattering becomes a significant mode of energy transfer only for heavy particles which are moving slowly and have a very large nuclear charge, such as do the "very heavy" fission fragments.

The main features of the interactions between heavy particles and absorbing materials were developed between about 1920 and 1935 by experimental and theoretical studies of the passage through air and other materials of the natural α rays, especially those of Po, RaC', and ThC'. By utilizing also the long-range α rays of ThC' ($E_\alpha = 10.54$ Mev), it was possible to explore the domain of particle velocities between 2.25×10^9 cm/sec ($\beta \sim 0.08$) and zero. All these interactions can therefore be discussed in terms of nonrelativistic theory. These studies on α range form the core of knowledge in this field and provide experimental data which have been routinely extrapolated to other particles, with the help of the theory.

The more recent availability of high-energy particle accelerators which are capable of producing well-collimated, nearly monoenergetic beams of atomic ions of the lightest elements has stimulated renewed interest in the field. Detailed studies of the behavior of swift protons in matter are occurring with increasing frequency. Important advances are being made in the accuracy of both the experimental and theoretical data, and the studies have been extended into the relativistic region of 300-Mev protons and into the domain of the "very heavy" swift atomic particles which are produced in nuclear fission. Because the bulk of the experimental material relates to α rays and protons, and these particles are often the instigators or the products of nuclear reactions, we shall emphasize the behavior of these particular "heavy" particles in most of this chapter.

1. *Capture and Loss of Electrons*

Rutherford and Royds (R51) first proved unambiguously that the α rays are swift helium nuclei. Alpha rays which were stopped in a glass wall or in mercury acquired two atomic electrons and subsequently displayed the optical spectrum of atomic helium.

The acquisition of atomic electrons by an α particle was shown to depend strongly upon the *velocity* of the α particle, when G. H. Henderson (H31), while carrying out magnetic deflection experiments on the α rays of RaC' in high vacuum, first observed α rays having a single charge and others having zero charge, in addition to the usual doubly charged α rays. Henderson, Rutherford (R48), Briggs (B120), Kapitza (K4), and others soon showed that an α ray, while passing through the electron cloud of the emitting atom and the other atoms which lie along its path, will capture one or two electrons and thus become a singly ionized or neutral helium atom. After this capture, the swiftly moving atom will be reionized quickly by collisions with other atoms. There is therefore a regular exchange of electrons between the moving α ray and its absorbing medium. *About 10^3 exchanges occur along the path of a single α ray*, the interchange becoming most rapid as the α-ray velocity declines near the end of its range.

a. Mean Free Path and Cross Section for Capture and Loss of Electrons. Consider, with Rutherford (R48), the doubly charged α ray (He^{++}) to have a mean free path for electron capture of λ_c mm of air at 15°C, 760 mm Hg. That is, on the average, the reaction

$$\text{He}^{++} + e^- \rightarrow \text{He}^+ \tag{1.1}$$

occurs after the He^{++} has traveled a distance λ_c air-mm. Similarly, let λ_l be the mean free path for loss of an electron, i.e., for ionization by collision,

$$\text{He}^+ \rightarrow \text{He}^{++} + e^- \tag{1.2}$$

At moderate velocities, λ_c and λ_l are very small, and we may consider that in a beam of α rays equilibrium is established in a thin layer Δs of absorbing material. Then the number of α rays losing an electron equals the number gaining an electron. That is,

$$(\text{He}^{++}) \frac{\Delta s}{\lambda_c} = (\text{He}^+) \frac{\Delta s}{\lambda_l} \tag{1.3}$$

If σ_c and σ_l are the cross sections per atom of absorber for the capture and loss processes, then Eq. (1.3) becomes

$$\frac{\text{He}^+}{\text{He}^{++}} = \frac{\lambda_l}{\lambda_c} = \frac{\sigma_c}{\sigma_l} \tag{1.4}$$

where He$^+$/He^{++} is statistically the ratio of the number of singly to doubly charged α rays in the beam, or the ratio of the chance that an individual α ray will be singly or doubly charged at the particular velocity for which Eq. (1.4) is evaluated.

Experimentally, He+/He++ is a relatively simple quantity to measure, as is the analogous ratio H⁰/H⁺ for the case of electron capture and loss by protons. It is found experimentally and theoretically (B47) that electron loss is much more probable than electron capture $\sigma_l \gg \sigma_c$, provided that the particle's velocity V is significantly greater than the Bohr orbital velocity u for a K electron in the moving particle. The capture of an electron by a moving particle whose atomic number is z becomes a highly probable "pickup" process at low velocities, $V \sim u$, where

$$u = z \frac{e^2}{\hbar} = \frac{z}{137} c$$

$$= 0.22 \times 10^9 \text{ cm/sec} \qquad \text{for protons } (E_p = 25 \text{ kev})$$
$$= 0.44 \times 10^9 \text{ cm/sec} \qquad \text{for } \alpha \text{ rays } (E_\alpha = 400 \text{ kev}) \qquad (1.5)$$

But at high velocities loss is much more probable than capture, and a direct determination of λ_l, hence σ_l, can be made (R48). In principle, this permits the measurement of both λ_l and λ_c. Illustrative numerical values are shown in Table 1.1, where we note especially that, for α rays whose energy is ~ 1 Mev, λ_l and λ_c are of the order of $\frac{1}{100}$ air-mm; thus there are of the order of 100 electron exchanges per millimeter of path in air.

TABLE 1.1 MEAN FREE PATHS FOR CAPTURE AND LOSS OF ELECTRONS λ_c AND λ_l (MILLIMETERS OF AIR AT 15°C AND 760 MM Hg) AT VARIOUS VELOCITIES V, AND THE MEAN α-RAY CHARGE CHARACTERISTIC OF THESE VELOCITIES (R48)

V, 10^9 cm/sec	E_α, Mev	λ_c, air-mm	λ_l, air-mm	λ_l/λ_c	z_{av}
1.81	6.78	2.2	0.011	0.005	1.995
1.46	4.43	0.52	0.0078	0.015	1.985
0.90	1.70	0.037	0.0050	0.133	1.883
0.56	0.65	~0.003	~0.003	~1	1.500

The theory (B95, B47, B137, J3) of capture and loss of electrons is complicated and only approximately valid. The loss of an electron is an ionization process and is dealt with by visualizing the collision in a coordinate system whose origin is on the particle. In this frame of reference, the α particle or proton is then bombarded by the atoms in the absorber. For very-low-Z absorbers, Bohr (B95) finds

$$\sigma_l \simeq 4\pi \left(\frac{a_H}{z}\right)^2 (Z^2 + Z) \left(\frac{u_H}{V}\right)^2 \qquad (1.6)$$

where V and z are the velocity and atomic number of the swift particle and Z is the atomic number of the absorber, while

$$a_H = \frac{\hbar^2}{m_0 e^2} = 0.53 \times 10^{-8} \text{ cm}$$

and $u_H = c/137$ are the Bohr radius and velocity in a hydrogen atom. The term in Z^2 represents ionization of the moving particle by nuclei in the absorber, while the term in Z represents the effect of its associated atomic electrons. For α rays ($z = 2$) in hydrogen ($Z = 1$), at a velocity $V = 1.75 \times 10^9$ cm/sec $\simeq 8u_H$, Jacobsen (J4) found $\lambda_l \simeq 0.07$ mm of H_2 at normal temperature and pressure; hence $\sigma_l \simeq 3 \times 10^{-18}$ cm^2. Equation (1.6) gives $\sigma_l \simeq 2.5 \times 10^{-18}$ cm^2 for the same conditions.

Equation (1.6) is expected to be valid only for the lightest absorbers, say, $Z = 1$ to 4. For $Z \simeq 4$ to 6, σ_l is expected to behave about as (B95, H8)

$$\sigma_l \simeq \pi a_H^2 \, Z^{\frac{1}{3}} \, z^{-1} \frac{u_H}{V} \tag{1.7}$$

For $Z > 6$ (carbon), the dependence of σ_l on V is expected to become still weaker, until σ_l becomes substantially independent of V in heavy elements such as gold.

The cross section for electron capture σ_c is even less amenable to accurate theoretical estimation. All theories (B95) agree that σ_c *is very strongly velocity-dependent*, varying from V^{-4} to V^{-12} under different conditions. Hall (H8) has found, for example, that, for protons of $\sim$350 kev passing through thin foils of Be, Al, Ag, and Au, σ_c varies about as V^{-11} in Be, V^{-10} in Al, V^{-9} in Ag, and V^{-7} in Au.

b. Average Charge. The ratio of the cross sections σ_c/σ_l is found experimentally to be substantially independent of the absorbing material, particularly for middleweight and light absorbers, say, $Z \leq 50$ (R48, H31, J4, B62, H8). Then all the ratios in Eq. (1.4) are dependent upon velocity alone. The mean free paths are so small that any individual α ray (or proton) may have many charge exchanges while traversing a small increment of its path. Therefore each such particle can be thought of as having some average net charge ez_{av} which is smaller than its nuclear charge ez. This average charge is the same as the mean charge carried in a parallel beam composed of many particles.

For α rays, let He^{++}, He^{+}, and He^{0} denote the number of doubly charged, singly charged, and neutral α particles in a beam composed of a total of He^{++} + He^{+} + He^{0} particles. Then the average charge is given by

$$z_{av} = \frac{2\text{He}^{++} + \text{He}^{+}}{\text{He}^{++} + \text{He}^{+} + \text{He}^{0}}$$
$$= \frac{2 + (\text{He}^{+}/\text{He}^{++})}{1 + (\text{He}^{+}/\text{He}^{++}) + (\text{He}^{0}/\text{He}^{++})} \tag{1.8}$$

For velocities above about $2u_H$ ($\sim$0.44 $\times 10^9$ cm/sec), the ratio He^{0}/He^{++} is thought to be very small (R48) and can be neglected in comparison with He^{+}/He^{++}. Then the mean charge can be expressed in terms of any of the equivalent measured ratios in Eq. (1.4), e.g.,

$$z_{av} = 1 + \frac{1}{1 + (\text{He}^{+}/\text{He}^{++})} = 1 + \frac{1}{1 + (\sigma_c/\sigma_l)} \tag{1.9}$$

Figure 1.1 collects the results of several observers (H31, R48, B120, K4) in terms of the mean charge of α rays, in light elements such as air and mica. Kapitza's (K4) observations consist of measurements of the curvature of α-ray tracks in an air-filled cloud chamber, under the influence of a magnetic field of 43,000 gauss. As these α rays lose their velocity, it is found that the final portions of their range have a constant radius of curvature. Therefore their effective charge ez_{av} is proportional to their velocity V as $V \rightarrow 0$. The dotted portion of the α-ray curve in Fig. 1.1 is therefore extrapolated linearly into the origin. In the very-low-energy domain from 0.10 to 0.48 Mev, accelerated helium ions have been used by Snitzer (S55) to measure the relative proportions of He++, He+, and He⁰ in helium ion beams traversing $\overset{\ast}{H}_2$, He, air, and A gas.

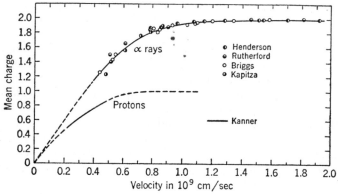

Fig. 1.1   Mean charge ez_{av} for α rays and protons, due to capture and loss of electrons.

Because the mean charge on a beam of α rays depends upon velocity, the quantity measured in a deflection experiment in moderate vacuum is ez_{av}/M, and the charge collected from n α rays is only nez_{av}. For α rays from a bare polonium source, for example, where $V = 1.6 \times 10^9$ cm/sec, the mean charge is $1.988e$, not $2e$.

Figure 1.1 also shows the mean charge for protons in air and is probably applicable up to, say, $Z \sim 50$, as in the case of α rays. The solid portion of the proton curve is calculated from Kanner's (K3) direct measurements of σ_l and σ_c for protons in the energy domain from about 30 kev to 120 kev, using, by analogy with Eq. (1.8),

$$z_{av} = \frac{1}{1 + (H^0/H^+)} = \frac{1}{1 + (\sigma_c/\sigma_l)} \tag{1.10}$$

Kanner finds by a modest extrapolation that, for protons in air, $\sigma_l = \sigma_c$ (= 2.37×10^{-16} cm²) when $V = u_H$ (= 0.22×10^9 cm/sec; $E_p = 25$ kev), i.e., when the protons have a velocity equal to the Bohr orbital electron velocity in a hydrogen atom. However, for protons traversing hydrogen gas, the combined results of Ribe (R16) and of Montague (M52) indicate that $\sigma_l = \sigma_c$ at a slightly greater velocity, $V = 1.44$ u_H.

Capture and loss of charge plays a decisive but complicated role in the passage of the "very heavy" fission fragments through matter, as discussed in Sec. 6.

2. *Energy Loss per Unit Path Length*

Theoretical descriptions of the various methods by which a swift charged particle transfers its kinetic energy to an absorbing medium were developed in Chap. 18. If the rest mass of the particle greatly exceeds the rest mass of an electron, then the overwhelmingly predominant mode of energy transfer is by inelastic collisions with atomic electrons. The resulting *ionization* can be measured if the absorbing medium is a gas, a photographic emulsion, or a scintillating solid or liquid. But an important fraction of the energy transfer results in *excitation*, without ionization, of atoms in the absorber. Ordinarily, the excitation losses are not susceptible to direct measurement. Experiments which are designed as tests of the theory must therefore be based on direct measurements of the kinetic energy of an incident particle and on its residual kinetic energy after traversing a selected thickness of absorber. Such energy measurements generally are made by magnetic or electric deflection of the incident and emergent particles.

a. Differential Theory of Energy Loss. For a particle of any spin having rest mass M ($\gg m_0$), charge ze, and velocity V ($= \beta c$), the energy dE transferred as excitation and ionization along an element of path ds to a homogeneous absorbing medium containing N atoms/cm³, each of atomic number Z, is well approximated by

$$\frac{dE}{ds} = \frac{4\pi e^4 z^2}{m_0 V^2}\, NZ \left[\ln \frac{2m_0 V^2}{I} - \ln (1 - \beta^2) - \beta^2 \right] \qquad (2.1)$$

The geometric-mean excitation and ionization potential I of the absorbing atoms cannot be calculated accurately from first principles, except in the case of hydrogen. Therefore I is to be regarded generally as a constant whose value must be determined experimentally for each element. Bloch has shown that we can expect

$$I = kZ \qquad (2.2)$$

where k is an empirical constant, for atoms which have Z large enough to justify the Thomas-Fermi model of electron charge distribution.

Equation (2.1) is valid only if ze is not subjected to reduction by capture and loss of electrons; only if the energy is small enough so that polarization of the medium is unimportant; only if ze/MV^2 is small enough so that nuclear scattering and bremsstrahlung may be neglected; only if ze is not too large so that the usual condition, $2zZ/137\beta \ll 1$, for the applicability of the Born approximation is not too strongly violated; and only if $\beta \gg Z/137$ so that V greatly exceeds the Bohr orbital speed of the K electrons, $u_K = cZ/137$, and hence of any atomic electron.

Atomic Stopping Number. It is convenient to separate Eq. (2.1) into two factors, so that it reads

$$\frac{dE}{ds} = \frac{4\pi e^4 z^2}{m_0 V^2} NB \tag{2.3}$$

where B is called the *atomic stopping number*. For the nonrelativistic case, we have simply

$$B = Z \ln \frac{2m_0 V^2}{I} \tag{2.4}$$

but this is valid only if $c \gg V \gg c(Z/137)$.

Corrections for Nonparticipating Electrons. In an absorbing atom, the K electrons have a binding energy of $\frac{1}{2}m_0 c^2 (Z_{\text{eff}}/137)^2$ and a speed $u_K = c(Z_{\text{eff}}/137)$, where Z_{eff} is the effective nuclear charge. If screening of the nuclear charge by one K electron is included, but screening by all $L, M, N, \ldots$ electrons is ignored, then $Z_{\text{eff}} \simeq (Z - 0.3)$. If the K electrons are to participate in interactions with the incident particle, then energy transfers at least as large as the K-shell ionization potential must be energetically possible. But the maximum energy transfer (Chap. 18), when $M \gg m_0$ and $\beta^2 \ll 1$, is $2m_0 V^2$. Therefore, if the K electrons are to be effective, the energy E of the incident particle must be

$$E = \frac{1}{2} M V^2 = \frac{M}{4m_0} 2m_0 V^2 \gg \frac{1}{8} M c^2 \left(\frac{Z - 0.3}{137}\right)^2 \tag{2.5}$$

For protons passing through Al, the right-hand side of Eq. (2.5) equals 1.0 Mev. Equation (2.5) is a direct consequence of the conservation of momentum and energy.

An analogous restriction on the validity of Eq. (2.4) at low energies arises from the assumption $V \gg u_K$ made in the derivation of Eq. (2.1). With Bethe, we define a parameter $1/\eta$ as

$$\frac{1}{\eta} = \left(\frac{u_K}{V}\right)^2 \simeq \left(\frac{Z - 0.3}{137\beta}\right)^2 = \frac{M}{m_0} \left(\frac{Z - 0.3}{137}\right)^2 \frac{m_0 c^2}{2E} \tag{2.6}$$

Then Eqs. (2.1) and (2.4) are valid only when $1/\eta \ll 1$. Numerically,

$$\frac{1}{\eta} = 1 \quad \text{for} \begin{cases} \text{4.8-Mev } \alpha \text{ ray in air} \\ \text{4.1-Mev proton in Al} \\ \text{155-Mev proton in Au} \end{cases} \tag{2.7}$$

Clearly, there will be many practical cases in which the condition $V \gg u_K$ is not satisfied, and in which some of the hard collisions and all the soft collisions which are included in Eqs. (2.1) and (2.4) will, in fact, not occur.

Bethe and coworkers (L32, B47, W6) have derived a correction term C_K which represents the deficit in the atomic stopping number B, due to the ineffectiveness of K electrons. When this correction term is used, we write

$$B = Z \left[\ln \frac{2m_0 V^2}{I} - \ln (1 - \beta^2) - \beta^2 - \frac{C_K}{Z} \right] \tag{2.8}$$

and for the very common nonrelativistic case

$$B = Z \ln \frac{2m_0 V^2}{I} - C_K \qquad (2.9)$$

Figure 2.1 shows the theoretical values of C_K, as a function of $1/\eta$, and of a second parameter ϑ, which is the ratio of the actual K-shell binding energy to the "ideal ionization potential," $\frac{1}{2} m_0 c^2 [(Z - 0.3)/137]^2$, which ignores screening of the nuclear charge by the $L, M, N, \ldots$ electrons.

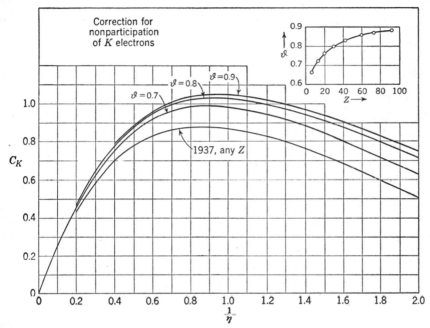

Fig. 2.1 The correction C_K to the atomic stopping number, Eqs. (2.8) and (2.9), due to the binding of K electrons. The parameter $1/\eta$ is inversely proportional to the particle energy E and is defined by Eq. (2.6). The parameter ϑ is the K-shell binding energy divided by the "ideal ionization potential" and depends on Z only. Numerical values of ϑ can be read directly from the inset graph, which is from a table by Bethe and Ashkin (p. 171 of B47). The curves for C_K are from Walske (W6). For comparison, the curve marked "1937, any Z" is the C_K vs. $1/\eta$ curve of Livingston and Bethe (L32).

Figure 2.1 also includes an older form (L32) of the C_K correction, marked "1937, any Z," which was used for the interpretation of experimental data up to 1953. Use of the upper curves (larger C_K) will impose a slight general reduction on all the values of I which have been derived from experimental data between 1937 and 1953. When B, V, and Z are experimentally determined quantities, Eq. (2.9) becomes

$$I = 2m_0 c^2 \beta^2 e^{-B/Z} e^{-C_K/Z} \qquad (2.10)$$

In some cases, corrections C_L may also be needed for nonparticipation of L electrons. These have been computed by Walske (W5). A semi-empirical evaluation of a correction for all shells,

$$C = C_K + C_L + C_M + \cdots$$

has been proposed for the case of 18-Mev protons by Sachs and Richardson (S1).

b. Experimental Determination of I. Although many measurements have been made of the *relative* stopping power of various elements, there are only a few *absolute* measurements which can be compared directly with Eq. (2.9). Such absolute measurements are especially valuable, because they provide the reference standards against which other elements and compounds may be compared. Air and Al are among the most common and convenient standard absorbing materials. In Al, the Bohr orbital speed of the K electrons is $u_K \simeq 2.8 \times 10^9$ cm/sec, or about the same as that of a 4.1-Mev proton or a 16-Mev α ray.

Aluminum. The absolute rate of energy loss dE/ds by protons in thin foils of Al has been measured by Sachs and Richardson (S1, C2) at about 18 Mev, and by Kahn and others (K1) at various energies between 0.05 and 2.0 Mev. The incident and emergent energies were measured by magnetic deflection in the higher-energy experiments and by electrostatic deflection in the low-energy domain.

The most probable energy loss (S1) and the mean energy loss (C2) by 17.8-Mev protons passing through Al foils of 10 different thicknesses were measured by Sachs and Richardson. For foils between 7 and 77 mg/cm², the average energy loss per milligram per square centimeter was about 22.2 kev. A weighted average, using Eqs. (2.3) and (2.10), leads to the proposed (C2) absolute value

$$I_{Al} = 164 \pm 3 \text{ ev} \tag{2.11}$$

It needs to be emphasized that the absolute value of I, which is calculated from any experimental determination of dE/ds, *depends very strongly on the numerical values chosen for the physical constants* which appear in Eq. (2.3). The origin of this strong dependence is primarily the exponential term $e^{-B/Z}$ in Eq. (2.10). For example, in the experiments just cited, $B/Z \simeq 5.5$; then a 1 per cent shift in e^4, or in N, will produce more than a 5 per cent shift in I, because $(dI/I) = -d(B/Z)$. Of course, the same strong dependence exists with respect to experimental uncertainties in dE/ds or in V^2. The particular value $I_{Al} = 164$ ev proposed in Eq. (2.11) is associated with the following values of the physical constants: $e^2/m_0c^2 = r_0 = 2.818 \times 10^{-13}$ cm; $m_0c^2 = 0.5108$ Mev; $N = 6.0228 \times 10^{23}$ atoms/g mole (*chemical* scale), and atomic weight $A = 26.98$ g/mole (*chemical* scale).

Many of the discrepancies in the literature on I are more apparent than real and have their origin in the selection of numerical constants (often unstated) by various authors.

In the proton energy range from 0.5 to 1.3 Mev, Kahn (K1) has measured the most probable energy loss and the mean energy loss in thin foils of Be, Al, Cu, and Au and has summarized the measurements by

Warshaw (W9) and others just below and above this energy domain.   At 1.00 Mev Kahn reports an energy loss per milligram per square centimeter of 177 kev in Al.   Because $1/\eta = 4.0$ for these conditions, the calculation of I with Eq. (2.10) is reasonably sensitive to C_K.   Using values of C_K by Brown, which have subsequently been corrected by Walske (W6), Kahn reported agreement with Eq. (2.10) over the energy domain studied and a mean value of $I_{Al} = 159$ ev.   Perhaps the standard error is of the order of 5 per cent, or ± 8 ev.

Within the reasonably wide standard errors imposed by the exponential dependence of I on B, Eq. (2.10), these absolute values of I for Al are in agreement with each other and with determinations of the mean range of energetic protons in Al.   The integration of Eq. (2.3), to give the full range of an average proton in the stopping material, will be discussed in Sec. 3.   Here we may note that range measurements in Al have been interpreted in terms of I values, as shown in Table 2.1.

TABLE 2.1. EVALUATIONS OF THE GEOMETRIC-MEAN EXCITATION AND IONIZATION POTENTIAL I FOR Al
(Based on measurements of the mean range of protons in Al)

Observers	Incident proton energy, Mev	Mean range in Al, g/cm²	I, ev
Simmons (S40)..................	∼10	....	155 ± 3
Hubbard and MacKenzie (H66, C2)	18.00 ± 0.02	0.4770 ± 0.0005	165 ± 3
Bloembergen and van Heerden (B78)........................	35–50	....	164
	50–75	....	161
Mather and Segrè (M19)........	339.7	79.42	150.3
	338.5	78.63	145.5

Air.   Dry air has long been the standard reference absorber for α rays in the energy domain from 0 to about 10 Mev.   Argon makes up nearly 1 volume per cent of air, and if its K electrons are presumed to be wholly nonparticipating, then the average number of effective electrons per atom of air is about 7.22 (L32).   Taking 7.22 as the effective atomic number of air, we find $1/\eta = 1$ for a 4.8-Mev α ray.   Corrections for nonparticipating electrons are therefore needed in the K shell and, for accurate work, also in the L shell.   The extensive corrections required, coupled with the fact that air is not a simple substance, have caused the abundant measurements to receive a wide variety of interpretations, in terms of I values (80.5 ev to 131 ev), by various workers.   In the energy domain below about 5 Mev for α rays and 1.25 Mev for protons, where $1/\eta \geq 1$, the energy-loss and range information in air is best regarded as purely empirical.   We shall discuss some of these data, and possible theoretical interpretations, in Sec. 3.

   c. Relative Stopping Power.   The "relative stopping power" of a substance is always a ratio of the amount of a standard material to the amount of the substance in question, *for equal energy loss.*

Definitions. When the relative stopping power is expressed on a basis of relative path lengths for equal energy loss, we can write, from Eq. (2.3), the usual *linear* relative stopping power S_l as

$$S_l = \frac{ds_0}{ds_1} = \frac{N_1}{N_0} \frac{B_1}{B_0} \tag{2.12}$$

where the subscripts 0 refer to the reference standard and the subscripts 1 denote the material specified by S_l. Analogously, the relative stopping power *per atom* is

$$S_a = \frac{N_0}{N_1} \frac{ds_0}{ds_1} = \frac{B_1}{B_0} \tag{2.13}$$

which is simply the ratio of the atomic stopping numbers B. Finally, the *relative stopping power per atomic electron S_e* has a readily visualizable physical significance and is the quantity

$$S_e = \frac{N_0 Z_0}{N_1 Z_1} \frac{ds_0}{ds_1} = \frac{(B/Z)_1}{(B/Z)_0} \tag{2.14}$$

For simple substances, $N = \mathsf{N}\rho/A$ atoms/cm³, where N is Avogadro's number, ρ is the density, and A the atomic weight of the absorber. Then the ratio N_1/N_0 can be replaced by $(\rho_1 A_0/\rho_0 A_1)$, and Eq. (2.14) becomes

$$S_e = \frac{(A/Z)_1}{(A/Z)_0} \frac{(\rho\, ds)_0}{(\rho\, ds)_1} = \frac{(B/Z)_1}{(B/Z)_0} \tag{2.15}$$

In this expression, the ratio of the masses $\rho\, ds$ g/cm² penetrated for equal energy loss is called the relative *mass stopping power S_m*

$$S_m = \frac{(\rho\, ds)_0}{(\rho\, ds)_1} = S_e \frac{(A/Z)_0}{(A/Z)_1} = \frac{(B/A)_1}{(B/A)_0} \tag{2.16}$$

Variation of Stopping Power with Z and V. Qualitatively, the general behavior which is expected of the relative stopping power can be visualized by expressing B in terms of Eq. (2.4). For this restricted case ($C_K = 0; \beta^2 \ll 1$) we expect the stopping power per electron to vary with Z as

$$S_e = \frac{B_1/Z_1}{B_0/Z_0} = \frac{\ln(2m_0 V^2/I_1)}{\ln(2m_0 V^2/I_0)}$$

$$= 1 - \frac{\ln(I_1/I_0)}{\ln(2m_0 V^2/I_0)} \tag{2.17}$$

Because of the approximate proportionality between I and Z, the term in $\ln(I_1/I_0)$ is negative for $Z_1 < Z_0$. Then all materials of smaller Z than the standard will have a greater stopping power per electron than does the standard, that is, $S_e > 1$. Conversely, for $Z_1 > Z_0$, the effectiveness per electron diminishes as Z_1 increases, and $S_e < 1$. Physically, these general trends reflect simply the increased tightness of binding of electrons, as Z increases. In Eq. (2.17), the term $\ln(2m_0 V^2/I_0)$ in the denominator emphasizes the fact that the variation of S_e with Z is greatest for low-velocity particles, where the effects of electron binding are felt more profoundly.

Relative Stopping Power of Aluminum with Respect to Air.   For proton energies between 1.5 Mev and 4.0 Mev, Wilson (W65) found that the stopping power of Al relative to air is constant (and equal to 1.48 mg/cm² of Al per centimeter of air at 15°C and 760 mm Hg).   This constancy is in violation of Eq. (2.17).   It is due to a fortuitous balancing of the effects of nonparticipating electrons.   Rewriting S_e in terms of Eq. (2.9), i.e., with C_K included, we obtain

$$S_e = \frac{B_1/Z_1}{B_0/Z_0} = \frac{\ln\ (2m_0V^2/I_1) - (C_K/Z)_1}{\ln\ (2m_0V^2/I_0) - (C_K/Z)_0}$$
$$= 1 - \frac{\ln\ (I_1/I_0) + (C_K/Z)_1 - (C_K/Z)_0}{\ln\ (2m_0V^2/I_0) - (C_K/Z)_0} \qquad (2.18)$$

In the 1.5-Mev to 4-Mev domain, Wheeler pointed out (W65) that, with increasing proton energy, $(C_K/Z)_{Al}$ increases but $(C_K/Z)_{air}$ decreases, and by just the right amounts to make S_e independent of V.   This important result provides a clear and independent experimental justification for the theoretical correction term C_K in Eq. (2.9).   Wheeler also interpreted Wilson's experiment in terms of the relative I values of Al and air.   In terms of a value $I_{air} = 80.5$ ev proposed in 1937 by Livingston and Bethe (L32), and based on α-ray ranges in air, Wheeler deduced $I_{Al} = 150$ ev, using the 1937 values of C_K.   This value of $I_{Al} = 150$ ev has been used widely as a substandard in the literature between 1941 and 1953.   It is important to recall that it is an indirect result and is subject to the uncertainties involved in the theoretical analysis of the data on α rays in air.

Measurements of Relative and Absolute Stopping Power.   Figure 2.2 collects representative experimental data covering elements from hydrogen to uranium.   The upper curve presents the observations on 12 elements by Bakker and Segrè (B7), who determined the number of grams per square centimeter required to produce the same diminution in the range of 340-Mev protons as is produced by a fixed thickness of about 30 g/cm² of Cu.   This produces a decrease of about 75 Mev in the energy of the protons; hence the mean energy of the protons in the "foil" is taken as about 300 Mev.   These relative mass stopping powers S_m were converted to a scale of absolute stopping number per electron B/Z by normalizing the data to the Wilson-Wheeler reference value of $I_{Al} = 150$ ev, which gives $(B/Z)_{Al} = 8.096$ from Eq. (2.8) with $C_K = 0$.

In Fig. 2.2, the 18-Mev proton data are from the mass-stopping-power experiments of Sachs and Richardson (S1).   These authors did not report their direct experimental data on S_m, and so their presumed B/Z observations have been computed using Eq. (2.4) and the effective, or uncorrected, I values, as reported for this experiment by Caldwell and Richardson (C2).   The 1-Mev proton data are from the absolute measurements by Kahn (K1), in the energy range from 0.5 to 1.3 Mev.

In Fig. 2.2, the ~8-Mev α-ray data are from the compilation by Mano

(M8), in 1934, of his own measurements on the gases H_2, He, air, Ne, and A, together with the measurements by Rosenblum, Briggs, and others on metal and mica foils. In Mano's experiments, the α rays from a bare ThC' source were retarded by passing through 10.86 cm of air, or other gas, at a known but adjustable pressure and temperature. They emerged through a slit in a thin (0.003-mm) window of cellulose acetate into an evacuated magnetic deflection chamber. Mano's method actually employed air as the absorbing material and hence rejoiced in a directness not found in earlier experiments, in which mica foils of separately determined air equivalence were substituted for air in the magnetic deflection

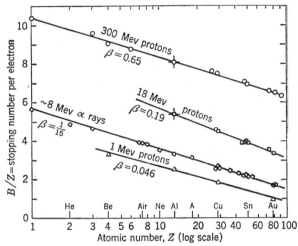

Fig. 2.2 Illustrative measurements (S1, C2, K1, M8) of relative stopping power, expressed as the observed stopping number per electron (B/Z). Normalization points are indicated by a cross, at Al, for the 300-Mev and 18-Mev proton data.

apparatus. The B/Z values plotted for $\sim$8-Mev α rays are computed from Mano's tabulation of the atomic stopping powers S_a relative to air, for $V = 2.0 \times 10^9$ cm/sec ($E_\alpha = 8.34$ Mev), for which Mano's experiments gave the value $dE/ds = 0.066$ Mev/mm of dry air at 15°C, 760 mm Hg, or $(B/Z)_{air} = 3.95$ and $I_{air} = 87$ ev for $C_K = 0$, using 1934 values of the physical constants.

In Fig. 2.2, for any one velocity β, the stopping number B/Z per electron is seen to decrease approximately linearly with log Z. This is in accord with Eq. (2.17) and the rough proportionality between Z and the average excitation energy I. The spacing of the four experimental lines reflects the influence of the particle velocity V when Z is constant. For the higher velocities, each electron is able to accept a larger maximum energy transfer, $Q_{max} \simeq 2m_0V^2$; hence the stopping number per electron increases with particle velocity, as represented analytically in Eqs. (2.4) and (2.17).

Relationship between I and Z. Each of the stopping-power experiments shown in Fig. 2.2 has been interpreted by its authors in terms of the geometric-mean excitation and ionization potential I, as a function of Z. Figure 2.3 shows the results, as calculated values of the mean ionization potential per electron, I/Z.

For each experimental point on Fig. 2.2, there corresponds an effective, or "uncorrected," value of I. These uncorrected values are obtained from Eq. (2.8) by setting $C_K = 0$. In the nonrelativistic cases, this amounts to assuming that $B/Z = \ln [(2m_0V^2)/I]$. The resulting uncorrected values of I/Z are shown as open symbols in Fig. 2.3.

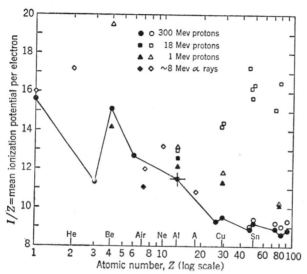

Fig. 2.3 Experimental results for I/Z, in ev. The shape of the symbol and its Z value show the experimental value B/Z, as given in Fig. 2.2, from which I/Z was computed. Solid symbols show I/Z corrected for nonparticipation of K electrons; open symbols are "uncorrected" values, that is, $C_K = 0$. In order to simplify the diagram, the α-ray data are restricted here to the gases H_2, He, air, Ne, and A, which were measured by Mano. For 300-Mev protons, all values are relative to the normalization point $(I/Z)_{Al} = 11.5$ ev, shown with a cross. These points are connected by a broken line as an aid to visualizing trends in the data.

For the experiments with 300-Mev protons and 1-Mev protons, corrected values of I have been determined by utilizing the appropriate values of C_K. These corrected values of I/Z are shown by the corresponding solid symbols in Fig. 2.3. In the case of 300-Mev protons, the K binding exerts only a slight influence at large Z ($1/\eta = 0.31$ for Sn, $Z = 50$) and is negligible in the lower-Z domain. Hence only solid circles appear in Fig. 2.3, except for the five heaviest elements used (Ag, Sn, W, Pb, U), where there is a slight difference between the corrected and uncorrected values of I/Z. None of these 300-Mev values is absolute. The 300-Mev values of I/Z were all computed (B47, B7) relative to the 1941 Wilson-Wheeler value for aluminum, $I_{Al} = 150$ ev, or $I/Z = 11.5$ ev.

The broad distribution of these data is due in part to experimental uncertainties, in part to the lack of theoretical correction terms for non-participation of L, M, . . . electrons, and in part to the use by different authors of different and often unspecified values of the fundamental physical constants. Recall that I/Z is extremely sensitive to variations in any of these quantities, Eq. (2.10).

Considering any one set of self-consistent values of I/Z, such as those of Bakker and Segrè on 300-Mev protons, it is clear that: (1) I/Z is *not constant* but decreases slowly as Z increases (roughly, the decrease is as log Z) and (2) the variation of I/Z with Z is *not monotonic;* there are real local variations, for particular values of Z, which exceed the experimental and theoretical uncertainties.

Additional experimental data will be found in the excellent reviews by Bethe and Ashkin (B47) and Allison and Warshaw (A17).

Stopping Power of Compounds and Mixtures. When compounds or mixtures of elements are used as absorbers, as in the case of mica, plastics, methane, or of helium-air mixtures, the atomic stopping power of each atom is taken as independent of the presence of atoms of other types (Chap. 18, Sec. 5), because the chemical binding energies are usually negligible. Then the mean atomic stopping power in a mixture of independent atoms is

$$(S_a)_{\text{av}} = \frac{(ds)_0}{(ds)_{\text{av}}} \frac{N_0}{N} = \frac{B_{\text{av}}}{B_0} = n_1 S_1 + n_2 S_2 + n_3 S_3 + \cdots \quad (2.19)$$

where n_1, n_2, . . . are the atomic fractions of the elements whose relative atomic stopping powers are S_1, S_2, . . . , and N is the total number of *atoms* per cubic centimeter of absorber. For mica (K_2O, $3Al_2O_3$, $6SiO_2$, $2H_2O$) the mean relative atomic stopping power is

$$(S_a)_{\text{av}} = \tfrac{2}{42} S_K + \tfrac{6}{42} S_{Al} + \tfrac{6}{42} S_{Si} + \tfrac{4}{42} S_H + \tfrac{24}{42} S_O \quad (2.20)$$

Problems

1. A certain cloud chamber contains air and small amounts of alcohol vapor and of a volatile compound of boron. Thermal neutrons produce the reaction $B^{10}(n,\alpha)Li^7$, for which $Q = 2.79$ Mev. The He^4 and Li^7 products are oppositely directed, away from the site of the compound nucleus, and hence they form one straight track. The variations of specific ionization along this track can be measured with a microphotometer and are indicated schematically in the sketch.

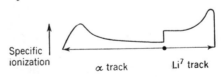

Specific ionization

α track Li^7 track

(a) What is the initial kinetic energy of the He^4?
(b) What is the initial kinetic energy of the Li^7 nucleus?
(c) What is the ratio of the initial velocities, $V(\text{He})/V(\text{Li})$?
(d) What is the ratio of the initial specific ionization produced by the two fragments, if the geometric-mean excitation potential of the medium is $I = 100$ ev?

2. Taking the composition of dry air, in volume per cent, as 78.02 nitrogen, 21.01 oxygen, 0.94 argon, and 0.03 carbon dioxide, calculate the average number of electrons per atom for air. *Ans.:* 7.26.

3. *Range-Energy Relationships*

The total range of a "heavy" swift charged particle is almost exactly equal to its total path length, because elastic nuclear scattering and bremsstrahlung are negligible when $M \gg m_0$, if z is small. The total range is then the integral of ds, which can be written as an element of range dr.

a. Integration of the Energy-loss Equation. The differential equation for energy loss can be integrated analytically if $\beta^2 \ll 1$ and $C_K = 0$. Otherwise, extensive computational work is involved in the numerical integration of Eq. (2.3), using B as given by Eq. (2.8).

For the common nonrelativistic case, we can write $E = \frac{1}{2}MV^2$, $dE = MV\, dV$, and $ds = dr$. Then Eq. (2.1) becomes

$$dr = \frac{M}{z^2} \frac{m_0}{4\pi e^4} \frac{1}{NZ} \frac{V^3\, dV}{\ln\,(2m_0 V^2/I)} \tag{3.1}$$

This equation, like Eq. (2.1), is not valid for small velocities because (1) capture and loss of electrons will alter z, (2) corrections C_K for nonparticipating electrons will alter I, and (3) the logarithmic term passes through zero to negative values when $2m_0 V^2 = I$, which is equivalent to $E = \frac{1}{2}MV^2 = (M/4m_0)I$, or about 0.2 Mev for α rays in air, or 0.1 Mev for protons in Al. Therefore Eq. (3.1) cannot be integrated over the entire range of the particle. However, it can be very profitably employed to describe the difference in range $(R_2 - R_1)$ between any two higher velocities $(V_2 - V_1)$ and also to relate the ranges of particles which have the same initial velocity but different values of M/z^2.

To integrate Eq. (3.1), we substitute

$$y \equiv \left(\frac{2m_0 V^2}{I}\right)^2 \tag{3.2}$$

Then Eq. (3.1) becomes

$$\int_{R_1}^{R_2} dr = \frac{M}{z^2} \frac{1}{32\pi e^4 m_0} \frac{I^2}{NZ} \int_{y_1}^{y_2} \frac{dy}{\ln y} \tag{3.3}$$

For ease of computation, let $u = \ln y$; then

$$Y_1 \equiv \int_0^{y_1} \frac{dy}{\ln y} = \int_{-\infty}^{\ln y_1} \frac{e^u}{u}\, du \equiv Ei(\ln y_1) \tag{3.4}$$

The "exponential integral" $Ei(x)$ has been tabulated, for example, in "Tables of Sine, Cosine, and Exponential Integrals," vol. 2, National Bureau of Standards, Washington, D.C., 1940. Then

$$R_2 - R_1 = \frac{M}{z^2} \frac{1}{32\pi e^4 m_0} \frac{I^2}{NZ} (Y_2 - Y_1) \tag{3.5}$$

b. Velocity-Distance Relationship for α Rays in Air. Substituting the "1952 values" (D44) of the physical constants, Eq. (3.5) becomes, for α rays in dry air at 15°C, 760 mm Hg,

$$R_2 - R_1 = 2.370 \times 10^{-6} I^2 (Y_2 - Y_1) \tag{3.6}$$

where R is in centimeters of air and I is in electron volts. When Eq. (3.6) is fitted to the measured ranges and velocities of the α rays of ThC', RaC', and Po, as given in Table 1.1 of Chap. 16, one obtains

$$I_{air} = 98.1 \text{ ev} \tag{3.7}$$

Because $C_K = 0$ was assumed in order to make Eq. (2.1) integrable, this value for I_{air} is an effective, or "uncorrected," mean ionization potential for air. It can be used in the integral equations, Eqs. (3.5) and (3.6), for interpolation and extrapolation over a reasonable domain of particle velocities. For example, the normal and long-range ThC' α rays have velocities of $V_1 = 2.0535 \times 10^9$ cm/sec and $V_2 = 2.2495 \times 10^9$ cm/sec. Equations (3.6) and (3.7) give $R_2 - R_1 = 3.00$ air-cm for these velocities. The experimentally determined ranges are 8.570 and 11.580 air-cm, or a difference of 3.01 air-cm.

A value for I_{air}, corrected for nonparticipation of K electrons, can be obtained with the aid of Eq. (2.10). For $E_\alpha \simeq 8$ Mev in air, Eq. (2.6) gives $1/\eta = 0.59$; then from Fig. 2.1, $C_K \simeq 0.9$. If $I_{air} = 98$ ev with $C_K = 0$, then from Eq. (2.10) the corrected value, with $C_K/Z \simeq 0.12$, is $I_{air} \simeq 86$ ev. This value, or Bethe's (L32) 1937 value of $I_{air} = 80.5$ ev, or the Bogaardt and Koudijs (B85) value of $I_{air} = 77.5$ ev, could then be used in numerical or graphical integrations in which C_K is taken as finite.

Figure 3.1 summarizes the experimental data on the velocity-distance relationship for ThC' α rays, whose initial energy is 8.776 Mev, as they are slowed down and stopped in air. The curve is Eq. (3.6) with $I_{air} = 98$ ev. It will be seen that the uncorrected theory ($C_K = 0$) matches the experimental data down to a velocity of less than 1.0×10^9 cm/sec ($\sim$2.1 Mev). At this velocity, capture and loss of electrons are becoming significant, Fig. 1.1. The continued agreement between Eq. (3.6) and experiment, at even lower velocities, is fortuitous.

Near the end of the range, the reduced mean charge ez_{av} of the particle and the nonparticipation of inner electron shells greatly reduce the rate of energy loss dE/ds and permit the particle to "coast" on out to a longer range than it would have otherwise. Because these effects cannot be described by any existing theory, the velocity-distance relationship in air for particles slower than about 1.5×10^9 cm/sec ($\sim$4.8-Mev α rays, or $\sim$1.2-Mev protons) must be regarded as wholly empirical.

c. Range-Energy Curves for α Rays in Air. Because all α rays are alike, if measured back from the end of their range, a range-velocity and range-energy relationship for slow α rays in air can be read from Fig. 3.1. It is only necessary to convert the distance scale r to a scale of *residual range* $(8.57 - r)$. For example, the initial velocity of an α ray whose range is 2.00 air-cm is the same as the velocity of a ThC′ α ray which has already traveled a distance $r = 6.57$ and is $V = 1.27 \times 10^9$ cm/sec, or 3.4 Mev.

Figure 3.2 is a range-energy relationship for α rays in air, constructed in part from Fig. 3.1, from measurements on the long-range ThC′ α rays, and from extrapolation with the aid of the theory. The accuracy and availability of a wide variety of empirical and theoretical range-energy

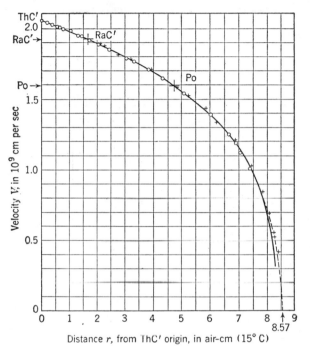

Fig. 3.1 Retardation of α rays by dry air. V is the velocity of ThC′ α rays which have passed through r cm of dry air at 15°C and 760 mm Hg. The smooth curve corresponds to Eq. (3.6) with $I_{air} = 98$ ev. Open circles are Mano's (M8) data on air absorption of ThC′ α rays. Crosses are Briggs's (B120) data on mica absorption of RaC′ α rays, referred to air by Briggs, and corrected to the ThC′ scale by adding 1.76 air-cm to his experimental values of r. The mean range of 8.57 air-cm is from Holloway and Livingston (H62). The initial velocity of the α rays from ThC′ and Po is indicated along the scale of velocities, and by crosses on the V vs. r curve.

curves steadily improve with time, as a result of continued efforts by individuals (A32, B47, B46, J12, B44, T9) and of correlative activities by a committee of the National Research Council.

d. Range-Energy for Hydrogen Ions. Recall Eq. (3.1). The moving particle is characterized by M, z, and V. We note that dr/dV, the distance traversed for a given velocity loss in a specified medium, is proportional to M/z^2 and to a complicated function of V. Then for two particles which have different values of M/z^2, such as He³ and He⁴, but the *same initial velocity*, every element of range dr will be proportional to

M/z^2; thus

$$\frac{dr_1}{dr_2} = \frac{(M/z^2)_1}{(M/z^2)_2} \tag{3.8}$$

This relationship is valid even when one introduces into Eq. (3.1) corrections for nonparticipation of inner electrons, because C_K depends upon V but not on M or z. If the capture and loss of electrons are significant, then Eq. (3.8) is valid only if the effective value of z^2 depends on velocity in the same way for the two particles. This is the case for all particles

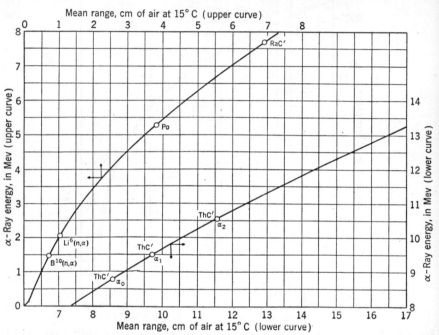

Fig. 3.2 Range-energy relationship for α rays in dry air at 15°C and 760 mm Hg. The curves agree with those of Bethe (B44) and with the tables by Jesse and Sadauskis (J12). Two low-energy calibration points (J12) are provided by the α rays emitted in the thermal neutron reactions $B^{10}(n,\alpha)Li^7$ and $Li^6(n,\alpha)H^3$.

which have the same z, for example, He^4 compared with He^3, but not He^4 compared with H^3. If Eq. (3.8) is valid at any specified velocity, then it is valid over the entire range R, and we can write, for particles of equal initial velocity,

$$\frac{R_{He^3}}{R_\alpha} = \frac{(M/z^2)_{He^3}}{(M/z^2)_\alpha} = 0.753 \simeq \tfrac{3}{4} \tag{3.9}$$

$$\frac{R_d}{R_p} = \frac{(M/z^2)_d}{(M/z^2)_p} = 1.999 \simeq 2 \tag{3.10}$$

$$\frac{R_t}{R_p} = \frac{(M/z^2)_t}{(M/z^2)_p} = 2.993 \simeq 3 \tag{3.11}$$

where α, p, d, t denote He^4, H^1, H^2, and H^3.

Range comparisons can be made between particles of different z provided that we know how to allow for the difference in capture and loss of electrons by the two particles. The α particle, because it has two charges to capture and lose, has its range extended somewhat farther than does the proton. It can be seen from Fig. 1.1 that $(z_{av})^2$ begins to fall off for α rays at somewhat higher velocities than for protons. Hence we expect proton ranges to be shorter than the corresponding α-ray ranges. This deficit has been evaluated in direct experiments by Blackett (B62) who found that the range of slow protons is 0.2 air-cm (15°C, 760 mm Hg) ·

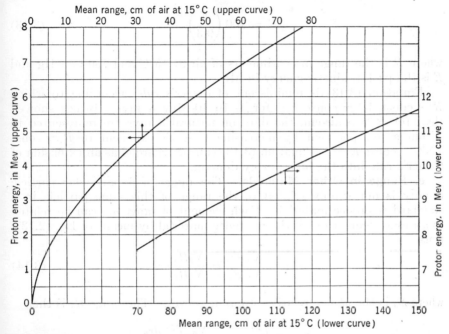

Fig. 3.3 Range-energy relationship for protons in dry air at 15°C and 760 mm Hg. [*From Bethe* (B44).]

shorter than the range of slow α rays of the same initial velocity. With Eqs. (3.10) and (3.11) in view, this observation can be generalized to read

$$R_H = \frac{(M/z^2)_H}{(M/z^2)_\alpha}\,(R_\alpha - 0.2 \text{ air-cm}) \qquad (3.12)$$

where H refers to a hydrogen ion of any mass, 1, 2, or 3.

Range-energy relations for p, d, and t can therefore be constructed from those for α rays, such as Fig. 3.2. For convenience, we give a range-energy relationship for protons in Fig. 3.3. Values for deuterons and tritons can be read from it also, using Eqs. (3.10) and (3.11).

Mesons. Range-energy relationships for μ and π mesons can be inferred from the proton range-energy curves, with correction for M/z^2.

These will be approximate, because of variations in their behavior near the end of their range.

High-energy Protons. For proton energies from about 15 Mev to 10^4 Mev, Smith (S49) has reported energy-loss values dE/ds, and ranges R, for air and Al, obtained by numerical integration of Eq. (2.3), using B from Eq. (2.8) and $I_{air} = 80.5$ ev, $I_{Al} = 150$ ev. Wilson and Brobeck (W66) have pointed out that, in the energy domain of about 10 Mev $<$ $E < 200$ Mev, simplifying assumptions can be made which permit easy integration and lead to the approximate relationship

$$R = 100 \left(\frac{E}{9.3}\right)^{1.8} \tag{3.13}$$

where R is the range in centimeters of air at 15°C and 760 mm Hg and E is the proton kinetic energy in Mev.

Equation (3.13) is reminiscent of *Geiger's rule*, according to which $R \simeq$ const $V^3 =$ const $E^{1.5}$ for 4- to 10-Mev α rays. Briggs showed that, for $R > 5$ air-cm, the data on natural α rays are represented to within a few per cent by increasing Geiger's exponent to $R \simeq$ const $V^{3.26} =$ const $E^{1.63}$. Equation (3.13) can be regarded as an extension of Geiger's rule into the high-energy domain.

e. Range in Other Materials. The range of a particular particle usually is not simply related to the range of this same particle in a standard reference material. Each element of range dr_1 can be related to a range element dr_0 in the reference material by means of Eq. (2.13); thus

$$dr_1 = \frac{N_0}{N_1}\frac{dr_0}{S_a} = \frac{N_0 B_0}{N_1 B_1} dr_0 \tag{3.14}$$

where S_a is the *atomic* relative stopping power. The range R_1 is then

$$R_1 = \int_0^{R_1} dr_1 = \frac{N_0}{N_1} \int_0^{R_0} \frac{dr_0}{S_a} \tag{3.15}$$

Because S_a is dependent upon the velocity [recall Eq. (2.17)], S_a cannot be taken outside the integral. The relationship $R_1 = (N_0/N_1)(R_0/S_a)$ is erroneous but not uncommon. Where relative stopping powers are known as a function of velocity, relative ranges may be obtained by numerical integration of Eq. (3.15). Otherwise it is usually simpler to employ Eq. (3.5), with effective, or "uncorrected," values of I.

Bragg-Kleeman Rule. Many instances arise in which a quick but rough estimate of relative ranges is useful. Bragg's early measurements of the range of α rays in a number of substances showed that the effective atomic stopping power is approximately proportional to $\sqrt{A}$. Then

$$\frac{R_1}{R_0} = \frac{N_0}{N_1} \cdot \frac{1}{S_1} \simeq \frac{(\rho_0/A_0)}{(\rho_1/A_1)} \cdot \frac{\sqrt{A_0}}{\sqrt{A_1}} = \frac{\rho_0}{\rho_1}\frac{\sqrt{A_1}}{\sqrt{A_0}} \tag{3.16}$$

where R is the range, ρ is the density, and A is the atomic weight.   Usually the Bragg-Kleeman rule is good to within ± 15 per cent.   Note especially that $R\rho$ is not "constant," as it is for β rays, but rather that $R\rho/\sqrt{A}$ is approximately constant for heavy particles whose ranges are not appreciably shortened by multiple scattering in high-Z materials. Compounds and mixtures follow the same empirical rule, provided that, in accord with Eqs. (2.19) and (3.16), the effective atomic weight is written as

$$\sqrt{A} = \frac{n_1 A_1 + n_2 A_2 + n_3 A_3 + \cdots}{n_1 \sqrt{A_1} + n_2 \sqrt{A_2} + n_3 \sqrt{A_3} + \cdots} \qquad (3.17)$$

where $n_1, n_2, \ldots$ are the atomic fractions of the elements whose atomic weights are $A_1, A_2, \ldots$.   Then for air, $\sqrt{A_0} = 3.82$, and

$$\rho_0 = 1.226 \times 10^{-3} \text{ g/cm}^3$$

at 15°C, 760 mm Hg.   The Bragg-Kleeman rule, Eq. (3.16), then takes its most common form

$$R_1 = 3.2 \times 10^{-4} \frac{\sqrt{A_1}}{\rho_1} R_{\text{air}} \qquad (3.18)$$

In aluminum, the range of α rays and protons in the domain of 1 to, say, 10 Mev is then about 1/1,600 of the range in air.   Comparison of Eqs. (3.15) and (3.16) shows that the Bragg-Kleeman rule functions because the variation of I with Z and the relative constancy of Z/A cause the atomic stopping power to be approximately proportional to $\sqrt{A}$ in this energy domain.

Problems

1. An α ray moving 2×10^9 cm/sec has a kinetic energy of 8.34 Mev and, if traveling in air, loses energy by ionization at the rate of 0.066 Mev/air-mm of path.   The loss in velocity per air-millimeter is 0.0080×10^9 cm/sec.   What is the kinetic energy of a proton and of a deuteron, if moving at the same velocity as this α ray?   What is their rate of loss of energy per air-millimeter of path, due to the ionization, while moving at 2×10^9 cm/sec?   If the α-ray range is 7.86 air-cm, what is the range for the proton and deuteron?

2. Assuming the following values for α rays, construct similar tables for protons and deuterons, over the ranges which are conveniently deduced from these α-ray data.

Range, air-cm.............	160	120	80	40	20	10	5
Energy, Mev.............	47.5	40.3	32.2	21.7	14.5	9.68	6.30

3. Using known data for α rays, determine the mean range in air at 15°C and 760 mm Hg of a group of He^3 nuclei whose initial velocity is 0.75×10^9 cm/sec.

4. Based on known empirical data for α particles, find the mean range in argon, at 15°C and 0.5-atm pressure, of a H^3 nucleus whose initial velocity is 1.0×10^9 cm/sec.   Assume that the average atomic stopping power of argon relative to air is 1.70 over the entire range.

5. Estimate (± 15 per cent) by the Bragg-Kleeman rule the mean range of 12-Mev deuterons in cobalt, if their mean range in air at 15°C and 760 mm Hg is 93 cm.

6. The initial velocities of the normal and long-range α rays from RaC' and ThC' are given in the table below. From the mean range of 8.570 air-cm for the normal ThC' α rays, compute the mean range of the other α rays listed.

	ThC'			RaC'	
	V, 10^9 cm/sec	R, air-cm		V, 10^9 cm/sec	R, air-cm
Normal.......	2.0535	8.570	Normal.......	1.9215	6.907
Long α_1.......	2.1348	9.724	Long α_1.......	1.9945	7.792
Long α_2.......	2.2495	11.580	Long α_2.......	2.0870	9.04
			Long α_3.......	2.2460	11.51

4. *Ionization of Gases*

Heavy charged particles are commonly detected, and their properties evaluated, by the ionization which the particle produces. Whereas energy losses are susceptible to theoretical description, the ionization produced by this energy loss is at present purely empirical. Roughly, an average expenditure of about 35 ev is required for each ion pair produced in air, but the exact value depends upon the velocity of the heavy particle. In air, more than half the energy loss results in excitation without ionization, as can be seen from the fact that the ionization potentials of O_2 and N_2 are only 13.6 ev and 14.5 ev, or less than half the average energy lost per ionization.

The more important types of empirical information relate to (1) the *specific ionization*, or number of ion pairs per unit path length, along the path of α rays and other swift ions in air and other gases and (2) the *total ionization* produced by swift ions of known initial energy while being absorbed in various gases.

a. Specific Ionization. In each ionizing event an originally neutral atom is divided into a free negative electron and a residual positive ion. Depending upon the nature of the nearby atoms, the liberated electron may remain free or it may become attached to a neutral atom to form a negative ion. The term *ion pair* means the residual positive ion and its negative counterpart, regardless of whether the electron is free or attached. In an ionization chamber, the electric charge which is collected is equal to the electronic charge times the number of ion pairs. Along the path of an α ray in normal air, some 2,000 to 6,000 ion pairs per millimeter are produced, depending upon the velocity of the α ray at the point under consideration. The number of ion pairs per unit path length is called the *specific ionization*.

The earliest direct studies of the specific ionization along the paths of the *individual* α rays were made in 1928 by Feather and Nimmo (F15), who measured with a photometer the intensity of scattered light along α-ray tracks in a cloud chamber. It had to be assumed that the ionization along the track was proportional to the number of water droplets formed, and hence to the light-scattering power of the track. By making all distance measurements back along the track from the end of the range, and considering only the final 2 cm of the track, the effects of straggling were largely eliminated, and an approximate "specific ionization" curve was inferred.

Subsequent developments in electrical detection instruments have permitted the direct measurement of the ionization produced within path elements only 1 mm long, at various points along the path of a single α ray. At the exact end of the range the specific ionization is zero. To locate this point by any kind of ionization measurements therefore requires an extrapolation of the measured specific ionization to zero.

For this reason, the location of the true end of an α-ray track is difficult to establish within about ± 0.02 air-cm.

The experimental work has been reviewed from time to time, and especially informative summaries have been given by L. H. Gray (G45) and by Bethe and Ashkin (B47). Figure 4.1 shows the specific ionization curve for α rays in air, as obtained by Holloway and Livingston (H62), who used as movable probe a shallow parallel-plate ionization chamber, 1 mm deep, coupled to a linear pulse amplifier and a thyratron-type discriminator circuit. Distances were measured along the path of a collimated beam of α rays from a polonium α-ray source. Uncertainties in residual range, due to the straggled distribution of α-ray velocities at any particular distance from the source, were minimized by making all the ionization measurements on the α rays of mean range. The discriminator bias which allowed just one-half the α rays to be counted was taken

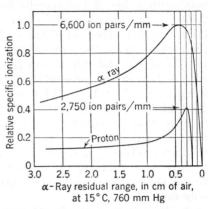

Fig. 4.1 Specific ionization of a single α ray and of a single proton in air at 15°C and 760 mm Hg. On the vertical scale, unity corresponds to about 6,600 ion pairs per millimeter of air. The horizontal scale is such that this proton and α ray will have substantially the same velocity throughout the left half of the diagram. Then the proton range is 0.2 air-cm shorter than the α-ray range, for the same initial velocity, by Eq. (3.12). [*α-Ray curve from Holloway and Livingston* (H62); *proton curve from Jentschke* (J10).]

as proportional to the specific ionization of the median α ray, at a point in its total path which is at the electrical center of the ionization chamber. The end of the mean range was taken as the position of the back face of the 1-mm-deep ionization chamber when the median α ray produces the same ionization in a similar chamber which is greater than 1 mm deep.

In Fig. 4.1 note especially that the maximum specific ionization occurs at a residual α-ray range of 0.40 ± 0.02 air-cm, where the average charge on the α ray has fallen to $ez_{av} = 1.5e$, as shown in Fig. 1.1. With the further rapid decline in ez_{av}, the specific ionization, which depends on the square of the charge, declines nonlinearly toward zero as the velocity decreases. At the peak of the α-ray curve, the specific ionization is 6,600 ion pairs per air-millimeter, according to direct measurements by Stetter and Jentschke (S74).

Figure 4.1 also shows the specific ionization curve for protons in air, according to the direct measurements by Jentschke (J10). Recall Eq. (3.12), according to which $R_p = 1.007(R_\alpha - 0.2)$ air-cm for protons and α rays of equal velocity. The two curves in Fig. 4.1 are drawn so that the proton and α ray have equal velocities when the residual range of the α ray is about 1 air-cm or greater. In this way we can visualize the 0.2-air-cm deficit in proton range as compared with α-ray range. The maximum value of the specific ionization for protons (G45) is close to 2,750 ion pairs per air-millimeter and occurs at a distance of only about 0.1 air-cm from the end of the proton range. For deuterons and tritons the maxima have the same values as for protons but occur at distances (B105) of 0.2 and 0.3 air-cm from the end of the range, as would be expected from the proportionality between path length and mass for equal energy loss, Eqs. (3.10) and (3.11). Notice also that, throughout the high-velocity region, the specific ionizations are strictly proportional to z^2, so that for equal velocities the specific ionization by the proton is one-fourth that for the α ray. However, near the end of the range this relationship breaks down, and the peak of the proton curve is 42 per cent of the α-ray peak. Qualitatively, this is because the α ray has two electronic charges available for capture and loss whereas the proton has only one.

b. Energy Loss per Ion Pair. Nearly half the kinetic energy lost by a swift proton or α ray is transferred in "hard" collisions (Chap. 18). The resulting δ rays may have kinetic energies as large as several kev. Thus about half the ultimate ionization is actually produced by slow electrons. In many of the "soft" collisions the incident particle (or a δ ray) may transfer less energy than is required for ionizing the absorbing atom, but enough to produce excitation of optical states of the atom. In spite of the very complicated character of the ultimate ionizing processes, it is found experimentally that the average energy w required to form an ion pair differs only about twofold among all common gases and for incident heavy particles of any velocity. This remarkable experimental constancy of w has been discussed in terms of semiquantitative physical arguments by Fano (F6), who concludes that "the greater the ionization potential the greater is the share of the absorbed energy which is actually spent in ionization." In the noble gases the ionization potentials are large, but the excitation potentials lie very close to the ionization potentials. Most energy transfers result in ionization even though this requires a relatively large expenditure of energy. In atoms not consisting of closed electron shells, the ionization potentials are much lower, but also the excitation and ionization potentials are more widely spaced. Although ionization requires only a relatively small energy transfer, there is a much larger probability in these atoms that energy transfers will result in excitation only. Hence w varies only moderately from one type of atom to another.

Velocity Dependence.   Early experiments by Gurney indicated (G48, G45) that for the noble gases He, Ne, and A the total ionization, produced by α rays of 0.25- to 2.0-air-cm range, is proportional to the initial kinetic energy E_α of the α ray.   This observation indicates that the energy w per ion pair is independent of α-ray velocity over the domain studied.   Contrariwise, Gurney found that in air, N_2, or O_2 the ratio of ionization to α-ray energy decreased with decreasing E_α.   For these gases, therefore, w increases as E_α decreases.   These findings were confirmed in later and more extensive measurements for air by Stetter (S73) and for argon and other gases by Jesse and coworkers (J11, J14a).

Figure 4.2 shows how the ratio of the ionization in argon to the ionization in air varies with α-ray energy, as determined in careful measurements by Jesse and Sadauskis (J12) on the total ionization produced by individual α rays.

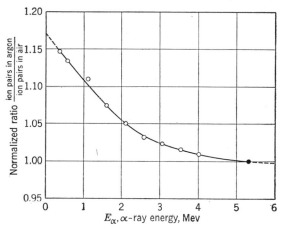

Fig. 4.2   Variation, with α-ray energy, of the ratio (total ionization produced in argon)/(total ionization produced in air).   The ratios are normalized to unity for the polonium α rays ($E_\alpha = 5.298$ Mev).   The vertical coordinate is also the variation of the energy per ion pair w in air (averaged over the energy domain from E_α to 0), because w for argon appears to be independent of E_α.   The air samples used in these experiments had been pretreated for removal of CO_2 as well as water vapor.   [*From Jesse and Sadauskis (J12).*]

Effects of Impurities in Gases.   Jesse and Sadauskis (J13) have shown clearly that minute amounts of impurities will profoundly alter the ionization produced by polonium α rays in the noble gases.   This finding requires that all such measurements prior to 1952 be reinterpreted.

Table 4.1 shows how small amounts of argon impurity in He and Ne greatly increase the ionization and reduce the derived value of w.   The same alterations in ionization are found for the secondary electrons produced by radium γ rays.   Hence the effect appears to be a secondary one.   The helium atom, whose first ionization potential is at 24.5 ev, has a metastable excited level at 19.8 ev.   The first ionization potential for argon is at 15.7 ev.   Hence an excited helium atom, in a collision with a normal argon atom, can transfer its excitation energy and ionize the argon atom, according to

$$He^* + A \rightarrow He + A^+ + e^- \tag{4.1}$$

This entirely plausible explanation appears to be confirmed by the additional observation that the ionization in pure argon can be increased nearly 25 per cent by the addition of 0.2 per cent acetylene. In this case, the metastable excited level in argon is at 11.6 ev, while the first ionization potential of acetylene is at about 11.2 ev.

In all the older experiments, and in most laboratory situations, He and Ne contain traces of impurities such as argon. Then the lower values of w are seen for He and Ne. In argon, the effects of impurities are generally much less marked, because the common contaminants are N_2 and O_2, whose ionization potentials of 15.5 ev and 12.5 ev do not lie below the 11.6-ev metastable level of argon.

TABLE 4.1. TOTAL IONIZATION, AND AVERAGE ENERGY w TO FORM AN
ION PAIR, IN PURE AND CONTAMINATED NOBLE GASES

Gas	Ion pairs/Po α ray	w = av. energy/ ion pair, ev	Reference
Purest helium used................	1.283×10^5	41.3	J13
Helium + 0.13 per cent argon......	1.784×10^5	29.7	J13
Purest neon......................	1.460×10^5	36.3	J13
Neon + 0.12 per cent argon........	2.030×10^5	26.1	J13
Purest argon.....................	....	26.4	J14
Argon + 0.2 per cent acetylene.....	....	21	J14

Average Energy to Form an Ion Pair in Pure Gases. Measurements of w for various gases and for low- and high-energy α rays and protons have been summarized by Jesse and Sadauskis (J14) and by Bethe and Ashkin (B47). Table 4.2 lists representative results, for polonium α rays, in highly purified gases. Note that among all the noble gases the observed ratio of w to the lowest ionization potential B_0 has a small and substantially constant value of $w/B_0 \simeq 1.7$.

Results by other workers (B99) using highly purified gases are comparable. When ordinary tank gases are used, the w values for the noble gases fall to those listed in Table 4.1. Results for 340-Mev protons in tank gases (B7) generally agree with the polonium α-ray values of w within about 1 ev.

c. Columnar Ionization and Ion Recombination. Immediately after the passage of a heavy charged particle all the ionization is located in a cylindrical or needlelike volume enclosing the path of the ray. Thus the volume density of ionization along the particle's path is enormous and is briefly described by the term *columnar ionization*. In air and other gases which contain traces of oxygen or water vapor, the freed electrons become attached to neighboring neutral atoms to form negative ions. Because of the great volume density of ion pairs in the case of columnar ionization, and the kinetic diffusion which takes place in the gas, a portion of the positive and negative ions are neutralized by recombination before they can be separated and collected by the electrostatic field within the ionization chamber. If the collecting field is at right angles to the path of the particle, and thus to its column of ions, a greater fraction of the ions can be collected than if the field is at any other angle with the ray. If the field is parallel to the particle's path, all ions which are collected must be drawn through the diffused column of ions, and in this way the probability of their loss by recombination is a maximum.

TABLE 4.2. AVERAGE ENERGY w TO FORM AN ION PAIR, IN CAREFULLY PURIFIED GASES, BY α RAYS FROM POLONIUM ($E_\alpha = 5.298$ MEV)

[As measured by Jesse and Sadauskis (J14). Ionization and excitation potentials from Brown (B132)]

Gas	w, ev/ion pair ± 0.5 per cent	Metastable excitation potential, ev	Lowest ionization potential B_0, ev	Ratio w/B_0
He	42.7	19.8	24.5	1.74
Ne	36.8	16.6	21.5	1.71
A	26.4	11.6	15.7	1.68
Kr	24.1	9.9	14.0	1.73
Xe	21.9	8.3	12.1	1.81
H_2	36.3	....	15.6	2.33
CO_2	34.5	....	14.4	2.40
Air	35.5	....		
O_2	32.5	....	12.5	2.60
N_2	36.6	....	15.5	2.36
CH_4	29.2	....	14.4	2.03
C_2H_2	27.5	....	11.6	2.37
C_2H_6	26.6	....		
C_2H_4	28.0	....		

The ratio of the number of ions collected to the number formed is called the *relative saturation*. It depends not only on the magnitude of the field and its orientation with respect to the particle's trajectory but also on the type and density of the gas. In the case of air at 15°C and atmospheric pressure, about 98 per cent of the ions can be collected by a field of 100 volts/cm, normal to an α-ray path, while the same field, if parallel to column of ions, will collect only about 88 per cent of the ions. At other angles the relative saturation is intermediate (K2) between these extremes and is in accord with Jaffé's theory (J7) of columnar ionization. The relative saturation at higher gas density is greatly decreased.

Figure 4.3 shows Moulin's data (M73) on the relative saturation for α-ray ionization in air at 1 atm. Moulin also made similar measurements in CO_2 and H_2, while Kanne and Bearden have given data for air at 1 and 2 atm, using several values of field intensity and angles of 0° to 45° between the field and the ray.

All absolute ionization measurements on heavy particles should include corrections for relative saturation. Unfortunately, this point has been overlooked or inadequately treated in some otherwise valuable experiments. The correction should be obtained empirically for each apparatus. This is best done by observing the ionization i at various values of the total collecting potential U and extrapolating a graph of i/U vs. i to $i/U = 0$, ($U = \infty$).

Certain gases, notably CO_2, are exceptionally difficult to saturate, fields of over 3,300 volts/cm being required for about 99 per cent relative saturation at atmospheric pressure (H46). On the other hand, the noble gases, He, A, Ne, etc., when carefully purified, show very high relative saturations, because in these gases the probability of negative ion formation by electron attachment is very small.

All the experiments discussed in this section have been done without the use of extreme ion collecting potentials, i.e., under "normal" laboratory operating conditions. When saturation is sought, through the use of collecting fields of the order of 10^4 volts/cm, Kimura and coworkers (K16) have shown that Fig. 4.1 is altered in a manner such that w for air is less dependent on α-ray velocity. Similarly, Adler and coworkers (A9) have found that $w = 34.7 \pm 0.5$ ev per ion pair for air, under extremely high ion collecting fields, as compared with $w = 35.5 \pm 0.5$ ev per ion pair given in Table 4.2.

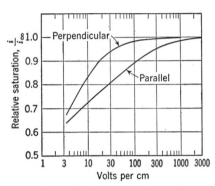

Fig. 4.3 Relative saturation of α-ray ionization in air at 15°C and 760 mm Hg for rays parallel to the collecting field and perpendicular to the collecting field.

5. *Straggling*

Identical charged particles, all having the same initial velocity, do not all have the same range. The observed ranges of individual particles from any monoenergetic source will show a substantially normal (or "gaussian") distribution about the mean range. The standard deviation of this distribution is of the order of 1 per cent for polonium α rays in any absorber. As early as 1912, Darwin (D4) correctly identified this distribution as due to statistical fluctuations in the individual collisions between the charged particle and atomic electrons and named the effect *range straggling*.

As has been emphasized recently by Lewis (L21), the harder collisions actually account for most of the straggling, as would be expected from the general theory of statistical fluctuations in composite distributions, Chap. 26, Eq. (3.2). Because the very hard collisions are few in number, the actual distribution is somewhat asymmetric, with a longer tail in the direction of short ranges, and with a mean range which is slightly shorter than the modal range (L21, C1).   The assumption of a symmetric normal law distribution is, however, within the accuracy of most experiments and is the basis for the conventional theory of straggling.

a. Energy Straggling.   Energy straggling refers to the variations in energy noted in a beam of initially monoenergetic particles after passing through some fixed amount of absorber.   Let A_x be the average number of collisions per unit path length in which an energy between Q_x and $Q_x + dQ$ is transferred.   Then, from the classical collision theory of Bohr (Chap. 18), we have

$$A_x = NZ \, d\sigma = \frac{2\pi z^2 e^4}{m_0 V^2} \, NZ \, \frac{dQ}{Q_x^2} \qquad \text{per cm} \qquad (5.1)$$

where all the symbols have their usual meaning.   The energy transfer in a distance Δr will be

$$\Delta E = Q_1 A_1 \, \Delta r + Q_2 A_2 \, \Delta r \cdots \qquad (5.2)$$

giving an energy transfer per unit path length of

$$\frac{\Delta E}{\Delta r} = \sum_x Q_x A_x \qquad (5.3)$$

Writing Eq. (5.3) in the corresponding integral form and using Eq. (5.1), we have

$$\frac{dE}{dr} = \frac{2\pi z^2 e^4}{m_0 V^2} \, NZ \int_{Q_{\min}}^{Q_{\max}} \frac{dQ}{Q} \qquad \text{ergs/cm} \qquad (5.4)$$

The statistical fluctuations in energy loss ΔE arise from fluctuations about the average number of collisions $A_x \, \Delta r$.   We assume that the collisions are randomly distributed and that they therefore fulfill the conditions for a Poisson distribution (Chap. 26).   Then the standard deviation (S.D.) in the number of collisions is $\sqrt{A_x \, \Delta r}$.   The S.D. of the energy loss is $Q_x \sqrt{A_x \, \Delta r}$.   The variance, or (S.D.)², of the energy loss ΔE is $Q_x^2 A_x \, \Delta r$.

In the addition of independent random processes the individual variances are additive.   Hence the variance, called $P \, \Delta r$, in the energy loss ΔE over the range element Δr is

$$P \, \Delta r = Q_1^2 A_1 \, \Delta r + Q_2^2 A_2 \, \Delta r + \cdots$$
$$= \Delta r \sum_x Q_x^2 A_x \qquad (5.5)$$

Substituting Eq. (5.1) for A_x and replacing the summation by its corresponding integral give

$$P = \frac{2\pi z^2 e^4}{m_0 V^2} \, NZ \int_{Q_{\min}}^{Q_{\max}} dQ = \frac{2\pi z^2 e^4}{m_0 V^2} \, NZ(Q_{\max} - Q_{\min})$$

If $Q_{\min} \ll Q_{\max} = 2m_0 V^2 [M/(M + m_0)]^2$, and $M \gg m_0$, we obtain Bohr's classical value (B93) for the variance P_0 of the energy transfer per unit path length

$$P_0 = 4\pi z^2 e^4 NZ \qquad \text{ergs}^2/\text{cm} \qquad (5.6)$$

E. J. Williams (W56) derived a quantum-mechanical treatment of the effects of electron binding on the soft collisions. The result is

$$P = P_0 \left(1 + \frac{kI}{m_0 V^2} \ln \frac{2m_0 V^2}{I}\right) \quad \text{ergs}^2/\text{cm} \tag{5.7}$$

where $k \simeq \frac{4}{3}$ for hydrogenlike electrons. It is assumed that $k = \frac{4}{3}$ can be used to obtain approximate results for any atom.

b. Range Straggling. Consider a large number n_0 of α rays, each having exactly energy E_0 at $r = 0$. Between $r = 0$ and $r = \Delta r$, a variance of $P \, \Delta r$ in E is developed. This distribution of energies at Δr implies that the particles which have each lost exactly ΔE are *not* all at distance Δr, but are at various distances distributed about a mean value of Δr.

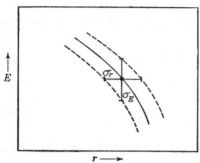

Now let σ_E be the S.D. of the mean residual energy and σ_r be the standard deviation of the distance traversed by the individual particles which have energy E. σ_E and σ_r are indicated in Fig. 5.1 where, parallel to the curve representing the mean value of E vs. r, we have drawn curves which are ± 1 S.D. away. The region between these two curves brackets the actual values of E and r for 68 per cent of the particles.

Fig. 5.1 Schematic representation of the standard deviations σ_E and σ_r, showing the region bordering the mean E vs. r curve, in which 68 per cent of all particles will be found. The usual E vs. r curve (or a V vs. r curve) actually represents only the mean value of E vs. r and is more physical when visualized in three dimensions, with the distribution of the number of particles plotted normal to the plane of the diagram.

The ratio between σ_E and σ_r is seen from Fig. 5.1 to be the same as the absolute value of the slope of the E vs. r curve, i.e.,

$$\frac{\sigma_E}{\sigma_r} = \left|\frac{dE}{dr}\right| \tag{5.8}$$

Then, in general, the variance σ_r^2 of r is

$$\sigma_r^2 = \sigma_E^2 \left(\frac{dE}{dr}\right)^{-2} \tag{5.9}$$

Then the increment $\Delta(\sigma_r^2)$ in the variance of r, produced between $r = 0$ and $r = \Delta r$, is

$$\Delta(\sigma_r^2) = \Delta \left[\sigma_E^2 \left(\frac{dE}{dr}\right)^{-2}\right] = P \left(\frac{dE}{dr}\right)^{-2} \Delta r \tag{5.10}$$

The variance σ_r^2, developed between $r = 0$ and $r = r$, is the sum of the increments of the variance, or

$$\sigma_r^2 = \sum \Delta(\sigma_r^2) = \int_0^r P \left(\frac{dE}{dr}\right)^{-2} dr \tag{5.11}$$

and the S.D. of the actual ranges of the particles, about their mean range R, is

$$\sigma_R = \left[\int_0^R P \left(\frac{dE}{dr} \right)^{-2} dr \right]^{\frac{1}{2}} = \left[\int_0^E P \left(\frac{dE}{dr} \right)^{-3} dE \right]^{\frac{1}{2}} \qquad (5.12)$$

Equation (5.12) has to be evaluated by numerical integration. For orientation, we may note that, for polonium α rays in air, $E = 5.298$ Mev, $R = 3.84$ air-cm, $\sigma_R = 0.036$ air-cm, $\sigma_R/R \simeq 0.9$ per cent.

The number of collisions per unit path is large ($\sim 10^3$ per millimeter of air). Hence the Poisson distribution is well represented by a normal distribution whose S.D. is given by the Poisson value deduced from P, as in Eq. (5.12). Then in a large group of n_0 α rays having the same initial velocity V_0, the number dn, having actual ranges between x and $x + dx$, will be given by the normal distribution and is

$$\frac{dn}{n_0} = \frac{1}{\sigma_R \sqrt{2\pi}} e^{-[(x-R)^2/2\sigma_R^2]} \, dx \qquad (5.13)$$

The literature on straggling has usually followed a precedent set by Bohr (B93) who did not explicitly use S.D. but rather a *range-straggling parameter* α_0 defined by

$$\alpha_0 \equiv \sqrt{2} \, \sigma_R \qquad (5.14)$$

When instrumental effects (slit widths, etc.) add to the true straggling as represented by α_0, the observed range-straggling parameter α is

$$\alpha^2 = \alpha_0^2 + \alpha_1^2 + \alpha_2^2 + \cdots \qquad (5.15)$$

In practice, α^2 may easily equal $2\alpha_0^2$; see, for example, the informative cloud-chamber measurements on the α rays from normal uranium, by King and Rayton (K17). Then Eq. (5.13) becomes

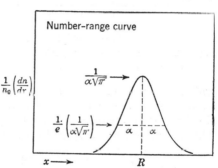

Fig. 5.2   Schematic "number-range curve," illustrating a symmetric distribution of ranges about the mean range R. The "range-straggling parameter" α is $\sqrt{2}$ times the standard deviation of the range distribution.

$$\frac{dn}{n_0} = \frac{1}{\alpha \sqrt{\pi}} e^{-[(x-R)/\alpha]^2} \, dx \qquad (5.16)$$

where α is the half width of the range distribution at $1/e$ of maximum, as illustrated in Fig. 5.2.

c. **Range-straggling Parameter.** Measurements of the range-straggling parameter α_0 have been undertaken by Lewis and Wynn-Williams (L25), Briggs (B119), Bennett (B33), and others. Figure 5.3 gives illustrative results, for α rays in air, according to the differential ionization-chamber measurements by Lewis and Wynn-Williams. It will be noted that α_0 is approximately linear with R and can be represented within about ± 10 per cent by

$$\alpha_0 \simeq 0.015R \qquad (5.17)$$

d. Straggling for Protons. With α-ray data in hand, we can make use of the theory in order to infer values of the range-straggling parameter for other conditions. For particles of the *same initial velocity* V_0, but different *mass* M, and *charge* ze, we can substitute into Eq. (5.12) the following previously derived expressions: for P, Eq. (5.7); for dE/dr, Eqs. (2.3) and (2.4); for dr, Eq. (3.1); and for α_0, Eq. (5.14). When this is done, we obtain the following general relationships

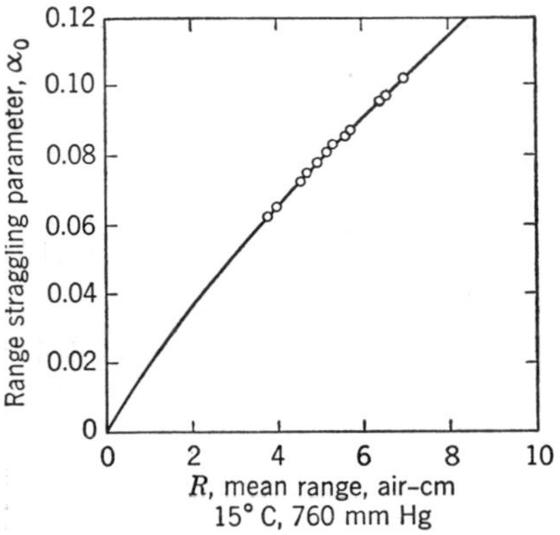

$$\alpha_0 = \frac{\sqrt{M}}{z^2} \frac{1}{NZ} F_1(V_0, I) \qquad (5.18)$$

$$R = \frac{M}{z^2} \frac{1}{NZ} F_2(V_0, I) \qquad (5.19)$$

$$\frac{\alpha_0}{R} = \frac{1}{\sqrt{M}} F_3(V_0, I) \qquad (5.20)$$

Fig. 5.3 Range-straggling parameter α_0 for natural α rays in air (L25).

in which F_1, F_2, and F_3 are complicated functions of the initial velocity V_0 and of the geometric-mean excitation and ionization potential I, which characterizes the absorber. Qualitatively, $F_3(V_0, I)$ and hence α_0/R can be shown to (1) be independent of N, and of z, (2) decrease slowly with increasing V_0, and (3) increase slowly with increasing I. Then, for particles having the same V_0,

$$\frac{(\alpha_0/R)_M}{(\alpha_0/R)_{\alpha \text{ ray}}} = \sqrt{\frac{4}{M}} \qquad (5.21)$$

Protons will therefore be expected to have about twice the range-straggling parameter of an α ray which has the same initial velocity and hence about the same range.

Equation (5.21) is not valid for very heavy ions, such as fission fragments, where nuclear scattering interactions involve very large energy transfers and hence greatly increase the straggling.

e. Number-Distance Curve. Several common types of particle detectors measure the number of particles which are still present in a collimated beam at a distance x from the source. These particles, which are "still going" at x, have actual ranges equal to or greater than x. Their number n is given by

$$n = n_0 - \int_{-\infty}^{x} dn \qquad (5.22)$$

where dn/n_0 is given by the normal law distribution of Eq. (5.16). The normal distribution is nonintegrable but has been tabulated (Chap. 26, Fig. 1.2).

The so-called "number-distance curve," n/n_0 against x, is shown in Fig. 5.4. Its slope $(dn/n_0)/dx$ at the mean range $x = R$ is $1/\alpha \sqrt{\pi}$. The central portion of the number-distance curve is approximately linear and extrapolates into the distance axis at the so-called *extrapolated number-distance range* R_n. From Fig. 5.4, the relationship between R_n and the mean range R is

$$\frac{\frac{1}{2}}{R_n - R} = \frac{1}{\alpha \sqrt{\pi}} \tag{5.23}$$

so that the mean range, in terms of a measured extrapolated range R_n and straggling parameter α, is

$$R = R_n - \frac{\sqrt{\pi}}{2}\alpha = R_n - 0.886\alpha \tag{5.24}$$

f. Bragg Ionization Curve. In a collimated beam of α rays, or similar particles, the relationship between the *average* specific ionization and the distance from the source is named the *Bragg curve*, in honor of W. H.

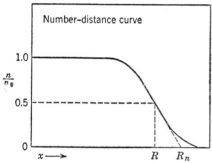

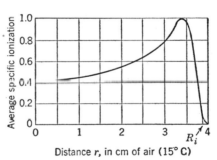

Fig. 5.4 The extrapolated number-distance range R_n exceeds the mean range R by 0.886α, where α is the range-straggling parameter.

Fig. 5.5 Bragg ionization curve for polonium α rays in air at 15°C and 760 mm Hg. [*From Naidu* (N3).]

Bragg, who first examined it systematically (B109) and who first observed that the α rays from each radioactive nuclide have a characteristic range in air and ionize most heavily near the end of that range.

The Bragg curve for various particles, especially the α rays from Po and RaC′, has since been studied carefully by many experimenters. Although no two observers have obtained identical results, it seems probable that the geometrical factors which lead to spurious effects have been most nearly eliminated in the work of Naidu (N3). Figure 5.5 shows the Bragg ionization curve for polonium α rays according to Naidu.

Bragg curves differ in principle from curves of the specific ionization of an individual particle, Fig. 4.1. A Bragg curve is an *average over a large number of individual particles,* hence includes effects of straggling, and has a pronounced tail well beyond the mean range.

A Bragg curve can be constructed by combining the specific ionization curve for a single particle with the straggled distribution of actual ranges. Let

x = range of individual particle

dn = number of particles with range between x and $x + dx$

r = distance from source

$i(x - r)$ = specific ionization along path of individual particle, at distance $(x - r)$ from *end* of its path

$I(r)$ = Bragg curve ordinate (average ionization per unit path length)

Then
$$d[I(r)] = [i(x - r)] \frac{dn}{n_0}$$

$$I(r) = \int_r^\infty \frac{i(x - r)}{\alpha \sqrt{\pi}} \, e^{-[(x-R)/\alpha]^2} \, dx \tag{5.25}$$

Equation (5.25) can be evaluated by numerical or graphical integration. Figure 5.6 illustrates a typical result. Note that the Bragg curve has a broad peak and a nearly straight-line descent followed by a long tail, in contrast with the specific ionization curve for an individual particle.

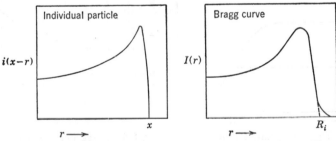

Fig. 5.6 The Bragg curve is the *average* specific ionization along a collimated beam of heavy particles. Extrapolation of the slope of the final portion of the Bragg curve leads to the "extrapolated ionization range" R_i.

g. Extrapolated Ionization Range. Many α-ray and proton "range" measurements have been obtained by extrapolating the descending straight-line portion of a Bragg ionization curve into the distance axis, as indicated in Fig. 5.6. This *extrapolated ionization range R_i* was devised by Marsden and Perkins in 1914, and a great many range measurements are made employing this concept. We require a justifiable method for converting extrapolated ionization ranges R_i into mean ranges R.

Evidently the extrapolated intercept, like the Bragg curve itself, is determined jointly by the effective straggling parameter α and by the specific ionization curve for a single particle. For α rays in air, Holloway and Livingston (H62) have evaluated Eq. (5.25) using Fig. 4.1 and a series of assumed values for α (0.062, 0.100, 0.124, and 0.150 air-cm).

The family of Bragg curves so constructed leads, on graphical analysis, to the empirical relationship

$$R = R_i - 0.47\alpha + 0.006 \qquad \text{air-cm} \tag{5.26}$$

for α rays in air. We recall that the effective straggling parameter α includes instrumental effects and therefore is always greater than the theoretical value α_0. The actual value of α in any particular experiment may be estimated from the slope of the descending portion of the observed Bragg curve (H62). Because of the uncertainties in this estimate, it is highly preferable to design experiments so that the mean range is measured directly, or at least so that extrapolated ionization ranges are used only as reference points.

h. Comparison of "Ranges." Figure 5.7 summarizes the effects of straggling on various types of particle "range." Among all these, only the mean range R has basic physical significance and is the type of "range" which is meant in all range-energy relationships.

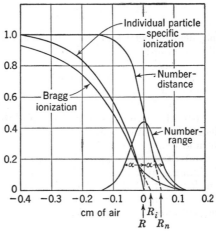

Fig. 5.7 Comparison of ranges R, R_n, and R_i for the particular case of polonium α rays in air. The Bragg curve corresponds to a group of particles with the range distribution as given by the number-range curve, and with individual-particle specific ionization as shown here and in Fig. 4.1. [*From Holloway and Livingston* (H62).]

Problems

1. An initially monoenergetic beam of 14-Mev deuterons is passed through absorbing material of such thickness that one-half emerge. What fraction of the emergent deuterons will have a residual kinetic energy greater than 1 Mev?

2. A homogeneous beam of 1.29-Mev protons is to pass through an absorber which has atomic properties similar to air, and the emerging protons are to be counted by a proportional counter. The minimum ionization which will produce a count is about 700 ion pairs and corresponds exactly to the ionization produced in the last 0.5 air-mm of path of a proton. Thus only those protons whose residual range is 0.5 air-mm or greater will produce counts. When the absorber thickness is exactly equal to the mean range of the protons, what is the counting rate relative to the counting rate with no absorber?

3. A certain cloud chamber is filled with *helium* gas and is operated at 2.0-atm pressure and 15°C. The cloud chamber also contains a small amount of alcohol vapor and of a volatile compound of lithium. (The effects of the alcohol and the lithium compound on the stopping power of the gas can be neglected as simplifying assumptions in the calculations to follow.)

Thermal neutrons produce the reaction $Li^6(n,\alpha)H^3$, for which $Q = 4.78$ Mev. The H^3 and He^4 products are oppositely directed, away from the site of the compound nucleus, and hence they form one straight track. The variations of specific ionization along this track can be measured with a microphotometer and are indicated schematically in the sketch.   Determine and tabulate the following

H³ track   α track   Specific ionization

physical properties of the α particle and the H³ particle which are produced in this reaction:

(a) Ratio of initial velocities of H³ and He⁴.

(b) Ratio of initial specific ionization by H³ and He⁴, using the "uncorrected" mean excitation potential $I \simeq 35$ ev and $C_K = 0$ for helium gas.

(c) Initial kinetic energy of H³ and He⁴, in Mev.

(d) Mean range of H³ and He⁴ and the mean value of the total H³ + He⁴ track length in helium gas at 2-atm pressure and 15°C, if the *atomic* stopping power of helium relative to air is 0.36 and is taken as independent of velocity.

(e) Straggling parameters in air and the standard deviation of ranges in helium gas at 2 atm and 15°C for the H³ track, the He⁴, and the total H³ + He⁴ track.   Note that the straggling parameter for the total H³ + He⁴ track is not the simple arithmetic sum of the parameters for H³ and He⁴.   For simplicity, neglect effects of I on α/R.

6. *Range of Fission Fragments*

Range-energy relationships for particles which are much heavier than protons and α rays are largely empirical.   This group of "very heavy" particles can be thought of as including all ions which have a nuclear charge $z \gg 1$.   Thus ions like C^+, N^+, Ne^+, and A^+ are included (E17, W30), along with the very highly ionized fission fragments.

Theoretical discussions of the mechanisms of energy loss by very heavy particles have been given by Bohr (B95) and others and have been reviewed by Bethe and Ashkin (B47).   These theories are quite approximate in character, but they serve to outline the main physical processes and are in sufficiently close agreement with experiments to suggest that the gross physical behavior of very heavy particles is understood.   We can illustrate these principles by explicit consideration of the passage of fission fragments through absorbing materials.

TABLE 6.1. APPROXIMATE PHYSICAL PROPERTIES OF THE MOST PROBABLE
PRODUCTS OF THE FISSION OF U²³⁵ BY THERMAL NEUTRONS
(p. 64 of G31)

	Light fragment	Heavy fragment
Mass number A.............	97	138
Nuclear charge z............	38 (Sr)	54 (Xe)
Kinetic energy E............	97 Mev	65 Mev
Initial velocity V_0..........	1.4×10^9 cm/sec	0.93×10^9 cm/sec
Initial ionic charge ez_{av}.......	$20e$	$22e$
Mean range in air R........	2.5 air-cm	1.9 air-cm

Recall from Fig. 3.11, Chap. 11, that fission which is produced by low- and moderate-energy agents results generally in an asymmetric splitting of the compound nucleus. We have then a "heavy fragment" and a "light fragment," whose most probable mass numbers are about 138 and 97 in the case of $U^{235}(n,f)$. Table 6.1 summarizes the approximate physical properties of these fragments. Conservation of momentum dictates that the heavy fragment has the smaller velocity and the smaller kinetic energy.

a. Ordinary Ionization Losses. Both fission fragments are initially highly ionized, having carried with them roughly one-half their full complement of atomic electrons. Thus the most probable heavy fragment has a net ionic charge of $ez_{av} \simeq 22e$ and is moving with a velocity comparable with a 2-Mev α ray. Although the theory of ionization losses is not strictly valid, because it contemplates a fully ionized incident nuclear particle, some guidance can be obtained from Eq. (2.3). We may expect the excitation and ionization losses to be roughly proportional to $(z_{av})^2 Z/m_0 V^2$, where Z refers to the absorbing medium.

As the fragment moves through the absorber, capture and loss of electrons will be a process of major importance. Roughly, the moving fragment can be expected to capture electrons into atomic states for which the Bohr orbital speed u is $u \geq V$. Theoretical (B28) and experimental (L10) values of the mean ionic charge ez_{av} are in general agreement. As the particle's velocity V is reduced, it will capture more and more atomic

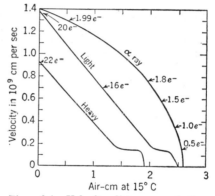

Fig. 6.1 Velocity distance relationships for average heavy and light fission fragments from $U^{235}(n,f)$, compared with the α-particle curve from Fig. 3.1. Typical values of the mean ionic charge ez_{av} are indicated along the curves. [*From Bøggild, Brostrøm, and Lauritsen* (B86).]

electrons, thus continuously reducing its net ionic charge ez_{av} and also reducing its energy losses $(dE/dr)_{ion}$ by ionization and excitation. This continuous *reduction* in $(dE/dr)_{ion}$ along the path of the particle is analogous to the behavior of α rays in the final 3 to 4 air-mm of range (recall Fig. 4.1) where capture and loss of electrons also control the magnitude of the ionization losses.

Figures 6.1 and 6.2 show representative experimental data on the loss of energy per unit path, and on V, as functions of distance, for the heavy and light fission fragments.

b. Nuclear Collisions. As the fission particles slow down, the cross section for energy losses by elastic nuclear scattering increases in importance. Roughly, these nuclear collision losses (see Appendix B, Sec. 3) are proportional to $z^2 Z^2/M_2 V^2$, where M_2 and Z are the mass of and nuclear charge of the absorbing atoms. We see that the ratio of the elastic nuclear collision losses to the ordinary ionization losses may be proportional to

$$\frac{z^2 Z^2 / M_2 V^2}{(z_{av})^2 Z / m_0 V^2} = \left(\frac{z}{z_{av}}\right)^2 Z \frac{m_0}{M_2} \tag{6.1}$$

As the particle velocity V slows down to the order of

$$\frac{e^2}{\hbar} = \frac{c}{137} = 0.22 \times 10^9 \text{ cm/sec}$$

the net ionic charge $e z_{av}$ may be expected to tend toward very small values, even zero.

This situation is similar to the end of an α-ray track, where swift neutral He^0 particles occasionally produce a burst of ionization in an elastic nuclear collision (S19). Cloud-chamber photographs of fission fragments show clearly that the final portion of the range is characterized by elastic nuclear collisions, in which relatively large energy transfers take place. This behavior is indicated schematically in Fig. 6.2. The number-energy distribution of these close nuclear "knock-on" collisions has been studied experimentally by Bøggild and coworkers (B86) and is in agreement with a statistical theory by Bohr. The number of nuclear collisions with close to the maximum possible energy transfer averages about two collisions per fission track and exhibits a Poisson distribution with "practical" extreme values of 0 and about 9.

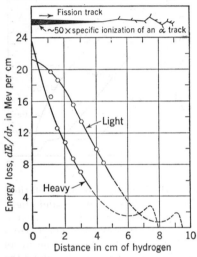

Fig. 6.2 Energy loss per unit path length for average heavy and light fission fragments from $U^{235}(n,f)$. The inset shows schematically the appearance of a typical fission-particle track in a cloud chamber, for correlation with dE/dr. [*From Lassen* (L9).]

In the final portion of the range, i.e., for $V \leq e^2/\hbar = c/137$, the ordinary ionization losses are very small, and the predominant mechanism for energy loss is the elastic nuclear collision. The transition between these two mechanisms accounts for the plateaus in Figs. 6.1 and 6.2.

c. Range-Mass Relationship. The mass number A of a particular fission fragment primarily determines the velocity V, energy E, atomic number z, and ionic charge $e z_{av}$ of the fragment. Therefore the mean range may be expected actually to be a function of A. In Figs. 6.1 and 6.2 we considered only the most probable, or modal, values of A for the heavy and light fragments. Katcoff, Miskel, and Stanley (K6) have utilized radiochemical methods for identifying the mass number A of the fission fragments which are caught on thin lacquer films after traversing predetermined path lengths of air at about 130-mm Hg pressure. In this way, a series of number-distance curves, for fission products of various

A, is constructed.   From these curves, the extrapolated number-distance range R_n and the mean range R can be determined as a function of A.

Figure 6.3 shows the range-mass relationship so determined for the fission products of $Pu^{239}(n,f)$. The effective straggling parameter α as determined by comparing R_n and R [Eq. (5.24)] is found to be independent of A, and proportional to R, according to

$$\alpha \simeq 0.07R \qquad (6.2)$$

This straggling parameter is vastly greater than would be predicted by Eq. (5.21) because a large proportion of the straggling is due to the elastic nuclear collisions, in each of which a large proportion of the fragment's residual energy is transferred.

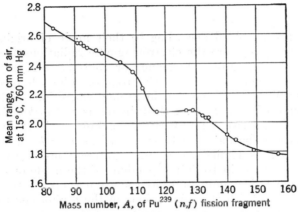

Fig. 6.3   Mean range R (in centimeters of air at 15°C and 760 mm Hg) of plutonium fission products, as a function of mass number A.   [*From Katcoff, Miskel, and Stanley* (K6).]

d. Relative Stopping Power. Segrè and Wiegand (S27) have determined the relative stopping power of collodion, Al, Cu, Ag, and Au for the averaged fission products of $U^{235}(n,f)$.   Table 6.2 summarizes these results in terms of mass stopping power, S_m of Eq. (2.16), relative to Al. There is little difference between S_m for these averaged fission products and for the 4.66-Mev α rays of U^{234}.

TABLE 6.2. RELATIVE MASS STOPPING POWER FOR AVERAGED FISSION
PRODUCTS OF $U^{235}(n,f)$, AND FOR 4.66-MEV α RAYS
[From Segrè and Wiegand (S27)]

Material	Mass stopping power S_m	
	Fission products	4.66-Mev α rays
Collodion..........	1.70	1.38
Aluminum.........	1.00	1.00
Copper............	0.66	0.69
Silver.............	0.55	0.51
Gold.............	0.34	0.36

The Interaction of Electromagnetic Radiations with Matter. Compton Scattering and Absorption

Photons are classified according to their mode of origin, not their energy. Thus, γ *rays* are the electromagnetic radiations accompanying nuclear transitions. Bremsstrahlung, or *continuous* X *rays*, are the result of the acceleration of free electrons or other charged particles. *Characteristic* X *rays* are emitted in atomic transitions of bound electrons between the $K, L, M, \ldots$ shells in atoms. *Annihilation radiation* is emitted when a positron and negatron combine. The quantum energy of any of these radiations can be expressed as $E = h\nu$, where ν is the frequency and h is Planck's constant. Interactions of these photons with matter are thought to be independent of the mode of origin of the photon and dependent only upon its quantum energy. In this section we shall deal only with the interactions of these photons; therefore we shall use the term γ ray to refer to any type of electromagnetic radiation, regardless of origin.

Unlike charged particles, a well-collimated beam of γ rays shows a truly exponential absorption in matter. This is because photons are absorbed or scattered in a single event. That is, those collimated photons which penetrate the absorber have had no interaction, while the ones absorbed have been eliminated from the beam in a single event. This can easily be shown to lead to a truly exponential attenuation.

There are a number of processes which can cause γ rays to be scattered or absorbed. A catalogue of the possible processes by which the electromagnetic field of the γ ray may interact with matter has been put in the following systematic form by Fano (F7):

Kinds of interaction	Effects of interaction
1. Interaction with atomic electrons	(a) Complete absorption
2. Interaction with nucleons	(b) Elastic scattering (coherent)
3. Interaction with the electric field surrounding nuclei or electrons	(c) Inelastic scattering (incoherent)
4. Interaction with the meson field surrounding nucleons	

There are 12 ways of combining columns 1 and 2; thus in theory there are 12 different processes by which γ rays can be absorbed or scattered. Many of these processes are quite infrequent, and some have not yet been observed. It turns out that in the energy domain met most frequently in nuclear transitions, say, 0.01 to 10 Mev, all but a few of the very minor effects are explainable in terms of just three of the above 12 processes. These are the Compton effect (1c), the photoelectric effect (1a), and pair production (3a). We shall study these effects in detail in this chapter and in Chap. 24. The minor effects which are of interest in special cases are as follows:

Rayleigh Scattering (1b). Even at energies of 0.1 Mev and above, elastic coherent scattering by tightly bound atomic electrons can be significant in heavy elements. The permissible Rayleigh scattering angles are always small, because the recoil imparted to the atom must not produce atomic excitation or ionization. Some 60 to 70 per cent of the Rayleigh scattering is confined to deflections which are smaller than the following angles, in degrees (F7):

Photon energy	0.1 Mev	1 Mev	10 Mev
Al	15	2	0.5
Fe	20	3	0.8
Pb	30	4	1

Rayleigh scattering cross sections for small $h\nu$ and large Z have been included in the numerical tables by G. R. White (W38). For large $h\nu$ and small Z, Rayleigh scattering is negligible in comparison with Compton scattering, as shown in Chap. 25, Figs. 1.2 to 1.6.

Thomson Scattering by the Nucleus (2b). Thomson scattering can combine coherently with Rayleigh scattering. Because of the large mass of the nucleus, the effects are small but appear to have been detected (S77, W67, D6).

Delbruck Scattering (3b). Delbruck scattering, or elastic "nuclear potential scattering," is due to virtual electron pair formation in the field of the nucleus. The effect, if present, is extremely small and does not show up clearly in experiments designed to detect it when 1.3-Mev and 2.7-Mev γ rays are scattered by Pb (W67, D6).

Nuclear Resonance Scattering (2c). This type of scattering involves the excitation of a nuclear level by an incident photon, with subsequent reemission of the excitation energy. After many unsuccessful searches, suitable conditions appear to have been found for producing a Doppler broadened emission line which is wide enough to overlap the scattering resonance and thus permit detection of nuclear resonance scattering (I1).

Photodisintegration of Nuclei (2a). Photodisintegration, or the "nuclear photoeffect," is energetically possible whenever the photon energy exceeds the separation energy of a neutron or proton. Except for $Be^9(\gamma,n)$ and $H^2(\gamma,n)$, these effects are generally confined to the high-energy region above about 8 Mev. Even when photodisintegration is energetically allowed, the cross sections are negligible compared with those for the Compton effect and for absorption by nuclear pair production.

Meson Production (4a).   Meson production requires photon energies above about 150 Mev.   Even then the cross sections are negligible ($\sim 10^{-3}$ barn/atom) compared with other attenuation processes.

1. *Compton Collision and the Conservation Laws*

The scattering of very-low-energy photons ($h\nu \ll m_0c^2$) by free electrons is described adequately by the nonrelativistic classical theory of J. J. Thomson (see Appendix A and Chap. 1).   This theory, however, breaks down quickly as $h\nu$ approaches $m_0c^2 = 0.51$ Mev.   It is therefore necessary to develop a relativistic theory of scattering.

When the incident photon has an energy $h\nu_0$ which cannot be neglected in comparison with m_0c^2, a new and complicated set of phenomena occurs.   The photon momentum $h\nu_0/c$ can no longer be neglected.   This incident momentum must be conserved between the scattered photon and the struck electron.   Except for the trivial case of zero scattering angle, the direction of the scattered photon is not parallel to the direction of the incident photon.   The scattered photon must therefore have a smaller momentum, and hence a smaller quantum energy, than the incident photon.   The remaining momentum and energy are imparted to the struck electron.

We shall consider the case in which the struck electron is at rest.   If desired, the general case can be obtained from this special case by a Lorentz transformation.   The struck electron is also considered to be unbound.   In practice, this simply limits the theory to those cases for which the atomic binding energy of the struck electron is small compared with $h\nu_0$.   Almost all practical cases fall within this region.   In those cases where the photon energy is comparable with the binding energy of the atomic electrons, the photoelectric cross section usually greatly exceeds the Compton scattering cross section so that the Compton scattering becomes of minor importance.

In Fig. 1.1, and in the following discussion, we represent the energy $h\nu_0$ of the incident photon by the dimensionless parameter $\alpha \equiv h\nu_0/m_0c^2$. The scattered photon is emitted at an angle of ϑ with an energy of $h\nu'$, and the electron recoils at an angle φ with a momentum p and kinetic energy T.   The paths of the incident and scattered photon define the *scattering plane*.   The momentum normal to this plane is zero; therefore the path of the recoiling electron must also lie in the same plane.   The three paths, therefore, must be coplanar, as shown in Fig. 1.1.   Polarization has, of course, no influence on these momentum relationships. Remembering that the momentum of a photon is $h\nu/c$, we can now write the relations for the conservation of momentum for this collision.   Conservation of momentum in the direction of $h\nu_0$ is expressed by

$$\frac{h\nu_0}{c} = \frac{h\nu'}{c} \cos \vartheta + p \cos \varphi \qquad (1.1)$$

while conservation of momentum normal to this direction gives

$$0 = \frac{h\nu'}{c} \sin \vartheta - p \sin \varphi \qquad (1.2)$$

A third relation between these variables is obtained from the conservation of energy.

$$h\nu_0 = h\nu' + T \qquad (1.3)$$

Using the relativistic relationship

$$pc = \sqrt{T(T + 2m_0c^2)} \qquad (1.4)$$

and some algebra, one can eliminate any two parameters from these three equations. It should be noted that these equations represent only the fundamental conservation laws as applied to a two-body collision. They

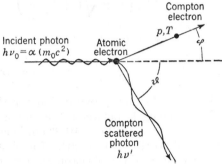

Fig. 1.1 Trajectories in the scattering plane for the incident photon $h\nu_0$, the scattered photon $h\nu'$, and the scattering electron which acquires momentum p and kinetic energy T.

must, therefore, be obeyed *regardless of the details of the interaction* at the scene of the collision. A number of useful relationships follow directly from algebraic combinations of the three basic conservation equations. These include the following, in which $\alpha = h\nu_0/m_0c^2$:

The Compton shift

$$\frac{c}{\nu'} - \frac{c}{\nu_0} = \lambda' - \lambda_0 = \frac{h}{m_0c} (1 - \cos \vartheta) \qquad (1.5)$$

Energy of the scattered quantum

$$h\nu' = \frac{m_0c^2}{1 - \cos \vartheta + (1/\alpha)} \qquad (1.6)$$

$$\frac{\nu'}{\nu_0} = \frac{1}{1 + \alpha(1 - \cos \vartheta)} \qquad (1.7)$$

Note that for very large incident photon energy, $\alpha \gg 1$, the energy of the backscattered photon approaches $m_0c^2/2 = 0.25$ Mev at $\vartheta = 180°$, while the energy of photons scattered at $\vartheta = 90°$ approaches $m_0c^2 = 0.51$ Mev.

Energy of the struck electron

$$T = h\nu_0 - h\nu' \tag{1.8}$$

$$T = h\nu_0 \frac{2\alpha \cos^2 \varphi}{(1 + \alpha)^2 - \alpha^2 \cos^2 \varphi} \tag{1.9}$$

$$T = h\nu_0 \frac{\alpha(1 - \cos \vartheta)}{1 + \alpha(1 - \cos \vartheta)} \tag{1.10}$$

The maximum energy transfer T_{max}

$$T_{max} = \frac{h\nu_0}{1 + (1/2\alpha)} \tag{1.11}$$

or $$h\nu_0 = \tfrac{1}{2}T_{max}\left(1 + \sqrt{1 + \frac{2m_0c^2}{T_{max}}}\right) \tag{1.12}$$

Relation between the scattering angles, φ and ϑ,

$$\cot \varphi = (1 + \alpha) \frac{1 - \cos \vartheta}{\sin \vartheta} = (1 + \alpha) \tan \frac{\vartheta}{2} \tag{1.13}$$

Equation (1.5) is the well-known expression for the *Compton shift*, or the difference in wavelength between the incident and scattered quantum. The length $h/m_0c = 2.426 \times 10^{-10}$ cm is called the *Compton wavelength* λ_c. It is equal to the wavelength of a photon whose energy is just equal to the rest energy of the electron $m_0c^2 = 0.51$ Mev. In the domain of nuclear γ-ray energies, the Compton shift can be visualized more readily when the incident and scattered photons are described by their energies, rather than by their wavelengths. Rewriting Eq. (1.5), we have

$$\frac{1}{h\nu'} - \frac{1}{h\nu_0} = \frac{1}{m_0c^2} (1 - \cos \vartheta) \tag{1.14}$$

It is of great practical importance to note that the Compton *shift in wavelength*, in any particular direction, is independent of the energy of the incident photon. In sharp contrast, the Compton *shift in energy* is very strongly dependent upon $h\nu_0$. Low-energy photons are scattered with only a moderate energy change, but high-energy photons suffer a very large change in energy. For example, at $\vartheta = 90°$ if $h\nu_0 = 10$ kev, then $h\nu' = 9.8$ kev (a 2 per cent change); but if $h\nu_0 = 10$ Mev, then $h\nu' = 0.49$ Mev (a 20-fold change)!

Numerous careful experiments have shown (C57) that momentum and energy are indeed conserved in each individual collision as envisaged in the relationships just written. Experiments also show that the scattered photon and the recoil electron do arise simultaneously within the resolution of present-day coincidence counters, which is about 1.5×10^{-8} sec (H59).

2. Klein-Nishina Cross Sections for Polarized and Unpolarized Radiation

Although Thomson scattering has a simple classical interpretation in terms of induced oscillations of the scattering electron by the incident electric vector, the collisions involving higher photon energy defy accurate description in terms of the mechanisms known in classical physics. Perhaps the most that can be said is that magnetic forces would be expected to play some role, in addition to the electrostatic forces. The finite magnetic dipole moment of the electron must have some interaction with the magnetic vector of the incident and scattered waves. Since the oscillating electron is a current element, one would expect it to experience a Lorentz force normal to the magnetic vector of the incident electromagnetic radiation. For photons of moderate energy, some improvements on the Thomson formula were developed by Compton, Breit, and others, but classical methods are incapable of coping with the general collision involving very-high-energy photons.

a. Quantum-mechanical Model. In 1928, Klein and Nishina (K21) successfully applied Dirac's then new relativistic theory of the electron to this problem and obtained a general solution which is in remarkable agreement with all good experiments. The so-called "Klein-Nishina formula" has had many brilliant successes and stands as one of the earliest confirmations of the Dirac electron theory. Strong support is given especially to the utility of Dirac's concept of negative energy states for the electron. In this theory, the momentum p of a free electron does not determine its state completely. For each value of the momentum p, there correspond *two* energy states, one of positive total energy and one of negative total energy. These two states may be regarded as the two roots of Eq. (1.4).

$$T + m_0 c^2 = \pm \sqrt{(pc)^2 + (m_0 c^2)^2}$$

The positive root is the energy state of ordinary experience. All negative energy states are regarded as normally filled by a "universal sea of electrons," and these states become experimentally observable only when a vacancy occurs in one of them; then this "hole" is seen as a positron in the laboratory. The normally unobserved negative energy states are capable of playing a role in the interaction between a quantized electromagnetic field and a free electron. In the quantum electrodynamics, these interactions involve an initial state, an intermediate state, and a final state. Momentum and energy are conserved between the initial and final state, but in the intermediate state the theory requires only momentum conservation and not energy conservation. It is in these intermediate states that negative energies are invoked for the electron. Then a free electron of momentum p can have either of *two energy values*. In addition, each of these states may have either of two *spin directions*. Thus for each intermediate momentum, four states exist altogether.

It must also be noted that, in the quantum electrodynamics, the classical distinctness of the mechanism of interaction between an electromagnetic field and an electron disappears. The mathematical process of quantizing an electromagnetic field is equivalent to breaking it up into particles, the photons. During an intermediate state, electrons can absorb photons and can emit photons. An electron at rest can, during an intermediate state, emit a *virtual* photon, in violation of the ordinary energy-conservation laws, and can subsequently absorb energy in the form of another quantum from an incident radiation field, in order to restore energy conservation and make possible the transition to the final state.

Then the over-all scattering of electromagnetic radiation by electrons becomes the sum of the two types of process, each involving different intermediate states. These two processes are:

1. The incident photon $h\nu_0$ is absorbed by the electron. In the intermediate state the electron has momentum $h\nu_0/c$, and no photon is present. In the transition to the final state, the photon $h\nu'$ is emitted by the electron.

2. The electron first emits a photon $h\nu'$. In the intermediate state the electron has momentum $-h\nu'/c$, and two photons $h\nu'$ and $h\nu_0$ are present. In the transition to the final state the photon $h\nu_0$ is absorbed by the electron.

b. Differential Collision Cross Section for Polarized Radiation. It can be shown (H29) that this representation of the scattering mechanism leads to the following expression for the differential *collision* cross section in the case of plane-polarized incident radiation:

$$d(_e\sigma) = \frac{r_0^2}{4} d\Omega \left(\frac{\nu'}{\nu_0}\right)^2 \left(\frac{\nu_0}{\nu'} + \frac{\nu'}{\nu_0} - 2 + 4\cos^2\Theta\right) \qquad \text{cm}^2/\text{electron} \qquad (2.1)$$

Here Θ is the angle between the electric vectors of the incident radiation and scattered radiation $\boldsymbol{\varepsilon}_0$ and $\boldsymbol{\varepsilon}'$, respectively; r_0 is the classical electron radius; and $d\Omega$ is the element of solid angle through which the scattered photon emerges after the collision. The energy of the scattered photon is $h\nu'$; therefore the scattering angle is implicitly specified through Eq. (1.7). Physically, $d(_e\sigma)$ is the absolute value of the probability that a photon of energy $h\nu_0$, while passing through an absorber whose thickness is such that the absorber contains one electron per square centimeter, will suffer a particular collision from which the scattered photon emerges with energy $h\nu'$, within solid angle $d\Omega$, and is so polarized that its electric vector makes an angle Θ with the electric vector $\boldsymbol{\varepsilon}_0$ of the incident photon. All the other types of cross section and the corresponding absorption coefficients for the Compton effect can be derived from this one fundamental equation.

In nearly every practical case, the direction of polarization of the scattered photon will not be experimentally important. Thus our first step is to sum Eq. (2.1) over all possible directions of polarization of the scattered photon. The angles and directions involved can be visualized with the aid of Fig. 2.1*a*, *b*, and *c*, in which

OA = direction of scattered photon
OAB = scattering plane (as in Fig. 1.1)
ϑ = scattering angle (as in Fig. 1.1)
$\mathcal{E}_0$ = electric vector of incident photon
ξ = angle between $\mathcal{E}_0$ and OA
ODB = plane of polarization of incident photon
η = angle between plane of incident polarization ODB and scattering plane
$\mathcal{E}'$ = electric vector of scattered photon
$ODAC$ = plane of polarization of incident photon
β = angle between $\mathcal{E}'$ and $ODAC$ plane
$\mathcal{E}'_\parallel = \mathcal{E}' \cos \beta$ = component of $\mathcal{E}'$ in $ODAC$ plane
$\mathcal{E}'_\perp = \mathcal{E}' \sin \beta$ = component of $\mathcal{E}'$ perpendicular to $ODAC$ plane
Θ = angle between $\mathcal{E}_0$ and $\mathcal{E}'$

Since $\mathcal{E}'_\parallel = \mathcal{E}' \cos \beta$, and $\mathcal{E}'_\perp = \mathcal{E}' \sin \beta$, we have $(\mathcal{E}'_\perp)^2 + (\mathcal{E}'_\parallel)^2 = (\mathcal{E}')^2$. The total scattered intensity in the direction ξ is proportional to $(\mathcal{E}')^2$

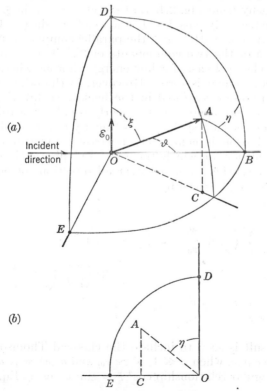

(a)

Incident direction

(b)

Fig. 2.1 (*a*) A Compton interaction at O. $\mathcal{E}_0$ is the electric vector of the incident photon, OA the direction of the scattered photon. (*b*) The projection of A and C on the ODE plane shows the angle η.   (*Continued*)

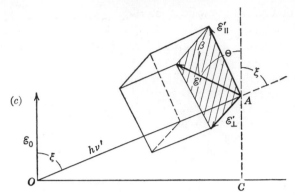

Fig. 2.1   (c) The Compton interaction in the $ODAC$ plane, showing the polarization of the scattered photon. The electric vector of the scattered photon $\mathbf{\varepsilon}'$ makes an angle Θ with the direction of $\mathbf{\varepsilon}_0$, and an angle β with the $ODAC$ plane.

and hence to the sum of the orthogonal components $(\mathbf{\varepsilon}'_\perp)^2$ and $(\mathbf{\varepsilon}'_\parallel)^2$. For $\mathbf{\varepsilon}'_\perp$ we have, in effect, $\cos \beta = 0$, and hence $\cos \Theta = 0$, because it can be shown easily from Fig. 2.1c that $\cos \Theta = \cos \beta \sin \xi$. In the case of $\mathbf{\varepsilon}'_\parallel$ we have, effectively, $\cos \beta = 1$, and $\cos \Theta = \sin \xi$. Then, regardless of the direction of scattering ξ, the parallel component $\mathbf{\varepsilon}'_\parallel$ tends to be the more intense of the two components of $\mathbf{\varepsilon}'$. This is to be expected because, in the classical case, for low-energy photons where $\nu' \simeq \nu_0$, the perpendicular component is zero. However, in the other extreme, that of high-energy photons scattered in the backward direction ($\vartheta \sim 180°$, $\nu' \ll \nu_0$), the two components become nearly equal. For this reason, the backscattered photons are spoken of as "nearly unpolarized" even when the incident radiation is completely polarized. The differential cross section for a collision in which the scattered photon is emitted at a particular ϑ and ξ, when summed over all directions of polarization of the scattered photon, is given by

$$
\begin{aligned}
d(_e\sigma) &= d(_e\sigma)_\parallel + d(_e\sigma)_\perp \\
&= \frac{r_0^2}{4} d\Omega \left(\frac{\nu'}{\nu_0}\right)^2 \left(\frac{\nu_0}{\nu'} + \frac{\nu'}{\nu_0} - 2 + 4 \sin^2 \xi\right) \\
&\qquad\qquad + \frac{r_0^2}{4} d\Omega \left(\frac{\nu'}{\nu_0}\right)^2 \left(\frac{\nu_0}{\nu'} + \frac{\nu'}{\nu_0} - 2\right) \\
&= \frac{r_0^2}{2} d\Omega \left(\frac{\nu'}{\nu_0}\right)^2 \left(\frac{\nu_0}{\nu'} + \frac{\nu'}{\nu_0} - 2 \cos^2 \xi\right)
\end{aligned}
\tag{2.2}
$$

This general result is seen to include the classical Thomson result as a limiting case, because when $\alpha \ll 1$, $\nu' \simeq \nu_0$, and $d(_e\sigma) = r_0^2 \, d\Omega \sin^2 \xi$.

Using the angular relationship $\cos^2 \xi = \sin^2 \vartheta \cos^2 \eta$, Eq. (2.2) can be rewritten as

$$
d(_e\sigma) = \frac{r_0^2}{2} d\Omega \left(\frac{\nu'}{\nu_0}\right)^2 \left(\frac{\nu_0}{\nu'} + \frac{\nu'}{\nu_0} - 2 \sin^2 \vartheta \cos^2 \eta\right)
\tag{2.3}
$$

For any scattering angle ϑ we see that the scattering probability has its maximum value when $\eta = 90°$. Therefore, the scattered photon and the scattered electron tend to be ejected *at right angles to the electric vector* $\mathcal{E}_0$ *of the incident radiation.*

Equation (2.3) forms the operating basis for several types of practical γ-ray polarimeters. In one of these, shown schematically in Fig. 2.2, the scattered photons are observed at fixed values of the scattering angle ϑ as a function of the angle η. A minimum in the coincidence counting rate locates the angle $\eta = 0$, for which $\mathcal{E}_0$ is parallel to the scattering plane, while a maximum counting rate is observed at $\eta = 90°$. The asymmetry ratio between the maximum and minimum values of the scattering intensities depends on both $h\nu_0$ and ϑ and falls to unity for $\vartheta = 0$ or $180°$. In general, the greatest asymmetry is found for scattering angles which are slightly less than $90°$. For example, the optimum scattering angle ϑ is about $82°$ for 0.51-Mev photons, and about $78°$ for 1.0-Mev photons (M44). The maximum asymmetry ratio is 5 for 0.51-Mev photons in ideal geometry and decreases as the photon energy increases.

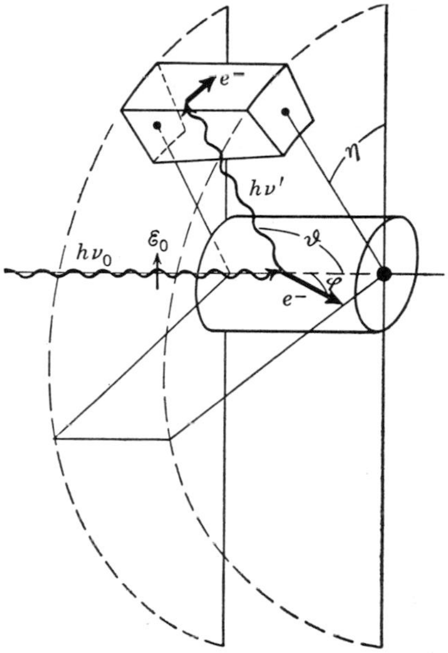

Fig. 2.2 Schematic illustration of a basic element for a γ-ray polarimeter. Two scintillation counters are used in a coincidence circuit. A coincidence is registered when the incident photon $h\nu_0$ produces a Compton recoil electron in one counter, while the photon scattered at ϑ, η is detected in a second counter, in which it produces a Compton electron or a photoelectron. At fixed scattering angle ϑ, the coincidences are minimum in the direction ($\eta = 0$) of the incident electric vector $\mathcal{E}_0$ and maximum in a direction ($\eta = 90°$) normal to $\mathcal{E}_0$. [*Metzger and Deutsch* (M44).]

c. Differential Scattering Cross Section for Polarized Incident Radiation. Now let us turn our attention to the amount of *energy* carried by the scattered photons. Consider a broad incident beam, of area S cm², consisting of n incident photons per second, each photon having energy $h\nu_0$. Then the incident intensity is

$$I_0 = \frac{n}{S} h\nu_0 \qquad \text{ergs/(sec)(cm}^2\text{)} \qquad (2.4)$$

When this beam passes over one single electron, $d(_e\sigma)$ of Eq. (2.3) is the fraction of the n/S incident photons per square centimeter–second which are scattered in such a way that $h\nu'$ goes into a solid angle $d\Omega$ at ϑ, η. That is, $dn = (n/S) d(_e\sigma)$ photons/sec. Let $d(_eQ)$ be the total energy scattered into this unit solid angle $d\Omega$ over a time t. We then have

$$\frac{d(_eQ)}{t} = h\nu'\, dn = h\nu'\, \frac{n}{S}\, d(_e\sigma) = I_0\, \frac{\nu'}{\nu_0}\, d(_e\sigma)$$

$$= I_0\, \frac{r_0^2}{2}\, d\Omega \left(\frac{\nu'}{\nu_0}\right)^3 \left(\frac{\nu_0}{\nu'} + \frac{\nu'}{\nu_0} - 2\cos^2\xi\right) \qquad (2.5)$$

The fraction $d(_eQ)/I_0 t$ has the dimensions of square centimeter per electron and is known as the *differential scattering cross section*, $d(_e\sigma_s)$. Note that the simple relationship

$$d(_e\sigma_s) = \frac{\nu'}{\nu_0}\, d(_e\sigma) \qquad (2.6)$$

emerges. This is because $d(_e\sigma)$ represents the probability of *collision*, resulting in the removal of the incident photon $h\nu_0$ from the collimated beam. Not all the energy $h\nu_0$ is scattered, however, but only the fraction $h\nu'/h\nu_0$. Therefore the differential *scattering* cross section, which is proportional to the energy scattered into $d\Omega$ at ϑ, η, is only ν'/ν_0 times the differential *collision* cross section.

Equation (2.5) takes on its more conventional form when it is expressed explicitly in terms of α, ϑ, and ξ. By making the substitution for ν_0/ν' given in Eq. (1.7), the differential cross section for the energy scattered from polarized incident radiation becomes

$$d(_e\sigma_s) = \frac{d(_eQ)}{I_0 t} = r_0^2\, d\Omega \left[\frac{1}{1 + \alpha(1 - \cos\vartheta)}\right]^3$$
$$\left\{\sin^2\xi + \frac{\alpha^2(1 - \cos\vartheta)^2}{2[1 + \alpha(1 - \cos\vartheta)]}\right\} \qquad \text{cm}^2/\text{electron} \quad (2.7)$$

as was first shown by Klein and Nishina (K21) and later by Tamm (T3). It is helpful to note the physical significance of the individual terms. The term in the square brackets can be shown (C37) to correspond to the diminution of scattering due to the motion of the electron during the "collision." In the curly braces, the $\sin^2\xi$ term represents the fully polarized classical component of the scattered energy. The second term in the curly braces could be called the Klein-Nishina correction term. This correction term is independent of ξ and hence represents scattered radiation which is *unpolarized* with respect to the primary radiation. This unpolarized component is zero in the forward direction ($\vartheta = 0$) and maximum in the backward direction ($\vartheta = 180°$). It depends strongly on the energy of the incident photons, increasing as α^2. Thus, for high-energy photons, the backscattered radiation consists predominantly of this unpolarized component.

d. Differential Collision and Scattering Cross Sections for Unpolarized Incident Radiation. All the expressions we have derived up to now have been for the special case of polarized incident radiation. Let us now look at the more common case of incident unpolarized radiation. It is convenient to resolve all the incident radiation into two orthogonally polarized components, each carrying one-half the incident intensity. We choose the orientation of these two components so that one lies perpendicular to the scattering plane ($\eta = 90°$), while the other lies parallel to it ($\eta = 0°$). Then the differential *collision* cross section for incident unpolarized radiation is the sum of two components obtained from Eq. (2.3) and is

$$d(_e\sigma) = \tfrac{1}{2}[d(_e\sigma)_{\eta=90°}] + \tfrac{1}{2}[d(_e\sigma)_{\eta=0°}]$$

$$= \frac{r_0^2}{2} \, d\Omega \left(\frac{\nu'}{\nu_0}\right)^2 \left(\frac{\nu_0}{\nu'} + \frac{\nu'}{\nu_0} - \sin^2 \vartheta\right) \tag{2.8}$$

where the scattered photon $h\nu'$ goes into solid angle $d\Omega = 2\pi \sin \vartheta \, d\vartheta$. Figure 2.3 is a polar plot of Eq. (2.8). Note the tremendous increase in the fraction of forward-scattered photons, as α increases.

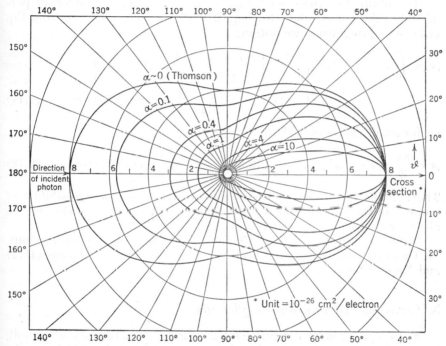

Fig. 2.3 The *number* of photons scattered into unit solid angle $d(_e\sigma)/d\Omega$, at a mean scattering angle ϑ, Eq. (2.8). [*From Davisson and Evans* (D12).]

The differential *scattering* cross section for unpolarized radiation can now be written with the aid of Eq. (2.6) and is

$$d(_e\sigma_s) = \frac{d(_e Q)}{I_0 t} = \frac{r_0^2}{2} \, d\Omega \left(\frac{\nu'}{\nu_0}\right)^3 \left(\frac{\nu_0}{\nu'} + \frac{\nu'}{\nu_0} - \sin^2 \vartheta\right) \tag{2.9}$$

or $d(_e\sigma_s) = r_0^2 \, d\Omega \left[\dfrac{1}{1 + \alpha(1 - \cos \vartheta)}\right]^3 \left(\dfrac{1 + \cos^2 \vartheta}{2}\right)$

$$\left\{1 + \frac{\alpha^2(1 - \cos \vartheta)^2}{(1 + \cos^2 \vartheta)[1 + \alpha(1 - \cos \vartheta)]}\right\} \tag{2.10}$$

In Eq. (2.10), the terms have been arranged to display the quantum-mechanical correction term of Klein and Nishina as the second term in the curly braces. For low energies, $\alpha \to 0$, the limiting value of the entire general expression is seen to be just the classical Thomson-scattering value.

e. Average Collision Cross Section $_e\sigma$. The summation of the probabilities of all possible collisions between the incident photon and each free electron is generally called the *total collision cross section*. Because it represents the integrated probability, per electron, that some scattering event will occur, it is physically clearer to speak of this integral as the *average collision cross section*. The average collision cross section is, of course, the same for polarized or unpolarized incident radiation.

To obtain the expression for $_e\sigma$, we integrate Eq. (2.8) over all permissible values of ϑ. Substituting $d\Omega = 2\pi \sin \vartheta \, d\vartheta$, and ν'/ν_0 from Eq. (1.7), then integrating, we obtain:

$$_e\sigma = \int_0^\pi d(_e\sigma) = 2\pi r_0^2 \left\{ \frac{1+\alpha}{\alpha^2} \left[\frac{2(1+\alpha)}{1+2\alpha} - \frac{1}{\alpha} \ln (1+2\alpha) \right] \right.$$
$$\left. + \frac{1}{2\alpha} \ln (1+2\alpha) - \frac{1+3\alpha}{(1+2\alpha)^2} \right\} \qquad \text{cm}^2/\text{electron} \qquad (2.11)$$

or, for small values of α (L18),

$$_e\sigma = \frac{8\pi}{3} r_0^2 (1 - 2\alpha + 5.2\alpha^2 - 13.3\alpha^3 + \cdots) \qquad \text{cm}^2/\text{electron} \qquad (2.12)$$

The average (or total) collision cross section $_e\sigma$ is the probability of removal of the photon from a collimated beam while passing through an absorber containing one electron/cm².

Tables and graphs of the differential and the average cross sections, for Compton collisions, have been given by Davisson and Evans (D12) and Nelms (N8).

3. *Compton Attenuation Coefficients*

a. Compton Linear Attenuation Coefficient. In a thin absorbing foil, having N atoms/cm³, each with Z electrons/atom, and of thickness dx, there are (NZ) electrons/cm³ and $(NZ \, dx)$ electrons/cm². Let a collimated beam of n photons/sec, each of energy $h\nu_0$, pass normally through the foil. The number dn of the primary photons which are removed from the collimated beam per second by such a foil is

$$-\frac{dn}{n} = (NZ \, dx) \, _e\sigma \qquad (3.1)$$

The electronic cross section is taken as independent of Z because it was assumed at the beginning that $h\nu_0$ greatly exceeds the atomic binding energies of the electrons. Then $_e\sigma$ is a function of only the incident photon energy and decreases monotonically as $h\nu_0$ increases.

In calculating the fractional transmission of photons through real absorbers it is often convenient to use linear attenuation coefficients. We therefore define the Compton *total linear attenuation coefficient* σ as

$$\sigma = NZ \, _e\sigma \qquad \text{cm}^{-1} \tag{3.2}$$

From Eq. (3.1) we have $dn/n = -\sigma \, dx$. Then the fractional transmission n/n_0 of unmodified *primary photons* through an absorber of thickness x is

$$\frac{n}{n_0} = e^{-\sigma x} \tag{3.3}$$

if the only significant interactions are Compton collisions.

Figures 3.1 and 3.2 include numerical values for σ for Pb and Al calculated from $_e\sigma$ by assuming:

for Al: density 2.70 g/cm³, $NZ = 0.786 \times 10^{24}$ electrons/cm³
for Pb: density 11.35 g/cm³, $NZ = 2.71 \times 10^{24}$ electrons/cm³

Values of the σ may be obtained for any other elementary material, of density ρ, atomic weight A, and atomic number Z from the values for

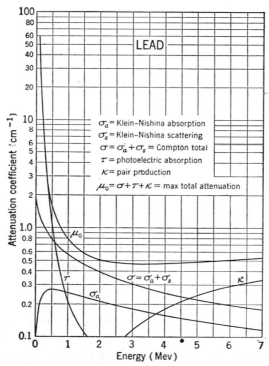

Fig. 3.1 Linear coefficients for various γ-ray interactions in Pb.   See also Fig. 2.4 of Chap. 24.   The value of $_e\sigma$ may be obtained by multiplying σ by 0.369×10^{-24} cm³/electron.   See Fig. 1.5 of Chap. 25 for mass attenuation coefficients.   [*From Evans and Evans (E22).*]

either lead or aluminum, by using the simple relation

$$\sigma_1 = \sigma_2 \frac{\rho_1}{\rho_2} \frac{A_2}{A_1} \frac{Z_1}{Z_2} \tag{3.4}$$

where the subscripts 2 refer to element whose σ is known and subscripts 1 refer to element whose σ is to be determined.

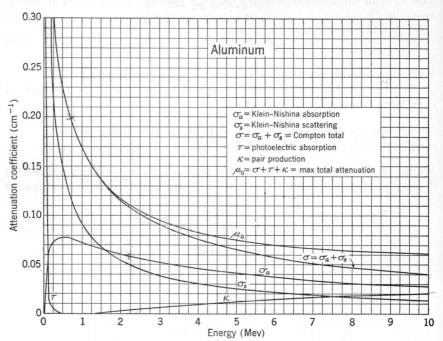

Fig. 3.2 Linear coefficients for various γ-ray interactions in Al. The value of $_e\sigma$ may be obtained by multiplying $_o$ by 1.27×10^{-24} cm³/electron. [*From Evans and Evans* (E22).]

b. Mass-attenuation Coefficient. In place of the linear attenuation coefficient it is often useful to use the *mass attenuation coefficient* (σ/ρ) cm²/g. The thickness of the absorber now must be measured in units of (ρx) g/cm², and

$$\frac{n}{n_0} = e^{-(\sigma/\rho)(\rho x)} \tag{3.5}$$

The great advantage in using units of grams per square centimeter to measure absorber thicknesses is that equal amounts of various absorbers measured in these units give roughly the same Compton attenuation. The mass attenuation coefficient σ/ρ is nearly independent of the nature of the absorber, because of the approximate constancy of Z/A for all elements. Graphs of σ/ρ are given in Chap. 25, Figs. 1.2 to 1.6.

c. Compton Scattering Coefficients $_e\sigma_s$ and σ_s. Experimental interest often centers on the average properties of the scattered radiation, rather than on the detailed distribution of $h\nu'$ and ϑ. Returning to Eqs. (2.9) and (2.10), we note that the total energy $_eQ$ scattered in a time t by one electron, from a beam having incident intensity I_0, is

$$\frac{_eQ}{t} = \frac{1}{t} \int d(_eQ) = I_0 \int_0^\pi d(_e\sigma_s) \equiv I_0(_e\sigma_s) \qquad (3.6)$$

The *average scattering cross section* $_e\sigma_s$ is obtained by a straightforward integration of Eq. (2.10) with $d\Omega = 2\pi \sin \vartheta \, d\vartheta$ and is

$$_e\sigma_s = \pi r_0^2 \left[\frac{1}{\alpha^3} \ln(1+2\alpha) + \frac{2(1+\alpha)(2\alpha^2 - 2\alpha - 1)}{\alpha^2(1+2\alpha)^2} + \frac{8\alpha^2}{3(1+2\alpha)^3} \right]$$
$$\text{cm}^2/\text{electron} \qquad (3.7)$$

or, for sufficiently small values of incident energy α (L18),

$$_e\sigma_s = \frac{8\pi}{3} r_0^2 (1 - 3\alpha + 9.4\alpha^2 - 28.0\alpha^3 + \cdots) \qquad \text{cm}^2/\text{electron} \qquad (3.8)$$

Note that $_e\sigma_s$ approaches the Thomson cross section of $(8\pi/3)r_0^2 = \frac{2}{3}$ barn as the photon energy decreases. This is because in the Thomson case all energy is scattered and none is absorbed by the electron.

Average Energy per Scattered Photon. We have seen that a beam of n photons/sec of quantum energy $h\nu_0$, and hence intensity $I_0 = nh\nu_0/S$, will, on the average, suffer $dn = n(NZ \, dx)(_e\sigma)$ collisions/sec on passing through an absorbing foil which contains $(NZ \, dx)$ electrons/cm². The total scattered energy, in photons of various energies $h\nu'$, is $I_0S(NZ \, dx) _e\sigma_s$. Therefore the average energy per scattered photon $(h\nu')_{\text{av}}$, or the average scattered energy per collision, is

$$(h\nu')_{\text{av}} = \frac{I_0 S(NZ \, dx) \,_e\sigma_s}{n(NZ \, dx) \,_e\sigma}$$
$$= h\nu_0 \frac{_e\sigma_s}{_e\sigma} \qquad (3.9)$$

Linear Scattering Coefficient. Figures 3.1 and 3.2 show numerical values of the linear scattering coefficient

$$\sigma_s = \,_e\sigma_s NZ \qquad \text{cm}^{-1} \qquad (3.10)$$

for Pb and Al. From these, the value of $_e\sigma_s$ or σ_s may be found for other elemental substances by using Eq. (3.4) with σ replaced by σ_s, the known scattering coefficient. In Figs. 3.1 and 3.2 the *fraction* of the incident photon energy which is *scattered* in the *average* collision is

$$\frac{(h\nu')_{\text{av}}}{h\nu_0} = \frac{\sigma_s}{\sigma} \qquad (3.11)$$

and is seen to decrease as $h\nu_0$ increases. At very low energies $\sigma_s/\sigma \simeq 1$, but as $h\nu_0$ increases a smaller average fraction of $h\nu_0$ is available for the scattered photons, because a larger average portion of $h\nu_0$ goes into the kinetic energy of the struck electron. The photon energy $h\nu_0$ is divided equally, on the average, between the scattered photon and the electron, when $h\nu_0 \simeq 1.6$ Mev.

d. Compton Absorption Coefficients $_e\sigma_a$ and σ_a. Each scattered photon $h\nu'$ has associated with it a recoil electron whose energy is

$$T = h\nu_0 - h\nu'$$

The total energy removed from the incident beam by Compton collisions is measured by $_e\sigma$, Eq. (2.11), while the average scattered energy is given by $_e\sigma_s$, Eq. (3.7). It is now obvious, from conservation of energy, that the energy absorbed by the electron must be the total energy involved in collisions minus the energy scattered as photons, and so we can write for the *average absorption cross section*, $_e\sigma_a$,

$$_e\sigma_a = {}_e\sigma - {}_e\sigma_s \tag{3.12}$$

An explicit expression for $_e\sigma_a$ follows from Eqs. (2.11) and (3.7) and is

$$
\begin{aligned}
_e\sigma_a &= {}_e\sigma - {}_e\sigma_s \\
&= 2\pi r_0^2 \left[\frac{2(1+\alpha)^2}{\alpha^2(1+2\alpha)} - \frac{1+3\alpha}{(1+2\alpha)^2} - \frac{(1+\alpha)(2\alpha^2 - 2\alpha - 1)}{\alpha^2(1+2\alpha)^2} \right. \\
&\quad \left. - \frac{4\alpha^2}{3(1+2\alpha)^3} - \left(\frac{1+\alpha}{\alpha^3} - \frac{1}{2\alpha} + \frac{1}{2\alpha^3} \right) \ln(1+2\alpha) \right]
\end{aligned}
$$
$$\text{cm}^2/\text{electron} \tag{3.13}$$

For small α, Lea (L18) has given the following approximation

$$_e\sigma_a = \frac{8\pi}{3} r_0^2 (\alpha - 4.2\alpha^2 + 14.7\alpha^3 - \cdots) \qquad \text{cm}^2/\text{electron} \tag{3.14}$$

Average Energy per Compton Electron. The *average* kinetic energy $(T)_{av}$ of all recoil electrons from Compton interactions will be

$$(T)_{av} = h\nu_0 - (h\nu')_{av}$$

Hence
$$\frac{(T)_{av}}{h\nu_0} = 1 - \frac{(h\nu')_{av}}{h\nu_0} = 1 - \frac{_e\sigma_s}{_e\sigma} = \frac{_e\sigma_a}{_e\sigma} \tag{3.15}$$

Thus we see that $_e\sigma_a$ physically represents a true *absorption* of energy from the incident photon and *not* just a *deflection*. This absorbed energy appears in the absorbing body as the kinetic energy of the recoil or Compton electrons. These electrons then lose their energy in ionizing and radiative collisions.

Emphasis needs to be laid on the sharp physical distinction between:

  $_e\sigma$, representing the probability of any kind of *collision*
  $_e\sigma_s$, representing *scattering*, or mere deflection of electromagnetic radiation
  $_e\sigma_a$, representing true *absorption* of energy from the electromagnetic radiation

The fraction $_e\sigma_a/_e\sigma$ of the incident photon energy which is absorbed in the average collision starts at zero for very-low-energy radiation and increases monotonically with $h\nu_0$, passing through the value $\frac{1}{2}$ at $h\nu_0 \simeq 1.6$ Mev.

Linear Absorption Coefficient. As in the preceding cases, we define the *linear absorption coefficient* σ_a as

$$\sigma_a = NZ \, {}_e\sigma_a \tag{3.16}$$

If we multiply Eq. (3.12) through by (NZ) electrons/cm³ it is clear that

$$\sigma = \sigma_s + \sigma_a \tag{3.17}$$

Numerical values of σ_a are found in Figs. 3.1 and 3.2 for the cases of Pb and Al. Figure 3.3 gives the total *absorption* coefficient for air (including absorption from photoelectric effect and pair production).

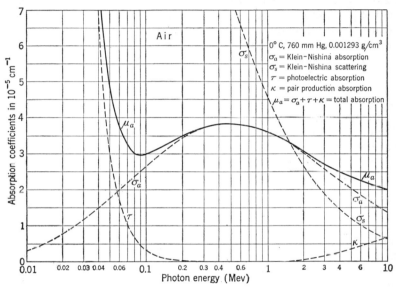

Fig. 3.3 Absorption coefficients for various γ-ray interactions in air (0°C, 760 mm Hg). μ_a represents the total *absorption* coefficient.

Note that this is due almost entirely to σ_a in the range of $h\nu_0 = 0.1$ Mev to 10 Mev. The great physical importance of the quantity σ_a is emphasized because the only significant effects on an absorbing body by Compton interactions are produced by the Compton electrons. This means that *only* the absorption coefficient σ_a is effective in producing detectable effects of the interaction of radiation by the Compton process. These effects include ionization in an ionization chamber, counts in a proportional counter, developable images in photographic emulsions, or biological effects in a living organism.

The average energy absorbed per unit volume in an absorber as a result of Compton interactions is simply $I_0\sigma_a$ ergs/(cm³)(sec). In absolute value, ${}_e\sigma_a$ and σ_a for any absorber pass through a maximum when $\alpha = 1$, i.e., for $h\nu_0 = 0.51$ Mev.

4. *Angular Distribution of Compton Scattered Photons and Recoil Electrons*

In a large number of experimental situations the average directional distribution of the Compton scattered photons and electrons is of great importance. For illustrative purposes, we shall consider here only the distribution of the *number* of photons scattered between the angles ϑ and $\vartheta + d\vartheta$, and the number of electrons scattered between the corresponding angles φ and $\varphi + d\varphi$.

a. Angular Distribution of Scattered Photons. The *number* of scattered photons per unit solid angle $d(_e\sigma)/d\Omega$ is given by Eq. (2.8) and Fig. 2.3. When we consider the scattering per unit of scattering angle ϑ instead of per unit solid angle, the results are remarkably different. This is because the total solid angle available per unit angle is $d\Omega/d\vartheta = 2\pi \sin \vartheta$ and approaches zero in the forward direction. As ϑ increases from zero, the element of solid angle between two cones whose half angles are ϑ and $\vartheta + d\vartheta$ increases, while the scattering per unit solid angle decreases. The product of these two functions, which is the scattering per unit angle $d(_e\sigma)/d\vartheta$, passes through a maximum which turns out to be quite sharp for large α.

Figure 4.1 is a polar plot of the *number-vs.-angle* distribution of scattered photons, for several values of α, as given by

$$\frac{d(_e\sigma)}{d\vartheta} = \frac{d(_e\sigma)}{d\Omega} 2\pi \sin \vartheta \qquad \text{cm}^2/\text{electron} \qquad (4.1)$$

where $d(_e\sigma)/d\Omega$ is given by Eq. (2.8).

The angular distribution of scattered *energy* is even more sharply peaked, because of the variation of $h\nu'$ with ϑ. Tables and graphs for these and related distributions have been given by Davisson and Evans (D12).

b. Angular Distribution of Compton Electrons. The ionization which actuates many radiation detectors is primarily due to the Compton electrons resulting from Compton interactions in the detector or its walls. Obviously, the initial directional distribution of these electrons is sometimes of considerable experimental importance in determining the response characteristics of the detector.

The directional distribution of the Compton electrons is obtained from the directional distribution of the scattered photons $d(_e\sigma)/d\Omega$, combined with the relationships connecting the photon scattering angle ϑ with the angle of projection φ of the Compton electron. In effect, this amounts to evaluating $(h\nu_0/T)\, d(_e\sigma_a)$ explicitly.

For each photon which is scattered into the solid angle between ϑ and $\vartheta + d\vartheta$, there will be an electron projected at an angle between φ and $\varphi + d\varphi$, that is, into a solid angle $d\Omega' = 2\pi \sin \varphi\, d\varphi$. Because the num-

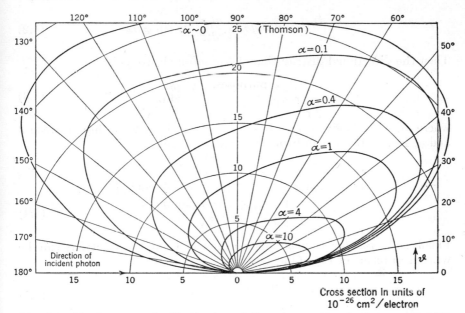

Fig. 4.1   Number-vs.-angle distribution of Compton scattered photons, $d(_e\sigma)/d\vartheta$, Eq. (4.1).   [*From Davisson and Evans* (D12).]

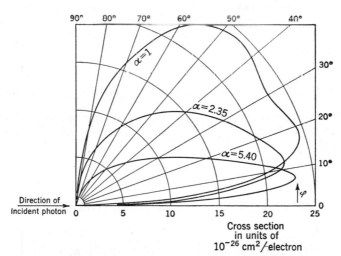

Fig. 4.2   Number-vs.-angle distribution of Compton electrons, $d(_e\sigma)/d\varphi$, Eq. (4.5), for primary photon energies $h\nu_0 = 0.51$ Mev ($\alpha = 1$), 1.2 Mev ($\alpha = 2.35$), and 2.76 Mev ($\alpha = 5.40$).   [*From Davisson and Evans* (D12).]

ber of photons and electrons must be equal, we obtain the relationship

$$\frac{d(_e\sigma)}{d\Omega} 2\pi \sin \vartheta \, d\vartheta = \frac{d(_e\sigma)}{d\Omega'} 2\pi \sin \varphi \, d\varphi \tag{4.2}$$

Then the directional distribution of Compton electrons is

$$\frac{d(_e\sigma)}{d\Omega'} = \frac{d(_e\sigma)}{d\Omega} \frac{\sin \vartheta \, d\vartheta}{\sin \varphi \, d\varphi} \tag{4.3}$$

where $d(_e\sigma)/d\Omega$ is given by Eq. (2.8). Using the relationship between ϑ and φ, Eq. (1.13), it can be shown that

$$\begin{aligned}
\frac{d\Omega}{d\Omega'} &= \frac{\sin \vartheta \, d\vartheta}{\sin \varphi \, d\varphi} = - \frac{4(1 + \alpha)^2 \cot \varphi \csc^3 \varphi}{[(1 + \alpha)^2 + \cot^2 \varphi]^2} \\
&= - \frac{1}{1 + \alpha} \frac{(1 + \cos \vartheta) \sin \vartheta}{\sin^3 \varphi}
\end{aligned} \tag{4.4}$$

Finally, the *number-vs.-angle* distribution of Compton electrons can be written in terms of Eqs. (4.3) and (4.4) as

$$\frac{d(_e\sigma)}{d\varphi} = \frac{d(_e\sigma)}{d\Omega'} 2\pi \sin \varphi \tag{4.5}$$

The number-vs.-solid-angle distribution $d(_e\sigma)/d\Omega'$ is sharply peaked in the direction of $\varphi = 0$. But the number-vs.-angle distribution $d(_e\sigma)/d\varphi$ is zero in the forward direction and exhibits its maxima at values of φ which depend upon the photon energy $h\nu_0$. Figure 4.2 shows the number-vs.-angle distribution of Compton electrons for $h\nu_0 = 0.51$ Mev, 1.2 Mev, and 2.76 Mev.

5. *Energy Distribution of Compton Electrons and Photons*

In certain experimental situations the "energy spectrum" of Compton electrons is important. This number-energy distribution can be represented as

$$\frac{d(_e\sigma)}{dT} = \frac{d(_e\sigma)}{d\varphi} \frac{d\varphi}{dT} \tag{5.1}$$

where $d(_e\sigma)/d\varphi$ is Eq. (4.5). It can be shown (D12) that

$$\frac{d(_e\sigma)}{dT} = \frac{d(_e\sigma)}{d\Omega} \frac{2\pi}{\alpha^2 m_0 c^2} \left[\frac{(1 + \alpha)^2 - \alpha^2 \cos^2 \varphi}{(1 + \alpha)^2 - \alpha(2 + \alpha) \cos^2 \varphi} \right]^2 \tag{5.2}$$

where $d(_e\sigma)/d\Omega$ is Eq. (2.8) and $\alpha = h\nu_0/m_0 c^2$ as usual.

Figure 5.1 shows the number-energy spectrum of Compton electrons produced by incident photons whose energies are $h\nu_0 = 0.51$ Mev, 1.2 Mev, and 2.76 Mev. The number-energy spectrum of scattered photons can be deduced easily from Eq. (5.2) or Fig. 5.1 because $h\nu' = h\nu_0 - T$.

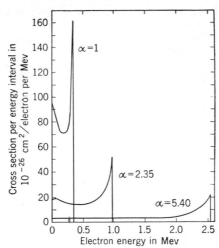

Fig. 5.1 Energy distribution of Compton electrons produced by primary photons whose energies are 0.51 Mev ($\alpha = 1$), 1.2 Mev ($\alpha = 2.35$), and 2.76 Mev ($\alpha = 5.40$). [*From Davisson and Evans* (D12).]

Problems

1. Calculate from the equation of Klein and Nishina the relative scattered energy per unit solid angle, at angles of 0°, 5°, 15°, 30°, 45°, 60°, 90°, 120°, 150°, and 180°, with an incident beam of unpolarized 1.20-Mev quanta. Normalize the results to a forward scattering of unity, and plot the relative values of scattered energy per unit solid angle, as a function of angle.

2. Calculate the energy per scattered quantum in each of the directions of Prob. 1.

3. Calculate the relative number of quanta scattered per unit solid angle in each of the directions of Prob. 1. Normalize the results to a forward scattering of unity, and plot as a function of angle on the graph of Prob. 1.

4. From the results of Prob. 1, calculate and plot the scattered energy per unit of scattering angle. Integrate graphically and thus determine the electronic cross section $_e\sigma_s$ for the scattering of 1.20-Mev photons.

5. In the Klein-Nishina formula for scattered energy vs. scattering angle, set $\alpha = 0$, and integrate the resulting analytical expression in order to obtain the energy scattered over all angles. Compare with the Thomson cross section

$$\sigma = \frac{8\pi}{3}\left(\frac{e^2}{m_0 c^2}\right)^2 \quad \text{cm}^2/\text{electron} \qquad \text{for } h\nu_0 \ll m_0 c^2$$

6. Calculate the angles φ of electron projection corresponding to the angles ϑ of scattered photons given in Prob. 1.

7. Show that, in the relation between the number of electrons projected into unit solid angle and the number of photons scattered into unit solid angle, the ratio

$$\frac{\sin\vartheta\,d\vartheta}{\sin\varphi\,d\varphi} = -\frac{4(1+\alpha)^2\cot\varphi\csc^3\varphi}{[(1+\alpha)^2+\cot^2\varphi]^2}$$

8. Calculate and plot the relative number of electrons per second projected per unit solid angle in the direction φ, as a function of φ.

9. Calculate and plot the number of electrons per second projected at angles between φ and $\varphi + d\varphi$. Integrate graphically to find $_e\sigma$.

10. Calculate and plot the number of photons per second scattered at angles between ϑ and $\vartheta + d\vartheta$ and show that graphical integration of this also leads to $_e\sigma$.

11. Calculate and plot the sum of the kinetic energies carried by all the electrons which are projected between φ and $\varphi + d\varphi$ and integrate graphically to find $_e\sigma_a$.

12. Compare results and show that

$$_e\sigma = {_e\sigma_a} + {_e\sigma_s}$$

State the exact physical meaning of the quantities of $_e\sigma$, $_e\sigma_a$, and $_e\sigma_s$.

13. Calculate and plot the number-energy distribution of Compton electrons produced by 1.20-Mev primary photons. Show that the number-energy distribution of scattered photons can be read from this same plot by a transformation of the energy axis. Integrate graphically to find $_e\sigma$, $(T)_{av}$, and $(hv')_{av}$.

14. It is desired to measure the Compton scattering of 10-Mev γ rays in a thin foil of graphite. If the scattered quanta are to be observed, about how thin must the carbon foil be made to ensure that less than 1 per cent of the observed quanta have been scattered twice? State explicitly your assumptions and approximations made in this calculation, and if possible estimate the errors introduced by these assumptions.

About how thin must the carbon foil be made to ensure that the recoil electron energies can be measured within 0.1 Mev? Again state assumptions used.

15. (a) Compute the maximum energy of the Compton recoil electrons resulting from the absorption in aluminum of 2.19-Mev γ rays.

(b) A monochromatic 50-kev X ray passes through an Al foil. What is the maximum and minimum energy found among the scattered quanta?

CHAPTER **24**

Photoelectric Effect and Pair Production

1. *Photoelectric Effect*

Below energies of about 0.1 Mev the predominant mode of γ-ray interaction in all medium- and high-Z absorbers is the photoelectric process.

a. General Features of the Photoelectric Interaction. An incident photon cannot be totally absorbed by a free electron. This is evident from our previous considerations of the momentum relationships in Compton collisions. However, total absorption can take place if the electron is initially bound in an atom. Then momentum is conserved by the recoil of the entire residual atom. As might be expected, the most tightly bound electrons have the greatest probability of absorbing a photon which is incident upon an atom. It is found both experimentally and theoretically that about 80 per cent of the photoelectric absorption processes take place in the K shell, provided that the incident photon energy $h\nu$ clearly exceeds the K-shell binding energy.

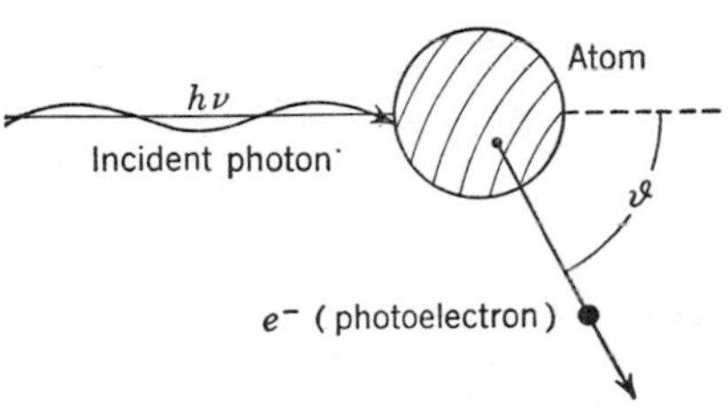

Because the entire atom participates, the photoelectric process may be visualized as an interaction of the primary photon with the atomic electron cloud in which the

Fig. 1.1 Schematic representation of the photoelectric process. The primary photon is completely absorbed and a photoelectron is ejected at an angle ϑ with energy $T = h\nu - B_e$. Momentum is conserved by the recoil of the entire residual atom. Because the presence and participation of the atom are essential, the photoelectric interaction is thought of as one between the incident photon $h\nu$ and the entire atom.

entire photon energy $h\nu$ is absorbed and an electron (usually K or L) is ejected from the atom with an energy

$$T = h\nu - B_e$$

where B_e is the binding energy of the ejected electron. The remainder of the energy appears as characteristic X rays and Auger electrons from the filling of the vacancy in the inner shell. Schematically, the photoelectric interaction is illustrated in Fig. 1.1.

Unlike the Compton effect, the photoelectric effect does not lend itself easily to theoretical treatments. Exact solutions are both difficult and tedious, because the Dirac relativistic equation for a bound electron must be used. In the energy region between 0.35 Mev and 2 Mev a set of nearly rigorous numerical solutions has been obtained by Hulme, McDougall, Buckingham, and Fowler (H75). At other energies, approximations can be made which simplify the problem and permit the development of complicated but closed formulas. The theoretical results can be divided into three energy regions: (1) above 2 Mev, (2) between 2 Mev and 0.35 Mev, and (3) below 0.35 Mev. Davisson and Evans (D12) have given a comprehensive review of the theoretical and experimental results obtained up to 1952.

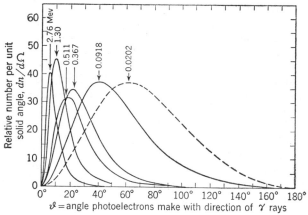

Fig. 1.2 Directional distribution of photoelectrons per unit solid angle, for energies as marked. The curves are not normalized with respect to each other. Solid curves are calculated from Sauter's (S6) relativistic formula; dashed curve from Fischer's (F50) nonrelativistic formula. [*From Davisson and Evans* (D12).]

Because of the restricted and approximate character of the theoretical results, the quantitative aspects of the photoelectric effect are largely empirical. The theories are especially useful for interpolation and extrapolation.

b. Directional Distribution of Photoelectrons. The discrete energy distribution of photoelectrons provides a useful experimental method for the determination of γ-ray energies. In such work the angular distribution of photoelectrons is often relevant. Especially at low photon energies, the photoelectrons tend to be ejected in the direction of the electric vector of the incident radiation, hence at right angles to the direction of incidence. At higher energies, the angular distribution is more in the forward direction. Of course, the kinetic energy of the photoelectron, $T = h\nu - B_e$, is the same for all directions of emission.

Figure 1.2 shows theoretical values for the directional distribution of photoelectrons, per unit solid angle, as calculated by Davisson from the relativistic formula of Sauter (S6) and the nonrelativistic formula of Fischer (F50), for several photon energies. These curves are applicable

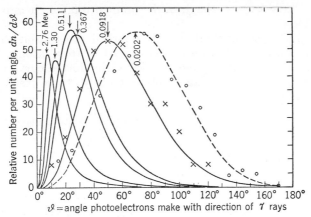

Fig. 1.3   Angular distribution of photoelectrons ejected between two cones having half angles of ϑ and $\vartheta + d\vartheta$.   *Crosses,* measured values by Lutz (L36) at 0.0918 Mev. *Circles,* measured values by Williams et al. (W60) at 0.0202 Mev.   Measurements at 0.4 Mev and 1.3 Mev by Hedgran and Hultberg (H28) and at 2.62 Mev by Latishev (L12) are also in satisfactory agreement with these predicted distributions.   [*From Davisson and Evans* (D12).]

to experimental arrangements in which the photons are unpolarized, and in which the detector subtends a fixed solid angle, as it does in several types of counter experiments.

Figure 1.3 shows the same data but converted to the angular distribution between two cones having half angles of ϑ and $\vartheta + d\vartheta$, by use of the relationship $d\Omega/d\vartheta = 2\pi \sin \vartheta$. These angular distributions are applicable to experiments performed in cloud chambers (L36, W60) or with axial focusing magnetic-lens spectrometers (H28).

Figure 1.4 shows the half angle of a cone within which one-half the photoelectrons should be ejected (bipartition angle), as a function of $h\nu$.   Note that at high energies the photoelectrons tend to be ejected at only a small angle with the forward direction.

c. Average Forward Momentum. Whenever $h\nu$ clearly exceeds the electron binding energy, the resulting

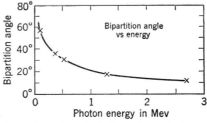

Fig. 1.4   One-half the photoelectrons should be ejected within a cone whose half angle is defined as the bipartition angle, shown here as a function of $h\nu$. The crosses represent the bipartition angles calculated from Fig. 1.3 by graphical integration.   [*From Davisson and Evans* (D12).]

photoelectron will have nearly the same energy as the incident photon. But because of the finite rest mass of the electron, its momentum will greatly exceed the momentum of the incident photon.   This "increase" in momentum, combined with the predominantly forward directional distribution of the photoelectrons, means that the residual atom must, on the average, have a finite "backward" momentum, i.e., it moves toward the left in Fig. 1.1.

Hulme (H74) has evaluated by numerical integration the average forward momentum of photoelectrons ejected from atoms for which $Z/137 \ll 1$. He finds the values shown by the dotted curve in Fig. 1.5. The average value of $\cos \vartheta$ can be obtained from these results, through the relationship

$$R = \frac{\text{average forward momentum of photoelectrons}}{\text{photon momentum}}$$

$$= \left(1 + \frac{2m_0c^2}{h\nu}\right)^{\frac{1}{2}} (\cos \vartheta)_{\text{av}} \qquad (1.1)$$

Figure 1.5 also shows the values of R obtained by numerical integration from Fig. 1.3, and hence based on Sauter's (S6) theoretical treatment of the photoelectric effect.

d. Cross Section per Atom. The absolute probability of a photoelectric interaction is described by the *atomic* cross section $_a\tau$ cm²/atom. Nearly all the theories relate only to interactions with the K electrons and hence give a partial cross section $_a\tau(K)$. When detailed experimental knowledge of the cross sections for the electrons in the $L, M, \ldots$ shells is lacking, it is customary to increase the K-shell cross sections by a factor $\frac{5}{4}$, in order to account for the relatively infrequent interactions with $L, M, \ldots$ electrons.

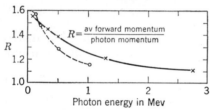

Consolidated theoretical estimates of $_a\tau$ are given in Fig. 1.6, as calculated by Davisson (D12). The strong dependence of the total photoelectric cross section upon Z and $h\nu$ is evident. For very rough orientation purposes, we may begin with a crude but useful approximation

$$_a\tau \simeq \text{const} \frac{Z^4}{(h\nu)^3} \qquad (1.2)$$

Fig. 1.5 The average forward momentum of the photoelectrons exceeds the momentum of the incident photons, for all values of $h\nu$. Solid curve, from Fig. 1.3; dotted curve from calculations by Hulme (H74). [*From Davisson and Evans* (D12).]

But both theory and experiment show clearly that the proper exponents of Z and $h\nu$ are each nonintegral and are each functions of $h\nu$.

Variation of $_a\tau$ with Z. Note that the vertical scale of Fig. 1.6 is $_a\tau/Z^5$. At $h\nu = 0.1$ Mev the individual curves for $Z = 0$ to $Z = 82$ have a spread of nearly a factor of 82. Therefore, in this energy region, $_a\tau$ varies about with Z^4. At higher photon energies, the individual curves are closer together, but they never cross over each other. Therefore $_a\tau$ always varies less rapidly than Z^5. From an analysis of the input data ($Z = 6$ to 83) for Fig. 1.6, N. C. Rasmussen has determined the empirical exponent of Z which best fits a power law

$$_a\tau \simeq \text{const} \, Z^n \qquad (1.3)$$

for fixed values of $h\nu$. The exponent n is found to increase from about 4.0 to 4.6 as $h\nu$ increases from 0.1 Mev to 3 Mev, as shown in Fig. 1.7.

Variation of $_a\tau$ with $h\nu$. In the energy region below 0.1 Mev the photoelectric cross section is further complicated by the absorption

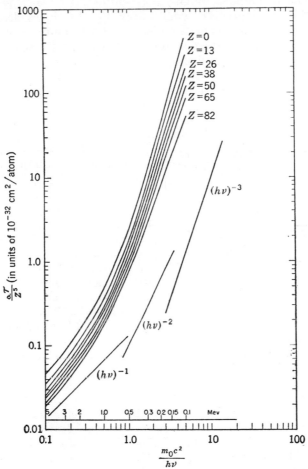

Fig. 1.6 Approximate "best" theoretical values of the photoelectric cross section $_a\tau$ cm²/atom, obtained by blending (1) the Sauter-Stobbe values below 0.35 Mev, (2) the Hulme, McDougall, Buckingham, and Fowler results between 0.35 Mev and 2 Mev, and (3) Hall's high-energy approximation above 2 Mev. For fixed Z, the lines marked $(h\nu)^{-1}$, $(h\nu)^{-2}$, and $(h\nu)^{-3}$ indicate the slopes expected if $_a\tau$ varied as $(h\nu)^{-1}$, $(h\nu)^{-2}$, or $(h\nu)^{-3}$. The horizontal scale $m_0c^2/h\nu$ is equal to the photon wavelength in units of the Compton wavelength, that is, $m_0c^2/h\nu = \lambda/(h/m_0c)$. [*From Davisson and Evans* (D12).]

edges. At these edges the cross section shows discontinuous jumps because $h\nu$ becomes smaller than the binding energy of some of the electrons, so that the number of electrons which it is energetically possible to eject is suddenly decreased. Jönsson, Allen, and others (p. 537 of C37) and more recently Victoreen (V5) have compiled the relevant experimental data and have proposed empirical formulas for $_a\tau$ in the very-low-energy region.   Tables which give the energies (rather than the wavelengths) for the X-ray absorption edges and emission lines, for all values of Z, have been compiled by Cauchois and others (C7a, H54a, F49a).

Even at energies greater than 0.1 Mev, Fig. 1.6 shows clearly that the variation of $_a\tau$ with $h\nu$ depends on both Z and $h\nu$ and can only be represented by expressions analogous to Eq. (1.2) over very restricted domains. It can be seen from Fig. 1.6 that (1) the variation of $_a\tau$ with $h\nu$ changes continuously as $h\nu$ increases and (2) in a given energy range the variation of $_a\tau$ with $h\nu$ is different for different Z, varying for low Z as a higher power of $h\nu$ than for high Z.

Tables and Graphs of $_a\tau$.   Where numerical values of the atomic photoelectric cross section $_a\tau$ are needed, it is usually best to rely on empirical values if they are available.   The experimental results up to 1950, on the elements C, Al, Fe, Cu, Ag, Sn, Ta, Pt, and Pb, have been presented in graphical form, accompanied by tables of theoretical values for 24 elements from $Z = 1$ to 83, by Davisson and Evans (D12).   G. R. White (W38) has given theoretical values for 19 elements from $Z = 1$ to 92. Values of $_a\tau$ for elements which have not been tabulated may be obtained by interpolating for Z, using Eq. (1.3) and Fig. 1.7, after finding $_a\tau$ for a nearby element at the required $h\nu$.

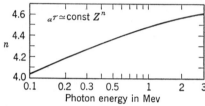

Fig. 1.7 Approximate variation of the photoelectric cross section $_a\tau$ cm²/atom with Z^n, for various values of $h\nu$. (*N. C. Rasmussen.*)

e. Linear Attenuation Coefficient τ for the Photoelectric Effect.   The linear attenuation coefficient τ cm⁻¹ is given by

$$\tau = {_a\tau}N \tag{1.4}$$

where N is the number of *atoms* per cubic centimeter and $_a\tau$ is the *atomic* cross section in square centimeters per atom.   Numerical values of τ for Pb will be found in Fig. 3.1 of Chap. 23 and Fig. 2.4 of this chapter, while τ for Al is shown in Fig. 3.2 of Chap. 23 and τ for air appears in Fig. 3.3 of Chap. 23.   Estimates of τ for other elements may be obtained from these, using the standard relationship

$$\tau_1 = \tau_2 \frac{\rho_1}{\rho_2} \frac{A_2}{A_1} \left(\frac{Z_1}{Z_2}\right)^n \tag{1.5}$$

where ρ is density, A is atomic weight, Z is atomic number, and n is obtained from Fig. 1.7.

f. Energy Absorption.   In a number of practical applications (biological effects, radiation shield design, etc.), the energy absorbed from incident photons is of major importance.   By analogy with the Compton collisions, we could write

$$\tau = \tau_s + \tau_a \tag{1.6}$$

where τ_a represents the true primary absorption, or conversion of photon energy into kinetic energy of photoelectrons. Then

$$\frac{\tau_a}{\tau} = \frac{h\nu - B_e}{h\nu} \tag{1.7}$$

The remaining fraction of the energy $h\nu$ is

$$\frac{\tau_s}{\tau} = \frac{B_e}{h\nu} \tag{1.8}$$

and is only converted into kinetic energy of free electrons as a result of secondary processes. B_e represents the excitation energy in the residual atom after ejection of the photoelectron. This may be given up as characteristic X rays or as Auger electrons. Even when the fluorescence yield is large, and the number of Auger electrons correspondingly small (Chap. 17, Fig. 3.10), the emitted X rays may be absorbed in a distance which is comparable with the range of the photoelectrons. Thus in most practical cases it is sufficiently accurate to consider the effective energy absorption as represented by τ, rather than by τ_a. We subsequently draw no practical distinction between the photoelectric linear *attenuation* coefficient τ and the linear *absorption* coefficient.

Problems

1. If a particular photon of energy $h\nu$ ejects a photoelectron in the forward direction, derive general (relativistic) expressions for the forward momentum of the photoelectron and for the backward momentum of the residual atom. Neglect the electron binding energy and the kinetic energy of the recoil atom in comparison with the energy of the incident photon.

2. From the value $_a\tau = 28$ barns/atom of Pb for 0.51-Mev photons, estimate the following photoelectric coefficients of tungsten: $_a\tau$ barns/atom, τ cm^{-1}, (τ/ρ) cm^2/g, at 0.51 Mev.

3. As^{74} emits (besides some other radiations) positrons and a 0.596-Mev γ ray. The energy of the γ ray is to be determined by studying the energies of photoelectrons ejected from thin foils, acting as "converters." What would be the energies of all the photoelectron groups between 0.4 and 0.6 Mev ejected from an Sn converter by the photons from As^{74}? Why are the usual converters of Pb or Bi not suitable for an accurate energy determination in this case?

2. *Pair Production by Photons*

Above incident photon energies of 1.02 Mev, a third type of interaction becomes increasingly important. In this interaction, known as pair production, the photon is completely absorbed and in its place appears a positron-negatron pair whose *total* energy is just equal to $h\nu$. Thus we write

$$h\nu = (T_- + m_0c^2) + (T_+ + m_0c^2) \tag{2.1}$$

where T_- and T_+ are the kinetic energy of the negatron and positron, respectively, and $m_0c^2 = 0.51$ Mev is the electronic rest energy. The process occurs *only* in the field of charged particles, mainly in the nuclear field but also to some degree in the field of an electron. The presence of this particle is necessary for momentum conservation. Schematically, the over-all process is shown in Fig. 2.1.

Careful measurements of the scattering and absorption of the 2.62-Mev γ rays from ThC″, by Chao (C18) and Tarrant (T5, T6) in 1930, first showed that the interactions of high-energy photons with high-Z

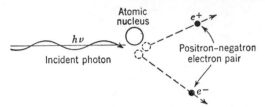

Fig. 2.1 Schematic representation of the pair-production process in the field of a nucleus. The incident photon is totally absorbed, and a positron-negatron pair emerges. Their total kinetic energy is $T_- + T_+ = h\nu - 2m_0c^2$.

absorbers exceed that which is expected from the Compton and photo-electric effects alone. Later, Anderson and Neddermeyer (A30) showed that these 2.62-Mev γ rays will eject positron-negatron pairs from a Pb foil and that under these conditions the total kinetic energy of the pair is 1.6 Mev. Combining these and related observations, Oppenheimer and Plessett (O4) first proposed an explanation of the experimental material in terms of the Dirac electron theory.

a. Basis of the Theory of Pair Production. The pair-production process lends itself nicely to a description in terms of the Dirac electron

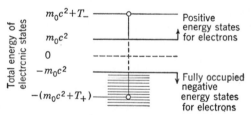

Fig. 2.2 Schematic representation of the positive and negative energy states of the electron. Negatron-positron pairs are created by transitions which add an energy of more than $2m_0c^2$ to an electron originally in a state of negative total energy. The "hole" (in the otherwise completely filled states of negative energy) is then a positron of total energy $m_0c^2 + T_+$, and the excited state is simply an electron of total energy $m_0c^2 + T_-$.

theory, which considers positrons as holes in an otherwise completely filled sea of negative energy states of negatrons (Chap. 23). This feature of the Dirac theory is illustrated by Fig. 2.2, where we see that to lift a negatron out of a negative energy state requires crossing an energy barrier of $2m_0c^2$. In doing this, the negatron is created in a positive energy state and so becomes observable. The vacancy in the negative energy region also is observable, having the same properties as the negatron except that its charge has the opposite sign.   The total energy between the hole and the electron is seen from Fig. 2.2 to be just equal to $h\nu$, as expressed by Eq. (2.1).

The pair-production process is intimately related to the bremsstrahlung process.   In bremsstrahlung, an electron undergoes a transition between two states, both of positive energy, and a photon is emitted instead of being absorbed.   Mathematically, the theories of the two processes are nearly identical and are usually treated together.   We shall note a number of similarities in the numerical results also.   The nuclear cross section, for example, will be of the order of $(Z^2/137)(e^2/m_0c^2)^2$ for both processes.   The appearance of the fine-structure constant $\frac{1}{137}$ is expected, because it represents the coupling between charged particles and an electromagnetic field.

A general quantum-mechanical solution has been obtained by Bethe and Heitler (B49), using plane waves for both electrons.   The conditions of the Born first approximation $Z/137\beta \ll 1$ are assumed to hold for both electrons.   Therefore this theory is in error (generally giving too large a cross section) when either electron has only a small energy.   This occurs for photon energies near the minimum possible value of $2m_0c^2$ ($= 1.02$ Mev) and also at the high and low ends of the distribution of positron energies.   Separate calculations for the low-energy domain have been made by Hough (H63).   Also, in Born's approximation the electrostatic potential energy between the nucleus and the electron occurs squared, and the sign of the charge disappears.   Therefore the slight asymmetry of the distribution of positron and negatron energies is missing from the general formulation.

For the nuclei of heavy elements, $Z/137\beta$ will not be negligible even for the fast components of the electron pairs.   For example, the minimum value of $Z/137\beta$ for Pb is 0.6.   Actually (A7, L16), the ratio of theoretical to experimental values for pair production by 88-Mev photons varies linearly with $(Z/137)^2$, as would be expected from inadequacy of the Born approximation.   For Pb, the theoretical cross section is 12 per cent higher than the observed value, at 88 Mev (L16).   Even at 17.6 Mev, the discrepancy appears to be about 10 per cent in the case of Pb (W4).

b. Angular Distribution of Pair Electrons.   The angular distribution of the positron and negatron is mainly forward for incident quanta of very high energy.   The average angle between the incident quantum and the created electrons is (B49) of the order of m_0c^2/T, for $T \gg m_0c^2$.   For incident photon energies of the order of $2m_0c^2$ the angular distribution is much more complicated, and the emphasis on the forward direction is much less marked.

c. Energy Distribution of Pair Electrons.   The differential cross section $d(_a\kappa)$ cm²/nucleus, for the creation of a positron of kinetic energy T_+ (and a negatron of kinetic energy $h\nu - 2m_0c^2 - T_+$), can be written as

$$d(_a\kappa) = \frac{\sigma_0 Z^2 P}{h\nu - 2m_0c^2}\, dT_+ \qquad (2.2)$$

where $$\sigma_0 = \frac{1}{137}\left(\frac{e^2}{m_0 c^2}\right)^2 = 5.80 \times 10^{-28} \text{ cm}^2/\text{nucleus} \qquad (2.3)$$

and the dimensionless quantity P is a complicated function of $h\nu$ and Z, which varies only between 0 (for $h\nu \leq 2m_0 c^2$) and about 20 (for $h\nu = \infty$), for all values of Z.   Figure 2.3 is a plot of P against the fraction of the total kinetic energy of both pair electrons which is received by the positron, $T_+/(h\nu - 2m_0 c^2)$.   It will be noted that these theoretical values

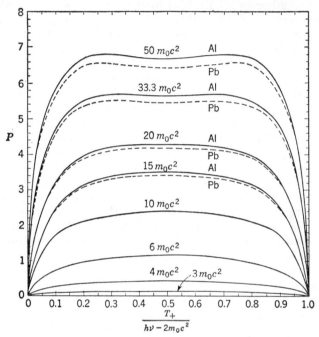

Fig. 2.3 Differential pair-production cross section, expressed as the dimensionless function P of Eq. (2.2).   The curves were calculated from the equations of Bethe and Heitler, including screening corrections for photon energies above $10m_0 c^2$. [*From Davisson and Evans* (D12).]

omit the slight asymmetry expected in the energy distribution between the positron and negatron.

If a pair is created at a distance r from the center of a nucleus of charge Ze, then the potential energy of each member of the pair is Ze^2/r. Nuclear repulsion on the positron and attraction of the negatron will then increase the original difference in their kinetic energies by $2Ze^2/r$.   The principal contribution to the matrix element for pair production comes (B49) from a region of the nuclear field for which r lies between $h/2\pi m_0 c$ and $(h/2\pi m_0 c)(h\nu/2m_0 c^2)$.   Therefore the average positron should receive a maximum of about $2Ze^2/(h/2\pi m_0 c) = 2m_0 c^2 Z/137 = 0.0075Z$ Mev more kinetic energy than the average negatron, for small values of $h\nu$. For very-high-energy photons, the asymmetry should be less.   For the special case of $h\nu = 2.62$ Mev (γ rays of ThC''), in Pb, calculations using exact wave functions (J6) indicate that the average positron energy would be expected to be 0.28 Mev greater than the average negatron energy.   This asymmetry appears to have been observed experimentally (A14), the most probable positron energy being 1.1 Mev instead of $(2.62 - 1.02)/2 = 0.8$ Mev for the 2.62-Mev γ rays of ThC''.

d. Screening Corrections.   For very-high-energy photons ($\sim$20 Mev and higher, in Pb) an appreciable contribution to the pair-production cross section may come from a distance r from the nucleus which is greater than the radius of the K-electron shell.   Then the effective nuclear charge is reduced, because of screening by the charge of the atomic electrons.   In the Bethe-Heitler theory of pair production the effect of the atomic electrons is approximated by using the Thomas-Fermi statistical model of the atom.   Then the electrostatic potential $U(r)$ at a distance r from the center of the nucleus can be represented as approximately

$$U(r) = \frac{Ze^2}{r} e^{-r/a} \tag{2.4}$$

where

$$a = \frac{\hbar^2}{m_0 e^2} \frac{1}{Z^{\frac{1}{3}}} = \frac{a_{\mathrm{H}}}{Z^{\frac{1}{3}}}$$

is the radius of a sphere which encloses a fixed fraction of all the atomic electrons, or, more loosely, the "radius" of the atomic electron cloud which screens the nucleus (S11).   The Thomas-Fermi model should be reasonably good for heavy elements and poorest for the light elements which contain too few atomic electrons to justify statistical averaging. The screening corrections (B49) have been included in Fig. 2.3, where separate curves are shown for Pb and Al.

Aside from the effects of screening, the pair-production cross sections in the field of a nucleus are theoretically and experimentally (L16, A7) dependent exactly on Z^2.

e. Total Pair-production Cross Section per Nucleus.   To find the total nuclear pair-production cross section, we integrate the differential cross section, Eq. (2.2), over all possible energies.   This is equivalent to finding the area under each curve in Fig. 2.3.   Thus we have

$$_a\kappa = \int d(_a\kappa) = \sigma_0 Z^2 \int_0^{h\nu - 2m_0 c^2} \frac{P\, dT_+}{h\nu - 2m_0 c^2} \tag{2.5}$$

$$_a\kappa = \sigma_0 Z^2 \int_0^1 P\, d\,\frac{T_+}{h\nu - 2m_0 c^2}$$

$$= \sigma_0 Z^2 \overline{P} \qquad \mathrm{cm}^2/\mathrm{nucleus} \tag{2.6}$$

where $\overline{P}$ can be regarded as the average value of P from Fig. 2.3. $\overline{P}$, and hence $_a\kappa$, increase approximately logarithmically with $h\nu$.

Analytical integration of Eq. (2.5) is possible only for extremely relativistic cases and gives, when screening is neglected (B49),

$$_a\kappa = \sigma_0 Z^2 \left(\tfrac{28}{9} \ln \frac{2h\nu}{m_0 c^2} - \tfrac{218}{27} \right) \tag{2.7}$$

for $m_0c^2 \ll h\nu \ll 137m_0c^2Z^{-\frac{1}{3}}$ (that is, about 16 Mev for Pb). In the case of complete screening one obtains

$$_a\kappa = \sigma_0 Z^2 [\tfrac{28}{9} \ln (183Z^{-\frac{1}{3}}) - \tfrac{2}{27}] \qquad (2.8)$$

for $h\nu \gg 137m_0c^2Z^{-\frac{1}{3}}$. It can be seen from Eq. (2.8) that for very high energies ($\sim 10^4$ Mev) the pair-production cross section depends only on screening and is independent of photon energy.

Table 2.1 gives the values of $_a\kappa/Z^2$ ($= \sigma_0\bar{P}$) which are obtained by graphical integration of the differential cross sections in Fig. 2.3, with screening included. For $h\nu > 5$ Mev, the magnitude of the screening corrections required for any Z can be estimated from the values of $\sigma_0\bar{P}$ for Al and Pb, in columns 3 and 4 of Table 2.1.

TABLE 2.1. PAIR-PRODUCTION ATTENUATION COEFFICIENTS, κ FOR PB, AND NUCLEAR CROSS SECTIONS $_a\kappa$ [IN TERMS OF $_a\kappa/Z^2 = \sigma_0\bar{P}$, OF EQ. (2.6)]

[Calculated (D12) by graphical integration under the curves of Fig. 2.3 (screening included). The values for $h\nu \geq 100m_0c^2$ are read from Fig. 18 of Heitler (H29).]

Photon energy		Pair-production coefficients		
		$(_a\kappa)/Z^2 = \sigma_0\bar{P}$, 10^{-27} cm²/atom		κ_{Pb}, cm⁻¹ Pb
$h\nu/m_0c^2$	Mev	Al	Pb	
2	1.02	0	0	0
3	1.53	0.050	0.050	0.011
4	2.04	0.189	0.189	0.042
6	3.06	0.524	0.524	0.116
10	5.10	1.15	1.15	0.255
15	7.66	1.70	1.66	0.368
20	10.22	2.12	2.08	0.462
33.3	17.0	2.94	2.84	0.630
50	25.5	3.56	3.46	0.768
100	51.0	5.0	4.5	1.00
200	102	5.9	5.3	1.18
500	255	6.5	6.0	1.33
1,000	510	7.2	6.3	1.40
2,000	1,020	7.5	6.5	1.44

f. Pair-production Linear Attenuation Coefficient. The linear attenuation κ for pair production is simply

$$\kappa = {}_a\kappa N \qquad \mathrm{cm}^{-1} \qquad (2.9)$$

where N is the number of atoms per cubic centimeter. For Pb,

$$N = 3.30 \times 10^{22} \ \mathrm{atoms/cm^3}$$

and κ has the numerical values shown in the right-hand column of Table 2.1.

Figure 2.4 gives κ on a linear scale, for Pb, in the energy domain up to

12 Mev. Values of κ cm^{-1} for any other element can be obtained, using the relationship

$$\kappa = \kappa_{\mathrm{Pb}} \frac{\rho}{11.35} \frac{207.2}{A} \left(\frac{Z}{82}\right)^2 \tag{2.10}$$

where ρ is the density (11.35 g/cm^3 for Pb), A is the atomic weight (207.2 for Pb), and Z is the atomic number (82 for Pb). Aside from minor screening corrections for $h\nu > 5$ Mev, as given in Table 2.1, the variation of κ with Z^2 is exact for all elements.

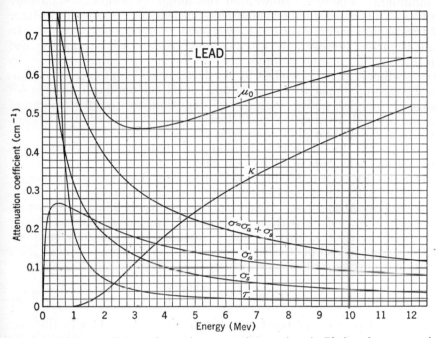

Fig. 2.4 Linear coefficients for various γ-ray interactions in Pb for photon energies up to 12 Mev. The total attenuation coefficient is $\mu_0 = \sigma$ (Compton) $+ \tau$ (photo) $+ \kappa$ (pair). Note that μ_0 passes through a minimum value at about 3.3 Mev, because of the increasing importance of pair production. This figure supplements Fig. 3.1 of Chap. 23 whose logarithmic scale cuts off the smallest values of κ. [*From Evans and Evans* (E22).]

Absorbers which contain a mixture of $N_1, N_2, N_3, \ldots$ atoms/cm^3 of elements having atomic numbers $Z_1, Z_2, Z_3, \ldots$ will exhibit a linear pair-production coefficient of

$$
\begin{aligned}
\kappa &= N_1(_a\kappa)_1 + N_2(_a\kappa)_2 + \cdots \\
&= (N_1 Z_1^2 + N_2 Z_2^2 + \cdots)\sigma_0 \bar{P} \\
&= \kappa_1 \left[1 + \frac{N_2}{N_1} \left(\frac{Z_2}{Z_1}\right)^2 + \cdots \right]
\end{aligned} \tag{2.11}
$$

It is important to notice that pair-production attenuation becomes of paramount importance in heavy elements and at high photon energies.

For example, in Pb the pair-production attenuation exceeds the Compton attenuation at $h\nu \geq 4.75$ Mev. At 17 Mev in Pb the measured pair-production attenuation (D18, M32) is in substantial agreement with the theoretical value of 0.63 cm^{-1} and is therefore about seven times larger than the total Compton attenuation coefficient of 0.09 cm^{-1} for Pb. Pair production is the only one of the three major processes whose cross section increases with increasing energy. Because of this, the total attenuation coefficient, $\mu_0 = \sigma + \tau + \kappa$, in heavy elements will go through a minimum. Figure 2.4 shows that this minimum occurs at $\sim$3.3 Mev in Pb. Thus a measured attenuation coefficient can correspond to either of two photon energies (in Pb, $\mu_0 = 0.5$ cm^{-1} for 2.0 and 5.5 Mev). In light elements, however, the attenuation coefficient will be single-valued up to very high photon energies, because the increase in pair-production cross section is more than offset by the decrease in Compton cross section. In the case of copper these two effects cancel one another over a broad range of energies, giving copper the interesting and useful property of having a total attenuation coefficient which is substantially constant at $\mu_0 = 0.28$ cm^{-1} for photon energies of 4 to 20 Mev.

Within the limits of the Born approximation, the measured pair-production coefficients in Al, Fe, Cu, and Pb at 11.0, 13.7, and 19.1 Mev (A7) and in Be, Al, Cu, Sn, Pb, and U at 88 Mev (L16) are in satisfactory agreement with the Bethe-Heitler theory of pair production.

g. Energy Absorption. When a photon is absorbed in a pair-production encounter, only a portion of its energy appears at once as kinetic energy of the electron pair. Thus, by analogy with our considerations of the Compton and photoelectric processes, the true primary *absorption* coefficient may be written as κ_a, where

$$\kappa_a = \kappa \left(1 - \frac{2m_0c^2}{h\nu} \right) \qquad (2.12)$$

The remaining $2m_0c^2$ of the total photon energy $h\nu$ resides in the rest masses of the electron pair. This energy is given up after the positron has been slowed down by ionizing and radiative collisions and has annihilated itself by combining with some negatron. The resulting two 0.51-Mev annihilation photons are then emitted from the scene of the annihilation. Their directional distribution is random, hence isotropic with respect to the direction of the original primary photon. These annihilation photons play the role of scattered radiation, when the overall energy-absorption process is considered. We may therefore write as a pair-production *scattering* coefficient κ_s the quantity

$$\kappa_s = \kappa \frac{2m_0c^2}{h\nu} \qquad (2.13)$$

The total pair-production attenuation coefficient κ is then made up of a true absorption κ_a and a scattering coefficient κ_s, or

$$\kappa = \kappa_a + \kappa_s \qquad (2.14)$$

At energies below about 3 Mev, the Compton effect is dominant, so that this scattering correction has a very small effect on the total scattering. At high energies, the fraction $2m_0c^2/h\nu$ becomes small, and again the scattering has only a small effect on any total absorption calculations. For these reasons, it is common practice in all but the most accurate work to use $\kappa_a \simeq \kappa$ as an approximation, and the terms pair *absorption coefficient* and pair *attenuation coefficient* are often used interchangeably.

h. Pair Production in the Field of an Electron. All our quantitative considerations thus far refer only to pair production in the electrostatic field of the nucleus. Perrin (P17) first pointed out in 1933 that pair production should also occur in the field of an atomic electron and showed from momentum conservation that the minimum photon energy would be $4m_0c^2 = 2.04$ Mev.

Theoretical developments made by Wheeler and Lamb (W35) and others up to 1952 have been reviewed by Bethe and Ashkin (B47). The effects of screening of the electrons by each other and by the nucleus make the theoretical treatment difficult and the results somewhat uncertain. Clearly, the theoretical cross sections are of the order of $\frac{1}{137}(e^2/m_0c^2)^2$ per electron, or roughly the same as for a proton. At about 6.5 Mev, present theories suggest that each electron in an atom of any Z is about 0.4 as effective as a proton would be. At larger photon energies this relative effectiveness of an electron increases, finally approaching unity for extremely high $h\nu$. In an atom of any Z, the ratio of the total cross section for all Z electrons, $\kappa_{electrons}$, to the cross section for nuclear pair production $_a\kappa = \kappa_{nucleus}$ can be written

$$\frac{\kappa_{electrons}}{\kappa_{nucleus}} = \frac{1}{CZ} \tag{2.15}$$

where C depends upon $h\nu$, but not upon Z. C is expected to be about 2.6 at 6.5 Mev, about 1.2 at 100 Mev, and to approach unity as $h\nu \rightarrow \infty$.

In a cloud chamber, pair production in the field of an electron can be observed as a *triplet* recoil track (one positron, two negatrons), in contrast to the characteristic *pair* recoil (one positron, one negatron) from the much more abundant pair production in the field of the nucleus. In these triplets one negatron usually has a small energy compared with the other two particles. Momentum and total energy have been shown to be conserved in individual triplets formed by 2.76-Mev γ rays of Na^{24} in an air-filled cloud chamber (O1).

By measuring the ratio of triplets to pairs, one obtains the ratio of electronic interactions to nuclear interactions. In this way, and using the 6- to 7-Mev γ rays from the $F^{19}(p,\alpha)$ reaction, Phillips and Kruger (P20) reported the following observations.

Gas	Number of triplets	Number of pairs	Ratio triplets/pairs = $1/CZ$	C in Eq. (2.15)
CH_4	97	1,430	0.068	3.6
Air	118	3,441	0.034	4.0
Argon	89	6,484	0.014	4.1

In spite of the greatest care, a few triplet tracks are likely to be misidentified as pairs in such experiments. Consequently, the average value, $C \simeq 3.9 \pm 0.3$, deduced from these observations may be regarded as an upper limit for 6.5-Mev photons. Analogous observations, on a smaller number of tracks, have been made of the interactions of the bremsstrahlung from 100-Mev electrons with air and saturated water vapor in a cloud chamber. In these studies Gaerttner and Yeater (G1) made approximate corrections for misidentified triplets and concluded that

$$C \simeq 1.3 \pm 0.3 \quad \text{for 5 to 20 Mev}$$
$$C \simeq 1.2 \pm 0.3 \quad \text{for 20 to 100 Mev}$$

Linear Attenuation Coefficient. Pair production in the field of the atomic electrons will account for a little additional attenuation, the amount depending upon both Z and $h\nu$. We may take the electronic effects into account by replacing Z^2 in Eq. (2.6) by $Z^2(1 + 1/CZ)$. Then

$$\kappa_{\text{total}} = \kappa \left(1 + \frac{1}{CZ} \right)$$

where κ is the usual nuclear pair-production coefficient and κ_{total} includes the effects of the atomic electrons. The correction term $1/CZ$ is zero for $h\nu < 2.04$ Mev.

Problems

1. Show that the minimum photon energy for the production of positron-negatron pairs in the field of a free electron is $4m_0c^2$.

2. From the data for Pb, determine the nuclear pair-production coefficient per centimeter of Ta for 2.76-Mev γ rays. Estimate what correction should be added for pair production in the field of the atomic electrons.

CHAPTER 25

Attenuation and Absorption of Electromagnetic Radiation

In the previous two chapters we have discussed in detail the major processes by which photons interact with matter. We can now examine some of the over-all effects of these processes on a beam of photons as it passes through an absorber.

1. Attenuation Coefficients

a. Total Linear Attenuation Coefficients. The probability of a photon traversing a given amount of absorber without any kind of interaction is just the product of the probabilities of survival for each particular type of interaction. The probability of traversing a thickness x of absorber without a Compton collision is just $e^{-\sigma x}$, where $\sigma = \sigma_a + \sigma_s$ is the total linear attenuation coefficient for the Compton process. Similarly, the probability of no photoelectric interaction is $e^{-\tau x}$, and of no pair-production collision is $e^{-\kappa x}$. Thus a collimated γ-ray beam of initial intensity I_0 after traversing a thickness x of absorber will have a residual intensity I of unaffected primary photons equal to

$$\begin{aligned} I &= I_0 e^{-\sigma x} e^{-\tau x} e^{-\kappa x} \\ &= I_0 e^{-(\sigma + \tau + \kappa)x} \\ &= I_0 e^{-\mu_0 x} \end{aligned} \tag{1.1}$$

where the quantity

$$\mu_0 = \sigma_a + \sigma_s + \tau + \kappa \tag{1.2}$$

is the *total linear attenuation coefficient*. This attenuation coefficient is a measure of the number of primary photons which have interactions. It is to be distinguished sharply from the *absorption* coefficient, which is always a smaller quantity, and which measures the energy absorbed by the medium.

Extensive measurements have been made to determine the values of μ_0 for various Z and $h\nu$. Compilations of the experimental results are available (D12, W38), and tables of theoretical values have been prepared by White (W38), Latter and Kahn (L11), Fano (F7), and Davisson and Evans (D12). Graphs and formulas for converting from one Z to another have been given in Chaps. 23 and 24.

The relative importance of σ, τ, and κ is shown graphically in Fig. 1.1. Photoelectric collisions are important only for small $h\nu$ and large Z and are responsible for the practical saying "lead is opaque to photons below ~0.3 Mev." Pair production is of major importance only for large $h\nu$ and large Z. Compton collisions predominate in the entire domain of intermediate $h\nu$, for all Z.

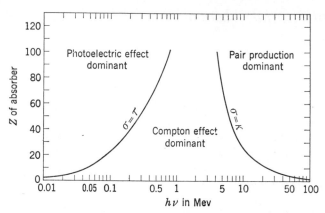

Fig. 1.1 Relative importance of the three major types of γ-ray interaction. The lines show the values of Z and $h\nu$ for which the two neighboring effects are just equal.

b. Mass Attenuation Coefficients. For any type of interaction, the mass attenuation coefficient is the linear coefficient divided by the density, ρ g/cm^3. These mass attenuation coefficients are really of more fundamental value than are the linear coefficients, because all mass attenuation coefficients are *independent of the actual density and physical state* (gas, liquid, or solid) of the absorber. This is because the fundamental interactions are expressible as cross sections per atom, $_a\kappa$, $_a\tau$, and $_a\sigma = _e\sigma Z$, and when these are multiplied by the number of atoms per gram we obtain the mass-absorption coefficients directly.

Expressing this mathematically, we have, for example,

$$\kappa(\text{cm}^{-1}) = {}_a\kappa \left(\frac{\text{cm}^2}{\text{atom}}\right) N \left(\frac{\text{atoms}}{\text{cm}^3}\right)$$

$$N \left(\frac{\text{atoms}}{\text{cm}^3}\right) = \mathsf{N} \left(\frac{\text{atoms}}{\text{mole}}\right) \frac{\rho(\text{g/cm}^3)}{A\,(\text{g/mole})}$$

Hence

$$\frac{\kappa}{\rho} \left(\frac{\text{cm}^2}{\text{g}}\right) = {}_a\kappa \frac{\mathsf{N}}{A} \tag{1.3}$$

with analogous relationships for τ/ρ, σ/ρ, σ_s/ρ, σ_a/ρ, and μ_0/ρ. Special convenience attaches to the mass coefficients for Compton interactions because the atomic cross sections are simply Z times the electronic cross sections. Then, for example,

$$\frac{\sigma}{\rho} \left(\frac{\text{cm}^2}{\text{g}}\right) = {}_a\sigma \frac{\mathsf{N}}{A} = {}_e\sigma \frac{Z}{A} \mathsf{N} \tag{1.4}$$

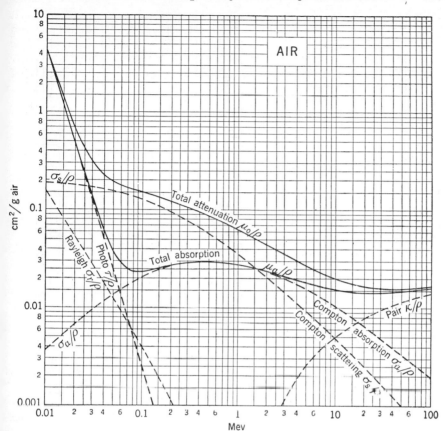

Fig. 1.2 Mass attenuation coefficients for photons in air, computed from the tables of atomic cross sections prepared by G. R. White (W38). The curve marked "total absorption" is $(\mu_a/\rho) = (\sigma_a/\rho) + (\tau/\rho) + (\kappa/\rho)$, where σ_a, τ, and κ are the corresponding linear coefficients for Compton absorption, photoelectric absorption, and pair production. When the Compton scattering coefficient σ_s is added to μ_a, we obtain the curve marked "total attenuation," which is $(\mu_0/\rho) = (\mu_a/\rho) + (\sigma_s/\rho)$. The total Rayleigh scattering cross section (σ_r/ρ) is shown separately. Because the Rayleigh scattering is elastic and is confined to small angles, it has not been included in μ_0/ρ. In computing these curves, the composition of "air" was taken as 78.04 volume per cent nitrogen, 21.02 volume per cent oxygen, and 0.94 volume per cent argon. At 0°C and 760 mm Hg pressure, the density of air is $\rho = 0.001\ 293$ g/cm³.

and σ/ρ is nearly independent of Z because $Z/A \simeq 0.45 \pm 0.05$ for all elements except hydrogen, for which $Z/A \simeq 1$.

Figures 1.2 to 1.6 give theoretical values of the mass attenuation coefficients for air, water, Al, Pb, and NaI, for $h\nu = 0.01$ Mev to 100 Mev, plotted from theoretical tables by White (W38).

c. Mixtures of Materials. The primary attenuation of γ rays in chemical compounds or other mixtures of elements is assumed to depend only upon the sum of the cross sections presented by all the atoms in the

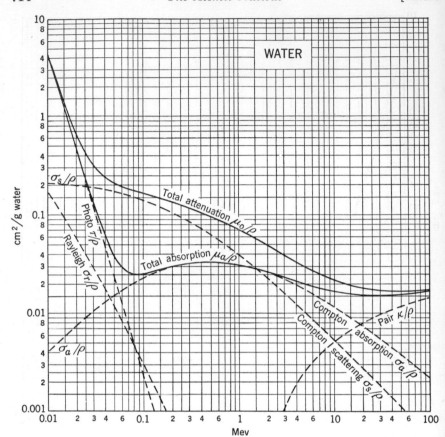

Fig. 1.3 Mass attenuation coefficients for photons in water. The individual curves have the same significance as in Fig. 1.2 and were computed from the tables of atomic cross sections prepared by G. R. White (W38).

mixture. Because chemical bonds are only of the order of a few electron volts, these have no significant effects on the Compton, photo, or pair interactions. Then, with the help of Eq. (1.3) and its analogues, it can be shown that an absorber whose bulk density is ρ, and which is made up of a mixture of elements whose mass attenuation coefficients are (μ_1/ρ_1), (μ_2/ρ_2), . . . , will have an over-all mass attenuation coefficient given by

$$\frac{\mu}{\rho} = \frac{\mu_1}{\rho_1} w_1 + \frac{\mu_2}{\rho_2} w_2 + \cdots \tag{1.5}$$

where w_1, w_2, . . . are the *fractions by weight* of the elements which make up the absorber. Equation (1.5) is valid when all the (μ/ρ)'s represent the total attenuation coefficients (Compton + photo + pair), and also when all the (μ/ρ)'s represent any selected one or more partial effects.

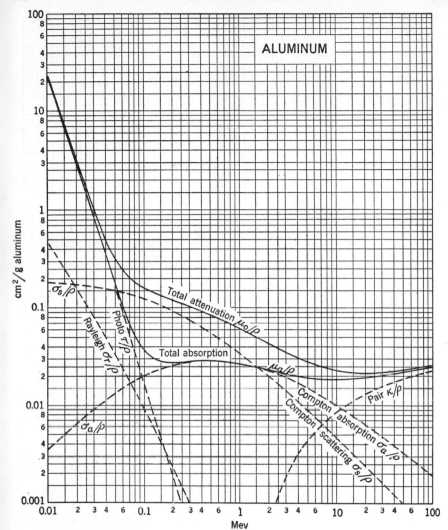

Fig. 1.4 Mass attenuation coefficients for photons in aluminum. The individual curves have the same significance as in Fig. 1.2 and were computed from the tables of atomic cross sections prepared by G. R. White (W38). The corresponding linear coefficients for aluminum may be obtained by multiplying all curves by $\rho = 2.70$ g/cm³ Al.

d. Mean Free Path. While a photon is traversing a material in which the total linear attenuation coefficient is μ_0, the probability of a collision in any short distance Δx is $\mu_0 \Delta x$, provided that $\mu_0 \Delta x \ll 1$. Then the probability that a photon can travel a distance x without experiencing a collision is $e^{-\mu_0 x}$, Eq. (1.1). Mathematically, this is entirely analogous to the probability law of radioactive decay, where $e^{-\lambda t}$ represents the probability of survival after a time t, when $\lambda \Delta t$ is the

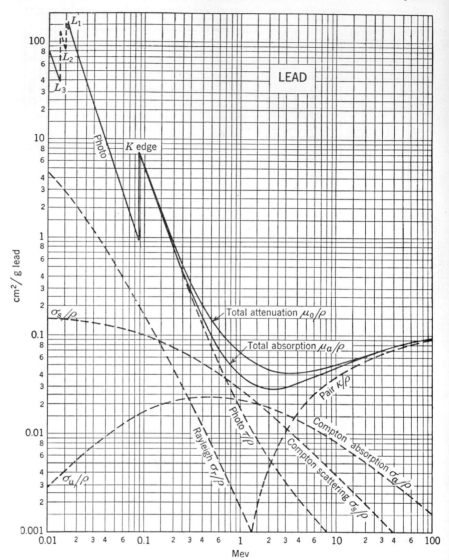

Fig. 1.5 Mass attenuation coefficients for photons in lead. The individual curves have the same significance as in Fig. 1.2 and were computed from the tables of atomic cross sections prepared by G. R. White (W38). The corresponding linear coefficients for lead may be obtained using $\rho = 11.35$ g/cm^3 Pb.

chance of decay in Δt. Both expressions are representations of the Poisson distribution (Chap. 26) and correspond to the probability of no event when, on the average, $\mu_0 x$ or λt events should occur.

If a large number n of identical photons enter an infinite absorber, the number which travel a distance x without having a collision is $ne^{-\mu_0 x}$, and the number which have a collision between x and $x + dx$ is $n\mu_0 e^{-\mu_0 x}\, dx$.

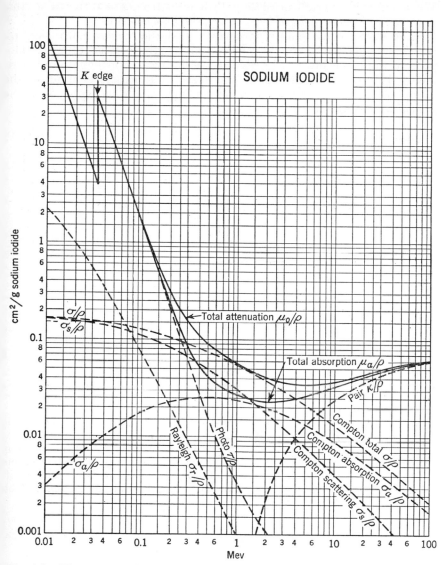

Fig. 1.6   Mass attenuation coefficients for sodium iodide.   The individual curves have the same significance as in Fig. 1.2 and were computed from tables of atomic cross sections prepared by G. R. White (W38).   Additionally, the "Compton total" attenuation coefficient $(\sigma/\rho) = (\sigma_a/\rho) + (\sigma_s/\rho)$ is shown explicitly, because of its usefulness in predicting the behavior of NaI scintillators.   Linear attenuation coefficients for NaI may be obtained using $\rho = 3.67$ g/cm^3 NaI.

When summed over all possible path lengths from $x = 0$ to $x = \infty$, thi: gives a *mean path length* of $1/\mu_0$ before the first collision.

The distance μ_0^{-1} cm is variously called the "mean path length," the "mean free path," or the "relaxation length." It is entirely analo gous to the mean life $1/\lambda$ in radioactive decay. In attenuation experi ments, it is common to express the absorber thickness in units of the mean free path μ_0^{-1}; then a thickness of x cm would be expressed as the *dimensionless* quantity $x/\mu_0^{-1} = \mu_0 x$.

Problems

1. A collimated, narrow beam of 2.04-Mev photons passes through a very thin Pb converter. The secondary electrons ejected at an angle of 20° are observed. At this angle, what will be the kinetic energy of (*a*) the photoelec trons, (*b*) the pair electrons, and (*c*) the Compton electrons?

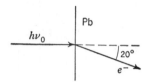

(*d*) Estimate qualitatively the relative intensity of the photo-, pair, and Compton electrons, per unit solid angle, at the mean angle of 20°. Give you reasons, in terms of the known cross sections and any other pertinent factors.

(*e*) When the Compton electron is ejected at an angle of 20°, through what angle has the primary photon been scattered?

NOTE: The energy of the K edge of Pb is 88.1 kev and of the L edge is 15 kev

2. From values for Pb, calculate κ, τ, and $(\sigma_s + \sigma_a)$ for Cu, in cm^{-1}, fo: 4-Mev and 8-Mev γ rays.

3. For what energies does the Compton effect predominate over the photo- electric effect and over pair production in the absorption of photons by Al?

4. The energy of a γ ray is to be determined from the energy of the electrons produced in a thin carbon converter. The maximum energy of these electrons is determined by placing an aluminum absorber between two β-ray counters in coincidence. The counters have glass walls of thickness of 10 mg/cm^2. The

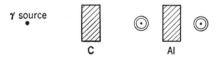

coincidence rate reduces to substantially zero when a thickness of 150 mg/cm^2 of Al absorber is used.

(*a*) What is the energy of the γ ray?

(*b*) If the electrons of maximum energy from the converter are allowed to move through a transverse magnetic field of 300 gauss, what will be their radius of curvature?

(*c*) What would be the maximum energy of the electrons if a thin Pb con verter replaced the carbon converter?

5. The 3-yr isotope of radioactive iron Fe^{55} decays by orbital electron capture and emits only the 5.9-kev X rays of its decay product, manganese. A counter, specially designed to detect this 5.9-kev radiation, is to be supplied with a beryllium window 0.030 in. thick. The density of beryllium is 1.85. Tables (C37) show that X rays of 6.38 kev have a total attenuation coefficient of 5.65 cm⁻¹ in Be, including 0.33 cm⁻¹ for Compton effect.

(*a*) What is the photoelectric absorption coefficient for 6.38-kev X rays in Be?

(*b*) Calculate the photoelectric absorption coefficient for 5.9-kev X rays in Be.

(*c*) What is the total attenuation coefficient of 5.9-kev X rays in Be?

(*d*) What fraction of the incident 5.9-kev X rays will penetrate the 0.030-in. Be window?

6. Pure beryllium windows are not available, and beryllium containing 1 per cent (by weight) of titanium is substituted in the previous problem. Pure titanium has an atomic weight of 47.9 and a density of 4.50. Assume that the alloy of Be-Ti has a density of 1.88.

(*a*) Estimate the photoelectric absorption coefficient in pure titanium ($Z = 22$) from the data on Be.

(*b*) Calculate the total attenuation coefficient for 5.9-kev X rays in the alloy.

(*c*) Calculate the fraction of the incident 5.9-kev X rays which will penetrate 0.030 in. of the alloy.

2. *Energy Absorption*

The effects which photons produce in matter are actually almost exclusively due to the secondary electrons. A photon produces *primary* ionization only when it removes an electron from an atom by a photoelectric collision or by a Compton collision, but from each primary ionizing collision the swift secondary electron which is produced may have nearly as much kinetic energy as the primary photon. This secondary electron dissipates its energy mainly by producing ionization and excitation of the atoms and molecules in the absorber. For electrons of the order of 1 Mev, an average of about 1 per cent of the electron's energy is lost as bremsstrahlung. If, on the average, the electron loses about 32 ev per ion pair produced, then a 1-Mev electron produces the order of 30,000 ion pairs before being stopped in the absorber. The one primary ionization is thus completely negligible in comparison with the very large amount of *secondary* ionization. For practical purposes, we can regard all the effects of photons as due to the electrons which they produce in absorbers.

a. Energy Absorption in a Medium. By "energy absorption" we mean the photon energy which is converted into kinetic energy of secondary electrons. This kinetic energy eventually is dissipated in the medium as heat and in principle could be measured with a calorimeter. The energy carried away from the primary collisions as degraded secondary photons is not absorbed energy.

Suppose that a collimated beam containing n photons/(cm²)(sec), each having energy $h\nu$ Mev, is incident on an absorber in which the linear attenuation coefficients are σ, τ, and κ cm⁻¹. The incident γ-*ray intensity*

I of this beam is

$$I = nh\nu \qquad \text{Mev}/(\text{cm}^2)(\text{sec}) \tag{2.1}$$

In passing a distance dx into the absorber, the number of primary photons suffering collisions will be

$$dn = n(\sigma + \tau + \kappa)\, dx = n\mu_0\, dx \qquad \text{photons}/(\text{cm}^2)(\text{sec}) \tag{2.2}$$

The total energy thus removed from the collimated beam is $h\nu\, dn$ Mev/ $(\text{cm}^2)(\text{sec})$, but a significant portion of this energy will be in the form of secondary photons.

In the Compton collisions, the average kinetic energy of the Compton electrons is $h\nu(\sigma_a/\sigma)$, and the Compton linear *absorption* coefficient σ_a is of the order of $\frac{1}{2}\sigma$ for 1- to 2-Mev photons. In the photoelectric collisions, the energy of the photoelectrons is $(h\nu - B_e)$, where B_e is the average binding energy of the atomic electron. In the pair-production collisions the total kinetic energy of the positron-negatron pair is $(h\nu - 2m_0c^2)$. Combining these considerations, we find that the true energy absorption in a thickness of dx cm is

$$dI = n\left[\sigma h\nu \frac{\sigma_a}{\sigma} + \tau(h\nu - B_e) + \kappa(h\nu - 2m_0c^2)\right] dx \qquad \text{Mev}/(\text{cm}^2)(\text{sec}) \tag{2.3}$$

In Chap. 24 we have seen that B_e and $2m_0c^2$ can usually be neglected, especially in light elements. Then the usual, but approximate, expression for energy absorption becomes

$$dI = I(\sigma_a + \tau + \kappa)\, dx = I\mu_a\, dx \qquad \text{Mev}/(\text{cm}^2)(\text{sec}) \tag{2.4}$$

where $\mu_a = (\sigma_a + \tau + \kappa)$ is the *linear absorption* coefficient. Note that μ_a is smaller than the total linear *attenuation* coefficient μ_0, because μ_0 includes a scattering coefficient μ_s which represents the energy content of all the secondary photons (Compton, X rays, and annihilation radiation). Then, rigorously,

$$\mu_0 = \mu_a + \mu_s \qquad \text{cm}^{-1} \tag{2.5}$$

and in the usual approximation, neglecting B_e and $2m_0c^2$,

$$\mu_a = \sigma_a + \tau + \kappa \qquad \text{cm}^{-1} \tag{2.6}$$
$$\mu_s = \sigma_s \qquad \text{cm}^{-1} \tag{2.7}$$

A simple and very general result, which follows at once from Eq. (2.4), is that the rate of *energy absorption per unit volume* is simply the incident intensity times μ_a

$$\frac{dI}{dx} = I\mu_a \qquad \text{Mev}/(\text{cm}^3)(\text{sec}) \tag{2.8}$$

This is valid for any size and shape of volume element, throughout which the intensity I is essentially constant.

Dose Rate.   Finally, the rate of energy absorption per gram, which is called the *dose rate R*, is

$$R = I\frac{\mu_a}{\rho} = I\left(\frac{\sigma_a}{\rho} + \frac{\tau}{\rho} + \frac{\kappa}{\rho}\right) \qquad \text{Mev}/(\text{g})(\text{sec}) \qquad (2.9)$$

where ρ g/cm³ is the density of the absorber.   Notice that only the mass-absorption coefficients (σ_a/ρ), (τ/ρ), and (κ/ρ) enter the formulation of dose rate.   Thus for a given intensity I, energy $h\nu$, and material, the *dose rate is independent of the density of the material.*

b. Roentgen Unit.   The roentgen was originally developed as a unit of radiological dose.   Workers in physics and related areas make frequent use of the roentgen and a number of units derived from it.

As redefined in 1937, the roentgen unit (r) is (I5) "that quantity of x- or γ radiation such that the associated corpuscular emission per 0.001 293 gm of air produces, in air, ions carrying 1 electrostatic unit of quantity of electricity of either sign."

The full meaning of this definition is not always apparent at first reading.   The mass of air referred to is 1 cm³ of dry air at 0°C and 760 mm Hg.   One electrostatic unit is $[1/(3 \times 10^9)]$ coulomb, or

$$\frac{1}{(4.80 \times 10^{-10})} = 2.08 \times 10^9 \text{ ion pairs}$$

The secondary electrons which produce this ionization are to originate in the stated air mass of 0.001 293 g, but they will do most of their ionizing somewhere outside the stated mass. The situation is represented in Fig. 2.1.   Correct use of the roentgen as a unit of "quantity of γ radiation" requires us to recognize that the roentgen does not involve any precise physical information at all about the quality $(h\nu)$ or intensity (I) of γ ra-

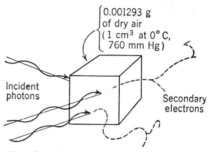

Fig. 2.1   Schematic representation of the roentgen unit of photon energy dissipation in air. Photons of any energy are incident from any direction, over an unstated time. The absorption of these photons, per 0.001 293 g of dry air, produces secondary electrons which, if completely absorbed *in air*, would produce a total ionization of 1 statcoulomb, i.e., $1/4.80 \times 10^{-10} = 2.08 \times 10^9$ ion pairs. This ionization would be distributed along the relatively long individual paths of the secondary electrons.   [*From Evans* (E20).]

diation.   It is really "quantity of ionization" which is defined.   Thus the roentgen is a *unit of energy dissipation in air*, by γ rays or X rays. It is not a unit of energy incidence nor of intensity.   Experimentally, evaluation of a dose in roentgens is difficult if $h\nu$ is large enough to cause appreciable pair production in the detection instruments; hence the roentgen unit is best used in the domain below about 3 Mev.

The roentgen unit does not depend on the *time* required for the accumulation of the ionization.   Consequently γ-ray *dose rates* are expressed in roentgens per unit time, very commonly in milliroentgens (mr) per hour for low intensities or roentgens (r) per minute for higher levels.

In summary, the 1937 international definition of the roentgen, when combined with current values of the physical constants, leads to

$$1 \text{ r} = 1 \text{ statcoulomb/cm}^3 \text{ std. air}$$
$$= 2.08 \times 10^9 \text{ ion pairs/cm}^3 \text{ std. air}$$
$$= 1.61 \times 10^{12} \text{ ion pairs/g air} \tag{2.10}$$

and if the secondary electrons expend an average energy of 32.5 ev (B56, G45) to form an ion pair in air, then also

$$1 \text{ r} = 6.77 \times 10^4 \text{ Mev/cm}^3 \text{ std. air}$$
$$= 5.24 \times 10^7 \text{ Mev/g air}$$
$$= 84 \text{ ergs/g air} \tag{2.11}$$

c. γ Output of Radionuclides. In many practical cases, an evaluation of the quantity of a radionuclide can be obtained most easily by

TABLE 2.1. MILLIROENTGENS PER HOUR PRODUCED AT 1 M BY THE NUCLEAR γ RAYS AND THE ANNIHILATION RADIATION FROM 1 MC OF THE RADIONUCLIDES LISTED

Nuclide	Half-period	$\dfrac{\text{mr}}{(\text{hr})(\text{mc})}$ at 1 m	Nuclide	Half-period	$\dfrac{\text{mr}}{(\text{hr})(\text{mc})}$ at 1 m
Na^{22}	2.6 yr	1.29	As^{76}	26.8 hr	0.4
Na^{24}	15.0 hr	1.92	Br^{82}	35.9 hr	1.5
Mn^{52}	6.0 d	1.93	I^{128}	25 min	0.018
Mn^{54}	310 d	0.49	I^{130}	12.6 hr	1.25
Fe^{59}	45 d	0.65	I^{131}	8.1 d	0.24
Co^{58}	72 d	0.56	Cs^{137}	33 yr	0.32
Co^{60}	5.3 yr	1.35	Ta^{182}	111 d	0.6
Cu^{64}	12.8 hr	0.12	Au^{198}	2.7 d	0.25
Zn^{65}	250 d	0.30	Ra^{226}	1,620 yr	0.84†

† Average of measured values, using cavity chambers, per milligram of radium, with 0.5-mm Pt filtration (E20); when corrected for density effect, the cavity-chamber measurements are reported (W44) to give 0.82 mr/(hr)(mg), in agreement with free-air measurements. All other values are calculated using "1952 decay schemes" as given by Hollander, Perlman, and Seaborg, *Revs. Mod. Phys.*, 25: 469 (1953).

measuring the γ radiation emitted by the unshielded sample. When the decay scheme of the radionuclide is known, γ-ray measurements give the absolute activity of the sample, with less accuracy but with vastly less effort than methods which depend upon absolute β counting, coincidence counting, or calorimetry (M9).

The basis of the γ-ray method can be illustrated by considering Co^{60}, which emits one γ ray of 1.17 Mev and one of 1.33 Mev per disintegration, in accord with the decay scheme shown in Fig. 7.2 of Chap. 6. One *curie* is the amount of any radionuclide in which the number of disintegrations per second is 3.700×10^{10} (P3). Then at a distance of

1 m (meter) from 1 curie of unshielded Co^{60}, the γ-ray *intensity* is

$$I = \frac{3.70 \times 10^{10}}{4\pi (100)^2} (1.17 + 1.33) \qquad Mev/(cm^2)(sec) \qquad (2.12)$$

The mass-absorption coefficients in air are $(\mu_a/\rho) = 0.0270$ cm^2/g for 1.17 Mev, and 0.0263 cm^2/g for 1.33 Mev. Therefore the total dose rate [Eqs. (2.9) and (2.11)] is

$$R = \sum I \frac{\mu_a}{\rho}$$

$$= \frac{3.70 \times 10^{10}}{4\pi (100)^2} \frac{(1.17 \times 0.0270 + 1.33 \times 0.0263)(3,600 \text{ sec/hr})}{[5.24 \times 10^7 \text{ Mev}/(\text{r})(\text{g air})]}$$

$$= 1.35 \text{ r/hr} \qquad \text{at 1 m from 1 curie of } Co^{60} \qquad (2.13)$$

Table 2.1 gives calculated values for the γ radiation from a number of common radionuclides. Because (μ_a/ρ) for air varies only slightly (± 15 per cent) throughout the energy domain of nuclear γ rays, a convenient approximate rule is

$$R \simeq 0.55 \Sigma (h\nu) \qquad mr/(hr)(mc) \text{ at 1 m} \qquad (2.14)$$

where $\Sigma(h\nu)$ is the *total* photon energy per disintegration, in Mev.

d. The Bragg-Gray Cavity Theorem. In the case of Co^{60} [Eq. (2.13)], some of the Compton electrons will have initial energies of the order of 1 Mev, hence ranges of as much as 0.4 g/cm^2, or 3 m of air. Yet the definition of the roentgen requires that we measure the ionization produced by all the secondary electrons formed per cubic centimeter of standard air. To avoid large and cumbersome apparatus, small "air-wall" ionization chambers, or *cavity chambers*, have been developed (W63). These follow the general principles (B109, F68, G42, G43, F2) governing the ionization produced in a small cavity (e.g., air) in a large mass of absorbing material traversed by γ rays.

When a sufficiently tiny cavity is introduced into a large homogeneous absorbing medium which is uniformly irradiated, the atmosphere of secondary electrons traversing the cavity is identical in every respect with the electron atmosphere which existed in the medium before the cavity was introduced. The cavity must be small compared with the range of the secondary electrons in the gas with which the cavity is filled (G43, S39). In a series of careful experiments, L. H. Gray (G43) verified this cavity principle and showed that

$$E_m = J_{air}(w_{air} S_l)_{av} \qquad (2.15)$$

where $E_m = \gamma$-ray energy absorbed in medium, ev/cm^3 of medium

J_{air} = ionization produced in small air-filled cavity, ion pairs/cm^3 of air

w_{air} = average energy to form an ion pair, ev/ion pair in air

$S_l = (dT/ds)_m/(dT/ds)_{air}$ = linear stopping power of medium relative to air, Chap. 22, Eq. (2.12); dT/ds for secondary electrons given by Eq. (2.25) of Chap. 18.

The linear relative stopping power S_l is almost independent of the electron's velocity but decreases slowly with increasing atomic number Z. (Compare the analogous stopping power and B/Z relationships for α rays and protons in air, Fig. 2.2 of Chap. 22.) In agreement with theory, Gray found S_l to be proportional to the relative electron densities NZ of the medium and the gas, except for the expected small decrease in S_l with increasing Z, which is due to the dependence of the relative stopping power *per electron* S_e on the geometric-mean ionization potential I. This decrease amounts to about 9 per cent between $Z = 6$ (C) and $Z = 13$ (Al), and an additional 8 per cent between $Z = 13$ (Al) and $Z = 29$ (Cu). Thus in a set of cavity chambers, the ionization per cubic centimeter of air will *increase* slightly, with increasing Z of the medium. Provided that the medium is composed of light elements between $Z = 6$ and 13, an error of less than 5 per cent is made by regarding S_l as simply the ratio of the densities of the medium and the cavity gas, because

$$S_l = \frac{\rho_m}{\rho_{\mathrm{air}}} \frac{(Z/A)_m}{(Z/A)_{\mathrm{air}}} S_e \simeq \frac{\rho_m}{\rho_{\mathrm{air}}} \qquad (2.16)$$

where ρ and A represent density and atomic weight.

   e. "Air-walled" Cavity Chambers. The thickness of medium necessary to validate the Bragg-Gray cavity-ionization principle, Eq. (2.15),

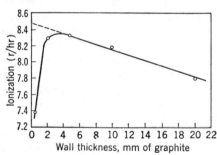

Fig. 2.2 Variation of ionization, due to a constant source of radium γ rays, with wall thickness, for a small graphite chamber filled with air. A wall thickness of ~ 4 mm is required to produce effective equilibrium between the γ rays and their secondary electrons. For thicker walls, the continued attenuation of the γ rays by the walls is noticeable. [*From Mayneord and Roberts* (M30).]

is small. It is only required that the medium be thick enough to establish equilibrium between the primary photons and their secondary electrons, i.e., about as thick as the maximum range of the secondary electrons in the medium. As this is only of the order of a few millimeters in media such as graphite, bakelite, common plastics, and aluminum, one can simply employ, as both the cavity and the medium, a small air-filled ionization chamber having walls a few millimeters thick. Figure 2.2 shows the effect of wall thickness on the ionization produced in a small graphite chamber (20 by 20 mm) filled with air and irradiated with γ rays from RaB + C. Actually, the wall of such an "air-wall" chamber can be somewhat thinner than the maximum range of the secondary electrons, because more than 90 per cent of the ionization is produced by electrons formed in the inner 1 mm of wall material, if $h\nu < 2$ Mev. It is to be noted also that the walls of the chamber should be thick enough to prevent secondary electrons from the surroundings, or from filters, as well as β rays from the γ-ray source, from reaching the sensitive volume of the chamber.

A satisfactory "air-walled" ionization chamber is one in which the ionization per cubic centimeter is

1. Independent of the volume of the chamber
2. Proportional to the density of the gas in the chamber
3. Proportional to the γ-ray energy absorbed per cubic centimeter of wall material
4. Inversely proportional to the stopping power of the walls for electrons

If the walls of the ionization chamber are composed of materials having an atomic number Z near that of air, and if the chamber gas is air, then the ionization per gram of air in the chamber will be substantially the same as the γ-ray energy loss per gram of air at the point where the chamber is located.

In an ideal "air-walled" cavity chamber, and if all the ions formed are collected,

$$1\,\frac{r}{sec} = \frac{1}{3 \times 10^9} \quad coulomb/(sec)(cm^3\ air)$$

$$= 3.33 \times 10^{-10} \quad amp/cm^3\ std.\ air$$

and $$1\,\frac{mr}{hr} = 0.926 \times 10^{-16} \quad amp/cm^3\ std.\ air \qquad (2.17)$$

Some of the more subtle characteristics of cavity chambers have been reviewed recently by Wang (W7) and by Whyte (W44).

f. Spectral Sensitivity of γ-Ray Detectors. A tremendous variety of instruments for measuring γ rays is available, and many reviews and books have been written on the detailed characteristics of some of them (J20, S67, F60, etc.). Currently, the most popular types are ionization chambers, Geiger-Müller counters, scintillation counters, and photographic emulsions. Within a given type, individual instruments may have widely different γ-ray response characteristics. Measurements of the behavior of γ rays in matter generally depend in a complicated way upon the spectral sensitivity of the detector. We shall consider only a few fundamental illustrative cases.

It is possible to construct γ-ray detectors whose spectral sensitivities approach the four idealized types shown in Fig. 2.3. These response characteristics will be exhibited, by any given instrument, only over a limited domain of photon energies. In Fig. 2.3 the *intrinsic efficiency* ϵ means the relative response of the instrument *per photon* of energy $h\nu$.

A detector whose spectral response is *linear*, $\epsilon = ah\nu$, will give an output reading which is proportional to the γ-ray *intensity* I, Eq. (2.1), regardless of the energy or mixture of energies in the incident photon beam. This is evident because the detector response, $\Sigma\epsilon = \Sigma(ah\nu)$, is simply equal to aI, if $a = \epsilon/h\nu$ is constant.

An "air-walled" cavity chamber can be made nearly linear (± 10 per cent) between about $h\nu = 0.2$ Mev and $h\nu = 2$ Mev. Mathematically, this can be seen from Eqs. (2.8) and (2.15), because the energy-absorption coefficient μ_a is nearly constant over this energy domain.   Physically, the probability that an incident photon will produce a secondary electron in the chamber wall is nearly independent of $h\nu$ in this energy region. But the probability that this secondary electron will penetrate the inner thickness of wall and enter the air cavity is proportional to its range, which in turn is proportional to the energy of the electron and also to the energy of the incident quantum.   Thus, physically, the response is approximately proportional to the incident intensity, or energy transport, because high-energy photons produce high-energy electrons, which have a higher penetration in the walls of the chamber.   Depending upon the details of construction (wall thickness, size, and arrangement of any metal leads or electrodes, etc.), the chamber may be oversensitive or undersensitive to low-energy photons, say, $h\nu < 0.2$ Mev, because of the

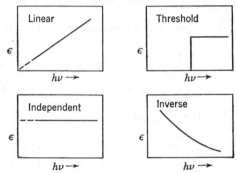

Fig. 2.3 Idealized representations of four types of spectral sensitivity, which can be approached in various types of γ-ray detectors, over limited energy domains.   The *intrinsic efficiency* ϵ describes the relative response of the instrument per photon.

importance of photoelectric absorption.   [Most commercial γ-ray and X-ray dosimeters are oversensitive between about 0.20 Mev and 0.05 Mev (D13).]

Analogous considerations apply to Geiger-Müller counters whose jackets and cathodes are made from low-Z materials.   The counting rate in aluminum- or copper-cathode counters is well known to be nearly proportional to the total incident photon energy (D38, M5) and not to the number of photons which traverse the counter.   By using high-Z materials for the cathode, the production of photoelectrons can be enhanced, and ϵ can be made nearly constant.   For a typical (R21) platinum screen-cathode counter, ϵ decreases only by about 40 per cent as $h\nu$ decreases from 1.0 Mev to 0.36 Mev.

For a sodium iodide scintillator, the photon cross section decreases rapidly with increasing $h\nu$ from 0.06 Mev to about 1 Mev (Fig. 1.6). Hence such a detector can be given an ϵ vs. $h\nu$ response which is "inverse," "threshold," or nearly "independent" (see Fig. 2.3), depending on how the photomultiplier pulses are sorted in the electronic counting circuits.

In our later discussion of practical cases of γ-ray attenuation and energy absorption, it should be recognized that the experimental results may be strongly dependent upon the spectral sensitivity of the γ-ray detector, and that the ϵ vs. $h\nu$ response characteristics often are not known accurately.

Problems

1. It is found that a certain beam of 1.65-Mev γ rays produces the same ionization per cubic centimeter of air as does another beam of 0.55-Mev γ rays. Calculate the ratio: number of 1.65-Mev photons/number of 0.55-Mev photons.

2. The predominant components of the decay scheme of 16-day V^{48} are shown.

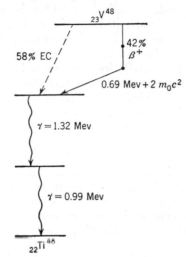

A small-sized source of V^{48}, whose activity is 10^8 disintegrations per second, is enclosed in a thin capsule which absorbs all the positrons and X rays but does not appreciably attenuate the γ rays and annihilation radiation. Determine the number of milliroentgens per hour produced at a distance of 1 m from this source.

3. The nuclear decay scheme of K^{42} is as shown, with 25 per cent of the transitions giving a 1.51-Mev γ ray. A 10-mc source of K^{42} is placed in a small spherical aluminum capsule whose walls are just thick enough to absorb all the β rays.

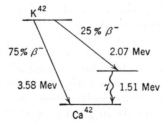

(*a*) What is the required thickness of the walls?
(*b*) If the external γ radiation is to be detected by a copper-cathode Geiger-Müller counter, or by an air-filled ionization chamber, what will be the effective fractional transmission through the walls of the aluminum sphere?

(*c*) What current will be produced by the transmitted γ rays in an "air-wall" ionization chamber situated 2 m from the source capsule, and containing 3 liters of air at a pressure of 2 atm, and 0°C?

(*d*) To a reasonable approximation, what additional ionization current will be produced in this chamber by the external bremsstrahlung from the β rays which are absorbed in the walls of the aluminum capsule?

3. Multiple Scattering of Photons

a. Secondary Radiations Produced by Photons. The extremely complicated family of secondary radiations which is produced by photons in matter may be visualized with the aid of Fig. 3.1, which shows a systematic arrangement of the more important primary processes and the secondary radiations which are produced in the first encounters. In turn, these secondary radiations undergo interactions which give rise to a new generation of additional radiations which can be called tertiary radiations. This third generation of photons and electrons produces a fourth generation, and so on. For many purposes the aggregate of secondary, tertiary, and all succeeding generations of radiations is simply lumped together under the family name of "secondary radiations." Interpretation of the word "secondary" often has to be made from context.

b. Narrow-beam Attenuation. In Fig. 3.2, the upper sketch illustrates the common experimental arrangement for measuring the total attenuation coefficient, $\mu_0 = \sigma + \tau + \kappa$. A narrow beam of photons is defined by circular apertures in two or more massive shields, or collimators. When the chosen absorber is placed in this beam, and between the collimators, all photons which are incoherently or coherently scattered by a few degrees are prevented from reaching the detector, as are nearly all secondary photons from photo and pair encounters in the absorber. Such arrangements are spoken of as *narrow-beam*, or as *"good-geometry,"* experiments.

If radionuclides which have relatively simple γ-ray spectra are chosen as sources, then the spectral sensitivity of the detector is of minor importance because substantially all the photons which reach the detector have the full primary energy. When performed with great care, narrow-beam experiments, with various $h\nu$ and Z, give evaluations of the absolute total attenuation coefficients which have a standard error of the order of 1 per cent. They therefore provide tests of the theories of photon cross sections and have shown (D12, W78, H65, C31) that the Klein-Nishina formula appears to be exact for all Z and $h\nu$. Theory and experiment are in good agreement with respect to pair production, and in fair agreement regarding photoelectric cross sections.

Attenuation measurements in good geometry have proved useful in nuclear spectroscopy and have been responsible for the discovery of low-abundance high-energy components such as the 0.5-per cent 1.34-Mev γ ray from Cu^{64} and the 15-per cent 0.638-Mev γ ray in I^{131} (D11).

c. Broad-beam Attenuation. Substantially every practical problem in γ-ray shielding, or in energy absorption, is not in narrow-beam geom-

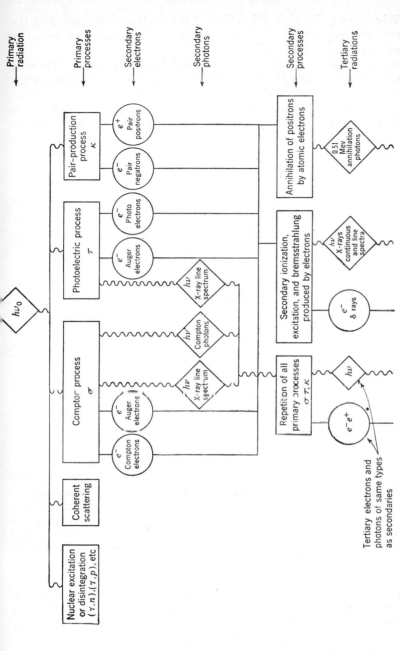

Fig. 3.1 Block diagram of the interaction of photons with matter. The types of interaction are in rectangles, photons of various sorts are in diamonds, and electron radiations are in circles. The reader may obtain a helpful review of electron and photon interactions by adding to this diagram information on the relative probability of the various interactions and on the energy and mean free paths of the various radiations.

etry.   Whenever a significant fraction of the scattered photons and the
secondary photons can reach the detector, the arrangement is called
broad beam or *"poor geometry."*

Figure 3.2 illustrates three typical broad-beam situations.   Because
the secondary radiations affect the detector, the apparent attenuation
coefficient will usually be less than the theoretical, or narrow-beam,
attenuation.   Just how much the response differs from the narrow-beam
case will be determined in any particular case by the sensitivity of the

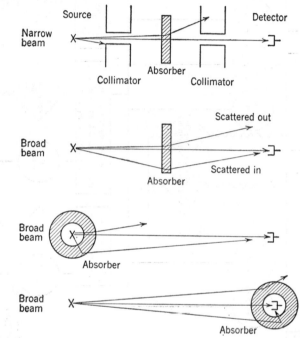

Fig. 3.2   Typical arrangements of source, absorber, and detector.   In ideal "narrow
beam," or "good geometry," no secondary or scattered photon may reach the detector.
Broad-beam, or "poor-geometry," situations, in which secondaries do reach the
receiving system, are the common ones.   Three typical cases are shown: (1) a slab
absorber, (2) a spherical or cylindrical absorber totally enclosing the source, and (3)
an absorber totally enclosing the receiving system.

detector to photons whose energy is smaller than that of the primaries.
Detectors whose spectral sensitivity ϵ vs. $h\nu$ is characterized in Fig. 2.3
as "independent" or "inverse" will be more sensitive to secondary
photons than will a detector for which ϵ is linear with $h\nu$.

Note that the total number of photons in any system is not altered
by Compton collisions, because one scattered photon always replaces one
primary photon.   In every pair-production interaction the total number
of photons is increased because, after one photon is absorbed, two are

produced as annihilation radiation.   Only by photoelectric absorption is the *number* of photons ultimately reduced.

From the complexity of the family of secondary radiations shown in Fig. 3.1 it is easy to see why accurate theoretical calculation of broad-beam attenuation is so very difficult.   This is also true for calculations of energy absorbed in a medium.   Even though energy absorption is, in general, difficult to measure experimentally, one usually has to use an empirical result in most practical cases where any degree of accuracy is desired.   This is especially true in cases where the absorber has an irregular geometry.

Only one generalization can be relied upon in all cases.   Because each primary photon can make only one collision before it ceases to be a primary photon, we can say that *the primary radiation is always in good geometry*.   This simple rule greatly facilitates the solution of many practical problems, as we shall see later.

d. Finite Absorber Surrounding a Point Source.   In Fig. 3.2, the second arrangement from the bottom typifies many practical shielding problems in which a totally enclosing shield contains a radioactive source, or a nuclear reactor, or any other radiation source.   Only a few sets of detailed measurements have been published concerning these important cases.

Figure 3.3 illustrates the physical principles involved.   Here a source of Co^{60} is placed inside a series of cylindrical lead shields having various wall thicknesses.   The transmitted γ rays were measured at some distance from the lead container, using as detector an ionization chamber whose outer wall was 0.5 cm of Pb lined with 0.5 cm of Al.   Although the primary γ rays from Co^{60} are essentially homogeneous, the observed transmission curve is clearly not a straight line.   Therefore the effective attenuation coefficient, as measured by the slope of the transmission curve, is not constant but is seen to increase as the wall thickness increases.

We can gain a qualitative understanding of the shape of this transmission curve.   For very small wall thickness, the transmission is seen to follow the straight line marked $\mu_0 - \sigma_s$, which corresponds to the true *absorption* coefficient

$$\mu_a = \mu_0 - \sigma_s = \tau + \kappa + \sigma_a \tag{3.1}$$

This is the attenuation in total γ-ray intensity which is expected when the Compton scattering σ_s produces no effective attenuation.   The fractional diminution in the energy flux outside the cylindrical shield is simply that fraction of the primary photon energy which is converted into kinetic energy of secondary electrons in the lead, through Compton absorption, photoelectric absorption, and pair production.   The photon energy which is merely scattered will still traverse the detector.   Owing to the circular symmetry of the shield, there is no preferred direction in the plane of Fig. 3.2.   Consequently, the number of photons scattered away from the detector is the same as the number scattered toward the detector.   (If the shield were spherical, this generalization would be exact.) These phenomena account for the initial slope of the transmission curve, because the detector is an ionization chamber which is roughly linear in its spectral response (except for a low-energy cutoff because of the Pb in its walls).

As the wall thickness is increased, Compton scattered photons which are produced in the inner layers of the shield are preferentially removed by photoelectric absorption in the outer layers of the shield. Hence the transmission curve begins to drop off more steeply.

The lower straight line, marked μ_0, is the transmission curve for the primary photons, which are always in good geometry. It will be seen that the *slope* of the actual transmission curve approaches, but never reaches, that of the primary photons. This failure of the transmitted secondary photons to come into an equilibrium proportion with the transmitted primaries is now thought to be characteristic (F9, F56, H57, H56, P12, P23, F7) of the attenuation of photons by thick absorbers of any shape. It can be made plausible by an analogy with the decay of a series of radioactive substances $A \rightarrow B \rightarrow C \rightarrow \cdots$ (Chap. 15). The primary photon plays the role of the radioactive parent A. With a mean free path μ_0^{-1}, instead of a mean life λ^{-1}, this parent transforms into the first generation of daughter photons B. These in turn suffer collisions, but with a different mean free path, and transform into photons of the C generation. So long as each successive collision has a finite chance of giving rise to a photon of the succeeding generation, the total length of the chain will increase without limit, and true equilibrium with the residual amount of primaries A will never be reached.

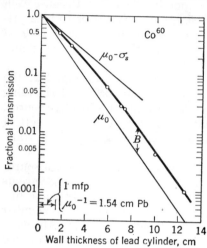

Fig. 3.3 Transmission of Co⁶⁰ γ rays through cylindrical Pb shields. Theoretical lines for the transmission of primary photons (μ_0) and for the true absorption of primary energy ($\mu_0 - \sigma_s = \mu_a$) are shown for comparison. The build-up factor is B. [*Experimental data are from Morrison* (M56).]

e. Build-up Factor. Experimental and theoretical results on the transmission of photons through thick absorbers are described conveniently in terms of the so-called *build-up factor* B, which is defined as

$$B \equiv \frac{\text{observed dose rate}}{\text{primary dose rate}}$$

$$= 1 + \frac{\text{dose rate due to scattered radiation}}{\text{primary dose rate}} \tag{3.2}$$

In Fig. 3.3, the build-up factor B for any wall thickness is the separation (logarithmic scale) between the observed transmission and the transmission curve μ_0 for the primary photons.

Analysis of Fig. 3.3 shows that, in this case, B increases linearly with the absorber thickness, starting at $B = 1$ for zero thickness and reaching $B = 3.1$ at a thickness of five mean free paths (7.7 cm Pb). In the next three mean free paths there are only two additional experimental points, and these show only a slight additional increase in B, to $B \simeq 3.3$. This tendency for B to level off, after an initial linear increase, has been observed also by Braestrup for radium in cylindrical Pb shields, and by Robertson and Morgan for Co^{60} in cylindrical Pb shields (B108, M55, E21). Additional data, with other values of $h\nu$ and Z, would be of interest.

f. Point Source in an Infinite Isotropic Medium. The dose rate at various distances from a point source in an essentially infinite homogeneous medium has been measured for radium in aluminum by L. H. Gray

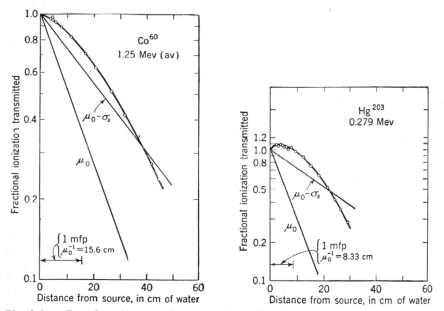

Fig. 3.4 γ-Ray dose from a point source in an infinite medium. [*From Van Dilla* (V2).]

(G44); by White (W37), Van Dilla (V2, V3), and others for Co^{60} in water; by Garrett and Whyte (G9a) for Co^{60} in iron and lead; and by Van Dilla for Hg^{203} ($h\nu = 0.279$ Mev), Au^{198} ($h\nu = 0.411$), and Ra in water. In all these cases, the detector is, of course, located within the homogeneous absorbing medium. Multiply scattered radiation therefore can and does reach the detector from behind. Van Dilla has measured the semi-infinite cases as well, when the sources are near and at the interface between water and air.

Figure 3.4 illustrates Van Dilla's measurements, within the first few mean free paths, for the cases of Co^{60} and Hg^{203}. Note the fundamental difference between these curves and that of Fig. 3.3 where the detector was outside the absorbing medium. In Fig. 3.4 the geometrical factors have been eliminated experimentally; the fractional ionization transmitted is the measured ratio of the dose rate in water to that in air, as a function of the source-to-detector distance. Note especially in Fig. 3.4 that close to the Hg^{203} source the presence of the water *increases* the transmitted ionization. The apparent attenuation coefficient here is negative in sign. This is clearly due to multiple backscattering, which produces a more intense radiation field near the source when the water is present. In both cases (and also for Au^{198}), the observed ionization does not fall to the $\mu_0 - \sigma_s$ line until nearly three mean free paths from the source.

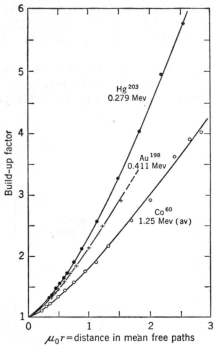

Fig. 3.5 Build-up factor for γ radiation from a point source in an infinite water medium. [*From Van Dilla* (V2).]

In Fig. 3.5, the same data are presented in terms of the build-up factor B, as a function of distance from the source. Note that for the case of an infinite isotropic medium, B increases steadily with $\mu_0 r$ and shows no tendency to level off. Measurements on the Co^{60} radiation in water have been extended by White to a distance of 253 cm, or 16 mean free paths, where the calculated transmission of primary radiation is only 1.1×10^{-7}. The build-up factor was found to rise continuously, reaching a value of about 33 at $\mu_0 r = 16$. Fano and coworkers (S63, F7) have developed a theoretical treatment of the infinite isotropic medium case, which is in good agreement with the measurements on Co^{60} γ rays at large distances from the source.

Problems

1. A solid lead sphere 30 cm in diameter has at its center a point source emitting γ rays. An "air-walled" ionization chamber located 5 cm from its surface indicates an ionization rate of 10^{-3} r/hr. When the temperature of the sphere is increased by 10°C the current in the ionization chamber increases by 2.0 per cent.

(*a*) What is the effective mass attenuation coefficient for these γ rays in Pb?

(*b*) What is the quantum energy of these γ rays?

(c) What would the ionization chamber read if the source were bare (without the lead sphere)? Coefficient of linear expansion for Pb $= 3 \times 10^{-5}$ C^{o-1}. Density of Pb $= 11.3$ g/cm^3.

2. A pencil of 2-Mev γ rays is incident on a 1-cm cube of Pb. Describe qualitatively all the emergent corpuscular and electromagnetic radiations in a table like the one shown below. Be thorough; there are at least 10 items.

Origin or type of secondary radiation	Approximate energy	Approximate relative intensity (check one)		
		large	medium	small
Compton electrons..............	0 to 1.8 Mev	x		

3. Investigate the production of secondary electrons by a beam of homogeneous γ rays which is incident on a thin layer of absorbing material, such as the wall of an ionization chamber. Let n_0 primary photons/sec, of energy $h\nu_0$, be incident on a wall of thickness t cm, in which the Compton scattering and absorption coefficients are σ_s and σ_a cm^{-1}.

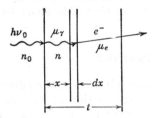

(a) What is the number n of primary photons still present at a depth x cm in the wall?

(b) What is the total kinetic energy dE_0 of the Compton electrons produced between x and $x + dx$ in the wall?

(c) If these electrons suffer exponential energy absorption, with an effective linear absorption coefficient μ_e cm^{-1}, while traversing the rest of the wall (whose *total* thickness is t cm), what is the emergent energy dE of the electrons which were produced between x and $x + dx$?

(d) Note the close mathematical analogy to the equations of radioactive series decay; the loss of primary photons is like the decay of a parent substance, while the build-up of secondary electrons is analogous to the growth of a radioactive daughter. Integrate dE and find the total electron energy E emerging from a wall of thickness t. (The result should look similar to that for the activity of a daughter radioactive substance at time t.)

(e) What is the optimum wall thickness t_1 in order to obtain the maximum possible energy flux of emergent electrons?

(f) Make a schematic graph showing the nature of the variation of (1) *emergent* primary photon energy and (2) emergent secondary electron energy, as a function of wall thickness t. (Draw on your knowledge of the analogous radioactive case, if desired.)

(g) Compare this result with an experiment by Laughlin et al. [*Am. J. Roentgenol.*, **65**: 787 (1951)] who found that when bremsstrahlung from a 22-Mev betatron is directed into a water phantom, the ionization is maximum at a depth of about 4 cm (see graph). For the incident photons, assume an effective average energy of about 10 Mev, and determine an approximate linear Compton coefficient for water.

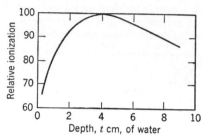

(*h*) For the secondary electrons, assume that their mass-absorption coefficient (μ_e/ρ) is the same in Al and water and that the effective absorption coefficient is substantially the same as that exhibited by continuous β rays having the same maximum energy, and thus estimate a linear attenuation coefficient for the Compton electrons in water.

(*i*) Using these estimated values of μ_γ and μ_e, calculate the depth, t_1 cm of water, where the maximum ionization should occur. (Even with all these simplifying assumptions, you should hit within about 10 per cent of the observed value of 4 cm of water.)

4. Distributed γ-Ray Sources

Because γ-ray fields are scalar fields, the effects of distributed sources can be obtained by simple summation of the intensities and local energy absorption from an assembly of point sources. Precise calculations are often exceedingly complicated, even for relatively simple situations. We review briefly here some simple semiempirical approaches, which will always indicate the general nature of the true result, and which are often sufficiently accurate for practical purposes.

a. Self-absorption in a Linear Source. In Fig. 4.1, let an amount A of a radionuclide, which emits a single line spectrum of γ rays, be uniformly distributed in a source of length $2l$, which has a small and uniform rectangular cross section, normal to l. Then the contribution to the ionization produced in a detector at a distance a along the extended axis of the source, by the activity contained in the shaded element dx, will be

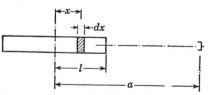

Fig. 4.1 Schematic representation of a linear source, for Eqs. (4.1) to (4.3a).

$$dI = k \frac{(A/2l)\,dx}{(a-x)^2} e^{-\mu(l-x)}$$

$$= I_0 e^{-\mu l} \left[\frac{e^{\mu x}}{(1-x/a)^2} \frac{dx}{2l} \right] \quad (4.1)$$

where $I_0 = kA/a^2$ is the ionization which would be produced if all the active material were concentrated at the center of the source, and if the effective attenuation coefficient μ were zero. The effect of self-absorption within the rectangular source is then given by the integral of Eq. (4.1), which is

$$\frac{I}{I_0} = e^{-\mu l} \int_{-l}^{l} \frac{e^{+\mu x} \, dx}{2l(1 - x/a)^2} \tag{4.2}$$

When this integrand is expanded, and integrated term by term, the general solution (E22) can be put in the form of a series which is rapidly convergent if $\mu l < 1$. In a number of practical cases of internal absorption, μl is of the order of 0.1 or less. When $\mu^2 l^2 \ll 1$, Eq. (4.2) becomes

$$\frac{I}{I_0} = e^{-\mu l} \left[\frac{1}{(1 - l^2/a^2)} + \mu l \left(\frac{2l}{3a} + \frac{4}{5} \frac{l^3}{a^3} + \cdots \right) \right] \tag{4.3}$$

The first term in the square brackets of Eq. (4.3) represents the purely geometric correction, because of the inverse-square law, for a linearly distributed source. For with $\mu = 0$, Eq. (4.3) becomes

$$\frac{I}{I_0} = \frac{1}{1 - l^2/a^2} = \frac{a^2}{(a + l)(a - l)} \tag{4.3a}$$

showing that the *effective distance* between a point detector and an extended uniformly distributed linear source is the geometric mean of the distances from the detector to the near end $(a - l)$ and the far end $(a + l)$ of the source. Alternatively, the *increase* in I, due to the geometric extension of the source, is the same as though the source were concentrated at a distance whose squared value is less than a^2 and equal to $(a^2 - l^2)$. It can be shown easily that Eq. (4.3a) also applies to the reciprocal case of a point source and a finite detector volume element of length $2l$.

The effective attenuation coefficient μ for the linear source of Fig. 4.1 will approach μ_0 when the dimensions normal to the axis of the source are small compared with l and with the mean free path of *scattered* photons in the source. This is because photons scattered once will usually emerge through the sides of the source and cannot be rescattered by additional source material so as to reach the detector.

Self-absorption in Disks and Cylinders. A source in the form of a disk can be visualized as a plane assembly of linear sources, laid side by side. If R is the radius of such a disk, then integration over the assembly of linear sources gives a result (E22) which reduces, for $R^2/a^2 \ll 1$, to

$$\frac{I}{I_0} = 1 - \frac{8}{3\pi} \mu R + \frac{1}{2} \mu^2 R^2 - \cdots \tag{4.4}$$

If $\mu R \leq 0.12$, as occurs in many practical cases, then Eq. (4.4) can be represented within 0.2 per cent by

$$\frac{I}{I_0} \simeq e^{-(8/3\pi)\mu R} \tag{4.5}$$

A cylinder of radius R and height h can be constructed from a stack of equal disks.   Then if $h^2/a^2 \ll 1$, Eqs. (4.4) and (4.5) also represent the self-absorption in a cylinder, for radiation emerging normal to its axis.

Self-absorption in a Sphere.   A sphere can be visualized as a vertical assembly of disks of appropriately varying radii, or as an assembly of linear rectangular sources.   When the appropriate integrals are evaluated, and the approximations $R^2/a^2 \ll 1$ and $\mu R \leq 0.12$ are taken, the result becomes simply

$$\frac{I}{I_0} \simeq e^{-(3/4)\mu R} \tag{4.6}$$

b. Distribution of Primary and Secondary Ionization Produced by a Point Source in an Infinite Isotropic Medium.   As indicated in Fig. 4.2,

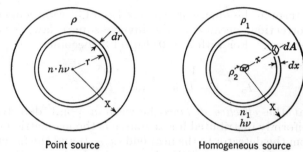

Point source   Homogeneous source

Fig. 4.2   Geometry and notation for energy-absorption considerations from a point source (left) and within a uniform spherical cloud of radioactivity (right), Eqs. (4.7) to (4.29).

assume that a point source which emits n photons/sec, each of energy $h\nu$, is situated in a very large isotropic medium.   Then the primary intensity I_{prim} at a distance r from the source is

$$I_{\text{prim}} = \frac{nh\nu}{4\pi r^2} e^{-\mu_0 r} \qquad \text{Mev}/(\text{cm}^2)(\text{sec}) \tag{4.7}$$

and the energy absorption from primary encounters at r is

$$R_{\text{prim}} = I_{\text{prim}} \frac{\mu_a}{\rho} \qquad \text{Mev}/(\text{g})(\text{sec}) \tag{4.8}$$

where ρ is the density, $\mu_0 = \tau + \kappa + \sigma_a + \sigma_s$ is the total attenuation coefficient, and $\mu_a = \mu_0 - \sigma_s$ is the energy-absorption coefficient of the medium.   In a spherical shell of thickness dr, the total rate of energy absorption, or power dP_{prim}, absorbed in primary collisions is R_{prim} times the mass of the shell, or

$$\begin{aligned} dP_{\text{prim}} &= \rho 4\pi r^2 \, dr \, R_{\text{prim}} \\ &= nh\nu\mu_a e^{-\mu_0 r} \, dr \qquad \text{Mev/sec} \end{aligned} \tag{4.9}$$

Note that the inverse-square spreading of the radiation intensity has been exactly compensated geometrically by the increased surface area of the shell, so that the primary power absorption in the shell is independent of r, except for the attenuation factor $e^{-\mu_0 r}$.

Integrating Eq. (4.9), we obtain the total power P_{prim} absorbed in primary collisions within a sphere of any arbitrary radius X. This is

$$P_{\text{prim}} = \int dP_{\text{prim}} = nh\nu\mu_a \int_0^X e^{-\mu_0 r} \, dr$$

$$= nh\nu \frac{\mu_a}{\mu_0} (1 - e^{-\mu_0 X}) \qquad \text{Mev/sec} \qquad (4.10)$$

Extending X to infinity, we have for the total power absorbed in all primary collisions throughout all space

$$P_{\text{prim}} = nh\nu \frac{\mu_a}{\mu_0} = nh\nu \frac{\mu_0 - \sigma_s}{\mu_0}$$

$$= nh\nu - nh\nu \frac{\sigma_s}{\mu_0} \qquad \text{Mev/sec} \qquad (4.11)$$

which is less than the emitted power $nh\nu$ Mev/sec. The deficit, $nh\nu(\sigma_s/\mu_0)$ Mev/sec, must be accounted for as energy losses from secondary photons.

Energy Absorption from Secondary Collisions. The build-up factor Eq. (3.2) can be written as

$$B = 1 + \frac{dP_{\text{sec}}}{dP_{\text{prim}}} \qquad (4.12)$$

where dP_{sec} is the rate of energy absorption at distance r due to all types of secondary collisions. Empirically, Fig. 3.5 shows that, to a first approximation, B increases linearly with the number of mean free paths $\mu_0 r$ traversed by the primary radiation. Then we will assume temporarily that

$$dP_{\text{sec}} \simeq a(\mu_0 r) \, dP_{\text{prim}} \qquad (4.13)$$

where the dimensionless coefficient a is to be evaluated by considerations of energy conservation.

Substituting Eq. (4.9) into Eq. (4.13), we obtain

$$dP_{\text{sec}} = a(\mu_0 r)nh\nu\mu_a e^{-\mu_0 r} \, dr \qquad (4.14)$$

which, upon integration over a sphere of radius X, gives

$$P_{\text{sec}} = \int dP_{\text{sec}} = a\mu_0\mu_a nh\nu \int_0^X re^{-\mu_0 r} \, dr$$

$$= a \frac{\mu_a}{\mu_0} nh\nu[1 - e^{-\mu_0 X}(1 + \mu_0 X)] \qquad \text{Mev/sec} \qquad (4.15)$$

Figure 4.3 shows the relative increase of primary power absorption P_{prim}, Eq. (4.10), and of secondary power absorption P_{sec}, Eq. (4.15), as a function of the radius X of the arbitrary sphere, in units of mean free paths $\mu_0 X$ for the primary radiation. Note that the secondary power builds up more slowly than P_{prim}. More than 99 per cent of the total power is seen to be absorbed within $\mu_0 X \simeq 7$, and within this distance Eq. (4.13) is a good approximation for moderate values of $h\nu$, absorbed in water or other low-Z materials such as air.

Extending Eq. (4.15) on to $\mu_0 X \gg 1$, we find that the total power absorption from secondary collisions throughout all space is

$$P_{sec} = a \frac{\mu_a}{\mu_0} nh\nu \qquad \text{Mev/sec} \tag{4.16}$$

and this has to be equal to the deficit between the primary absorption, Eq. (4.11), and the total emitted power $nh\nu$. Thus we find that

$$P_{sec} = a \frac{\mu_a}{\mu_0} nh\nu = \frac{\sigma_s}{\mu_0} nh\nu \tag{4.17}$$

from which

$$a = \frac{\sigma_s}{\mu_a} \tag{4.18}$$

Thus the simple assumption that the build-up factor increases linearly

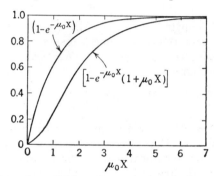

Fig. 4.3 Fraction of total available primary and secondary photon power from a point source which is absorbed within a sphere of radius $\mu_0 X$ mean free paths, Eqs. (4.10) and (4.15).

with distance leads to an evaluation of dP_{sec} solely in terms of the absorption and scattering coefficients of the *primary* radiation and gives, from Eqs. (4.9), (4.13), and (4.18),

$$dP_{sec} \simeq \frac{\sigma_s}{\mu_a} (\mu_0 r) \, dP_{prim}$$

$$\simeq nh\nu\sigma_s(\mu_0 r)e^{-\mu_0 r} \, dr \qquad \text{Mev/sec} \tag{4.19}$$

c. Primary and Secondary Energy Absorption at the Center of a Homogeneous Sphere of Radioactive Material. In the homogeneous cloud represented at the right of Fig. 4.2, let there be n_1 disintegrations per gram per second, each giving one photon of energy $h\nu$. Then if ρ_1 is the density of the cloud, the γ-ray energy emission is

$$n_1 h\nu\rho_1 \qquad \text{Mev/(cm}^3\text{)(sec)} \tag{4.20}$$

We wish to estimate the rate of energy absorption, due to primary and secondary radiations, in a small test object, density ρ_2, at the center of the cloud. The usual absorption and scattering coefficients with added subscripts 1 and 2 will denote the properties of the cloud and the test object.

In an element of cloud volume $dA \times dx$ (Fig. 4.2) the total emission is $n_1 h\nu \rho_1 \, dA \, dx$, and the intensity of primaries at the center is

$$dI_{\text{prim}} = n_1 h\nu \rho_1 \, dA \, dx \, \frac{1}{4\pi x^2} \, e^{-\mu_{01} x} \tag{4.21}$$

In an entire spherical shell as source, $dA = 4\pi x^2$, and

$$dI_{\text{prim}} = n_1 h\nu \rho_1 e^{-\mu_{01} x} \, dx \qquad \text{Mev}/(\text{cm}^2)(\text{sec}) \tag{4.22}$$

At the center of the cloud, the energy absorption of primary radiation from this shell is

$$dR_{\text{prim}} = dI_{\text{prim}} \frac{\mu_{a2}}{\rho_2} \qquad \text{Mev}/(\text{g})(\text{sec}) \tag{4.23}$$

Then the dose rate at the center, for primary radiation from a uniform sphere whose outer radius is X and whose inner radius is nearly zero, is

$$R_{\text{prim}} = \int dR_{\text{prim}} = n_1 h\nu \rho_1 \frac{\mu_{a2}}{\rho_2} \int_0^X e^{-\mu_{01} x} \, dx$$

$$= n_1 h\nu \frac{\mu_{a2}/\rho_2}{\mu_{01}/\rho_1} (1 - e^{-\mu_{01} X}) \tag{4.24}$$

We may note from Fig. 1.1 and Eq. (1.4) that if $h\nu \sim 1$ Mev, and $Z \sim 1$ to 50, the mass-absorption coefficients will be substantially independent of medium, that is, $(\mu_{a2}/\rho_2) \simeq (\mu_{a1}/\rho_1)$. Then Eq. (4.24) takes on the simpler form

$$R_{\text{prim}} \simeq n_1 h\nu \frac{\mu_{a1}}{\mu_{01}} (1 - e^{-\mu_{01} X}) \qquad \text{Mev}/(\text{g})(\text{sec}) \tag{4.25}$$

which is completely analogous to Eq. (4.10), in which the roles of source and absorber are just inverted. This physical interrelationship between Eqs. (4.10) and (4.25) is an explicit example of the general reciprocity theorem for radiation, as formulated by Mayneord (M29).

Energy Absorption from Secondary Photons. Making use of Eq. (4.19), the energy absorption from secondary photons in the test object at the center of the homogeneous sphere is

$$dR_{\text{sec}} \simeq \frac{\sigma_{s1}}{\mu_{a1}} (\mu_{01} x) \, dR_{\text{prim}} \qquad \text{Mev}/(\text{g})(\text{sec}) \tag{4.26}$$

Hence

$$R_{\text{sec}} = \int dR_{\text{sec}} = n_1 h\nu \rho_1 \frac{\mu_{a2}}{\rho_2} \frac{\sigma_{s1}}{\mu_{a1}} \mu_{01} \int_0^X x e^{-\mu_{01} x} \, dx$$

$$= n_1 h\nu \frac{\mu_{a2}/\rho_2}{\mu_{a1}/\rho_1} \frac{\sigma_{s1}}{\mu_{01}} [1 - e^{-\mu_{01} X}(1 + \mu_{01} X)] \tag{4.27}$$

Again, all the scattering and attenuation coefficients are those which characterize the *primary* photons, and for $h\nu \sim 1$ Mev, and $Z \sim 1$ to 50, we can equate the mass-absorption coefficients in the two media. Then Eq. (4.27) becomes simply

$$R_{\text{sec}} \simeq n_1 h\nu \frac{\sigma_{s1}}{\mu_{01}} [1 - e^{-\mu_{01} X}(1 + \mu_{01} X)] \qquad \text{Mev}/(\text{g})(\text{sec}) \tag{4.28}$$

Total Dose in an Infinite Homogeneous Source. If $\mu_{01}X \gg 1$, the total dose rate at the center becomes

$$R = R_{\text{prim}} + R_{\text{sec}} = \left[n_1 \frac{\text{disint}}{(\text{g})(\text{sec})} \right] \left(h\nu \frac{\text{Mev}}{\text{disint}} \right) \tag{4.29}$$

which simply and correctly states that the total energy emitted per gram must equal the total energy absorbed per gram, if the dimensions of the source are much larger than the mean free path of the radiation.

If we now put practical units into Eq. (4.29), writing C μc/g as the concentration of radioactive material in the source, we have

$$R = \left[C \frac{\mu c}{g} \times 3.7 \times 10^4 \frac{\text{disint}}{(\text{sec})(\mu c)} \right]$$
$$\left(h\nu \frac{\text{Mev}}{\text{disint}} \right) \left[\frac{1(\text{r})(\text{g air})}{5.24 \times 10^7 \text{ Mev}} \right] \left(\frac{3{,}600 \times 24 \text{ sec}}{\text{day}} \right)$$
$$= 61 C h\nu \quad \text{r/day} \tag{4.30}$$

This is the well-known "60 formula" which has been widely used for estimating radiation doses in radiobiological work and in radioisotope therapy (E19). It is based only on conservation of energy and is, of course, applicable to any types of radiation α, β, or γ. Recently a new and welcome unit of radiation dose has been recommended by the International Commission on Radiological Units (I5). This is the *rad*, defined as

$$1 \text{ rad} = 100 \text{ ergs/g} \tag{4.31}$$

The rad is applicable to any type of radiation, whereas the roentgen is restricted to X rays and γ rays below 3 Mev. As

$$1 \text{ Mev} = 1.60 \times 10^{-6} \text{ erg}$$

the rad is equivalent to

$$1 \text{ rad} = 6.25 \times 10^7 \text{ Mev/g} \tag{4.32}$$

Then, in rad units, the old "60 formula" becomes

$$R \left(\frac{\text{rad}}{\text{day}} \right) = 51 C \left(\frac{\mu c}{g} \right) E \left(\frac{\text{Mev}}{\text{disint}} \right) \tag{4.33}$$

The grimly practical applications of the "cloud problem," Eqs. (4.20) to (4.33), to the navigation of aircraft and submarines in heavily contaminated areas will be found among the following problems.

Problems

1. At what distance from the end of a radioactive wire, 12 in. long and containing 25 μg of radium per inch, will the γ-ray ionization be 12.5 mr/hr, if self-absorption be neglected?

2. Calculate, from first principles, the self-absorption in a small uniform sphere, radius R, density ρ, for γ radiation measured at distance a from the center of the sphere, for the case $R/a < 0.1$; $\mu R < 1$.

3. (*a*) The decay scheme of Al²⁸ involves one quantum of 1.8-Mev γ radiation per disintegration, as shown.   At 1 m from 1 mc of Al²⁸, what is the rate of γ-ray

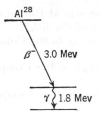

ionization of standard air (i.e., 0°C and 760 mm Hg) in milliroentgens per hour?

(*b*) A hollow sphere of aluminum is fabricated with inner radius *a* and outer radius *b*.   It is then irradiated with thermal neutrons to produce a uniform specific activity q mc/cm³ of Al²⁸ throughout the material.   The sphere is filled with standard air.   If μ represents the effective attenuation coefficient for the 1.8-Mev γ rays of Al²⁸ in Al, show that the ionization intensity at the center is

$$ I = \frac{4\pi q K}{\mu} (1 - e^{-\mu(b-a)}) $$

where K is the ionization produced by 1 mc of Al²⁸ in unit time at unit distance.

(*c*) Evaluate the central ionization I under the following conditions: $a = 20$ cm, $b = 30$ cm, $q = 2.7$ mc/cm³, and $K = 0.015$ mr/(min)(mc) at 1 m.   Notice that the μ appears twice in the equation.   Select a reasonable numerical value for μ in the exponent.   Give very briefly the reasons for your choice.   Select a reasonable value for μ in the denominator; give your reasons.   Evaluate I, in roentgens per minute.   (Avoid dimensional errors!)

4. A thin disk of metallic zinc is irradiated with thermal neutrons   The Zn⁶⁴(*n,γ*)Zn⁶⁵ reaction produces a total activity A μc in the disk.   We want to find the dose rate in the vicinity of the disk.

(*a*) Zn⁶⁵ ($T_{\frac{1}{2}} = 250$ days) decays to Cu⁶⁵ mainly by electron capture.   In 46 per cent of the disintegrations a single 1.14-Mev γ ray is emitted.   Calculate the energy absorption, in *milliroentgens* per *hour*, at 1 *cm* from a point source of 1 μc of Zn⁶⁵, due only to this primary γ radiation.

(*b*) Show that, if self-absorption be neglected, the dose rate R along the axis of a uniformly activated disk is always given by

$$ R = k \frac{A}{X^2} \ln \left(1 + \frac{X^2}{h^2} \right) $$

where X = radius of disk
h = height along axis
A = total activity
k = dose rate at unit distance from unit amount of particular radionuclide

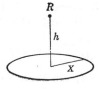

(c) If a particular disk is 4 cm in *diameter* and has a total activity of 20 μc, what is the dose rate in milliroentgens per hour at a point on the axis of the disk and 1 cm from the disk?

(d) What would be the dose rate at the same point if all the activity were concentrated at the exact center of the disk?

(e) What is the *maximum* energy of the Compton electrons produced at this same point?

(f) What is the *average* energy of the Compton electrons produced at this point by the primary photons?

(g) What is the *maximum range* of the Compton electrons, in centimeters of standard air?

5. Zn^{65} decays by K capture with the subsequent emission of a single 1.14-Mev γ ray. A small sample of Zn^{65} is placed at 10 cm from a small γ-ray counter, and the number of counts per second is determined. This sample is then dissolved in 1 cm^3 of Hg, and the solution is placed in a cubic vessel whose center is 10 cm from the counter. One of the sides of the cube is parallel to the direction from the center of the cube to the counter. Compare the number of counts per second, in this case, with that in the first measurement. Assume the counter used has (a) a constant sensitivity which is independent of γ-ray energy and (b) a sensitivity increasing linearly with energy and vanishing for zero energy.

6. (a) Estimate the γ-ray dose on an individual standing on a level plane at the center of an infinitely large uniform hemispherical cloud containing 1 μc Kr^{85} per liter of air. Assume that Kr^{85} emits one 0.37-Mev photon per disintegration.

(b) Approximately what radius must such a cloud have to give, say, 90 per cent of the dose due to an infinite cloud?

7. Estimate the γ-radiation dose rate in the cabin of an aircraft flying near the center of a radioactive cloud which is 3 miles in radius, contains 10^{11} curies of fission products, which emit an average of 1 Mev of γ radiation per disintegration, and is at a mean altitude of 40,000 ft. (This altitude corresponds to the normal base of the stratosphere, temperature $-60°C$, density 0.33 mg/cm^3.)

8. Consider the radiation dose inside a spherical diving bell, whose steel walls have a thickness t, and a total γ-ray attenuation coefficient μ_{02}. Show that, when the bell is immersed in uniformly radioactive water, the dose inside is uniform throughout the bell and to a good approximation is

$$R = n_1 h \nu e^{-\mu_{02}t} \left(1 + \frac{\sigma_s}{\sigma_a + \sigma_s} \mu_{02}t\right) \qquad \text{Mev}/(g)(sec)$$

where all symbols are as defined in the text.

9. Assume that the underwater detonation of a nominal 20-kiloton fission bomb (E5) produces, 1 hr afterward, a uniform distribution of 6×10^9 curies in a cylindrical region of water 3 miles in diameter and 200 ft deep.

(a) What is the dose rate on a swimmer in this water?

(b) What is the total radiation dose received by crew members in a submarine which crosses this contaminated region at a speed of 12 knots, if the hull has a thickness of 3 cm of steel?

10. If the build-up factor B increases a little faster than linearly with $\mu_0 r$, so that in place of Eq. (4.13) we can represent dP_{sec} by

$$\frac{dP_{sec}}{dP_{prim}} = a(\mu_0 r)^k$$

show that the total power absorption from secondaries throughout all space becomes

$$P_{\text{sec}} = anh\nu \frac{\mu_a}{\mu_0} \Gamma(k+1)$$

and that the build-up factor is

$$B = 1 + \frac{1}{\Gamma(k+1)} \frac{\sigma_s}{\mu_a} (\mu_0 r)^k$$

where $\Gamma(k+1)$ is the gamma function of $k+1$, hence $\Gamma(k+1) = k!$, if k is an integer.

11. If a γ-ray emitter is uniformly distributed in a disk having finite thickness and finite self-absorption, show that the primary ionization at a height h above

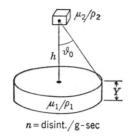

$$n = \text{disint.}/\text{g-sec}$$

the center of the disk is (when absorption in the distance h is negligible)

$$R_{\text{prim}} = \frac{nh\nu}{2} \frac{\mu_{a2}/\rho_2}{\mu_{01}/\rho_1} \int_1^{\sec \vartheta_0} \frac{dz}{z^2} (1 - e^{-\mu_{01}Yz})$$

where $z = \sec \vartheta$; and that

$$\int_1^Z \frac{dz}{z^2} e^{-bz} = \{e^{-b} - b[-Ei(-b)]\} - \frac{1}{Z} \{e^{-bZ} - bZ[-Ei(-bZ)]\}$$

where $[-Ei(-b)] = \int_1^\infty \frac{e^{-bz}}{z} dz$ is the logarithmic integral.

CHAPTER 26

Statistical Fluctuations in Nuclear Processes

It is well recognized that we can never measure any physical magnitude exactly, i.e., with no error. Progressively more elaborate experimental or theoretical efforts result only in reducing the possible error of the determination. In reporting the result of any measurements it is therefore obligatory to specify also the probability that the result is in error by some specified amount, since *a gamble on relative correctness is always involved in all physical determinations.* The theory of statistics and fluctuations, summarized here, describes the mathematical procedure involved in the reduction of data, particularly data of the type encountered in nearly every measurement in nuclear physics.

Nuclear processes, in common with all microscopic processes, are random in ultimate character. Because of the relatively large energies released in nuclear processes, it is possible to study single random events. The application of statistical theory to such measurements is therefore doubly important because it contributes to our understanding of nuclear processes and it gives insight into the statistical distributions which describe other random processes whose individual events are not observable. The exponential decay distribution is an example of a result derivable solely from probability considerations (Chap. 15), without detailed knowledge of the mechanism involved.

In any series of measurements, the frequency of occurrence of particular values is expected to follow some "probability distribution law," or "frequency distribution." There are about a half dozen distributions which are used most often in the statistical appraisal and interpretation of nuclear data. We begin by discussing the four most fundamental of these frequency distributions. Later the very useful generalized Poisson distribution (Sec. 3) and the generalized interval distribution (Chap. 28, Sec. 2) will be considered.

The theory presented here is called *efficient statistics* for it extracts the maximum amount of statistical information from the data. A recent development termed *inefficient statistics* can extract a major portion, but not all, of the information by very much simpler calculations. It does this by making reasonable approximations in the efficient theory. It is thus necessary to understand the efficient theory presented here and in Chaps. 27 and 28 in order to be able to use the inefficient theory wisely. For this reason, only the efficient theory is treated here; however, the reader will find some useful inefficient statistics in Appendix G.

1. *Frequency Distributions*

a. The Binomial Distribution. The binomial distribution is the fundamental frequency distribution governing random events. The other frequency distributions can be derived from it.† Historically, it was the first probability distribution to be enunciated theoretically. Bernoulli, early in the eighteenth century, showed that if p is the probability that an event will occur, and $q = 1 - p$ is the probability that it will not occur, then in a random group of z independent trials the probability P_x that the event will occur x times is represented by that term in the binomial expansion of $(p + q)^z$ in which p is raised to the x power. Thus the expansion of $(p + q)^z$, which is always equal to unity, represents the sum of the individual probabilities of observing $x = z$ events, $x = (z - 1)$ events, . . . , $x = 0$ events, as follows:

$$(p + q)^z = p^z + zp^{z-1}q + \frac{z(z - 1)}{2!} p^{z-2}q^2 + \cdots + q^z$$

$$= p^z + zp^{z-1}(1 - p) + \frac{z(z - 1)}{2!} p^{z-2}(1 - p)^2 + \cdots + (1 - p)^z$$

$$= P_z + P_{z-1} + P_{z-2} + \cdots + P_0 = 1$$

Any individual term in this binomial expansion can be written as

$$P_x = \frac{z!}{x!(z - x)!} p^x(1 - p)^{z-x} \tag{1.1}$$

which is the general form of the binomial distribution. The binomial distribution, Eq. (1.1), contains the two independent parameters p and z and rigorously applies to those phenomena in which the total number of trials z and the number of successes x are both *integers*.

It therefore describes the fluctuations in counting α rays from radioactive bodies, provided that p, which is equivalent to the probability $\lambda \Delta t$ that a particular atom will decay during an observation of short duration Δt, is constant. Like the normal and Poisson distributions, to be considered next, it represents the true probability only when the total amount of radioactive material is essentially unaltered during the

---

† Representative treatises containing detailed proofs of many of the statements in this chapter include:

T. C. Fry, "Probability and Its Engineering Uses," D. Van Nostrand Company, Inc., New York, 1928.

R. A. Fisher, "Statistical Methods for Research Workers," Oliver & Boyd, Ltd., Edinburgh and London, 1930.

S. S. Wilks, "Mathematical Statistics," Princeton University Press, Princeton, N.J., 1943.

P. G. Hoel, "Introduction to Mathematical Statistics," 2d ed., John Wiley & Sons, Inc., New York, 1954.

N. Arley and K. R. Buch, "Introduction to the Theory of Probability and Statistics," John Wiley & Sons, Inc., New York, 1950.

period of the observations. The tests must, therefore, be made in a time interval Δt which is very short compared with the half-period of the radioactive substance. But under this restriction of small p, Poisson's distribution is a satisfactory approximation to the binomial distribution.

Applications of the binomial distribution to the tossing of coins and the throwing of dice are doubtless familiar to the reader. Here, it applies rigorously because p is constant. Thus the chance of throwing three, two, one, or zero aces in three throws of a single die (or in one throw of three dice) is

$$
\begin{aligned}
(\tfrac{1}{6} + \tfrac{5}{6})^3 &= (\tfrac{1}{6})^3 + 3(\tfrac{1}{6})^2(\tfrac{5}{6}) + 3(\tfrac{1}{6})(\tfrac{5}{6})^2 + (\tfrac{5}{6})^3 \\
&= \tfrac{1}{216} + \tfrac{15}{216} + \tfrac{75}{216} + \tfrac{125}{216} \\
&= P_3 + P_2 + P_1 + P_0 = 1
\end{aligned}
$$

Note that the chance of getting no ace in three throws is $\tfrac{125}{216} = 58$ per cent, although the average number of aces is $pz = 0.50$.

The binomial distribution is a special case of the multinomial distribution describing processes in which several results having fixed probabilities $p_1, p_2, \ldots, p_s$ are possible. The separate probabilities are then given by terms of the expansion $(p_1 + p_2 + \cdots + p_s)^z$, where $p_1 + p_2 + \cdots + p_s = 1$.

b. The Normal Distribution. The normal distribution† is an analytical approximation to the binomial distribution when z is very large. It is applicable to distributions in which the observed variable is not confined to integer values but can take on any value from $-\infty$ to $+\infty$. The normal distribution thus generally applies to a continuously variable observed magnitude, such as the distance separating two spectral lines, while the binomial and Poisson distributions are applied to discontinuous variables, such as particle counting rates, which take on successive whole-number integral values. The statistical theory of errors (D19) is ordinarily based on the normal distribution.

Near the center of the distribution curve the binomial distribution, for large z and constant average value $m = pz$, approaches identity with the normal distribution, which states that the probability dP_x that x will lie between x and $x + dx$ is

$$
dP_x = \frac{1}{\sigma \sqrt{2\pi}} e^{-(x-m)^2/2\sigma^2} \, dx \tag{1.2}
$$

where $e = 2.7183$ is the base of the natural system of logarithms, m is the true value of the quantity whose measured values are x, and σ is the *standard deviation*, a parameter which describes the breadth of the distribution of *deviations* $(x - m)$ from the mean. The standard deviation is discussed in detail in Sec. 2, but for the present it may be regarded simply as one of the two parameters, m and σ, of the normal distribution.

Figure 1.1 illustrates the general form of the normal distribution, drawn for a mean value of $m = 100$ and a standard deviation of $\sigma = 10$.

† The normal-distribution curve is sometimes erroneously referred to as the Gaussian error curve, but its derivation by Gauss (1809) was antedated by those of Laplace (1774) and DeMoivre (1735).

The ordinates are normalized so that the total area under the curve is unity. Thus the area included between any two abscissas x_1 and x_2 is the probability that a single measurement of x will lie between x_1 and x_2, while a very large number of measurements of x would have a mean value of m. The correspondence between Fig. 1.1 and Eq. (1.2) lies in the relationships

$$dP_x = dA = y\,dx \qquad \int_{-\infty}^{\infty} dP_x = A = 1 \qquad (1.3)$$

in which y is the ordinate of Fig. 1.1 and dA is an element of area. The coefficient $1/\sigma\sqrt{2\pi}$ in Eq. (1.2) normalizes the area to unity, as given by Eq. (1.3).

Differentiation of Eq. (1.2) shows that the points of maximum slope, at which $d^2y/dx^2 = 0$, fall at the points $(x - m) = \pm\sigma$, where the slope

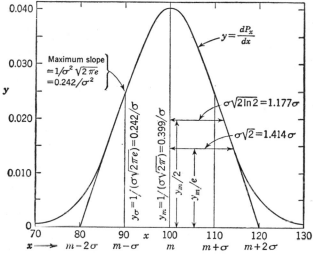

Fig. 1.1   Normal distribution for the special case of a mean value $m = 100$ and a standard deviation $\sigma = 10$.

has the value $1/\sigma^2\sqrt{2\pi e}$. Tangents to the distribution curve at these inflection points intersect the x axis at $(x - m) = \pm 2\sigma$. The ratio of the ordinate y_σ at these symmetrical points of maximum slope to the maximum ordinate $y_m = 1/\sigma\sqrt{2\pi}$ at $x = m$ is $y_\sigma/y_m = e^{-\frac{1}{2}} = 0.6065$. The half width is $\sigma\sqrt{2\ln 2} = 1.177\sigma$ at $y = y_m/2$ (half maximum) and is $\sigma\sqrt{2} = 1.414\sigma$ at $y = y_m/e$ (1/e of maximum). These geometrical relationships offer a convenient method of determining σ graphically from an experimentally determined distribution curve.

Figure 1.2 gives the results of integration of the normal distribution between various limits; from it can be read the chance that a single observation of x will differ from the mean value m by more than any arbitrary assigned amount. Figure 1.2 has many other uses which will be referred to later.

c. The Poisson Distribution. Poisson's distribution *describes all random processes whose probability of occurrence is small and constant.* It therefore has wide and diverse applicability and describes the statistical fluctuations in such random processes as the number of soldiers kicked and killed yearly by cavalry horses, the disintegration of atomic nuclei, the emission of light quanta by excited atoms, and the appearance of

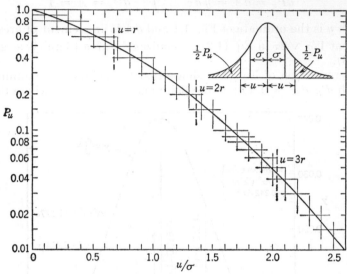

Fig. 1.2 The ordinate P_u is the fraction of the total area of a symmetric normal distribution which falls farther from the mean value than a distance u, measured in units of the standard deviation, σ. The area P_u is shown shaded in the inset and corresponds analytically to $P_u = 2 \int_{m+u}^{\infty} dP_x$. Thus for $u/\sigma = 1$, $P_u = 0.317$, and 31.7 per cent of the individual values of x may be expected to fall farther than one standard deviation from the mean value. The value of u for which $P_u = 0.50$ is called the probable error (see Sec. 2e). It will be seen that $P_u = 0.50$ for $u = r = 0.6745\sigma$. Particular numerical values which find frequent use are

u/σ.....	0.5	0.6745	1	1.349	2	2.024	2.698	3
P_u......	0.617	0.500	0.317	0.178	0.0455	0.0431	0.00706	0.00272

cosmic-ray bursts. The Poisson distribution applies to substantially all observations made in experimental nuclear physics.

The Poisson distribution can be deduced as a limiting case of the binomial distribution, for those random processes in which the probability of occurrence is very small, $p \ll 1$, while the number of trials z becomes very large and the mean value $m = pz$ remains fixed. Then in Eq. (1.1) $m \ll z$ and $x \ll z$, and so we can write, approximately,

$$\frac{z!}{(z-x)!} \simeq z^x$$

$$(1 - p)^{z-x} \simeq e^{-p(z-x)} \simeq e^{-pz}$$

and in the limiting case of small probability p, Eq. (1.1) approaches

$$P_x = \frac{z^x p^x}{x!} e^{-pz} = \frac{m^x}{x!} e^{-m}$$

which is the Poisson distribution.

A much clearer feeling for the statistical principles underlying the Poisson distribution is obtained by deriving this frequency distribution from first principles. Specializing the general conditions under which the Poisson distribution holds to the readily visualized case of a radio-active disintegration, we would write the following necessary and sufficient conditions:

1. The chance for an atom to disintegrate in any particular time interval is the same for all atoms in the group (all atoms identical).

2. The fact that an atom has disintegrated in a given time interval does not affect the chance that other atoms may disintegrate in the same time interval (all atoms independent).

3. The chance for an atom to disintegrate during a given time interval is the same for all time intervals of equal size (mean life long compared with the total period of observation).

4. The total number of atoms and the total number of equal time intervals are large (hence statistical averages significant).

Let a be the average rate of appearance of particles from such a random process; then the average number of events in a time interval t is at. Then in a short time interval, dt, such that $a\,dt \ll 1$, the quantity $a\,dt$ is simply the probability $P_1\,(dt)$ of observing one particle in the time dt. As dt decreases without limit, the probability of observing two or more particles in the time dt becomes vanishingly small in comparison with the probability of observing one particle, that is, $P_1\,(dt) \gg P_2\,(dt) \gg P_3\,(dt)$ . . . . The probability of observing no particle in dt is

$$P_0\,(dt) = 1 - P_1\,(dt) = 1 - a\,dt$$

We may now write the probability of observing x particles in the time $(t + dt)$ as the combined probabilities of $(x - 1)$ particles in t and one in dt, and of x particles in t and none in dt; thus

$$\begin{aligned} P_x(t + dt) &= P_1\,(dt)\,P_{x-1}(t) + P_0\,(dt)\,P_x(t) \\ &= a\,dt\,P_{x-1}(t) + (1 - a\,dt)\,P_x(t) \end{aligned} \qquad (1.4)$$

Rewriting Eq. (1.4) in differential form, we have

$$\begin{aligned} \frac{dP_x(t)}{dt} &= \frac{P_x(t + dt) - P_x(t)}{dt} \\ &= a[P_{x-1}(t) - P_x(t)] \end{aligned} \qquad (1.5)$$

The solution (B19) of Eq. (1.5) is

$$P_x(t) = \frac{(at)^x}{x!} e^{-at} \qquad (1.6)$$

as can be verified by differentiation. Now if the equal time intervals are chosen of length t, then the average number of particles per interval is $at = m$; substituting this in Eq. (1.6), we have the usual form of the Poisson distribution

$$P_x = \frac{m^x}{x!}\, e^{-m} \tag{1.7}$$

in which P_x is the probability of observing x events when the average for a large number of tries is m events. Although m may have any positive value, x is restricted to integer values only. It is easy to show that Eq. (1.7) correctly leads to

$$\sum_{x=0}^{x=\infty} P_x = 1$$

It must be noted that, in contrast with the two previous frequency distributions, *the Poisson distribution has but one parameter* m. The binomial distribution with parameters p and z becomes identical with the Poisson distribution when $p \to 0$ in such a way that $zp = m$. The normal distribution, near the center of the distribution, approaches equality with Poisson's distribution when m is large, so that the histogram of Poisson's discontinuous distribution approaches the continuous normal distribution (compare Figs. 1.1 and 1.3).

Following the numerical evaluation† of a particular value of P_x, other neighboring values may be computed quickly by using the following exact relationships, which can be derived easily from Eq. (1.7)

$$P_{x-1} = \frac{x}{m}\, P_x \tag{1.8}$$

$$P_{x+1} = \frac{m}{x+1}\, P_x \tag{1.9}$$

$$P_0 = e^{-m} \tag{1.10}$$

The Poisson distribution is slightly asymmetric, favoring low values of x. Thus substitution of $x = m$ in Eq. (1.8) shows that if the mean value is an integer *the probability of observing one less than the mean value is the same as the probability for the mean value.*

In computations with Eq. (1.7) it is often convenient to use Stirling's approximation to the factorial

$$x! = \sqrt{2\pi x}\; x^x\, e^{-x} \left(1 + \frac{1}{12x} + \cdots\right) \tag{1.11}$$

in which neglect of the final parentheses involves a negative error of only

---

† Extremely useful tables of the individual terms P_x and especially of the cumulated terms $\sum_{x}^{\infty} P_x$ for Poisson distributions with $m = 0.001$ to 100 have been published by E. C. Molina (M49).

0.8 per cent for $x = 10$, and 0.08 per cent when $x = 100$.   Then Eq. (1.7) becomes, to a good approximation, for $x > 10$

$$P_x \simeq \frac{1}{\sqrt{2\pi x}} \left(\frac{m}{x}\right)^x e^{-(m-x)} \tag{1.12}$$

The probability of actually observing the mean value m in a series of observations on a random process of constant average value is surprisingly small.   This is seen by substitution of $x = m$ in Eq. (1.12) which gives the following values

$$
\begin{array}{cccc}
m = & 10 & 100 & 1{,}000 \\
P_m = & 0.127 & 0.040 & 0.013
\end{array}
$$

The Poisson distribution must always be represented by a histogram, since x must assume whole-number values only.   Figure 1.3 illustrates the Poisson distribution for $m = 100$; the slight asymmetries should be noted, as well as the similarity with the symmetric normal distribution

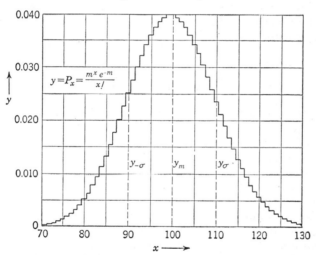

Fig. 1.3 Poisson distribution for $m = 100$.   Note that $P_{90} > P_{110}$, whereas $P_{70} < P_{130}$; also that $P_{99} = P_{100}$, illustrating the asymmetries of the Poisson distribution. The envelope of this histogram is very similar to the normal distribution shown in Fig. 1.1 only because of our arbitrary choice of $\sigma = \sqrt{m}$ in Fig. 1.1.   The standard deviation, σ for the Poisson distribution, Eq. (2.7), is always $\sqrt{m}$, but σ is an independent parameter in the normal distribution.

of Fig. 1.1.   For small values of m, say, between $m = 1$ and $m = 10$, the Poisson distribution is very asymmetric and is not well approximated by the normal distribution.

The Poisson frequency distribution treats all the *intervals* as *independent;* this restriction in application is removed by the interval distribution.

d. The Interval Distribution.   The interval distribution is derived from Poisson's distribution and describes the distribution in size of the time intervals between successive events in any random process in which the mean rate has the constant value of a events per unit time (M12, R20). From Eq. (1.7) or (1.10) the probability that there will be no events in a time interval t, during which time there should be at events on the average, is†

$$P_0 = \frac{(at)^0}{0!} e^{-at} = e^{-at} \tag{1.13}$$

The probability that there will be an event in the time interval dt is simply $a\,dt$. The combined probability that there will be no events during the time interval t, but one event between time t and $t + dt$, is $ae^{-at}\,dt$. Hence, in a random distribution which follows the Poisson distribution and has a constant average interval of $1/a$, the probability dP_t that the duration of a particular interval will be between t and $t + dt$ is

$$dP_t = ae^{-at}\,dt \tag{1.14}$$

We see at once that *small time intervals have a higher probability* than large time intervals between the randomly distributed events.

If the data concern a large number N of intervals, then the number of intervals greater than t_1 but less than t_2 is

$$
\begin{aligned}
n &= N \int_{t_1}^{t_2} ae^{-at}\,dt \\
&= N(e^{-at_1} - e^{-at_2})
\end{aligned} \tag{1.15}
$$

where a is the average number of events per unit time. Equations (1.14) and (1.15) are the general differential and integral forms of the interval distribution for randomly spaced events.

Two limiting cases are of special interest. Letting $t_2 \to \infty$, we find that *the number of intervals greater than any duration t is Ne^{-at}*, in which at is simply the average number of events in the interval t. Because the average interval is $\bar{t} = 1/a$, we note that the fraction of the intervals which are longer than the average is $n/N = e^{-1} = 0.37$.

Letting $t_1 \to 0$, Eq. (1.15) shows that *the number of intervals shorter than any duration t is $N(1 - e^{-at})$*. Examples of the usefulness of the interval distribution in α-ray counting experiments and in cosmic-ray-burst observations will be given in Chap. 27, Sec. 4. A generalization of the interval distribution, giving the frequency distribution of intervals which contain any predetermined number of random events, is derived in Chap. 28, Sec. 2.

Problems

"The reader is, however, advised that the detailed working of numerical examples is essential to a thorough grasp, not only of the technique, but of the principles by which an experimental procedure may be judged to be satisfactory

† That factorial zero equals unity follows from the gamma functions:

$$n! = \Gamma(n + 1) \qquad \Gamma(1) = 1 \qquad \Gamma(0 + 1) = 1$$

and effective." (R. A. Fisher, in the preface to the first edition of his "The Design of Experiments," Oliver & Boyd, Ltd., Edinburgh and London, 1935.)

1. From elementary probability arguments and consideration of the number of combinations and permutations of z things taken x at a time, "derive" the binomial distribution.

2. In 1693 (hence pre-Bernoulli and pre-binomial distribution), Samuel Pepys propounded the following question to his friend Isaac Newton, who prepared a lengthy response and engaged the tax accountant George Tollet in a protracted controversy over the answer:

"*A* has 6 dice in a box, with which he is to fling a six, *B* has in another box 12 dice, with which he is to fling 2 sixes, *C* has in another box 18 dice, with which he is to fling 3 sixes. Question—whether *B* and *C* have not as easy a task as *A* at even luck."

(*a*) Assuming Pepys meant *exactly* one, two, and three sixes for the three contestants, what are their chances of succeeding on a single throw?

(*b*) Assuming he meant *at least* one, two, and three sixes, in what direction will this modify their chances of success?

3. With a simultaneous throw of six dice, calculate the probabilities of obtaining just zero, one, two, three, four, five, and six sixes. Show that the sum of these probabilities is unity when the solutions are obtained using the binomial distribution. Compare with these the probabilities for the same events as given by the Poisson distribution. Point out the reasons for these differences.

4. On June 5, 1951, Dom DiMaggio had a batting average of 0.359, had been at bat 189 times in 44 games, and had hit safely at least once in each of his last 25 consecutive games.

(*a*) What is the probability that he will hit safely if he is at bat four times in the baseball game on June 6, 1951?

(*b*) What is the probability of his hitting safely in 26 consecutive games, if he is at bat four times in each game?

(*c*) Explain concisely why the odds in (*a*) and (*b*) are so different.

5. Consider the chances of a bomber pilot surviving a series of statistically identical raids, in which the chance of being shot down is always 5 per cent.

(*a*) From an original group of 1,000 such pilots, how many should survive 1, 5, 10, 15, 20, 40, 80, and 100 raids? Plot the survival curve, with the number of flights as abscissa.

(*b*) Estimate the mean life of a pilot in number of raids.

(*c*) In a single raid of 100 planes, what are the chances that zero, one, five, or ten planes will be lost?

6. Calculate and plot a normal distribution having a mean value of 10 and a standard deviation of 3.

7. Show that the sum of the probabilities $P_x = e^{-m}m^x/x!$ of all possible positive values $x = 0, 1, 2, \ldots$ is unity for the Poisson distribution.

8. In any Poisson distribution, show analytically that the probability of observing one less than the mean value is the same as the probability for the mean value.

9. In any Poisson distribution,

(*a*) Show that the ratio of the probability P_{2m} of observing twice the mean value to the probability P_m of observing the mean value is

$$P_{2m}/P_m = m^m m!/(2m)!$$

or when $m \gg 1$, $$P_{2m}/P_m = 0.707(0.824)^{2m}$$

(*b*) Compare P_{2m}/P_m for $m = 2, 10, 100$.

10. Calculate and plot a Poisson distribution with a mean value of 10 and values of x from 0 to 20. Compare with the normal distribution for $m = 10$, $\sigma = 3$.

11. The average background of a certain α-ray counter is 20 α rays per hour. In how many hours out of 200 would you expect to observe only 10 α rays?

12. In an α-ray counting experiment, on a source of constant average intensity, a total of 19,278 α rays are counted in 51 hr of continuous observations. The time of arrival of each α ray is recorded on a tape, so that the number of α rays recorded in each successive 1-min interval can be determined.

(*a*) What is the average number of α rays per 1-min interval?

(*b*) In how many of the total number of 1-min intervals would you expect to observe no α rays?

(*c*) In how many 1-min intervals should one observe one α ray?

(*d*) In how many 1-min intervals should one observe six α rays?

13. A Geiger-Müller counter having a resolving time of 300 μsec is placed in a plane parallel beam of 5-Mev photons from a pulsed generator. The counter has a cylindrical cathode 2 cm in diameter and 10 cm long, is placed with its axis perpendicular to the beam, and has an absolute efficiency of 2 per cent for 5-Mev photons. Each pulse of photons from the generator is 50 μsec in duration, and the repetition rate is 120 pulses per second. Under these conditions of operation, the counter displays an average counting rate of 3,600 counts per minute. During each pulse, what is the flux in photons per second per square centimeter at the counter position?

14. In a random distribution having an average interval $\bar{t}$, show by application of the interval distribution that the average value of the *absolute* deviations from the mean interval $\bar{t}$ is

$$|t - \bar{t}|_{\text{av}} = \frac{2}{e}\,\bar{t} = 0.7358\bar{t}$$

15. The average background of a certain α-ray counter is 30 α rays per hour.

(*a*) What fraction of the intervals between successive counts will be longer than 5 min?

(*b*) What fraction of the intervals will be longer than 10 min?

(*c*) What fraction of the intervals will be shorter than 30 sec?

16. A certain radioactive sample contains a mixture of an α-ray emitter and a β-ray emitter. The two substances are assumed to be independent. Using a particular pair of counters, the observed activities are A α counts per minute and B β counts per minute.

(*a*) What is the combined probability that a particular interval between two successive α rays will have a duration between t and $t + dt$ and will also contain exactly x β rays?

(*b*) Show that the probability $M(x)$ of observing just $x(x = 0, 1, 2, \ldots)$ β rays in the time interval between *any* two successive α-ray counts is

$$M(x) = \frac{R^x}{(R + 1)^{x+1}}$$

where $R = B/A$.

(*c*) What is the probability of observing just one α ray in the time interval between *successive* β rays if $A = 100$ and if $B = 500$ counts per minute?

17. Derive an interval distribution governing the output of a scale-of-2 circuit if the input receives randomly distributed pulses at an average rate of a pulses per minute. Specifically, (*a*) Show that the number n of observed intervals of length between t_1 and t_2 min, when N is the total number of scale-of-2 intervals studied, is

$$\frac{n}{N} = (at_1 + 1)e^{-at_1} - (at_2 + 1)e^{-at_2}$$

(*b*) Derive an expression for the fraction n/N of the intervals which will be longer than t.

(*c*) Derive an expression for the fraction of the intervals which will be shorter than t.

18. A scale-of-2 counter gave 292 pulses in 11 hr.

(*a*) What are the duration of the average interval and the average rate of the statistical process (scale of 1)?

(*b*) Compute the number of scale-of-2 intervals expected to be longer than 7.5 min. (Four were observed.)

(*c*) Compute the number of scale-of-2 intervals expected to be shorter than 5 sec. (One was observed.)

19. An interval distribution is to be derived, which will describe the distribution of time intervals between the arrival of π^+ mesons in a counter and the decay of the daughter μ^+ meson. The events to be considered are:

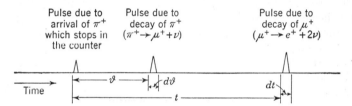

If λ_1 and λ_2 are the decay constants of the π^+ and μ^+ meson,

(*a*) What is the probability that the π^+ meson will decay in the time interval between ϑ and $\vartheta + d\vartheta$?

(*b*) What is the probability that a μ^+ meson will decay in the time interval between t and $t + dt$ after the arrival of its parent π^+ meson?

(*c*) What is the most probable time interval t_0 between arrival of π^+ and decay of μ^+? Use a mean life of 0.02 μsec for π^+, and of 2.0 μsec for μ^+.

2. *Statistical Characterization of Data*

a. Mean Value. In any *finite* series of measurements we can never find the *exact* value of the true mean value m, which corresponds to the infinite population of (i.e., an infinite amount of) data. Although the mean value† is constant, our individual measurements should be distributed about this mean value in a manner given by the particular frequency distribution which describes the process being studied. For the

---

† The *mean* value (i.e., the average value) is to be distinguished from the *modal* value (i.e., the most probable value) and from the *median* value (i.e., the value which is as frequently exceeded as not). Only for a symmetric distribution are the mean, mode, and median coincident. For an asymmetric distribution of numbers such as: 2, 3, 5, 6, 7, 8, 8, 9, 9, 9, 11, 11, 12, the mean value is 7.69, the mode is 9, and the median is 8.

four frequency distributions discussed in the previous section, it can be shown that our best approximation to m is simply the arithmetic average $\bar{x}$ of the n separate measurements, $x_1, x_2, x_3, \ldots, x_n$; that is,

$$m \simeq \bar{x} = \frac{1}{n} \sum_{1}^{n} x_i \tag{2.1}$$

The "expectation value" of any function of a statistical variable is synonymous with the mean value obtained for this variable in a large number of trials. Thus the *expectation value* of $\bar{x}$ is m.

b. Standard Deviation and Variance. The breadth of the statistical fluctuations of our individual readings about the true mean value is expressed quantitatively by the fundamentally important parameter, the *standard deviation σ*. For a particular mean value m, a small σ gives a sharply peaked distribution, whereas a large σ gives a broad, flattened distribution. In any case, the significance of the standard deviation as descriptive of the spread of the data is best seen in the normal distribution. Figure 1.2 shows that, in the normal distribution, about 32 per cent of a large series of individual observations must deviate from the mean value by more than $\pm\sigma$ and consequently that 68 per cent of the individual observations should lie within the band ($\bar{x} \pm \sigma$).

For any frequency distribution, the standard deviation (often abbreviated S.D.) is defined as the square root of the average value of the square of the individual deviations $(x - m)$, for a large number of observations. Thus

$$\sigma^2 = \sum_{x=-\infty}^{x=\infty} (x - m)^2 P_x \tag{2.2}$$

or, in terms of a large series of n measurements of x,

$$\sigma^2 = \frac{1}{n} \sum_{i=1}^{i=n} (x_i - m)^2 \tag{2.3}$$

The square of the S.D. is thus seen to be simply the second moment of the frequency distribution taken about the mean. The quantity σ^2 is usually called the *variance*. As is suggested by the form of Eq. (2.3), σ occasionally is called the *root-mean-square error*.

We can now use Eq. (2.2) for the derivation of analytical expressions for the S.D. of the various distributions.

For the binomial distribution, with mean value $m = zp$, the square of the standard deviation is

$$\sigma^2 = \sum_{x=0}^{x=z} (x - zp)^2 P_x = \sum_{x=0}^{x=z} \frac{(x - zp)^2 z! p^x (1 - p)^{z-x}}{x!(z - x)!}$$

Upon expansion and summation, this expression reduces to simply

$$\sigma^2 = zp(1 - p) \tag{2.4}$$

or, because the mean value of x is $m = zp$, we have also

$$\sigma^2 = m(1 - p) \tag{2.5}$$

Note especially that, for the binomial distribution, the variance σ^2 is always less than the mean value m ($\simeq \bar{x}$).

For the normal distribution, the evaluation of Eq. (2.2) by integration gives, of course,

$$\sigma^2 = \int_{-\infty}^{+\infty} (x - m)^2 \, dP_x = \frac{1}{\sigma \sqrt{2\pi}} \int_{-\infty}^{+\infty} (x - m)^2 e^{-(x-m)^2/2\sigma^2} \, dx = \sigma^2 \tag{2.6}$$

because the S.D. is simply one of the two independent parameters of the normal distribution and therefore may have any value.

For the Poisson distribution, however, the S.D. has a definite value in terms of the mean value, which is the only parameter of the Poisson distribution. From Eq. (2.2), we find on expansion that

$$\sigma^2 = \sum_{x=0}^{x=\infty} \frac{(x - m)^2 m^x}{x!} e^{-m} = m \tag{2.7}$$

Hence for the Poisson distribution, the S.D. of the distribution of individual observations is simply $\sqrt{m}$. This result is, of course, in agreement with the S.D. of the binomial distribution, Eq. (2.5), in the limiting case for $p \ll 1$.

For the interval distribution governing randomly distributed events occurring at an average rate a, hence with average interval $\bar{t} = 1/a$, Eqs. (1.14) and (2.2) lead to

$$\sigma^2 = \int_0^{\infty} \left(t - \frac{1}{a}\right)^2 ae^{-at} \, dt = \left(\frac{1}{a}\right)^2 \tag{2.8}$$

Thus the S.D. is just equal to the average interval $1/a$.

Table 2.1 now summarizes the properties of the four frequency distributions which apply to random processes having a constant average value.

c. **Estimate of Standard Deviation from a Finite Series of Observations.** In a finite series of n observations, we can never know m exactly. Hence we can never determine σ exactly, as implied in Eq. (2.2) which applies to the infinite population of data. Our best approximation to the S.D. of the distribution, in terms of our finite number n of observations, can be shown to be

$$\sigma^2 \simeq \frac{n}{n-1} \left[\frac{1}{n} \sum_1^n (x_i - \bar{x})^2\right] = \frac{1}{n-1} \sum_1^n (x_i - \bar{x})^2 \tag{2.9}$$

TABLE 2.1. SUMMARY OF FREQUENCY DISTRIBUTIONS DESCRIBING RANDOM PROCESSES

For ease of reference we include two generalizations which are to be described in Sec. 3 of this chapter and in Chap. 28, Sec. 2.

Frequency distribution	Distribution	Average value	Standard deviation	Distribution is approximation to binomial when
Binomial................	$P_x = \dfrac{z!}{x!(z-x)!}\, p^x(1-p)^{z-x}$	$\bar{x} = zp$	$\sqrt{zp(1-p)}$	
Normal................	$dP_x = \dfrac{1}{\sigma\sqrt{2\pi}}\, e^{-(x-m)^2/2\sigma^2}\, dx$	$\bar{x} = m$	σ	$z \gg 1$
Poisson................	$P_x = \dfrac{m^x}{x!}\, e^{-m}$	$\bar{x} = m$	$\sqrt{m}$	$p \ll 1;\; pz = m$
Interval................	$dP_t = ae^{-at}\, dt$	$\bar{t} = \dfrac{1}{a}$	$\dfrac{1}{a}$	
Generalized Poisson, this chapter, Sec. 3....	$P_u = aP_x + bP_y + cP_z + \cdots$ $\quad u = ax + by + cz + \cdots$ $\quad \sigma = \sqrt{a^2x + b^2y + c^2z + \cdots}$			
Generalized interval, Chap. 28, Sec. 2......	$dP_t = \dfrac{a^s t^{s-1}\, e^{-at}}{(s-1)!}\, dt$	$\bar{t} = \dfrac{s}{a}$	$\dfrac{\sqrt{s}}{a}$	

760

This practical expression for the (S.D.)^2 differs from Eq. (2.3) only in its denominator $(n - 1)$ and in the use of $\bar{x}$ in place of m. The term $(n - 1)$ is to be correlated with the view that the dispersion among the data is associated with the number of "degrees of freedom." From n independent observations of x we are provided originally with n independent equations. We reduce this number by one when we compute $\bar{x}$ and hence have only $(n - 1)$ independent data from which to compute σ. It can be seen readily that, in the special case in which only one observation is made, $\bar{x} = x$, and σ is indeterminate. The latter condition is correctly given by Eq. (2.9) but could not be obtained from Eq. (2.3) directly.

In the theory of mathematical statistics the so-called "sample variance" s^2 is defined as

$$s^2 \equiv \frac{1}{n} \sum_1^n (x_i - \bar{x})^2 \tag{2.10}$$

It can be shown quite generally that the *expectation value $E[s^2]$* for the *sample variance* of n observations is

$$E[s^2] = \frac{n - 1}{n} \sigma^2 \tag{2.11}$$

This is the formal basis for our Eq. (2.9) which we shall use hereafter without further explicit reference to the sample variance.

d. Standard Deviation of the Mean Value (Standard Error). If our n individual measurements of x exhibit, say, an approximately normal distribution about the mean value $\bar{x}$, then Fig. 1.2 shows that some 68 per cent of our individual observations have fallen within the central band $\bar{x} \pm \sigma$. This means that *one* additional single observation, if made, would have a 68 per cent chance of lying within $\bar{x} \pm \sigma$. In recognition of this probability interpretation, the "*standard deviation of the distribution*" σ, as determined from Eq. (2.3) or (2.9), can be called more precisely the "*standard deviation of a single observation.*"

Obviously, if we, or another observer, were to repeat our entire experiment of n observations, we should expect the new mean value to have much greater than a 68 per cent chance of falling within $\bar{x} \pm \sigma$. Therefore, in reporting our mean value $\bar{x}$, we wish to assign to it a S.D. of the mean value $\sigma_{\bar{x}}$ such that there is approximately a 68 per cent chance that some new mean value $\bar{x}_2$ will lie within the band $(\bar{x} \pm \sigma_{\bar{x}})$. Obviously, $\sigma_{\bar{x}}$ is smaller than σ.

It is well known in the theory of errors that a series of k mean values, $\bar{x}_1, \bar{x}_2, \bar{x}_3, \ldots, \bar{x}_k$, each based on n observations, will tend to exhibit a normal distribution about their grand average $\bar{\bar{x}}$. This is true if n is sufficiently large, even if the parent population x_i is not normally distributed but is, for example, an asymmetric Poisson distribution. In general, *the distribution of mean values tends to be much more nearly normal than the parent population.* This is the justification for a theoretical derivation of the relationship between σ and $\sigma_{\bar{x}}$, based on a normal distribution of $\bar{x}$. Then it can be shown that in a large series of k measurements of the mean value $\bar{x}$, each based on n measurements of x, the grand average $\bar{\bar{x}}$ approaches the true mean m and that the S.D. of $\bar{x}$ depends upon n in the following way

$$\sigma_{\bar{x}}^2 = \frac{1}{k} \sum_{j=1}^{j=k} (\bar{x}_j - m)^2 = \frac{\sigma^2}{n} \tag{2.12}$$

The result of a single series of n measurements of x is then to be reported as $(\bar{x} \pm \sigma_{\bar{x}})$, where

$$\bar{x} = \frac{1}{n} \sum_1^n x_i$$

$$\sigma_{\bar{x}} = \frac{\sigma}{\sqrt{n}}$$

$$\simeq \sqrt{\frac{1}{n(n-1)} \sum_1^n (x_i - \bar{x})^2} \tag{2.13}$$

Then a repetition of the series of n measurements would, in general, give a different mean value, but the chance that the new mean value would lie within $(\bar{x} \pm \sigma_{\bar{x}})$ is 68 per cent. The S.D. of the mean value $\sigma_{\bar{x}}$ is often called the *standard error*.

The validity of Eq. (2.12) or (2.13) is almost self-evident for the Poisson distribution. Suppose a total of $v = \sum_1^n x_i$ random events are observed. Then by Eq. (2.7) the S.D. in this single observation is $\sqrt{\sum_1^n x_i}$, so that the result would be reported as

$$v \pm \sigma = \sum_1^n x_i \pm \sqrt{\sum_1^n x_i} \tag{2.14}$$

and the *fractional S.D.* would be

$$\text{F.S.D.} \equiv \frac{\sigma}{v} = \frac{1}{\sum\limits_1^n x_i} \sqrt{\sum_1^n x_i} = \frac{1}{\sqrt{\sum\limits_1^n x_i}} \tag{2.15}$$

Suppose now that a zealous assistant was present, while you tallied only the total number $\sum_1^n x_i$ events, and that he broke the data into n contiguous and equal intervals, recording

$$x_1 + x_2 + x_3 + \cdots + x_n = \sum_1^n x_i$$

Then he would obtain

$$\bar{x} = \frac{1}{n} \sum_1^n x_i$$

$$\sigma = \sqrt{m} \simeq \sqrt{\bar{x}}$$

$$\sigma_{\bar{x}} = \frac{\sigma}{\sqrt{n}} = \frac{1}{n} \sqrt{\sum_1^n x_i}$$

and the result of the measurements would be reported as

$$\bar{x} \pm \sigma_{\bar{x}} = \frac{1}{n} \left(\sum_1^n x_i \pm \sqrt{\sum_1^n x_i} \right) \tag{2.16}$$

which has the same *fractional* S.D. as Eq. (2.15). In fact, Eq. (2.16) could have been obtained directly from Eq. (2.14) by simply dividing by the number of classifications n into which the data were subdivided. In either case, and in general, the observation of a total of $\sum_1^n x_i$ randomly distributed events has a *fractional* S.D. of $1 / \sqrt{\sum_1^n x_i}$. Thus the S.D. in counting 100 random events is 10 per cent, and one must count 10,000 events to reduce the S.D. to 1 per cent. *No mere method of treating the same total data can ever reduce the magnitude of the fractional uncertainty due purely to randomicity.*

e. Probable Error. A result quoted as $\bar{x} \pm \sigma_{\bar{x}}$ implies that the chance that the average value $\bar{x}$ differs from the true mean value m by more than $\sigma_{\bar{x}}$ is 0.317, if the error distribution is normal. While the S.D. has a definite statistical value and a basic significance in the principal frequency distributions, it is becoming increasingly common to fail to use it in reporting physical results. Instead, a quantity derived from the S.D. and called the probable error is often given. Its wide adoption rests on its easily visualized interpretation and perhaps also on the fact that, of all the common types of error specification, the probable error has the least value and hence makes the data look best.

The probable error is, by definition, *exactly as likely to be exceeded as not.* The probable error is ordinarily derived from the S.D. From Fig. 1.2 it can be seen that the particular error r which has exactly a 0.50

chance of being exceeded in a *normal distribution* is

$$r = 0.6745\sigma \qquad \text{and } r_{\bar{x}} = 0.6745\sigma_{\bar{x}} \tag{2.17}$$

Similarly, for a normal distribution, the chance that the actual error $(m - \bar{x})$ exceeds $r_{\bar{x}}$, $2r_{\bar{x}}$, $3r_{\bar{x}}$, etc. (without regard to sign) is given in the following table:

Chance that $|m - \bar{x}|$ is greater than............	$r_{\bar{x}}$	$2r_{\bar{x}}$	$3r_{\bar{x}}$	$4r_{\bar{x}}$
Is..	0.500	0.178	0.043	0.0071

Intermediate values may be read from Fig. 1.2. It is customary therefore to regard $3r_{\bar{x}}$ (or $2\sigma_{\bar{x}}$) as equivalent to the *limit of error*, though this is clearly arbitrary and unreal rigorously. Moreover, the specification of a physical result as $\bar{x} \pm r_{\bar{x}}$ is exact *only* for a symmetric normal distribution.

Any asymmetry in the actual distribution will result in the probable positive error differing from the probable negative error for single observations; that is, ordinates of the distribution curve at $x = 0$, $(m - r)$, m, $(m + r)$, ∞, no longer divide the errors (area) into four equal parts (quartiles). Of course, an analogous objection can often be made to the lack of significance of the plus and minus sign if used with the S.D. of an asymmetric distribution. The only rigorous interpretation of S.D. of an asymmetric distribution is as root-mean-square error, Eqs. (2.9) and (2.13), and not as a plus or minus value having symmetric probabilities of being exceeded. It is only because the asymmetry of the Poisson distribution becomes small, and because this distribution approaches the normal distribution in the vicinity of the mean value when $m \gg 1$, that probable error can have any exact significance.

Graphical integration of Poisson distributions shows that the asymmetry is of the order of 10 to 4 per cent for $m = 10$ to 100 and vanishes as $m \to \infty$. The asymmetry for $m \geq 10$ does not invalidate Eq. (2.17), but for $m < 10$ much more significance attaches to the S.D. than to the probable error. The general dependence of r on $\sigma = \sqrt{x}$ for the Poisson distribution is given in the following table (R25):

x....................	20	60	100	200	400	1,000	∞
$\dfrac{r}{\sigma} = \dfrac{r}{\sqrt{x}}$..............	0.575	0.613	0.628	0.640	0.647	0.660	0.6745

It will be noted that use of the conventional expression $r = 0.6745\sigma$ even for the Poisson distribution results in a conservative estimate of the probable error and is a safe procedure to follow.

If the mean value of an asymmetric distribution is estimated from a very large number n of observations, then the probable error of the mean value can have a true "plus-or-minus" significance, because the distribution of mean values is always more nearly normal than the parent population.

f. Dimensions of Statistical Parameters. From consideration of Eq. (2.7) or (1.7), it is evident that both x and σ must be *dimensionless* quantities, since σ has the same dimensions as x and $\sqrt{x}$. It is generally true that all such quantities in the distribution functions and in other statistical expressions are without dimensions. For example, $\bar{x}$ may be physically the average number of counts per minute, but statistically the time unit chosen is only an arbitrary interval or classification by which the data have been taken. It is to be regarded statistically as dimensionless. This can be visualized by considering time intervals measured off on a chronograph tape, in which case the particular interval used for classification might equally well be one second, or an equivalent length of tape, or even an equivalent mass of tape. The interval itself does not have the dimensions of time, length, or mass but is always statistically dimensionless, as are all the other basic statistical quantities.

While the interval distribution Eq. (1.14) contains the rate a in events per unit time, it always occurs in the product at or $a\,dt$, which is again dimensionless.

Problems

1. Prove analytically that the standard deviation is $\sqrt{m}$ for any Poisson distribution.

2. In the interval distribution for single randomly distributed events, show that the standard deviation is just equal to the average interval, that is, $\sigma = 1/a$.

3. In computing the standard deviation σ of a series of observations x_i, the arithmetic often can be greatly simplified by referring the individual readings to some arbitrary value x_0 (usually chosen as a round number near $\bar{x}$). Then if, as usual,

$$\bar{x} = \frac{1}{n}\sum_1^n x_i \qquad \text{and} \qquad \sigma^2 \simeq \frac{1}{n-1}\sum_1^n (x_i - \bar{x})^2$$

show that

$$(a)\ \ \bar{x} = x_0 + \frac{1}{n}\sum_1^n (x_i - x_0)$$

$$(b)\ \ \sigma^2 \simeq \left[\frac{1}{n-1}\sum_1^n (x_i - x_0)^2\right] - \left[\frac{n}{n-1}(\bar{x}-x_0)^2\right]$$

4. In successive 30-min intervals, the number of α rays observed on a certain counter are 13, 9, 16, 9, 14, 11, 17, 12, 7, 12, 15.

(a) Compute the average rate in α rays per hour.

(b) If a single additional 30-min observation is made, what are its probable value, standard deviation, and probable error?

(c) What is the probable error of the mean value determined in (a)?

(d) Compare (c) with the value expected if the data follow the Poisson distribution.

5. Calculate and plot a Poisson distribution having a mean value of 1.2 for values of x from 0 to 6. What is the standard deviation? What can be said concerning probable error in such an asymmetric distribution?

6. Consider an asymmetric normal distribution having a *modal* (most probable) value of $x = q$, a standard deviation σ_1 for $x < q$, and of σ_2 for $x > q$. The *median* value $x = r$ divides the distribution into two equal areas. The *mean*

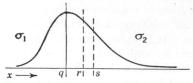

value $x = s$ is the average value of x. If the separation $(r - q)$ between the mode and median is small compared with σ_2, show that

$$\text{(median-mode)} = r - q = \sqrt{\frac{\pi}{8}}\,(\sigma_2 - \sigma_1) = 0.627(\sigma_2 - \sigma_1)$$

$$\text{(mean-mode)} = s - q = \sqrt{\frac{2}{\pi}}\,(\sigma_2 - \sigma_1) = 0.798(\sigma_2 - \sigma_1)$$

HINT: Does the assumption $q = 0$ result in any loss of generality?

7. Show that

$$\sum_1^n (x_i - \bar{x})^2 = \sum_1^n x_i^2 - \frac{1}{n}\left(\sum_1^n x_i\right)^2$$

This form is useful when x_i contains one or at most two digits.

3. *Composite Distributions*

Most measurements or calculations in physics involve more than one source of error or of statistical fluctuations. The joint effect of simultaneous but independent sources of statistical fluctuations is now to be considered.

a. Generalized Poisson Distribution. Superposition of Several Independent Random Processes. The complete generalization of the Poisson distribution is usually required in nuclear problems, because several types of radiation will actuate most detection instruments simultaneously. Thus, in ionization-chamber measurements of α rays, there will be present a background composed of α and β rays from radioactive contamination of the walls of the instrument, of cosmic rays, and of γ rays from the earth and the surrounding building materials. If each of several such processes is itself random, the resulting over-all fluctuations may be derived (E24).

Let $x, y, z, \ldots$ be the average number of particles from the several independent random processes, in the time interval chosen. Let them respectively produce specific effects (such as ion pairs) of $a, b, c, \ldots$ per particle. Then the average effect on the instrument is

$$u = ax + by + cz + \cdots \tag{3.1}$$

Generalization of Eq. (2.2) shows (E24) that the square of the S.D. of a single observation of u is given by

$$\sigma^2 = a^2 x + b^2 y + c^2 z + \cdots \tag{3.2}$$

Equations (3.1) and (3.2) are applied to differential measurements by noting that instrumentally subtracted effects correspond simply to negative values of the appropriate coefficient a, b, c, . . . in Eq. (3.2) and leave the fluctuations unchanged.

In Eqs. (3.1) and (3.2), dimensions may be associated with a, b, c, . . . and u, but not with x, y, z, ... In this case, both the mean value u and the S.D. σ have the dimensions of a, b, c, ...

Suppose that a certain ionization chamber receives in unit time an average of $x = 100$ α rays, each producing $a = 10^5$ ion pairs, and also $y = 10^4$ β rays, each producing $b = 10^3$ ion pairs. Then the total average ionization produced is

$$u = 10^5 \times 100 + 10^3 \times 10^4 = 2 \times 10^7 \text{ ion pairs}$$

However, the standard deviation in u is

$$\sigma = \sqrt{(10^5)^2 \times 100 + (10^3)^2 \times 10^4} = \sqrt{10^{12} + 10^{10}}$$
$$= \sqrt{1.01 \times 10^{12}} = 1.005 \times 10^6 \text{ ion pairs}$$

or 5 per cent of u. Thus the α rays produce only half the total ionization but, because of their small number and their large ionization per particle, they account for 99.5 per cent of the statistical fluctuations in the combined ionization effects.

Let this chamber and a second identical ionization chamber be connected in a differential circuit such that an electrometer reads the difference of the ionization in the two chambers. If the second chamber also receives in unit time an average of $z = 100$ α rays, each producing 10^5 ion pairs, then $c = -10^5$ ion pairs because the instrument subtracts cz from $ax + by$. Then the net average differential ionization will be

$$u = 10^5 \times 100 + 10^3 \times 10^4 - 10^5 \times 100 = 10^7 \text{ ion pairs}$$

However, the S.D. in this differential reading is increased to

$$\sigma = \sqrt{(10^5)^2 \times 100 + (10^3)^2 \times 10^4 + (-10^5)^2 \times 100}$$
$$= \sqrt{2.01 \times 10^{12}} = 1.41 \times 10^6 \text{ ion pairs}$$

or 14 per cent of the net u. Note that the differential circuit does not decrease the fluctuations in the total ionization. In fact, *σ has the same value whether the two ionization chambers are connected to oppose each other or to supplement each other.*

In single-particle counting apparatus, such as a Geiger-Müller counter, $a = b = 1$, because the counter discharges once whether the initiating ray is an α ray or a β ray. Thus the $x = 100$ α rays and $y = 10^4$ β rays, if acting in a Geiger-Müller counter, would produce a total of

$$u = 1 \times 10^2 + 1 \times 10^4 = 1.01 \times 10^4$$

counts with a S.D. of

$$\sigma = \sqrt{1 \times 10^2 + 1 \times 10^4} = 1.005 \times 10^2 \text{ counts}$$

or only 1 per cent of u.

We shall return later to Eq. (3.2) for the discussion of the statistics of scaling circuits (Chap. 28).

b. Propagation of Errors. The laws for the propagation of errors are rigorous for the S.D. and can, in fact, be inferred from Eqs. (3.1) and (3.2). In the present section we use probable error merely as a symbol for 0.6745σ, or for $0.6745\sigma_{\bar{x}}$, as required by the context.

Where a physical magnitude is to be obtained from the *summation or the differences* of independent observations on two or more physical quantities, the final probable error R of the derived magnitude is obtained from

$$R^2 = r_1^2 + r_2^2 + \cdots \tag{3.3}$$

where r_1, r_2, . . . are the *absolute* values of the probable errors in the mean values of the several quantities, expressed, of course, in the same units. Thus,

$$(100 \pm 3) + (6 \pm 4) = (106 \pm 5)$$

while

$$(100 \pm 3) - (105 \pm 4) = -(5 \pm 5)$$

The arithmetic of subtraction may be further illustrated by the problem of measuring a counting rate due to some radiation source. A separate measurement must always be made of the natural-background counting rate of the instrument when the source is absent. Suppose that in a time t_b a total of bt_b background counts is recorded. Then the average background rate B and its probable error would be

$$B = (bt_b \pm 0.67 \sqrt{bt_b}) \frac{1}{t_b}$$

$$= b \pm 0.67 \sqrt{\frac{b}{t_b}} \tag{3.4}$$

We note at once that the statistical uncertainty in our evaluation of the background rate depends inversely on the square root of the duration of our observation. Suppose that we now bring a radioactive source near the counter, increasing the true average counting rate to $(S + B)$, where S is due to the source and B to the background. Let $(s + b)$ be the observed counting rate over a period t_s, during which a total of $(s + b)t_s$ counts is recorded. Then our best estimate of $(S + B)$ and its probable error is

$$S + B = [(s + b)t_s \pm 0.67 \sqrt{(s + b)t_s}] \frac{1}{t_s}$$

$$= s + b \pm 0.67 \sqrt{\frac{s}{t_s} + \frac{b}{t_s}} \tag{3.5}$$

Subtracting Eq. (3.4) from Eq. (3.5) in order to obtain the average counting rate due to the source, we obtain, by Eq. (3.3),

$$S = s \pm 0.67 \sqrt{\frac{s}{t_s} + \frac{b}{t_s} + \frac{b}{t_b}} \tag{3.6}$$

It will be noted that the background uncertainty enters twice, once for its fluctuation during the measurement of $(s + b)$ and once for its fluctuation during the measurement of b alone.   In the design of counting experiments, it is clear from Eq. (3.6) that the uncertainty in s, measured for a fixed time t_s, can always be reduced by prolonging the independent background measurements t_b.

On the other hand, if a physical magnitude Y is to be obtained by *multiplication* or *division* of results of several independent observations on two or more physical magnitudes $y_1, y_2, \ldots$, the *fractional* probable error R/Y in the resulting value of Y depends upon the fractional probable errors $r_1/y_1, r_2/y_2, \ldots$ in the measurement of $y_1, y_2, \ldots$ and is given by

$$\left(\frac{R}{Y}\right)^2 \simeq \left(\frac{r_1}{y_1}\right)^2 + \left(\frac{r_2}{y_2}\right)^2 + \cdots + \left(\frac{r_n}{y_n}\right)^2 \tag{3.7}$$

or its equivalent

$$R \simeq Y \sqrt{\left(\frac{r_1}{y_1}\right)^2 + \left(\frac{r_2}{y_2}\right)^2 + \cdots + \left(\frac{r_n}{y_n}\right)^2} \tag{3.8}$$

Thus we have, for example,

$$(100 \pm 0.3)(6 \pm 0.4) = 600 \pm 600 \sqrt{(\tfrac{0.3}{100})^2 + (\tfrac{0.4}{6})^2} - 600 \pm 40$$
$$(100 \pm 3)(100 \pm 4) = 10^4 \pm 10^4 \sqrt{(\tfrac{3}{100})^2 + (\tfrac{4}{100})^2} = 10{,}000 \pm 500$$
$$\frac{100 \pm 40}{10 \pm 3} = 10 \pm 10 \sqrt{(\tfrac{40}{100})^2 + (\tfrac{3}{10})^2} = 10 \pm 5$$

Equation (3.7) is a good approximation if the fractional errors are small, that is, if $n(r_i/y_i)^2 \ll 1$, as often happens.

c. **Significance of the Difference of Two Means.**   Especially in nuclear physics, many experiments have to be statistically designed as optimum compromises between maximum resolution and maximum intensity.   It often happens that the statistical fluctuations in the natural background of a detecting instrument may be comparable with the average value of some feeble radiation effect which is to be measured.   In such cases, special care must be taken in interpreting the results of the measurements, and standard tests of the "significance of the difference of means" may need to be applied to the data.

Let m_u and m_v be the true mean values of two independent populations of normally distributed data, while $(\bar{u} \pm \sigma_{\bar{u}})$ and $(\bar{v} \pm \sigma_{\bar{v}})$ are measured values of samples from the two populations, each measurement being based on a sufficient number of observations so that the uncertainty in $\sigma_{\bar{u}}$ and in $\sigma_{\bar{v}}$ is small.   Then our best estimate of the difference, $(m_u - m_v)$, of the two means is

$$m_u - m_v \simeq (\bar{u} \pm \sigma_{\bar{u}}) - (\bar{v} \pm \sigma_{\bar{v}})$$
$$= (\bar{u} - \bar{v}) \pm \sqrt{\sigma_{\bar{u}}^2 + \sigma_{\bar{v}}^2} \tag{3.9}$$

It can be shown† that $(\bar{u} - \bar{v})$ is normally distributed about the true

† See P. G. Hoel, "Introduction to Mathematical Statistics," p. 70, John Wiley & Sons, Inc., New York, 1947, or S. S. Wilks, "Mathematical Statistics," p. 98, Princeton University Press, Princeton, N.J., 1943, on the problems of significance.

mean value $(m_u - m_v)$ with a standard deviation of

$$\sigma_{(\bar{u}-\bar{v})} = \sqrt{\sigma_{\bar{u}}^2 + \sigma_{\bar{v}}^2} \qquad (3.10)$$

If, for example, the true mean value is $(m_u - m_v) = 0$, then from Fig. 1.2 there is about a 32 per cent chance that the absolute value of $(\bar{u} - \bar{v})$ will be numerically greater than the standard deviation of its own measurement, $\sigma_{(\bar{u}-\bar{v})}$. Similarly, because Fig. 1.2 shows $P_u = 0.045$ for $u = 2\sigma$, there is only about a 5 per cent chance that the observed absolute value of $(\bar{u} - \bar{v})$ would exceed $2\sigma_{(\bar{u}-\bar{v})}$ if $(m_u - m_v) = 0$.

It is customary but arbitrary in the theory of errors to reject any hypothesis which falls below a "*significance level*" of 5 per cent. Thus, the hypothesis being tested is usually rejected if it predicts that the observation made was so unusual that it should occur less than 5 per cent of the time. Accordingly, an observation of a difference of at least twice the S.D. (or three times the probable error) between two mean values would be said to be "*significant*" and would lead to rejection of any tentative hypothesis that the two true mean values were identical.

For example, suppose that a radiation-safety monitor is searching for β-ray contamination, using an ionization chamber whose natural background has an average value of 10 α rays (10^5 ion pairs per α ray) plus 100 β rays (10^3 ion pairs per β ray) per minute. What is the minimum number of additional β rays per minute which can just be detected in a 30-sec inspection, using the conventional significance level of 5 per cent? From Eq. (3.1), the average background ionization per 30-sec interval is

$$u = ax + by = 10^5 \times 5 + 10^3 \times 50 = 5.5 \times 10^5 \text{ ion pairs}$$

while the S.D. of u is, by Eq. (3.2),

$$\sigma = \sqrt{a^2 x + b^2 y} = \sqrt{(10^5)^2 \times 5 + (10^3)^2 \times 50} = 2.24 \times 10^5 \text{ ion pairs}$$

Making the valid and simplifying assumption that the additional β-ray activity cz which is just detectable will not alter σ appreciably, we require $cz = 2\sigma$ for the 5 per cent significance level. Taking $c = b = 10^3$ ion pairs per β ray, we find that $z = 2\sigma/c = 2 \times 2.24 \times 10^5/10^3 = 450 \ \beta$ rays in 30 sec, or 900 β rays/min, as the least amount of β-ray activity which can be "detected" in 30 sec with this instrument.

Evidently, instruments designed for the detection of small activities should have small fluctuations in the background. In the example cited, the major portion of the statistical fluctuations is due to the α rays. Another ionization chamber, having no appreciable α-ray background but the same total average background due entirely to 1,100 β rays/min, would have $\sigma = \sqrt{(10^3)^2 \times 550} = 2.34 \times 10^4$ ion pairs for 30-sec readings. Such a chamber could therefore detect an addition of 2σ ion pairs, or 47 β rays in 30 sec, or an average activity of about 100 β rays/min in a 30-sec observation. Although both ionization chambers considered here have the same average background, their "useful sensitivities" to small sources differ by a factor of 9 (!) because of the important effects of fluctuations in the background.

This numerical example illustrates a broad general principle which is too often overlooked in discussions of the relative sensitivity of various types of detecting equipment. A measure of goodness, or of effective relative sensitivity, is the instrument's response to some small standard source, divided not by the average background but by the magnitude of the fluctuations of the background in unit time. The mere ratio of response divided by average background is meaningless.

In principle, a huge background would be perfectly acceptable if it could be absolutely steady in value. It is the inevitable increase in the absolute value of the statistical fluctuations with increasing background which directs instrument designers to seek low backgrounds.

Problems

1. Two measured quantities and their probable errors are $a = 50 \pm 4$ and $b = 30 \pm 3$. Find the values, with probable error, of the quantities ab, a/b, $(a - b)$, $(a + b)$.

2. A counter has a background of 90 counts per minute as determined from a 1-hr observation. A small sample, tentatively thought to be nonradioactive, is placed near the counter for 5 min. During this time 475 counts are recorded.

(a) On a basis of this evidence, is the sample radioactive?

(b) If in a period of 20 min 1,900 counts were recorded with the sample present, would it be judged as radioactive?

3. Using a counter having a very accurately measured average background of 120 counts per minute, what must be the duration of an observation of a radioactive source having a constant average activity of about 240 counts per minute if the activity of the source is to be measured with a probable error of 2 per cent?

4. The rate of emission of β rays from a single radioactive substance, for example, P^{32}, is being observed by counting the particles emitted during accurately measured time intervals of equal duration t. The background of the counter is first observed for a time t and is 3,000 counts. Then the source is brought up, and the counting rate rises to 7,000 counts in a time t.

(a) From these two observations alone, what is the fractional probable error (in per cent) of the observed counting rate due to the β rays?

(b) Why must t be much shorter than the half-period of the radioactive substance for the calculation in (a) to be valid?

5. The radioactivity of a long-lived substance emitting β rays is to be measured, using a Geiger-Müller counter. The background of the counter is such that a total of 3,200 counts are recorded in a total running time of t_b min. With the source in position, a total of 3,200 counts are recorded in t_s min.

(a) Show that the per cent probable error in the measurement of the source strength, in terms of the observed quantities t_b and t_s, is

$$\left(\frac{67}{\sqrt{3,200}} \right) \left[\frac{\sqrt{t_b^2 + t_s^2}}{(t_b - t_s)} \right]$$

(b) What is the per cent probable error if $t_b/t_s = 2$?

(c) What is the per cent probable error if $t_b/t_s = 10$?

6. Two Geiger-Müller counters are exposed to the same radiation to determine whether they have the same absolute sensitivity.

(a) In the first trial, counter 1 gives a total of 900 counts in the same time counter 2 gives 940 counts. Can this be considered a "statistically significant" difference?

(b) If counter 2 gave 990 counts instead of the 940, would this be a "statistically significant" difference?

7. In successive 10-min intervals, the background of a counter is 1,020; 970; 990; 1,040; 950; 1,010; and 980. A radioactive source of long half-period is brought up to the counter, and the increased counting rate, for successive 10-min intervals, is 3,060; 3,100; 2,980; 3,010; 2,950; and 3,030. Calculate the average values and probable errors for (a) the background, (b) the background and source, and (c) the source alone.

8. A time T is available in which to measure the counting rate s due to a radiation source, using an instrument whose background counting rate b is not known accurately and must be measured during part of T. Show that maximum accuracy is obtained in the measurement of s by using a time αT for observing the source, and $(1 - \alpha)T$ for observing the background, where

$$\text{"background time"} = 1 - \alpha = \frac{1}{1 + \sqrt{(b + s)/b}}$$

Plot α vs. log (b/s) for $0.01 \leq (b/s) \leq 10$. What is the limiting value of α for very weak sources? For very strong sources?

9. The background b of a counter is to be measured and then the counter is to be used to measure the activity s of a source, all in a fixed time T. If the true mean values are $b = 30$ counts per minute (cpm) and $s = 300$ counts per minute, and if $T = 20$ min, what is the probable error of s in counts per minute when T is divided between background and source measurements such that (a) the same total number of counts are recorded for background as with the source in position, (b) one-half the time available is used for background, and (c) the optimum division of time is utilized? *Ans.:* (a) 9.5 counts per minute; (b) 4.0 counts per minute; (c) 3.6 counts per minute.

10. Measurements are made with a γ-ray counter on a source of substantially constant average activity.

(a) A total count (source plus background) of 8,000 is observed in 10 min. Then, with the source removed, 10 min gave a total of 2,000 background counts. What is the average source strength in counts per minute? What is the standard deviation in this value?

(b) If the total time to make measurements is fixed, what is the optimum fraction of time to spend measuring background in part (a)?

11. A choice is to be made between two somewhat similar α-ray counters. One is distinguished especially by its low background, the other by its high efficiency.

(a) If the average background of a counter is B counts per hour, and the calibration constant or "sensitivity" is S counts per hour per micromicrocurie of, say, radon, show that the fractional standard deviation in the measurement of A $\mu\mu c$ in a time T is

$$\frac{\sigma}{SA} = \sqrt{\frac{SA + B}{TS^2A^2}}$$

(b) What is the fractional standard deviation for very weak sources $(A \to 0)$? For very strong sources $(A \to \infty)$?

(c) The two instruments which are available have $B_1 = 10$, $S_1 = 100$ and $B_2 = 150$, $S_2 = 250$. For very weak sources, should the instrument with the low background or the one with the high sensitivity be used? Which instrument is preferable for strong sources?

(d) What is the particular source strength A_0, in micromicrocuries, for which these two instruments give the same fractional statistical error of measurement in any fixed time T?

12. A large group of atoms, whose number is exactly N at $t = 0$, undergoes radioactive decay with decay constant λ and mean life $\tau = 1/\lambda$.

(a) State the probability that a given atom has survived at time t.

(b) State the probability that a given atom has decayed between $t = 0$ and $t = t$.

(c) What is the expectation value $\bar{n}$ of the number of survivors at time t (i.e., the mean number of survivors for many such groups of N similar atoms)?

(d) If $t = \tau$, which of the distribution laws studied describe(s) the fluctuation of the number of survivors n about $\bar{n}$?

(e) What is the standard deviation of n about $\bar{n}$?

(f) What is the probability that a given atom will survive through τ and decay between τ and $\tau + \Delta t$?

(g) What is the expectation value $\overline{\Delta n}$ of the number of atoms decaying between τ and $\tau + \Delta t$?

(h) If $\Delta t = \frac{1}{10}\tau$, which of the distribution laws studied describe(s) the fluctuation about $\overline{\Delta n}$ of the number of atoms, Δn, decaying between τ and $\tau + \Delta t$?

(i) What is the standard deviation of Δn about $\overline{\Delta n}$?

(j) At $t = 0$ we have 100 groups of N atoms, each of the above type, which we shall call A, and 100 groups of N atoms, each of a second type B. Observations between τ and $\tau + \Delta t$ result in the following

Type of atom	Mean Δn	S.D. of Δn about mean
A	$\overline{\Delta n_A}$	σ_A
B	$\overline{\Delta n_B}$	σ_B

If $\delta - |\overline{\Delta n_A} - \overline{\Delta n_B}|$, how large a value may δ have without seriously upsetting the hypothesis that types A and B are actually the same atoms?

13. The radium content of an unknown sample is to be determined on an absolute basis by comparison with the γ-ray activity of a radium standard. If A is the observed activity of the unknown and B is the observed activity of the radium standard, then the best value of the ratio A/B is the quantity sought from the measurements. A standardized technique is used, such that each individual measurement of A or of B has a fractional standard deviation of 0.5 per cent.

(a) If only one measurement of A and one of B are made, what is the fractional standard deviation of A/B?

(b) If three measurements of A are made, what is the fractional S.D. of the average activity $\bar{A}$ of the sample?

(c) If three measurements of A and n measurements of B are made, what is the fractional S.D. in the average ratio $\bar{A}/\bar{B}$?

(d) It is desired to make enough measurements n on the standard so that no appreciable statistical error is introduced in the final ratio $\bar{A}/\bar{B}$ by uncertainty in the activity $\bar{B}$ of the standard. Again, three measurements are made on A. What is the minimum number n of measurements of B such that the fractional S.D. in $\bar{A}/\bar{B}$ will not exceed 1.2 times the fractional S.D. in $\bar{A}$?

CHAPTER 27

Statistical Tests for Goodness of Fit

Two statistical tests for "goodness of fit" between data and hypothesis will be discussed. It has long been clear that all individual nuclear processes are random in character and hence obey Poisson's distribution and the interval distribution based on it. Data illustrating this fact will be given in Sec. 4 as examples of the application of statistical principles.

1. Lexis' Divergence Coefficient

In 1877 the German economist Lexis introduced a divergence coefficient Q^2, defined as the ratio of the average of the squares of the deviations to the arithmetical mean or, in the nomenclature of Chap. 26,

$$Q^2 = \frac{\sum_{1}^{n} (x_i - \bar{x})^2}{n\bar{x}} \tag{1.1}$$

Comparison of Eq. (1.1) with Eq. (2.9) of Chap. 26 shows that

$$Q^2 = \frac{n - 1}{n} \frac{\sigma^2}{\bar{x}} \tag{1.2}$$

which, for the normal distribution, can have any value since σ is a parameter of the normal distribution.

For the Poisson distribution, however, Q^2 has a definite value because σ is expressible in terms of the mean value m. Thus, if the data were in perfect agreement with *Poisson's distribution*, we should have, by Eq. (2.7) of Chap. 26,

$$Q^2 = \frac{\sum_{1}^{n} (x_i - m)^2}{nm} = \frac{\sigma^2}{m} = 1 \tag{1.3}$$

We can then compute Q^2 from our data, using Eq. (1.1), and if the observed Q^2 is close to unity we may say that the data seem to follow the Poisson distribution.

While this is very helpful, it is by no means enough, for we need to know how different from unity Q^2 may be expected to be before we should question the randomicity of the process. Such a quantitative test is offered by Pearson's chi-square test.

2. *Pearson's Chi-square Test*

Pearson's (P10) chi-square test determines the probability P that a repetition of the observations would show *greater* deviations from the frequency distribution which is assumed to govern the data. While derived on a basis of the normal distribution, it is successfully used on Poisson and interval distributions because, as stated earlier, the frequency curve of the means of samples drawn from a nonnormal infinite parent population of data is usually more nearly normal than the original population. Moreover, a parent Poisson distribution in which $m \gg 1$ approaches the normal form, as was seen in Figs. 1.1 and 1.3 of Chap. 26.

Whereas the chi-square test provides one of the most decisive statistical criteria, it is too seldom used by physicists, partly because of its unfamiliarity and partly because a large amount of data is required for its most useful applications. Its use should be encouraged.

Pearson's chi-square test may be most simply stated as follows: We define the quantity

$$\chi^2 = \sum^i \frac{[(\text{observed value})_i - (\text{expected value})_i]^2}{(\text{expected value})_i} \qquad (2.1)$$

where the summation is over the total number of independent classifications i in which the data have been grouped. The "expected values" are computed from any a priori assumed frequency distribution, e.g., normal, Poisson, interval, etc. In general, the data should be subdivided into at least five classifications, each containing at least five events. Secondly, we determine the number of *degrees of freedom F*, which is the number of independent classifications in which the observed series of data may differ from the hypothetical. Then enter Fig. 2.1 and from the values of χ^2 and F determine P, which is the probability that χ^2 should exceed its observed value. Put differently, *P is the probability that, on repeating the series of measurements, larger deviations from the expected values would be observed.*

In interpreting the value of P so obtained, we may say that, if P lies between 0.1 and 0.9, the assumed distribution very probably corresponds to the observed one, while if P is less than 0.02 or more than 0.98 the assumed distribution is extremely unlikely and is to be questioned seriously.

The practical uses of the chi-square test will be illustrated by numerical examples in Sec. 4 below.

For values of $F > 29$, which are neither shown in Fig. 2.1 nor given in the usual chi-square-test tables, it is sufficient to assume that $\sqrt{2\chi^2}$ has a normal distribution with unit standard deviation about a mean

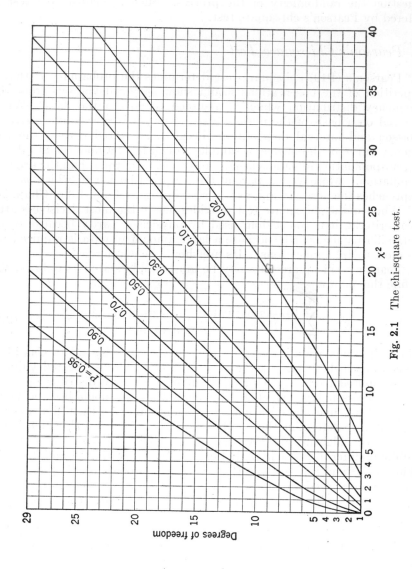

Fig. 2.1 The chi-square test.

value of $\sqrt{2F - 1}$. Then Fig. 1.2 of Chap. 26 may be used for such chi-square tests. In actual statistical practice F seldom exceeds 30 and is usually less than 12.

The chi-square test may be used to determine the validity of any proposed distribution law. Whereas statisticians have devised a number of tests for goodness of fit, physicists should find the chi-square test the most useful of these.

3. *An Extension of the Chi-square Test*

As expressed by Eq. (2.1), χ^2 measures the square of the observed deviations from some assumed frequency distribution. If we fail to specify the distribution assumed but do assume that in a series of n observations of a process, over equal time intervals, the expected value in each interval is constant and equal to the mean value $\bar{x}$ for all the intervals studied, then we would write

$$\chi^2 = \sum_1^n \frac{(x - \bar{x})^2}{\bar{x}} = nQ^2 \tag{3.1}$$

where n values of x are observed and Q^2 is Lexis' divergence coefficient, Eq. (1.1).

It must be emphasized that in Eq. (3.1) we have not yet assumed what distribution governs the observed process; in fact, we have assumed the expected value to be constant. But if the process follows the Poisson distribution, we have seen in Eq. (1.3) that $Q^2 = 1$; hence $\chi^2 = n$. Here the number of degrees of freedom is $F = n - 1$, because our only restriction on the n independent expected values is that they each be equal to $\bar{x}$. It will be seen from Fig. 2.1 that if $n > 5$ then P is between 0.3 and 0.4 for Poisson data so treated. This differs from 0.5 only slightly more than corresponds to the asymmetry of the Poisson distribution and is one justification for a type of application of the chi-square test which is often made on small samples. This test tells far more than can be learned from other readily applied statistical tests.

4. *Examples of Random Fluctuations*

In this section, numerical examples will be given to serve the double purpose of elucidating the application of the statistical principles given in preceding sections and to establish the random character of certain nuclear processes.

a. The Emission of α Rays by Polonium. All modern theories of radioactive decay involve the assumption that in an assembly of nuclei of a given type, e.g., polonium, all the nuclei are identical, independent, and that they each have a definite and constant probability of decaying in unit time (Chap. 15). Since these conditions are precisely the same as the necessary and sufficient conditions for Poisson's distribution, it becomes of fundamental importance to compare the observed statistical fluctuations in the emission of radioactive radiations, from a source of essentially constant strength, with the predictions of Poisson's distribution. The agreement which is found is illustrated by the following example. This is one of the experimental justifications on which many nuclear considerations rest.

To test adequately the random time of emission of α rays from a radioactive substance, a solid angle of 4π should be used so that every emitted ray can be counted, regardless of its direction of emission. This has been experimentally inconvenient but has been done in a few unpublished experiments by Constable and Pollard. Feather (F10) used a 2π solid angle and reported the interval distribution valid for his scintillation study of some 10,000 α rays.

It has been established adequately that at least in noncrystalline sources α rays are ejected uniformly in all directions. This and experimental convenience are the justification for the use of a small solid angle, and such experiments have been made by several workers. Of these, we shall discuss the data of Curtiss (C65), who employed a Geiger point counter to record the α rays emitted within a small solid angle from a polonium source. Between 20,000 and 30,000 α rays were counted in each of eighteen 6- to 7-hr runs extending over an elapsed time of 42 days. Lexis' divergence coefficient was computed for each of the 18 sets of data and showed a gradual approach to $Q^2 = 1.0$ as the source aged and as loose molecular aggregates were detached from the source by the recoil from the disintegration of one of the atoms in the aggregate. After all easily detached aggregates had been torn off, the source more exactly approximated one of constant strength, and the observed emission of α rays approached randomicity.

The resolving time of the counter was sufficiently small that the very short intervals could be faithfully observed. Finite resolving time always tends to lower Q^2 and χ^2 by ignoring short intervals, thus artificially reducing the true dispersion of the counts.

We now consider one of the 18 runs in detail. The number of α rays observed per time interval is recorded for $n = 3{,}455$ equal time intervals. Table 4.1 shows the number of these intervals l_x in which x α rays were observed. Thus no α rays were observed in eight of the intervals, one α ray in 59 intervals, etc., and in all, $\Sigma x l_x = 20{,}305$ α rays were observed. The average number of α rays per interval is thus

$$m \simeq \bar{x} = \frac{20{,}305}{3{,}455} = 5.88 \tag{4.1}$$

Knowing the total number of intervals and the average number of rays per interval, we can now assume that the Poisson distribution may describe the distribution of counts, and compare its predictions with observations. The number of intervals L_x in which x particles would be expected is given by the Poisson formula, Eq. (1.7) of Chap. 26,

$$L_x = nP_x = n\,\frac{m^x}{x!}\,e^{-m} \tag{4.2}$$

Hence, substituting $x = 0$, we expect $L_0 = 3{,}455e^{-5.88} = 9.7$ intervals with no α rays. Table 4.1 shows the calculated values for $x = 0$ to 15 particles per interval. Inspection of the table, or of Fig. 4.1, in which L_x and l_x are plotted against x, shows qualitatively that the observations are in reasonable agreement with Poisson's distribution governing random processes.

TABLE 4.1. CURTISS'S α-RAY DATA

x	l_x (obs)	L_x (calc)	$(l_x - L_x)$	$(l_x - L_x)^2/L_x$
0	8	9.7	-1.7	0.298
1	59	56.9	2.1	0.078
2	177	167.3	9.7	0.562
3	311	327.7	-16.7	0.853
4	492	481.4	10.6	0.233
5	528	565.8	-37.8	2.525
6	601	554.3	46.7	3.930
7	467	465.3	1.7	0.006
8	331	341.8	-10.8	0.342
9	220	223.2	-3.2	0.046
10	121	131.2	-10.2	0.793
11	85	70.1	14.9	3.170
12	24	34.3	-10.3	3.095
13	22	15.5	6.5	2.723
14	6	6.5	-0.5	0.038
15	3	2.6	$\left.\begin{array}{r}+0.4\\-1.4\end{array}\right\} -1.0$	0.250
≥ 16	0	1.4		
	$n = 3{,}455$			$\chi^2 = 18.942$

Degrees of freedom $= 16 - 2 = 14$ $\qquad$ $\therefore P = 0.2$

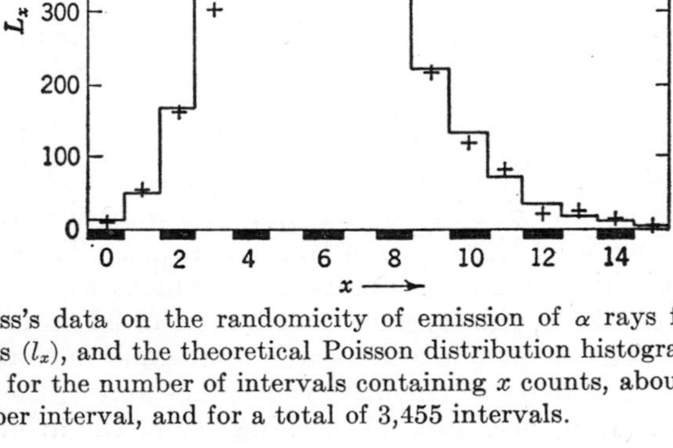

Fig. 4.1 Curtiss's data on the randomicity of emission of α rays from polonium. Observed values (l_x), and the theoretical Poisson distribution histogram (L_x in Table 4.1), are shown for the number of intervals containing x counts, about a mean value of 5.88 counts per interval, and for a total of 3,455 intervals.

[Handwritten marginalia:] Hoel: Since the χ^2 curve is only an approx. to the true dist., care must be exercised so that the χ^2 test will be used only when this approx. is good. Experience and theoretical investigation indicate that the expected value for each bin should be greater than or equal to five and that the number of degrees of freedom should be greater than or equal to five. If the number of degrees of freedom is less than five, it is best to have the expected value for each bin somewhat greater than five.

To determine the degree of agreement quantitatively, we apply the chi-square test to the data. To compute χ^2 we employ Eq. (2.1), which now takes the form

$$\chi^2 = \sum_x \frac{(l_x - L_x)^2}{L_x} \tag{4.3}$$

Table 4.1 summarizes the calculation leading to $\chi^2 = 18.9$.

The data have been divided into 16 classifications corresponding to $x = 0$ to 15; hence there are originally 16 independent ways in which the observations may be different $(l_x - L_x)$ from the calculations. However, there are not 16 degrees of freedom because two restrictions are placed on these 16 differences. First,

$$\Sigma l_x = \Sigma L_x$$

and secondly,

$$\Sigma x l_x = \Sigma x L_x$$

that is, we have used up two degrees of freedom by specifying (1) the total number of intervals and (2) the total number of events. The second restriction is, of course, equivalent to specifying the average number of rays per interval. There remain, then, $F = 16 - 2 = 14$ degrees of freedom. Entering Fig. 2.1 with these values of χ^2 and F, we find $P = 0.2$, i.e., in 2 cases out of 10 the deviations from Poisson's distribution would be expected to be greater than those here observed. The chi-square test thus gives us quantitative confidence in the randomicity of the process studied.

Studies of statistical theory and applications to cases of radioactive decay have been made by many workers, all tending to substantiate the view that the law of radioactive decay is a statistical law (K31). Kovarik (K43) showed that the β rays from a radium D + E + F mixture follow the Poisson distribution. In fact, all *independent* nuclear processes seem to follow the Poisson and the interval frequency distributions. This does not include some cases of series disintegration, as will be discussed in Chap. 28.

b. Distribution in Time of Cosmic-ray Bursts. As an example of the application of the chi-square test to the interval distribution, we consider the distribution of the time intervals between successive cosmic-ray bursts, as observed by the Montgomerys (M53).

The time of occurrence of 213 bursts in a total of 30.8 hr was observed. Equation (1.15) of Chap. 26 for the distribution of time intervals between randomly spaced events is assumed as a working hypothesis. The chi-square test is then applied to see how closely the observed time intervals between bursts agree with the assumption of random distribution in time. The results are summarized in Table 4.2. In analyzing the data, arbitrary choice is made of the range of time intervals. These are shown in the second and third columns. Thus if two bursts were separated by a time interval of 30 sec, this event would be one of 22 observed entries in the first row. The nomenclature used is analogous to that employed in Table 4.1. Thus l_x denotes the observed values and L_x the values calculated from Eq. (1.15) of Chap. 26, making use of the arbitrarily chosen time intervals, t_1 to t_2, and, from the data (1) the average rate of appearance of bursts (= 1/average interval between bursts) and (2) the total number of observed bursts.   Thus the number of degrees of freedom is two less than the number of patterns, or "classifications," studied.

The distribution curve of χ^2 (Fig. 2.1) is to be regarded as only an approximation to the true distribution if the number of independent classifications of data and the minimum number of events per classification are small.   Experience and theoretical studies show that *the approximation is usually satisfactory if there are at least five classifications, each containing at least five events*.   If there are less than five classifications, each should contain appreciably more than five events.   *It is best to combine classifications containing less than five events with an adjacent classification*.   Hence in Table 4.2 the intervals between 2,000 sec and

TABLE 4.2. DISTRIBUTION OF COSMIC-RAY BURSTS IN TIME (M53)

Classification	t_1, sec	t_2, sec	l_x (obs)	L_x (calc)	$(l_x - L_x)$	$(l_x - L_x)^2/L_x$
1	0	50	22	19.4	+2.6	0.35
2	50	100	17	17.9	−0.9	0.05
3	100	200	26	30.5	−4.5	0.66
4	200	500	68	63.5	+4.5	0.32
5	500	1,000	47	50.5	−3.5	0.24
6	1,000	2,000	31⎫			
7	2,000	5,000	2⎬	31.2	+1.8	0.10
8	5,000	∞	0⎭			
Total			213	213.0	0	$\chi^2 = 1.72$

Average interval between bursts = 521.6 sec
Degrees of freedom = 6   2 = 4
$P = 0.8$

infinity are to be combined with those between 1,000 and 2,000 sec. There are therefore six classifications, or patterns, studied and $6 - 2 = 4$ degrees of freedom.

Entering Fig. 2.1 for Pearson's chi-square test, we find $P = 0.8$, i.e., in 8 out of 10 similar experiments, the deviations from the interval distribution (which rests on the Poisson distribution) would be greater than here observed.   There is therefore strong support for the conclusion that the observed phenomena obey the interval distribution as proposed by Eq. (1.15) of Chap. 26, which describes a random process.

c. Randomicity of Geiger-Müller Counter Data.   Tables 4.3 and 4.4 show data taken on two Geiger-Müller counters used in radioactivity measurements.   The values of x are the number of impulses per 5-min interval and are due principally to local γ rays and cosmic rays actuating the instrument.   We wish to determine, from the spread of these data, whether or not the counter is operating satisfactorily.   Abundant evidence exists to show that these counts should be randomly distributed in time.   If they are not randomly distributed but tend to show periodicities, then we should suspect the counter in question of some anomalous behavior, such as a spurious periodic discharge superimposed on the true random effect of the incident radiation. The same arguments obviously apply to linear amplifiers, proportional counters, scintillation counters, and all similar detection instruments.

The routine statistical appraisal of these data is shown in the lower half of each table. In Table 4.3 it will be noted that the actual S.D. is slightly less than $\sqrt{\bar{x}}$, suggesting that the dispersion among the data is slightly subnormal. Two of the seven measurements fall outside ($\bar{x} \pm \sigma$), which is about the correct proportion. The result of the experiment and

TABLE 4.3. ANALYSIS OF GEIGER-MÜLLER COUNTER DATA

Test	x	$x - \bar{x}$	$(x - \bar{x})^2$
1	209	−18	324
2	217	−10	100
3	248	21	441
4	235	8	64
5	224	−3	9
6	223	−4	16
7	233	6	36
Total	1,589	0	990

Eq. (2.1), Chap. 26: $\bar{x} = \dfrac{1{,}589}{7} = 227$

Eq. (2.9), Chap. 26: $\sigma = \sqrt{\frac{990}{6}} = 12.8$ (from residuals)

Eq. (2.7), Chap. 26: $\sigma = \sqrt{227} = 15.1$ (expected)

Eq. (2.13), Chap. 26: $\sigma_{\bar{x}} = \dfrac{12.8}{\sqrt{7}} = 4.9$ (from residuals)

Eq. (2.17), Chap. 26: $r_{\bar{x}} = 0.6745 \times 4.9 = 3.3$ (from residuals)

Eq. (2.17), Chap. 26: $r_{\bar{x}} = 0.6745 \times \dfrac{15.1}{\sqrt{7}} = 3.8$ (expected)

Eq. (1.1), Chap. 27: $Q^2 = \dfrac{990}{7 \times 227} = 0.623$

Eq. (3.1), Chap. 27: $\chi^2 = \frac{990}{227} = 4.37$
$$F = 7 - 1 = 6$$
$$\therefore P = 0.6$$

its probable error of measurement would be recorded as 227 ± 4 counts per 5-min interval, or 45.4 ± 0.7 counts per minute. It is noted that Q^2 is not close to the expected value of unity for a Poisson distribution. Because $Q^2 < 1$, it is again evident that the dispersion of the data is subnormal, i.e., that even greater fluctuations should have been expected from a random distribution. But only the χ^2 test gives us definite information on just how well the data fit a random distribution. The only potential degree of freedom used up in the calculation of the expected values is the average rate $\bar{x} = 227$. With $\chi^2 = 4.37$ and $F = 6$, Fig. 2.1 gives $P = 0.6$. Therefore in 6 out of 10 similar tests we could expect fluctuations greater than those here observed. This is a satisfying result and suggests that this counter is behaving properly.

We now consider the data of Table 4.4, which led to the discovery of a faulty instrument. The very low value of the standard deviation computed from the residuals and the low value of Q^2 at once warn that the dispersion of the data is quite subnormal. However, the chi-square test provides us with a definite numerical gage of the improbability of our result. In 99 cases out of 100, we should expect a greater dispersion of data. We conclude that *either* (1) a very unusual observation has been made or (2) the instrument is faulty and devoted to spurious periodic discharges. The cautious experimenter will surely choose the latter

TABLE 4.4. ANALYSIS OF GEIGER-MÜLLER COUNTER DATA

Test	x	$x - \bar{x}$	$(x - \bar{x})^2$
1	242	-2	4
2	241	-3	9
3	249	5	25
4	246	2	4
5	236	-8	64
6	250	6	36
Total	1,464	0	142

Eq. (2.1), Chap. 26: $\bar{x} = \dfrac{1,464}{6} = 244$

Eq. (2.9), Chap. 26: $\sigma = \sqrt{\frac{142}{5}} = 5.3$ (from residuals)

Eq. (2.7), Chap. 26: $\sigma = \sqrt{244} = 15.6$ (expected)

Eq. (1.1), Chap. 27: $Q^2 = \dfrac{142}{6 \times 244} = 0.097$

Eq. (3.1), Chap. 27: $\chi^2 = \frac{142}{244} = 0.58$

$\qquad\qquad\qquad F = 6 - 1 = 5$

$\qquad\qquad\qquad \therefore P = 0.99$

explanation tentatively and will proceed with further examination of the instrument.

It is instructive to reread and contemplate on the observed values x in Tables 4.3 and 4.4. The naïve observer would usually choose the instrument of Table 4.4, because of the self-consistency and reproducibility of its readings. These are false clues. Variability comparable with or even greater than that exhibited in Table 4.3 *must be exhibited* by a reliable instrument operating on a random process.

Problems

1. Among 927 cosmic-ray bursts observed in 1,344 hr the interval between bursts was less than 30 sec in four instances, between 30 and 60 sec in 10 instances, and greater than 60 sec in the remaining 913 instances. [Cairns, *Phys. Rev.*, **47**: 194L, 631L (1935).] Compute the number of expected intervals of these durations if the bursts are randomly distributed in time. Apply Pearson's chi-square test and estimate the probability that greater deviations from randomicity would be observed in a repetition of the experiment.

2. The results of certain Army records, extending over a period of years, give among other things the number of soldiers killed by the kick of horses.

Number of deaths/time interval	Frequency observed
0	109
1	65
2	22
3	3
4	1
5	0
6	0

(a) What is the mean value of the number of deaths per time interval?

(b) What frequencies would you expect for 0, 1, 2, 3, 4, 5, 6 deaths per time interval?

(c) What is the probability that, on repeating this "series of measurements," larger deviations from the expected values would be observed?

3. Consider the spatial distribution of "flying-bomb" hits in a region south of London during World War II. For purposes of analysis, the entire region was divided into 576 squares of equal area ($\frac{1}{4}$ km² each). In the total region there were 537 hits altogether. The number of squares, l_x, receiving $x = 0$, 1, 2, . . . hits was as given in the table [from R. D. Clarke, *J. Inst. Actuaries*, **72**: 481 (1946)]. Many people believed that the points of impact tended to cluster.

No. hits in one square, x	No. squares receiving x hits, l_x
0	229
1	211
2	93
3	35
4	7
5	0
6	0
7	1
≥ 8	0

(a) Analyze the data given, and determine the probability that a purely random distribution of hits would show *better* agreement with the Poisson distribution.

(b) In what mathematical ways, if any, does this problem differ from an analysis of the number l_x of 1-min intervals, out of a total of 576 min, which contain $x = 0$, 1, 2, . . . nuclear disintegrations when the average rate is

$$\bar{x} = \tfrac{537}{576} = 0.932$$

disintegrations per minute?

4. A counter detects the radiation from a small solid angle of a source. A statistical analysis shows these data to obey an interval distribution. Why does this *not* definitely indicate that the disintegrations within the source are randomly distributed in time?

5. In successive 15-min intervals the background of a certain counter is 310, 290, 280, 315, 315, 275, 315. A radioactive source, whose half-period is 14 days, is brought up to the counter, and the increased counting rate, for successive 15-min intervals, is 720, 760, 770, 740, 780, 710, 780, 740. Calculate in counts per minute the average value and probable errors for the (a) background, (b) background plus source, and (c) source alone. Show quantitatively whether or not the data on source plus background can safely be considered to be randomly distributed.

CHAPTER 28

Applications of Poisson Statistics to Some Instruments Used in Nuclear Physics

There are many situations in experimental nuclear physics in which the effect of the detection apparatus is to alter or conceal the randomicity which is actually present in the nuclear process being observed. In some cases this alteration of the statistics of the process can be calculated from the laws which describe purely random distributions. We consider now some of the common practical cases.

1. Effects of the Finite Resolving Time of Counting Instruments

Every detection instrument used for counting single rays or particles exhibits a characteristic time constant having the nature of a recovery time. After recording one pulse, the counter is unresponsive to successive pulses until a time interval equal to or greater than its resolving time ρ has elapsed.

The interval distribution [Chap. 26, Eq. (1.14)] shows that short intervals are more likely to occur than are long intervals between successive events in a random distribution. If the interval between two true events is shorter than the resolving time ρ, then only the first event will be recorded. Thus there are both a loss of counts and a distortion of the distribution. Very short intervals are missing in the output. The observed distribution will have an average value and a standard deviation which differ from the true values for the primary random process.

a. Counting Losses Due to Finite Resolving Time. Counter systems really do not count the nuclear events, such as β rays, but rather the intervals between such events. Thus *all counting systems are really interval counters*. The conditions under which ionizing events fail to be recorded depend strongly on the characteristics of the detector and of the amplifier and recording system. Two limiting cases, or types, may be identified easily.

Type I ("Paralyzable"). This type is unable to provide a second output pulse unless there is a time interval of at least ρ between two successive true events. During the response time ρ to an initial event, the recovery of the apparatus is further extended for an additional time ρ

by any additional true events which occur before full recovery has taken place.   Thus if five true events are spaced at successive intervals of 2ρ, 0.5ρ, 0.8ρ, 3ρ, only the first, second, and fifth event (corresponding to the first and last intervals) can be recorded.   Figure 1.1 illustrates the continued paralysis of the detector until a free interval of at least ρ shall permit relaxation of the apparatus.

Systems of Type I (paralyzable) count only those intervals which are longer than ρ.   The interval distribution [Chap. 26, Eq. (1.15)] gives at once the fraction of the intervals which are longer than ρ as $e^{-N\rho}$, where

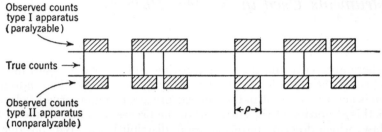

Fig. 1.1   Schematic illustration of the behavior of counting systems having a resolving time ρ.   The time axis is from left to right.   True counts occur at the times shown by vertical lines along the center section.   Apparatus of Type I responds only to intervals longer than ρ.   The number of observed counts and the time during which the Type I apparatus is insensitive are shown by shaded blocks.   Apparatus of Type II is insensitive for a time ρ after one pulse but then can respond again even if the interval between successive true counts is less than ρ, as illustrated by the triplet.   In the hypothetical example shown, there are eight true counts, of which six are recorded by a Type II apparatus and only five are recorded by a Type I apparatus.

N is the average number of true events per unit time.   Then if the total number of intervals counted is large compared with unity, the observed counting rate n is simply

$$n = Ne^{-N\rho} \tag{1.1}$$

If the true counting rate N is small enough, only a few intervals (or counts) are missed.   Then the observed counting rate is given by the useful approximations

$$n \simeq N(1 - N\rho) \tag{1.2}$$

or

$$N \simeq n(1 + n\rho) \tag{1.3}$$

when $N\rho \ll 1$.

As the true counting rate is increased, differentiation of Eq. (1.1) with respect to N shows that, when $N\rho = 1$, the observed counting rate n passes through a maximum given by

$$n_{\max} = \frac{N}{e} = \frac{1}{e\rho} \tag{1.4}$$

It is to be noted that the maximum of the observed counting rate occurs when the average number of true pulses expected per resolving time is unity, that is, $N\rho = 1$.   Then $1/e = 0.368$ of the true events is registered.   Also the maximum rate of response to *uniformly* spaced pulses (as from an oscillator) would be simply $1/\rho$, which is just e times the maximum observable rate of response of the same apparatus to randomly spaced input pulses.

If the true rate N is increased through values greater than $1/\rho$, then the observed rate n actually decreases, as paralysis of the apparatus becomes increasingly worse because of the scarcity of intervals longer than the resolving time ρ. The behavior is shown in Fig. 1.2.

As the true counting rate approaches infinity, the observed rate will approach zero, i.e., a condition of complete paralysis. Examples of paralyzable apparatus include most forms of electromechanical registers and certain (non-self-quenching) Geiger-Müller counters connected to a conventional high-resistance preamplifier.

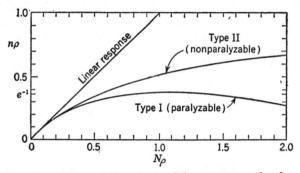

Fig. 1.2 Because of the finite resolving time ρ of the apparatus, the observed counting rate n is always less than the true counting rate N. Here $n\rho$ is plotted against $N\rho$ for two limiting cases. Type I (paralyzable) apparatus counts all intervals which are longer than ρ; note that the maximum observed counting rate corresponds to $n\rho = 1/e$ and occurs when $N\rho = 1$. Type II (nonparalyzable) apparatus is completely insensitive for a time ρ after each observed count, then regains full sensitivity. An apparatus with zero resolving time would follow the straight line marked "linear response."

An excellent generalized statistical treatment of resolving time losses in Type I apparatus for single-channel and coincidence counters, on constant and on decaying sources, has been developed by Schiff (S8).

Type II ("*Nonparalyzable*"). The opposite statistical extreme is found in apparatus which is not affected in any way by events which occur during its recovery time ρ.

Under these circumstances, the apparatus is dead for a time ρ after each recorded event. If the observed counting rate is n, then the fraction of the unit running time during which the apparatus is dead is $n\rho$. The fraction of the time during which the apparatus is sensitive is $1 - n\rho$. This is therefore the fraction of the true number of events which can be recorded, so that

$$\frac{n}{N} = 1 - n\rho \qquad (1.5)$$

or

$$N = \frac{n}{1 - n\rho} \qquad (1.6)$$

At relatively low counting rates, when $N\rho \ll 1$, we can write Eq. (1.5), to a good approximation, as

$$N \simeq n(1 + n\rho) \tag{1.7}$$

which is the same as for Type I apparatus, Eq. (1.3), provided that $N\rho$, and consequently $n\rho$, is small compared with unity.

Type II apparatus never exhibits complete paralysis. As N is increased, the observed counting rate n rises uniformly, approaching asymptotically the value

$$n_{max} = \frac{1}{\rho} \qquad \text{for } N = \infty \tag{1.8}$$

The general nature of the response curve is shown in Fig. 1.2. To an infinitely strong source of radiation, the apparatus responds periodically, with a frequency of $1/\rho$, all traces of statistical randomicity having been erased.

Equipment of Type II is illustrated by a fixed-gas counter (non-self-quenching) connected to a quenching preamplifier designed to maintain the applied voltage below the counting threshold for a time ρ, during which both the counter and the recording circuit are able to effect complete recovery. The same characteristics would be exhibited by a self-quenching counter connected to a very sensitive preamplifier capable of responding to all pulses received after the dead time of the counter. Most proportional counters and scintillation counters also follow the behavior of Type II.

b. Measurement of Resolving Time in Single-channel Counters. All that has been said above assumes that the resolving time is independent of the counting rate. There is some evidence (M74) that the dead time ρ in self-quenching counters may decrease when the counting rate is elevated to very high values. But at the lower counting rates met in most measurements, the assumption of constant resolving time agrees well with the observations. Many apparatus, however, do not conform perfectly to either of the limiting cases treated above but show resolution characteristics intermediate between Types I and II. Happily, the expressions for both limiting types converge at low counting rates. If $N\rho \leq 0.05$, the exact expressions for n/N differ from each other by less than 0.1 per cent, and the relation

$$N \simeq n(1 + n\rho) \tag{1.9}$$

may be used for any single-channel counting apparatus.

The resolving time of a reasonably well-designed Geiger-Müller counter and amplifier will usually be found to be between 3 and 6 $\times$ 10^{-4} sec, which is equivalent to between 5 and 10 $\times 10^{-6}$ min. Then at an observed counting rate of 1,000 counts per minute, the fraction of the counts which are lost is $n\rho = 5$ to 10×10^{-3}, or 0.5 to 1 per cent. At 2,000 counts per minute, the same apparatus loses 1 to 2 per cent of the counts. Based on Eq. (1.9), counting losses are often cited simply as *"per cent loss per thousand counts per minute."* Observed counting rates can be corrected easily and accurately for counting losses if $N\rho < 0.05$, i.e., up to observed rates of 5,000 to 10,000 counts per minute for most Geiger-Müller counters.

Scintillation counters, employing anthracene or similar phosphors, can have pulse widths of less than 10^{-7} sec. With suitably fast amplifiers, resolving times of 10^{-8} sec have been realized. Hence counting experiments with such equipment can be carried out accurately at counting rates of the order of 500,000 per minute. Certain proportional counters and linear pulse amplifiers can also have resolving times of the order of a microsecond or less.

One of the simplest satisfactory methods (B26, R12) for measuring the resolving time of single-channel counting apparatus is to compare the response of the apparatus to the radiation from two approximately equal sources, taken separately and then taken simultaneously. Let B be the true average background counting rate when neither source is present, and let N_A and N_B be the true elevation of the counting rate for each of the two sources. Then the observed counting rates for each of the two sources, including background, are n_A and n_B, where

$$N_A + B = n_A(1 + n_A\rho) \tag{1.10}$$
$$N_B + B = n_B(1 + n_B\rho) \tag{1.11}$$

Then when both sources are measured simultaneously, the sum of their radiation will elevate the true rate to $N_S + B = N_A + N_B + B$, but the observed rate will be only n_S, where

$$N_A + N_B + B = n_S(1 + n_S\rho) \tag{1.12}$$

provided that all counting rates are small enough that $n_S\rho \ll 1$. Subtracting Eq. (1.12) from the sum of Eqs. (1.10) and (1.11), and solving for ρ, we have

$$\rho = \frac{n_A + n_B - n_S - B}{n_S^2 - n_A^2 - n_B^2} \tag{1.13}$$

A useful transformation of Eq. (1.13) is obtained by setting

$$\delta = n_A + n_B - n_S - B \tag{1.14}$$

where, physically, δ is the difference between the counting losses in the observation on both sources taken simultaneously and the sum of the counting losses in the two observations on the two sources taken singly. Then Eq. (1.13) becomes

$$\rho = \frac{\delta}{2n_An_B - 2(\delta + B)n_S - (\delta + B)^2} \tag{1.15}$$

or, to an approximation which is usually satisfactory,

$$\rho \simeq \frac{\delta}{2n_An_B} \tag{1.16}$$

In carrying out an estimation of the resolving time ρ by this "two-source method," the observations should be taken in the order n_A, n_S,

n_B, that is, on A, $A + B$, and finally B alone. In this way, the single and the combined readings on each source are obtainable without moving the source between successive readings. This procedure avoids errors due to failure to reproduce the source positions accurately, as can occur when the order n_A, n_B, n_S is used. It is also important that, when the combined radiation of both sources is measured, the two sources should be sufficiently separated from each other so that neither source can scatter any of the radiation from the other source into the counter.

The National Bureau of Standards distributes standard γ-ray sources of certified radium or Co⁶⁰ content, which are convenient for calibrating counting apparatus. One series includes 5 ml of dilute HCl in flame-sealed glass ampoules containing Ra in the accurately graduated amounts 0.1, 0.2, 0.5, 1, 2, 5, 10, etc., μg. Pairs of these ampoules may be used in the two-source method of Eq. (1.13).

Alternatively, a series of such standard sources may be used to obtain a direct plot of observed counting rate n against source strength S. By fitting the best straight line (linear response, as in Fig. 1.2) to the lower end of such a curve, the nonlinearity of response of the counting apparatus can be evaluated empirically without making any assumptions regarding the detailed mechanism by which it loses counts. The slope of the straight line representing linear response N can be adjusted most accurately by noting that the counting loss $(N - n)$ and especially the counting loss per unit source strength, that is, $(N - n)/S$, must both extrapolate to zero at zero net counting rate. Thus the slope of the line of linear response N can be accurately adjusted, by successive approximations (K36), from auxiliary plots of $(N - n)/S$ against source strength S.

In the mathematical treatment, we have assumed thus far that the apparatus has only one controlling time constant, which is independent of counting rate. Certain scaling circuits, connected to slowly operating mechanical registers or recorders, may exhibit two important time constants. At low counting rates, the losses may be determined only by the resolving time of the counter and the first stage of the amplifier, as described in the preceding paragraphs. As the counting rates are elevated, a situation will occur in which, for example, a scale of 4 will occasionally receive five or more pulses in less than the time interval required for action of the mechanical register which it should be driving each time four counts are received. Then the resolving time of the mechanical register also becomes important. Consequently, the mathematical analysis of the scaling losses in such cases is more complicated (L30, L23) and will not be discussed here because usually it can be avoided by proper design of apparatus, e.g., by increasing the scaling factor.

c. Effect of Loss of Short Intervals on the Standard Deviation of the Output of Single-channel Counters. When N is the true average rate of a random process which is observed for a total time T, the "expectation," or average, number of true events is NT. In the preceding sections we have seen that the average, or expected, number of *observed* events nT is smaller than NT by an amount which depends on the resolving time ρ, the average rate N, and the type of apparatus. All the expressions developed there concern the usual nuclear laboratory case in which a large number of events are observed, that is, $NT \gg 1$. A much more complicated analysis must be performed to determine nT when only a few events are observed.

The variance (square of the standard deviation) of the expected true number of events is also NT, by Eq. (2.7) of Chap. 26. However, the variance of the *observed* number of events is not given simply by nT, even when $nT \gg 1$, because the number of short intervals which are lost depends both on the type of apparatus and on $n\rho$ or $N\rho$. Because the more abundant short intervals are removed, the variance of the observed distribution may be markedly smaller than of the parent distribution.

Various approximate or asymptotic solutions for the average number of registrations nT and for the variance σ^2 of the number of registrations have been developed by several workers.

For Type I (paralyzable) apparatus, the expected average number of registrations nT is (F29)

$$nT = (NT - N\rho - 1)e^{-N\rho} + 1 \tag{1.17}$$

which reduces to Eq. (1.1) for the usual experimental case in which $T \gg \rho$. The variance is approximately (K42)

$$\sigma^2 = NT \left(1 - 2N\rho + \frac{N\rho^2}{T} \right) \tag{1.18}$$

which for inferior apparatus arrangements can be (L19) even as small as $NT/2$. Feller (F29) has developed a much more complicated and presumably more exact expression for the variance of paralyzable apparatus.

For Type II (nonparalyzable) apparatus, the asymptotic expansion of the general solutions obtained with the use of operational calculus leads to an approximate expression for the average expected value of (F29)

$$nT \sim \frac{NT}{1 + N\rho} + \frac{N^2\rho^2}{2(1 + N\rho)^2} \tag{1.19}$$

which reduces to Eq. (1.6) when $N\rho \ll 1$. The variance of the number of registrations is approximately (F29)

$$\sigma^2 \sim \frac{NT}{(1 + N\rho)^3} \tag{1.20}$$

which is some 20 per cent smaller than the simple Poisson value nT when $N\rho = 0.1$.

d. Random Coincidences in Coincidence and Anticoincidence Circuits. Many types of measurement are made using two (or more) counters exposed to the same source of nuclear radiation. The outputs from the two counters may then be fed through a coincidence circuit, from which an output pulse is delivered only if pulses were received "simultaneously" from the two counters.

For example, a source of Al^{28}, whose decay scheme is shown in Fig. 4.2 of Chap. 3, might be placed between a β-ray counter and a γ-ray counter. Then a *true coincidence* would be registered when the two counters were triggered by the β ray and the prompt γ ray emitted by the same atom. In addition to such true coincidences, there will be false or *random coincidences* which are produced when a β ray and an unrelated γ ray actuate the counters within the resolving time of the apparatus.

Figure 1.3 is an illustrative experimental situation. Channel 1 receives random pulses (e.g., from β rays) at an average true rate N_1 and has a resolving time ρ_1. Channel 2 also receives randomly distributed pulses (for example, γ rays from the same source) at an average true rate N_2 and has a resolving time ρ_2. Let $N_{1,2}$ represent the true coincidence rate, which is generally much smaller than the singles rates N_1 and N_2.

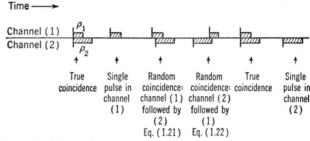

Fig. 1.3 Schematic illustration of true and random coincidences in a two-channel coincidence-counting circuit. For anticoincidence circuits, read "anticoincidence" for "coincidence" everywhere.

Then, in channel 1, the rate for those single pulses which are *not* associated with a true coincidence is $(N_1 - N_{1,2})$. Therefore, in the coincidence circuit, channel 1 is "set up," or "alive," for the fraction $(N_1 - N_{1,2})\rho_1$ of the running time, in addition to the time which it spends responding to true coincidences. In channel 2, single pulses which are not associated with true coincidences are arriving at an average rate $(N_2 - N_{1,2})$. The random-coincidence rate due to single pulses in channel 1 being followed, within its resolving time ρ_1, by single pulses in channel 2 is therefore

$$(N_1 - N_{1,2})\rho_1(N_2 - N_{1,2}) \qquad (1.21)$$

To these we must add additional random coincidences due to single pulses in channel 2 which are followed within its resolving time ρ_2 by random single pulses in channel 1. Because channel 2 is alive for the fraction $(N_2 - N_{1,2})\rho_2$ of the running time, aside from its response to true coincidences, this additional random-coincidence rate is

$$(N_2 - N_{1,2})\rho_2(N_1 - N_{1,2}) \qquad (1.22)$$

Both these two types of random coincidence are illustrated in Fig. 1.3. "Double random coincidences," such as would be caused by two pulses in channel 1 within the resolving time of channel 2, can be made negligible by keeping $N_1\rho_1 \ll 1$ and $N_2\rho_2 \ll 1$. Then the total random-coincidence rate is

$$N_{\text{random}} = (N_1 - N_{1,2})\rho_1(N_2 - N_{1,2}) + (N_2 - N_{1,2})\rho_2(N_1 - N_{1,2})$$
$$= (N_1 - N_{1,2})(N_2 - N_{1,2})(\rho_1 + \rho_2) \tag{1.23}$$

In practice, the singles rates N_1 and N_2 are usually large compared with the true coincidence rate $N_{1,2}$. Then Eq. (1.23) becomes approximately

$$N_{\text{random}} \simeq N_1 N_2(\rho_1 + \rho_2) \tag{1.24}$$

If N_1 and N_2 are each proportional to source strength, we note from Eq. (1.24) that the random coincidences increase with the square of the source strength. This condition imposes an upper limit on the useful source strength in any coincidence experiment, because at least half the total observed coincidences should be true coincidences.

In anticoincidence circuits, pulses are recorded from channel 1 provided that there is no coincident pulse in channel 2. It can be seen that the number of random anticoincidences is also given by Eq. (1.23).

Problems

1. The decay $N = N_0 e^{-\lambda t}$ of a radioactive substance is being observed with a paralyzable counter whose resolving time is ρ. Write an expression for the observed counting rate n as a function of time. Assume that $N_0\rho \sim 0.1$ and no resolving-time corrections are made. Under what conditions will the apparent half-period of radioactive decay be of the order of 10 per cent greater than the true half-period $0.693/\lambda$?

2. The resolving time of a γ-ray counter and amplifier is to be determined. Two radioactive sources A and B are first measured separately and then together. The observed counting rates are n_A for source A, n_B for source B, and n_S for $(A + B)$, each including the small background rate B.

(a) Derive an expression for the resolving time ρ of the apparatus, in terms of these three observed counting rates. Assume that n_S is small compared with the reciprocal of the resolving time.

(b) Calculate the resolving time of an apparatus if $B = 100$ counts per minute, $n_A = n_B = 4{,}800$ counts per minute, and $n_S = 9{,}120$ counts per minute.

(c) What would be the true counting rate for the source A?

Ans.: (a) See Eq. (1.16); (b) 8.25 μmin; (c) 4,890 counts per minute.

3. The resolving time of a γ-ray counter and amplifier is to be determined. Two radioactive sources C and D are available, and D is known to be exactly R times as strong as C. The observed counting rates are n_C counts per minute for source C and n_D for source D, including a background counting rate of B. Assume that n_D is small compared with the reciprocal of the resolving time.

(a) Show that the resolving time ρ of the apparatus is given by

$$\rho = \frac{n_C R - n_D - (R - 1)B}{n_D^2 - n_C^2 R}$$

(b) Calculate the resolving time of an apparatus if $n_C = 3{,}050$ counts per minute, $n_D = 8{,}690$ counts per minute, $B = 100$ counts per minute, and $R = 3.00$.

(c) What would be the true counting rate for the source C?

Ans.: (b) 5.5 μmin; (c) 3,001 counts per minute.

4. In the two-source method for determining the resolving time ρ, show that a close approximation for the standard error $\sigma(\rho)$ in the determination of ρ, in an experiment of total duration $3T$, is

$$\sigma(\rho) \simeq \frac{1}{n_A} \sqrt{\frac{1}{n_A T}}$$

if $n_A \simeq n_B$ and a total time of $3T$ is approximately equally divided between measurement of n_A, n_B, and n_S, the background B being known in advance with negligible error.

5. A certain electromechanical register is found to follow just 120 periodic pulses per second without jamming.

(a) What is its maximum counting rate of randomly distributed pulses, as the average rate of random pulses is increased without limit?

(b) At the maximum observed rate of counting, what is the true average rate?

6. A Western Electric telephone register is found to have a maximum counting rate of 240 per minute for random pulses. Compute the true counting rate when this register shows 10, 30, 60, 90, 120, 180, 240 counts per minute from a random process. Plot these observed counting rates as abscissas against true rates as ordinates.

7. In the fall of 1947 an amateur long-range weather forecaster set out to predict the times of the snowstorms in Boston for the coming winter. Assuming that winter lasts from December 17 to March 15, a total of 90 days, and that the average number of snowstorms per winter for the last 20 years is 15, he predicted a total of 15 snowstorms and assigned a date to each one at random. Thus he divided the winter into 24-hr intervals and for 15 of these intervals, chosen at random, he predicted snow. It turned out, however, that there were actually 27 snowstorms that winter. Assume that each of these lasted exactly 6 hr and that they were randomly distributed throughout the winter. If we agree to call a prediction successful when some snow (not necessarily the whole amount coming down in a snowstorm) fell during an interval for which snow was predicted, then what is the probable number of successful predictions? *Ans.:* About six.

2. Scaling Circuits

In a typical scaling circuit, one output pulse is produced for every s input events. If the events at the input are randomly distributed in time and have an average rate a, the scaling circuit conceals the short intervals, tends to average out the variations of interval length, and produces an approximately periodic output (H67) whose mean frequency is a/s. Those counting losses which are due to the resolving time of electromechanical registers can be made negligibly small by the use of scaling circuits having a sufficiently large scaling factor s. Electronically, two types of scaler are now in common use. The two types are the scale of 2, which is cascaded to give instruments having $s = 2^n = 2, 4, 8, 16, 32, 64, \ldots, 4,096, \ldots$, and decade scalers having $s = 10^n = 10, 100, 1,000$.

a. Generalized (s-fold) Interval Distribution. We shall assume at first that the input pulses delivered to the scaler are randomly distributed in time, at an average rate a, or average interval $1/a$. The length of an interval between output, or "s-fold," pulses may be called an "s-fold interval." The intervals *between* successive input pulses contain zero events; the intervals between successive s-fold pulses contain $s - 1$ events (such as counts from a Geiger-Müller counter or from a scintillation counter).

The Poisson distribution [Chap. 26, Eq. (1.6)] shows that the probability that an s-fold interval of duration t will contain exactly $s - 1$ events is

$$P_{s-1}(t) = \frac{(at)^{s-1}}{(s-1)!} e^{-at} \tag{2.1}$$

The probability of one event occurring in an additional time dt is simply

$$P_1(dt) = a\, dt \tag{2.2}$$

The probability of $s - 1$ events in t, and the sth event between t and $t + dt$, is therefore

$$dP_t = P_{s-1}(t)\, P_1(dt)$$

$$= \frac{a^s t^{s-1}}{(s-1)!} e^{-at}\, dt \tag{2.3}$$

which is the generalized s-fold interval distribution. Equation (1.14) of Chap. 26 is seen to correspond to the special case in which $s = 1$. Equation (2.3) expresses the probability that an s-fold interval will have a duration between t and $t + dt$ when a is the average rate and a/s is the average rate of s-fold counting.

We note that Eq. (2.3) is already normalized, and this can be verified by finding the probability that the s-fold interval will have some duration between zero and infinity. Thus

$$\int_0^\infty dP_t = \frac{a^s}{(s-1)!} \int_0^\infty t^{s-1} e^{-at}\, dt = \frac{a^s}{(s-1)!} \frac{(s-1)!}{a^s} = 1 \tag{2.4}$$

The probability P_T that an s-fold interval will be equal to or shorter than a time T can be obtained by integration of Eq. (2.3). Then

$$P_T = \int_0^T dP_t = \frac{a^s}{(s-1)!} \int_0^T t^{s-1} e^{-at}\, dt \tag{2.5}$$

This integral can be evaluated by successive integration by parts, yielding

$$P_T = 1 - e^{-aT} - \frac{aT}{1} e^{-aT} - \frac{(aT)^2}{1 \times 2} e^{-aT} - \cdots - \frac{(aT)^{s-1}}{(s-1)!} e^{-aT} \tag{2.6}$$

Each of these terms is simply the Poisson probability of 0, 1, 2, . . . $(s - 1)$ events in the time T, or

$$P_T = 1 - (P_0 + P_1 + P_2 + \cdots + P_{s-1}) \tag{2.7}$$

or, since $\sum_0^\infty P_i = 1$,

$$P_T = P_s + P_{s+1} + \cdots + P_\infty \tag{2.8}$$

This result could have been written directly by noting that the probability for an s-fold pulse within the time T is simply the Poisson probability of s, *or more*, events in the time T.

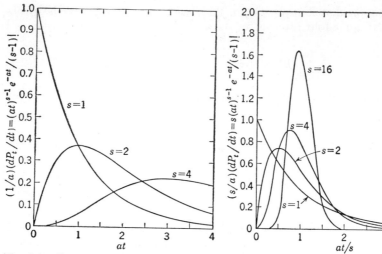

Fig. 2.1 Generalized s-fold interval distribution. Abscissas: average number of randomly distributed events at in time interval t. Ordinates: probability of s-fold interval, of duration between at and $a(t + dt)$. The area under each curve between time zero and at is the probability that an s-fold interval will be shorter than at, Eq. (2.5). Note that the duration at of the most probable s-fold interval is $s - 1$, Eq. (2.10), i.e., the average time for $s - 1$ random events. The average interval, however, is $at = s$, Eq. (2.9). Note the great reduction in the probability of short intervals which is produced even by these very small scaling factors. Because of the analytical form of Eq. (2.3), these curves also represent the Poisson probability of getting $s - 1$ random events in the time t when the average expected number is at, Eq. (2.1), or Eq. (1.6) of Chap. 26.

Fig. 2.2 Curves similar to Fig. 2.1 but normalized to a time axis at/s, so that the average s-fold interval is $at/s = 1$. The most probable s-fold interval is $at/s = (s - 1)/s$. The ordinates are adjusted so that the area under each curve is unity. Note the strong regularizing action of the larger scaling factors, e.g., for $s = 16$ the distribution of intervals appears almost normal. The fractional standard deviation of the distribution of s-fold intervals decreases as $\sqrt{1/s}$, as given by Eq. (2.15). Thus the chance that the duration of an s-fold interval will vary greatly from the average s-fold interval decreases markedly as s increases.

Of course, the probability that an s-fold interval will be longer than T is simply $1 - P_T$. Useful numerical tables of P_T have been compiled by Molina (M49).

The distribution of s-fold intervals is shown in Figs. 2.1 and 2.2.

b. Average s-fold Interval. The average s-fold interval has the duration

$$\bar{t}_s = \int_0^\infty t \, dP_t$$

$$= \frac{a^s}{(s-1)!} \int_0^\infty t^s e^{-at} \, dt$$

$$= \frac{a^s}{(s-1)!} \frac{s!}{a^{s+1}}$$

$$= \frac{s}{a} \tag{2.9}$$

as expected from the fact that the average interval of the parent random process is $1/a$.

c. Most Probable s-fold Interval. The probability that an s-fold interval lies between t and $t + dt$ is given by Eq. (2.3). Then $y = dP_t/dt$ is the differential probability of an interval of duration t, and dy/dt is the variation of this probability with the duration t of the s-fold interval. The most probable duration t_0 occurs when

$$\frac{dy}{dt} = \frac{d}{dt}\left[\frac{a^s t^{s-1} e^{-at}}{(s-1)!}\right] = 0$$

which is when $t = (s-1)/a$, thus

$$t_0 = \frac{s-1}{a} \tag{2.10}$$

It will be noted that the most probable interval is slightly shorter than the average interval $\bar{t}$, such that

$$t_0 = \frac{s-1}{s}\,\bar{t} \tag{2.11}$$

For scale of 1 the most probable interval is zero, while when s is very large the most probable interval approaches the average interval.

d. Standard Deviation of s-fold Intervals. The deletion of short intervals and the approximately periodic output of the scaler is sometimes referred to as the *regularizing action* of a scaler. The variance σ^2 of the s-fold intervals is a measure of this "smoothing effect" and is

$$\sigma^2 = \int_0^\infty (t - \bar{t})^2 \, dP_t = \frac{a^s}{(s-1)!} \int_0^\infty \left(t - \frac{s}{a}\right)^2 t^{s-1} e^{-at} \, dt \tag{2.12}$$

which, on expansion and evaluation, leads to

$$\sigma^2 = \frac{s}{a^2} \tag{2.13}$$

or, for the standard deviation σ, we have

$$\sigma = \frac{\sqrt{s}}{a} = \frac{\bar{t}}{\sqrt{s}} \tag{2.14}$$

Then the *fractional* standard deviation of s-fold intervals is

$$\frac{\sigma}{\bar{t}} = \frac{1}{\sqrt{s}} \tag{2.15}$$

Thus the fractional standard deviation in the time $\bar{t}$, required to accumulate s random events, decreases with the inverse square root of the total number of counts, for it does not matter what type of apparatus is used to tally the s events.

This important result shows directly what fluctuations are to be expected in counting observations based on measurements of the time required to accumulate a predetermined number of counts. Thus the fractional standard deviation of the time required to accumulate a total of, for example, $2^{12} = 4,096$ counts is simply $\sqrt{1/4,096} = \frac{1}{64} = 1.56$ per cent.

It should be especially noted that this is the same as the algebraic form Eq. (2.15) of Chap. 26 for the fractional fluctuation, or error, which would be associated with observations of the number of counts accumulated in a predetermined time.

Scaling circuits may also be understood from the viewpoint of the generalized Poisson distribution of Eqs. (3.1) and (3.2) of Chap. 26. If x is the expectation number of random events, and if the specific effectiveness is $1/s$ per event, then Eq. (3.1) of Chap. 26 shows that the expected average number of s-fold pulses is simply

$$u = \frac{x}{s} \qquad \text{if } u \text{ is integral or if } x \gg s \tag{2.16}$$

while the expected standard deviation σ is given by Eq. (3.2) of Chap. 26 as

$$\sigma^2 = \frac{x}{s^2} \tag{2.17}$$

and the fractional standard deviation of the number of s-fold registrations in a fixed time is

$$\frac{\sigma}{u} = \frac{\sqrt{x/s^2}}{x/s} = \frac{1}{\sqrt{x}}$$

$$= \frac{1}{\sqrt{su}} \tag{2.18}$$

which is the same as Eq. (2.15) of Chap. 26 and as Eq. (2.15) above, because u can have any integral value and is unity for the case considered in Eq. (2.15) above.

e. Interpolation. Many conventional scaling circuits are provided with interpolation lights or meters. Then if counting is stopped at a predetermined time, the exact number of input counts x is given by

$$x = su + \Delta \tag{2.19}$$

where u is the number of s-fold pulses and Δ is the number of single interpolation pulses.   It is to be noted that the interpolation pulses Δ are only statistically significant if they are comparable with or greater than the standard deviation of x.   We can ignore the interpolation pulses in many practical cases without introducing a statistically significant error.   Suppose that we decide that Δ is to be ignored whenever its maximum possible value, $\Delta_{max} = s - 1$, cannot exceed some arbitrary fraction β of the standard deviation in x.   Then we can omit the chore of interpolation whenever

$$\Delta_{max} = s - 1 < \beta \sqrt{su + \Delta} > \beta \sqrt{su} \qquad (2.20)$$

Squaring, and solving the second inequality for u, we have

$$u > \frac{(s - 1)^2}{\beta^2 s} \qquad (2.21)$$

or, in the practical case of $s \gg 1$, and $\beta \sim \frac{1}{2}$, interpolation is pointless whenever

$$u > 4s \qquad (2.22)$$

f. Chi-square for the Output from a Scaler.   The output from a scale of s may be tested for fidelity and for randomicity of the input process by computing the standard deviation of the s-fold output from its residuals, Eq. (2.9) of Chap. 26, and comparing with the theoretically expected values of Eq. (2.15) or Eq. (2.18).

A more objective appraisal of the data is obtained by applying the χ^2 test.   This can be done by computing the input events, from the s-fold output readings, and then applying Eq. (3.1) of Chap. 27 to the input or scale-of-1 events.   More conveniently, one may wish to compute χ^2 for the input process directly from the s-fold output readings. Then two cases arise, depending on whether the series of output observations are made over a predetermined and fixed time interval (variable number of counts) or over a predetermined total number of counts (time variable).

Case I, Constant Time Interval.   In a series of n successive equal time intervals, let the number of observed s-fold output pulses be $u_1, u_2, \ldots, u_n$ (u can be nonintegral if interpolation has been resorted to, thus $u = x/s$).   Then the average s-fold output is

$$\bar{u} = \frac{1}{n} \sum_{1}^{n} u_i \qquad (2.23)$$

and χ^2, of Eq. (3.1) of Chap. 27 but in terms of the s-fold output counts, becomes

$$\chi^2 = \sum_{1}^{n} \frac{(x_i - \bar{x})^2}{\bar{x}} = \sum_{1}^{n} \frac{(su_i - s\bar{u})^2}{s\bar{u}}$$

$$= \frac{s}{\bar{u}} \sum_{1}^{n} (u_i - \bar{u})^2 \qquad (2.24)$$

The expected value of the summation in Eq. (2.24) is n times the variance σ^2 of u. If the input process is random, then Eq. (3.2) of Chap. 26 gives $\sigma^2 = \bar{x}/s^2$; hence

$$\sum_1^n (u_i - \bar{u})^2 = n\sigma^2 = \frac{n\bar{x}}{s^2} = \frac{n\bar{u}}{s}$$

and the expectation value of Eq. (2.24) is

$$\chi^2 = \frac{s}{\bar{u}}\frac{n\bar{u}}{s} = n \qquad (2.25)$$

as in Eq. (3.1) of Chap. 27. The number of degrees of freedom would again be $F = n - 1$, and Fig. 2.1 of Chap. 27 is to be used with χ^2 from Eq. (2.24).

Case II, Constant Number of Counts. In a series of n successive observations, let the total time required to accumulate a predetermined number of input counts s be $t_1, t_2, \ldots, t_n$. Then the average interval for s input counts is

$$\bar{t} = \frac{1}{n}\sum_1^n t_i \qquad (2.26)$$

Because of the general requirement that statistically distributed parameters be dimensionless, we cannot proceed toward χ^2 by forming

$$\sum \left[\frac{(t_i - \bar{t})^2}{\bar{t}}\right]$$

which would have dimensions of time and a numerical value which would depend on the units of time (seconds, minutes, etc.) used in the observations.

We may proceed by obtaining from our observations of t a substantially equivalent distribution of the effective number of input counts in a hypothetical and arbitrary fixed time interval T, which can be given the value $\bar{t}$ without loss of generality. Then if s input counts require a time t, the average rate for this interval is s/t and the corresponding number of input events x, in a fixed time $\bar{t}$, would be expected to be approximately

$$x \simeq \frac{s}{t}\bar{t} \qquad (2.27)$$

while

$$\bar{x} = s \qquad (2.28)$$

Then we can form a corresponding dimensionless expression for χ^2, by the substitutions

$$\chi^2 = \sum_1^n \frac{(x_i - \bar{x})^2}{\bar{x}} = \sum_1^n \frac{[(s\bar{t}/t_i) - s]^2}{s}$$

$$= s\sum_1^n \left(\frac{\bar{t}}{t_i} - 1\right)^2 \qquad (2.29)$$

The expected value of the summation in Eq. (2.29), for large n, is

$$\sum_{1}^{n} \left(\frac{\bar{t}}{t_i} - 1 \right)^2 = n \int_0^{\infty} \left(\frac{\bar{t}}{t} - 1 \right)^2 dP_t \qquad (2.30)$$

Inserting dP_t from Eq. (2.3) and $\bar{t} = s/a$ from Eq. (2.9), expanding, and evaluating the three resulting integrals lead to

$$n \int_0^{\infty} \left(\frac{\bar{t}}{t} - 1 \right)^2 dP_t = n \frac{s+2}{(s-1)(s-2)} \qquad (2.31)$$

or approximately

$$n \int_0^{\infty} \left(\frac{\bar{t}}{t} - 1 \right)^2 dP_t \simeq \frac{n}{s} \left(1 + \frac{5}{s} + \cdots \right)$$

$$\simeq \frac{n}{s} \qquad (2.32)$$

for large values of s (4,096, etc.), such as are customarily used in scalers operating toward a preset number of counts. Then the expectation value of Eq. (2.29) is

$$\chi^2 = s \frac{n}{s} = n \qquad (2.33)$$

The number of degrees of freedom is again $F = n - 1$, and Fig. 2.1 of Chap. 27 is to be used with χ^2 from Eq. (2.29).

g. Effects of Resolving Time at Input and Output of Scaler. Counting losses due to the finite reaction time of an electromechanical register or other output device can be made negligibly small through the use of an adequately large scaling factor. With a properly designed counting system, the losses can be restricted mainly to the Geiger-Müller counter or scintillation counter preamplifier, which provides the input to the scaling circuit. Such losses remove the shortest intervals in the distribution of input pulses to the scaler, as discussed in Sec. 1. An exact reanalysis of subsequent losses in the various scaling stages would be both complicated and of little practical value. An upper limit to the losses in the scaler can be computed readily by assuming that the scaler input is truly random.

Then the fractional losses of s-fold pulses from the sth stage is given simply by Eq. (2.8) with T set equal to the resolving time ρ_s of the sth stage. For $a\rho_s \ll 1$, $P_{s+1} \ll P_s$, and Eq. (2.8) reduces simply to

$$P_T \simeq \frac{(a\rho_s)^s}{s!} \qquad (2.34)$$

This is really an overestimate of the fractional loss in the sth stage because actually many of these pulses will have been lost in previous stages. In scalers of the 2^n variety, composed of cascaded scales of 2, only the resolving time of the early stages need be very short (D34). DeVault has developed a circuit in which $\rho_8 = 2\rho_4 = 8\rho_2 = 40\rho_1$, and he estimates that, if the first stage misses 1 per cent of the pulses, subsequent stages should not lose more than an additional 0.1 per cent.

If the input counting rate is large, and the scaling factor s is too small, the resolving time of the output register may become the governing factor in determining counting losses. This situation is more commonly encountered with scintillation counters than with Geiger-Müller counters because of the very short resolving time which can be realized with scintillation counters. If two s-fold output pulses occur within the resolving time ρ_s of the recorder, then the electronic scaling circuit clears and begins counting over at 0, 1, 2, . . . input pulses, without recording the second s-fold pulse. Electromechanical registers generally are a Type I (paralyzable) apparatus, as described in Sec. 1, and therefore respond only to intervals which are longer than their resolving time. The ratio of observed to true counting rate is, by analogy with Eq. (1.1), the fraction of s-fold intervals which are longer than ρ, or, from Eq. (2.6),

$$1 - P_\rho = e^{-a\rho} + a\rho e^{-a\rho} + \tfrac{1}{2}(a\rho)^2 e^{-a\rho} + \cdots + \frac{1}{(s-1)!}(a\rho)^{s-1}e^{-a\rho}$$

$$(2.35)$$

Problems

1. A β-ray counter has both a direct recording output and a scale-of-4 output. The following readings were made in successive 5-min intervals on the direct output (scale of 1): 200, 215, 195, 175, 225, 205, 185, 205, 190, 180, 210, 230.

(a) Compute the average value and its probable error as determined by the residuals. Compare with the probable error expected if the data follow a Poisson distribution.

(b) What will be the output of the scale of 4 for each of the 5-min intervals (remember to carry over 0, 1, 2, or 3 counts from each interval to the next interval)?

(c) Compute the average value of the scale-of-4 counts and its probable error from the residuals.

(d) Compute the probable error expected if the scale-of-4 data follow a Poisson distribution.

(e) Calling the solution to (c) $\bar{y} \pm r$, is the correct value for the average number of β rays per 5-min interval given by $4\bar{y} \pm 4r$?

(f) Calling the solution to (d) $\bar{y} \pm s$, is the correct value for the average given by $4\bar{y} \pm 4s$? Why? Compare with solution to (a).

2. In 22 successive 30-min intervals a scale-of-2 output gave the following numbers of pulses: 10, 15, 17, 9, 17, 15, 13, 16, 13, 14, 17, 21, 11, 12, 16, 8, 15, 8, 7, 15, 15, 8.

(a) Compute the average rate of the scale-of-2 process.

(b) Compare the standard deviation from the residuals with the expected S.D. based on the average number of scale-of-2 counts. Does the dispersion of the data seem excessive?

(c) Compute χ^2 and compare with the expected χ^2 if the scale-of-1 process is random.

(d) Estimate the probability that a truly random process would give a larger dispersion.

3. Verify Eq. (2.6) by integration of Eq. (2.5).

4. Show that the standard deviation of the duration of s-fold intervals is $\sqrt{s}/a$, where a is the average rate of random input events.

5. Show that Eq. (2.29) can be expressed in the more convenient form

$$\chi^2 = \frac{s}{(\bar{t})^2} \sum_1^n (\bar{t} - t_i)^2$$

if $\bar{t}/t_i$ is nearly unity.

6. A certain scaling circuit has an output which operates a printing timer after $10 \times 4{,}096 = 40{,}960$ input pulses have been received. With a certain radioactive source of constant strength, the number of seconds required to accumulate 40,960 input counts in each of 15 separate runs was: 2,595; 2,616; 2,624; 2,632; 2,648; 2,610; 2,638; 2,597; 2,605; 2,619; 2,622; 2,626; 2,615; 2,618; 2,623. Do these data satisfy the χ^2 test for randomicity of the primary process? *Ans.:* $\chi^2 = 16.9$; $F = 14$; $P \simeq 0.2$; yes.

7. Random pulses from a scintillation counter are fed into a scale of 8 which actuates a mechanical register. Two output pulses from the scale of 8 within a time interval of 5×10^{-2} sec will not be resolved by the mechanical register; only the first pulse will be recorded. If the register is counting at the rate of 600 per minute, what is the true rate at which pulses are arriving at the input of the scale of 8? Neglect all counting losses besides those in the mechanical register. *Ans.:* 5,160 counts per minute.

3. *Counting-rate Meters*

In counting-rate meters (often called CRM) each pulse from a counter is converted electronically into a charge q which is added to the charge Q on a tank condenser C. A resistance R shunts the tank condenser. The charge Q on the condenser can be read continuously, either by reading the potential difference

$$V = \frac{Q}{C} \tag{3.1}$$

across the condenser with a vacuum-tube voltmeter, or by reading the current

$$i = \frac{V}{R} = \frac{Q}{RC} \tag{3.2}$$

through the shunt resistance.

The statistical interpretation of the counting-rate-meter output readings due to randomly distributed input pulses requires a special statistical theory (S12, K19) because the integrating and averaging circuit RC produces an *exponential interdependence of successive observations on all preceding observations.*

a. Average Rate. Let the charge Q on the tank condenser be zero at $t = 0$, when a radiation source begins producing randomly distributed input pulses at a constant average rate a. The average number of pulses during the time interval from t to $t + dt$ will be $a\,dt$, and the expected increment of charge on the condenser in this interval is $qa\,dt$. If now a reading of Q is taken at a later time t_0, this increment of charge will have decayed to $qae^{-(t_0-t)/RC}\,dt$, because of leakage of charge through the resistance, with the time constant RC of the tank circuit. Thus the *expectation value* Q_m for the charge at any time t_0 is

$$Q_m(t_0) = \int_0^{t_0} qae^{-(t_0-t)/RC}\,dt = qaRC(1 - e^{-t_0/RC}) \tag{3.3}$$

and the expected equilibrium charge, after the counting-rate meter has been operating for a time $t_0 \gg RC$, has the value

$$Q_m = qaRC \tag{3.4}$$

It will be noted that Q_m is simply the specific charge q per pulse times the average number of pulses aRC occurring in one time constant RC of the tank circuit. Alternatively, each pulse can be considered to have a mean life RC in the tank circuit. Then, by analogy with radioactive series decay, the mean number of pulses in the tank at equilibrium is the pulse rate a times the mean life RC; compare Eq. (3.27).

We note also that the mean potential difference across the tank is

$$V_m = \frac{Q_m}{C} = qaR \tag{3.5}$$

which is independent of C. This is equivalent to noting that at equilibrium Q is constant, and that therefore the average current qa simply passes through the resistance R, in which it produces a potential difference qaR, by Ohm's law.

b. Standard Deviation of a Single Reading. Suppose that the counting-rate meter has been operating for a time $t_0 \gg RC$, and we make a single observation of the charge Q on the tank condenser at time t_0. The mean expected value is Q_m, but individual single observations will be distributed about Q_m with some standard deviation $\sigma(Q)$, which we now must evaluate.

Because a is randomly distributed, the number of events in a small time interval obeys Poisson's distribution, and the standard deviation of the number of events $a\,dt$ between t and $t + dt$ is $(a\,dt)^{\frac{1}{2}}$. Then the standard deviation of the increment of charge is $q(a\,dt)^{\frac{1}{2}}$. When observed at a later time, t_0, this deviation will make a contribution $q(a\,dt)^{\frac{1}{2}}e^{-(t_0-t)/RC}$ to the deviation of Q at t_0. All such contributions are statistically independent. Therefore, their total effect is to be obtained from the sum of the squares of the individual deviations, by the usual principles of the propagation of errors. Hence the total variance $\sigma^2(Q)$, of Q at t_0, is

$$\sigma^2(Q) = \int_0^{t_0} q^2ae^{-2(t_0-t)/RC}\,dt$$
$$= \tfrac{1}{2}q^2aRC(1 - e^{-2t_0/RC}) \tag{3.6}$$

and the variance for single observations of Q when $t_0 \gg RC$ is

$$\sigma^2(Q) = \tfrac{1}{2}q^2aRC \tag{3.7}$$

Thus the variance is only one-half as great as would be given by the

Poisson variance aRC of the pulses received in one time constant RC. This is because the square-law dependence on individual fluctuations emphasizes the fluctuations which have occurred only a short time before the reading is taken at t_0.

The *fractional* standard deviation of a single instantaneous reading of the counting-rate meter is then

$$\frac{\sigma(Q)}{Q_m} = \frac{1}{\sqrt{2aRC}} \qquad (3.8)$$

or the same as would be expected in a direct counting observation over a time $2RC$.

c. Standard Deviation of the Average of n Independent Readings. Suppose that at $t_0 \gg RC$ a single reading of Q_1 is taken, and that additional readings are taken at subsequent times ϑRC, $2\vartheta RC$, . . . , $(n-1)\vartheta RC$. Then, because the expectation value of Q is the same for each reading, the best estimate of the true mean value of Q will be given by the arithmetic average of these n readings

$$Q_m \simeq \bar{Q} \equiv \frac{1}{n} \sum_{1}^{n} Q_i \qquad (3.9)$$

The standard error of this average value $\bar{Q}$ about the true mean value Q_m will be given by the usual principles [Chap. 26, Eq. (2.12)] only if $\vartheta \gg 1$. In the more applicable cases of small ϑ, the successive readings of Q are not statistically independent of one another, because of the exponential memory of the tank circuit. We may consider as our set of truly independent readings those parts of the various readings which are due to charge accumulated *since* the preceding reading. Only this much of any reading is independent of preceding readings. We must now determine the manner in which the standard error of the mean value $\bar{Q}$ depends on both n and ϑ.

The second reading Q_2, which is taken at a time ϑRC after Q_1, will have the value

$$Q_2 = Q_1 e^{-\vartheta} + G_1 \qquad (3.10)$$

Here $Q_1 e^{-\vartheta}$ is the residual charge from the decay of Q_1, and G_1 is due to new charge accumulated between t_0 and $t_0 + \vartheta RC$. Because all the readings Q_i have the same expectation value Q_m, the expectation value $E[G_i]$ of G_i can be written from Eq. (3.10) or (3.3) and is

$$E[G_i] = (1 - e^{-\vartheta})Q_m \qquad (3.11)$$

For algebraic convenience we will hereafter use the definition

$$r \equiv e^{-\vartheta} \qquad (3.12)$$

where r denotes the residual fraction of any observation Q_i which is present in the subsequent observation Q_{i+1}, by Eq. (3.10). The series of n consecutive observations Q_1, Q_2, . . . , Q_n, equally spaced in time, are exponentially linked by the following recurrence relations

$$Q_2 = rQ_1 + G_1$$
$$Q_3 = rQ_2 + G_2 = r^2Q_1 + rG_1 + G_2$$
$$\cdots\cdots\cdots\cdots\cdots\cdots\cdots\cdots$$
$$Q_i = rQ_{i-1} + G_{i-1} \qquad (1 < i \le n)$$
$$= r^{i-1}Q_1 + r^{i-2}G_1 + \cdots + rG_{i-2} + G_{i-1}$$

(3.13)

The mean value $\bar{Q}$ of Eq. (3.9) is obtained by collecting terms in Eq. (3.13) and has the value

$$\bar{Q} = \frac{1}{n}[(1 + r + \cdots + r^{n-1})Q_1 + (1 + r + \cdots + r^{n-2})G_1 + \cdots$$
$$+ (1 + r + \cdots + r^{n-i-1})G_i + \cdots + G_{n-1}] \quad (3.14)$$

Summing the indicated geometric series, we obtain the simpler expression

$$n\bar{Q} = \frac{1}{1 - r}[(1 - r^n)Q_1 + (1 - r^{n-1})G_1 + \cdots$$
$$+ (1 - r^{n-i})G_i + \cdots + (1 - r)G_{n-1}] \quad (3.15)$$

The quantities $Q_1, G_1, G_2, \cdots, G_{n-1}$ are all independent. Therefore the variance in $n\bar{Q}$ is the sum of the variances of each of the terms in Eq. (3.15). The expectation value of the variance of any Q_i is given by Eq. (3.7) and is the same for all readings. The expectation value for the variance $\sigma^2(G)$ of any G_i can then be obtained with the help of the recurrence relations, Eqs. (3.10) and (3.13). From the principles of the propagation of errors, we can write the expectation values for the variances as

$$\sigma^2(Q) = \sigma^2(rQ) + \sigma^2(G) \qquad \text{for any } i \tag{3.16}$$

The residue of any $\sigma(Q)$ at a later time ϑRC is $r\sigma(Q)$. Therefore Eq. (3.16) becomes

$$\sigma^2(Q) = [r\sigma(Q)]^2 + \sigma^2(G) \tag{3.17}$$

Therefore the expectation value of the variance $\sigma^2(G)$ for any G_i is given by

$$\sigma^2(G) = (1 - r^2)\sigma^2(Q) = (1 - r^2)\tfrac{1}{2}q^2aRC \tag{3.18}$$

which is confirmed by Eq. (3.6). By applying the principles of the propagation of errors to Eq. (3.15), and making use of Eq. (3.18), we can write for the variance of $n\bar{Q}$

$$\sigma^2(n\bar{Q}) = \frac{\sigma^2(Q)}{(1 - r)^2}[(1 - r^n)^2 + (1 - r^{n-1})^2(1 - r^2) + \cdots$$
$$+ (1 - r^{n-i})^2(1 - r^2) + \cdots + (1 - r)^2(1 - r^2)] \quad (3.19)$$

When the indicated summations are carried out we obtain

$$\sigma^2(n\bar{Q}) = \frac{\sigma^2(Q)}{(1 - r)^2}[n(1 - r^2) - 2r(1 - r^n)] \tag{3.20}$$

Then the standard deviation, or standard error, in $\bar{Q}$ can be written as

$\sigma_n(\bar{Q})$ and from Eqs. (3.20) and (3.12) has the value

$$\sigma_n(\bar{Q}) = \frac{1}{n}\,\sigma(n\bar{Q})$$

$$= \frac{1}{n(1-e^{-\vartheta})}\,[n(1-e^{-2\vartheta}) - 2e^{-\vartheta}(1-e^{-n\vartheta})]^{\frac{1}{2}}\sigma(Q) \qquad (3.21)$$

Equation (3.21) is the relationship sought for the standard error in the average value $\bar{Q}$ of Eq. (3.9). If $\vartheta \gg 1$, so that the n readings are really statistically independent, then Eq. (3.21) correctly reduces to

$$\sigma_n(\bar{Q}) = \frac{\sigma(Q)}{\sqrt{n}} \qquad \text{for } \vartheta \gg 1 \qquad (3.22)$$

which is in accord with the elementary principles given by Eq. (2.12) of Chap. 26.

d. **Standard Deviation of Continuous Observations.** The output of a counting-rate meter is often a recording voltmeter or galvanometer. The continuous observation of Q over a finite time T corresponds to an infinite number of single readings, with an infinitely close spacing, or $n \to \infty$, $\vartheta \to 0$, but such that

$$n\vartheta = \frac{T}{RC} \qquad (3.23)$$

Then the standard error $\sigma(T)$ of the average deflection $\bar{Q}$ is obtained by substituting Eq. (3.23) into Eq. (3.21). In the limit of $\vartheta \ll 1$, this leads to†

$$\frac{\sigma(T)}{\sigma(Q)} = \left\{\frac{2RC}{T}\left[1 - \frac{RC}{T}\left(1 - e^{-T/RC}\right)\right]\right\}^{\frac{1}{2}} \qquad (3.24)$$

where $\sigma(Q) = q(aRC/2)^{\frac{1}{2}}$ is the standard deviation of a single instantaneous observation as given by Eq. (3.7). Figure 3.1 is a plot of the dependence of $\sigma(T)/\sigma(Q)$ on T/RC as given by Eq. (3.24).

When $T \gg RC$, the general expression of Eq. (3.24) reduces to

$$\frac{\sigma(T)}{\bar{Q}} \simeq \frac{\sigma(T)}{Q_m} = \frac{1}{\sqrt{aT}} \qquad (3.25)$$

which is equivalent to Eq. (2.15) of Chap. 26 because aT is the total number of pulses observed in the interval T.

In the practical uses of a continuously recorded output, the mean deflection $\bar{Q}$ divides the instantaneous readings into two equal areas, as illustrated in Fig. 3.2. The fractional standard deviation of a single

† Equations (3.21) and (3.24) are rigorous and were first obtained by R. E. Burgess, *Rev. Sci. Instr.*, **20**: 964L (1949). They replace equations developed in 1936 by Schiff and Evans (S12) which are algebraically dissimilar but which give substantially identical numerical values, as in Fig. 3.1. The derivation of Eq. (3.21) by means of the recurrence relationships of Eq. (3.13) is due to Professor George P. Wadsworth and Dr. Joseph G. Bryan.

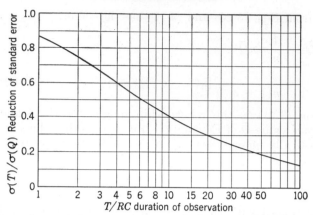

Fig. 3.1 Dependence of the ratio of the standard error $\sigma(T)$ of $\bar{Q}$ to the standard deviation $\sigma(Q)$ of a single observation, for continuous observations of various duration T/RC, Eq. (3.24).

observation can also be estimated directly from the recorded output, because the readings will exceed twice the standard deviation of a single observation only 4.6 per cent of the time. Thus if we draw dotted lines, as in Fig. 3.2, which include all but about 2 per cent of the highest observations and 2 per cent of the lowest observations, we shall have made a

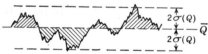

Fig. 3.2 Schematic representation of counting-rate-meter output, displaying exaggerated statistical fluctuations for purposes of illustration. The base line is off the bottom of the page. The heavy dotted line locates the average value $\bar{Q}$, the equal shaded areas representing the observations above and below the average value. The light dotted lines locate the region $\bar{Q} \pm 2\sigma(Q)$, where $\sigma(Q)$ is the standard deviation of any single point on the curve. The standard error of the average $\bar{Q}$ is then obtained with $\sigma(Q)$ and Fig. 3.1.

reasonably accurate graphical evaluation of the standard deviation $\sigma(Q)$ of any single point on the curve. From this, the standard error of the mean value can be obtained from Eq. (3.24), which is plotted in Fig. 3.1.

e. Equilibrium Time. Equation (3.3) shows that the approach to an equilibrium output is a characteristic exponential growth curve, similar in every respect to the growth of activity in a radioactive daughter substance, of mean life RC, from a long-lived parent radioactive substance of constant activity. For practical measurements, we may say that a condition experimentally indistinguishable from equilibrium exists when the charge $Q(t_0)$ differs from the average value by less than one probable error $[= 0.6745\sigma(Q)]$ occasioned by statistical fluctuations. Then the time t_0 necessary to establish this practical equilibrium is

$$Q(t_0)e^{-t_0/RC} = \frac{0.6745Q(t_0)}{\sqrt{2aRC}}$$

from which $\qquad t_0 = RC(0.394 + \tfrac{1}{2}\ln 2aRC)$ $\qquad\qquad$ (3.26)

Figure 3.3 shows this dependence of t_0 on the counting rate a for several common values of RC.

f. Use of Counting-rate Meter on Rapidly Decaying Sources. It can be shown (S12) that the mean output of a counting-rate meter is always related to variations in the input in exactly the same way as the radioactivity of a daughter radioactive substance of mean life RC is related to the activity of its parent radioactive substance. The counting rate a is equivalent to the activity of the hypothetical parent radioactive substance. The term aRC is then equivalent to the number of atoms of daughter substance present at equilibrium, because it is of the form (activity × mean life). The exponential term $(1 - e^{-t_0/RC})$ in Eq. (3.3) is equivalent to the growth of a daughter substance of decay constant $(1/RC)$ from a long-lived parent of essentially constant activity. If the radiation source had been a radioactive substance of mean life τ, the input counting rate at any time t_0 would have been $ae^{-t_0/\tau}$ instead of the constant value a. Then the expectation value for the charge $Q_m(t_0)$ on the tank condenser at time t_0 would become

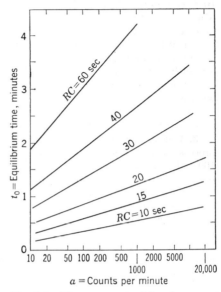

Fig. 3.3 Time t_0 required for the output to rise from zero to within one probable error of the final equilibrium value, for various counting rates a and time constants RC of the counting-rate meter.

$$Q_m(t_0) = qaRC \, \frac{1/RC}{(1/RC) - (1/\tau)} \, (e^{-t_0/\tau} - e^{-t_0/RC}) \qquad (3.27)$$

which is entirely analogous to the amount of daughter substance present with a parent substance of decay constant $1/\tau$, as determined in Chap. 15. Similarly, the mean charge $Q_m(t_0)$ would pass through a maximum value at a time given by $[\ln (\tau/RC)]/[(1/RC) - (1/\tau)]$. After a time which is large compared with $[(1/RC) - (1/\tau)]$ the mean charge will be in transient equilibrium with the exponentially decreasing input counting rate.

Problems

1. Randomly distributed pulses, at an average rate a, are fed through a scale-of-s scaler and then into a counting-rate meter. Each scale-of-s pulse puts a charge q into the counting-rate-meter tank circuit whose time constant is RC.

    (a) What is the equilibrium value of the tank-circuit voltage?

    (b) Derive an analytical expression for the F.S.D. (fractional standard deviation) of a single observation of the equilibrium tank-circuit voltage.

(*c*) How does the expression obtained in (*b*) compare with the F.S.D if the scaler is removed from the circuit?

2. A Geiger-Müller counter is connected to a counting-rate meter having a tank circuit whose voltage is measured by a vacuum-tube voltmeter. The tank condenser has a capacitance of 10 μf and the specific charge per pulse is 10^{-10} coulomb. A long-lived radioactive source produces pulses in the Geiger-Müller tube at an average rate of 1,000 per minute. It is desired to have a 6-mv input to the voltmeter.

(*a*) What value should the tank resistor have?

(*b*) If a single reading of the voltmeter is taken after equilibrium has been established, what is its fractional standard deviation?

(*c*) If the output is recorded on a recording milliammeter for a 2-min period, what is the fractional standard error of the average output?

(*d*) If it is desired to read the equilibrium voltage as soon after the source is presented to the counter as possible, how long should one wait?

3. Compare the fractional standard deviation (F.S.D) of observations on a process whose random counting rate is 3,000 counts per minute, using a scale-of-100 scaler and alternatively a counting-rate meter whose time constant is $RC = 15$ sec.

(*a*) If the background counting rate can be neglected, how many seconds must one wait for the counting-rate meter to come to equilibrium?

(*b*) If a single observation is taken after equilibrium is reached, what is its F.S.D?

(*c*) If the counting-rate-meter readings for the next 75 sec are averaged, what is the F.S.D in the average value?

(*d*) If a single scaler reading is taken over the same 75 sec, what is its F.S.D?

(*e*) If a single scaler reading is taken over the same total period that the counting-rate meter is operating (equilibrium time + 75 sec), what is its F.S.D?

(*f*) Compare the numerical values in (*c*), (*d*), and (*e*) and explain clearly the statistical origin of the differences, especially why (*c*) is less than (*d*).

4. One minute is available for a measurement of the background rate of a certain discharge counter. A scaler and a counting-rate meter ($RC = 15$ sec) are available, and it is known that the background rate of this counter should be about 100 counts per minute.

(*a*) What will be the expected value of the F.S.D of the scaler reading?

(*b*) If the tank condenser is charged up to its equilibrium value in a few seconds by an adjustment of the calibration switch, what is the F.S.D of the counting-rate-meter reading?

(*c*) Explain any difference between the answers to (*a*) and (*b*).

(*d*) If the measurement time is now increased to 5 min, calculate the F.S.D for the scaler.

(*e*) What is the F.S.D of the counting-rate-meter reading, assuming that the calibration switch has been used to charge up the condenser quickly?

(*f*) What is the F.S.D of the counting-rate-meter reading, assuming that no "trick" is used to charge the condenser quickly?

(*g*) Explain any differences among the answers to (*d*), (*e*), and (*f*).

4. *Ionization Chambers*

The major features of the statistical behavior of ionization chambers can be inferred by comparison with the detailed statistical theory for counters. When ionization measurements are made by the *rate-of-drift* method, the total deflections are statistically analogous to readings of a total number of counts observed with a scaling circuit. When ionization measurements are made by the *steady-deflection* method, the readings are analogous to observations of a counting rate using a counting-rate meter. The controlling time constant RC is usually found in the input capacitance C and shunt resistance R of the ionization chamber and its electrometer circuit. Less frequently, the period of an output galvanometer may be the controlling time constant.

The theory of counter circuits thus leads toward an understanding of ionization-chamber circuits. However, one major characteristic of ionization chambers introduces mathematical complications which prevent the development of a detailed theory, except for unrealistic or trivial special cases.

In the statistical theory of counter circuits, each recorded ionizing particle produces the same effect on the instrument, namely, one count.

However, the number of ion pairs produced in an ionization chamber, per ionizing particle, not only depends on the type of particle but is statistically distributed about some mean value, even for identical particles of identical initial energy. Even an initially homogeneous group of α particles produces slightly different amounts of ionization, because of straggling. β rays, in addition to individual straggling, have a continuous initial distribution of energies and produce widely varying amounts of ionization per particle. Similar variations exist for the ionization per particle produced by the secondary electrons by which γ rays give rise to ionization, and by the ionizing recoil particles produced by fast neutrons.

Therefore, the statistical theory of counting-rate meters can be extended to ionization circuits only after realizing that the effectiveness q per particle is not constant but is distributed about some mean value. This distribution in q is generally not a random or Poisson one, nor even a normal distribution. It may be highly asymmetric, as is a primary spectrum of β-ray energies. Even its standard deviation may not be predictable on purely theoretical grounds. These fluctuations in q, that is, in the ionization per particle, therefore have the effect of increasing the observed fluctuations to some value greater than that predicted by the counter theory, in which q is a constant. Thus the statistical theory for the counting-rate meter gives the *lower limit* for the statistical fluctuations in an ionization current.

Similarly, the theory of scaling circuits serves as the *lower limit* for the statistical fluctuations in total ionization collected over a measured period of time, as in rate-of-drift measurements with an ionization chamber. In the theory of scaling circuits, the effectiveness per particle is implicitly taken as unity and is included in the term a of Eq. (2.1) et seq. for the average counting rate.

A second circumstance which can greatly increase the fluctuations in ionization is the fact that several types of ionizing particle may be acting simultaneously on the chamber. On this point, reference should be made to the generalized Poisson distribution in Chap. 26 and the illustrative examples given there. Circumstances can easily occur in which heavily ionizing particles, such as α rays or recoil protons, may produce only a small portion of the total ionization but may at the same time dominate the statistical fluctuations in ionization.

Finally, it should be pointed out that, when ionization chambers are operated as *proportional counters*, there are statistical fluctuations in the gas-amplification ratio. This again has the effect of making the specific effectiveness per particle [as represented by a, b, . . . , in Eq. (3.1) of Chap. 26] a statistically distributed quantity. The general effect is to impair the resolution in studies of spectral distribution using proportional counters (H16). Similar statistical considerations apply to other multiplicative processes, such as the luminescent counter systems and photomultipliers used with fluorescent counters (S28).

5. *Rapid Decay of a Single Radionuclide*

In the derivation of the Poisson distribution we imposed the condition that the average rate of the process be constant over the period of the observations. Poisson's distribution and the statistical results of its simple application therefore cannot be applied directly to data which are taken in time intervals which are comparable with the mean life of the radioactive substance being studied. Poisson's distribution can be used as a basis for developing special statistical treatments which are applicable to measurements on rapidly decaying sources.

a. Mean-life Determination by Peierls's Method. The statistics of the rapidly decaying source have been treated in detail by Peierls (P14) whose minimum-error method for determining exponential coefficients is of general importance in many physical processes. For example, it applies to the determination of γ-ray absorption coefficients as well as to the determination of radioactive decay constants.

Peierls's method recognizes that the detecting apparatus possesses a finite background counting rate whose average rate is constant. Therefore the rapidly decaying radioactive source must be counted as an additional effect superimposed upon a statistically distributed background.

Peierls has shown that the radioactive decay constant λ is to be obtained with minimum error by designing the experiment so that the data can be used to calculate the *mean life* for the atoms whose disintegrations are observed. Figure 5.1 illustrates the method and the principal statistical problems which are encountered.

At time $t = 0$, let there be N_0 atoms whose disintegrations can be detected. (The actual initial number of atoms will be greater than N_0, except when a 4π-geometry detector possessing 100 per cent counting efficiency is used.) Then the initial instantaneous counting rate due to the source has the expectation value

$$\left(\frac{dN}{dt}\right)_{t=0} = N_0\lambda = \frac{N_0}{\tau} \tag{5.1}$$

where τ is the mean life of all the N_0 atoms. This initial counting rate should be at least several times the background counting rate.

Based upon preliminary approximate knowledge of the half-period and the initial activity, select a time interval Δt which is less than about one-third the mean life τ, yet is long enough to contain a statistically significant number of counts. In an unbroken sequence of n contiguous equal time intervals Δt, observe the total number of counts x_1, x_2, x_3, . . . , x_n due to the source plus the background. Then our best estimate of the number of counts ΔN_1, ΔN_2, . . . , due to the source alone, is

$$\Delta N_1 = x_1 - b\Delta t$$
$$\Delta N_2 = x_2 - b\Delta t$$
$$\cdot \cdot \cdot \cdot \cdot \cdot \cdot \cdot \cdot \quad (5.2)$$
$$\Delta N_n = x_n - b\Delta t$$

where $b\Delta t$ is the expectation value of the number of background counts in a time Δt.

Average Life of the Observed Atoms. The ΔN_1 atoms which decay during the first time interval Δt can be assigned an average lifetime of $\frac{1}{2}\Delta t$. Similarly, the ΔN_2 atoms which decay during the second time interval Δt to $2\Delta t$ can be assigned an average lifetime of $\frac{3}{2}\Delta t$. Then the total lifetimes of all the atoms which decay between $t = 0$ and $t = n\Delta t$ are

$$\Delta N_1(\tfrac{1}{2}\Delta t) + \Delta N_2(\tfrac{3}{2}\Delta t) + \Delta N_3(\tfrac{5}{2}\Delta t)$$
$$+ \cdot \cdot \cdot + \Delta N_n \frac{2n-1}{2}\Delta t \quad (5.3)$$

During this time, the total number of atoms whose individual lifetimes are observed is

$$N \equiv \Delta N_1 + \Delta N_2 + \Delta N_3$$
$$+ \cdot \cdot \cdot + \Delta N_n \quad (5.4)$$

Hence the average life s of all the observed atoms is given by Eq. (5.3) divided by Eq. (5.4) which is

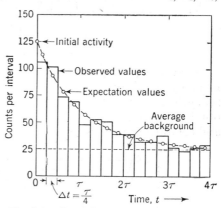

Fig. 5.1 Graphical presentation of typical statistical fluctuations encountered in measuring the mean life of a rapidly decaying source. The instantaneous value of the initial activity N_0/τ of this source is only four times the background. In a sequence of contiguous time intervals Δt, the expectation values of the number of counts per interval are shown as circles, plotted at the mid-points of the time intervals, and connected by the dotted decay curve. The actual observations, shown by the histogram, involve statistical fluctuations due both to background and to the source. Table 5.1 shows that in the calculation of the average life, by means of Eq. (5.5), observations beyond $T_0 \simeq 2.8\tau$ should be excluded. Each time interval here is $\Delta t = \tau/4$; therefore only the first $n = 11$ time intervals should be included in Eq. (5.5). After $t = n\Delta t = 2.75\tau$, the statistical fluctuations in the background are comparable with the residual activity of the source.

$$s = \frac{\Delta N_1 + 3\Delta N_2 + 5\Delta N_3 + \cdot \cdot \cdot + (2n-1)\Delta N_n}{\Delta N_1 + \Delta N_2 + \Delta N_3 + \cdot \cdot \cdot + \Delta N_n} \frac{\Delta t}{2} \quad (5.5)$$

By terminating the observations at the finite time $t = n\Delta t$ we have excluded the longest-lived atoms. Therefore the average life s of the *observed* atoms is less than the true mean life τ of *all* the atoms. The expectation value of s is given by

$$s = \frac{\int_0^{n\Delta t} t\, dN}{\int_0^{n\Delta t} dN} = \frac{(N_0/\tau) \int_0^{n\Delta t} t e^{-t/\tau}\, dt}{(N_0/\tau) \int_0^{n\Delta t} e^{-t/\tau}\, dt} \tag{5.6}$$

$$s = \tau \left[1 - \frac{n\Delta t/\tau}{(e^{n\Delta t/\tau} - 1)} \right] \tag{5.7}$$

Equation (5.6) furnishes the means of calculating τ from the experimentally determined average life s of the observed atoms. Figure 5.2 relates the observed quantities s and $n\Delta t$ to the true mean life τ. It is obtained from Eq. (5.7) by assuming a series of arbitrary values $n\Delta t/\tau$ and computing the corresponding values of τ/s and hence $n\Delta t/s$.

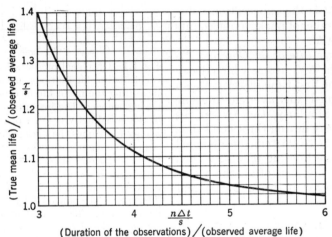

Fig. 5.2 The relation, Eq. (5.7), between the true mean life τ of *all* the atoms and the observed average life s of the atoms decaying in time $n\Delta t$.

Equation (5.7) and Fig. 5.2 are exact representations of the relationship between τ and s only if $\Delta t \ll \tau$, when the summation in Eq. (5.3) becomes equivalent to the numerator of Eq. (5.6). In any experiment, Δt must be finite and long enough to accumulate a significant number of counts. Peierls has shown that τ, as given by Eq. (5.7) and Fig. 5.2, is 1 to 1.5 per cent high if $\Delta t = 0.3\tau$. This systematic error in τ varies with $(\Delta t/\tau)^2$; therefore it is reduced to about 0.1 to 0.2 per cent if $\Delta t \leq 0.1\tau$. Actually, very few decay constants are known within an accuracy of 1 per cent.

Optimum Duration of Observations. If the measurements $x_1, x_2, \ldots$ are continued for many mean lives, the residual activity of the source may become small compared with the ever-present statistical fluctuations in the background. This situation can be seen in Fig. 5.1, beyond $t \sim 3\tau$. There comes a time when it is foolish to continue the measurements because the additional data which can be obtained are so inaccurate that their use will actually increase the error in the calculation of the mean life. Conversely, the measurements should not be discontinued too soon. Otherwise, data which would be useful statistically will not be obtained.

It is seen that there is some optimum time during which counting should be continued. This optimum duration T_0 is of the order of three to five mean lives for most practical cases. Peierls has shown that the minimum error in the determination of the mean life τ is obtained by selecting an optimum duration T_0 which depends upon the ratio of the initial activity of the source N_0/τ to the mean background rate b. These values are given in Table 5.1. The actual number of intervals used in Eq. (5.5) should therefore be chosen so that n is the nearest integer to $T_0/\Delta t$, that is,

$$n \simeq \frac{T_0}{\Delta t} \tag{5.8}$$

The initial activity N_0/τ of the source is, of course, greater than $\Delta N_1/\Delta t$. The preliminary estimates of the instantaneous initial activity and of the mean life, which are needed for the application of Peierls's method, are

TABLE 5.1. OPTIMUM DURATION T_0 OF OBSERVATIONS ON A RAPIDLY DECAYING SOURCE WHOSE MEAN LIFE IS τ, WHEN THE INITIAL RATIO OF SOURCE ACTIVITY TO BACKGROUND IS $N_0/\tau b$.

The table also gives typical values of the ratio τ/s of the true mean life τ to the average life s of the N atoms observed; the fraction N/N_0 of the atoms observed; and the standard error σ in the measurement of τ, as determined by Peierls (P14).

$\dfrac{N_0}{\tau}\dfrac{1}{b}$	2	5	10	30	65	100
$\dfrac{T_0}{\tau}$	2.6	3.0	3.5	4.0	4.5	5.0
$\dfrac{\tau}{s}$	1.263	...	1.122	1.081	....	1.035
$\dfrac{T_0}{s}$	3.29	...	3.93	4.32	....	5.18
$\dfrac{N}{N_0}$	0.925	...	0.970	0.982	....	0.993
$\dfrac{\sigma}{\tau}\sqrt{N}$	2.84	...	1.81	1.47	....	1.23

obtained most readily from a semilogarithmic graph of the experimental values of $\Delta N/\Delta t$ [Eq. (5.2)] plotted at the mid-points of their respective time intervals.

Standard Error of Mean Life. One of the greatest advantages of Peierls's method is that it also allows a calculation of the standard error in τ whenever *counting* methods have been employed to obtain the data for Eqs. (5.2) and (5.5). Peierls's lengthy computations are summarized in Fig. 5.3, where the fractional standard error σ/τ is given as a function of the total number of counts N due to the source, Eq. (5.4), and of T_0/s. This standard error includes the effects of statistical fluctuations in the background, and of the decay of the source.   In the limiting case of a negligible background, σ approaches the Poisson value

$$\sigma = \frac{\tau}{\sqrt{N_0}} \qquad \text{for} \begin{cases} b \to 0 \\ T_0 \to \infty \\ N \to N_0 \end{cases} \tag{5.9}$$

Peierls's results have been confirmed by Bartlett (B17), using the powerful and elegant statistical method introduced by Fisher (F51) and known as the "method of maximum likelihood."

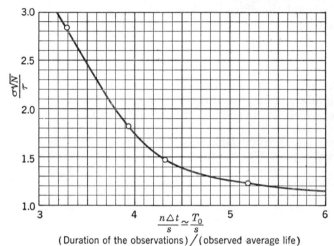

(Duration of the observations)/(observed average life)

Fig. 5.3   The standard error σ in the mean life τ determined from counting N particles in a total time T_0, when T_0 has been chosen in accord with Table 5.1.   The probable error in τ would be given approximately by 0.67σ.   The four points shown are based on Peierls's calculations (P14).

b. Determination of Initial Activity of a Source Whose Mean Life Is Known.   Tandberg (T4) has considered the problem of obtaining minimum statistical error in the determination of the activity of a radioactive source, from a single observation of the total number of counts observed in a time T_0.   If the mean life τ of the source is known accurately, and the background counting rate b is comparable with the initial activity N_0/τ of the source, Tandberg showed that

$$\frac{N_0}{\tau}\frac{1}{b} = e^{T_0/\tau} - \frac{2T_0/\tau}{1 - e^{-T_0/\tau}} \tag{5.10}$$

where T_0 is the *optimum* duration of the single counting observation. In this interval T_0, the expected number of background counts is bT_0, the expected number of counts due to the source is $N_0(1 - e^{-T_0/\tau})$, and both counts are subject to random fluctuations.   Values of T_0 for several values of $(N_0/\tau b)$, the ratio of initial source strength N_0/τ to background b, are given in the following table.

TABLE 5.2. OPTIMUM DURATION T_0 OF COUNTING WHEN τ IS KNOWN AND THE INITIAL ACTIVITY N_0/τ IS TO BE EVALUATED (T4)

$\dfrac{N_0}{\tau}\dfrac{1}{b}$	$\ll 1$	2	5	10	20
$\dfrac{T_0}{\tau}$	1.3	1.8	2.3	2.7	3.3

It will be noted that these values of the optimum counting time T_0 are slightly less than the values deduced by Peierls (Table 5.1) for the optimum duration of counting when τ is initially unknown and the best value of τ is to be determined from a *series* of observations on a single decaying source.

Problems

1. The usual experimental approximation to the true instantaneous activity dN/dt at any time t is obtained from the particle count ΔN over the finite time interval of duration Δt extending from $(t - \frac{1}{2}\Delta t)$ to $(t + \frac{1}{2}\Delta t)$. Show that this average activity $\Delta N/\Delta t$ always exceeds the instantaneous activity dN/dt at the mid-point of the time interval Δt and is given by

$$\frac{\Delta N}{\Delta t} = \frac{dN}{dt}\left[\frac{\sinh(\Delta t/2\tau)}{\Delta t/2\tau}\right] = \frac{dN}{dt}\left[1 + \frac{1}{24}\left(\frac{\Delta t}{\tau}\right)^2 + \cdots\right]$$

2. Show that the total lifetimes of the atoms which decay between $t = 0$ and $t = \Delta t$ are

$$\int_0^{\Delta t} t\,dN - \tfrac{1}{2}\Delta t\,\Delta N\left(1 - \frac{1}{6}\frac{\Delta t}{\tau} + \cdots\right)$$

3. Carry out the integrations indicated in Eq. (5.6) and show also that:
(*a*) The expectation value of N, the number of atoms whose disintegrations are observed, is

$$N = N_0(1 - e^{-n\Delta t/\tau})$$

(*b*) The expectation value of s becomes the ordinary mean life τ when the mean life is negligible compared with the duration of the observations.

4. Show that the greatest contribution to the sum of the lifetimes, Eq. (5.3), is due to those atoms which have an actual lifetime equal to the mean life τ.

5. Determine the half-period, and its probable error, from the following data. The average background of the counter is 25 counts per minute (scale of 1). In successive 1-min intervals, the number of counts due to source plus background is 106, 102, 73, 68, 48, 52, 51, 38, 38, 32, 32, 37, 27, 23, 26, 28. *Ans.:* From semi-logarithmic graph of $\Delta N/\Delta t$: $N_0/\tau \simeq 100$ counts per minute; $\tau \simeq 4$ min; therefore, $T_0 \simeq 11$ min; $n = 11$. Finally, $\tau = 4.07 \pm 0.58$ (S.E.) min, or $T_{\frac{1}{2}} = 2.8 \pm 0.3$ (P.E.) min.

6. If the experimental conditions are such that the radionuclide studied in Prob. 5 cannot be made with greater initial activity, how many times must experiments like that of Prob. 5 be repeated in order to obtain a value of τ which has a probable error of 1 per cent?

7. Calculate by Peierls's method (*a*) the mean life and (*b*) the probable error in the mean life of a radioactive isotope, from the following data. Using a scale-of-2 recorder, the total number of impulses, including background, in successive 10-min intervals were 960, 820, 650, 560, 450, 420, 350, 330, 290, 260, 240, 230, 220, 210, 205. The scale-of-2 background is 180 per 10 min, the initial activity of the sample is about five times the background, and the half-period of the isotope is about 28 min.

6. *Radioactive-series Disintegrations*

In the derivation of the Poisson distribution we required that each event be independent of all others. In radioactive-series decay this condition is sometimes violated, depending on the time intervals chosen for observation. Thus AcA, the 0.0018-sec half-period decay product of Ac, gives α rays whose appearance is strongly governed by the decay of its parent product. The discovery of AcA by Geiger (G11) was directed by the excessive number of short intervals between successive α rays from actinon and its decay products, i.e., by deviations from the Poisson and interval distributions.

Cases of series decay can often be treated statistically by proper compounding of simple Poisson distributions. Adams (A8) has so treated the statistics of α-ray counting from Th in equilibrium with its decay products RdTh, ThX, Tn, ThA, ThB, ThC, etc. The half-period of ThX is 3.64 days. If in any 5-min observational interval a ThX α ray is counted, this will be closely followed by α rays from the successive disintegration products Tn and ThA (half-periods 54.5 sec and 0.158 sec, respectively). These latter α rays are therefore *not* randomly distributed in the time intervals chosen because they are dependent on the emission of the ThX α ray. Alternatively, it is seen that the total equilibrium amount of Tn and ThA present in this experiment is vanishingly small, being only those few atoms which have decayed out of the ThX state but not yet out of the ThA state. They therefore do not satisfy one of the conditions for the validity of Poisson's distribution because their probability of decay in the large time interval chosen is nearly unity, instead of nearly zero. Adams found the standard deviation for α counting in 5-min intervals on the Th series to be 1.45 times the Poisson value for a purely random process.

In general, the statistics of counting a series of substances which are in radioactive equilibrium can be deduced from the Poisson distribution if (S9) each radioactive mean life is either much longer or much shorter than the duration of the individual observations.

Thomson Scattering as an Illustration of the Wave and Corpuscular Concepts of Cross Section

This appendix has two purposes: (1) to outline the classical electromagnetic wave theory concerning the scattering of electromagnetic radiation by electrons (Thomson scattering) and (2) to illustrate the physical relationship between the concepts of *cross section* as met in wave or field theory and as met in corpuscular models of collision phenomena.

1. *Thomson Scattering*

In a somewhat simplified classical treatment, and using Gaussian centimeter-gram-second (cgs) units, we here consider the interaction of a plane-polarized electromagnetic wave with a single free electron. The electric field $\mathcal{E}$ of the incident wave at the average position of the electron can be written as

$$\mathcal{E} = \mathcal{E}_0 \sin 2\pi \nu t \tag{1}$$

where ν is the frequency and $\mathcal{E}_0$ the amplitude of the incident radiation, and t is time. Then the force on a free electron of charge e esu is $e\mathcal{E}$, and in the low-energy nonrelativistic case the equation of its motion is

$$m_0 \frac{d^2 z}{dt^2} = e\mathcal{E} = e\mathcal{E}_0 \sin 2\pi \nu t \tag{2}$$

where m_0 is the rest mass of the electron and z is a space coordinate chosen in the direction of $\mathcal{E}_0$, which is here defined as the direction of polarization.

A solution for the displacement z is seen to be

$$z = - \frac{e}{m_0 (2\pi \nu)^2} \mathcal{E}_0 \sin 2\pi \nu t \tag{3}$$

Then the instantaneous value of the equivalent electric dipole moment is (ez), and its maximum value, or amplitude, is

$$(ez)_0 = \frac{e^2 \mathcal{E}_0}{m_0 (2\pi \nu)^2} \tag{4}$$

The oscillating electron also constitutes an oscillating current element

$i\,dz$, which has the instantaneous value, in electromagnetic units, of

$$i\,dz = \frac{e}{c}v = \frac{e}{c}\frac{dz}{dt} = -\frac{e^2}{m_0c}\frac{1}{2\pi\nu}\,\mathcal{E}_0\cos 2\pi\nu t \tag{5}$$

where v is the instantaneous velocity of the electron in the z direction. The interaction of this current element with the magnetic vector of the incident radiation produces a small force on the electron (and is responsible for a net drift of the electron along the direction of the incident radiation) which can be neglected in comparison with $e\mathcal{E}$ in the low-energy non-relativistic case. In the case actually calculated we have neglected the damping effect which occurs when the electron reradiates energy. Consequently the electron velocity is exactly 90° out of phase with the incident $\mathcal{E}$ and H fields, and no net forward thrust will result. However, in an actual case the phase of the electron lags the phase of the incident fields, thus producing the forward thrust and allowing the electron to absorb energy from the $\mathcal{E}$ field for reradiation. This net drift velocity can be shown classically to be smaller than v_0 (the maximum value of v) by approximately the ratio v_0/c. For the low-energy nonrelativistic case ($h\nu \ll m_0c^2 = 0.51$ Mev) the ratio $v_0/c \ll 1$, and therefore the magnetic interaction can be neglected in comparison with the simple electric interaction of Eq. (2). It should be noted also that Eq. (2) neglects any atomic restoring forces on the displaced electron and is therefore equivalent to neglecting the atomic binding energy B_e of the electron in comparison with the quantum energy $h\nu$. These two simplifications restrict the Thomson formulas to electromagnetic radiation for which

$$B_e \ll h\nu \ll m_0c^2 \tag{6}$$

At a distance R which is large compared with z_0 and with the wavelength c/ν (that is, in the wave zone) the oscillating dipole produces an electromagnetic field in which the magnitudes of the electric vector $\mathcal{E}'$ and of the magnetic vector H' have the absolute values (p. 64 of R18), in cgs units, of

$$|\mathcal{E}'| = |H'| = \frac{e}{Rc^2}\frac{d^2z}{dt^2}\sin\xi \tag{7}$$

$$|\mathcal{E}'| = |H'| = \left(\frac{1}{R}\frac{e^2}{m_0c^2}\sin\xi\right)\mathcal{E}_0\sin 2\pi\nu\left(t - \frac{R}{c}\right) \tag{8}$$

The vectors $\mathcal{E}'$ and H' are normal to each other and to the direction of R, which lies at an angle ξ with z (compare Fig. 2.1, Chap. 23). The instantaneous *intensity* at distance R from the scattering center is given by the magnitude of the Poynting vector $(c/4\pi)\mathcal{E}' \times H' = (c/4\pi)(\mathcal{E}')^2$, while the *average* intensity I' at R is $(c/8\pi)(\mathcal{E}'_{\max})^2$, where

$$I' = \frac{c}{8\pi}(\mathcal{E}'_{\max})^2 = \frac{1}{R^2}\left(\frac{e^2}{m_0c^2}\right)^2\frac{c}{8\pi}\mathcal{E}_0^2\sin^2\xi\,\frac{\text{ergs}}{(\text{cm}^2)(\text{sec})} \tag{9}$$

In a time t, each electron radiates an average energy $d(_eQ)$, hence an average power $d(_eQ)/t$, into the element of solid angle $d\Omega$, at angle ξ.

The radiated power is

$$\frac{d(_eQ)}{t} = I'R^2\,d\Omega = \left(\frac{e^2}{m_0c^2}\right)^2 d\Omega\,\frac{c}{8\pi}\,\mathcal{E}_0^2\,\sin^2\xi\,\frac{\text{ergs}}{(\text{sec})(\text{electron})} \quad (10)$$

The intensity I_0 of the incident wave is given by the average value of its Poynting vector

$$I_0 = \frac{c}{8\pi}\,\mathcal{E}_0^2\,\frac{\text{ergs}}{(\text{cm}^2)(\text{sec})} \quad (11)$$

and hence the power radiated into the solid angle $d\Omega$ by a single electron can be written

$$\frac{d(_eQ)}{t} = I_0\left(\frac{e^2}{m_0c^2}\right)^2 d\Omega\,\sin^2\xi\,\frac{\text{ergs}}{(\text{sec})(\text{electron})} \quad (12)$$

This is the differential form of the Thomson scattering formula.

The total energy $_eQ$ radiated by each electron is the integral of $d(_eQ)$ over all angles, with $d\Omega = 2\pi\sin\xi\,d\xi$. The result is

$$_eQ = I_0t\frac{8\pi}{3}\left(\frac{e^2}{m_0c^2}\right)^2\frac{\text{ergs}}{\text{electron}} \quad (13)$$

It should be noted that both the differential (12) and integral (13) forms contain the mass of the scattering center squared in the denominator. The scattering of electromagnetic radiation by a proton or by heavier atomic nuclei is therefore less than one-millionth of the scattering from one electron.

2. *Comparison of Wave and Corpuscular Concepts of Cross Section*

The concept of "cross section" is used in a wide variety of interactions. The precise definition of the term depends on what particular phenomenon is being studied. When met at random in the literature, the exact meaning of "cross section" may have to be deduced from context or even by dimensional analysis.

There are, in fact, two quite distinct interpretations of the term "cross section," depending on whether a wave model or a corpuscular model is to be visualized. Loose and occasionally garbled use of these concepts in the literature is a continuing source of unnecessary confusion to new workers. In the following discussion we begin with the wave or field model of cross section and then follow a stepwise transfer to the corpuscular model.

Many types of collision problems are best treated by some sort of wave theory. Thus the diffraction of visible light by small obstacles, the absorption and scattering of sound by suspended spheres, the scattering of fast neutrons by atomic nuclei, and the interaction of high-energy photons with atomic electrons all have a parallel physical approach. In each theory, the incident radiation is regarded as a plane wave, whose dimensions normal to the direction of propagation are infinite compared with the wavelength of the radiation or with the physical dimensions of the scattering body. The energy transported in this infinite incident wave has to be expressed in terms of energy flux, i.e., *intensity* I_0 in units of energy per unit time and area, or of power per unit area.

The rate of removal of energy from the incident beam by one target particle is then calculated. In general, it is found that the total power removed from the incident collimated beam is proportional to the incident intensity. Thus we can write

$$\frac{_eQ}{t} = {_e\sigma} I_0 \frac{\text{ergs}}{(\text{sec})(\text{electron})} \tag{14}$$

where $_e\sigma$ is merely the proportionality constant derived from the theory and the subscript e emphasizes that we are speaking of cross section per electron. This proportionality $_e\sigma$ between incident power per unit area I_0 and the power $_eQ/t$ removed from the incident beam always has the dimensions of area per target particle. Therefore it is a mnemonic convenience to call $_e\sigma$ the *"cross section"* for the interaction.

a. Differential and Total Thomson Cross Sections. Where a number of distinguishable types of interaction may take place in competition with one another, it is convenient to speak of the "partial cross section" for each particular type of interaction, and also of a "differential cross section." For example, in Thomson scattering, the "differential cross section" $d(_e\sigma)$ for the particular interaction which removes an amount of power $d(_eQ)/t$ from the incident collimated beam and scatters this power into the solid angle $d\Omega$ at mean angle ξ is

$$d(_e\sigma) = \frac{d(_eQ)}{I_0 t} = \left(\frac{e^2}{m_0 c^2}\right)^2 d\Omega \sin^2 \xi \frac{\text{cm}^2}{\text{electron}} \tag{15}$$

Similarly the "total" Thomson cross section refers to the removal of power $_eQ/t$ from the beam by any and all scattering interactions and has the value

$$_e\sigma = \frac{8\pi}{3} \left(\frac{e^2}{m_0 c^2}\right)^2 \equiv \frac{8\pi}{3} r_0^2 \frac{\text{cm}^2}{\text{electron}} \tag{16}$$

b. Classical Electron Radius. These and numerous other types of interaction involving electrons contain the common factor $(e^2/m_0 c^2)^2$, which has dimensions of a length squared. For convenience and brevity, the length $e^2/m_0 c^2 = 2.818 \times 10^{-13}$ cm is generally referred to as the *"classical electron radius"* denoted by the symbol r_0. This is not to be interpreted as having any significance in respect to the probable finite "size" of an actual electron. Indeed, we have just seen that, in the derivation of the Thomson cross sections, the theory treated the electron as if it were a point charge.

c. Wave Concept of Cross Section. In the wave or field theory, the cross section does not appear as a physical property of the struck particle. Its proper physical interpretation is as a property of the entire interaction

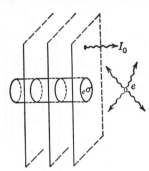

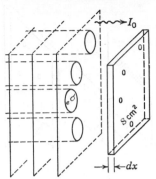

Fig. 1 The intensity, or power per unit area, in the infinite plane wave front advancing from the left is I_0 ergs/(sec)(cm²). As derived from wave theory, the average power removed from the incident collimated beam, through interaction with a point electron having no finite size, corresponds to the power $_e\sigma I_0$ which is transported in a cylinder whose area on the wave front is $_e\sigma$ cm².

Fig. 2 The foil containing $(NZ\ dx)$ electrons/cm², each acting independently, removes the power $Q/t = _e\sigma I_0 S(NZ\ dx)$ ergs/sec from the infinite incident plane wave.

which can be conveniently described as an area $_e\sigma$ cm² in the incident wave front. Then, as illustrated in Fig. 1, the *energy* $_eQ$ removed from the incident collimated beam is equivalent to the energy content of a cylinder whose area is $_e\sigma$ and whose length corresponds to a time t. Even this interpretation is only a convenient fiction, because *actually a broad and diffuse area on the wave front cooperated in the interaction* with the electron.

Physically, the target electron is generally presented to the incident beam as only one of many electrons attached to atoms, as in some absorbing foil. For definiteness, consider in Fig. 2 an experimentally possible arrangement, consisting of an absorbing foil whose area normal to the direction of propagation of the infinite incident plane wave is S cm², and whose thickness is dx cm. Let the foil contain N atoms/cm³, each having Z electrons per atom. Then the foil contains $(NZ\ dx)$ electrons/cm², and $(SNZ\ dx)$ electrons altogether. Assume now that each electron acts independently of all others in its interactions with the wave, in other words, that the scattering is incoherent, and that therefore the total scattering is $(SNZ\ dx)$ times the scattering for one electron. Then the total power removed from the incident plane wave is

$$\frac{Q}{t} = \frac{_eQ}{t}(SNZ\ dx)$$

$$= \left(_e\sigma\ \frac{cm^2}{electron}\right)\left(I_0\ \frac{ergs}{(cm^2)(sec)}\right)(S\ cm^2)\left(NZ\ dx\ \frac{electrons}{cm^2}\right)$$

$$= {_e\sigma}I_0 S(NZ\ dx)\ \frac{ergs}{sec} \tag{17}$$

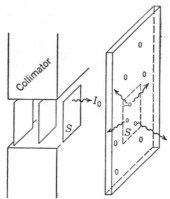

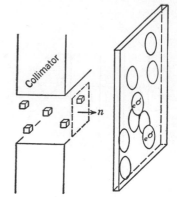

Fig. 3 The incident wave front is now collimated to a finite area S cm², with $\sqrt{S} \gg \lambda$, and the area of the absorber is made $\gg S$. Only the electrons in the area S cm² which is struck by the incident radiation are effective. The total incident power is now finite and equal to $I_0 S$ ergs/sec. The power removed from the incident beam is, however, the same as in Fig. 2.

Fig. 4 The incident power is quantized by dividing it into n particles/sec which carry the total incident power $I_0 S$ ergs/sec. The incident particles can be actual incident deuterons, neutrons, etc., previously treated as a plane matter wave. If the incident radiation was an electromagnetic wave with frequency ν, the incident "particles" are photons each having the energy $h\nu$. When these are regarded as having no physical size, then the cross section $_e\sigma$ is visualized as the area associated with each target particle.

Our third step, shown in Fig. 3, is to collimate the incident radiation, so that the incident wave front has the finite area of S cm². The linear dimensions of the collimating aperture are understood to be very large compared with the wavelength of the radiation, that is, $\sqrt{S} \gg \lambda$. Then edge effects, at the periphery of the incident wave front, can be neglected. Let this finite wave front traverse an absorbing foil whose area is anything greater than S cm² and whose thickness and electron concentration are the same as in Fig. 2. Then only the electrons within the area S are effective. The energy Q removed from the finite incident wave is the same as in Fig. 2, i.e.,

$$\frac{Q}{t} = {}_e\sigma I_0 S N Z \, dx \, \frac{\text{ergs}}{\text{sec}} \tag{18}$$

However, we can now put a different physical interpretation on the experiment:

$I_0 S$ ergs/sec is the total incident power.
$I_0 S t$ ergs is the total incident energy.
Q ergs is the energy removed from the incident collimated beam.

d. Corpuscular Concept of Cross Section. We can now make the transition to a corpuscular viewpoint and can develop a statistical, or probability-law, interpretation of "cross section." We quantize the incident plane wave, as in Fig. 4. For the case of incident electromagnetic radiation, this consists of dividing the incident radiation up into photons, each containing the energy $h\nu$ ergs. Then the total number of photons per second in the incident radiation is n, where

$$n = \frac{(I_0 S \text{ ergs/sec})}{(h\nu \text{ ergs/photon})} = \frac{I_0 S}{h\nu} \frac{\text{photons}}{\text{sec}} \tag{19}$$

The number of incident photons removed from the collimated beam per second is

$$dn = \frac{[(Q/t) \text{ ergs/sec}]}{(h\nu \text{ ergs/photon})} = \frac{Q/t}{h\nu} \frac{\text{photons}}{\text{sec}} \tag{20}$$

Then the Thomson equation (18) becomes

$$\frac{Q}{t} = {}_e\sigma(I_0 S)(NZ \, dx)$$

$$h\nu \, dn = {}_e\sigma(nh\nu)(NZ \, dx) \frac{\text{ergs}}{\text{sec}} \tag{21}$$

or

$$\frac{dn}{n} = \left({}_e\sigma \frac{\text{cm}^2}{\text{electron}}\right)\left(NZ \, dx \frac{\text{electrons}}{\text{cm}^2}\right)$$

$$= {}_e\sigma(NZ \, dx) \text{ dimensionless} \tag{22}$$

In this corpuscular model we see that the *fraction* dn/n of the incident particles removed from the incident beam by some interaction is independent of time t, and of area S, of beam or absorber. If only one particle is incident, then dn/n is the probability that it will suffer some interaction in passing through the foil, and $(1 - dn/n)$ is the probability that it will experience no interaction.

The "cross section" ${}_e\sigma$ no longer corresponds to an area in the incident wave front, for the wave front is absent from the corpuscular model. Therefore, in the corpuscular model, the cross section is visualized as a property of the target centers. It can be written as

$$_e\sigma = \frac{dn/n}{(NZ \, dx \text{ electrons/cm}^2)} = \frac{dn/n}{(NZ \, dx)} \frac{\text{cm}^2}{\text{electron}} \tag{23}$$

from which we interpret the cross section as the *probability* that one incident particle would suffer the interaction specified while passing through a foil containing just one target center per square centimeter. If there are $(NZ \, dx)$ target centers per square centimeter, then the probability becomes ${}_e\sigma(NZ \, dx)$. Now the cross section is playing the role of a target area or disk surrounding each target particle. The probability of removing an incident particle from the beam is visualized as the fractional target area represented by all the $(NZ \, dx)$ electrons in each square centimeter of absorber.

Here we should emphasize again that the theory has nowhere assumed that the target particles have any finite dimensions. Physically, they can still be point particles. But collisionwise they behave the same as if they were particles of definite finite size being bombarded by incident particles which have zero size.

Differential cross sections receive a similar statistical interpretation. Thus $d(_e\sigma)$ becomes the probability that the particular interaction specified will actually occur when one incident particle passes through a foil containing one target center per unit area.

e. The Dimensions of Differential Cross Section. It is convenient sometimes to express the differential cross section as some function multiplied by a differential element. For example, instead of $d(_e\sigma)$ in Eq. (15), we would write $_e\sigma(\xi)\, d\Omega$, where

$$_e\sigma(\xi) \equiv r_0^2 \sin^2 \xi \tag{24}$$

In this particular case it happens that the quantity $_e\sigma(\xi)$ also has dimensions of an area (because $d\Omega$ is dimensionless). Some workers therefore refer to $_e\sigma(\xi)$ as the differential cross section, but this loose usage can lead to confusion and is to be avoided. If we consider other types of differential cross section, such as that describing the energy distribution of bremsstrahlung [Chap. 20, Eq. (1.3)], after integration over all angles, but before integration over the energy spectrum, then we have to deal with a quantity of the form

$$d(\sigma_{\text{rad}}) \equiv \sigma_{\text{rad}}(h\nu)\, d(h\nu) \tag{25}$$

Here it is evident that the function $\sigma_{\text{rad}}(h\nu)$ does not have dimensions of an area, but of square centimeters per erg. The functional relation $\sigma_{\text{rad}}(h\nu)$ *and* the differential parameter $d(h\nu)$ together make up the differential cross section. Therefore, in partial cross sections where dimensionless quantities such as $d\Omega$ or $d\vartheta$ do occur, it is in keeping with a uniform viewpoint to *retain the differential element as part of the cross section.* Thus we call $_e\sigma(\xi)\, d\Omega$, and not $_e\sigma(\xi)$ alone, the differential cross section for Thomson scattering.

In such processes as the emission of bremsstrahlung, the energy of a particle scattered at an angle ϑ may extend over a range of values. Then a "cross section," or more exactly a "differential cross section," may contain both energy and angle as differential parameters. All differential and total cross sections should have dimensions of *area per target particle*.

f. Summary. 1. In the wave or field model, the "cross section" for a particular interaction is the ratio between the rate of energy removal (power) and the incident intensity (power per unit area) per target particle. The cross section can be visualized as an *area in the incident wave front* (Fig. 1) through which flows the amount of power which is removed by the interaction with one target particle.

2. In the corpuscular model, the "cross section" is the fraction of the incident particles which suffer the specified interaction, divided by the number of target particles per unit area of a thin target. Alternatively, the cross section times the number of target particles per unit area of a thin target is the probability, or statistical chance, that *one* incident

particle will undergo the specified interaction while passing through the target. The cross section can be visualized as the hypothetical *area associated with each target particle* (Fig. 4), through which those incident particles pass which undergo the specified interaction. The incident particles in this model have no physical size. The cross section is not a true physical property of the target particle, but rather it is a convenient method for visualizing and comparing the probabilities of various types of competing interactions.

Problem

Let $\mu = NZ\,_e\sigma$ cm^{-1} be the linear absorption coefficient for X rays in matter. Show that in an absorber of thickness x the fraction I/I_0 of the incident intensity which is transmitted without scattering is $I/I_0 = e^{-\mu x}$, and hence that the *relaxation length* is $1/\mu$ cm. Considering the incident intensity to be made up of n_0 photons/(cm^2)(sec), each with energy $h\nu$, show that the *mean free path*, or average distance which a photon travels in this absorber before having a collision in which it is scattered, is also $1/\mu$ cm.

Center-of-mass Coordinates, and the Nonrelativistic Elastic Collision in Classical Mechanics

We discuss here the motion of an incident particle of mass M_1 in its collision with a free particle of mass M_2 which is initially stationary in the laboratory coordinates. The motion of M_1 in the laboratory coordinates is easily derived if its mass can be regarded as negligible in comparison with the mass of the struck particle, which then remains stationary throughout the collision. However, in the majority of important cases, M_1 cannot be neglected in comparison with M_2. It is then most convenient to discuss the dynamics of the collision in a coordinate system whose origin is at rest at the center of mass of the colliding particles. We must therefore use two sets of coordinates, one whose origin is at rest in the laboratory (L coordinates) and one whose origin is at rest at the center of mass of the two colliding particles (C coordinates). The total linear momentum of the colliding particles is zero in the C coordinates, which are therefore also called the *zero-momentum coordinates*.

1. Relations between L (Laboratory) and C (Center-of-mass) Coordinates

a. Elastic Collision in L Coordinates. A particle of mass M_1, whose initial velocity in the laboratory coordinates is V, collides with a free particle of mass M_2 which is initially at rest. The center of mass of these two particles moves with velocity V_c, in a direction parallel to V, such that the linear momentum of the system of two particles is

$$M_1 V = (M_1 + M_2) V_c \tag{1}$$

Thus
$$V_c = V \frac{M_1}{M_1 + M_2} = V \frac{M_0}{M_2} \tag{2}$$

where M_0 is called the *reduced mass* of the system of particles and is defined by

$$\frac{1}{M_0} \equiv \frac{1}{M_1} + \frac{1}{M_2} \qquad \text{or} \qquad M_0 \equiv \frac{M_1 M_2}{M_1 + M_2} \tag{3}$$

The reduced mass always lies between 0.5 and 1.0 times the mass of the lighter particle.   The domain of possible values for the reduced mass M_0 can be visualized with the aid of Fig. 1.

As a result of the collision, the incident particle is deflected through an angle ϑ, while the struck particle M_2 is projected at an angle φ with the original direction of M_1.   The linear momentum of the system is unchanged by the occurrence of the collision, and so the velocity V_c of the center of mass in the L coordinates is the same before, during, and after the collision.   These concepts are shown schematically in Fig. 2. As a result of the collision, the struck particle acquires a velocity V_2, while the velocity of the incident particle is reduced to the value V_1.

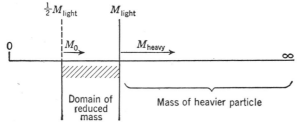

Fig. 1   Mnemonic representation of the reduced mass M_0, which equals $\frac{1}{2}M_{\text{light}}$ when $M_{\text{light}} = M_{\text{heavy}}$ and can increase only to $M_0 = M_{\text{light}}$, as M_{heavy} approaches infinity.

Kinetic energy is conserved in elastic collisions; that is, the total kinetic energy of the particles when they are widely separated is the same before and after the collision.   Hence we write

Conservation of energy: $\frac{1}{2}M_1V^2 = \frac{1}{2}M_1V_1^2 + \frac{1}{2}M_2V_2^2$ $\qquad$ (4)

The linear momentum normal to the plane of Fig. 2 is always zero, but in this plane of motion we write

Conservation of momentum: $M_1V = M_1V_1 \cos \vartheta + M_2V_2 \cos \varphi$ $\quad$ (5)
Conservation of momentum: $\qquad 0 = M_1V_1 \sin \vartheta - M_2V_2 \sin \varphi$ $\quad$ (6)

These three conservation equations may be solved simultaneously to eliminate any two parameters.   If we choose to eliminate V_2 and φ, we obtain an expression for the final velocity V_1 in terms of the deflection angle ϑ, which is

$$\left(\frac{V_1}{V}\right)^2 - 2\left(\frac{V_1}{V}\right)\frac{M_1}{M_1 + M_2}\cos \vartheta - \frac{M_2 - M_1}{M_1 + M_2} = 0 \qquad (7)$$

Note that Eq. (7) is quadratic in V_1.   [Expressions for V_2 and V_1 in terms of φ are given in Eqs. (29) and (30).]

All these relationships, Eqs. (1) to (7), are independent of the nature of the forces involved in the collision, because they depend only on conservation of kinetic energy and momentum and are essentially "before and after" quantities.

b. Elastic Collision in C Coordinates.   We reconsider the collision illustrated in Fig. 2, referring all motion to coordinates which are at rest at the center of mass of the two particles.   This is equivalent to translating the laboratory coordinates at a uniform velocity, $(-V_c)$. Then, as illustrated schematically in Fig. 3, M_1 approaches the origin with velocity

$$V - V_c = V\left(1 - \frac{M_0}{M_2}\right) = V\frac{M_2}{M_1 + M_2} = V\frac{M_0}{M_1} \tag{8}$$

Also M_2 approaches the center of mass with velocity V_c.

The initial *mutual velocity of approach* is $(V - V_c) + V_c = V$, which is the same in the C coordinates as in the L coordinates.

Laboratory coordinates

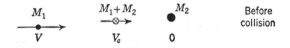

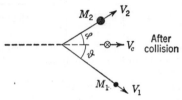

Fig. 2   In L coordinates, the center of mass, marked $\otimes$, moves with constant velocity V_c before, during, and after the collision.

The *total linear momentum of the system is zero*, because the center of mass is stationary.   Thus

$$M_1(V - V_c) - M_2 V_c = M_0 V - M_0 V = 0 \tag{9}$$

and therefore the velocities are in inverse ratio to the masses

$$\frac{V - V_c}{V_c} = \frac{M_2}{M_1} \tag{10}$$

The linear momenta of the two individual particles are equal and opposite at all times before, during, and after the elastic collision.   Therefore, after the collision, the two particles must depart from the center of mass in exactly opposite directions.   If M_1 is deflected through an angle Θ, then M_2 will also be deflected through the same angle Θ; see Fig. 3. The path of M_2 after the collision is at an angle Φ with the original direction of M_1, where

$$\Phi = \pi - \Theta \tag{11}$$

The net results of the collision are that the line joining M_1 and M_2 is rotated through the angle Θ, and the two particles recede from the center of mass after the collision.

Moreover, the individual velocities of the two particles are the same after the collision as they were before.   This is an immediate consequence of the conservation of kinetic energy in the (elastic) collision. If the velocity of M_1 were decreased by the collision, then the velocity of M_2 would also have to decrease in order to satisfy momentum conservation. But this would decrease the total kinetic energy of the system. Therefore, both the initial and final velocities of M_1 are $(V - V_c)$, and of M_2 are V_c. The *initial and final linear momentum of each particle is $M_0 V$,* by Eqs. (8) and (9), and the total linear momentum is always zero.

The *total kinetic energy* $(KE)_0$ before and after the collision in the C coordinates is

$$(KE)_0 = \tfrac{1}{2}M_1(V - V_c)^2 + \tfrac{1}{2}M_2 V_c^2 = \tfrac{1}{2}M_1 V^2 - \tfrac{1}{2}(M_1 + M_2)V_c^2 \quad (12)$$

This is simply the kinetic energy of M_1 in the L coordinates, diminished by the kinetic energy equivalent to the motion of the center of mass in the L coordinates. Substituting the value of V_c in terms of V from Eq. (2) into Eq. (12) and simplifying, we obtain the more general expression

$$(KE)_0 = \tfrac{1}{2}M_0 V^2 \tag{13}$$

Thus the initial kinetic energy in the C coordinates is most simply expressed in terms of the reduced mass of the system and the initial mutual velocity of approach of the two particles.

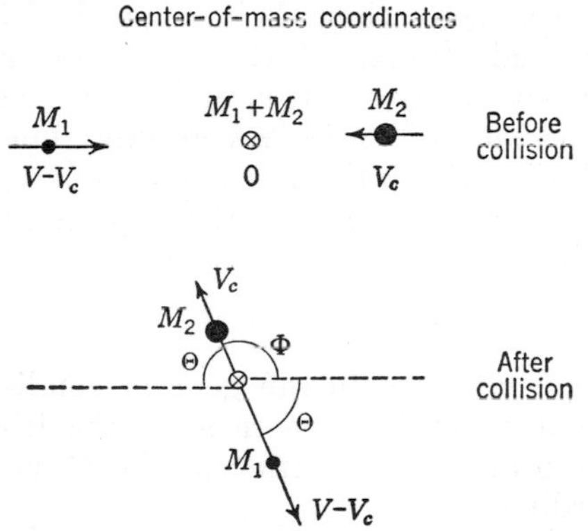

We should note especially that the collision is now generalized. In the L coordinates M_1 represented

Center-of-mass coordinates

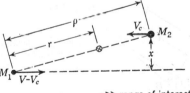

Fig. 3 In C coordinates the center of mass, marked $\otimes$, is stationary.

Fig. 4 The impact parameter x is the separation at which the particles would pass each other if there were no interaction.

the projectile and M_2 the target. But in the C coordinates this distinction disappears. *Two* particles approach *each other.* They have an initial velocity of approach V, reduced mass M_0, total linear momentum zero, total kinetic energy $\tfrac{1}{2}M_0 V^2$, and deflection angle Θ.

c. Impact Parameter, Angular Momentum, Moment of Inertia, Kinetic Energy. In considering the over-all collision, we have so far dealt only with the initial and final states. We must now examine the actual collision in more detail. Especially, we must recognize that most collisions are not "head-on." In Fig. 4, the two particles are at a large distance ρ from each other. If no forces were to exist between the two particles, they would eventually pass each other at a distance x called the *impact parameter*.

The *angular momentum J* of this system of two particles is a constant of their motion, because *no external torques act* on the system. The angular momentum, taken about the center of mass, has the same value in both the L and C coordinates, because these coordinate systems differ only in the value of the translational velocity of the center of mass (V_c in L, 0 in C). The angular momentum about the center of mass, evaluated in the C coordinates, is

$$J = M_1(V - V_c)\frac{r}{\rho} x + M_2 V_c \frac{\rho - r}{\rho} x = M_0 V \frac{r}{\rho} x + M_0 V \left(1 - \frac{r}{\rho}\right) x$$

$$= M_0 V x \tag{14}$$

As the particles approach more closely to one another, the forces which are to be effective in the collision gradually begin to be felt. For example, if the interaction is to be due to coulomb repulsion, then the force between the particles will increase with $1/\rho^2$. During the effective "time of impact" the velocities of both particles will change in direction and in magnitude. The change in magnitude will correspond to the changing potential energy between the two particles, the potential energy of their interaction having been taken as zero when their separation ρ was very large. Throughout the actual "impact" the total linear momentum must remain zero in the C coordinates. If v_1 and v_2 are the instantaneous velocities at any time during the impact, then v_1 and v_2 must always be exactly oppositely directed. The momentum

$$0 = M_1 v_1 - M_2 v_2$$

leads at once to the general condition governing the ratio of the instantaneous velocities in the C coordinates,

$$\frac{v_2}{v_1} = \frac{M_1}{M_2} \tag{15}$$

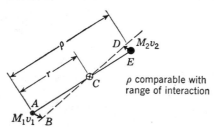

Fig. 5 In the region of interaction, during the "collision," conservation of momentum requires $v_2/v_1 = M_1/M_2$, and $r/\rho = M_0/M_1$ [Eqs. (15) and (17)].

This facilitates an independent evaluation of the relationship between the separation distance ρ and the corresponding instantaneous distance r between M_1 and the center of mass. Thus, in Fig. 5, assume (virtual) displacements $v_1\,dt$ and $v_2\,dt$ of the positions of M_1 and M_2 during the time interval dt. Then in the similar triangles ABC and CDE, we have

$$\frac{v_1\,dt}{r} = \frac{v_2\,dt}{\rho - r}$$

Simplifying and making use of Eq. (15), we obtain

$$\frac{v_2}{v_1} = \frac{\rho}{r} - 1 = \frac{M_1}{M_2} \tag{16}$$

Then at any time during the motion

$$\frac{r}{\rho} = \frac{M_2}{M_1 + M_2} = \frac{M_0}{M_1} \quad \text{or} \quad M_0\rho = M_1 r = M_2(\rho - r) \quad (17)$$

because at any instant both particles have the same angular velocity about the center of mass.

The *moment of inertia* I of the system about the center of mass is then given by

$$I = M_1 r^2 + M_2(\rho - r)^2 = M_0\rho r + M_0\rho(\rho - r) = M_0\rho^2 \quad (18)$$

which is an important general relationship.

The *kinetic energy* KE *during the collision* will differ from the initial and final kinetic energy $(KE)_0$ if the particles interact with each other, i.e., if they have a finite mutual potential energy during the "collision." Then at any time during the collision, when the instantaneous velocity of M_1 is v_1 in C coordinates, the instantaneous kinetic energy in C coordinates is

$$KE = \tfrac{1}{2}M_1 v_1^2 + \tfrac{1}{2}M_2 v_2^2 \quad (19)$$

$$KE = \tfrac{1}{2}M_0\left(\frac{M_1}{M_2} + 1\right)v_1^2 + \tfrac{1}{2}M_0\left(\frac{M_2}{M_1} + 1\right)v_2^2$$

$$= \tfrac{1}{2}M_0\left(\frac{v_2}{v_1} + 1\right)v_1^2 + \tfrac{1}{2}M_0\left(\frac{v_1}{v_2} + 1\right)v_2^2$$

$$= \tfrac{1}{2}M_0(v_1 + v_2)^2 \quad (20)$$

which is the general expression, whose limiting value for large ρ corresponds to $(KE)_0 = \tfrac{1}{2}M_0 V^2$, as given in Eq. (13). Substituting

$$v_2 = \frac{v_1 M_1}{M_2}$$

into Eq. (20) and simplifying, we obtain the alternative expression

$$KE = \tfrac{1}{2}M_0 v_1^2\left(\frac{M_1}{M_0}\right)^2 = \tfrac{1}{2}M_1 v_1^2\left(\frac{M_1}{M_0}\right) \quad (21)$$

d. Deflection Angles in L and C Coordinates. In Fig. 6 the uniform motion V_c of the center of mass in the L coordinates is superimposed on the angular and velocity relations of the C coordinates as taken from Fig. 3. For example, the final velocity V_1 of M_1 is the vector sum of V_c and of $(V - V_c)$ at angle Θ with respect to the direction defined by V_c.

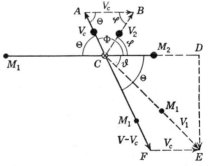

Fig. 6 Solid vectors represent the velocities of M_1 and M_2 in the C coordinates, as given in Fig. 3. The velocity V_c of the center of mass in the L coordinates is added vectorially, to obtain the final velocities V_1 and V_2 in the L coordinates as given first in Fig. 2.

In Fig. 6, t   therefore the angle ACB equals
φ, and

But from E   ıck particle
M_2 is projected at an   imply

$$\varphi = \tfrac{1}{2}(\pi - \Theta) \tag{22}$$

Note that this relationship is independent of M_1/M_2.

The relationship between the angles ϑ and Θ, for the incident particle M_1, is not quite as simple.   In the triangle CDE

$$\frac{CD}{DE} = \cot \vartheta = \frac{V_c + (V - V_c) \cos \Theta}{(V - V_c) \sin \Theta}$$

or $$\cot \vartheta = \frac{(M_1/M_2) + \cos \Theta}{\sin \Theta} = \frac{M_1}{M_2} \csc \Theta + \cot \Theta \tag{23}$$

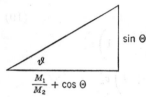

sin Θ

$\dfrac{M_1}{M_2} + \cos \Theta$

Fig. 7 Graphical representation of Eq. (23) connecting the laboratory angle ϑ with the center-of-mass angle Θ for the deflection of an incident particle of mass M_1 by a target particle of mass M_2.

The relationship between Θ, ϑ, and M_1/M_2 can be summarized by the mnemonically convenient graphical representation of Fig. 7.

An equivalent and alternative relationship, which expresses Θ in terms of the observed laboratory angle ϑ, can be obtained by applying the law of sines to triangle CEF of Fig. 6 and is

$$\sin (\Theta - \vartheta) = \frac{M_1}{M_2} \sin \vartheta \tag{24}$$

Depending on the mass ratio M_1/M_2, there are three special cases of Eq. (23) or (24) which are of particular interest.   These are

1. If $M_1 \ll M_2$: $\Theta \simeq \vartheta + \dfrac{M_1}{M_2} \sin \vartheta$ or $\vartheta \simeq \Theta$ (25)

2. If $M_1 = M_2$: $\cot \vartheta = \cot \Theta + \csc \Theta = \cot \dfrac{\Theta}{2}$ or $\vartheta = \dfrac{\Theta}{2}$ (26)

3. If $M_1 \gg M_2$: $\tan \vartheta \simeq \dfrac{M_2}{M_1} \sin \Theta$ or $\vartheta \simeq \dfrac{M_2}{M_1} \sin \Theta$ (27)

e. Velocities in L and C Coordinates.   In this section we consider only the initial and final velocities, i.e., the velocities when the separation ρ of the particles is sufficiently large so that their mutual potential energy is negligible.

The velocities in the C coordinates are unchanged by the elastic collision.   The velocities in the L coordinates are changed because some kinetic energy is transferred from M_1 to M_2 in the collision; therefore, $V_1 < V$.

In Fig. 6, apply the law of cosines to triangle CAB, obtaining

$$V_2^2 = V_c^2 + V_c^2 - 2V_c^2 \cos \Theta = 2V_c^2(1 - \cos \Theta)$$

$$= 2 \left(V \frac{M_0}{M_2} \right)^2 (1 - \cos \Theta) \tag{28}$$

Making use of a trigonometric identity and Eq. (22), we have

$$(1 - \cos \Theta) = 2 \sin^2 \frac{\Theta}{2} = 2 \cos^2 \varphi \tag{28a}$$

which, on substitution into Eq. (28), gives

$$V_2 = 2V \frac{M_0}{M_2} \cos \varphi \tag{29}$$

for the velocity acquired in the L coordinates by the struck particle, M_2. The residual velocity V_1 of the incident particle in the L coordinates can be obtained from triangle CEF of Fig. 6 or directly from conservation of energy, Eqs. (4) and (29). Thus

$$\tfrac{1}{2} M_1 V_1^2 = \tfrac{1}{2} M_1 V^2 - \tfrac{1}{2} M_2 V_2^2$$

$$V_1^2 = V^2 - \frac{M_2}{M_1} \left(2V \frac{M_0}{M_2} \cos \varphi \right)^2$$

$$= V^2 \left(1 - \frac{4M_0^2}{M_1 M_2} \cos^2 \varphi \right) \tag{30}$$

$$V_1^2 = V^2 \left[1 - 2(1 - \cos \Theta) \frac{M_1 M_2}{(M_1 + M_2)^2} \right] \tag{31}$$

Each of these is, of course, equivalent to Eq. (7). It is also useful to note, from the line DE in Fig. 6, the relationship

$$V_1 \sin \vartheta = V \frac{M_0}{M_1} \sin \Theta \tag{32}$$

Problems

1. Show that, whenever a particle of mass M and velocity V has an elastic collision with a particle having the same mass M but initially unbound and at rest in the laboratory system, the paths of the two particles in the laboratory coordinates after the collision are always at 90° to one another.

2. Obtain the expression for V_2 in terms of φ, Eq. (29), directly from the conservation laws, Eqs. (4), (5), and (6).

3. Consider an elastic collision between an incident particle having mass M_1 and a target particle M_2 for those cases in which $M_1 > M_2$.

(a) Show that the largest possible angle of scattering ϑ_m in the L coordinates is given by

$$\cos \Theta_m = - \frac{M_2}{M_1}$$

$$\sin \vartheta_m = \frac{M_2}{M_1}$$

$$\sin \varphi_m = \sqrt{\frac{M_1 - M_2}{2M_1}}$$

(*b*) Evaluate the angles Θ_m, ϑ_m, and ($\vartheta_m + \varphi_m$) for elastic collisions between incident deuterons and target protons. Integer values may be used for the deuteron and proton masses. Evaluate the angles in degrees.

(*c*) Are any of the results in (*a*) and (*b*) dependent on the nature of the scattering forces? Why?

2. *Equation of the Hyperbola in Polar Coordinates*

For comparison with results to be obtained in the subsequent section, we review here the analytical properties of the hyperbola in polar coordinates.

In Fig. 8 (which we shall find later corresponds to repulsive coulomb forces in elastic scattering), we establish at C the origin of polar coordinates, r, ψ. Now establish a point C' at $\psi = 0$, $r = 2a\epsilon$. This point is the inner focus of the hyperbola to be constructed with its vertex at $r = a\epsilon + a$, $\psi = 0$. C and C' are the *foci*, and $2a$ is the distance between the *vertices*, of the two branches of the hyperbola which can be drawn between C and C' with *eccentricity* ϵ.

The hyperbola is the locus of all points whose distances r and r', from two fixed points C and C', have a constant difference $2a$. Thus

$$r - r' = 2a \tag{33}$$

or
$$(r')^2 = r^2 - 4ar + 4a^2$$

From Fig. 8, the law of cosines gives

$$(r')^2 = r^2 + (2a\epsilon)^2 - 2r(2a\epsilon)\cos\psi$$

Equating these two values of $(r')^2$, collecting terms, and simplifying give

$$r = \frac{a(\epsilon^2 - 1)}{\epsilon\cos\psi - 1} \tag{34}$$

which is the hyperbola of Fig. 8.

The *asymptotes* correspond to $r = \infty$ and occur at angles $\pm\psi_\infty$, such that

$$\cos\psi_\infty = \frac{1}{\epsilon} \tag{35}$$

The angle between the asymptotes will be found later to correspond to the deflection angle Θ and is given by

$$\Theta = \pi - 2\psi_\infty \qquad \text{or} \qquad \psi_\infty = \frac{\pi}{2} - \frac{\Theta}{2} \tag{36}$$

so that
$$\cos\psi_\infty = \sin\frac{\Theta}{2} = \frac{1}{\epsilon} \tag{37}$$

and
$$\epsilon^2 - 1 = \csc^2\frac{\Theta}{2} - 1 = \cot^2\frac{\Theta}{2} \tag{38}$$

Equation (38) shows that the minimum value of the eccentricity for any hyperbola is unity. From Eq. (34), the minimum positive value of r

(vertex) is $r = a(\epsilon + 1)$, for $\psi = 0$. In Eq. (34), positive values of r correspond to the hyperbola shown in Fig. 8 and occur for values of ψ between ψ_∞ and $-\psi_\infty$, that is,

$$\psi_\infty \geq \psi \geq -\psi_\infty \qquad \text{for } r \text{ positive} \tag{39}$$

Similarly, negative values of r occur for the larger values of ψ, such that

$$\psi_\infty \leq \psi \leq -\psi_\infty \qquad \text{for } r \text{ negative} \tag{40}$$

These negative values form the second branch of the hyperbola, which

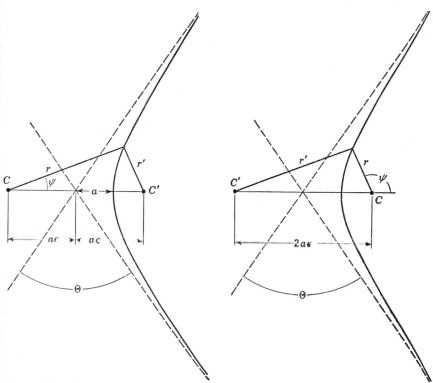

Fig. 8 Hyperbolic orbit of Eqs. (33) to (40), characteristic of coulomb *repulsive* forces between particles whose center of mass is at the *external* focus and origin C. Drawn for an eccentricity $\epsilon = 1.8 = 1/\sin(\Theta/2)$, so that $\Theta \simeq 67°$.

Fig. 9 Hyperbolic orbit of Eqs. (41) to (46), characteristic of coulomb *attractive* forces between particles whose center of mass is at the *internal* focus and origin C. Same eccentricity as Fig. 8.

contains the origin C as its *inner* focus. This branch is not **drawn** in Fig. 8. Instead, we will make a direct derivation of the equation of a hyperbola having its origin as inner focus.

In Fig. 9, consider the branch of the hyperbola defined by

$$r' - r = 2a \tag{41}$$

Then, from the law of cosines,

$$(r')^2 = r^2 + (2a\epsilon)^2 + 2r(2a\epsilon) \cos \psi$$

which, when combined with Eq. (41), gives the polar equation of the hyperbola drawn in Fig. 9 as

$$r = \frac{a(\epsilon^2 - 1)}{1 - \epsilon \cos \psi} \tag{42}$$

This is simply the negative of Eq. (34), as expected. The asymptotes $r = \infty$ correspond as before to $\cos \psi_\infty = 1/\epsilon$. The deflection angle is again $\Theta = \pi - 2\psi_\infty$. Therefore

$$\cos \psi_\infty = \sin \frac{\Theta}{2} = \frac{1}{\epsilon} \tag{43}$$

so that, as before,

$$\epsilon^2 - 1 = \cot^2 \frac{\Theta}{2} \tag{44}$$

Positive values of r occur only for the large angles ψ given by

$$\psi_\infty \leq \psi \leq -\psi_\infty \qquad \text{for } r \text{ positive} \tag{45}$$

The negative values of r which occur for the small angles

$$\psi_\infty \geq \psi \geq -\psi_\infty$$

correspond to the other branch of this hyperbola, for which C is the external focus and C' is the internal focus. The minimum positive value of r now occurs for $\psi = \pi$, when $\cos \psi = -1$, and locates the vertex at

$$r = a(\epsilon - 1) \qquad \psi = \pi \tag{46}$$

The hyperbola of Fig. 9 and Eq. (42) will be found to correspond to the path of a particle experiencing an *attractive* coulomb force, when C is the center of mass of the two interacting particles.

3. *Elastic Collision between Charged Particles*

All the results of the first section are independent of the type of interaction between the particles. The use of center-of-mass coordinates reduces any two-body problem to a one-body problem, namely, the interaction of one particle having a mass M_0 and velocity V with a potential field which can be considered as centered at the origin of the C coordinates. This is true for either classical mechanics, Eq. (55), or wave mechanics, Appendix C, Eq. (38).

We must now consider the collision in more detail, under the assumption that the interaction is an inverse-square force. The general results will therefore include Rutherford-Darwin scattering of α rays, protons, electrons, etc., by nuclei, as well as the ionizing collisions of these same charged particles with atomic electrons.

a. Velocity and Acceleration in Polar Coordinates. The problem of determining the orbit of the charged particles is greatly simplified by the use of polar coordinates, with the origin at the center of mass. Then, if r, ψ are the coordinates of M_1 at any time t, the components of its velocity and acceleration, v_r, v_ψ, a_r, a_ψ, are well-known results of analytical geometry (p. 56 of S45, p. 236 of P19). These components, in the directions of increasing r and of increasing ψ, are

$$v_r = \frac{dr}{dt} \qquad v_\psi = r\frac{d\psi}{dt} \tag{47}$$

where dr/dt is the radial velocity and $d\psi/dt$ is the angular velocity of M_1 at r, ψ. The radial component of acceleration, in the direction of increasing r, is

$$a_r = \frac{d^2r}{dt^2} - r\left(\frac{d\psi}{dt}\right)^2 \tag{48}$$

where the final term is the "centripetal acceleration." The angular component of acceleration in the direction of increasing ψ is

$$a_\psi = r\frac{d^2\psi}{dt^2} + 2\frac{dr}{dt}\frac{d\psi}{dt} \tag{49}$$

where the final term is the "Coriolis acceleration." The last equation can also be written in the form

$$a_\psi = \frac{1}{r}\frac{d}{dt}\left(r^2\frac{d\psi}{dt}\right) \tag{50}$$

where the term in parentheses is the angular momentum per unit mass.

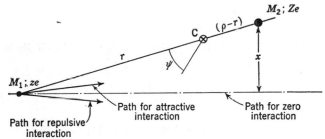

Fig. 10 Schematic of center-of-mass polar coordinates for discussion of collisions involving coulomb attraction or repulsion. The direction of $\psi = 0$ is arbitrary for the present.

b. Conservation of Angular Momentum. For central forces between M_1 and M_2 (Fig. 10), the torque about the center of mass C is zero. Therefore the angular component of acceleration a_ψ is zero, because the entire force is along r. Then Eq. (50) becomes

$$a_\psi = 0 = \frac{1}{r}\frac{d}{dt}\left(r^2\frac{d\psi}{dt}\right) \tag{51}$$

Upon integration, this gives

$$r^2 \frac{d\psi}{dt} = H \tag{52}$$

where H is a constant of integration and is shown in Eq. (54) to be proportional to the constant angular momentum of the system. We note that $d\psi/dt$ is the angular velocity of the line ρ joining M_1 and M_2 about the center of mass. Then $d\psi/dt$ times the moment of inertia I equals the angular momentum J which, by Eq. (14), has the constant value of $M_0 Vx$. Using Eq. (18) for the moment of inertia as a function of r, and inserting a negative sign because $d\psi/dt$ is negative as drawn in Fig. 10, the angular momentum of the system about C is

$$J = -r^2 M_0 \left(\frac{M_1}{M_0}\right)^2 \frac{d\psi}{dt} = M_0 Vx = \text{const} \tag{53}$$

Hence

$$r^2 \frac{d\psi}{dt} = -\left(\frac{M_0}{M_1}\right)^2 Vx = H \tag{54}$$

The negative sign depends only on our arbitrary choice of the direction of $\psi = 0$ in Fig. 10. It will not influence the final equations, because only H^2 appears later on. Equation (54) is one of the equations restricting the orbit.

c. Coulomb Force. We now assume that the only force between M_1 and M_2 is the coulomb force between their charges ze and Ze. (If other central forces, such as a meson attractive force, were to be included, they should be added at this step.) The coulomb force is entirely along ρ and hence r. Remembering that $\rho = r M_1/M_0$, from Eq. (17), the coulomb force is

$$f_r = \frac{Zze^2}{\rho^2} = \frac{Zze^2}{r^2}\left(\frac{M_0}{M_1}\right)^2 \tag{55}$$

This force is attractive if Zz is negative and is repulsive if Zz is positive. The component of acceleration of M_1 along r is

$$a_r = \frac{f_r}{M_1} = \frac{Zze^2}{r^2}\left(\frac{M_0}{M_1}\right)^2 \frac{1}{M_1} \equiv \frac{G}{r^2} \tag{56}$$

where G represents the masses and charges of M_1 and M_2. Both G and a_r are positive for repulsive interaction and are negative for attractive forces. Then Eq. (48) becomes

$$a_r = \frac{d^2 r}{dt^2} - r\left(\frac{d\psi}{dt}\right)^2 = \frac{G}{r^2} \tag{57}$$

which is a second equation restricting the path of M_1 with respect to the center of mass.

d. Equation of the Path of M_1. We now wish to obtain the differential equation of the orbit, in terms of r and ψ. This can be done by eliminating the time t between Eqs. (57) and (54). Physically, we are combining the principle of conservation of angular momentum, Eq. (54), and the coulomb interaction between the particles, Eq. (57), in order to obtain the differential equation of the path of M_1.   These steps, and the resulting differential equation, are greatly simplified if we make the substitution

$$r \equiv \frac{1}{\mu} \tag{58}$$

Then

$$\frac{dr}{dt} = \frac{dr}{d\psi}\frac{d\psi}{dt} \tag{59}$$

$$\frac{dr}{d\psi} = \frac{d}{d\psi}\frac{1}{\mu} = -\frac{1}{\mu^2}\frac{d\mu}{d\psi} \tag{60}$$

Equation (54) becomes

$$\frac{d\psi}{dt} = H\mu^2 \tag{61}$$

Substitution of Eqs. (60) and (61) into Eq. (59) gives

$$\frac{dr}{dt} = -\frac{1}{\mu^2}\frac{d\mu}{d\psi} H\mu^2 = -H\frac{d\mu}{d\psi} \tag{62}$$

The second derivative is then

$$\frac{d^2r}{dt^2} = -H\frac{d^2\mu}{d\psi^2}\frac{d\psi}{dt} = -H^2\mu^2\frac{d^2\mu}{d\psi^2} \tag{63}$$

Substituting Eq. (63) into (57), and writing $r = 1/\mu$, we have

$$-H^2\mu^2\frac{d^2\mu}{d\psi^2} - \frac{1}{\mu}H^2\mu^4 = G\mu^2 \quad \text{or} \quad \frac{d^2\mu}{d\psi^2} + \mu = -\frac{G}{H^2} \tag{64}$$

which is the differential equation of the path of M_1.   The general solution of Eq. (64) can be written in the form

$$\mu = \frac{1}{r} = -\frac{G}{H^2} + A\cos(\psi - \psi_0) \tag{65}$$

where A and ψ_0 are constants of integration, to be evaluated later.   Equation (65) can be arranged in the form

$$r = \frac{H^2/G}{(AH^2/G)\cos(\psi - \psi_0) - 1} \tag{66}$$

This is the equation of a hyperbolic orbit.   For repulsive forces, G is positive, and Eq. (66) takes the form of Eq. (34) and Fig. 8.   For attractive forces, G is negative, and Eq. (66) takes the form of Eq. (42) and Fig. 9.   In both cases $\epsilon = AH^2/G$ is positive, and ϵ is to be evaluated from the expression

$$\epsilon^2 - 1 = \frac{A^2H^4}{G^2} - 1 \tag{67}$$

The scale factor a of Eq. (34) or (42) is then given by

$$a = \frac{H^2}{G(\epsilon^2 - 1)} = \frac{G}{A^2H^2 - (G^2/H^2)} \tag{68}$$

and has the same sign as G.

For repulsive forces, the smallest value of r occurs when

$$\cos(\psi - \psi_0) = 1 \quad \text{or} \quad \psi = \psi_0$$

therefore we set ψ_0 as the direction *toward* the vertex, as in Fig. 8. For attractive forces, the smallest value of r occurs when $\cos(\psi - \psi_0) = -1$, or $\psi = \psi_0 + \pi$; therefore we set ψ_0 as the direction *away* from the vertex, as in Fig. 9. By choosing these directions for the initial line we can set

$$\psi_0 = 0 \tag{69}$$

e. Conservation of Energy. To evaluate the integration constant A of Eq. (66), we apply the principle of conservation of energy to this elastic collision.

In general, the instantaneous velocity v_1 of M_1 is given by

$$v_1^2 = \left(\frac{dr}{dt}\right)^2 + \left(r\frac{d\psi}{dt}\right)^2 = \left[\left(\frac{dr}{d\psi}\right)^2 + r^2\right]\left(\frac{d\psi}{dt}\right)^2 \tag{70}$$

From Eq. (65) for the path of M_1, we obtain, with $\psi_0 = 0$,

$$\frac{dr}{d\psi} = \frac{dr}{d\mu}\frac{d\mu}{d\psi} = \left(-\frac{1}{\mu^2}\right)(-A\sin\psi) = Ar^2\sin\psi \tag{71}$$

Using this, and $d\psi/dt = H/r^2$ from Eq. (52), Eq. (70) becomes

$$v_1^2 = A^2H^2\sin^2\psi + \frac{H^2}{r^2} \tag{72}$$

Now when the separation ρ is finite, the sum of the kinetic energy, Eq. (21), and the electrostatic potential energy must equal the initial kinetic energy, Eq. (13), of the system. The potential energy is

$$\frac{Zze^2}{\rho} = \frac{Zze^2}{r}\frac{M_0}{M_1} \tag{73}$$

Conservation of energy then gives the relationship

$$\tfrac{1}{2}M_0V^2 = \tfrac{1}{2}M_1v_1^2\frac{M_1}{M_0} + \frac{Zze^2}{r}\frac{M_0}{M_1}$$

or

$$V^2\left(\frac{M_0}{M_1}\right)^2 = v_1^2 + \frac{2Zze^2}{rM_1}\left(\frac{M_0}{M_1}\right)^2$$

$$= v_1^2 + \frac{2G}{r} \tag{74}$$

Substituting v_1^2 from Eq. (72) and $1/r$ from Eq. (65), with $\psi_0 = 0$, into this expression and simplifying lead at once to

$$V^2\left(\frac{M_0}{M_1}\right)^2 = \frac{A^2H^4 - G^2}{H^2} \tag{75}$$

which is independent of r and ψ, and which expresses the integration constant A in terms of the other parameters of the collision. Instead of solving this equation for A, we may proceed directly to evaluate the eccentricity, Eq. (67), of the hyperbolic path of M_1 about the center of mass. Thus

$$\epsilon^2 = \frac{A^2 H^4}{G^2} = V^2 \left(\frac{H}{G}\right)^2 \left(\frac{M_0}{M_1}\right)^2 + 1 \tag{76}$$

Solving for ϵ and substituting the values of G and H, which were defined in Eqs. (54) and (56) as

$$H = -Vx \left(\frac{M_0}{M_1}\right)^2 \qquad G = \frac{Zze^2}{M_1} \left(\frac{M_0}{M_1}\right)^2$$

we obtain for the eccentricity of the path

$$\epsilon = \sqrt{1 + \left(\frac{M_0 V^2 x}{Zze^2}\right)^2} \tag{77}$$

It will be noted that Zz appears only in a squared term, and so the eccentricity is the same for attractive and for repulsive forces. Moreover, the last equation gives direct verification of the fact that the eccentricity is always

$$\epsilon \geq 1$$

so that the path is always hyperbolic and never elliptical.

f. Collision Diameter. In examining the physical consequences of the equations which describe the collision, it is convenient and instructive to group the principal parameters in a particular way. We therefore define a fundamental length, to be called the *collision diameter b*, as

$$b = \frac{2|Zz|e^2}{M_0 V^2} \tag{78}$$

where $|Zz|$ is the absolute value of Zz. Then the equation of the orbit of M_1, Eq. (66), becomes

$$r = \frac{a(\epsilon^2 - 1)}{\epsilon \cos \psi - 1} \tag{79}$$

where

$$\epsilon = \sqrt{1 + \left(\frac{2x}{b}\right)^2} \tag{79a}$$

$$\epsilon^2 - 1 = \left(\frac{2x}{b}\right)^2 \tag{79b}$$

$$a = \pm \left(\frac{b}{2}\right)\left(\frac{M_0}{M_1}\right) \tag{79c}$$

$$a(\epsilon^2 - 1) = \pm \left(\frac{2x^2}{b}\right)\left(\frac{M_0}{M_1}\right) \tag{79d}$$

and a has the same sign as Zz. Referring to the general equations of the hyperbola, we recall from Eqs. (38) and (44) that

$$\epsilon^2 - 1 = \cot^2 \frac{\Theta}{2}$$

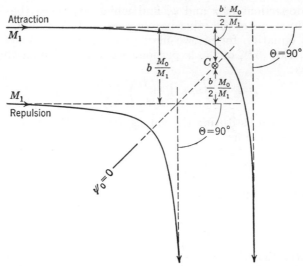

Fig. 11 The collision diameter b defines the impact parameter $x = b/2$ which results in 90° deflections, in the C coordinates, for both attractive and repulsive forces. In the figure, C is the center of mass and is the origin of polar coordinates r, ψ defining the paths as in Eq. (79), with the direction $\psi_0 = 0$. The impact parameter x is the separation of the initial paths of the two particles, and so the distance between C and the initial path of M_1 is $x(M_0/M_1)$, in general, and is $(b/2)(M_0/M_1)$ for the special case of $\Theta = 90°$ shown here.

and so Eq. (79b) gives us the relationship sought between impact parameter x, collision diameter b, and the deflection angle Θ in the C coordinates. Thus we obtain

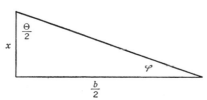

Fig. 12 Graphical representation of Rutherford scattering, Eqs. (80) and (80a).

$$x = \frac{b}{2} \cot \frac{\Theta}{2} \qquad (80)$$

This equation clearly exhibits the physical concept of *collision diameter* b. When the impact parameter x is one-half the collision diameter, the deflection Θ is 90°. This is true for both attractive and repulsive forces, as illustrated in Fig. 11.

The essential physical features of Rutherford (i.e., classical) scattering are most succinctly represented by Eq. (80), for which Fig. 12 is a convenient mnemonic representation.

From Eq. (22), $\frac{1}{2}\Theta = \frac{1}{2}\pi - \varphi$, so that the last equation can also be written in terms of the laboratory angle of projection of M_2 and then is

$$x = \frac{b}{2} \tan \varphi \qquad (80a)$$

g. Closest Distance of Approach. The separation ρ between the interacting particles is always $\rho = r(M_1/M_0)$, by Eq. (17).

For repulsive forces the minimum value of r is, by Eq. (34),

$$r = a(\epsilon + 1)$$

Therefore the minimum separation, when M_1 passes through the vertex of its hyperbolic path, is

$$\rho_{min} = r\frac{M_1}{M_0} = a(\epsilon + 1)\frac{M_1}{M_0}$$

$$= \frac{b}{2}(\epsilon + 1) = \frac{b}{2}\left[1 + \sqrt{1 + \left(\frac{2x}{b}\right)^2}\right]$$

$$= \frac{b}{2} + \sqrt{\left(\frac{b}{2}\right)^2 + x^2} \tag{81}$$

Alternatively, we may express ρ_{min} in terms of Θ instead of x, by using $1/\epsilon = \sin\Theta/2$; then

$$\rho_{min} = \frac{b}{2}\left(\csc\frac{\Theta}{2} + 1\right) \tag{82}$$

Then in a head-on collision, where $x = 0$, and $\Theta = \pi$, either expression gives

$$\rho_{min} = b \tag{83}$$

Note that this depends on M_0, but not on either M_1 or M_2 alone, and applies for all collisions between particles of like sign of charge. When, in the head-on collision, the two repelling particles are separated by the distance b, the electrostatic potential energy equals the original C-coordinate kinetic energy, and both particles are stationary ($v_1 = v_2 = 0$) in the C coordinates, i.e.,

$$\frac{Zze^2}{b} = \tfrac{1}{2}M_0V^2$$

Thus *the collision diameter is also the closest possible distance of approach in a head-on collision between repelling particles.*

For attractive forces, the minimum value of r is, by Eq. (46),

$$r = |a|(\epsilon - 1)$$

Therefore the minimum separation, when M_1 passes through the vertex of its hyperbolic path, is

$$\rho_{min} = r\frac{M_1}{M_0} = |a|(\epsilon - 1)\frac{M_1}{M_0}$$

$$= \frac{b}{2}(\epsilon - 1) = \frac{b}{2}\left[\sqrt{1 + \left(\frac{2x}{b}\right)^2} - 1\right]$$

$$= \sqrt{\left(\frac{b}{2}\right)^2 + x^2} - \frac{b}{2} \tag{84}$$

$$\rho_{min} = \frac{b}{2}\left(\csc\frac{\Theta}{2} - 1\right) \tag{85}$$

Then, in an exactly head-on collision between particles of unlike sign of charge, the minimum separation can have the value zero. This implies that even particles of very small radius would actually "strike," or make contact with, each other. The physical consequences of this special collision would then depend on the nature of the particles involved and on the possible existence of additional short-range forces. For example, a positron and negatron would annihilate each other.

h. Path of M_2. In the discussion following Eq. (13) we noted that in the C coordinates there is no distinction between projectile and target particles. V is merely the initial velocity of approach of two particles of mass M_1 and M_2, and both are deflected through the same angle Θ. Hence in deriving the path of M_1 we have also derived the path for M_2. The collision diameter, impact parameter, angle of deflection, and eccentricity of orbit are the same for both particles [Eqs. (78), (79a), and (79b) do not contain M_1 but only M_0]. The distances r and a do depend on which particle is being considered and were derived for M_1. To find the corresponding distances for M_2, merely substitute M_2 for M_1 in the appropriate equations, e.g., in Eq. (79) or (79c).

In our notation, r and $(\rho - r)$ have represented the distances from the center of mass to M_1 and M_2. If these distances were called r_1 and r_2, then Eq. (16) would read

$$\frac{r_2}{r_1} = \frac{M_1}{M_2} = \frac{v_2}{v_1} \tag{86}$$

Then Eq. (17) would become

$$r_1 = \rho \frac{M_0}{M_1} \qquad r_2 = \rho \frac{M_0}{M_2} \qquad r_1 + r_2 = \rho \tag{87}$$

While M_1 is traversing its hyperbolic path r_1 about the center of mass, M_2 is also traversing a similar path, $r_2 (= r_1 M_1/M_2)$ on the other side of the center of mass. The line, $\rho = r_1 + r_2$, joining the positions of the two particles passes through the center of mass at all times. For an example, see Fig. 3.2 of Chap. 1.

Problems

1. In an elastic collision, when the impact parameter x is just equal to the collision radius $b/2$, what are the values of the deflection angles Θ, φ, and ϑ? *Ans.:* For $x/(b/2) = 1$, $\Theta = 90°$, $\varphi = 45°$, $\tan \vartheta = M_2/M_1$.

2. (a) What is the approximate numerical value of the "collision radius" $b/2$ for a 5-Mev proton being deflected by a gold nucleus?

(b) Compare with the approximate radius of a gold nucleus.

(c) Compare the de Broglie wavelength of the 5-Mev proton. *Ans.:* (a) 11×10^{-13} cm; (b) 9×10^{-13} cm; (c) 13×10^{-13} cm.

3. An approximation which is especially useful for visualizing some details of elastic collisions is to assume that the principal part of the interaction occurs during an *effective collision time* τ, which is of the order of $2x/V$ (where x is the impact parameter and V the initial relative velocity of the particles).

(a) On this basis, develop an approximate expression for the distance through which the struck particle is displaced in the L coordinates during the effective collision time.

(b) Show that when $M_1 \gg M_2$ and $x \gg b$ this displacement of M_2 is of the order of one collision diameter b, and for all other collisions, the displacement of M_2 is less than b.

4. In an elastic coulomb collision,

(a) Show that the kinetic energy Q transferred to the struck particle M_2, in the L coordinates, is given by

$$Q = \frac{2}{M_2} \left(\frac{Zze^2}{V} \right)^2 \frac{1}{x^2 + (b/2)^2}$$

where, as usual, x is the impact parameter, b is the collision diameter, and V is the initial relative velocity of the colliding particles which have charges ze and Ze.

(b) For remote collisions ($x \gg b/2$), note that the energy transfer is inversely proportional to V^2, and show from elementary physical considerations why this should be so.

(c) In the center-of-mass coordinates, how much kinetic energy is transferred from M_1 to M_2 as a result of the collision?

4. Cross Sections for Elastic Scattering by Coulomb Forces

a. Cross Section for Rutherford Scattering. The differential cross section for scattering of M_1 into the solid angle $d\omega = 2\pi \sin \vartheta \, d\vartheta$ in the L coordinates will be called $d\sigma \equiv \xi_0(\vartheta) \, d\omega$. The fraction of the incident particles which are so scattered by a very thin foil of thickness Δs containing N of the target particles M_2 per cubic centimeter, and hence $N \Delta s$ per square centimeter, is $N \Delta s \, \xi_0(\vartheta) \, d\omega$. These are the same particles which, in the C coordinates, are scattered in the solid angle

$$d\Omega = 2\pi \sin \Theta \, d\Theta = 4\pi \sin \frac{\Theta}{2} \cos \frac{\Theta}{2} \, d\Theta$$

If the differential cross section, $d\sigma$, is called $\xi_0(\Theta) \, d\Omega$ in the C coordinates, then

$$\frac{d\sigma}{2\pi} = \xi_0(\vartheta) \sin \vartheta \, d\vartheta = \xi_0(\Theta) \sin \Theta \, d\Theta \tag{88}$$

The differential cross section $\xi_0(\Theta) \, d\Omega$ for an impact parameter between x and $x + dx$ is simply the area of a ring of radius x, and width dx, which is $2\pi x \, dx$. Then, from Eq. (80), we have

$$d\sigma \equiv \xi_0(\Theta) \, d\Omega = 2\pi x \, dx = 2\pi \left(\frac{b}{2} \cot \frac{\Theta}{2} \right) \frac{b}{2} \csc^2 \frac{\Theta}{2} \frac{d\Theta}{2}$$

$$= \pi \frac{b^2}{4} \frac{\cos (\Theta/2)}{\sin^3 (\Theta/2)} \, d\Theta = \frac{b^2}{16} \frac{1}{\sin^4 (\Theta/2)} \, d\Omega \tag{89}$$

This cross section can be transposed to the L coordinates when M_1/M_2, and hence the relationship between ϑ and Θ, is known from Eq. (23). For example, if $M_1 = M_2$, then $\vartheta = \Theta/2$, by Eq. (26). In this special case we have, for the differential cross section in the L coordinates,

$$
\begin{aligned}
d\sigma &= \xi_0(\vartheta)\, d\omega = \xi_0(\Theta) \frac{\sin \Theta\, d\Theta}{\sin \vartheta\, d\vartheta}\, d\omega \\
&= \xi_0(\Theta) \frac{4 \sin \vartheta \cos \vartheta\, d\vartheta}{\sin \vartheta\, d\vartheta}\, d\omega \\
&= \xi_0(\Theta)\, 4 \cos \vartheta\, d\omega \\
&= \frac{b^2}{4} \frac{\cos \vartheta}{\sin^4 \vartheta}\, d\omega \qquad \text{if } M_1 = M_2
\end{aligned} \tag{90}
$$

The factor $4 \cos \vartheta$ which arises in this transformation is the same solid-angle factor which appears in the electron-electron scattering cross sections given in Chap. 19.

An impact parameter of x or less will produce a deflection of Θ or greater. Therefore the cross section for scattering through an angle Θ or greater is simply

$$
\sigma(\geq \Theta) = \pi x^2 = \frac{\pi b^2}{4} \cot^2 \frac{\Theta}{2} \tag{91}
$$

For particles of equal mass, this reduces at once to

$$
\sigma(\geq \vartheta) = \pi x^2 = \frac{\pi b^2}{4} \cot^2 \vartheta
$$

and so there is no backscattering ($\vartheta > 90°$) in the L coordinates. If $M_1 \ll M_2$, then $\Theta \simeq \vartheta$, and the cross section for backscattering becomes simply $(\pi/4)b^2$, which is the area corresponding to the collision diameter.

b. Cross Section for Energy Transfers in Elastic Collision. In the L coordinates, an elastic collision confers on the struck particle M_2 a velocity V_2 in the direction φ, if it was initially at rest and unbound. Thus the struck particle acquires a kinetic energy $\frac{1}{2} M_2 V_2^2$, and this energy is lost by the incident particle M_1. The classical theory of the energy losses by swift charged particles, in the production of ionization, is based on the coulomb interactions of the incident particle with the atomic electrons in the absorber. Let

$$
Q \equiv \tfrac{1}{2} M_2 V_2^2 \tag{92}
$$

be the kinetic energy transferred to the struck particle, which is considered to be initially unbound and at rest in the L coordinates. The differential cross section for an energy transfer between Q and $Q + dQ$ can be written as before in the form

$$
d\sigma = 2\pi x\, dx
$$

and our analytical problem is only to transform the variable from x to Q. A transformation from x to Θ has already been made in Eq. (89). The connection between Θ and V_2 is given by Eq. (28), which leads to

$$
Q = \tfrac{1}{2} M_2 V_2^2 = \tfrac{1}{2} M_2 \left(\frac{2VM_0}{M_2} \right)^2 \sin^2 \frac{\Theta}{2} \tag{93}
$$

and its differential

$$dQ = 2 \frac{V^2 M_0^2}{M_2} \sin \frac{\Theta}{2} \cos \frac{\Theta}{2} \, d\Theta \tag{94}$$

Substituting into Eq. (89) the value of $\cos (\Theta/2) \, d\Theta$ from Eq. (94) and the value of $\sin^2 (\Theta/2)$ from Eq. (93) leads at once to

$$d\sigma = 2\pi x \, dx = b^2 \frac{\pi V^2 M_0^2}{2M_2} \frac{dQ}{Q^2}$$

and substitution of $b \equiv 2|Zz|e^2/M_0 V^2$ from Eq. (78) gives the desired cross section

$$d\sigma = \frac{2\pi Z^2 z^2 e^4}{M_2 V^2} \frac{dQ}{Q^2} \tag{95}$$

Equation (95) shows that the cross section for energy transfers will be most important for those struck particles having a small mass M_2. Energy transfers to nuclei are therefore unimportant compared with those to atomic electrons, for which $M_2 = m_0$, and $Z = -1$. Therefore the classical cross section per atomic electron for an energy transfer between Q and $Q + dQ$ is

$$d\sigma = \frac{2\pi z^2 e^4}{m_0 V^2} \frac{dQ}{Q^2} \qquad \text{cm}^2/\text{electron} \tag{96}$$

where ze is the charge and V is the velocity of the incident particle. Small energy transfers are greatly favored, and large transfers are improbable, as shown by the $1/Q^2$ relationship. Note that the mass M_1 of the *incident* particle does not appear in the classical cross section for energy transfers. This is also true in the analogous cross section based on wave mechanics [Chap. 18, Eq. (2.6)].

Classical collision theory is valid when the rationalized de Broglie wavelength of the relative motion, $\lambda/2\pi \equiv \lambdabar = \hbar/M_0 V$, is small compared with the collision diameter b. This inequality is equivalent to the condition

$$\frac{b}{\lambdabar} = \frac{2Zz}{137\beta} \gg 1 \qquad \text{or} \qquad \beta = \frac{V}{c} \ll \frac{2Zz}{137} \tag{97}$$

the origin of which is discussed in Appendix C, Sec. 4.

Problems

1. Show that, when the Rutherford scattering cross section is written in terms of the laboratory angle of projection φ of M_2, the probability of an energy transfer between Q and $Q + dQ$ is proportional to $1/Q^2$, and the differential scattering cross section is

$$d\sigma = 2\pi x \, dx = \frac{2\pi Z^2 z^2 e^4}{M_2 V^2} \frac{dQ}{Q^2}$$

2. If the differential cross section for elastic scattering in the C coordinates into the solid angle $d\Omega$ at mean angle Θ is $\xi(\Theta) \, d\Omega$, while the corresponding cross section in the L coordinates is $\xi(\vartheta)\, d\omega$, show that the general relationship between the functions $\xi(\Theta)$ and $\xi(\vartheta)$ is independent of the nature of the forces and is

$$\frac{d\Omega}{d\omega} = \frac{\xi(\vartheta)}{\xi(\Theta)} = \frac{\sin^3 \Theta}{\sin^3 \vartheta}\left[\frac{1}{1 + (M_1/M_2)\cos \Theta}\right]$$

and that two special cases are

for $M_1 = M_2$: $\vartheta = \Theta/2$ and $\xi(\vartheta) = \xi(\Theta)(4\cos\vartheta)$
for $M_1 \ll M_2$: $\vartheta = \Theta$ and $\xi(\vartheta) = \xi(\Theta)$

$[\xi(\vartheta)/\xi(\Theta)$ for *inelastic* interactions is given on p. 421, Prob. 17].

3. The classical scattering of elastic spheres provides useful illustrations of the concepts of differential cross section, etc. Consider the scattering of a small, lightweight sphere in collisions with a much larger and heavier sphere of radius R. Assume that the only forces involved are short-range repulsive (elastic) forces, such that the "angle of reflection" ψ equals the "angle of incidence" ψ with the normal, as shown in the figure. The incident particle whose impact parameter is $x = R\sin\psi$ is then scattered through an angle $\vartheta = \pi - 2\psi$.

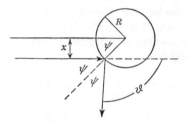

(*a*) Show that the differential cross section for scattering between ϑ and $\vartheta + d\vartheta$ can be written

$$d\sigma = 2\pi x\, dx = (R^2/4)\, d\omega$$

where $d\omega$ is the element of solid angle $2\pi\sin\vartheta\, d\vartheta$, and that therefore the scattering is *isotropic*, i.e., uniform in all directions per unit of solid angle.

(*b*) Integrate the differential cross section over all angles from $\vartheta = 0$ to π, and show that the total scattering cross section is simply the geometrical area $\sigma = \pi R^2$.

(*c*) Integrate $d\sigma$ from $\vartheta = \pi/2$ to π, and show that the cross section for backscattering is $\sigma_{\text{back}} = \pi R^2/2$, and that therefore any impact parameter $x \leq R/\sqrt{2}$ results in backscattering.

(*d*) If there are N target spheres per cubic centimeter, show that the chance that an incident particle will pass through a thin layer Δs thick without being scattered is $(1 - N\sigma\,\Delta s)$ and that the fraction of the randomly incident particles which are scattered is $N\sigma\,\Delta s$.

(*e*) If the ensemble of N target spheres per cubic centimeter is t cm thick, show that the fraction of normally incident particles transmitted without suffering any scattering is $e^{-N\sigma t}$.

(*f*) Show that the fraction of randomly incident particles which suffer some scattering in (*e*) is

$$1 - e^{-N\sigma t} = (N\sigma t) - (N\sigma t)^2/2 + (N\sigma t)^3/3! - \cdots$$

and point out the physical significance of each term in the expansion in comparison with the "shadowing" of target spheres deep in the ensemble by spheres near or at the front of the ensemble.

5. *Summary of Principal Symbols and Results*

Quantity	L coordinates		C coordinates	
Mass	M_1	M_2	M_1	M_2
Charge	ze	Ze	ze	Ze
Initial velocity	V	0	$V - V_c$	V_c
Instantaneous velocity	...	...	v_1	v_2
Final velocity	V_1	V_2	$V - V_c$	V_c
Angle of deflection	ϑ	φ	Θ	Θ
C coordinates	...		r, ψ	$(\rho - r), \psi$
Initial and final total kinetic energy	$\frac{1}{2}M_1V^2$		$\frac{1}{2}M_0V^2$	
Angular momentum about C	M_0Vx		M_0Vx	
Collision diameter	.....		$b = \dfrac{2|Zz|e^2}{M_0V^2}$	
Separation of M_1 and M_2	.....		$\rho = r\,\dfrac{M_1}{M_0}$	
Eccentricity	.....		$\epsilon = \csc\dfrac{\Theta}{2}$	
Time			t	
Reduced mass		$M_0 = \dfrac{M_1M_2}{M_1 + M_2}$		
Impact parameter			x	

$$\cot \vartheta = \frac{M_1}{M_2}\csc \Theta + \cot \Theta \qquad \begin{cases} \vartheta \simeq \Theta & \text{for } M_1 \ll M_2 \\ \vartheta \simeq \dfrac{\Theta}{2} & \text{for } M_1 = M_2 \end{cases} \qquad \text{Eq. (23)}$$

$$\varphi = \frac{\pi}{2} - \frac{\Theta}{2} \qquad\qquad \text{Eq. (22)}$$

$$V_2^2 = 2\left(V\frac{M_0}{M_2}\right)^2 (1 - \cos \Theta) = 4V^2\left(\frac{M_0}{M_2}\right)^2 \cos^2 \varphi \qquad \text{Eqs. (28), (29)}$$

$$r = \frac{Zze^2}{M_1V^2}\left(\frac{\epsilon^2 - 1}{\epsilon \cos \psi - 1}\right) \qquad \text{with } (\epsilon^2 - 1) = \left(\frac{2x}{b}\right)^2 \qquad \text{Eq. (79)}$$

$$x = \frac{b}{2}\cot\frac{\Theta}{2} = \frac{b}{2}\tan \varphi \qquad \text{Eqs. (80), (80}a)$$

$$\rho_{\min} = \frac{b}{2}(\epsilon + 1) \qquad \text{for repulsive forces} \qquad \text{Eq. (82)}$$

$$\rho_{\min} = \frac{b}{2}(\epsilon - 1) \qquad \text{for attractive forces} \qquad \text{Eq. (85)}$$

Cross sections:

$$(\text{single scattering } \Theta \text{ to } \Theta + d\Theta) = 2\pi x\,dx = \frac{\pi b^2}{4}\cot\frac{\Theta}{2}\csc^2\frac{\Theta}{2}\,d\Theta \qquad \text{Eq. (89)}$$

$$(\text{single scattering} > \Theta) = \pi x^2 = \frac{\pi b^2}{4}\cot^2\frac{\Theta}{2} \qquad \text{Eq. (91)}$$

$$(\text{energy transfer } Q \text{ to } Q + dQ) = 2\pi x\,dx = \frac{2\pi Z^2z^2e^4}{M_2V^2}\frac{dQ}{Q^2} \qquad \text{Eq. (95)}$$

The Wave Mechanics of Nuclear Potential Barriers

Applications of the wave equation to nuclear mechanics involve a set of mathematical principles and results which are common to a variety of nuclear phenomena, including scattering, disintegration, and transmutation. In this appendix we carry through the mathematical development of the wave description of these phenomena. Sufficient detail is given to serve the immediate requirements of those readers who have not yet completed a basic course in wave mechanics. The sequence of topics should permit the reader to use this appendix either by parts or as a single entity which has points of contact with the main text in a number of chapters, where emphasis has generally been laid on a briefer treatment of the physical principles, rather than on mathematical details.

1. Exact Solution of Schrödinger's Equations for a One-dimensional Rectangular Barrier

a. Wave Functions for the One-dimensional Barrier. With the help of the Schrödinger equation, Eq. (5.34) of Chap. 2, we can derive an exact expression for the transparency of a one-dimensional, rectangular, potential barrier, whose thickness in the z direction is a, and whose height is $U_2 - U_1 = U$, as shown in Fig. 1.

In region 1 (where the potential energy U_1 may, for convenience, be taken as zero), a particle whose total energy is W is incident on the barrier. In region 1, this particle has the kinetic energy

$$T_1 = W - U_1 \tag{1}$$

and hence the wave number [Chap. 2, Eq. (5.29)]

$$k_1 \equiv \frac{2\pi}{\lambda} = \frac{2\pi \sqrt{2M(W - U_1)}}{h} = \frac{2\pi \sqrt{2MT_1}}{h} \tag{2}$$

The incident plane wave which represents this particle travels in the positive direction of z and therefore can be written [Chap. 2, Eq. (5.20)] as

$$\Psi_{\text{incident}} = A_1 e^{i(k_1 z - 2\pi\nu t)} = (\psi_{\text{incident}})e^{-2\pi i\nu t} \tag{3}$$

We postulate in region 1 the existence of a reflected wave which travels toward negative values of z and hence can be written

$$\Psi_{\text{reflected}} = B_1 e^{i(-k_1 z - 2\pi \nu t)} = (\psi_{\text{reflected}}) e^{-2\pi i \nu t} \tag{4}$$

The total wave function in region 1 is the sum of the incident and reflected waves, or

$$\Psi_1 = (A_1 e^{ik_1 z} + B_1 e^{-ik_1 z}) e^{-2\pi i \nu t} \tag{5}$$

which is seen by inspection to be a solution of Schrödinger's equation for region 1, provided that the wave number k_1 has the value given in Eq. (2).

The frequency ν is determined by the total energy W of the particle and is $\nu = W/h$, by Eq. (5.7) of Chap. 2. This frequency will be the same for all three regions, because the total energy W must remain constant in the conservative fields which are involved here. The time-dependent factor $e^{-2\pi i \nu t}$ would cancel out later when the particle density

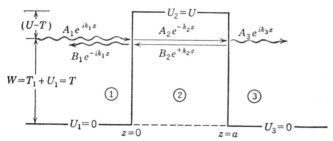

Fig. 1 Rectangular potential barrier. The components of the wave functions in each of the three regions are shown.

is computed from $\Psi\Psi^*$ for any of the three regions [Chap. 2, Eq. (5.41)] and is of no physical interest in problems involving beams of particles. We shall therefore omit it and shall consider only the amplitude, or time-independent wave function ψ, in all regions. Then in region 1, we have for the total disturbance

$$\psi_1 = A_1 e^{ik_1 z} + B_1 e^{-ik_1 z} \tag{6}$$

which is also a solution of Schrödinger's equation

$$\frac{\partial^2 \psi}{\partial z^2} + \frac{8\pi^2 M(W - U)}{h^2} \psi = 0 \tag{7}$$

provided that

$$k_1 = \frac{2\pi \sqrt{2MT_1}}{h} \quad \text{and} \quad T_1 = W \quad \text{when } U_1 = 0 \tag{8}$$

In region 2, there will generally be disturbances moving in both directions, and the nature of the solutions depends on whether the kinetic energy in region 2, $T_2 = W - U_2$, is positive or negative. If, as in Fig. 1, $W < U_2$, so that the kinetic energy is negative, then the solutions of Schrödinger's equation will correspond to a *nonoscillatory, exponentially damped disturbance*. This is analogous to the damping of electromagnetic waves just inside the surface of a metallic reflector, for which the optical refractive index is a complex quantity. We note that in the present wave-mechanical case the refractive index for particles passing from region 1 to 2 is also imaginary if $U_2 > W$ and is given by [Chap. 2, Eq. (5.17)]

$$\mu = \sqrt{\frac{W - U_2}{W - U_1}} = i\sqrt{\frac{U_2 - T_1}{T_1}} \qquad \text{if } U_1 = 0 \qquad (9)$$

For region 2, if we were to use a solution analogous to Eq. (6), but with subscripts 2 throughout, we should find on substitution in Eq. (7) that the wave number is $(2\pi/h)\sqrt{2M(W - U_2)}$, which is imaginary because $W < U_2$. For the sake of mathematical simplicity in some of the subsequent equations, we shall choose to make use of the complex conjugate of this wave number. With this preknowledge, we write for the disturbance under the barrier, in region 2,

$$\psi_2 = A_2 e^{-k_2 z} + B_2 e^{k_2 z} \qquad (10)$$

Substitution of Eq. (10) in Eq. (7) then gives for k_2 the real quantity

$$k_2 = \frac{2\pi \sqrt{2M(U_2 - W)}}{h} \qquad (11)$$

The physical significance of this propagation number k_2 is that it is the wave number which would be exhibited by a particle whose kinetic energy is positive and equal to the difference between the barrier height U_2 and the incident kinetic energy W. This energy $(U_2 - W)$ has the value $(U - T)$ for the barrier shown in Fig. 1.

In region 3, we expect only a disturbance moving to the right, because there are no further changes in potential, from which reflections could possibly arise.

Then for region 3, we can write

$$\psi_3 = A_3 e^{ik_3 z} \qquad (12)$$

Substitution of ψ_3 into Schrödinger's equation, Eq. (7), gives

$$k_3 = \frac{2\pi \sqrt{2M(W - U_3)}}{h}$$

which, because $U_3 = 0$, reduces to the same value as in region 1, or

$$k_3 = \frac{2\pi \sqrt{2M T_1}}{h} = k_1 \qquad (13)$$

and allows us to rewrite Eq. (12) as

$$\psi_3 = A_3 e^{ik_1 z} \qquad (14)$$

We have so far established three wave functions ψ_1, ψ_2, and ψ_3, as given by Eqs. (6), (10), and (14), each of which satisfies Schrödinger's equation as applied to its own region. These three equations contain five unknowns, A_1, A_2, A_3, B_1, and B_2, and so we obviously need some additional relationships which will connect them. These are obtained by considering conditions at the two boundaries which separate the three regions.

b. Boundary Conditions. In any application of the Schrödinger equation, the kinetic energy $(W - U)$ and the wave function ψ must have noninfinite values. Then, from Eq. (7), $\partial^2\psi/\partial z^2$ must also have only finite values. If $\partial^2\psi/\partial z^2$ is finite, then $\partial\psi/\partial z$ cannot have any sudden jumps. If $\partial\psi/\partial z$ has no sudden jumps, then neither has ψ. Therefore the simple requirement that the kinetic energy and the wave function be finite leads to the requirements that $\partial\psi/\partial z$ and ψ be continuous. These are the so-called *boundary conditions*. Applied to the present problem, they require that ψ and $\partial\psi/\partial z$ have the same values on both sides of the boundaries at $z = 0$ and $z = a$. Hence we obtain four additional equations which are

$$\psi_1 = \psi_2 \qquad \text{at } z = 0 \tag{15}$$

$$\frac{\partial\psi_1}{\partial z} = \frac{\partial\psi_2}{\partial z} \qquad \text{at } z = 0 \tag{16}$$

$$\psi_2 = \psi_3 \qquad \text{at } z = a \tag{17}$$

$$\frac{\partial\psi_2}{\partial z} = \frac{\partial\psi_3}{\partial z} \qquad \text{at } z = a \tag{18}$$

Substitution of ψ_1, ψ_2, and ψ_3, as given by Eqs. (6), (10), and (14), into Eqs. (15) to (18) gives us the following set:

$$A_1 + B_1 = A_2 + B_2 \tag{19}$$

$$ik_1 A_1 - ik_1 B_1 = -k_2 A_2 + k_2 B_2 \tag{20}$$

$$A_2 e^{-k_2 a} + B_2 e^{k_2 a} = A_3 e^{ik_1 a} \tag{21}$$

$$-k_2 A_2 e^{-k_2 a} + k_2 B_2 e^{k_2 a} = ik_1 A_3 e^{ik_1 a} \tag{22}$$

In these equations, k_1 and k_2 are both real numbers. These four equations connect the five amplitudes A_1, A_2, A_3, B_1, B_2. We can eliminate any three amplitudes and form the ratio between the remaining two. When our interest centers on barrier transparency, we want to find the relationship between the transmitted amplitude A_3 and the incident amplitude A_1. The elimination of B_1, A_2, and B_2 is a straightforward algebraic process and leads directly to the relationship

$$\frac{A_1}{A_3} = \left[\frac{1}{2} + \frac{i}{4}\left(\frac{k_2}{k_1} - \frac{k_1}{k_2}\right)\right] e^{(ik_1 + k_2)a} + \left[\frac{1}{2} - \frac{i}{4}\left(\frac{k_2}{k_1} - \frac{k_1}{k_2}\right)\right] e^{(ik_1 - k_2)a} \tag{23}$$

Because this ratio is complex, it is evident that one or both of the amplitude coefficients A_1 and A_3 are also complex.

c. Transmission Coefficient. The *density* of incident particles in region 1 is given by Eq. (5.43) of Chap. 2 and is

$$|\psi_{\text{incident}}|^2$$

which, from Eq. (3), is equal to $|A_1|^2$ because $|e^{ikz}|^2 = 1$. The *flux* of incident particles is the particle density times the particle velocity V_1 in region 1, or

$$\text{Incident flux} = |A_1|^2 V_1 \tag{24}$$

The transmitted flux, in region 3, where the velocity is V_3, is

$$\text{Transmitted flux} = |A_3|^2 V_3 \tag{25}$$

The fraction of the incident particles which are transmitted through the barrier, or, more fundamentally, the probability that an individual particle will be transmitted through the barrier, is

$$\mathsf{T}_l = \frac{|A_3|^2 V_3}{|A_1|^2 V_1} = \left|\frac{A_3}{A_1}\right|^2 \frac{V_3}{V_1} \tag{26}$$

where T_l is called the *transmission coefficient*, or the "transparency." In the present case, $V_3 = V_1$, and so Eq. (26) reduces to

$$\mathsf{T}_l = \left|\frac{A_3}{A_1}\right|^2 = \left(\frac{A_3}{A_1}\right)\left(\frac{A_3}{A_1}\right)^* \tag{27}$$

In order to evaluate Eq. (27), we return to Eq. (23) for (A_1/A_3) and form its complex conjugate, which is

$$\left(\frac{A_1}{A_3}\right)^* = \left[\frac{1}{2} - \frac{i}{4}\left(\frac{k_2}{k_1} - \frac{k_1}{k_2}\right)\right] e^{(-ik_1+k_2)a}$$
$$+ \left[\frac{1}{2} + \frac{i}{4}\left(\frac{k_2}{k_1} - \frac{k_1}{k_2}\right)\right] e^{(-ik_1-k_2)a} \tag{28}$$

We find, on carrying out the multiplication and simplifying the result with the aid of the identity

$$\sinh x = \tfrac{1}{2}(e^x - e^{-x}) \qquad \sinh^2 x = \tfrac{1}{4}(e^{2x} + e^{-2x}) - \tfrac{1}{2} \tag{29}$$

that

$$\left(\frac{A_1}{A_3}\right)\left(\frac{A_1}{A_3}\right)^* = 1 + \frac{1}{4}\left[2 + \left(\frac{k_2}{k_1}\right)^2 + \left(\frac{k_1}{k_2}\right)^2\right]\sinh^2 k_2 a \tag{30}$$

The propagation numbers k_1 and k_2 are both real numbers and are given by Eqs. (8) and (11). The subscripts of the energy terms used there may now be dropped, and we write simply

$$T = T_1 = W = \text{incident kinetic energy}$$
$$U = U_2 = \text{barrier height}$$

Then from Eqs. (8) and (11)

$$\left(\frac{k_2}{k_1}\right)^2 = \frac{U - T}{T} \tag{31}$$

Making this substitution in Eq. (30), and simplifying, we obtain

$$\left|\frac{A_1}{A_3}\right|^2 = 1 + \frac{U^2}{4T(U-T)}\sinh^2 k_2 a$$

and hence the transmission coefficient T_l for the rectangular barrier is

$$T_l = \left|\frac{A_3}{A_1}\right|^2 \frac{V_3}{V_1} = \left[1 + \frac{U^2}{4T(U-T)} \sinh^2 k_2 a\right]^{-1} \quad (32)$$

where
$$k_2 = \frac{2\pi \sqrt{2M(U-T)}}{h} = \frac{2\pi}{\lambda_2} \quad (33)$$

and λ_2 is the de Broglie wavelength for a hypothetical particle whose kinetic energy $(U - T)$ equals the energy by which the barrier height exceeds the kinetic energy of the incident particle.

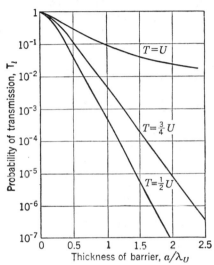

Fig. 2 The transmission coefficient T_l of Eq. (32), or probability of transmission through a rectangular barrier of height U and width a by a particle whose incident kinetic energy is T. The barrier thickness a is given here in units of the de Broglie wavelength λ_U of an incident particle whose kinetic energy just equals the barrier height, that is, $T = U$. Thus the shape of the barrier is fixed by the dimensionless abscissa a/λ_U and is the same for each of the three curves. Note that the transmission is not unity for particles whose kinetic energy equals the barrier height. Also, that for $T < U$, the transmission falls approximately exponentially with barrier thickness beyond about $a = \lambda_U/2$.

Figure 2 is a plot of Eq. (32) for a few selected values of T/U. Equation (32) shows that if T/U is not too close to 0 or 1, the transmission through barriers whose thickness is about $a = \lambda_2/2$ is of the order of $\frac{1}{10}$. For thicker barriers the transmission decreases approximately exponentially with thickness a.

d. Thick Rectangular Barriers. In nuclear physics, the interesting questions of barrier transparency occur mostly for barriers which are quite thick, and which therefore have a very small transmission coefficient T_l. Insight into these cases is gained by considering the simplified form which Eq. (32) takes for thick barriers, i.e., when

$$a \gg \frac{1}{k_2} = \frac{\lambda_2}{2\pi} \quad (34)$$

Then from Eq. (29)

$$\sinh^2 k_2 a \simeq \tfrac{1}{4} e^{2k_2 a} \qquad k_2 a \gg 1 \tag{35}$$

and the transmission coefficient as given exactly by Eq. (32) becomes approximately

$$\mathsf{T}_l \simeq 16 \frac{T}{U}\left(1 - \frac{T}{U}\right) e^{-2k_2 a} \qquad \text{for } k_2 a \gg 1 \tag{36}$$

Equation (36) displays the important physical result that, for reasonably thick barriers, the probability of transmission through the barrier decreases exponentially as the barrier thickness a increases.

The dominant term here is the exponential. The energy-dependent coefficient of the exponential is of the order of unity. This leads to the basic concept of a transparency, or barrier transmission coefficient T_l, of the form

$$\mathsf{T}_l \simeq e^{-\gamma} \tag{37}$$

where γ is a dimensionless barrier-transmission exponent whose explicit value depends on the type of barrier under discussion.

Problems

1. (a) Verify Eqs. (32) and (36) by carrying out all intermediate steps in their derivation.

(b) Calculate the transparency of rectangular barriers for the particular case in which $T = 0.8U$, and for barriers whose thickness a as measured in terms of the de Broglie wavelength λ of the incident particle is: $a = 0.2\lambda$, 0.5λ, λ, 2λ, 5λ. Plot these values of transparency on a logarithmic scale against a linear scale of barrier thickness expressed in units of a/λ.

2. For the rectangular barrier, determine the relative amplitude B_1 of the reflected wave in region 1 of Fig. 1, and show that the probability of reflection is indeed $(1 - \mathsf{T}_l)$, where T_l is the probability of transmission through the barrier. This important result verifies, for this particular case, the general requirement of conservation of particles, and hence of electric charge, in a scattering situation.

3. Consider the exponentially damped disturbance inside the rectangular barrier of Fig. 1, and described by Eq. (10). Show that the second term $B_2 e^{k_2 z}$ cannot override the exponentially decreasing first term, by determining the ratio B_2/A_2.

$$\frac{B_2}{A_2} = \frac{1 + ik_1/k_2}{1 - ik_1/k_2}\, e^{-2k_2 a} \qquad \text{or} \qquad \left|\frac{B_2}{A_2}\right|^2 = e^{-4k_2 a}$$

4. (a) Consider the behavior of particles whose incident kinetic energy T is greater than the height of a rectangular barrier U. Show that, for $T > U$, the chance that a particle will traverse the barrier is

$$\mathsf{T}_l \equiv \left|\frac{A_3}{A_1}\right|^2 \frac{V_3}{V_1} = \left[1 + \frac{U^2 \sin^2 k_2 a}{4T(T - U)}\right]^{-1}$$

where $k_2 \equiv (2\pi/h)\sqrt{2M(T - U)}$ is the (real) wave number over the barrier.

(b) Show that, when $T > U$, there is total transmission over the barrier only when $k_2 a = \pi$, 2π, ... Comment on any analogy which this result may bear to the optical transmission of light through thin refracting layers.

(c) When $T = U$, show that the chance of traversing the barrier becomes

$$T_l = \left(1 + \frac{2\pi^2 M T a^2}{h^2}\right)^{-1} = \left[1 + \left(\pi \frac{a}{\lambda_1}\right)^2\right]^{-1}$$

where λ_1 is the wavelength of the incident particle. Verify that this represents the curve for $T = U$ in Fig. 2.

5. Reflection is also produced by an attractive potential. Consider the passage of particles across a rectangular potential well. Show that the transmission is given by

$$T_l \equiv \left|\frac{A_3}{A_1}\right|^2 \frac{V_3}{V_1} = \left[1 + \frac{U^2 \sin^2 k_2 a}{4T(T + U)}\right]^{-1}$$

where $k_2 \equiv (2\pi/h) \sqrt{2M(T + U)}$.

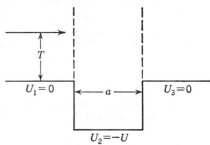

6. Show that the probability of transmission across the *step barrier* shown in the figure is

$$T_l = \frac{4k_1 k_2}{(k_1 + k_2)^2} = \frac{4p_1 p_2}{(p_1 + p_2)^2}$$

where k_1 and k_2 are the wave numbers and p_1 and p_2 are the momenta for the particle in regions 1 and 2. Show that the result is unchanged if $U < 0$, i.e., for a *step well*.

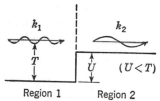

7. Show that the transmission coefficient for the one-dimensional barrier given below, for particles whose incident kinetic energy T is $U_2 > T > U_3$,

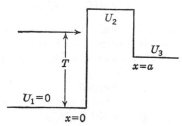

is

$$\mathsf{T}_l = 4\sqrt{\frac{T - U_3}{T}}\left[\left(1 + \sqrt{\frac{T - U_3}{T}}\right)^2 + \frac{U_2^2 - U_2 U_3}{T(U_2 - T)}\sinh^2 k_2 a\right]^{-1}$$

where $k_2 = (2\pi/h)\sqrt{2M(U_2 - T)}$. Note that this result reduces to Eq. (32) for $U_3 = 0$.

2. Schrödinger's Equation for a Central Field

The cartesian coordinates x, y, z have been useful for our preliminary considerations of the wave equation and for visualizing the wave model of the penetration of one-dimensional potential barriers. But for problems which involve the spherically symmetric potentials in the vicinity of nuclei we need a better set of coordinates, one in which it is easier to express radial distances r between a nuclear center of force and the position of some incident or emitted particle. The departure of an α ray from a parent nucleus can be represented mathematically as an outbound spherical wave, which would then contain e^{ikr} as a factor. Similarly, a particle which has been scattered by a nucleus can be represented as an outbound spherical wave containing e^{ikr}. However, particles which are incident on a nucleus will still have to be represented as a plane wave e^{ikz}.

From classical nonrelativistic mechanics we know that these two-body problems may be reduced to a pair of one-body problems (Chap. 5 of S45). The solution of one of these equations will give the motion of the center of mass and will be a function of three coordinates and the total mass of the system. The other solution describes the relative motion of the particles and is a function of the *relative separation* of the particles and of the reduced mass. The quantum-mechanical problem may also be separated by this method into two one-body problems.

When one applies this technique to the two-body Schrödinger equation, the equation of the relative motion is (p. 80 of S11)

$$\nabla^2\psi + \frac{8\pi^2 M}{h^2}[W - U(r)]\psi = 0 \tag{38}$$

where M is reduced mass and r is separation of particles. Then the de Broglie wavelength of relative motion is

$$\lambda = \frac{h}{\sqrt{2M[W - U(r)]}} \tag{39}$$

a. Spherical Polar Coordinates. The most useful three-dimensional coordinate system for nuclear interactions is the system of spherical polar coordinates r, ϑ, φ, which is connected with cartesian coordinates by the usual relationships

$$\begin{aligned} z &= r\cos\vartheta \\ x &= r\sin\vartheta\cos\varphi \\ y &= r\sin\vartheta\sin\varphi \end{aligned} \tag{40}$$

when z is the direction of the polar axis, as shown in Fig. 3. We use here, and in the remainder of this appendix, the lower-case ϑ for the *polar angle* and the lower-case φ for the *azimuthal angle*. These angles are measured in the C coordinates, but the lower-case symbols are used here in place of the upper-case symbols used for C coordinates in Appendix B and elsewhere, in order to conform to the conventional notation for the Legendre polynomials and other functions which arise in the present discussion.

b. Separation of Schrödinger's Equation in Spherical Polar Coordinates. When the value of the Laplacian operator ∇^2 which is appropriate to spherical polar coordinates is inserted in Eq. (38), Schrödinger's equation becomes

$$\left[\frac{1}{r^2}\frac{\partial}{\partial r}\left(r^2\frac{\partial}{\partial r}\right) + \frac{1}{r^2\sin\vartheta}\frac{\partial}{\partial\vartheta}\left(\sin\vartheta\frac{\partial}{\partial\vartheta}\right) + \frac{1}{r^2\sin^2\vartheta}\frac{\partial^2}{\partial\varphi^2}\right]\psi$$

$$+ \frac{8\pi^2 M}{h^2}\,[W - U(r)]\psi = 0 \quad (41)$$

where M is the reduced mass, W is the total energy in C coordinates, and $U(r)$ is the internal potential energy of the system.

If U is some function, $U(r)$, which depends only on r and not on ϑ and φ, then Eq. (41) can be separated into a differential equation containing the variable r only, another depending only on ϑ, and a third depending only on φ.

We carry out this separation in two steps. First, the radial and angular parts can be separated conveniently, by assuming that the radial dependence of ψ is given entirely by some function $R(r)$, while the angular dependence is confined entirely to some function $Y(\vartheta,\varphi)$. Substituting

$$\psi(r,\vartheta,\varphi) = R(r)Y(\vartheta,\varphi) \quad (42)$$

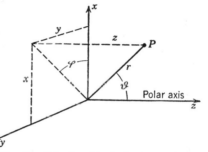

Fig. 3 Relationship between cartesian coordinates x, y, z, and spherical polar coordinates r, ϑ, φ, of a point P, with the *polar axis* shown as horizontal in order to correspond to Fig. 1 for propagation of a plane wave $e^{ikz} = e^{ikr\cos\vartheta}$ in the z direction.

into Eq. (41), and dividing through by ψ, gives

$$\frac{1}{R}\frac{d}{dr}\left(r^2\frac{dR}{dr}\right) + \frac{8\pi^2 Mr^2}{h^2}\,[W - U(r)]$$

$$= -\frac{1}{Y}\left[\frac{1}{\sin\vartheta}\frac{\partial}{\partial\vartheta}\left(\sin\vartheta\frac{\partial Y}{\partial\vartheta}\right) + \frac{1}{\sin^2\vartheta}\frac{\partial^2 Y}{\partial\varphi^2}\right] \quad (43)$$

The left side of Eq. (43) depends only on r, and the right side depends only on ϑ and φ. If these are to be equal for all values of r, ϑ, and φ, both sides must be equal to some constant. We will call this separation constant $l(l + 1)$ and will investigate later the possible values for l.

Secondly, the right-hand side of Eq. (43) can be separated into two differential equations by assuming that the dependence of Y, and hence ψ, on the polar angle ϑ is given entirely by some function $\Theta(\vartheta)$, while the dependence of Y and ψ on the azimuthal angle φ is confined entirely to some function $\Phi(\varphi)$. Substituting

$$Y(\vartheta,\varphi) = \Theta(\vartheta)\Phi(\varphi) \tag{44}$$

into the right-hand side of Eq. (43), and equating this to the separation constant, $l\,(l+1)$, gives us the relationship

$$\sin^2 \vartheta \left[\frac{1}{\Theta \sin \vartheta} \frac{d}{d\vartheta} \left(\sin \vartheta \frac{d\Theta}{d\vartheta} \right) + l\,(l+1) \right] = - \frac{1}{\Phi} \frac{d^2\Phi}{d\varphi^2} \tag{45}$$

Again, if the two sides of Eq. (45) are to be equal for all values of ϑ and of φ, both sides must equal some constant. We will call this separation constant for the angular equations m^2.

Schrödinger's equation, Eq. (41), has now been separated into the following three differential equations:

radial: $\quad \dfrac{1}{r^2 R} \dfrac{d}{dr} \left(r^2 \dfrac{dR}{dr} \right) + \dfrac{8\pi^2 M}{h^2} \left[W - U(r) - \dfrac{l(l+1)}{2Mr^2} \left(\dfrac{h}{2\pi} \right)^2 \right] = 0 \quad (46)$

polar: $\quad\quad \dfrac{1}{\Theta \sin \vartheta} \dfrac{d}{d\vartheta} \left(\sin \vartheta \dfrac{d\Theta}{d\vartheta} \right) + l(l+1) - \dfrac{m^2}{\sin^2 \vartheta} = 0 \quad\quad (47)$

azimuthal: $\quad\quad\quad\quad \dfrac{d^2\Phi}{d\varphi^2} + m^2\Phi = 0 \quad\quad\quad\quad\quad\quad (48)$

which are valid only if the potential $U(r)$ is spherically symmetric and if the constants l and m, which arose from the separation constants, $l(l+1)$ and m^2, are suitably chosen.

The solution of Eq. (48) is well known and, besides a normalizing constant of integration, is given by

$$\Phi_m(\varphi) = \binom{\sin}{\cos} m\varphi \quad\quad \text{or} \quad\quad \Phi_m(\varphi) = e^{\pm im\varphi} \tag{49}$$

It is physically necessary that ψ be single-valued, hence also Φ must have only one value for any particular φ. An increase of φ by 2π will bring us back to the same point in space and must give the same value of Φ. This can only be done if m is an integer. We conclude that m must be any positive or negative integer or zero. The integer m is known as the *magnetic quantum number*, having acquired this name as a consequence of its importance in connection with the theory of the Zeeman effect, which involves the components of the angular momentum of bound atomic states along the axis of an external magnetic field.

c. Legendre's Equation. Equation (47) is known as *Legendre's equation*. Because it is a second-order differential equation, it has in general two linearly independent solutions, each of which can be written as a power series in $\cos \vartheta$. Except for particular values (0, 2, 6, 12, . . .) of the separation constant $l(l+1)$, both these solutions for Θ can be shown to become infinite at $\cos \vartheta = \pm 1$, i.e., along the polar axis. Such solutions would cause $\psi = R\Theta\Phi$ also to become infinite and are therefore rejected as nonphysical. It is possible to show that if l is a positive integer or zero [so that $l(l + 1) = 0, 2, 6, 12, 20, 30, \ldots$], and if $|m| \leq l$, then one of these solutions is finite, single-valued, and continuous for all values of ϑ, and is therefore a physically acceptable solution for Θ. For other values of l and m, Eq. (47) has no finite single-valued solution. Thus l is restricted to integer values or zero, and $l \geq |m|$. For reasons which we shall look at soon, l is called the angular-momentum quantum number.

For the important but special case of $m = 0$ (hence $\Phi = $ const), these physically acceptable solutions of Legendre's equation are called the *Legendre polynomials* $P_l(\cos \vartheta)$. The values of the first few Legendre polynomials are

$$
\begin{aligned}
P_0(\cos \vartheta) &= 1 \\
P_1(\cos \vartheta) &= \cos \vartheta \\
P_2(\cos \vartheta) &= \tfrac{1}{2}(3 \cos^2 \vartheta - 1) = \tfrac{1}{4}(3 \cos 2\vartheta + 1) \\
P_3(\cos \vartheta) &= \tfrac{1}{2}(5 \cos^3 \vartheta - 3 \cos \vartheta) = \tfrac{1}{8}(5 \cos 3\vartheta + 3 \cos \vartheta)
\end{aligned}
\tag{50}
$$

When $m \neq 0$, and $l \geq |m|$, the solutions of Legendre's equation are called the *associated Legendre functions*, $P_l^m(\cos \vartheta)$. These can be expressed in terms of the Legendre polynomials and are (p. 72 of S11)

$$
P_l^m(w) = (1 - w^2)^{|m|/2} \frac{d^{|m|}}{dw^{|m|}} P_l(w)
\tag{51}
$$

where $w \equiv \cos \vartheta$.

d. Spherical Harmonics. The angular part, $Y(\vartheta,\varphi) = \Theta(\vartheta)\Phi(\varphi)$, of the complete wave function ψ is then the product of Eq. (49) and the associated Legendre function P_l^m for $l = 0, 1, 2, \ldots$, and $|m| \leq l$. This solution of the right-hand side of Eq. (43) is called a *spherical harmonic* and can be written

$$
Y_{lm}(\vartheta,\varphi) = N_{lm} P_l^m(\cos \vartheta) e^{im\varphi}
\tag{52}
$$

where N_{lm} is a normalizing constant. We note that, for each value of l, there are $(2l + 1)$ values of m, namely, $m = l, (l - 1), \ldots, 0, \ldots, -(l - 1), -(l)$. We can add together an infinite number of such solutions, for all values of l and m, in order to obtain a general solution, with the constants chosen to fit boundary conditions.

e. Radial Wave Equation. Finally we return to Eq. (46), which contains the radial dependence $R(r)$ of the complete wave function

$$
\psi = R(r)\Theta(\vartheta)\Phi(\varphi)
$$

This equation can be transformed into a form which is analogous to the simple one-dimensional wave equation. To accomplish this, we substitute into Eq. (46) the so-called *modified radial wave function* $\chi(r)$ defined by

$$
\chi(r) = r R(r)
\tag{53}
$$

Then the radial equation becomes simply

$$\frac{d^2\chi}{dr^2} + \frac{8\pi^2 M}{h^2}\left[W - U(r) - \frac{l(l+1)}{2Mr^2}\left(\frac{h}{2\pi}\right)^2\right]\chi = 0 \qquad (54)$$

when the complete wave function is of the form $\psi = r^{-1}\chi\Theta\Phi$. We note that the solutions χ of this radial wave equation are independent of m and depend only on l. They can therefore be denoted χ_l wherever specification of l is pertinent, and they will be identical for all the $(2l+1)$ values of m which can be associated with each value of l.

f. Angular Momentum. The modified radial wave equation, Eq. (54), is identical with the one-dimensional wave equation for the motion of a particle in a potential given by

$$U(r) + \frac{l(l+1)}{2Mr^2}\left(\frac{h}{2\pi}\right)^2 \qquad (55)$$

Therefore the second term has dimensions of an energy. We seek a physical interpretation of this term. The discussion can be simplified,

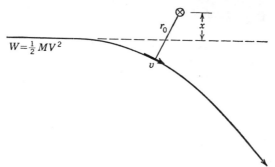

Fig. 4 The angular momentum of the classical particle, $J = MVx = Mvr_0$, is replaced in the radial wave equation by quantized angular momenta, $J = \sqrt{l(l+1)}(h/2\pi)$, Eq. (59), where l is the angular-momentum quantum number.

without loss of generality, if we determine the role which these energy terms would play in the classical scattering of an incident particle by an infinitely heavy nucleus. In a noncentral collision, let v be the velocity which the incident particle retains at its closest distance of approach, which we will call r_0, as shown in Fig. 4. The residual kinetic energy of the particle is then

$$\tfrac{1}{2}Mv^2 = W - U(r_0) \qquad (56)$$

where the total energy W is the initial kinetic energy. At the distance of closest approach, the particle has zero radial velocity and is therefore moving normal to r_0. The angular momentum about the center of mass is therefore

$$J = Mvr_0 \qquad (57)$$

Eliminating v between Eqs. (56) and (57) gives

$$W = U(r_0) + \frac{J^2}{2Mr_0^2} \tag{58}$$

This is equivalent to saying that, at the distance of closest approach, the total energy is the sum of the potential energy of position and the rotational kinetic energy, $J^2/2Mr_0^2$. Here, Mr_0^2 is simply the moment of inertia of the system when the separation is r_0 [compare Eq. (18) of Appendix B]. The angular momentum J is a constant of the motion [Appendix B, Eq. (14)], hence has the same value before, during, and after the actual impact. Comparison of Eq. (58) with Eq. (55) shows that

$$J = \sqrt{l(l+1)}\left(\frac{h}{2\pi}\right) \tag{59}$$

is to be interpreted as the *angular momentum* of the system about an axis through its center of mass and normal to the polar axis. The integer l is called the *angular-momentum quantum number*.

Returning to the modified radial wave equation, Eq. (54), and to Eq. (55), we see that the term

$$\frac{l(l+1)}{2Mr^2}\left(\frac{h}{2\pi}\right)^2 \tag{60}$$

corresponds physically to a varying amount of rotational kinetic energy, because Mr^2 always represents the classical moment of inertia of the system at separation r, and the rest of the expression is a constant of the motion. However, this term appears in Eqs. (54) and (55) with the *same* sign as the potential energy $U(r)$. Because it behaves in scattering problems as though it represented an outward repulsive force and were supplementing the repulsive field of the potential $U(r)$, this term is often associated with the classical concept of centrifugal force. For a central collision ($l = 0$) the distance of closest approach is determined solely by the potential barrier and is the value r_0, for which

$$W = U(r_0) \qquad \text{for } l = 0 \tag{61}$$

For noncentral collisions ($l > 0$), the classical distance of closest approach r_0 is given by

$$W = U(r_0) + \frac{l(l+1)}{2Mr_0^2}\left(\frac{h}{2\pi}\right)^2 \tag{62}$$

For this reason the term $(h/2\pi)^2 l(l+1)/2Mr^2$, which involves the angular momentum of the motion, is often referred to in collision problems as *the centrifugal barrier*.

g. Quantum Numbers. We see that the separation of the wave equation in spherical polar coordinates gives rise to two quantum numbers. This separation can be accomplished only if the potential energy $U(r)$ is spherically symmetric.

The quantum number l, which occurs in the radial wave equation and in the associated Legendre functions which are solutions of the angular equation, is called the *angular-momentum quantum number* in collision problems involving free particles. When bound states are involved, as in the determination of atomic levels, l is more frequently called the *orbital-angular-momentum quantum number*. The magnitude of the angular momentum of the system is $\sqrt{l(l+1)}\,(h/2\pi)$. The values of l which correspond to physical reality are zero and any positive integer. Thus $l = 0, 1, 2, 3, \ldots$.

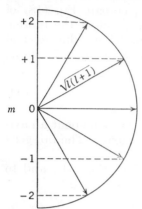

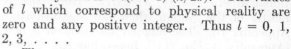

The quantum number m which arises in the equation dealing with the azimuthal angle φ is called the *magnetic quantum number*. This is because of the role which m plays when bound states are involved, as in the Zeeman effect of atomic spectroscopy. We have seen that Eq. (47), in the polar angle ϑ, can only give physically meaningful solutions if the absolute value of m is equal to or smaller than l but, in contrast with l, m can have both positive and negative integer values. Thus for each value of l there are $(2l + 1)$ possible values for m. It can be shown that, when an external magnetic field is applied to a free particle or a bound system having a finite angular momentum and an associated magnetic dipole moment, the angular momentum can take on any of $(2l + 1)$ possible angular orientations with respect to the applied field. These possible orientations are those for which the component of the angular momentum, in the direction of the field, has the values $m(h/2\pi)$. These relationships are conveniently shown in a vector representation, as illustrated by Fig. 5.

Fig. 5 Vector representation of the magnetic substates $m = 2, 1, 0, -1, -2$ for the components of a state having angular-momentum quantum number $l = 2$ and magnitude of angular momentum

$$\sqrt{l(l+1)}\,(h/2\pi)$$
$$= \sqrt{6}\,(h/2\pi).$$

The term "azimuthal quantum number" can lead to confusion. The azimuthal quantum number k of the older quantum theory of Sommerfeld has been replaced in the quantum mechanics by l. Therefore l is also called "azimuthal" by some writers (e.g., Gamow, Schiff, White). Others, such as Bohm, call m the azimuthal quantum number. We shall adhere to "orbital" or "angular" for l, and "magnetic" for m.

3. *Representation of the Plane Wave in Spherical Polar Coordinates*

In spherical polar coordinates, we shall want solutions of Schrödinger's equation which will describe the scattering of an incident plane wave by the spherically symmetric potential, $U(r)$, of a nucleus. We must first be able to express the incident plane wave in spherical polar coordinates.

The mathematical representation of a plane wave, propagated in the z direction, in terms of elementary spherical waves about the origin of polar coordinates r, ϑ, φ, was first carried out by Lord Rayleigh (formerly J. W. Strutt) for the solution of problems in the scattering of waves of sound by spherical obstacles (R10, S78).

In the plane wave

$$e^{ikz}\, e^{-2\pi i \nu t} \tag{63}$$

we are not interested in the time-dependent second term, but only in e^{ikz}, which depends on the spatial coordinate system.

a. Plane Wave as the Sum of Elementary Spherical Waves. The plane wave e^{ikz} is a solution of Schrödinger's equation in a region of constant potential. Therefore we may fruitfully seek to express the plane wave as the product of some functions $R(r)$, $\Theta(\vartheta)$, and $\Phi(\varphi)$, which are themselves solutions of the separated wave equation in polar coordinates.

Then the plane wave

$$\psi = e^{ikz} = e^{ikr \cos \vartheta} = R(r)\,\Theta(\vartheta)\Phi(\varphi) \tag{64}$$

is a solution of the elementary wave equation

$$\nabla^2 \psi + k^2 \psi = 0 \tag{65}$$

and the functions R, Θ, and Φ are solutions of the separated equations

$$\frac{1}{r^2}\frac{d}{dr}\left(r^2 \frac{dR}{dr}\right) + \left[k^2 - \frac{l(l+1)}{r^2}\right] R = 0 \tag{66}$$

$$\frac{1}{\Theta \sin \vartheta}\frac{d}{d\vartheta}\left(\sin \vartheta\, \frac{d\Theta}{d\vartheta}\right) + l(l+1) - \frac{m^2}{\sin^2 \vartheta} = 0 \tag{67}$$

$$\frac{d^2\Phi}{d\varphi^2} + m^2\Phi = 0 \tag{68}$$

Every surface of constant phase in the plane wave is symmetric about the axis of propagation. Hence $\Phi = \text{const}$, and Eq. (68) has only the solution $m = 0$.

Equation (67) is Legendre's equation, and its solutions (S44) when $m = 0$ are the Legendre polynomials $P_l (\cos \vartheta)$, as given in Eq. (50).

Equation (66) has a close resemblance to Bessel's equation. It has two solutions, one of which is not finite at the origin, and which therefore cannot represent the plane wave. The other solution of Eq. (66) is finite at the origin, is physically acceptable, and can be represented in terms of Bessel functions. This solution for $R(r)$ is the so-called *spherical Bessel function*, as defined by Morse (M59), $j_l(kr)$, which has the value

$$j_l(kr) \equiv \sqrt{\frac{\pi}{2kr}}\, J_{l+\frac{1}{2}}(kr) \tag{69}$$

where J is an ordinary Bessel function whose order is half an odd integer.

The values of the first few spherical Bessel functions are†

$$j_0 = \frac{\sin kr}{kr}$$

$$j_1 = \frac{\sin kr}{(kr)^2} - \frac{\cos kr}{kr} \tag{70}$$

$$j_2 = \left[\frac{3}{(kr)^3} - \frac{1}{kr}\right] \sin kr - \frac{3}{(kr)^2} \cos kr$$

Other values can be obtained from the recurrence formula

$$j_{l+1}(kr) = \frac{2l+1}{kr} j_l(kr) - j_{l-1}(kr) \tag{71}$$

Then if A_l are arbitrary constants, the most general solution of Eq. (65) which has axial symmetry and which is finite at the origin is

$$\sum_{l=0}^{l=\infty} A_l \, R(r) \, \Theta(\vartheta) = \sum_{l=0}^{l=\infty} A_l j_l \,(kr) P_l(\cos \vartheta) \tag{72}$$

The plane wave can therefore be expanded in the series

$$e^{ikz} = e^{ikr \cos \vartheta} = \sum_{l=0}^{l=\infty} A_l j_l(kr) P_l(\cos \vartheta) \tag{73}$$

when the constants A_l are properly evaluated. In a straightforward but laborious way it can be shown (M69) that for the plane wave,

$$A_l = (2l + 1)i^l \tag{74}$$

Therefore the required representation of the plane wave in terms of elementary spherical partial waves about the origin of polar coordinates is

$$e^{ikz} = \sum_{l=0}^{l=\infty} (2l + 1)i^l j_l(kr) P_l(\cos \vartheta) \tag{75}$$

The first few terms of the expansion usually are the most important ones, and these *partial waves* have the following values:

† The spherical Bessel functions have the asymptotic values:

$$j_l(kr) \xrightarrow[(kr) \ll l]{} \frac{(kr)^l}{1 \times 3 \times 5 \cdots (2l + 1)} \qquad \text{for very small } kr$$

$$j_l(kr) \xrightarrow[(kr) \gg l]{} \frac{1}{kr} \sin\left(kr - l\frac{\pi}{2}\right) \qquad \text{for very large } kr$$

for $l = 0$: $+ \dfrac{\sin kr}{kr}$

for $l = 1$: $+3i \cos \vartheta \left[\dfrac{1}{(kr)^2} \sin kr - \dfrac{1}{kr} \cos kr \right]$

for $l = 2$: $-\tfrac{5}{4}(3 \cos 2\vartheta + 1) \left[\left(\dfrac{3}{(kr)^3} - \dfrac{1}{kr} \right) \sin kr - \dfrac{3}{(kr)^2} \cos kr \right]$ (76)

for $l = 3$: $-\tfrac{7}{8}i(5 \cos 3\vartheta$

$+ 3 \cos \vartheta) \left[\left(\dfrac{15}{(kr)^4} - \dfrac{6}{(kr)^2} \right) \sin kr - \left(\dfrac{15}{(kr)^3} - \dfrac{1}{kr} \right) \cos kr \right]$

Note that the partial wave for $l = 0$ is independent of angle and therefore is spherically symmetric about the origin.

Problem

Verify any one of the partial waves of Eq. (76) by showing that it does satisfy the separated wave equations, Eqs. (66) and (67).

4. *Physical Correspondence between Partial Waves and Classical Impact Parameters*

a. Limitations of Classical Collision Theory. Consider, as in Fig. 6, a parallel beam of particles which are incident on a single scattering center. In the laboratory, these incident particles are characterized by a well-defined velocity V, reduced mass M, and a *random* distribution of

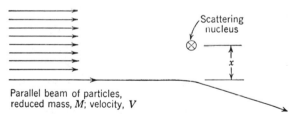

Parallel beam of particles, reduced mass, M; velocity, V

Fig. 6 A parallel beam of particles is incident on a single scattering center at $\otimes$. Classical collision theory visualizes the random distribution of impact parameters as composed of a continuum of discrete values x.

impact parameters x. The classical theory of scattering (Appendix B) proceeds by visualizing these random impact parameters as broken down into discrete values x (or, more exactly, x to $x + dx$). The classical deflection is then calculated for each discrete impact parameter, and these results are reintegrated in order to obtain a prediction of the statistical distribution of scattering angle which is actually observed in the laboratory. We shall need to inquire whether this detailed model of the interaction would be capable of experimental verification for a single incident particle.

In the classical model, the angular momentum for each incident particle can be written as

$$J = MVx = l\hbar \tag{77}$$

where, classically, l is not confined to integer values. Then the impact parameter x has the value

$$x = l\,\frac{\hbar}{MV} = l\lambdabar \tag{78}$$

where $\lambdabar$ is the rationalized de Broglie wavelength $\lambda/2\pi$ of the incident particles.

The classical model of the interaction would be admissible if the extra details which it visualizes could be observed experimentally in a hypothetical experiment with ideal instruments.   We know that every act of measurement alters the phenomenon being measured.   The minimum disturbance imposed by even ideal apparatus is expressed quantitatively by Heisenberg's uncertainty principle

$$\Delta x\,\Delta p \geq \hbar \tag{79}$$

We can use this relationship to estimate the minimum disturbance which would be involved in an experimental effort to observe both the impact parameter x and the momentum transfer p in a classical collision.   Figure 7 indicates a possible hypothetical arrangement in which a slit system admits only incident particles whose impact parameter is close to a

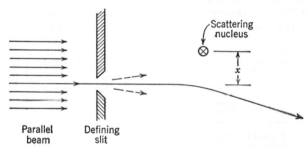

Fig. 7 Hypothetical ideal apparatus for watching the progress of a particular collision, for which the impact parameter is set at x by means of a slit. When the incident parallel beam is regarded as a plane wave, the slit introduces diffraction (dotted arrows) and hence an uncontrollable uncertainty in the impact parameter x and in the angle of scattering. [*From N. Bohr* (B95).]

predetermined value x.   It will suffice for the present estimate to consider collisions in which x is reasonably large compared with the collision diameter, and in which the deflections are therefore small.   Then the momentum transferred in the collision will be essentially at right angles to the path of the incident particle, hence is in the direction of x, and can be called p_x.   To sufficient accuracy, this momentum transfer is the product of an effective coulomb force Zze^2/x^2 acting during an effective collision time which is about $2x/V$.   The momentum transfer is therefore approximately

$$p_x \simeq \frac{Zze^2}{x^2} \frac{2x}{V} = \frac{2Zze^2}{Vx} \tag{80}$$

In the uncertainty relationship, Eq. (79), Δp represents the uncertainty in the momentum which we are willing to accept in the direction x. If we accept 50 per cent uncertainty, we could use $\Delta p = p_x/2$. More commonly, one evaluates Eq. (79) by accepting 100 per cent uncertainty in momentum; thus, $\Delta p = p_x$. Under these circumstances, Δx corresponds to what is often called the "minimum uncertainty" in x. Combining Eqs. (79) and (80), with $\Delta p = p_x$, we obtain for the minimum uncertainty in x

$$\Delta x \simeq (\Delta x)_{\min} = \frac{\hbar}{p_x} = x \frac{\hbar V}{2Zze^2} \tag{81}$$

By expressing the velocity in terms of the velocity of light, $V = \beta c$, and introducing the fine-structure constant, $e^2/\hbar c = \frac{1}{137}$, Eq. (81) takes on the useful form

$$\left(\frac{\Delta x}{x}\right)_{\min} \simeq \frac{137\beta}{2Zz} \tag{82}$$

We see that the minimum fractional uncertainty $\Delta x/x$ in the impact parameter is small only when

$$\frac{2Zz}{137\beta} \gg 1 \tag{83}$$

This means that the subdivision of random impact parameters into discrete values could be verified only when Eq. (83) is satisfied. This inequality is the usual quantitative expression of the domain of validity of classical collision theory [Appendix B, Eq. (97)]. E. J. Williams (W59) has pointed out that this expression is independent of distance r (or x) only for the case of an inverse-square field; hence the *classical theory is valid for all parts of the field, or not at all.* Numerically, the coulomb interaction of a 4-Mev α ray with a gold nucleus corresponds to $2Zz/137\beta \sim 50$, so that Rutherford's classical impact-parameter treatment of such a collision is quite fully valid.

However, the coulomb interaction of, say, a 4-Mev proton ($\beta \sim 0.1$) with a nitrogen nucleus corresponds to $2Zz/137\beta \sim 1$, and no validity could be claimed for the classical impact-parameter model of such a collision. For such cases, the disturbance produced by the apparatus can be interpreted in the wave model as the diffraction produced by the slit in Fig. 7, where the dotted arrows denote the possibility of changes in the direction of the particle due to diffraction. This diffraction pattern can only be evaluated as a probability distribution and cannot be evaluated as an exact correction to be applied to the path of an individual particle. This diffraction can be thought of as the physical origin of the relationship in Eq. (82) for the minimum disturbance produced by the ideal hypothetical apparatus, and also for our inability to evaluate this disturbance for a single individual particle.

b. Angular Momentum Associated with the Partial Waves. It is convenient to visualize the incident parallel beam of particles as divided up into cylindrical zones whose radii are $l\lambda = \lambda,\ 2\lambda,\ 3\lambda,\ \ldots$, as indicated in Fig. 8. Then all the particles whose classical impact parameters lie between $l\lambda$ and $(l + 1)\lambda$ would travel in the cylindrical zone whose inner radius is $l\lambda$. According to classical mechanics, these particles would have angular momenta between $l\hbar$ and $(l + 1)\hbar$.

In the wave mechanics, the angular-momentum quantum number is restricted to integer values $l = 0, 1, 2, 3, \ldots$. We need to inquire whether the resulting quantization of angular momentum $\sqrt{l(l + 1)}\ \hbar$ would really restrict the classical impact parameters x to the series of corresponding quantized values $\sqrt{l(l + 1)}\ \lambda$.

For a swift particle whose classical impact parameter would be $x = l\lambda$, we see from Eq. (82) that an indefiniteness at least as large as λ is easily

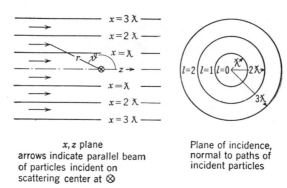

x, z plane
arrows indicate parallel beam
of particles incident on
scattering center at $\otimes$

Plane of incidence,
normal to paths of
incident particles

Fig. 8 The parallel beam of particles is divided up into cylindrical zones whose radii are $l\lambda = \lambda,\ 2\lambda,\ 3\lambda,\ \ldots$. Particles traveling in the cylinder whose inner radius is $l\lambda$ and whose outer radius is $(l + 1)\lambda$ constitute the main bulk of a group whose angular-momentum quantum number is l and whose angular momentum is $\sqrt{l(l + 1)}\ \hbar$. These particles correspond to the lth partial wave in Eq. (76).

accounted for. Hence we are not justified in speaking of a well-defined impact parameter when $2Zz/137\beta$ is small.

This means that in Fig. 8 it is admissible to assume that a group of particles which have angular-momentum quantum number l may be smeared out but will move mostly in the zone whose inner radius is $l\lambda$. The particles in this zone can be thought of as having the angular momentum $\sqrt{l(l + 1)}\ \hbar$, in accord with Eq. (59). Those particles which travel in the axial zone correspond to $l = 0$ and are the wave analogue of the central collisions in the classical model. Those in the next zone correspond to $l = 1$, and so forth.

It can be shown that the first and largest maximum of the radial part $j_l(kr)$ of the wave function, Eq. (76), occurs in the vicinity of $kr \equiv r/\lambda \sim 1.5l$. This is to be associated physically with the relative density of particles in the l group at various *radial* distances from the origin. Thus when the influence of the polar angle ϑ is included, most of the particles whose angular-momentum quantum number is l will be found somewhere along the length of the cylinder whose inner radius is $l\lambda$ and whose outer radius is $(l + 1)\lambda$.

Nuclear collisions are classified in the wave model using the letter designations for the l values, as borrowed from Rydberg's notation in atomic spectroscopy. These are

l	Letter	Rydberg notation
0	s	sharp
1	p	principal
2	d	diffuse
3	f	fundamental
4	g	(follow the alphabet from here on)

Thus the $l = 0$ collisions are called "s-wave collisions," etc. We shall find that the s-wave collisions are usually the most significant in dealing with the physical interpretation of many types of collision experiments.

The area of each zone in Fig. 8 is

$$\pi(l + 1)^2\lambda^2 - \pi l^2\lambda^2 = \pi(2l + 1)\lambda^2 \tag{84}$$

which is seen to be proportional to $(2l + 1)$. This gives a rough physical interpretation to the weighting factor $(2l + 1)$ in Eqs. (74) and (75) for the individual partial waves which make up a plane wave.

It may be pointed out in passing that the area $\pi(2l + 1)\lambda^2$ of the zones in the wave front representing a stream of particles at once puts an upper limit on the *absorption* cross section for all types of nuclear reactions. This upper limit is

$$\sigma_l = \pi(2l + 1)\lambda^2 \tag{85}$$

for the lth partial wave. This simple generalization does not, however, apply to elastic potential *scattering*, for which Eq. (122) will show that the maximum cross section is $4\pi(2l + 1)\lambda^2$.

Problems

1. Plot the normalized amplitude $(2l + 1)i^l j_l(kr)$ of the first few partial waves in Eq. (75) against kr, for some fixed value of ϑ, say, $\vartheta = 0$.

2. Determine the approximate value of kr, for which each of the first few partial waves has its maximum amplitude. Tabulate against l the quantities kr and kr/l for these maxima. Comment on the physical significance of the location of these maxima in connection with the three-dimensional extension of the cylindrical zones in Fig. 8.

3. In a classical coulomb scattering collision, show that the exact value of the momentum transfer p_x normal to the incident momentum, in L coordinates, is

$$p_x = \frac{2Zze^2}{Vx}\left[\frac{1}{1 + (b/2x)^2}\right]$$

Compare with the approximation, Eq. (80).

4. Show from the uncertainty and complementarity principles that the minimum disturbance, Eq. (81), of the slit in Fig. 7 can also be expressed as

$$(\Delta x)_{\min} \simeq \lambda\, \frac{\frac{1}{2}MV^2}{Zze^2/x}$$

Give a physical interpretation for the numerator and the denominator terms. Must their ratio always be greater than unity? If the exact value of momentum transfer p_x as determined in Prob. 3 is used in Eq. (81), show that for all values of x

$$(\Delta x)_{\min} \geq \lambda$$

5. *Transmission through a Nuclear Potential Barrier*

We have now reviewed the principles which must be applied, in spherical polar coordinates, in order to explain the experimental results on the transparency of nuclear barriers. It can be shown that the dominant terms in the wave-mechanical expression for the transmission through nuclear barriers are the same for outgoing and for incoming particles. The theory of α-ray decay and the theory of the capture of swift bombarding particles involve the same general expressions for the transparency of a nuclear potential barrier.

Without serious loss of generality, we shall proceed from the viewpoint of an outgoing particle, as in α decay. The only case for which relatively simple formulas can be developed is that of $l = 0$. This corresponds to the numerous and important cases of α-ray emission in which the mutual angular momentum of the emitted α ray and its residual nucleus, about their center of mass, is zero, i.e., "s-wave" emission.

a. Transmission of s Waves through a High Nuclear Barrier. Figure 9 represents the potential barrier between an α particle ($z = 2$) and the decay product nucleus Z, which remains after the emission of the α ray. The parent nucleus itself has the atomic number $Z + z = Z + 2$. The radius R refers to the decay product, and the barrier height is taken as

$$B = \frac{Zze^2}{R} \tag{86}$$

A rectangular potential well is used, and the potential of the α particle in this well is U_0. The exact value of U_0 is not of great importance, because the principal part of the integral which determines the barrier transparency occurs out under the coulomb barrier. It is assumed, however, and with good experimental justification, that $U_0 \ll B$.

The total energy W of the α particle is taken as the total kinetic energy T when the emitted α ray and the residual nucleus are widely separated. Thus T is the sum of the kinetic energy T_α of the α ray and the kinetic energy T_z of the residual recoiling nucleus. When V is the mutual velocity of recession of the emitted α ray and the residual nucleus, we have

$$V = V_\alpha + V_z \tag{87}$$

where V_α and V_z are the laboratory velocities of the α ray and the recoil nucleus.   Then it is easy to show that

$$T = T_\alpha \frac{M_\alpha}{M} = \tfrac{1}{2}MV^2 \tag{88}$$

where M is the *reduced mass* of the α ray and the residual nucleus.   Also in Fig. 9, the radial separation of the α particle from the center of the residual nucleus is r, and the coulomb barrier potential is

$$U(r) = \frac{Zze^2}{r} \qquad \text{for } r > R \tag{89}$$

The value of r for which the coulomb potential equals the total energy T is

$$b = \frac{Zze^2}{T} = \frac{2Zze^2}{MV^2} \tag{90}$$

which would equal the "collision diameter" if the α ray were directed toward the nucleus.

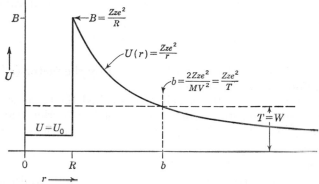

Fig. 9   Nuclear potential barrier and associated parameters used in evaluating the transparency to particles whose charge is ze, velocity V, reduced mass M.

We shall assume that the wave function of the α particle is spherically symmetric, corresponding to an $l = 0$, or "s state," both inside and outside the potential barrier.   Then the wave function ψ of the α particle is independent of angle, depends only on r, and can be written as

$$\psi = \frac{1}{r}\chi(r) \tag{91}$$

where $\chi(r)$ satisfies the modified radial wave equation, Eq. (54), with $l = 0$, i.e.,

$$\frac{d^2\chi}{dr^2} + \frac{8\pi^2 M}{h^2}(W - U)\chi = 0 \tag{92}$$

We see that this radial equation, when $l = 0$, is identical with the one-dimensional wave equation.   Therefore we can turn back to Eqs. (5.71) and (5.72) of Chap. 2 and can write at once the dominant term in the resulting radial barrier transparency.

This gives us for the probability T_0 of transmission of s waves

$$T_0 \simeq e^{-\gamma} \tag{93}$$

where

$$\gamma = \frac{4\pi}{h} \sqrt{2M} \int_R^b \left(\frac{Zze^2}{r} - T\right)^{\frac{1}{2}} dr \tag{94}$$

The result of a straightforward integration is

$$\gamma = \frac{8\pi Zze^2}{hV} \left[\cos^{-1}\left(\frac{T}{B}\right)^{\frac{1}{2}} - \left(\frac{T}{B}\right)^{\frac{1}{2}}\left(1 - \frac{T}{B}\right)^{\frac{1}{2}} \right] \tag{95}$$

As an approximation for the important case in which the barrier is much higher than the kinetic energy of the emitted α ray, that is, $B \gg T$, the square brackets become

$$\left\{ \left[\frac{\pi}{2} - \left(\frac{T}{B}\right)^{\frac{1}{2}} - \frac{1}{6}\left(\frac{T}{B}\right)^{\frac{3}{2}} - \cdots \right] - \left[\left(\frac{T}{B}\right)^{\frac{1}{2}} - \frac{1}{2}\left(\frac{T}{B}\right)^{\frac{3}{2}} - \cdots \right] \right\}$$
$$\text{for } B \gg T \quad (96)$$

and the approximate result for the barrier transmission exponent for s waves is

$$\gamma \simeq \frac{4\pi^2 Zze^2}{hV} - \frac{8\pi}{h} (2Zze^2 MR)^{\frac{1}{2}} \tag{97}$$

The first term is larger than the second term by the factor $(\pi/4)\sqrt{B/T}$ and is therefore the dominant term.

The first term of Eq. (97) is sometimes called the Gamow exponent, and the corresponding approximate value of the barrier transparency, for s waves $(l = 0)$ through very high spherical barriers, is called the *Gamow factor*

$$T_0(R \to 0) \equiv G \simeq e^{-(4\pi^2 Zze^2/hV)} \tag{98}$$

In terms of the fine-structure constant, $2\pi e^2/hc = \frac{1}{137}$, and the velocity in terms of the velocity of light, $V = \beta c$, the Gamow factor becomes

$$G \simeq e^{-\pi(2Zz/137\beta)} \tag{99}$$

This last expression indicates that the nuclear barrier will be quite impenetrable when

$$\frac{2Zz}{137\beta} \gg 1 \tag{100}$$

and that this inequality is again found to represent the domain in which classical collision theory can be expected to be valid.

The second term in Eq. (97) expresses the influence of nuclear radius R on the barrier transparency. It will be noted that the transparency *increases* as R increases. This is because the spherical barrier becomes thinner as R increases, if all other parameters remain constant. The physical significance becomes clearer when the second term of Eq. (97) is rewritten as

$$-\frac{8\pi}{h} (2Zze^2 MR)^{\frac{1}{2}} = -\frac{4}{137}\left(2Zz \frac{M}{m_0} \frac{R}{r_0}\right)^{\frac{1}{2}} \tag{101}$$

where $\frac{1}{137} = 2\pi e^2/hc$ = fine-structure constant

M/m_0 = reduced mass in terms of rest mass m_0 of electron

R/r_0 = nuclear radius in terms of classical electron radius

$$r_0 = e^2/m_0 c^2 = 2.82 \times 10^{-13} \text{ cm}$$

The radii of all known nuclei fall well within the domain of $R/r_0 = 1$ to 4.

In the notation of Eqs. (99) and (101), the barrier transmission exponent of Eq. (97) can be put in the more eloquent form

$$\gamma \simeq \pi \left(\frac{2Zz}{137\beta}\right) - \frac{4}{137}\left(2Zz \frac{M}{m_0}\frac{R}{r_0}\right)^{\frac{1}{2}} \tag{102}$$

b. Barrier Transparency for $l \neq 0$. When compared with its sensitive dependence on the kinetic energy T and on R, the transparency of a nuclear barrier is only slightly dependent on l. Figure 10 indicates schematically that the potential barrier includes both the coulomb barrier and the centrifugal barrier, as given in Eq. (55).

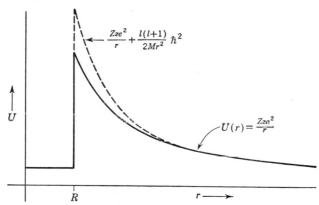

Fig. 10 Schematic representation of the coulomb and centrifugal barriers for $l > 0$.

The analytical evaluation of the transparency of coulomb barriers for particles with finite l values can only be accomplished by making numerous approximations. For light nuclei, the results have been obtained by numerical integration and are available in the form of tables and graphs (B77, C23).

For heavy nuclei, an approximate analytical form due to Gamow (p. 173 of G7) is

$$\gamma \simeq \frac{4\pi^2 Zze^2}{hV} - \frac{8\pi}{h}(2Zze^2 MR)^{\frac{1}{2}}\left(1 - \frac{\sigma}{2}\right) \tag{103}$$

where

$$\sigma \equiv \frac{[l(l+1)/2MR^2](h/2\pi)^2}{Zze^2/R} \ll 1 \tag{104}$$

The correction parameter σ is the ratio of the centrifugal barrier to the coulomb barrier, when both are evaluated at the nuclear radius. Equation (103) is obtained by inserting the centrifugal potential in Eq. (94), expanding the square root in powers of σ, and integrating. It can be used as a guide when $\sigma \ll 1$, as is the case for the very heavy radioactive nuclei [$Z \sim 90$; $R \sim 10^{-12}$ cm; $\sigma \sim 0.002 l(l + 1)$]. It is not valid for estimating the effects of angular momentum in the penetration of light nuclei by charged particles, because then σ is not small enough.

A better approximate formula has been developed by Mott (p. 55 of M69) and by Yost, Wheeler, and Breit (Y4), but these expressions are quite complicated. Preston (P31, P33) has evaluated the errors in Gamow's approximation, Eq. (103), and has developed and evaluated analytical expressions of greater generality. Preston's theory is based on the spherical-well model but has the advantage of retaining *both* U_0 and R as parameters which can be evaluated from the experimental data on α decay.

Problems

1. Verify Eq. (88) for the total kinetic energy in center-of-mass coordinates, for the case of α-ray emission.

2. Show that the Gamow factor can be written as

$$G \simeq e^{-\pi k b}$$

where $k = 2\pi/\lambda = MV/\hbar$ is the wave number of relative motion for the emitted α ray when at a large distance from the nucleus, and b is the collision diameter $2Zze^2/MV^2$. Compare and contrast with Eq. (36) for the rectangular one-dimensional barrier.

3. From a qualitative examination of Eqs. (97) and (102), state whether the transmission through a nuclear barrier is increased by large values or by small values of M, V, Z, z, and R. Correlate each decision with the qualitative effect on the shape of the barrier and other parameters of Fig. 9.

4. Show that the s-wave barrier transmission exponents of Eq. (95) can be expressed as the converging series

$$\gamma = \pi \frac{2Zz}{137\beta} \left[1 - \frac{4}{\pi} \left(\frac{T}{B} \right)^{\frac{1}{2}} + \frac{2}{3\pi} \left(\frac{T}{B} \right)^{\frac{3}{2}} + \frac{1}{10\pi} \left(\frac{T}{B} \right)^{\frac{5}{2}} + \cdots \right]$$

where $T/B = MV^2R/2Zze^2 = R/[\lambda(2Zz/137\beta)]$, and the first and second terms in the square brackets correspond to the two terms used in the common approximate expression, Eq. (97). When the higher correction terms are used, show that Eq. (102) becomes

$$\gamma \simeq \pi \left(\frac{2Zz}{137\beta} \right) - \frac{4}{137} \left(2Zz \frac{M}{m_0} \frac{R}{r_0} \right)^{\frac{1}{2}} \left[1 - \frac{1}{6} \frac{T}{B} - \frac{1}{40} \left(\frac{T}{B} \right)^2 - \cdots \right]$$

6. *Elastic Scattering of Particles Incident on a Nuclear Potential Barrier*

If $U(r)$ is a spherically symmetric nuclear potential, we can obtain from the wave model a general expression for the differential scattering cross section for elastic collisions.

The parallel beam of incident particles can be represented by the plane wave e^{ikz}, where $k \equiv 2\pi MV/h = 2\pi/\lambda$.

The probability of scattering in the direction ϑ can be represented in terms of the square of the amplitude of a spherical wave going out from the origin of coordinates. This scattered wave must have the form

$$f(\vartheta) \frac{e^{ikr}}{r} \tag{105}$$

where the function $f(\vartheta)$ of angle is to be evaluated in terms of k, $U(r)$, and other parameters of the collision.

At a large distance from the scattering center, the variation with radial distance r must be as shown in Eq. (105) for the following reasons. An outgoing wave must contain the factor e^{ikr}, and not e^{-ikr} which would represent an incoming wave. This rests on the previous arbitrary selection of $e^{-2\pi i\nu t}$ as the time-dependent factor [Chap. 2, Eqs. (5.30) and (5.38)] for solutions of the time-dependent Schrödinger equation. Thus, by analogy with Eqs. (5.22) and (5.30) of Chap. 2, $e^{i(kr-2\pi\nu t)}$ represents a wave in which surfaces of constant phase move radially outward from the origin. The variation of Eq. (105) with r^{-1} provides for conservation of particles in the outgoing wave. This is because the probability of finding the particle in any spherical shell, between r and $r + dr$, must be constant if there are no sinks or sources of particles. The volume of such a spherical shell is $4\pi r^2\, dr$; hence the density of particles in it must vary with $1/r^2$. The density of particles, or the probability of finding one particle in the spherical shell, is proportional to the square of the amplitude of the scattered wave in the shell. Consequently the amplitude must vary exactly with $1/r$.

The *density* of particles in the incident plane wave is $|e^{ikz}|^2 = 1$ particle per unit volume. The incident *flux* of bombarding particles is therefore $|e^{ikz}|^2 V = V$ particles per square centimeter per second. In the scattered wave, the number of scattered particles crossing an element of area dS, at the location (r,ϑ,φ), is the product of the probability density, the area dS, and the velocity V of the elastically scattered particles, or

$$V \left| f(\vartheta) \frac{e^{ikr}}{r} \right|^2 dS \qquad \text{particles/sec} \tag{106}$$

The *differential cross section* $d\sigma$ for elastic scattering into the solid angle $d\Omega = dS/r^2$ at mean angle ϑ is the ratio of Eq. (106) to the incident flux, or

$$d\sigma = |f(\vartheta)|^2\, d\Omega \qquad \text{cm}^2/\text{scattering center} \tag{107}$$

The *total cross section* for elastic scattering is simply the integral of Eq. (107) over all possible angles, or

$$\sigma = \int d\sigma = 2\pi \int_0^\pi |f(\vartheta)|^2 \sin \vartheta\, d\vartheta \qquad \text{cm}^2/\text{scattering center} \tag{108}$$

a. General Equation for Elastic Scattering Cross Section. Our problem is to evaluate $f(\vartheta)$. This is done in two steps. First, we must find a wave function ψ_{total}, which represents the total disturbance of the incident wave and the scattered wave. This is to be in the form

$$\psi_{\text{total}} = e^{ikz} + f(\vartheta)\,\frac{e^{ikr}}{r} \tag{109}$$

and is to be valid for large distances r, that is, for $kr \gg l$. Secondly, we subtract the incident wave

$$\psi_{\text{incident}} = e^{ikz} \tag{110}$$

in order to obtain the scattered wave as

$$\psi_{\text{scattered}} = \psi_{\text{total}} - \psi_{\text{incident}} \tag{111}$$

Expressions must be found for each of the three wave functions in Eq. (111), in terms of sums of partial waves. We have already found the required expansion for ψ_{incident}, which was given by Eq. (75) as

$$e^{ikz} = \sum_{l=0}^{l=\infty} (2l + 1)i^l j_l(kr)P_l(\cos\vartheta) \tag{112}$$

where, for large values of r, j_l has the asymptotic form

$$j_l(kr) \simeq \frac{1}{kr}\sin\left(kr - l\frac{\pi}{2}\right) \qquad \text{for } kr \gg l \tag{113}$$

The wave function ψ_{total} for the combined disturbance has to be a solution of the wave equation, Eq. (41), containing the scattering potential $U(r)$. The solution which is desired can be written, by analogy with Eq. (72), as

$$\psi_{\text{total}} = \sum_{l=0}^{l=\infty} A_l R_l(kr)P_l(\cos\vartheta) \tag{114}$$

where the A_l are constants chosen so that Eq. (109) is satisfied, and the $R_l(kr)$ are solutions of the unmodified radial wave equation, Eq. (46), with the potential $U(r)$.

It can be shown (p. 23 of M69) that, if the potential $U(r)$ decreases *faster than* $1/r$ as r tends to infinity, then the asymptotic value of $R_l(kr)$, which is finite at the origin, is given by

$$R_l(kr) \simeq \frac{1}{kr}\sin\left(kr - l\frac{\pi}{2} + \delta_l\right) \qquad \text{for } kr \gg l \tag{115}$$

where δ_l is called the *phase shift* of the lth partial wave, caused by the scattering potential $U(r)$.

The phase shift is independent of angle ϑ but depends on $U(r)$ and on the particle energy as expressed by its wave number k. There are only a few very simple potentials $U(r)$ for which any values of δ_l can be evaluated analytically. However, for more complicated potentials, the phase shifts can usually be determined by numerical integration.

When the constants A_l in Eq. (114) are chosen so that ψ_{total} represents the sum of an incident plane wave and an outgoing spherical wave, these constants are found to have the values

$$A_l = (2l + 1)i^l e^{i\delta_l} \tag{116}$$

and the total disturbance is represented by

$$\psi_{\text{total}} = \sum_{l=0}^{l=\infty} (2l + 1)i^l e^{i\delta_l} R_l(kr) P_l(\cos \vartheta) \tag{117}$$

Upon subtracting the incident plane wave, Eq. (112), from Eq. (117), and equating the difference to the scattered wave, $f(\vartheta)e^{ikr}/r$, it is found that

$$f(\vartheta) = \frac{1}{2ik} \sum_{l=0}^{l=\infty} (2l + 1)(e^{2i\delta_l} - 1)P_l(\cos \vartheta) \tag{118}$$

which is the desired general expression for $f(\vartheta)$. Equation (118), through Eq. (107), gives the required scattering cross sections, in terms of the phase shifts δ_l for the individual partial waves $l = 0, 1, 2, \ldots$. Like Eq. (115), Eq. (118) is valid if $U(r)$ decreases faster than $1/r$ for large r.

It will be noted that $f(\vartheta)$ is complex. The scattering cross section involves only the square of the absolute value, which can be written

$$|f(\vartheta)|^2 = A^2 + B^2 \tag{119}$$

where

$$A = \frac{1}{2k} \sum (2l + 1)(\cos 2\delta_l - 1)P_l(\cos \vartheta) \tag{120}$$

and

$$B = \frac{1}{2k} \sum (2l + 1)(\sin 2\delta_l)P_l(\cos \vartheta) \tag{121}$$

The total elastic scattering cross section is obtained by carrying out the integration indicated in Eq. (108), which gives

$$\sigma = \frac{4\pi}{k^2} \sum_{l=0}^{l=\infty} (2l + 1)\sin^2 \delta_l \tag{122}$$

where the phase shifts δ_l are each functions of k and $U(r)$, and $U(r)$ must decrease faster than $1/r$ for very large r.

b. Elastic Scattering by a Spherical Potential Well. The origin and physical significance of the phase shift, and its relationship to the scattering potential, can be visualized by considering a very simple but important special case. As illustrated in Fig. 11, let the potential $U(r)$ be a narrow spherical well having a depth D and radius b, that is,

$$\begin{aligned} U(r) &= -D &\quad \text{for } r < b \\ U(r) &= 0 &\quad \text{for } r > b \end{aligned} \tag{123}$$

Such a potential is known to give a fairly good representation of many of the features of the short-range attractive interaction between a nucleus and an incident neutron. The radius b of the well for a light nucleus is found experimentally to be small compared with the rationalized de Broglie wavelength $\lambdabar$ of neutrons whose energy is of the order of 10 Mev or less. Therefore incident particles which have one unit or more of angular momentum cannot reach the edge of the potential well. Only s-wave collisions are effective, as can be seen from Fig. 8, and we need consider only the partial wave for $l = 0$.

As an explicit illustration of the phase-shift method, we can carry out the calculations for this special case. The incident plane wave, with unit amplitude, is

$$\psi_{\text{incident}} = e^{ik_1 z} \simeq \frac{\sin k_1 r}{k_1 r} = \frac{e^{ik_1 r} - e^{-ik_1 r}}{2ik_1 r} \qquad \text{for } l = 0 \qquad (124)$$

where

$$k_1^2 = \frac{8\pi^2 M}{h^2} W \qquad (125)$$

and M = reduced mass

W = incident kinetic energy in C coordinates

r = separation of centers of interacting particles

Note from Eq. (124) that the incident $l = 0$ wave can be considered as the sum of an outbound wave (term in $e^{ik_1 r}$) and an inbound wave (term in $e^{-ik_1 r}$) having equal amplitude $1/2ik_1 r$.

The total disturbance, due to the incident plane wave and the scattered wave, is

$$\psi_{\text{total}} = e^{ik_1 z} + f_0 \frac{e^{ik_1 r}}{r} \qquad (126)$$

where f_0 is the amplitude of the scattered $l = 0$ wave. The asymptotic form of this wave function is, by Eqs. (114) and (115),

$$\psi_{\text{total}} \simeq \frac{A \sin (k_1 r + \delta_0)}{k_1 r} \qquad (127)$$

$$= \frac{A}{2ik_1 r} \left(e^{i(k_1 r + \delta_0)} - e^{-i(k_1 r + \delta_0)} \right) \qquad (128)$$

where δ_0 is the phase shift for the $l = 0$ wave.

The scattered wave is

$$\psi_{\text{scattered}} = \psi_{\text{total}} - \psi_{\text{incident}} = f_0 \frac{e^{ik_1 r}}{r}$$

$$= \frac{1}{2ik_1 r} [(A e^{i\delta_0} - 1)e^{ik_1 r} - (A e^{-i\delta_0} - 1)e^{-ik_1 r}] \qquad (129)$$

This scattered wave must contain no incoming wave. Therefore the coefficient of the $e^{-ik_1 r}$ term is zero, or

$$A = e^{i\delta_0} \qquad (130)$$

and the total wave, for $r > b$, becomes

$$\psi_{\text{total}} \simeq \frac{e^{i\delta_0}}{k_1 r} \sin(k_1 r + \delta_0) \tag{131}$$

Then Eq. (129) can be solved for f_0, which is

$$f_0 = \frac{1}{2ik_1}(e^{2i\delta_0} - 1) = \frac{e^{i\delta_0} \sin \delta_0}{k_1} \tag{132}$$

in agreement with the more general relationship given in Eq. (118). The amplitude f_0 of the scattered wave is complex, and the square of its absolute value is easily shown to be

$$|f_0|^2 = f_0 f_0^* = \left(\frac{\sin \delta_0}{k_1}\right)^2 \tag{133}$$

Then the total elastic scattering cross section is

$$\sigma = 4\pi |f_0|^2 = \frac{4\pi}{k_1^2} \sin^2 \delta_0 \tag{134}$$

For many important nuclear cases, such as the scattering of slow neutrons by nuclei, the phase change δ_0 is close to 0° or 180°, and f_0 is, with good approximation, a real number. Then the length f_0 is called the "*scattering amplitude*" in the terminology of Wollan and Shull (W69), while for "zero-energy" neutrons $k_1 \to 0$, and $-f_0$ is known as the "*scattering length*" $+a$ in the terminology of Fermi and Marshall (F40) [Chap. 10, Eq. (3.6)].

To evaluate δ_0 in terms of $U(r)$, we note that the wave equation

$$\nabla^2 \psi + k^2 \psi = 0 \tag{135}$$

must be satisfied both inside and outside the well. This means that the modified radial wave equation, Eq. (54), for $l = 0$, must be satisfied by the modified radial wave function $\chi = r\psi$, in both regions, i.e.,

$$\frac{\partial^2 \chi}{\partial r^2} + \frac{8\pi^2 M}{h^2}(W - U)\chi = 0 \tag{136}$$

Inside the well ($r < b$), Eq. (136) is satisfied by

$$\chi = B \sin k_2 r \tag{137}$$

or

$$\psi_{\text{inside}} = \frac{\chi}{r} = \frac{B}{r} \sin k_2 r \tag{138}$$

where the propagation number k_2 is given by

$$k_2^2 = \frac{8\pi^2 M}{h^2}(W - U) = \frac{8\pi^2 M}{h^2}(W + D) \tag{139}$$

We now have Eq. (131) for the wave function outside the well ($r > b$) and Eq. (138) for the wave function inside the well. The constants B and δ_0 must be chosen in such a way that ψ and $\partial\psi/\partial r$, and therefore χ

and $\partial\chi/\partial r$, are continuous across the boundary at $r = b$. This gives

$$\frac{e^{i\delta_0}}{k_1} \sin (k_1 b + \delta_0) = B \sin k_2 b \tag{140}$$

$$e^{i\delta_0} \cos (k_1 b + \delta_0) = B k_2 \cos k_2 b \tag{141}$$

Dividing, in order to eliminate B, we obtain

$$\tan (k_1 b + \delta_0) = \frac{k_1}{k_2} \tan k_2 b \tag{142}$$

This can be rearranged as an explicit solution for δ_0

$$\delta_0 = -k_1 b + \tan^{-1} \left(\frac{k_1}{k_2} \tan k_2 b \right) \tag{143}$$

which expresses the phase shift δ_0 in terms of the kinetic energy

$$W = k_1^2 \left(\frac{h^2}{8\pi^2 M} \right)$$

of the incident particle, the depth $D = (k_2^2 - k_1^2)(h^2/8\pi^2 M)$, and radius b of the potential well $U(r)$.

The scattering cross section, Eq. (134), could now be expressed in terms of W and $U(r)$, if desired, through Eq. (143). In place of the general expression, we will note here that the cross section $(4\pi \sin^2 \delta_0)/k_1^2$ has a finite limit for very slow incident particles $W \to 0$, $k_1 \to 0$, which is

$$\sigma \xrightarrow[k_1 \to 0]{} 4\pi b^2 \left(\frac{\tan k_0 b}{k_0 b} - 1 \right)^2 \tag{144}$$

where

$$k_0^2 \equiv k_2^2 - k_1^2 = \frac{8\pi^2 M D}{h^2} \tag{145}$$

This cross section has infinite values for $k_0 b = \pi/2, 3\pi/2, \ldots$, which are associated physically with the distribution of allowed energy levels, with zero angular momentum $(l - 0)$, within the potential well.

Except when $k_0 b$ is near these values, the solution of Eqs. (140) and (141) for B shows that the amplitude of the wave function inside the well is very small compared with the wave function outside. This is in qualitative agreement with the small value expected for the transmission $4k_1 k_2/(k_1 + k_2)^2$ for a step well (Sec. 1, Prob. 6).

c. Physical Significance of the Phase Shift. For s-wave scattering by the "rectangular" spherical potential well, we have now found that the pertinent wave functions outside $(r > b)$ the well are

$$\psi_{\text{incident}} = \frac{1}{k_1 r} \sin k_1 r \tag{146}$$

$$\psi_{\text{scattered}} = \frac{\sin \delta_0}{k_1 r} e^{i(k_1 r + \delta_0)} \tag{147}$$

$$\psi_{\text{total}} \equiv \psi_1 = \frac{e^{i\delta_0}}{k_1 r} \sin (k_1 r + \delta_0) \tag{148}$$

Inside the well, we have, for $(r < b)$

$$\psi_{\text{inside}} \equiv \psi_2 = \frac{B}{r} \sin k_2 r \qquad (149)$$

And at the boundary, $r = b$, the inside wave and the total outside wave must join smoothly, as represented by the conditions

$$\psi_1 = \psi_2 \qquad \frac{\partial \psi_1}{\partial r} = \frac{\partial \psi_2}{\partial r} \qquad \text{at } r = b \qquad (150)$$

We seek a pictorial representation of all these relationships. Externally, $\psi_{\text{scattered}}$ is best represented by the complex-plane presentation (p. 255 of S45), as illustrated in Prob. 4 of this section. The three other wave functions, and the boundary conditions, can be visualized as in Fig. 11.

In Fig. 11, the horizontal scale corresponds to the separation r between the centers of any two nuclear particles whose interaction conforms essentially to a rectangular well. There are two vertical scales. One is an energy scale and shows the potential well, Eq. (123), together with the asymptotic value of the kinetic energy $T_1 = W$ for the incident and the elastically scattered particles. The other vertical scale, $k_1 r \psi(r)$, is used for the

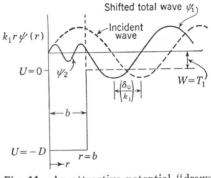

Fig. 11 An attractive potential "draws in" the incident wave and produces a positive phase shift δ_0 between the incident wave and the total wave, outside the range of the potential.

three wave functions. These are plotted by using the $T_1 = W$ line as a convenient horizontal axis.

The dotted curve represents the incident wave (e.g., a neutron) in the region outside the well, where $k_1 r \psi(r) = \sin k_1 r$. It can also be thought of as representing the incident wave, for $r < b$, in the absence of the potential due to the scattering nucleus. Its kinetic energy and its de Broglie wavelength $\lambda_1 = 2\pi/k_1$ are constant. The solid line represents the neutron when the scattering potential is present. Within the potential well, the amplitude is generally smaller, Eq. (149), than outside. Also the kinetic energy of the neutron is greater inside the well, because of the attractive potential, and its de Broglie wavelength $\lambda_2 = 2\pi/k_2$ is correspondingly shorter. This wave, Eq. (149), starts out from the origin with a shorter wavelength, and a more rapid oscillation, until it reaches $r = b$. Then it must join smoothly to the outside wave, with equal value and equal slope, Eq. (150), at the edge of the potential well. In order to satisfy these boundary conditions, it can be seen from Fig. 11 that there must be a difference in phase between the incident wave and the wave which now represents the total system ψ_1 outside the well. We can represent the phase shift δ_0 in terms of a length in Fig. 11. Let

r_{incident} and r_{total} be radial distances for which the incident and total wave functions have equal phase. Then

$$k_1 r_{\text{incident}} = k_1 r_{\text{total}} + \delta_0 \tag{151}$$

and

$$r_{\text{incident}} - r_{\text{total}} = \frac{\delta_0}{k_1} \tag{152}$$

Thus points of equal phase occur at distances outside the well which are uniformly δ_0/k_1 closer to the origin for the total wave than they would be for the incident wave alone.

It is seen that the wave can be thought of as "drawn in" toward the origin, as a result of the presence of the attractive potential. Conversely, it can be shown that for repulsive potentials δ_0 is negative, and the total wave can be thought of as "pushed out" from the origin.

When the amplitude inside the well is very small compared with that outside the well, we are dealing with substantially pure *potential scattering*. This is usually the case when an inside wave of large wave number k_2 is to be joined to an outside wave of small wave number k_1. The inside wave number k_2 depends on the excitation energy of the compound nucleus which could be formed by the coalescence of the two interacting particles. There may exist certain exceptional values of the incident energy $T_1 = W$ for which the corresponding interior wave function ψ_2 has nearly a zero derivative at $r = b$. Then the outside and inside wave functions could be joined with substantially equal amplitudes. These exceptional energies correspond to what is called *resonance scattering*. Pure potential scattering and pure resonance scattering are extreme limiting cases, and in practice all possible intermediate situations are observed. These are discussed and illustrated in Chap. 14, Fig. 1.1.

d. Rutherford Scattering. The scattering of incident particles whose charge is ze by the coulomb field due to another particle whose charge is Ze is a fundamental problem for which the wave equation has been solved with varying degrees of rigor by a variety of approximate methods. An exact solution was obtained first by Gordon (G33) and is identical with the classical solution. This is a remarkable result.

It is only for the case of an inverse-square field of force that the classical and wave-mechanical cross sections can be identical. E. J. Williams (W59) has pointed out the dimensional generalization that if the force between two particles varies with r^n, then their scattering cross section will vary with h^{4+2n}. It is only for the inverse-square field r^{-2} that the scattering cross section is independent of h. This independence from h is a necessary condition for equality between any classical theory and its wave-mechanical counterpart.

It has been noted in connection with the derivation of Eq. (117) that the phase-shift method of dealing with scattering problems is generally valid only if the potential $U(r)$ decreases faster than $1/r$ for large values of r. The coulomb potential

$$U(r) = \frac{Zze^2}{r} \tag{153}$$

for a bare nucleus does not satisfy this requirement and therefore does not lead to the usual asymptotic form given by Eq. (115) for the radial part of the total wave function. Nevertheless, Gordon was able to show that, for the special case of the coulomb $(1/r)$ potential, the total wave function can be obtained in the form of Eq. (117), and further that this series can be summed in terms of confluent hypergeometric functions. The asymptotic result, for the scattering amplitude $f(\vartheta)$ of Eq. (109), is

$$f(\vartheta) = \frac{Zze^2}{2MV^2} \frac{1}{\sin^2 (\vartheta/2)} \tag{154}$$

which leads to the usual Rutherford value [Appendix B, Eq. (89)] for the differential cross section $|f|^2$ in the wave treatment. This result, by Gordon's method, is valid for all values of that crucial parameter $2Zz/137\beta$.

We have seen previously that the classical theory is fully valid if the charge parameter $2Zz/137\beta \gg 1$. For small values of this parameter, the uncertainty principle removed our confidence in the classical model of the collision, Eq. (82). Also the nuclear coulomb barrier was found in Eq. (99) to become appreciably transparent when $2Zz/137\beta \sim 1$. We may wonder, then, why universal validity can be claimed for Gordon's result. The answer is that Eq. (154) is the solution for the potential $U(r) = Zze^2/r$. This is a coulomb potential which extends all the way into the origin of coordinates. No inner potential well is involved. Therefore Eq. (154) can be valid even for $2Zz/137\beta \ll 1$ because barrier transmission has been *mathematically* excluded. Physically, whenever barrier transmission is conceivable, it will occur within the domain of small values of $2Zz/137\beta$; it will alter the observed scattering and may produce disintegrations as well.

e. The Born Approximation. A broadly useful approach to many types of interaction problems is an approximate method based on a perturbation method and due to Born. The method may be illustrated by applying it to the coulomb scattering problem.

If the total energy W of a particle is everywhere large compared with the potential $U(r)$, then the form of the incident wave cannot be greatly perturbed by the scattering field. Under these conditions, one can assume that each volume element $d\tau$ within the scattering field produces a scattered wavelet whose amplitude is proportional to the potential $U(r)$ at $d\tau$, and to the amplitude of the incident wave. Then it can be shown (M68) that the scattering amplitude $f(\vartheta)$ of Eq. (105) can be expressed in this approximation by the integral

$$f(\vartheta) = \frac{8\pi^2 M}{h^2} \int_0^\infty U(r) \frac{\sin \mu r}{\mu r} r^2 \, dr \tag{155}$$

where

$$\mu \equiv 2k \sin \frac{\vartheta}{2} \qquad k = \frac{2\pi}{\lambda} = 2\pi \frac{MV}{h} \tag{156}$$

If now the nuclear scattering potential is represented by the screened coulomb potential

$$U(r) = \frac{Zze^2}{r} e^{-r/d} \tag{157}$$

where d is of the order of atomic dimensions ($\sim 10^{-8}$ cm) and the exponential term is thought of as a rough representation of the screening effect of bound electrons, then the integration in Eq. (155) can be carried out. The result is

$$f(\vartheta) = \frac{8\pi^2 M}{h^2} \frac{Zze^2}{\mu^2 + 1/d^2} \tag{158}$$

Now, if we neglect $1/d^2$ in comparison with μ^2, we come to the usual Rutherford formula again.

E. J. Williams (W59) has pointed out that the domain of validity of the Born approximation always corresponds to the extreme opposite of the domain of validity of classical theory and is

$$\frac{2Zz}{137\beta} \ll 1 \tag{159}$$

Thus the Born approximation is valid for small values of Zz and for very swift particles, but not for slow particles.

f. Anomalous Scattering of Charged Particles. Charged particles of sufficiently high velocity and small charge, so that $2Zz/137\beta$ is not large, are able to penetrate a nuclear barrier such as that shown in Fig. 9, and defined by a potential

$$U(r) = U_0 \qquad \text{for } r < R \tag{160}$$

$$U(r) = \frac{Zze^2}{r} \qquad \text{for } r > R$$

The resulting scattering will be a combination of scattering by the long-range coulomb potential and scattering from the discontinuity in potential at the surface of the nucleus ($r = R$), for those particles which penetrated the coulomb barrier. Both types of scattering can take place simultaneously and coherently, so that interference terms can be expected (Chap. 2, Sec. 7).

Qualitatively, we can still express the total wave function as in Eq. (109). But now the scattering amplitude $f(\vartheta)$ includes coulomb scattering f_c and nuclear scattering f_n. The cross section becomes

$$d\sigma = |f_c + f_n|^2 \, d\Omega \tag{161}$$

and thus contains a cross term $f_c f_n$ as well as the coulomb term f_c^2 and the nuclear term f_n^2. This cross term couples, in effect, the nuclear scattering to the coulomb scattering and gives rise to observable effects even when $f_c^2 \gg f_n^2$.

When experimental deviations from Rutherford scattering were first observed, these were named *anomalous scattering*. The results are attributable to phenomena accompanying penetration of the nuclear barrier. Examples are discussed in Chaps. 2, 10, and 14.

Problems

1. Show that each term in the usual expansion of a plane wave, Eq. (76), represents the sum of a wave coming into the origin (proportional to e^{-ikr}) and a wave going out from the origin (proportional to e^{ikr}), both with magnitude of the angular momentum given by $\sqrt{l(l+1)}\,\hbar$, and with zero component of angular momentum in the direction of propagation of the plane wave. Express the $l = 1$ wave as the sum of an inbound and an outbound wave. Comment in a general way on the relative values of the amplitude and of the phase for the inbound and outbound waves.

2. Starting with Eq. (118), show that the differential cross section for elastic s-wave scattering is

$$d\sigma = \frac{\sin^2 \delta_0}{k^2}\, d\Omega$$

and that its integral σ is in agreement with Eq. (122).

3. Write the explicit expressions for the incident and the scattered waves, for s-wave scattering by a rectangular potential well, and show analytically that they do add up to Eq. (131) for the total wave.

4. Show that the scattered wave $\psi_{\text{scattered}}$ of Eq. (129) can be expressed as

$$\chi = r\psi_{\text{scattered}} = \frac{\sin \delta_0}{k_1}\, e^{i(k_1 r + \delta_0)}$$

and therefore χ can be represented in a complex plane as a vector whose absolute magnitude is $(\sin \delta_0)/k_1$, and whose phase angle is $(k_1 r + \delta_0)$.

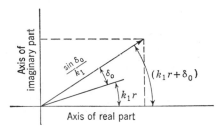

5. By application of the boundary conditions, Eqs. (140) and (141), show that the ratio of the square of the amplitude inside the well of Fig. 11 to that outside the well is given by

$$\left(\frac{B}{e^{i\delta_0}/k_1}\right)^2 = \frac{1}{1 + [(k_2^2/k_1^2) - 1]\cos^2 k_2 b}$$

Show that ordinarily this is of the order of $(k_1/k_2)^2$, if $k_2 \gg k_1$, except near the resonances $k_2 b = \pi/2,\ 3\pi/2,\ \ldots$, where the ratio of the amplitudes approaches unity.

Relativistic Relationships between Mass, Momentum, Energy, and Magnetic Rigidity

For ease of reference, we review and collect here a number of useful relationships concerning the relativistic properties of moving particles.

The rest mass of the electron is so small that the relativistic increase in the mass of an electron is 1 per cent of the rest mass for each 5 kev of kinetic energy. In almost all cases encountered in nuclear physics, the motion of electrons must be treated relativistically.

We shall use the symbol m_0 for the rest mass of the moving particle but are to understand that this refers to electrons only in those special cases where numerical values appropriate to the electron are introduced in the equations. In all the general relationships, the symbol m_0 can represent the rest mass of a meson, proton, α particle, etc.

The principal symbols needed will be:

c = velocity of light in vacuum, cm/sec
v = velocity of particle, cm/sec
$\beta = v/c$ = velocity of particle in relation to c
m_0 = rest mass of particle, g
m = mass = total mass = relativistic mass of particle
$p = mv$ = momentum of particle, g-cm/sec
m_0c = natural unit of momentum
$\eta = p/m_0c$ = momentum of particle, units of m_0c
E = kinetic energy of particle, Mev
T = kinetic energy of particle, ergs
$mc^2 = T + m_0c^2$ = total energy of particle, ergs
m_0c^2 = natural unit of energy
$W = mc^2/m_0c^2 = (T/m_0c^2) + 1$ = total energy of particle, units
of m_0c^2
B = magnetic induction, gauss
ρ = radius of curvature of path, cm
e = electron charge, electrostatic units
e/c = electron charge, electromagnetic units
ze = charge on particle
M = rest mass of particle, atomic mass units
N = Avogadro's number, on physical scale
$F = \mathsf{N}e$ = the faraday = 96,520 coulombs/(g mole)

a. Relationships between Momentum and Total Energy. We have the fundamental relativistic relationships

$$m = \frac{m_0}{(1 - \beta^2)^{\frac{1}{2}}} \tag{1}$$

$$p = mv \tag{2}$$
$$T = mc^2 - m_0c^2 \tag{3}$$

Numerous useful expressions follow from these three equations. By squaring Eq. (1) we obtain

$$m^2 \frac{c^2 - v^2}{c^2} = m_0^2$$

or $$(mc)^2 - (m_0c)^2 = (mv)^2 = p^2$$

or $$(pc)^2 = (mc^2)^2 - (m_0c^2)^2 \tag{4}$$

Equation (4) is the basis for the occasional representation of the momentum of particles in units of (pc), which has the dimensions of energy (e.g., Mev).

Writing $\eta = p/m_0c$, and $W = mc^2/m_0c^2$, we have the extremely useful general relationship

$$W^2 = \eta^2 + 1 \tag{5}$$

A right triangle serves as a mnemonic device for Eqs. (4) and (5); thus

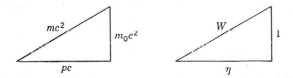

Useful forms involving β include the following

$$\beta = \frac{v}{c} = \frac{p}{mc} = \frac{\eta}{W} \tag{6}$$

$$\beta^2 = \frac{\eta^2}{1 + \eta^2} = 1 - \frac{1}{W^2} = 1 - \left(\frac{m_0}{m}\right)^2 \tag{7}$$

$$\frac{\beta^2}{1 - \beta^2} = \eta^2 = \left(\frac{T}{m_0c^2}\right)^2 \left(1 + \frac{2m_0c^2}{T}\right) \tag{8}$$

The connection between a small change in momentum and the corresponding change in energy follows by differentiation of Eq. (5) and is

$$dW = \frac{\eta}{W} d\eta = \beta \, d\eta \tag{9}$$

$$dT = m_0c^2\beta \frac{dp}{m_0c} = v \, dp \tag{10}$$

Explicit relationships between momentum and kinetic energy are obtained by combining Eqs. (3) and (4) and are

$$p = \frac{1}{c} \sqrt{T(T + 2m_0c^2)} = \frac{T}{c} \sqrt{1 + \frac{2m_0c^2}{T}} \tag{11}$$

$$T = \sqrt{(pc)^2 + (m_0c^2)^2} - m_0c^2 \tag{12}$$

The last equations show that for "particles" which have zero rest mass (photon, neutrino) the momentum is simply $p = T/c$. The relativistic mass, from Eq. (3), is $m = T/c^2$, and the velocity, from Eq. (7), is $\beta = 1$, thus

$$\left.\begin{array}{l} p = T/c \\ m = T/c^2 \\ v = c \end{array}\right\} \qquad \text{for } m_0 = 0 \tag{13}$$

The usual nonrelativistic relationships of Newtonian mechanics are contained in Eqs. (1), (2), and (3). When $\beta^2 \ll 1$, these reduce at once to the familiar $m = m_0$, $p = m_0v$, $T = m_0v^2/2$.

b. Magnetic Deflection of Relativistic Particles. The momentum of any charged particle can be measured by observing the radius of curvature ρ of the particle's path normal to a uniform magnetic field B. If the rest mass of the particle is known, its energy can be deduced from the measured momentum. We have

$$B \frac{ze}{c} v = \frac{mv^2}{\rho}$$

or

$$B\rho \frac{ze}{c} = mv = p$$

$$(B\rho)(ze) = pc = \sqrt{T(T + 2m_0c^2)} \tag{14}$$

The quantity $B\rho$ (or $H\rho$ in the older periodical literature) has dimensions of gauss-centimeter and is a direct measure of the momentum per unit charge, p/ze. Often $B\rho$ is simply called "the momentum," and less frequently the *magnetic rigidity*.

Numerical factors for converting a measured value of the "momentum" $B\rho$ gauss-cm into the corresponding kinetic energy E in Mev may be developed for use with Eq. (5). Using Eq. (14), we have in general

$$\eta \equiv \frac{p}{m_0c} = B\rho \frac{ze}{m_0c^2} \tag{15}$$

For heavy particles (protons, deuterons, α rays, etc.) it is convenient to express the rest mass m_0 as M amu. Then, as in Eq. (4.5) of Chap. 3,

$$m_0c^2 = \frac{Mc^2}{N} \tag{16}$$

and with $eN = Fc/10$, as in Eq. (4.6) of Chap. 3, we have

$$\frac{ze}{m_0c^2} = \frac{zeN}{Mc^2} = \frac{z\,F}{10Mc} \tag{17}$$

so that finally

$$\eta = B\rho \frac{zF}{10Mc} = B\rho \left(3.2196 \times 10^{-7} \frac{z}{M} \right) \tag{18}$$

The connection between the kinetic energy T in ergs and E in Mev is given by the fundamental electrostatic relationship

$$T = e(10^6 E) \frac{10^8}{c} = 10^{14} E \frac{e}{c} \qquad \text{ergs} \tag{19}$$

where we have used the identity

$$1 \text{ volt} = \frac{10^8}{c} \text{ statvolts} (\simeq \tfrac{1}{300} \text{ statvolts}) \tag{20}$$

In order to evaluate W, we need a general relationship for T/m_0c^2. With m_0 expressed as M amu, this becomes

$$\frac{T}{m_0 c^2} = 10^{14} E \frac{e}{c} \frac{\mathsf{N}}{Mc^2} = E \frac{10^{13} F}{Mc^2} \tag{21}$$

$$= E \frac{1.0739 \times 10^{-3}}{M} \tag{22}$$

The most general relationship between $B\rho$ and E is then obtained by writing Eq. (5) as

$$\frac{T}{m_0 c^2} + 1 \equiv W = (\eta^2 + 1)^{\frac{1}{2}} \tag{23}$$

and substituting Eqs. (18) and (22), to obtain

$$E \frac{10^{13} F}{Mc^2} + 1 = \left[\left(B\rho \frac{z F}{10Mc} \right)^2 + 1 \right]^{\frac{1}{2}} \tag{24}$$

Low-energy Heavy Particles. For protons, α rays, etc., whose kinetic energy is small compared with their rest energy, that is, $T \ll m_0 c^2$, hence $\eta^2 \ll 1$, simple relationships between E and $B\rho$ may be obtained by expanding the right-hand side of Eq. (23), thus

$$\frac{T}{m_0 c^2} + 1 = 1 + \tfrac{1}{2}\eta^2 - \tfrac{1}{8}\eta^4 + \cdots$$

$$\frac{T}{m_0 c^2} = \tfrac{1}{2}\eta^2 (1 - \tfrac{1}{4}\eta^2 + \cdots) \tag{25}$$

Utilizing Eqs. (18) and (21), Eq. (25) becomes, for low-energy particles,

$$E \frac{10^{13} F}{Mc^2} = \tfrac{1}{2}(B\rho)^2 \left(\frac{z F}{10Mc} \right)^2 (1 - \tfrac{1}{4}\eta^2 + \cdots)$$

$$E = (B\rho)^2 \frac{z^2}{M} \left(\frac{F}{2 \times 10^{15}} \right) (1 - \tfrac{1}{4}\eta^2 + \cdots) \tag{26}$$

$$E = (B\rho)^2 \frac{z^2}{M} (4.8260 \times 10^{-11})(1 - \tfrac{1}{4}\eta^2 + \cdots) \tag{27}$$

where the final parentheses contain the small relativity correction term, $\eta^2/4 \simeq \frac{1}{2}(T/m_0 c^2)$, while all other factors are as they would appear in nonrelativistic electrodynamics. The relativistic correction is about 0.1 per cent for 2-Mev protons, 4-Mev deuterons, or 7-Mev α particles.

In applying Eq. (24) or (27) to heavy particles, recall that M is the mass of the *ion*, not of its corresponding neutral atom. The appropriate number of electron masses (0.000 549 amu) must be subtracted from the neutral atomic masses given in Table 5.1 of Chap. 3. Thus the proton mass is $M = 1.008\ 142 - 0.000\ 549 = 1.007\ 593$ amu, and the α-ray mass is $M = 4.003\ 873 - 0.001\ 098 = 4.002\ 775$ amu.

When the relativistic correction is ignored, Eq. (27) gives, with E in Mev and $B\rho$ in gauss-centimeters,

for protons
$$E = \left(\frac{B\rho}{1.445 \times 10^5}\right)^2 \tag{28}$$

for deuterons
$$E = \left(\frac{B\rho}{2.043 \times 10^5}\right)^2 \tag{29}$$

for α rays
$$E = \left(\frac{B\rho}{1.440 \times 10^5}\right)^2 \tag{30}$$

Electrons. Electrons are "always" relativistic. To obtain the relationship between E and $B\rho$, we could use Eq. (24), with $M = 0.000\ 549$ amu. However, the charge e and the specific charge $(e/c)/m_0$ of the electron are well known experimentally, and it is instructive to utilize these directly measured quantities. We adopt from the 1952 values of the physical constants by DuMond and Cohen (D44)

$$e = (4.802\ 88 \pm 0.000\ 21) \times 10^{-10}\ \text{esu}$$
$$\frac{e/c}{m_0} = (1.758\ 88 \pm 0.000\ 05) \times 10^7\ \text{emu/g} \tag{31}$$
$$c = (2.997\ 929 \pm 0.000\ 008) \times 10^{10}\ \text{cm/sec}$$

Then, for electrons, Eqs. (15) and (31) give for the momentum parameters

$$\eta = B\rho \left(\frac{e/c}{m_0}\right)\frac{1}{c} = \frac{B\rho}{1,704.4} \tag{32}$$

where $B\rho$ is in gauss-centimeters. The energy parameters for electrons, obtained directly from Eqs. (19) and (31), are

$$\frac{T}{m_0 c^2} = 10^{14} E \frac{e}{c}\frac{1}{m_0 c^2} = 10^{14} E \left(\frac{e/c}{m_0}\right)\frac{1}{c^2}$$
$$= \frac{E}{0.510\ 98} \tag{33}$$

where E is in Mev. Finally, for electrons of any energy,

$$W^2 = \eta^2 + 1$$

becomes
$$\left(\frac{E}{0.510\ 98} + 1\right)^2 = \left(\frac{B\rho}{1,704}\right)^2 + 1 \tag{34}$$

where E is in Mev and $B\rho$ is in gauss-centimeters. Figure 1 is a convenient plot of E vs. $B\rho$ over the energy domain from 0 to 35 Mev. The inset figure shows the electron velocity, as $\beta = v/c$, for $E = 0$ to 1 Mev. Tables relating E, $B\rho$, β, and η for electrons from 0 to 10 Mev are included in the National Bureau of Standards "Tables for the Analysis of β Spectra" (N5).

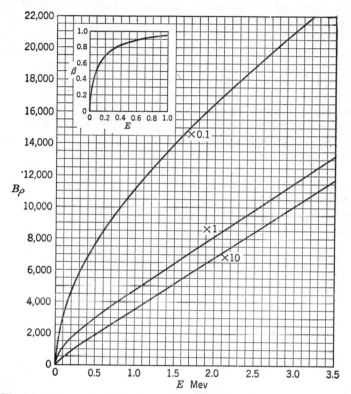

Fig. 1 The kinetic energy E of electrons in Mev vs. the momentum $B\rho$ in gauss-centimeters, as given by Eq. (34). Use the coordinates as shown for the center curve, marked ($\times 1$). For the upper curve ($\times 0.1$) multiply *both* coordinates by 0.1. The lower curve gives the high-energy domain; multiply *both* coordinate scales by 10. Beyond the maximum plotted value of 35 Mev, it is sufficiently accurate to write Eq. (34) as $E = 3 \times 10^{-4} B\rho$. The insert shows the electron velocity $\beta = v/c$ for electrons up to 1 Mev, from Eq. (6).

The numerical value for the rest energy of the electron,

$$m_0c^2 = 0.510\ 98 \text{ Mev}$$

which is implicit in Eq. (33) is identical with the value derived in Chap. 3, Eq. (4.11). But it is important to note the different bases on which the two calculations have been carried through. Equation (33) utilizes only the specific charge $(e/c)/m_0$ of the electron, and the velocity of light c. In Chap. 3 we used the velocity of light, the faraday F, and the ratio of the electron mass m_0 to the mass of the proton, as determined from optical spectroscopy. The two results are the same, within their respective probable errors, because of the use of a self-consistent set of numerical values of the fundamental physical constants, such as those developed by Birge, DuMond and Cohen, and others.

It should be especially noted that the numerical relationship between measured values of $B\rho$ gauss-cm and computed values of E Mev, Eq. (34), depends only on the numerical values adopted for c and for the specific charge $(e/c)/m_0$. Especially *the relationship is independent of the absolute charge e on the electron*. Recall that in 1935 (B24) an increase of about 0.6 per cent (from 4.77 to 4.80 $\times$ 10^{-10} esu) in the most probable value of e was adopted. This change in e caused a corresponding increase of 0.6 per cent in the numerical value of m_0c^2 in ergs, and in the ratio between ergs and Mev [Chap. 3, Eq. (4.4)]. On the other hand, it caused no change of the numerical value of m_0c^2 in Mev, nor of the relationship between $B\rho$ and E, because these depend only on c and on $(e/c)/m_0$, for which the most probable numerical values have been relatively stable for a long time. Some of the fundamental α-ray and β-ray energy standards (B121, E9, B122) of nuclear physics were established prior to 1935. Those which depended on accurate measurements of $B\rho$, but were reported in Mev, remain unchanged by the 1935 revision of e.

Some Basic Atomic and Nuclear Constants

In accord with current practice in the periodical literature of nuclear physics, cgs units are employed throughout. The numerical values cited are mainly from the compilation of DuMond and Cohen (D44). In every case, the number of significant figures retained here is such that the 1953 uncertainty is not more than unity in the last digit.

Quantity	Symbols and formulation	Numerical value and units
Classical electron radius	$r_0 = e^2/m_0 c^2$	$= 2.818 \times 10^{-13}$ cm
Fine-structure constant	$\alpha = 2\pi e^2/hc$	$= 1/137.04$
Compton wavelength of electron	$\lambda_c = h/m_0 c$ $= 2\pi r_0/\alpha$	$= 2.4262 \times 10^{-10}$ cm
Radius of first Bohr orbit of hydrogen atom	$a_{\mathrm{H}} = h^2/4\pi^2 e^2 m_0$ $= r_0/\alpha^2$ $= \lambda_c/2\pi\alpha$	$= 0.52917 \times 10^{-8}$ cm
Radius of n shell (screening neglected)	$a = a_{\mathrm{H}}(n^2/Z)$	
Bohr orbital velocity (screening neglected)	$u = 2\pi e^2 Z/hn$ $= \alpha c(Z/n)$	
Ionization energy of normal hydrogen atom	$I_0 = 2\pi^2 m_0 e^4/h^2$ $= e^2/2a_{\mathrm{H}}$ $= m_0 c^2(\alpha^2/2)$	$= 13.60$ ev
Ionization energy of n shell (screening neglected)	$I = I_0(Z^2/n^2)$	
Total electron binding energy of an atom [Thomas-Fermi model with empirical coefficient (F57)]	$B_e(Z)$	$= 15.73 Z^{\frac{7}{3}}$ ev
Thomson electron cross section	$_e\sigma = (8\pi/3)r_0^2$	$= 0.6652 \times 10^{-24}$ cm^2 $\simeq \frac{2}{3}$ barn

Quantity	Symbols and formulation	Numerical value and units
Bohr magneton	$\mu_\beta = eh/4\pi m_0 c$	$= 9.273 \times 10^{-21}$ erg/gauss $= 5.788 \times 10^{-9}$ ev/gauss
Nuclear magneton	$\mu_M = eh/4\pi M_p c$	$= 5.050 \times 10^{-24}$ erg/gauss $= 3.152 \times 10^{-12}$ ev/gauss
Ratio of proton mass to electron mass	M_p/m_0	$= 1,836.1$
Rest energy of the electron	$m_0 c^2$	$= 0.5110$ Mev
Electron rest mass	m_0	$= 0.5488 \times 10^{-3}$ amu $= 9.108 \times 10^{-28}$ g
Electron charge Specific electron charge	e $(e/c)/m_0$	$= 4.803 \times 10^{-10}$ esu $\;= 1.60206 \times 10^{-19} C$ $= 1.7589 \times 10^7$ emu/g
Velocity of light in vacuum	c	$= 2.99793 \times 10^{10}$ cm/sec
Planck constant	h $\hbar = h/2\pi$ $\hbar$ $\hbar c$	$= 6.625 \times 10^{-27}$ erg-sec $= 1.0544 \times 10^{-27}$ erg-sec $= 0.6582 \times 10^{-15}$ ev-sec $= 1.9732 \times 10^{-11}$ Mev-cm
Avogadro's number, on physical scale ($O^{16} = 16$)	N	$= 6.025 \times 10^{23}$ atoms/mole
Faraday (physical scale)	$F = Ne$	$= 2.8936 \times 10^{14}$ esu/mole $= 96,520$ coulombs/mole
Mass of hydrogen atom	M_H	$= 1.008142$ amu
Mass of neutron	M_n	$= 1.008982$ amu
Neutron-hydrogen mass difference	$(M_n - M_H)$	$= 0.782$ Mev
Binding energy of deuteron	B_d	$= 2.225 \pm 0.002$ Mev
Wavelength of photons having energy $h\nu = E$	$\lambda = c/\nu = hc/E$	$= \dfrac{0.012397}{E(\text{Mev})} \times 10^{-8}$ cm $= \dfrac{12.372}{E(\text{Mev})}$ X.U.
De Broglie wavelength of neutrons having energy $E \ll M_n c^2$	$\lambda = h/p$	$= \dfrac{2.8600 \times 10^{-9}}{[E(\text{ev})]^{\frac{1}{2}}}$ cm
Mass-energy conversion factors	1 amu 1 Mev 1 ev	$= 931.16$ Mev $= 0.001074$ amu $= 1.6020 \times 10^{-12}$ erg

$k = 1.38 \times 10^{-16}$ erg deg^{-1}

APPENDIX F

Table of the Elements

PERIODIC ARRANGEMENT OF THE ELEMENTS

Group / Period	O	I	II	III	IV	V	VI	VII	VIII		
1		1 H									
2	2 He	3 Li	4 Be	5 B	6 C	7 N	8 O	9 F			
3	10 Ne	11 Na	12 Mg	13 Al	14 Si	15 P	16 S	17 Cl			
4	18 A	19 K	20 Ca	21 Sc	22 Ti	23 V	24 Cr	25 Mn	26 Fe	27 Co	28 Ni
		29 Cu	30 Zn	31 Ga	32 Ge	33 As	34 Se	35 Br			
5	36 Kr	37 Rb	38 Sr	39 Y	40 Zr	41 Nb	42 Mo	43 Tc	44 Ru	45 Rh	46 Pd
		47 Ag	48 Cd	49 In	50 Sn	51 Sb	52 Te	53 I			
6	54 Xe	55 Cs	56 Ba	57–71 La†	72 Hf	73 Ta	74 W	75 Re	76 Os	77 Ir	78 Pt
		79 Au	80 Hg	81 Tl	82 Pb	83 Bi	84 Po	85 At			
7	86 Rn	87 Fr	88 Ra	89– Ac‡							

6 † Lanthanide series, rare earths	57 La	58 Ce	59 Pr	60 Nd	61 Pm	62 Sm	63 Eu	64 Gd	65 Tb	66 Dy	67 Ho	68 Er	69 Tm	70 Yb	71 Lu
7 ‡ Actinide series	89 Ac	90 Th	91 Pa	92 U	93 Np	94 Pu	95 Am	96 Cm	97 Bk	98 Cf	99 E	100 Fm	101 Mv	102	

TABLE OF THE CHEMICAL-SCALE ATOMIC WEIGHTS

Element	Symbol	Atomic number	Atomic weight†	Element	Symbol	Atomic number	Atomic weight
Actinium	Ac	89	227	Mendelevium	Mv	101	[256]
Aluminum	Al	13	26.98	Mercury	Hg	80	200.61
Americium	Am	95	[243]‡	Molybdenum	Mo	42	95.95
Antimony	Sb	51	121.76	Neodymium	Nd	60	144.27
Argon	A	18	39.944	Neptunium	Np	93	[237]
Arsenic	As	33	74.91	Neon	Ne	10	20.183
Astatine	At	85	[210]	Nickel	Ni	28	58.69
Barium	Ba	56	137.36	Niobium			
Berkelium	Bk	97	[249]	(Columbium)	Nb	41	92.91
Beryllium	Be	4	9.013	Nitrogen	N	7	14.008
Bismith	Bi	83	209.00	Osmium	Os	76	190.2
Boron	B	5	10.82	Oxygen	O	8	16
Bromine	Br	35	79.916	Palladium	Pd	46	106.7
Cadmium	Cd	48	112.41	Phosphorus	P	15	30.975
Calcium	Ca	20	40.08	Platinum	Pt	78	195.23
Californium	Cf	98	[249]	Plutonium	Pu	94	[242]
Carbon	C	6	12.011	Polonium	Po	84	210
Cerium	Ce	58	140.13	Potassium	K	19	39.100
Cesium	Cs	55	132.91	Praseodymium	Pr	59	140.92
Chlorine	Cl	17	35.457	Promethium	Pm	61	[145]
Chromium	Cr	24	52.01	Protoactinium	Pa	91	231
Cobalt	Co	27	58.94	Radium	Ra	88	226.05
Columbium				Radon	Rn	86	222
(see Niobium)				Rhenium	Re	75	186.31
Copper	Cu	29	63.54	Rhodium	Rh	45	102.91
Curium	Cm	96	[245]	Rubidium	Rb	37	85.48
Dysprosium	Dy	66	162.46	Ruthenium	Ru	44	101.1
Einsteinium	E	99	[254]	Samarium	Sm	62	150.43
Erbium	Er	68	167.2	Scandium	Sc	21	44.96
Europium	Eu	63	152.0	Selenium	Se	34	78.96
Fermium	Fm	100	[253]	Silicon	Si	14	28.09
Fluorine	F	9	19.00	Silver	Ag	47	107.880
Francium	Fr	87	[223]	Sodium	Na	11	22.991
Gadolinium	Gd	64	156.9	Strontium	Sr	38	87.63
Gallium	Ga	31	69.72	Sulfur	S	16	32.066
Germanium	Ge	32	72.60	Tantalum	Ta	73	180.95
Gold	Au	79	197.0	Technetium	Tc	43	[99]
Hafnium	Hf	72	178.6	Tellurium	Te	52	127.61
Helium	He	2	4.003	Terbium	Tb	65	158.93
Holmium	Ho	67	164.94	Thallium	Tl	81	204.39
Hydrogen	H	1	1.0080	Thorium	Th	90	232.05
Indium	In	49	114.76	Thulium	Tm	69	168.94
Iodine	I	53	126.91	Tin	Sn	50	118.70
Iridium	Ir	77	192.2	Titanium	Ti	22	47.90
Iron	Fe	26	55.85	Tungsten	W	74	183.92
Krypton	Kr	36	83.80	Uranium	U	92	238.07
Lanthanum	La	57	138.92	Vanadium	V	23	50.95
Lead	Pb	82	207.21	Xenon	Xe	54	131.3
Lithium	Li	3	6.940	Ytterbium	Yb	70	173.04
Lutetium	Lu	71	174.99	Yttrium	Y	39	88.92
Magnesium	Mg	12	24.32	Zinc	Zn	30	65.38
Manganese	Mn	25	54.94	Zirconium	Zr	40	91.22

† Atomic weights are from the Committee on Atomic Weights of the American Chemical Society, *J. Am. Chem. Soc.*, **76**: 2033 (1954).

‡ Atomic weights in brackets represent the mass number of the most stable known isotope.

Some Useful Inefficient Statistics†

Each body of experimental data, or "sample of the infinite population of data," contains a certain maximum amount of information. This information can be completely extracted from the sample of data by the use of conventional methods of statistical analysis. Thus, for a normal distribution of n measured values of x, the best possible estimate of the true mean m and standard deviation σ is obtained by using the "efficient" statistics (Chap. 26)

$$m \simeq \bar{x} \equiv \frac{1}{n} \sum x \quad \text{and} \quad \sigma^2 \simeq \frac{1}{n-1} \sum (x - \bar{x})^2$$

Situations arise when it is desirable to use an "inefficient" statistic, i.e., one which removes only part of the maximum amount of information, but which does it simply and much more quickly. Occasions also will arise where more information can be obtained in a given time, and for a given effort, by the "inefficient" analysis of larger samples of data. The degree of "inefficiency" has been quantified for a number of simple statistics. A statistic having an efficiency of, say, 0.64 is one which removes from n measurements only the amount of statistical information contained in $0.64n$ measurements.

1. *Macrostatistics* $(n > 100)$

a. Estimates of the Mean of a Large Sample $(n > 100)$ **Drawn from a Symmetrical Population.** 1. The median value (50-per cent point) is an estimate of the true mean which has an efficiency of 0.64, i.e., the same accuracy as the mean calculated from 64 per cent of the data. Thus 36 per cent of the information in the data is ignored if the median is taken as representing the mean.

2. The average of the two observations which are 29 per cent of the way in from the upper and lower extremes of the data (the 29- and the

---

† F. Mosteller, On Some Useful Inefficient Statistics, *Ann. Math. Statistics*, **17**: 377 (1946).

W. J. Dixon and F. J. Massey, Jr., "Introduction to Statistical Analysis," Chaps. 15–17, McGraw-Hill Book Company, Inc., New York, 1951.

G. W. Snedecor, "Statistical Methods," p. 98, 4th ed., Iowa State College Press, Ames, Iowa, 1946.

P. B. Patnaik, Mean Range as an Estimator of Variance, *Biometrika*, **37**: 78 (1950).

71-per cent points) is an estimate which has the same accuracy as the mean calculated from 81 per cent of the observations. Thus this average of two selected observations contains 81 per cent of the information available for an estimate of the mean of a large sample.

3. The more elaborate cases have been worked out also. For example, if the mean is to be estimated from the average of three individual readings, then the loss of information is minimized (and equals 12 per cent) if the average of the 20-, 50-, and 80-per cent points is chosen.

b. Estimate of the Standard Deviation for a Large Sample ($n > 100$) **Drawn from an Approximately Normal Population.** About 65 per cent of the information contained in the data is utilized in the simple estimate

$$\sigma \simeq \frac{(\text{93-per cent point}) - (\text{7-per cent point})}{3}$$

This approximation is equivalent to noticing that in a normal distribution 86 per cent of the data fall within $m \pm 1.5\sigma$.

2. *Microstatistics* ($n \le 10$)

a. Estimates of the Mean Value. 1. The *median* (middle value when n is odd; average of the two middle values when n is even) has an efficiency of ≥ 0.64 for all n. The median is a more efficient statistic than the *mid-range* (average of the largest and the smallest readings) for all n except 3 and 5. Tables are given by Dixon and Massey, p. 238.

2. For $n = 7$ to 10 (and probably greater) the average of the third term from each end has an efficiency of about 0.84.

3. *Example:* 44, 48, 52, 60, 61, 63, 66, 69 ($n = 8$)

True mean $= 57.88$

Median $= \dfrac{60 + 61}{2} = 60.5$

Mid-range $= \dfrac{44 + 69}{2} = 56.5$

Average of third terms $= \dfrac{52 + 63}{2} = 57.5$

b. Estimates of the Standard Deviation for a Small Sample. For $n \sim 2$ to 20 an estimate of σ can be based simply on the range.

Range $\equiv$ (largest reading) $-$ (smallest reading)

$$\sigma \simeq \sqrt{\frac{\Sigma(x - \bar{x})^2}{n - 1}} \simeq \frac{\text{range}}{\sqrt{n}}$$

The efficiency falls from 99 per cent for $n = 3$ to about 85 per cent at $n = 10$. Snedecor gives tables for these denominators, but $\sqrt{n}$ is a very good approximation for $n \le 10$. For $n > 10$, the values to use in place of $\sqrt{n}$ are:

n	10	15	20	30	50	100
Range/σ	3.08	3.47	3.73	4.09	4.50	5.02

Patnaik has shown that the relative efficiency of range as an estimator of standard deviation decreases as n increases. In practice, when $n > 12$, it is best to divide the data into a number of equal groups each containing about seven or eight observations and to use the average of the ranges of these groups.

c. Estimate of the Standard Error (Standard Deviation of the Mean Value) for a Small Sample.

$$\sigma_{\bar{x}} = \frac{\sigma}{\sqrt{n}} = \sqrt{\frac{\Sigma(x - \bar{x})^2}{n(n - 1)}}$$

$$\simeq \frac{\text{range}}{n}$$

d. Estimate of Chi-square for Small Samples from Poisson Distributions. There is no known literature on this.

$$\chi^2 = \frac{1}{\bar{x}} \Sigma(x - \bar{x})^2 = \frac{n\sigma^2}{\bar{x}} \simeq \frac{(\text{range})^2}{\text{mean}}$$

e. Examples. As an illustration, analyze the Geiger-Müller counter data of Chap. 27, Table 4.3.

$$\bar{x} \simeq \text{median} = 224$$

$$\sigma \simeq \frac{\text{range}}{\sqrt{n}} = \frac{248 - 209}{\sqrt{7}} = \frac{39}{2.65} = 14.8$$

$$\sigma_{\bar{x}} \simeq \frac{\text{range}}{n} = \frac{39}{7} = 5.6$$

$$\chi^2 \simeq \frac{(\text{range})^2}{\text{mean}} \simeq \frac{(39)^2}{224} = 6.8$$

Then $F = n - 1 = 6$, and $P \simeq 0.3$.

These results are compared with those obtained from the corresponding efficient statistics in the following table. The results are seen to be compatible.

	$\bar{x}$	σ	$\sigma_{\bar{x}}$	χ^2	P
Efficient statistics.........	227	12.8	4.9	4.4	0.6
Inefficient statistics.......	224	14.8	5.6	6.8	0.3

When analyzed in the same way, the data of Table 4.4, Chap. 27, give

	$\bar{x}$	σ	$\sigma_{\bar{x}}$	χ^2	P
Efficient statistics........	244	5.3	2.2	0.58	0.99
Inefficient statistics......	244	5.7	2.3	0.8	0.98

These inefficient statistics are so simple that they should be used routinely for the preliminary appraisal of all laboratory data.

Bibliography

A1   P. H. Abelson: *Phys. Rev.*, **56**: 753 (1939). [Chap. 1, Sec. 4]

A2   R. K. Adair: *Revs. Mod. Phys.*, **22**: 249 (1950). [Chap. 10, Sec. 3; Chap. 14, Sec. 1]

A3   R. K. Adair: *Phys. Rev.*, **86**: 155 (1952). [Chap. 2, Sec. 7]

A4   R. K. Adair: *Phys. Rev.*, **87**: 1041 (1952). [Chap. 12, Sec. 1]

A5   R. K. Adair: *Phys. Rev.*, **94**: 737L (1954). [Chap. 14, Sec. 2]

A6   R. K. Adair, A. Okazaki, and M. Walt: *Phys. Rev.*, **89**: 1165 (1953). [Chap. 10, Sec. 6]

A7   G. D. Adams: *Phys. Rev.*, **74**: 1707 (1948). [Chap. 24, Sec. 2]

A8   N. I. Adams, Jr.: *Phys. Rev.*, **44**: 651 (1933). [Chap. 28, Sec. 6]

A9   F. Adler, P. Huber, and F. Metzger: *Helv. Phys. Acta*, **20**: 234 (1947). [Chap. 22, Sec. 4]

A10   F. Ajzenberg and T. Lauritsen: *Revs. Mod. Phys.*, **24**: 321 (1952). [Chap. 6, Secs. 1, 9; Chap. 10, Sec. 6; Chap. 11, Sec. 4; Chap. 12, Secs. 1, 2; Chap. 13, Secs. 1, 4]

A11   R. D. Albert and C. S. Wu: *Phys. Rev.*, **74**: 847L (1948). [Chap. 17, Sec. 3]

A12   L. T. Aldrich and A. O. Nier: *Phys. Rev.*, **74**: 1590 (1948). [Chap. 7, Introd.]

A12a W. P. Alford and D. R. Hamilton: *Phys. Rev.*, **95**: 1351L (1954). [Chap. 17, Sec. 2]

A13   A. I. Alichanow, A. I. Alichanian, and M. S. Kosodaew: *Nature*, **136**: 475 (1935); *J. phys. radium*, **7**: 163 (1936). [Chap. 6, Sec. 5]

A14   A. I. Alichanow and B. S. Dzelepov: *Compt. rend. acad. sci. U.R.S.S.*, **20**: 115 (1938). [Chap. 24, Sec. 2]

A15   J. S. Allen: *Am. J. Phys.*, **16**: 451 (1948). [Chap. 17, Sec. 2]

A16   J. S. Allen, H. R. Paneth, and A. H. Morrish: *Phys. Rev.*, **75**: 570 (1949). [Chap. 17, Sec. 2]

A17   S. K. Allison and S. D. Warshaw: *Revs. Mod. Phys.*, **25**: 779 (1953). [Chap. 22, Sec. 2]

A18   J. C. Allred: *Phys. Rev.*, **84**: 695 (1951). [Chap. 10, Sec. 6]

A19   J. C. Allred, A. H. Armstrong, and L. Rosen: *Phys. Rev.*, **91**: 90 (1953). [Chap. 10, Secs. 3, 6]

A20   R. A. Alpher and R. C. Herman: *Revs. Mod. Phys.*, **22**: 153 (1950); erratum, **22**: 406 (1950). [Chap. 8, Sec. 2]

A21   R. A. Alpher and R. C. Herman: *Ann. Rev. Nuclear Sci.*, **2**: 1 (1953). [Chap. 8, Sec. 2]

A22   L. W. Alvarez: *Phys. Rev.*, **52**: 134L (1937). [Chap. 1, Sec. 4]

A23   L. W. Alvarez: *Phys. Rev.*, **54**: 486 (1938). [Chap. 1, Sec. 4; Chap. 6, Sec. 5]

A24   L. W. Alvarez and F. Bloch: *Phys. Rev.*, **57**: 111 (1940). [Chap. 4, Sec. 3]

A25   L. W. Alvarez and R. Cornog: *Phys. Rev.*, **56**: 379L (1939). [Chap. 3, Sec. 3]

A26   L. W. Alvarez and R. Cornog: *Phys. Rev.*, **56**: 613L (1939). [Chap. 7, Introd., Sec. 7]

A27   E. Amaldi, O. D'Agostino, E. Fermi, B. Pontecorvo, F. Rasetti, and E. Segrè: *Proc. Roy. Soc.* (*London*), **A149**: 522 (1935). [Chap. 14, Introd.]

A28   C. D. Anderson: *Science*, **76**: 238 (1932); *Phys. Rev.*, **43**: 491 (1933). [Chap. 13, Sec. 3]

A29   C. D. Anderson, R. A. Millikan, S. H. Neddermeyer, and W. Pickering: *Phys. Rev.*, **45**: 352 (1934). [Chap. 18, Introd.]

A30   C. D. Anderson and S. H. Neddermeyer: *Phys. Rev.*, **43**: 1034L (1933). [Chap. 13, Sec. 3; Chap. 24, Sec. 2]

A31   W. R. Arnold and A. Roberts: *Phys. Rev.*, **71**: 878 (1947). [Chap. 4, Sec. 3]

A32   W. A. Aron, B. G. Hoffman, and F. C. Williams: AECU-663 (UCRL-121), 1949. [Chap. 22, Sec. 3]

A33   W. J. Arrol, R. B. Jacobi, and F. A. Paneth: *Nature*, **149**: 235 (1942). [Chap. 8, Sec. 2]

A34   F. Asaro and I. Perlman: *Phys. Rev.*, **91**: 763L (1953). [Chap. 16, Sec. 4]

A34a   F. Asaro and I. Perlman: *Revs. Mod. Phys.*, **26**: 456 (1954). [Chap. 3, Sec. 5]

A35   F. W. Aston: *Nature*, **123**: 313 (1929). [Chap. 7, Sec. 6]

A36   F. W. Aston: "Mass Spectra and Isotopes," Edward Arnold & Co., London, 1933. [Introd.; Chap. 9, Secs. 1, 2]

A37   F. W. Aston: "Mass Spectra and Isotopes," Longmans, Green & Co., Inc., New York, 1942. [Chap. 3, Secs. 1, 3]

A38   G. H. Aston: *Proc. Cambridge Phil. Soc.*, **23**: 935 (1927). [Chap. 21, Sec. 2]

B1   G. E. Bacon and K. Lonsdale: *Repts. Progr. in Phys.*, **16**: 1 (1953). [Chap. 10, Sec. 3]

B2   R. H. Bacon: *Am. J. Phys.*, **8**: 354 (1940). [Chap. 12, Sec. 2]

B3   K. T. Bainbridge: *Phys. Rev.*, **44**: 123L (1933). [Chap. 3, Sec. 4]

B4   K. T. Bainbridge in E. Segrè (ed.): "Experimental Nuclear Physics," vol. 1, pt. V, John Wiley & Sons, Inc., New York, 1953. [Chap. 3, Secs. 3, 5; Chap. 7, Sec. 1; Chap. 9, Sec. 3; Chap. 11, Sec. 3]

B5   K. T. Bainbridge and E. B. Jordan: *Phys. Rev.*, **50**: 282 (1936). [Chap. 3, Sec. 3]

B6   K. T. Bainbridge and A. O. Nier: *Natl. Research Council (U.S.) Prelim. Rept.* 9, 1950. [Chap. 7, Secs. 1, 5]

B7   C. J. Bakker and E. Segrè: *Phys. Rev.*, **81**: 489 (1951). [Chap. 22, Secs. 2, 4]

B8   E. M. Baldwin: *Phys. Rev.*, **83**: 495 (1951). [Chap. 10, Sec. 9]

B9   A. Barber and F. C. Champion: *Proc. Roy. Soc. (London)*, **A168**: 159 (1938). [Chap. 21, Sec. 3]

B10   J. Bardeen and C. H. Townes: *Phys. Rev.*, **73**: 97 (1948). [Chap. 4, Sec. 5; Chap. 5, Sec. 3]

B11   W. H. Barkas: *Phys. Rev.*, **75**: 1109L (1949). [Chap. 2, Sec. 3]

B12   C. G. Barkla: *Phil. Mag.*, **21**: 648 (1911). [Introd.; Chap. 1, Sec. 2]

B13   H. H. Barschall: *Am. J. Phys.*, **18**: 535 (1950). [Chap. 12, Sec. 2]

B14   H. H. Barschall: *Phys. Rev.*, **86**: 431L (1952). [Chap. 14, Sec. 2]

B15   H. H. Barschall, C. K. Bockelman, and L. W. Seagondollar: *Phys. Rev.*, **73**: 659 (1948). [Chap. 14, Sec. 2]

B15a   H. H. Barschall and J. L. Powell: *Phys. Rev.*, **96**: 713 (1954). [Chap. 12, Sec. 2]

B16   G. A. Bartholomew and B. B. Kinsey: *Phys. Rev.*, **90**: 355A (1953). [Chap. 14, Introd.]

B17   M. S. Bartlett: *Proc. Roy. Soc. (London)*, **A154**: 124 (1936); *Phil. Mag.*, **44**: 249 (1953). [Chap. 28, Sec. 5]

B18   G. W. Barton, Jr., H. P. Robinson, and I. Perlman: *Phys. Rev.*, **81**: 208 (1951). [Chap. 1, Sec. 4]

B19   H. Bateman: *Phil. Mag.*, **20**: 704 (1910). [Chap. 26, Sec. 1]

B20   H. Bateman: *Proc. Cambridge Phil. Soc.*, **15**: 423 (1910). [Chap. 15, Introd., Sec. 8]

B21   J. W. Beams: *Revs. Mod. Phys.*, **10**: 245 (1938).   [Chap. 7, Sec. 8]

B22   J. W. Beams: *Repts. Progr. in Phys.*, **8**: 31 (1942).   [Chap. 7, Sec. 8]

B23   J. W. Beams and C. Skarstrom: *Phys. Rev.*, **56**: 266 (1939).   [Chap. 7, Sec. 8]

B24   J. A. Bearden: *Phys. Rev.*, **48**: 385 (1935).   [Appendix D]

B25   H. Becquerel: *Compt. rend.*, **122**: 420, 501 (1896).   [Introd.]

B26   Y. Beers: *Rev. Sci. Instr.*, **13**: 72 (1942).   [Chap. 28, Sec. 1]

B27   C. E. Behrens: *Am. J. Phys.*, **11**: 135 (1943).†   [Introd.]

B28   G. I. Bell: *Phys. Rev.*, **90**: 548 (1953).   [Chap. 22, Sec. 6]

B29   R. E. Bell and L. G. Elliott: *Phys. Rev.*, **79**: 282 (1950).   [Chap. 3, Sec. 4]

B30   R. E. Bell and R. L. Graham: *Phys. Rev.*, **86**: 212 (1952).   [Chap. 3, Sec. 4]

B31   R. S. Bender, F. C. Shoemaker, S. G. Kaufmann, and G. M. B. Bouricius: *Phys. Rev.*, **76**: 273 (1949).   [Chap. 14, Sec. 1]

B32   M. Benedict and C. Williams: "Engineering Developments in the Gaseous Diffusion Process," National Nuclear Energy Series, div. II, vol. 16, McGraw-Hill Book Company, Inc., New York, 1949.   [Chap. 7, Sec. 8]

B33   W. E. Bennett: *Proc. Roy. Soc. (London)*, **A155**: 419 (1936).   [Chap. 22, Sec. 5]

B34   W. E. Bennett, T. W. Bonner, C. E. Mandeville, and B. E. Watt: *Phys. Rev.*, **70**: 882 (1946).   [Chap. 6, Sec. 5]

B35   P. G. Bergmann: "Introduction to the Theory of Relativity," Prentice-Hall, Inc., New York, 1942.   [Chap. 1, Sec. 3]

B36   E. M. Bernstein and H. W. Lewis: *Phys. Rev.*, **95**: 83 (1954).   [Chap. 20, Sec. 1]

B37   H. A. Bethe: *Ann. Physik*, **5**: 325 (1930).   [Chap. 18, Secs. 2, 4]

B38   H. A. Bethe: *Z. Physik*, **76**: 293 (1932).   [Chap. 18, Sec. 2]

B39   H. A. Bethe: *Proc. Cambridge Phil. Soc.*, **30**: 524 (1934).   [Chap. 20, Sec. 1]

B40   H. A. Bethe: *Proc. Cambridge Phil. Soc.*, **31**: 108 (1935).   [Chap. 17, Sec. 2]

B41   H. A. Bethe: *Revs. Mod. Phys.*, **9**: 69 (1937).   [Chap. 2, Sec. 7]

B42   H. A. Bethe: *Phys. Rev.*, **70**: 821 (1946).   [Chap. 19, Sec. 1]

B43   H. A. Bethe: "Elementary Nuclear Theory," John Wiley & Sons, Inc., New York, 1947.   [Chap. 3, Sec. 5; Chap. 10, Secs. 3, 4; Chap. 17, Sec. 2]

B44   H. A. Bethe: BNL-T-7, 1949.   [Chap. 22, Sec. 3]

B45   H. A. Bethe: *Phys. Rev.*, **76**: 38 (1949).   [Chap. 10, Sec. 3]

B46   H. A. Bethe: *Revs. Mod. Phys.*, **22**: 213 (1950).   [Chap. 22, Sec. 3]

B47   H. A. Bethe and J. Ashkin in E. Segrè (ed.): "Experimental Nuclear Physics," vol. 1, p. 166, John Wiley & Sons, Inc., New York, 1953.   [Chap. 22, Secs. 1, 2, 3, 4, 6; Chap. 24, Sec. 2]

B48   H. A. Bethe and R. F. Bacher: *Revs. Mod. Phys.*, **8**: 82 (1936).   [Chap. 2, Sec. 2; Chap. 11, Secs. 2, 3; Chap. 17, Sec. 2]

B49   H. A. Bethe and W. Heitler: *Proc. Roy. Soc. (London)*, **A146**: 83 (1934).   [Chap. 20, Sec. 1; Chap. 24, Sec. 2]

B50   H. A. Bethe and C. Longmire: *Phys. Rev.*, **77**: 647 (1950).   [Chap. 10, Sec. 4]

B51   H. A. Bethe and L. C. Maximon: *Phys. Rev.*, **93**: 768 (1954).   [Chap. 20, Sec. 1]

B52   H. A. Bethe and G. Placzek: *Phys. Rev.*, **51**: 450 (1937).   [Chap. 10, Sec. 4; Chap. 14, Sec. 1]

B53   R. T. Beyer: "Foundations of Nuclear Physics," Dover Publications, New York, 1949.‡   [Chap. 1, Sec. 3]

B54   H. J. Bhabha: *Proc. Roy. Soc. (London)*, **A154**: 195 (1936).   [Chap. 18, Sec. 2]

† This is a critical review of the historical development of Bohr's model of the atom.

‡ Contains facsimile reprints of 13 fundamental papers on nuclear physics and an extensive bibliography of the periodical literature up to 1947.

B55   H. J. Bhabha: *Proc. Roy. Soc. (London)*, **A164**: 257 (1938). [Chap. 18, Sec. 2; Chap. 20, Sec. 2]

B56   W. Binks: *Repts. Progr. in Phys.*, **3**: 347 (1936). [Chap. 18, Secs. 2, 4; Chap. 25, Sec. 2]

B57   R. W. Birge, U. E. Kruse, and N. F. Ramsey: *Phys. Rev.*, **83**: 274 (1951). [Chap. 10, Sec. 9]

B58   G. R. Bishop, C. H. Collie, H. Halban, A. Hedgran, K. Siegbahn, S. du Toit, and R. Wilson: *Phys. Rev.*, **80**: 211 (1950). [Chap. 10, Sec. 4]

B59   G. R. Bishop, H. Halban, P. F. D. Shaw, and R. Wilson: *Phys. Rev.*, **81**: 219 (1951). [Chap. 10, Sec. 4]

B60   F. Bitter: *Phys. Rev.*, **75**: 1326A (1949); **76**: 150L (1949). [Chap. 4, Sec. 4]

B61   F. Bitter and H. Feshbach: *Phys. Rev.*, **92**: 837L (1953). [Chap. 2, Sec. 3]

B62   P. M. S. Blackett: *Proc. Roy. Soc. (London)*, **A135**: 132 (1932). [Chap. 22, Secs. 1, 3]

B63   J. S. Blair and G. F. Chew: *Ann. Rev. Nuclear Sci.*, **2**, 163 (1953). [Chap. 2, Sec. 3; Chap. 8, Sec. 1]

B64   J. Blake: *Am. J. Med. Sci.*, **15**: 63 (1848). [Chap. 1, Sec. 1]

B65   J. Blaton: *Kgl. Danske Videnskab. Selskab, Mat.-fys. Medd.*, **24**(20): 1 (1950). [Chap. 1, Sec. 3; Chap. 12, Sec. 2]

B66   J. M. Blatt: *Phys. Rev.*, **89**: 83 (1953). [Chap. 6, Sec. 3]

B67   J. M. Blatt and L. C. Biedenharn: *Revs. Mod. Phys.*, **24**: 258 (1952). [Chap. 6, Secs. 8, 9]

B68   J. M. Blatt and V. F. Weisskopf: "Theoretical Nuclear Physics," John Wiley & Sons, Inc., New York, 1952. [Chap. 2, Secs. 5, 6; Chap. 4, Introd., Secs. 1, 5; Chap. 6, Secs. 3–5, 8; Chap. 10, Secs. 2–5, 8; Chap. 11, Secs. 3, 4; Chap. 14, Secs. 1, 2; Chap. 17, Sec. 3]

B69   W. Bleakney and J. A. Hipple, Jr.: *Phys. Rev.*, **53**: 521 (1938). [Chap. 3, Sec. 3]

B70   F. Bloch: *Ann. Physik*, **16**: 285 (1933). [Chap. 18, Secs. 2, 3]

B71   F. Bloch: *Z. Physik*, **81**: 363 (1933). [Chap. 18, Secs. 2, 3]

B72   F. Bloch: *Phys. Rev.*, **50**: 272 (1936). [Chap. 21, Sec. 2]

B73   F. Bloch: *Phys. Rev.*, **70**: 460 (1946). [Chap. 5, Sec. 2]

B74   F. Bloch: *Phys. Rev.*, **83**: 839L (1951). [Chap. 4, Sec. 4]

B75   F. Bloch, W. W. Hansen, and M. Packard: *Phys. Rev.*, **69**: 127L (1946); **70**: 474 (1946). [Chap. 5, Sec. 2]

B76   F. Bloch, D. Nicodemus, and H. H. Staub: *Phys. Rev.*, **74**: 1025 (1948). [Chap. 4, Sec. 3]

B77   I. Bloch, M. M. Hull, Jr., A. A. Broyles, W. G. Bouricius, B. E. Freeman, and G. Breit: *Revs. Mod. Phys.*, **23**: 147 (1951). [Appendix C, Sec. 5]

B78   N. Bloembergen and P. J. van Heerden: *Phys. Rev.*, **83**: 561 (1951). [Chap. 22, Sec. 2]

B79   N. Bloembergen, E. M. Purcell, and R. V. Pound: *Phys. Rev.*, **73**: 679 (1948). [Chap. 5, Sec. 2]

B80   S. D. Bloom: *Phys. Rev.*, **88**: 312 (1952). [Chap. 6, Sec. 5]

B81   O. Blunck and S. Leisegang: *Z. Physik*, **128**: 500 (1950). [Chap. 21, Sec. 3]

B82   C. K. Bockelman, C. P. Browne, W. W. Buechner, and A. Sperduto: *Phys. Rev.*, **92**: 665 (1953). [Chap. 13, Sec. 5]

B83   A. R. Bodmer: *Proc. Phys. Soc. (London)*, **66**: 1041 (1953). [Chap. 2, Sec. 3]

B84   F. Boehm and C. S. Wu: *Phys. Rev.*, **93**: 518 (1954). [Chap. 21, Sec. 2]

B85   M. Bogaardt and B. Koudijs: *Physica*, **17**: 703 (1951). [Chap. 22, Sec. 3]

B86   J. K. Bøggild, K. J. Brostrøm, and T. Lauritsen: *Kgl. Danske Videnskab. Selskab. Mat.-fys. Medd.*, **18**: 4 (1940); *Phys. Rev.*, **59**: 275 (1941). [Chap. 22, Sec. 6]

B87   D. Bohm: "Quantum Theory," Prentice-Hall, Inc., New York, 1951. [Chap. 4, Sec. 7; Chap. 19, Sec. 2]

B88   A. Bohr: *Kgl. Danske Videnskab. Selskab, Mat.-fys. Medd.*, vol. 24, no. 19, 1948. [Chap. 18, Secs. 5, 6]

B89   A. Bohr and B. R. Mottelson: *Kgl. Danske Videnskab. Selskab, Mat.-fys. Medd.*, vol. 27, no. 16, 1953. [Chap. 4, Sec. 5; Chap. 14, Sec. 2]

B90   A. Bohr and V. F. Weisskopf: *Phys. Rev.*, **77**: 94 (1950). [Chap. 4, Sec. 4]

B91   N. Bohr: *Phil. Mag.*, **25**: 10 (1913). [Chap. 18, Sec. 1]

B92   N. Bohr: *Phil. Mag.*, **26**: 1 (1913); **26**: 476 (1913). [Introd.; Chap. 1, Secs. 3, 4]

B93   N. Bohr: *Phil. Mag.*, **30**: 581 (1915). [Chap. 18, Sec. 1; Chap. 22, Sec. 5]

B94   N. Bohr: *Nature*, **137**: 344 (1936). [Chap. 13, Sec. 3]

B95   N. Bohr: *Kgl. Danske Videnskab. Selskab, Mat.-fys. Medd.*, vol. 18, no. 8, 1948. [Chap. 18, Secs. 2, 3, 5; Chap. 22, Secs. 1, 6; Appendix C, Sec. 4]

B96   N. Bohr and J. A. Wheeler: *Phys. Rev.*, **56**: 426 (1939). [Chap. 11, Sec. 3]

B97   T. W. Bonner, R. A. Ferrell, and M. C. Rinehart: *Phys. Rev.*, **87**: 1032 (1952). [Chap. 11, Sec. 3]

B98   T. W. Bonner and L. M. Mott-Smith: *Phys. Rev.*, **46**: 258 (1934). [Chap. 13, Sec. 2]

B99   T. E. Bortner and G. S. Hurst: *Phys. Rev.*, **90**: 160L (1953). [Chap. 22, Sec. 4]

B100 W. Bothe: *Z. Physik*, **63**: 381 (1930). [Chap. 13, Sec. 1]

B101 W. Bothe and H. Becker: *Z. Physik*, **66**: 289 (1930). [Chap. 13, Sec. 2]

B102 W. Bothe and H. Fränz: *Z. Physik*, **49**: 1 (1928). [Chap. 13, Sec. 1]

B103 R. Bouchez: *Physica*, **18**: 1171 (1952). [Chap. 17, Sec. 3]

B104 I. S. Bowen: *Revs. Mod. Phys.*, **8**: 55 (1936). [Chap. 6, Sec. 4]

B105 J. C. Bower: *Proc. Cambridge Phil. Soc.*, **34**: 450 (1938). [Chap. 22, Sec. 4]

B106 K. Boyer, H. E. Gove, J. A. Harvey, M. Deutsch, and M. S. Livingston: *Rev. Sci. Instr.*, **22**: 310 (1951). [Chap. 12, Sec. 2]

B107 E. L. Brady and M. Deutsch: *Phys. Rev.*, **74**: 1541L (1948); *Phys. Rev.*, **78**: 558 (1950). [Chap. 6, Sec. 8]

B108 C. B. Bracstrup: *Radiology*, **46**: 385 (1946). [Chap. 25, Sec. 3]

B109 W. H. Bragg: "Studies in Radioactivity," Macmillan & Co., Ltd., London, 1912. [Chap. 22, Sec. 5; Chap. 25, Sec. 2]

B110 A. Bratenahl, S. Fernbach, R. H. Hildebrand, C. E. Leith, and B. J. Moyer: *Phys. Rev.*, **77**: 597 (1950). [Chap. 14, Sec. 2]

B111 G. Breit: *Phys. Rev.*, **42**: 348 (1932). [Chap. 2, Sec. 3]

B112 G. Breit: *Phys. Rev.*, **69**: 472 (1946). [Chap. 14, Sec. 1]

B113 G. Breit: *Revs. Mod. Phys.*, **23**: 238 (1951). [Chap. 10, Sec. 5]

B114 G. Breit and R. L. Gluckstern: *Ann. Rev. Nuclear Sci.*, **2**: 365 (1953). [Chap. 10, Secs. 3, 5]

B115 G. Breit and M. H. Hull, Jr.: *Am. J. Phys.*, **21**: 184 (1953). [Chap. 10, Sec. 5]

B116 G. Breit and I. I. Rabi: *Phys. Rev.*, **38**: 2082L (1931). [Chap. 5, Sec. 1]

B117 G. Breit, H. M. Thaxton, and L. Eisenbud: *Phys. Rev.*, **55**: 1018 (1939). [Chap. 10, Sec. 5]

B118 G. Breit and E. Wigner: *Phys. Rev.*, **49**: 519 (1936). [Chap. 11, Sec. 4; Chap. 13, Sec. 3; Chap. 14, Introd., Sec. 1]

B119 G. H. Briggs: *Proc. Roy. Soc. (London)*, **A114**: 313 (1927). [Chap. 22, Sec. 5]

B120 G. H. Briggs: *Proc. Roy. Soc. (London)*, **A114**: 341 (1927). [Chap. 22, Secs. 1, 3]

B121 G. H. Briggs: *Proc. Roy. Soc. (London)*, **A157**: 183 (1936). [Chap. 16, Sec. 1; Appendix D]

B122 G. H. Briggs: *Revs. Mod. Phys.*, **26**: 1 (1954); erratum, **26**: 472E (1954). [Chap. 16, Sec. 1; Appendix D]

B123 P. Brix and H. Kopfermann: *Z. Physik*, **126**: 344 (1949); *Festschr. Akad. Wiss. Göttingen, Math.-Phys. Kl.*, vol. 17, 1951. [Chap. 2, Sec. 3]

B124 R. B. Brode: *Revs. Mod. Phys.*, **5**: 257 (1933). [Chap. 18, Introd.]

B125 A. van den Broek: *Physik. Z.*, **14**: 32 (1913). [Chap. 1, Sec. 3]

B126 J. E. Brolley, Jr., J. H. Coon, and J. L. Fowler: *Phys. Rev.*, **82**: 190 (1951). [Chap. 10, Sec. 9]

B127 D. A. Bromley: *Phys. Rev.*, **88**: 565 (1952). [Chap. 6, Sec. 9]

B128 D. A. Bromley, J. A. Bruner, and H. W. Fulbright: *Phys. Rev.*, **89**: 396 (1953). [Chap. 6, Sec. 9]

B129 K. J. Broström, T. Huus, and R. Tangen: *Phys. Rev.*, **71**: 661 (1947). [Chap. 14, Sec. 1]

B130 A. B. Brown, C. W. Snyder, W. A. Fowler, and C. C. Lauritsen: *Phys. Rev.*, **82**: 159 (1951). [Chap. 2, Sec. 2; Chap. 10, Secs. 1, 6; Chap. 12, Sec. 2; Chap. 14, Sec. 1]

B131 H. Brown: *Revs. Mod. Phys.*, **21**: 625 (1949). [Chap. 8, Sec. 2]

B132 S. C. Brown: *Nucleonics*, **2**: 625 (1949). [Chap. 22, Sec. 4]

B133 S. C. Brown and L. G. Elliott: *Am. J. Phys.*, **11**: 311 (1943). [Chap. 5, Sec. 1]

B134 G. L. Brownell: *Nucleonics*, **10**(6): 30 (1952). [Chap. 21, Sec. 3]

B135 C. D. Broyles, D. A. Thomas, and S. K. Haynes: *Phys. Rev.*, **89**: 715 (1953). [Chap. 17, Sec. 3]

B136 G. Brubaker: *Phys. Rev.*, **54**: 1011 (1938). [Chap. 2, Sec. 7]

B137 J. H. M. Brunings, J. K. Knipp, and E. Teller: *Phys. Rev.*, **60**: 657 (1941). [Chap. 22, Sec. 1]

B138 W. W. Buechner, E. N. Strait, C. G. Stergiopoulos, and A. Sperduto: *Phys. Rev.*, **74**: 1569 (1948). [Chap. 12, Sec. 2; Chap. 16, Sec. 1]

B139 W. W. Buechner, R. J. Van de Graaff, E. A. Burrill, and A. Sperduto: *Phys. Rev.*, **74**: 1348 (1948). [Chap. 21, Sec. 2]

B140 W. W. Buechner, R. J. Van de Graaff, A. Sperduto, E. A. Burrill, Jr., and H. Feshbach: *Phys. Rev.*, **72**: 678 (1947). [Chap. 19, Sec. 1]

B141 W. E. Burcham: *Progr. Nuclear Phys.*, **2**: 174 (1952). [Chap. 11, Sec. 4; Chap. 12, Sec. 2]

B142 E. H. S. Burhop: "The Auger Effect and Other Radiationless Transitions," Cambridge University Press, London, 1952. [Chap. 17, Sec. 3]

B143 L. E. Burkhart, W. F. Peed, and B. G. Saunders: *Phys. Rev.*, **73**: 347 (1948). [Chap. 1, Sec. 4]

B144 L. E. Burkhart, W. F. Peed, and E. J. Spitzer: *Phys. Rev.*, **75**: 86 (1949). [Chap. 1, Sec. 4]

B145 L. E. Burkhart, G. Stukenbroeker, and S. Adams: *Phys. Rev.*, **75**: 83 (1949). [Chap. 7, Sec. 2]

B146 S. T. Butler: *Phys. Rev.*, **80**: 1095L (1950); *Proc. Roy. Soc. (London)*, **A208**: 559 (1951); *Phys. Rev.*, **88**: 685L (1952). [Chap. 6, Sec. 9]

C1 D. O. Caldwell: *Phys. Rev.*, **88**: 131 (1952). [Chap. 22, Sec. 5]

C2 D. O. Caldwell and J. R. Richardson: *Phys. Rev.*, **94**: 79 (1954). [Chap. 22, Sec. 2]

C3 M. Camac and H. A. Bethe: *Phys. Rev.*, **73**: 191 (1948). [Chap. 10, Sec. 3]

C4 M. Camac, A. D. McGuire, J. B. Platt, and H. J. Schulte: *Phys. Rev.*, **88**: 134L (1952). [Chap. 2, Sec. 3]

C5 J. R. Cameron: *Phys. Rev.*, **90**: 839 (1953). [Chap. 2, Sec. 7]

C6 H. Casimir: *Physica*, **2**: 719 (1935). [Chap. 5, Sec. 3]

C7   J. M. Cassels, T. G. Pickavance, and G. H. Stafford: *Proc. Roy. Soc. (London)*, **A214**: 262 (1952). [Chap. 10, Sec. 9]

C7a   Y. Cauchois: *J. phys. radium*, **13**: 113 (1952). [Chap. 24, Sec. 1]

C8   P. E. Cavanagh: *Progr. Nuclear Phys.*, **1**: 140 (1950). [Chap. 17, Introd., Secs. 1, 3]

C9   P. A. Čerenkov: *Compt. rend. acad. sci. U.R.S.S.*, **8**: 451 (1934); **14**: 105 (1937); *Phys. Rev.*, **52**: 378 (1937). [Chap. 18, Sec. 6]

C10   J. Chadwick: *Verhandl. deut. physik. Ges.*, **16**: 383 (1914). [Chap. 17, Sec. 1]

C11   J. Chadwick: *Phil. Mag.*, **40**: 734 (1920). [Chap. 1, Sec. 3]

C12   J. Chadwick: *Proc. Roy. Soc. (London)*, **A136**: 692 (1932). [Introd.; Chap. 13, Sec. 2]

C13   J. Chadwick and E. S. Bieler: *Phil. Mag.*, **42**: 923 (1921). [Chap. 2, Secs. 1, 7]

C14   J. Chadwick, J. E. R. Constable, and E. C. Pollard: *Proc. Roy. Soc. (London)*, **A130**: 463 (1931). [Chap. 13, Sec. 4]

C15   O. Chamberlain, E. Segrè, and C. Wiegand: *Phys. Rev.*, **83**: 923 (1951). [Chap. 10, Sec. 9]

C16   F. C. Champion: *Repts. Progr. in Phys.*, **5**: 348 (1938). [Chap. 19, Sec. 1]

C17   C. S. Wang Chang and D. L. Falkoff: *Phys. Rev.*, **76**: 365 (1949). [Chap. 21, Sec. 2]

C18   C. Y. Chao: *Proc. Natl. Acad. Sci. U. S.*, **16**: 431 (1930); *Phys. Rev.*, **36**: 1519 (1930). [Chap. 24, Sec. 2]

C19   G. F. Chew: *Phys. Rev.*, **84**: 710 (1951). [Chap. 10, Sec. 6]

C20   R. S. Christian and J. L. Gammel: *Phys. Rev.*, **91**: 100 (1953). [Chap. 10, Sec. 6]

C21   R. S. Christian and E. W. Hart: *Phys. Rev.*, **77**: 441 (1950). [Chap. 10, Sec. 9]

C22   R. S. Christian and H. P. Noyes: *Phys. Rev.*, **79**: 85 (1950). [Chap. 10, Sec. 9]

C23   R. F. Christy and R. Latter: *Revs. Mod. Phys.*, **20**: 185 (1948). [Appendix C, Sec. 5]

C24   E. T. Clarke and J. W. Irvine, Jr.: *Phys. Rev.*, **70**: 893 (1946). [Chap. 15, Sec. 6]

C25   G. H. Clewett: *Ann. Rev. Nuclear Sci.*, **1**: 293 (1952). [Chap. 7, Sec. 8]

C26   K. Clusius and G. Dickel: *Naturwiss.*, **26**: 546 (1938); *Z. Physik. Chem.*, **44B**: 397 (1939). [Chap. 7, Sec. 8]

C27   J. D. Cockroft and E. T. S. Walton: *Proc. Roy. Soc. (London)*, **A129**: 477 (1930); **A137**: 229 (1932). [Introd.; Chap. 2, Sec. 8]

C28   B. L. Cohen: *Phys. Rev.*, **80**: 105L (1950). [Chap. 2, Sec. 6]

C29   B. L. Cohen and T. H. Handley: *Phys. Rev.*, **92**: 101 (1953). [Chap. 10, Sec. 6]

C30   K. Cohen: *J. Chem. Phys.*, **8**: 588 (1940). [Chap. 7, Sec. 8]

C31   S. A. Colgate: *Phys. Rev.*, **87**: 592 (1952). [Chap. 25, Sec. 3]

C32   E. R. Collins, C. D. McKenzie, and C. A. Ramm: *Proc. Roy. Soc. (London)*, **A216**: 219 (1953). [Chap. 16, Sec. 1]

C33   G. B. Collins and V. G. Reiling: *Phys. Rev.*, **54**: 499 (1938). [Chap. 18, Sec. 6]

C34   T. L. Collins, W. H. Johnson, Jr., and A. O. Nier: *Phys. Rev.*, **94**: 398 (1954). [Chap. 3, Secs. 3, 5; Chap. 9, Sec. 1]

C35   T. L. Collins, A. O. Nier, and W. H. Johnson, Jr.: *Phys. Rev.*, **84**: 717 (1951). [Chap. 3, Secs. 3, 5; Chap. 9, Secs. 2, 3; Chap. 11, Sec. 3]

C36   T. L. Collins, A. O. Nier, and W. H. Johnson, Jr.: *Phys. Rev.*, **86**: 408 (1952). [Chap. 3, Secs. 3, 5; Chap. 9, Secs. 2, 3; Chap. 11, Sec. 3]

C37   A. H. Compton and S. K. Allison: "X-rays in Theory and Experiment,"

D. Van Nostrand Company, Inc., New York, 1935. [Chap. 1, Sec. 4; Chap. 20, Sec. 1; Chap. 21, Sec. 2; Chap. 23, Sec. 2; Chap. 24, Sec. 1; Chap. 25, Sec. 1]

C38   C. S. Cook, L. M. Langer, and H. C. Price, Jr.: *Phys. Rev.*, **74**: 548 (1948). [Chap. 17, Sec. 3]

C39   J. H. Coon: *Phys. Rev.*, **75**: 1355 (1949). [Chap. 7, Introd.]

C40   J. H. Coon, E. R. Graves, and H. H. Barschall: *Phys. Rev.*, **88**: 562 (1952). [Chap. 14, Sec. 2]

C41   E. P. Cooper: *Phys. Rev.*, **61**: 1 (1942). [Chap. 7, Sec. 10]

C42   L. N. Cooper and E. M. Henley: *Phys. Rev.*, **92**: 801 (1953). [Chap. 2, Secs. 2, 3]

C43   H. C. Corben: *Proc. Cambridge Phil. Soc.*, **34**: 540 (1938). [Chap. 21, Sec. 3]

C44   B. Cork: *Phys. Rev.*, **80**: 321 (1950). [Chap. 10, Sec. 9]

C45   D. R. Corson: *Phys. Rev.*, **84**: 605L (1951). [Chap. 21, Sec. 1]

C46   C. D. Coryell: *Ann. Rev. Nuclear Sci.*, **2**: 305 (1953). [Chap. 11, Sec. 3]

C47   C. D. Coryell and N. Sugarman: "Radiochemical Studies of the Fission Products," McGraw-Hill Book Company, Inc., New York, 1951. [Chap. 11, Sec. 3]

C47a   C. L. Cowan, Jr., F. Reines, and F. B. Harrison: *Phys. Rev.*, **96**: 1294 (1954). [Chap. 8, Sec. 1; Chap. 17, Sec. 2]

C48   R. T. Cox and C. T. Chase: *Phys. Rev.*, **51**: 140L (1937). [Chap. 19, Sec. 1]

C49   H. R. Crane: *Phys. Rev.*, **55**: 501 (1939). [Chap. 17, Sec. 2]

C50   H. R. Crane: *Revs. Mod. Phys.*, **20**: 278 (1948). [Chap. 17, Sec. 2]

C51   H. R. Crane and C. C. Lauritsen: *Phys. Rev.*, **45**: 430L, 497L (1934). [Chap. 13, Sec. 3]

C52   M. F. Crawford and A. L. Schawlow: *Phys. Rev.*, **76**: 1310 (1949). [Chap. 2, Sec. 3; Chap. 5, Sec. 1]

C53   R. J. Creagan: *Phys. Rev.*, **76**: 1769 (1949). [Chap. 13, Sec. 1]

C54   H. Crew: "The Rise of Modern Physics," The Williams & Wilkins Company, Baltimore, 1935. [Introd.]

C55   C. L. Critchfield and D. C. Dodder: *Phys. Rev.*, **76**: 602 (1949). [Chap. 2, Sec. 7]

C56   W. Crookes: *Nature*, **34**: 423 (1886). [Chap. 3, Sec. 1]

C57   W. G. Cross and N. F. Ramsey: *Phys. Rev.*, **80**: 929 (1950). [Chap. 23, Sec. 1]

C58   I. Curie: *Compt. rend.*, **193**: 1412 (1931). [Chap. 13, Sec. 2]

C59   I. Curie and F. Joliot: *Compt. rend.*, **194**: 273 (1932). [Chap. 13, Sec. 2]

C60   I. Curie and F. Joliot: *Compt. rend.*, **196**: 1105 (1933). [Chap. 13, Sec. 3]

C61   I. Curie and F. Joliot: *Compt. rend.*, **196**: 1885 (1933); *J. phys. radium*, **4**: 494 (1933). [Chap. 13, Sec. 3]

C62   I. Curie and F. Joliot: *Compt. rend.*, **198**: 254 (1934). [Introd.; Chap. 13, Sec. 3]

C63   I. Curie and F. Joliot: *Compt. rend.*, **198**: 559 (1934). [Chap. 13, Sec. 3]

C64   M. Curie, A. Debierne, A. S. Eve, H. Geiger, O. Hahn, S. C. Lind, St. Meyer, E. Rutherford, and E. Schweidler: *Revs. Mod. Phys.*, **3**: 427 (1931). [Chap. 21, Sec. 3]

C65   L. F. Curtiss: *J. Research Natl. Bur. Standards*, **4**: 595 (1930). [Chap. 27, Sec. 4]

D1   W. C. Dampier Whetham and M. Dampier Whetham: "Cambridge Readings in the Literature of Science," Cambridge University Press, London, 1924. [Introd.]

D2   S. M. Dancoff and P. Morrison: *Phys. Rev.*, **55**: 122 (1939). [Chap. 6, Sec. 5]

D3   K. K. Darrow: *Rev. Sci. Instr.*, **4**: 58 (1933); **5**: 66 (1934); *Bell System Tech. J.*, **10**: 628 (1931); **12**: 288 (1933), et seq. [Chap. 13, Introd.]

D4   C. G. Darwin: *Phil. Mag.*, **23**: 901 (1912). [Chap. 22, Sec. 5]

D5   C. G. Darwin: *Phil. Mag.*, **27**: 499 (1914). [Chap. 1, Sec. 3]

D6   W. G. Davey: *Proc. Phys. Soc. (London)*, **A66**: 1059 (1953). [Chap. 23, Introd.]

D7   J. P. Davidson, Jr.: *Phys. Rev.*, **82**: 48 (1951). [Chap. 17, Sec. 3]

D8   L. Davis, Jr., B. T. Feld, C. W. Zabel, and J. R. Zacharias: *Phys. Rev.*, **76**: 1076 (1949). [Chap. 5, Secs. 2, 3]

D9   L. Davis, Jr., D. E. Nagle, and J. R. Zacharias: *Phys. Rev.*, **76**: 1068 (1949). [Chap. 5, Secs. 1, 2; Chap. 6, Sec. 7]

D10   R. Davis, Jr.: *Phys. Rev.*, **86**: 976 (1952). [Chap. 17, Sec. 2]

D11   C. M. Davisson and R. D. Evans: *Phys. Rev.*, **81**: 404 (1951). [Chap. 25, Sec. 3]

D12   C. M. Davisson and R. D. Evans: *Revs. Mod. Phys.*, **24**: 79 (1952). [Chap. 23, Secs. 2, 4, 5; Chap. 24, Secs. 1, 2; Chap. 25, Secs. 1, 3]

D13   F. H. Day: X-ray Calibration of Radiation Detectors of the Health-Physics Type, *Natl. Bur. Standards (U.S.) Cir.* 507, 1951. [Chap. 25, Sec. 2]

D14   R. B. Day and R. L. Henkel: *Phys. Rev.*, **92**: 358 (1953). [Chap. 2, Sec. 6; Chap. 14, Sec. 2]

D15   S. De Benedetti, C. E. Cowan, W. R. Konneker, and H. Primakoff: *Phys. Rev.*, **77**: 205 (1950). [Chap. 21, Sec. 4]

D16   S. De Benedetti and G. H. Minton: *Phys. Rev.*, **85**: 944L (1952). [Chap. 16, Sec. 1]

D17   P. I. Dee: *Proc. Roy. Soc. (London)*, **A136**: 727 (1932). [Chap. 13, Sec. 2]

D18   L. A. Delsasso, W. A. Fowler, and C. C. Lauritsen: *Phys. Rev.*, **51**: 391 (1937). [Chap. 24, Sec. 2]

D19   W. E. Deming and R. T. Birge: *Revs. Mod. Phys.*, **6**: 119 (1934). [Chap. 26, Sec. 1]

D20   A. J. Dempster: *Proc. Am. Phil. Soc.*, **75**: 755 (1935). [Chap. 16, Sec. 2]

D21   A. J. Dempster: *Phys. Rev.*, **53**: 64 (1938). [Chap. 3, Sec. 3]

D22   A. J. Dempster: *Phys. Rev.*, **53**: 869 (1938). [Chap. 9, Secs. 1, 3]

D23   A. J. Dempster: *Phys. Rev.*, **71**: 829L (1947). [Chap. 7, Sec. 6]

D24   D. M. Dennison: *Proc. Roy. Soc. (London)*, **A115**: 483 (1927). [Chap. 5, Sec. 1]

D25   A. de Shalit: *Phys. Rev.*, **90**: 83 (1953). [Chap. 4, Sec. 4]

D26   M. Deutsch: *Phys. Rev.*, **72**: 729 (1947). [Chap. 21, Sec. 4]

D27   M. Deutsch: *Phys. Rev.*, **82**: 455L (1951). [Chap. 21, Sec. 4]

D28   M. Deutsch: *Phys. Rev.*, **83**: 866L (1951). [Chap. 21, Sec. 4]

D29   M. Deutsch: *Repts. Progr. in Phys.*, **14**: 196 (1951). [Chap. 6, Sec. 8]

D30   M. Deutsch and S. C. Brown: *Phys. Rev.*, **85**: 1047L (1952). [Chap. 21, Sec. 4]

D31   M. Deutsch and E. R. Dulit: *Phys. Rev.*, **84**: 601L (1951). [Chap. 21, Sec. 4]

D32   M. Deutsch and G. Scharff-Goldhaber: *Phys. Rev.*, **83**: 1059L (1951). [Chap. 6, Sec. 7]

D33   J. J. Devaney: Alpha Decay, Ph.D. thesis, Massachusetts Institute of Technology, Cambridge, Mass., 1950; *Phys. Rev.*, **91**: 587 (1953). [Chap. 2, Sec. 6]

D34   D. DeVault: *Rev. Sci. Instr.*, **12**: 83 (1941). [Chap. 28, Sec. 2]

D35   S. Devons: "Excited States of Nuclei," Cambridge University Press, London, 1949. [Chap. 11, Sec. 4]

D36   S. Devons, H. G. Hereward, and G. R. Lindsey: *Nature*, **164**: 586 (1949). [Chap. 6, Sec. 5]

D37   W. C. Dickinson: *Phys. Rev.*, **80**: 563 (1950). [Chap. 5, Sec. 1]
D38   G. F. v. Droste: *Z. Physik*, **100**: 529 (1936). [Chap. 25, Sec. 2]
D39   G. F. v. Droste: *Z. Physik*, **104**: 335 (1937). [Chap. 21, Sec. 2]
D40   W. Duane and F. L. Hunt: *Phys. Rev.*, **6**: 166 (1915). [Chap. 20, Sec. 1]
D40*a*   H. E. Duckworth, B. G. Hogg, and E. M. Pennington: *Revs. Mod. Phys.*, **26**: 463 (1954). [Chap. 3, Sec. 5]
D41   H. E. Duckworth, C. L. Kegley, J. M. Olson, and G. S. Stanford: *Phys. Rev.*, **83**: 1114 (1951). [Chap. 9, Sec. 3]
D42   R. A. Dudley: Measurement of Beta Radiation Dosage with Photographic Emulsions, Ph.D. thesis, Massachusetts Institute of Technology, Cambridge Mass., 1951. [Chap. 21, Sec. 3.]
D43   J. W. M. DuMond and E. R. Cohen: *Revs. Mod. Phys.*, **20**: 82 (1948). [Chap. 4, Sec. 3]
D44   J. W. M. DuMond and E. R. Cohen: *Revs. Mod. Phys.*, **25**: 691 (1953). [Chap. 3, Sec. 4; Chap. 4, Sec. 3; Chap. 7, Sec. 5; Chap. 22, Sec. 3; Appendix D; Appendix E]

E1   C. E. Eddy: *Proc. Cambridge Phil. Soc.*, **75**: 50 (1929). [Chap. 21, Sec. 3]
E2   J. E. Edwards and M. L. Pool: *Phys. Rev.*, **69**: 549 (1946). [Chap. 21, Sec. 2]
E3   R. R. Edwards: *Ann. Rev. Nuclear Sci.*, **1**: 301 (1952). [Chap. 7, Sec. 7]
E4   R. R. Edwards and T. H. Davis: *Nucleonics*, **2**(6): 44 (1948). [Chap. 7, Sec. 10]
E5   "Effects of Atomic Weapons," p. 38, U. S. Government Printing Office, Washington, D.C., 1950. [Chap. 25, Sec. 4]
E6   L. G. Elliott and R. E. Bell: *Phys. Rev.*, **76**: 168A (1949). [Chap. 17, Sec. 2]
E7   L. G. Elliott, R. L. Graham, J. Walker, and J. L. Wolfson: *Phys. Rev.*, **93**: 356L (1954). [Chap. 16, Sec. 1]
E8   C. D. Ellis: *Proc. Roy. Soc. (London)*, **A99**: 261 (1921); **A101**: 1 (1922). [Chap. 6, Sec. 5]
E9   C. D. Ellis: *Proc. Roy. Soc. (London)*, **A143**: 350 (1934). [Chap. 6, Sec. 5; Appendix D]
E10   C. D. Ellis and N. F. Mott: *Proc. Roy. Soc. (London)*, **A141**: 502 (1933). [Chap. 17, Sec. 1]
E11   C. D. Ellis and W. A. Wooster: *Proc. Roy. Soc. (London)*, **A117**: 109 (1927). [Chap. 17, Sec. 1]
E12   R. H. Ellis, H. H. Rossi, and G. Failla: *Phys. Rev.*, **86**: 562L (1952). [Chap. 18, Sec. 5]
E13   K. G. Emeleus: *Proc. Cambridge Phil. Soc.*, **22**: 400 (1924). [Chap. 17, Sec. 1]
E14   P. M. Endt and J. C. Kluyver: *Revs. Mod. Phys.*, **26**: 95 (1954). [Chap. 10, Sec. 6; Chap. 12, Sec. 1]
E15   I. Estermann: *Revs. Mod. Phys.*, **18**: 300 (1946). [Chap. 4, Sec. 3]
E16   I. Estermann, O. C. Simpson, and O. Stern: *Phys. Rev.*, **52**: 535 (1937).† [Chap. 4, Sec. 3]
E17   G. E. Evans, P. M. Stier, and C. F. Barnett: *Phys. Rev.*, **90**: 825 (1953). [Chap. 22, Sec. 6]
E18   R. D. Evans: *Field Museum Nat. History Geol. Ser.*, **7**: 79 (1943). [Chap. 7, Introd.; Chap. 8, Sec. 2]
E19   R. D. Evans: *Am. J. Roentgenol., Radium Therapy, Nuclear Med.*, **58**: 754 (1947). [Chap. 25, Sec. 4]
E20   R. D. Evans: *Nucleonics*, **1**(2): 32 (1947). [Chap. 25, Sec. 2]

† Presents the final results and a review of the earlier work.

E21   R. D. Evans: National Research Council, *Nuclear Sci. Series, Rept.* 11, Washington, D.C., 1954. [Chap. 25, Sec. 3]

E22   R. D. Evans and R. O. Evans: *Revs. Mod. Phys.*, **20**: 305 (1948). [Chap. 23, Sec. 3; Chap. 24, Sec. 2; Chap. 25, Sec. 4]

E23   R. D. Evans and M. S. Livingston: *Revs. Mod. Phys.*, **7**: 229 (1935). [Chap. 13, Sec. 3]

E24   R. D. Evans and H. V. Neher: *Phys. Rev.*, **45**: 144 (1934). [Chap. 26, Sec. 3]

F1   W. J. Fader and A. Sperduto: *Phys. Rev.*, **94**: 748A (1954). [Chap. 13, Sec. 1]

F2   G. Failla: *Radiology*, **29**: 202 (1937). [Chap. 25, Sec. 2]

F3   D. L. Falkoff: *Am. J. Phys.*, **18**: 30 (1950). [Chap. 9, Sec. 3]

F4   D. L. Falkoff: *Phys. Rev.*, **82**: 98L (1951). [Chap. 6, Sec. 8]

F5   D. L. Falkoff and G. E. Uhlenbeck: *Phys. Rev.*, **79**: 323, 334 (1950). [Chap. 6, Sec. 8]

F6   U. Fano: *Phys. Rev.*, **70**: 44 (1946). [Chap. 22, Sec. 4]

F7   U. Fano: *Nucleonics*, **11**(8): 8 (1953); **11**(9): 55 (1953). [Chap. 23, Introd.; Chap. 25, Secs. 1, 3]

F8   A. Farkas and L. Farkas: *Proc. Roy. Soc. (London)*, **A152**: 152 (1935). [Chap. 5, Sec. 2]

F9   W. R. Faust: *Phys. Rev.*, **77**: 227 (1950). [Chap. 25, Sec. 3]

F10   N. Feather: *Phys. Rev.*, **35**: 705 (1930). [Chap. 27, Sec. 4]

F11   N. Feather: *Proc. Roy. Soc. (London)*, **A136**: 709 (1932). [Chap. 13, Sec. 2]

F12   N. Feather: *Proc. Cambridge Phil. Soc.*, **34**: 599 (1938). [Chap. 17, Sec. 1; Chap. 21, Sec. 3]

F13   N. Feather: *Advances in Phys.*, **2**: 141 (1953). [Chap. 9, Sec. 4]

F14   N. Feather and E. Bretscher: *Proc. Roy. Soc. (London)*, **A165**: 530 (1938). [Chap. 6, Sec. 6]

F15   N. Feather and R. R. Nimmo: *Proc. Cambridge Phil. Soc.*, **24**: 139 (1928). [Chap. 22, Sec. 4]

F16   E. Feenberg: *Phys. Rev.*, **55**: 504 (1939). [Chap. 11, Sec. 3]

F17   E. Feenberg: *Revs. Mod. Phys.*, **19**: 239 (1947). [Chap. 2, Sec. 1; Chap. 11, Sec. 3]

F18   E. Feenberg: *Phys. Rev.*, **77**: 771 (1950). [Chap. 4, Sec. 5; Chap. 6, Sec. 6; Chap. 11, Sec. 2]

F19   E. Feenberg: *Ann. Rev. Nuclear Sci.*, **1**: 43 (1952). [Chap. 11, Sec. 2]

F20   E. Feenberg and K. C. Hammack: *Phys. Rev.*, **75**: 1877 (1949). [Chap. 11, Sec. 2]

F21   E. Feenberg, K. C. Hammack, and L. W. Nordheim: *Phys. Rev.*, **75**: 1968L (1949). [Chap. 11, Sec. 2]

F22   E. Feenberg and G. Trigg: *Revs. Mod. Phys.*, **22**: 399 (1950). [Chap. 6, Sec. 3; Chap. 17, Sec. 3]

F23   E. Feenberg and E. Wigner: *Phys. Rev.*, **51**: 95 (1937). [Chap. 9, Sec. 4]

F24   I. Feister: *Phys. Rev.*, **78**: 375 (1950). [Chap. 17, Sec. 3]

F25   B. Feld: *Phys. Rev.*, **72**: 1116L (1947). [Chap. 4, Sec. 5; Chap. 5, Sec. 3]

F26   B. Feld: *Natl. Research Council Prelim. Rept.* 2, Washington, D.C., 1949. [Chap. 4, Sec. 5]

F27   B. T. Feld: *Ann. Rev. Nuclear Sci.*, **2**: 239 (1953). [Chap. 4, Sec. 4]

F28   B. T. Feld and W. E. Lamb, Jr.: *Phys. Rev.*, **67**: 15 (1945). [Chap. 5, Sec. 3]

F29   W. Feller: "Studies and Essays," Interscience Publishers, Inc., New York, 1948. [Chap. 28, Sec. 1]

F30   A. J. Ferguson and L. R. Walker: *Phys. Rev.*, **58**: 666 (1940). [Chap. 2, Sec. 7]

F31   E. Fermi: *Z. Physik*, **60**: 320 (1930). [Chap. 5, Sec. 1]

F32   E. Fermi: *Nature,* **133**: 757 (1934); **133**: 898 (1934).   [Chap. 13, Sec. 3]

F33   E. Fermi: *Ricerca sci.,* **5**: 21, 282, 380 (1934); *Nature,* **133**: 757 (1934). [Introd.]

F34   E. Fermi: *Z. Physik,* **88**: 161 (1934).   [Chap. 6, Sec. 3; Chap. 13, Sec. 3; Chap. 17, Sec. 3]

F35   E. Fermi: *Phys. Rev.,* **48**: 570L (1935); **50**: 899 (1936); *Ricerca sci.,* **7**: 13 (1936).   [Chap. 10, Sec. 4]

F36   E. Fermi: *Phys. Rev.,* **56**: 1242 (1939).   [Chap. 18, Sec. 5]

F37   E. Fermi: *Phys. Rev.,* **57**: 485 (1940).   [Chap. 18, Secs. 5, 6]

F38   E. Fermi: LADC-255, 1946.†   [Chap. 11, Sec. 3]

F39   E. Fermi, E. Amaldi, O. D'Agostino, F. Rasetti, and E. Segrè: *Proc. Roy. Soc. (London),* **A146**: 483 (1934).   [Chap. 13, Sec. 3]

F40   E. Fermi and L. Marshall: *Phys. Rev.,* **71**: 666 (1947); **75**: 578 (1949). [Chap. 10, Sec. 3; Appendix C, Sec. 6]

F41   E. Fermi (notes compiled by J. Orear, A. H. Rosenfeld, and R. A. Schluter): "Nuclear Physics," University of Chicago Press, Chicago, 1950.   [Chap. 2, Sec. 5; Chap. 4, Sec. 1; Chap. 10, Secs. 4, 9; Chap. 11, Sec. 3; Chap. 17, Secs. 2, 3]

F42   S. Fernbach, R. Serber, and T. B. Taylor: *Phys. Rev.,* **75**: 1352 (1949). [Chap. 14, Sec. 2]

F43   H. Feshbach: *Phys. Rev.,* **84**: 1206 (1951).   [Chap. 2, Sec. 3; Chap. 19, Sec. 1]

F44   H. Feshbach: *Phys. Rev.,* **88**: 295 (1952).   [Chap. 19, Sec. 1]

F45   H. Feshbach, D. C. Peaslee, and V. F. Weisskopf: *Phys. Rev.,* **71**: 145 (1947); erratum, **71**: 564L (1947).   [Chap. 2, Sec. 7; Chap. 11, Sec. 4; Chap. 14, Sec. 1]

F46   H. Feshbach, C. E. Porter, and V. F. Weisskopf: *Phys. Rev.,* **90**: 166L (1953). [Chap. 14, Sec. 2]

F47   H. Feshbach, C. E. Porter, and V. F. Weisskopf: *Phys. Rev.,* **96**: 448 (1954). [Chap. 14, Sec. 2]

F48   H. Feshbach and J. Schwinger: *Phys. Rev.,* **84**: 194 (1951).   [Chap. 4, Sec. 5; Chap. 10, Secs. 4, 8]

F49   H. Feshbach and V. F. Weisskopf: *Phys. Rev.,* **76**: 1550 (1949).   [Chap. 2, Sec. 9; Chap. 14, Secs. 1, 2]

F49a   S. Fine and C. F. Hendee: *Nucleonics,* **13**(3): 36 (1955).   [Chap. 24, Sec. 1]

F50   J. Fischer: *Ann. Physik,* **8**: 821 (1931).   [Chap. 24, Sec. 1]

F51   R. A. Fisher: *Proc. Cambridge Phil. Soc.,* **22**: 700 (1925); **26**: 528 (1930); **28**: 257 (1932); *Proc. Roy. Soc. (London),* **A146**: 1 (1934); *J. Roy. Statistical Soc.,* **98**: 39 (1935).   [Chap. 28, Sec. 5]

F52   V. L. Fitch and J. Rainwater: *Phys. Rev.,* **92**: 789 (1953).   [Chap. 2, Sec. 3]

F53   W. H. Fleming and H. G. Thode: *Phys. Rev.,* **92**: 378 (1953).   [Chap. 11, Sec. 3]

F54   B. H. Flowers: *Progr. Nuclear Phys.,* **2**: 235 (1952).   [Chap. 11, Sec. 2]

F55   R. G. Fluharty and M. Deutsch: *Phys. Rev.,* **76**: 182 (1949).   [Chap. 6, Sec. 7]

F56   L. L. Foldy: *Phys. Rev.,* **81**: 395 (1951).   [Chap. 25, Sec. 3]

F57   L. L. Foldy: *Phys. Rev.,* **83**: 397 (1951).   [Chap. 3, Sec. 2; Appendix E]

F58   K. W. Ford and D. Bohm: *Phys. Rev.,* **79**: 745L (1950).   [Chap. 14, Sec. 2]

F59   E. W. Foster: *Repts. Progr. in Phys.,* **14**: 288 (1951).   [Chap. 2, Sec. 3; Chap. 7, Sec. 2]

F60   Fourth Scintillation Counter Symposium, *Nucleonics,* **12**(3): 14 (1954). [Chap. 25, Sec. 2]

F61   W. A. Fowler, L. A. Delsasso, and C. C. Lauritsen: *Phys. Rev.,* **49**: 561 (1936). [Chap. 2, Sec. 2]

† Notes by I. Halpern on Los Alamos lecture series on neutron physics.

F62   W. A. Fowler, C. C. Lauritsen, and T. Lauritsen: *Revs. Mod. Phys.*, **20**: 236 (1948). [Chap. 2, Sec. 8]

F63   W. A. Fowler and J. Oppenheimer: *Phys. Rev.*, **54**: 320 (1938). [Chap. 19, Sec. 1]

F64   I. Frank and I. Tamm: *Compt. rend. acad. sci. U.R.S.S.*, **14**: 109 (1937). [Chap. 18, Sec. 6]

F65   H. Fränz: *Z. Physik*, **63**: 370 (1930). [Chap. 13, Sec. 1]

F66   H. Fraunfelder: *Ann. Rev. Nuclear Sci.*, **2**: 129 (1953). [Chap. 6, Sec. 8]

F67   B. E. Freeman and J. L. McHale: *Phys. Rev.*, **89**: 223 (1953). [Chap. 14, Sec. 1]

F68   H. Fricke and O. Glasser: *Am. J. Roentgenol., Radium Therapy, Nuclear Med.*, **13**: 453, 462 (1925). [Chap. 25, Sec. 2]

F69   G. Friedlander and J. W. Kennedy: "Introduction to Radiochemistry," John Wiley & Sons, Inc., New York, 1949. [Chap. 11, Sec. 3]

F70   F. L. Friedman: Cosmic Ray Shower Theory, Ph.D. thesis, Massachusetts Institute of Technology, Cambridge, Mass., 1949. [Chap. 18, Sec. 2]

F71   D. H. Frisch: *Phys. Rev.*, **84**: 1169 (1951). [Chap. 11, Sec. 3]

F72   E. G. Fuller: *Phys. Rev.*, **76**: 576L (1949). [Chap. 6, Sec. 9]

G1   E. R. Gaerttner and M. L. Yeater: *Phys. Rev.*, **78**: 621L (1950). [Chap. 24, Sec. 2]

G2   G. Gamow: *Z. Physik*, **51**: 204 (1928). [Chap. 2, Sec. 6]

G3   G. Gamow: *Nature*, **126**: 397 (1930). [Chap. 16, Sec. 1]

G4   G. Gamow: *Proc. Roy. Soc. (London)*, **A146**: 217 (1934); *Physik. Z.*, **35**: 533 (1934). [Chap. 6, Sec. 3]

G5   G. Gamow: *Phys. Rev.*, **70**: 572L (1946); erratum, **71**: 273L (1947). [Chap. 8, Sec. 2]

G6   G. Gamow: *Phys. Today*, **1**(3): 4 (1948). [Chap. 17, Sec. 2]

G7   G. Gamow and C. L. Critchfield: "Theory of Atomic Nucleus and Nuclear Energy Sources," Oxford University Press, London, 1949. [Appendix C, Sec. 5]

G8   G. Gamow and E. Teller: *Phys. Rev.*, **49**: 895 (1936). [Chap. 6, Sec. 3]

G9   J. H. Gardner and E. M. Purcell: *Phys. Rev.*, **76**: 1262L (1949). [Chap. 4, Sec. 3]

G9a   C. Garrett and G. N. Whyte: *Phys. Rev.*, **96**: 889 (1954). [Chap. 25, Sec. 3]

G10   H. Geiger: *Proc. Roy. Soc. (London)*, **A83**: 482 (1910). [Introd.]

G11   H. Geiger: *Phil. Mag.*, **22**: 201 (1911). [Chap. 28, Sec. 6]

G12   H. Geiger: *Z. Physik*, **8**: 45 (1921). [Chap. 16, Sec. 4]

G13   H. Geiger and E. Marsden: *Proc. Roy. Soc. (London)*, **A82**: 495 (1909). [Introd.]

G14   H. Geiger and E. Marsden: *Phil. Mag.*, **25**: 604 (1913). [Introd.; Chap. 1, Sec. 3]

G15   H. Geiger and J. M. Nuttall: *Phil. Mag.*, **22**: 613 (1911); **23**: 439 (1912). [Chap. 16, Sec. 4]

G16   H. Gellman, B. A. Griffith, and J. P. Stanley: *Phys. Rev.*, **80**: 866 (1950); **85**: 944L (1952). [Chap. 6, Sec. 5]

G17   J. B. Gerhart: *Phys. Rev.*, **95**: 288L (1954). [Chap. 17, Sec. 3]

G18   E. Gerjuoy: *Phys. Rev.*, **91**: 645 (1953). [Chap. 6, Sec. 9]

G18a   S. Geschwind, G. R. Gunther-Mohr, and C. H. Townes: *Revs. Mod. Phys.*, **26**: 444 (1954). [Chap. 3, Sec. 5]

G19   I. Getting: *Phys. Rev.*, **71**: 123L (1947). [Chap. 18, Sec. 6]

G20   A. Ghiorso, G. H. Higgins, A. E. Larsh, G. T. Seaborg, and S. G. Thompson: *Phys. Rev.*, **87**: 163L (1952). [Chap. 11, Sec. 3]

G21   S. N. Ghoshal: *Phys. Rev.*, **80**: 939 (1950). [Chap. 14, Sec. 2]

G22   W. F. Giauque and H. L. Johnston: *J. Am. Chem. Soc.*, **51**: 1436, 3528 (1929). [Chap. 7, Sec. 5]

G23   R. L. Gluckstern and M. H. Hull, Jr.: *Phys. Rev.*, **90**: 1030 (1953). [Chap. 20, Sec. 1]

G24   R. L. Gluckstern, M. H. Hull, Jr., and G. Breit: *Phys. Rev.*, **90**: 1026 (1953). [Chap. 20, Sec. 1]

G25   M. Goldhaber and R. D. Hill: *Revs. Mod. Phys.*, **24**: 179 (1952). [Chap. 6, Secs. 5, 6, 7, 8; Chap. 11, Sec. 2]

G26   M. Goldhaber and G. Scharff-Goldhaber: *Phys. Rev.*, **73**: 1472L (1948). [Chap. 4, Sec. 7]

G27   M. Goldhaber and A. W. Sunyar: *Phys. Rev.*, **83**: 906 (1951). [Chap. 6, Secs. 4, 5, 6, 7]

G28   V. M. Goldschmidt: "Geochemische Verteilungsgesetze der Elemente," Norske Videnskaps-Akademi, Oslo, 1938. [Chap. 8, Sec. 2]

G29   H. H. Goldsmith, H. W. Ibser, and B. T. Feld: *Revs. Mod. Phys.*, **19**: 259 (1947). [Chap. 14, Introd., Sec. 1]

G30   E. L. Goldwasser, F. E. Mills, and A. O. Hanson: *Phys. Rev.*, **88**: 1137 (1952). [Chap. 18, Sec. 5]

G31   C. Goodman (ed.): "The Science and Engineering of Nuclear Power," Addison-Wesley Publishing Company, Cambridge, Mass., 1947. [Chap. 22, Sec. 6]

G32   M. Goodrich and W. B. Payne: *Phys. Rev.*, **94**: 405 (1954). [Chap. 21, Sec. 2]

G33   W. Gordon: *Z. Physik*, **48**: 180 (1928). [Appendix C, Sec. 6]

G34   W. Gordy: *Revs. Mod. Phys.*, **20**: 668 (1948). [Chap. 5, Sec. 3]

G35   W. Gordy, O. R. Gilliam, and R. Livingston: *Phys. Rev.*, **76**: 443L (1949). [Chap. 5, Sec. 3]

G36   W. Gordy, H. Ring, and A. B. Burg: *Phys. Rev.*, **78**: 512 (1950). [Chap. 5, Sec. 3]

G37   W. Gordy, W. V. Smith, and R. Trambarulo: "Microwave Spectroscopy," John Wiley & Sons, Inc., New York, 1953. [Chap. 5, Sec. 3]

G38   S. Goudsmit: *Phys. Rev.*, **43**: 636 (1933). [Chap. 5, Sec. 1]

G39   G. A. R. Graham and H. Halban, Jr.: *Revs. Mod. Phys.*, **17**: 297 (1945). [Chap. 10, Sec. 4]

G40   E. R. Graves and D. I. Meyer: *Phys. Rev.*, **76**: 183A (1949). [Chap. 21, Sec. 2]

G41   G. A. Graves, L. M. Langer, and R. D. Moffat: *Phys. Rev.*, **88**: 344 (1952). [Chap. 6, Sec. 5]

G42   L. H. Gray: *Proc. Roy. Soc. (London)*, **A122**: 647 (1928). [Chap. 25, Sec. 2]

G43   L. H. Gray: *Proc. Roy. Soc. (London)*, **A156**: 578 (1936). [Chap. 25, Sec. 2]

G44   L. H. Gray: *Proc. Roy. Soc. (London)*, **A159**: 263 (1937). [Chap. 25, Sec. 3]

G45   L. H. Gray: *Proc. Cambridge Phil. Soc.*, **40**: 72 (1944). [Chap. 18, Secs. 2, 4, 5; Chap. 22, Sec. 4; Chap. 25, Sec. 2]

G46   A. E. S. Green: *Phys. Rev.*, **95**: 1006 (1954). [Chap. 11, Sec. 3]

G47   P. C. Gugelot: *Phys. Rev.*, **81**: 51 (1951). [Chap. 11, Sec. 4]

G48   R. W. Gurney: *Proc. Roy. Soc. (London)*, **A107**: 332 (1925). [Chap. 22, Sec .4]

G49   R. W. Gurney: *Nature*, **123**: 565 (1929). [Chap. 13, Sec. 4]

G50   R. W. Gurney and E. U. Condon: *Nature*, **122**: 439 (1928); *Phys. Rev.*, **33**: 127 (1929). [Chap. 2, Sec. 6]

H1   J. Hadley, E. Kelly, C. Leith, E. Segrè, C. Wiegand, and H. York: *Phys. Rev.*, **75**: 351 (1949). [Chap. 10, Sec. 9]

H2   L. R. Hafstad and E. Teller: *Phys. Rev.*, **54**: 681 (1938). [Chap. 9, Sec. 4]

H3   F. Hagemann: *J. Am. Chem. Soc.*, **72**: 768 (1950). [Chap. 16, Sec. 2]

H4   O. Hahn and L. Meitner: *Physik. Z.*, **9**: 321 (1908); **9**: 697 (1908). [Chap. 17, Sec. 1]

H5   O. Hahn and F. Strassmann: *Naturwiss.*, **27**: 11 (1939). [Chap. 13, Sec. 3]

H6   O. Hahn, F. Strassmann, and E. Walling: *Naturwiss.*, **25**: 189 (1937). [Chap. 7, Introd.]

H7   II. H. Hall and J. L. Powell: *Phys. Rev.*, **90**: 912 (1953). [Chap. 10, Sec. 5]

H8   T. Hall: *Phys. Rev.*, **79**: 504 (1950). [Chap. 22, Sec. 1]

H9   O. Halpern and H. Hall: *Phys. Rev.*, **57**: 459L (1940). [Chap. 18, Sec. 5]

H10   O. Halpern and H. Hall: *Phys. Rev.*, **73**: 477 (1948). [Chap. 18, Sec. 5]

H11   R. E. Halsted: *Phys. Rev.*, **88**: 666 (1952). [Chap. 3, Sec. 5; Chap. 9, Sec. 3; Chap. 11, Sec. 3]

H12   D. R. Hamilton: *Am. J. Phys.*, **9**: 319 (1941). [Chap. 5, Sec. 2]

H13   D. R. Hamilton: *Phys. Rev.*, **71**: 456L (1947). [Chap. 17, Sec. 2]

H14   D. R. Hamilton: *Phys. Rev.*, **74**: 782 (1948). [Chap. 6, Sec. 8]

H15   D. R. Hamilton, W. P. Alford, and L. Gross: *Phys. Rev.*, **92**: 1521 (1953). [Chap. 17, Sec. 3]

H16   G. C. Hanna, D. H. W. Kirkwood, and B. Pontecorvo: *Phys. Rev.*, **75**: 985L (1949). [Chap. 28, Sec. 4]

H17   J. M. Harding and J. E. Henderson: *Phys. Rev.*, **74**: 1560A (1948). [Chap. 18, Sec. 6]

H18   H. Harmsen, G. Hertz, and W. Schütze: *Z. Physik*, **90**: 703 (1934). [Chap. 7, Sec. 8]

H19   G. P. Harnwell and J. J. Livingood: "Experimental Atomic Physics," McGraw-Hill Book Company, Inc., New York, 1933. [Chap. 3, Sec. 1]

H20   S. P. Harris, C. O. Muehlhause, D. Rose, H. P. Schroder, G. E. Thomas, Jr., and S. Wexler: *Phys. Rev.*, **91**: 125 (1953). [Chap. 10, Sec. 4]

H21   A. J. Hartzler and R. T. Siegel: *Phys. Rev.*, **95**: 185 (1954). [Chap. 10, Sec. 9]

H22   J. A. Harvey: *Phys. Rev.*, **81**: 353 (1951). [Chap. 11, Sec. 3]

H23   K. Harworth and P. Kirkpatrick: *Phys. Rev.*, **62**: 334 (1942). [Chap. 20, Sec. 1]

H24   O. Haxel, J. H. D. Jensen, and II. E. Suess: *Phys. Rev.*, **75**: 1766L (1949); *Z. Physik*, **128**: 295 (1950). [Chap. 11, Sec. 2]

H25   R. J. Hayden: *Phys. Rev.*, **74**: 650 (1948). [Chap. 7, Sec. 6]

H26   E. E. Hays, P. I. Richards, and S. A. Goudsmit: *Phys. Rev.*, **84**: 824 (1951). [Chap. 3, Sec. 3]

H27   M. H. Hebb and E. Nelson: *Phys. Rev.*, **58**: 486 (1940). [Chap. 6, Sec. 5]

H28   A. Hedgran and S. Hultberg: *Phys. Rev.*, **94**: 498L (1954). [Chap. 24, Sec. 1]

H29   W. Heitler: "The Quantum Theory of Radiation," Oxford University Press, London, 1944. [Chap. 20, Sec. 1; Chap. 21, Secs. 3, 4; Chap. 23, Sec. 2; Chap. 24, Sec. 2]

H30   A. Hemmendinger and W. R. Smythe: *Phys. Rev.*, **51**: 1052 (1937). [Chap. 7, Sec. 7]

H31   G. H. Henderson: *Proc. Roy. Soc. (London)*, **A102**: 496 (1922); **A109**: 157 (1925). [Chap. 22, Sec. 1]

H32   G. H. Henderson: *Proc. Roy. Soc. (London)*, **A145**: 591 (1934). [Chap. 15, Sec. 1]

H33   G. H. Henderson and S. Bateson: *Proc. Roy. Soc. (London)*, **A145**: 563 (1934). [Chap. 15, Sec. 1]

H34   G. H. Henderson and L. G. Turnbull: *Proc. Roy. Soc. (London)*, **A145**: 582 (1934). [Chap. 15, Sec. 1]

H35   M. C. Henderson, M. S. Livingston, and E. O. Lawrence: *Phys. Rev.*, **45**: 428L (1934). [Chap. 13, Sec. 3]

H36   W. J. Henderson: *Proc. Roy. Soc. (London)*, **A147**: 572 (1934). [Chap. **17,** Sec. 1]

H37   R. G. Herb, D. W. Kerst, D. B. Parkinson, and G. J. Plain: *Phys. Rev.*, **55**: 998 (1939). [Chap. 10, Sec. 5]

H38   R. G. Herb, S. C. Snowdon, and O. Sala: *Phys. Rev.*, **75**: 246 (1949). [Chap. 14, Sec. 1]

H39   F. L. Hereford: *Phys. Rev.*, **74**: 574 (1948). [Chap. 18, Sec. 5]

H40   F. L. Hereford: *Phys. Rev.*, **81**: 482L (1951). [Chap. 21, Sec. 4]

H41   G. Hertz: *Z. Physik*, **79**: 108 (1932). [Chap. 7, Sec. 8]

H42   G. Hertz: *Z. Physik*, **91**: 810 (1934). [Chap. 7, Sec. 8]

H43   G. Herzberg: "Molecular Spectra and Molecular Structure I: Diatomic Molecules," Prentice-Hall, Inc., New York, 1939. [Chap. 7, Sec. 3]

H44   G. Herzberg: "Atomic Spectra and Atomic Structure," Dover Publications, New York, 1944. [Chap. 4, Sec. 1; Chap. 9, Secs. 3, 4]

H45   R. Herzog: *Z. Physik*, **89**: 447 (1934). [Chap. 3, Sec. 3]

H46   V. F. Hess and M. Hornyak: *Sitzber Akad. Wiss. Wien, Math.-naturw. Kl.*, **129**(IIa): 661 (1920). [Chap. 22, Sec. 4]

H47   G. Hevesy: "Chemical Analysis by X rays and Its Applications," McGraw-Hill Book Company, Inc., New York, 1932. [Chap. 8, Sec. 2]

H48   G. Hevesy: "Radioactive Indicators," Interscience Publishers, Inc., New York, 1948. [Chap. 7, Sec. 7]

H49   C. W. Hewlett: *Phys. Rev.*, **19**: 266 (1922); **20**: 688 (1922). [Chap. 1, Sec. 2]

H50   N. P. Heydenburg, C. M. Hudson, D. R. Inglis, and W. D. Whitehead, Jr.: *Phys. Rev.*, **74**: 405 (1948). [Chap. 6, Sec. 9]

H51   R. H. Hildebrand and C. E. Leith: *Phys. Rev.*, **80**: 842 (1950). [Chap. 14, Sec. 2]

H52   D. L. Hill: *Phys. Rev.*, **87**: 1034 (1952). [Chap. 11, Sec. 3]

H53   D. L. Hill and J. A. Wheeler: *Phys. Rev.*, **89**: 1102 (1953). [Chap. 2, Sec. 6; Chap. 4, Sec. 5; Chap. 11, Sec. 3]

H54   R. D. Hill: *Phys. Rev.*, **76**: 998L (1949). [Chap. 4, Sec. 5]

H54a R. D. Hill, E. L. Church, and J. W. Mihelich: *Rev. Sci. Instr.*, **23**: 523 (1952). [Chap. 24, Sec. 1]

H55   J. A. Hipple, H. Sommer, and H. A. Thomas: *Phys. Rev.*, **76**: 1877L (1949). [Chap. 4, Sec. 3]

H56   J. O. Hirschfelder and E. N. Adams, II: *Phys. Rev.*, **73**: 863 (1948). [Chap. 25, Sec. 3]

H57   J. O. Hirschfelder and J. L. Magee: *Phys. Rev.*, **73**: 852 (1948). [Chap. 25, Sec. 3]

H58   R. Hofstadter, H. R. Fechter, and J. A. McIntyre: *Phys. Rev.*, **92**: 978 (1953). [Chap. 2, Sec. 3]

H59   R. Hofstadter and J. A. McIntyre: *Phys. Rev.*, **78**: 24 (1950). [Chap. 23, Sec. 1]

H60   L. E. Hoisington, S. S. Share, and G. Breit: *Phys. Rev.*, **56**: 884 (1939). [Chap. 10, Sec. 5]

H61   J. M. Hollander, I. Perlman, and G. T. Seaborg: *Revs. Mod. Phys.*, **25**: 469 (1953). [Chap. 2, Sec. 2; Chap. 4, Sec. 4; Chap. 6, Sec. 3; Chap. 8, Sec. 3; Chap. 11, Sec. 3; Chap. 16, Secs. 1, 2, 4; Chap. 17, Sec. 3]

H62   M. G. Holloway and M. S. Livingston: *Phys. Rev.*, **54**: 18 (1938). [Chap. 16, Sec. 1; Chap. 22, Secs. 3, 4, 5]

H63   P. V. C. Hough: *Phys. Rev.*, **73**: 266L (1948). [Chap. 24, Sec. 2]

H64   P. V. C. Hough: *Phys. Rev.*, **74**: 80 (1948). [Chap. 20, Sec. 1]

H65   P. R. Howland and W. E. Kreger: *Phys. Rev.*, **95**: 407 (1954). [Chap. 25, Sec. 3]

H66   E. L. Hubbard and K. R. MacKenzie: *Phys. Rev.*, **85**: 107 (1952). [Chap. 22, Sec. 2]

H67   A. L. Hughes: *Am. Phys. Teacher*, **7**: 271 (1939). [Chap. 28, Sec. 2]

H68   D. J. Hughes: "Pile Neutron Research," Addison-Wesley Publishing Company, Cambridge, Mass., 1953. [Chap. 8, Sec. 2; Chap. 10, Sec. 3; Chap. 11, Sec. 4; Chap. 14, Introd.]

H69   D. J. Hughes, R. C. Garth, and J. S. Levin: *Phys. Rev.*, **91**: 1423 (1953). [Chap. 8, Sec. 2; Chap. 11, Sec. 4]

H70   D. S. Hughes: *Phys. Rev.*, **38**: 857 (1931). [Chap. 7, Sec. 2]

H71   H. K. Hughes: *Phys. Rev.*, **72**: 614 (1947). [Chap. 5, Sec. 3]

H72   V. Hughes and L. Grabner: *Phys. Rev.*, **79**: 314 (1950). [Chap. 5, Sec. 3]

H73   M. H. Hull, Jr., and A. Herschman: *Phys. Rev.*, **90**: 482 (1953). [Chap. 10, Sec. 9]

H74   H. R. Hulme: *Proc. Roy. Soc. (London)*, **A133**: 381 (1931). [Chap. 24, Sec. 1]

H75   H. R. Hulme, J. McDougall, R. A. Buckingham, and R. H. Fowler: *Proc. Roy. Soc. (London)*, **A149**: 131 (1935). [Chap. 24, Sec. 1]

H76   R. F. Humphreys: *Phys. Rev.*, **56**: 684 (1939). [Chap. 7, Sec. 8]

H77   E. T. Hungerford and R. D. Birkhoff: *Phys. Rev.*, **95**: 6 (1954). [Chap. 21, Sec. 3]

I1   K. Ilakovac and P. B. Moon: *Phys. Rev.*, **93**: 254L (1954). [Chap. 23, Introd.]

I2   M. G. Inghram and J. H. Reynolds: *Phys. Rev.*, **78**: 822L (1950). [Chap. 8, Sec. 3]

I3   D. R. Inglis: *Phys. Rev.*, **74**: 21 (1948). [Chap. 6, Sec. 9]

I4   D. R. Inglis: *Revs. Mod. Phys.*, **25**: 390 (1953); erratum, **27**: 76 (1955). [Chap. 4, Secs. 1, 5; Chap. 9, Sec. 4; Chap. 10, Introd.; Chap. 11, Sec. 3; Chap. 12, Sec. 1]

I5   International Commission on Radiological Units, *Nucleonics*, **12**(1): 11 (1954); *Am. J. Roentgenol., Radium Therapy, Nuclear Med.*, **71**: 139 (1954). [Chap. 25, Secs. 2, 4]

I6   J. Irving: *Phys. Rev.*, **87**: 519L (1952); *Proc. Phys. Soc. (London)*, **A66**: 17 (1953). [Chap. 10, Sec. 3]

I7   A. V. Ivanov, A. K. Walter, K. D. Sinelnikov, A. J. Taranov, and A. M. Abramovich: *J. Phys. (U.S.S.R.)*, **4**: 319 (1941). [Chap. 21, Sec. 2]

J1   H. L. Jackson and A. I. Galonsky: *Phys. Rev.*, **89**: 370 (1953). [Chap. 14, Sec. 1]

J2   J. D. Jackson and J. M. Blatt: *Revs. Mod. Phys.*, **22**: 77 (1950). [Chap. 10, Sec. 5]

J3   J. D. Jackson and H. Schiff: *Phys. Rev.*, **89**: 359 (1953). [Chap. 22, Sec. 1]

J4   J. C. Jacobsen: *Nature*, **117**: 858 (1926); *Phil. Mag.*, **10**: 401 (1930). [Chap. 22, Sec. 1]

J5   J. C. Jaeger and H. R. Hulme: *Proc. Roy. Soc. (London)*, **A148**: 708 (1935). [Chap. 6, Sec. 5]

J6   J. C. Jaeger and H. R. Hulme: *Proc. Roy. Soc. (London)*, **A153**: 443 (1936). [Chap. 24, Sec. 2]

J7   G. Jaffé: *Ann. Physik*, **42**: 303 (1913); **1**: 977 (1929); *Physik. Z.*, **30**: 849 (1929); *Phys. Rev.*, **58**: 968 (1940). [Chap. 22, Sec. 4]

J8   R. Jastrow: *Phys. Rev.*, **81**: 165 (1951). [Chap. 10, Sec. 9]

J9   R. Jastrow: *Phys. Rev.*, **81**: 636L (1951). [Chap. 10, Sec. 9]

J10   W. Jentschke: *Physik. Z.*, **41**: 524 (1940). [Chap. 22, Sec. 4]

J11   W. P. Jesse, H. Forstat, and J. Sadauskis: *Phys. Rev.*, **77**: 782 (1950). [Chap. 22, Sec. 4]

J12   W. P. Jesse and J. Sadauskis: *Phys. Rev.*, **78**: 1 (1950). [Chap. 22, Secs. 3, 4]

J13   W. P. Jesse and J. Sadauskis: *Phys. Rev.*, **88**: 417L (1952). [Chap. 22, Sec. 4]

J14   W. P. Jesse and J. Sadauskis: *Phys. Rev.*, **90**: 1120L (1953). [Chap. 22, Sec. 4]

J14*a*   W. P. Jesse and J. Sadauskis: *Phys. Rev.*, **97**: 1668 (1955). [Chap. 18, Sec. 4; Chap. 22, Sec. 4]

J15   W. Jevons: "Report on Band Spectra of Diatomic Molecules," Cambridge University Press, London, 1932. [Chap. 7, Sec. 3]

J16   E. G. Johnson and A. O. Nier: *Phys. Rev.*, **91**: 10 (1953). [Chap. 3, Sec. 3]

J17   W. H. Johnson: *Phys. Rev.*, **87**: 166L (1952). [Chap. 8, Sec. 3]

J18   R. C. Jones and W. H. Furry: *Revs. Mod. Phys.*, **18**: 151 (1946). [Chap. 7, Sec. 8]

J19   E. B. Jordan and K. T. Bainbridge: *Phys. Rev.*, **50**: 98L (1936). [Chap. 3, Sec. 4]

J20   W. H. Jordan: *Ann. Rev. Nuclear Sci.*, **1**: 207 (1952). [Chap. 25, Sec. 2]

K1   D. Kahn: *Phys. Rev.*, **90**: 503 (1953). [Chap. 22, Sec. 2]

K2   W. R. Kanne and J. A. Bearden: *Phys. Rev.*, **50**: 935 (1936). [Chap. 22, Sec. 4]

K3   H. Kanner: *Phys. Rev.*, **84**: 1211 (1951). [Chap. 22, Sec. 1]

K4   P. Kapitza: *Proc. Roy. Soc. (London)*, **A106**: 602 (1924). [Chap. 22, Sec. 1]

K5   P. L. Kapur and R. Peierls: *Proc. Roy. Soc. (London)*, **A166,** 277 (1938). [Chap. 14, Sec. 1]

K6   S. Katcoff, J. A. Miskel, and C. W. Stanley: *Phys. Rev.*, **74**: 631 (1948). [Chap. 22, Sec. 6]

K7   L. Katz and A. S. Penfold: *Revs. Mod. Phys.*, **24**: 28 (1952). [Chap. 21, Sec. 3]

K8   S. G. Kaufmann, E. Goldberg, L. J. Koester, and F. P. Mooring: *Phys. Rev.*, **88**: 673 (1952). [Chap. 10, Sec. 4; Chap. 14, Sec. 1]

K9   J. Keilson: *Phys. Rev.*, **82**: 759L (1951). [Chap. 11, Sec. 2]

K10   C. P. Keim: *Ann. Rev. Nuclear Sci.*, **1**: 263 (1952). [Chap. 7, Sec. 7]

K11   C. P. Keim: *Nucleonics*, **10**(8): 29 (1952). [Chap. 7, Sec. 7]

K12   J. M. B. Kellogg and S. Millman: *Revs. Mod. Phys.*, **18**: 323 (1946). [Chap. 5, Secs. 1, 2]

K13   J. M. B. Kellogg, I. I. Rabi, N. F. Ramsey, Jr., and J. R. Zacharias: *Phys. Rev.*, **55**: 318L (1939); **57**: 677 (1940). [Chap. 4, Sec. 5; Chap. 5, Sec. 3]

K14   J. M. B. Kellogg, I. I. Rabi, and J. R. Zacharias: *Phys. Rev.*, **50**: 472 (1936). [Chap. 5, Sec. 2]

K15   E. Kelly, C. Leith, E. Segrè, and C. Wiegand: *Phys. Rev.*, **79**: 96 (1950). [Chap. 10, Sec. 9]

K16   K. Kimura, R. Ishiwari, K. Yuasa, S. Yamashita, K. Miyako, and S. Kimura: *J. Phys. Soc. Japan*, **7**: 111 (1952). [Chap. 22, Sec. 4]

K17   A. King and W. M. Rayton: *Phys. Rev.*, **51**: 826 (1937). [Chap. 22, Sec. 5]

K18   A. S. King and R. T. Birge: *Astrophys. J.*, **72**: 19 (1930). [Chap. 7, Sec. 3]

K18*a* R. W. King: *Revs. Mod. Phys.*, **26**: 327 (1954). [Chap. 3, Sec. 5; Chap. 6, Sec. 3]

K19   A. F. Kip, A. G. Bousquet, R. D. Evans, and W. N. Tuttle: *Rev. Sci. Instr.*, **17**: 323, 515 (1946). [Chap. 28, Sec. 3]

K20   P. Kirkpatrick: *Phys. Rev.*, **70**: 446A (1946). [Chap. 21, Sec. 2]

K21   O. Klein and Y. Nishina: *Z. Physik*, **52**: 853 (1929). [Chap. 23, Sec. 2]

K22   P. F. A. Klinkenberg: *Physica*, **11**: 327 (1945). [Chap. 7, Sec. 2]

K23   P. F. A. Klinkenberg: *Revs. Mod. Phys.*, **24**: 63 (1952). [Chap. 4, Secs. 4, 5; Chap. 5, Sec. 1]

K24   H. P. Knauss: *Science*, **107**: 324 (1948). [Chap. 15, Sec. 2]

K25   J. K. Knipp and G. E. Uhlenbeck: *Physica*, **3**: 425 (1936). [Chap. 21, Sec. 2]

K26   H. W. Koch and R. E. Carter: *Phys. Rev.*, **75**: 1950L (1949). [Chap. 20, Sec. 1]

K27   J. Koch and E. Rasmussen: *Phys. Rev.*, **77**: 722L (1950). [Chap. 7, Sec. 2]

K28   H. W. Koch, J. McElhinney, and E. L. Gasteiger: *Phys. Rev.*, **77**: 329 (1950). [Chap. 11, Sec. 3]

K29   L. J. Koester, Jr.: *Phys. Rev.*, **85**: 643 (1952). [Chap. 2, Sec. 7]

K30   O. Kofoed-Hansen and A. Winther: *Phys. Rev.*, **86**: 428L (1952). [Chap. 17, Sec. 3]

K31   K. W. F. Kohlrausch: *Ergeb. exakt. Naturw.*, **5**: 197 (1926). [Chap. 27, Sec. 4]

K32   T. P. Kohman: *Am. J. Phys.*, **15**: 356 (1947). [Chap. 3, Sec. 2]

K33   T. P. Kohman: *Phys. Rev.*, **73**: 16 (1948). [Chap. 8, Sec. 3; Chap. 11, Sec. 3; Chap. 16, Sec. 3]

K34   T. P. Kohman: *Phys. Rev.*, **76**: 448L (1949). [Chap. 16, Sec. 4]

K35   T. P. Kohman: *Phys. Rev.*, **85**: 530 (1952). [Chap. 11, Sec. 3]

K36   T. P. Kohman and P. Fineman: Unpublished preliminary report, Argonne National Laboratory, Aug. 18, 1948. [Chap. 28, Sec. 1]

K37   E. J. Konopinski: *Revs. Mod. Phys.*, **15**: 209 (1943). [Chap. 6, Sec. 3; Chap. 17, Sec. 3]

K38   E. J. Konopinski and H. A. Bethe: *Phys. Rev.*, **54**: 130 (1938). [Chap. 14, Sec. 2]

K39   E. J. Konopinski and L. M. Langer: *Ann. Rev. Nuclear Sci.*, **2**: 261 (1953). [Chap. 6, Sec. 3; Chap. 8, Sec. 3; Chap. 17, Introd., Sec. 3]

K40   E. J. Konopinski and G. E. Uhlenbeck: *Phys. Rev.*, **48**: 7 (1935). [Chap. 17, Sec. 3]

K41   E. J. Konopinski and G. E. Uhlenbeck: *Phys. Rev.*, **60**: 308 (1941). [Chap. 6, Sec. 3; Chap. 17, Sec. 3]

K42   L. Kosten: *Physica*, **10**: 749 (1943). [Chap. 28, Sec. 1]

K43   A. F. Kovarik: *Phys. Rev.*, **13**: 272 (1919). [Chap. 27, Sec. 4]

K44   H. A. Kramers: *Physica*, **13**: 401 (1947). [Chap. 18, Sec. 5]

K45   W. Krasny-Ergen: *Phys. Rev.*, **58**: 1078 (1940). [Chap. 7, Sec. 8]

K46   J. J. Kraushaar, E. D. Wilson, and K. T. Bainbridge: *Phys. Rev.*, **90**: 610 (1953). [Chap. 17, Sec. 3]

K47   H. Kulenkampff: *Physik. Z.*, **30**: 513 (1929). [Chap. 20, Sec. 1]

K48   C. H. Kunsman: *Science*, **62**: 269 (1925). [Chap. 3, Sec. 3]

K49   F. N. D. Kurie and G. D. Knopf: *Phys. Rev.*, **43**: 311 (1933). [Chap. 16, Sec. 4]

K50   F. N. D. Kurie, J. R. Richardson, and H. C. Paxton: *Phys. Rev.*, **48**: 167L (1935); **49**: 368 (1936). [Chap. 17, Sec. 3]

K51   P. Kusch and H. M. Foley: *Phys. Rev.*, **72**: 1256L (1947); **74**: 250 (1948). [Chap. 4, Sec. 3]

K52   P. Kusch, S. Millman, and I. I. Rabi: *Phys. Rev.*, **57**: 765 (1940). [Chap. 5, Sec. 2]

L1   W. E. Lamb, Jr.: *Phys. Rev.*, **60**: 817 (1941). [Chap. 4, Sec. 3; Chap. 5, Sec. 1]

L2   W. E. Lamb, Jr., and R. C. Retherford: *Phys. Rev.*, **72**: 241 (1947). [Chap. 4, Sec. 3]

L3   E. E. Lampi, G. D. Freier, and J. H. Williams: *Phys. Rev.*, **80**: 853 (1950). [Chap. 10, Sec. 3]

L4   L. Landau: *J. Phys.* (*U.S.S.R.*), **8**: 201 (1944). [Chap. 21, Sec. 3]

L5   L. M. Langer and R. J. D. Moffat: *Phys. Rev.*, **82**: 635 (1951). [Chap. 6, Secs. 3, 7; Chap. 17, Sec. 3]

L6   L. M. Langer and R. J. D. Moffat: *Phys. Rev.*, **88**: 689 (1952). [Chap. 17, Sec. 3]

L7   L. M. Langer, R. J. D. Moffat, and H. C. Price, Jr.: *Phys. Rev.*, **76**: 1725L (1949). [Chap. 17, Sec. 3]

L8   L. M. Langer and H. C. Price, Jr.: *Phys. Rev.*, **76**: 641 (1949). [Chap. 6, Sec. 7; Chap. 17, Sec. 3]

L9   N. O. Lassen: *Phys. Rev.*, **75**: 1762L (1949). [Chap. 22, Sec. 6]

L10   N. O. Lassen: *Kgl. Danske Videnskab. Selskab, Mat.-fys. Medd.*, vol. 26, no. 5, 1951. [Chap. 22, Sec. 6]

L11   R. Latter and H. Kahn: R-240, The Rand Corporation, Santa Monica, Calif., 1949. [Chap. 25, Sec. 1]

L12   G. D. Latyshev: *Revs. Mod. Phys.*, **19**: 132 (1947). [Chap. 6, Sec. 5; Chap. 24, Sec. 1]

L13   R. A. Laubenstein and M. J. W. Laubenstein: *Phys. Rev.*, **84**: 18 (1951). [Chap. 2, Sec. 7]

L14   E. O. Lawrence, M. S. Livingston, and M. G. White: *Phys. Rev.*, **42**: 150L (1932). [Chap. 2, Sec. 8]

L15   J. L. Lawson: *Phys. Rev.*, **56**: 131 (1939). [Chap. 17, Sec. 3]

L16   J. L. Lawson: *Phys. Rev.*, **75**: 433 (1949). [Chap. 24, Sec. 2]

L17   J. L. Lawson and J. M. Cork: *Phys. Rev.*, **57**: 982 (1940). [Chap. 17, Sec. 3]

L18   D. E. Lea: "Actions of Radiations on Living Cells," The Macmillan Company, New York, 1947. [Chap. 18, Sec. 4; Chap. 23, Secs. 2, 3]

L19   C. Levert and W. L. Scheen: *Physica*, **10**: 225 (1943). [Chap. 28, Sec. 1]

L20   J. S. Levinger: *Phys. Rev.*, **90**: 11 (1953). [Chap. 21, Sec. 2]

L21   H. W. Lewis: *Phys. Rev.*, **85**: 20 (1952). [Chap. 22, Sec. 5]

L22   L. G. Lewis and R. J. Hayden: *Rev. Sci. Instr.*, **19**: 599 (1948). [Chap. 7, Sec. 6]

L23   W. B. Lewis: "Electrical Counting," Cambridge University Press, London, 1942. [Chap. 28, Sec. 1]

L24   W. B. Lewis and B. V. Bowden: *Proc. Roy. Soc.* (*London*), **A145**: 235 (1934). [Chap. 16, Sec. 1]

L25   W. B. Lewis and C. E. Wynn-Williams: *Proc. Roy. Soc.* (*London*), **A136**: 349 (1932). [Chap. 22, Sec. 5]

L26   C. W. Li: *Phys. Rev.*, **88**: 1038 (1952); erratum, **90**: 1131E (1953). [Chap. 3, Secs. 4, 5]

L27   C. W. Li, W. Whaling, W. A. Fowler, and C. C. Lauritsen: *Phys. Rev.*, **83**: 512 (1951). [Chap. 3, Secs. 3, 4, 5; Chap. 11, Sec. 3; Chap. 12, Sec. 2; Chap. 17, Sec. 2]

L28   Y. Li: *Phys. Rev.*, **80**: 104L (1950). [Chap. 18, Sec. 6]

L29   W. F. Libby: *Science*, **93**: 283 (1941). [Chap. 7, Sec. 9]

L30   H. Lifschutz and O. S. Duffendach: *Phys. Rev.*, **54**: 714 (1938). [Chap. 28, Sec. 1]

L31   H. J. Lipkin and M. G. White: *Phys. Rev.*, **79**: 892L (1950); erratum, **80**: 770L (1950). [Chap. 19, Sec. 1]

L32   M. S. Livingston and H. A. Bethe: *Revs. Mod. Phys.*, **9**: 245 (1937). [Chap. 18, Sec. 2; Chap. 22, Secs. 2, 3]

L33   M. S. Livingston, F. Genevese, and E. J. Konopinski: *Phys. Rev.*, **51**: 835 (1937). [Chap. 20, Sec. 1]

L34   G. D. Louderback, R. D. Evans, B. Gutenberg, G. P. Kuiper, R. C. Tolman, and P. S. Epstein: *Science*, **82**: 51 (1935). [Chap. 8, Sec. 2]

L35   W. Low and C. H. Townes: *Phys. Rev.*, **80**: 608 (1950). [Chap. 5, Sec. 3]

L36   E. Lutze: *Ann. Physik,* **9**: 853 (1931). [Chap. 24, Sec. 1]

L37   E. M. Lyman, A. O. Hanson, and M. B. Scott: *Phys. Rev.,* **84**: 626 (1951). [Chap. 2, Sec. 3]

M1   J. Macnamara, C. B. Collins, and H. G. Thode: *Phys. Rev.,* **78**: 129 (1950). [Chap. 7, Sec. 6]

M2   L. Madansky, F. Lipps, P. Bolgiano, and T. H. Berlin: *Phys. Rev.,* **84**: 596L (1951). [Chap. 21, Sec. 2]

M3   L. Madansky and F. Rassetti: *Phys. Rev.,* **94**: 407 (1954). [Chap. 21, Sec. 2]

M4   E. Madgwick: *Proc. Cambridge Phil. Soc.,* **23**: 970 (1927). [Chap. 21, Sec. 3]

M5   H. Maier-Leibnitz: *Z. Naturforsch.,* **1**: 243 (1946). [Chap. 25, Sec. 2]

M6   B. J. Malenka: *Phys. Rev.,* **86**: 68 (1952). [Chap. 11, Sec. 2]

M7   A. K. Mann and P. Kusch: *Phys. Rev.,* **77**: 435 (1950). [Chap. 4, Sec. 3]

M8   G. Mano: *Ann. phys.,* **1**: 407 (1934). [Chap. 22, Secs. 2, 3]

M9   G. Manov: *Natl. Research Council (U.S.), Nuclear Sci. Ser. Prelim. Rept.* 13, 1953. [Chap. 25, Sec. 2]

M10   H. Margenau and E. Wigner: *Phys. Rev.,* **58**: 103 (1940). [Chap. 4, Sec. 4]

M11   L. D. Marinelli, R. F. Brinckerhoff, and G. J. Hine: *Revs. Mod. Phys.,* **19**: 25 (1947). [Chap. 17, Sec. 1; Chap. 21, Sec. 2]

M12   E. Marsden and T. Barratt: *Proc. Phys. Soc. (London),* **A23**: 367 (1911); **A24**: 50 (1911). [Chap. 26, Sec. 1]

M13   R. E. Marshak: *Phys. Rev.,* **61**: 431 (1942). [Chap. 17, Sec. 3]

M14   R. E. Marshak: *Ann. Rev. Nuclear Sci.,* **1**: 1 (1952). [Chap. 2, Sec. 3; Chap. 8, Sec. 1]

M15   R. E. Marshak: "Meson Physics," McGraw-Hill Book Company, Inc., New York, 1952. [Chap. 2, Sec. 3]

M16   J. Marshall: *Phys. Rev.,* **81**: 275L (1951). [Chap. 18, Sec. 6]

M17   J. S. Marshall and A. G. Ward: *Can. J. Research,* **A15**: 39 (1937). [Chap. 21, Sec. 3]

M18   R. L. Mather: *Phys. Rev.,* **84**: 181 (1951). [Chap. 18, Sec. 6]

M19   R. L. Mather and E. Segrè: *Phys. Rev.,* **84**: 191 (1951). [Chap. 22, Sec. 2]

M20   J. Mattauch: *Naturwiss.,* **25**: 189 (1937). [Chap. 6, Sec. 8; Chap. 7, Introd.]

M21   J. Mattauch and A. Flammersfeld: "Isotopic Report," Verlag der Zeitschrift für Naturforschung, Tübingen, Germany, 1949. [Chap. 3, Sec. 5]

M22   J. Mattauch and S. Fluegge: "Nuclear Physics Tables" and "An Introduction to Nuclear Physics," Interscience Publishers, Inc., New York, 1946. [Chap. 3, Sec. 5; Chap. 9, Secs. 1, 2, 3; Chap. 11, Sec. 3]

M22a   D. R. Maxson, J. S. Allen, and W. K. Jentschke: *Phys. Rev.,* **97**: 109 (1955). [Chap. 17, Sec. 2]

M23   M. G. Mayer: *Phys. Rev.,* **74**: 235 (1948). [Chap. 11, Sec. 2]

M24   M. G. Mayer: *Phys. Rev.,* **75**: 1969L (1949). [Chap. 4, Sec. 1; Chap. 11, Sec. 2]

M25   M. G. Mayer: *Phys. Rev.,* **78**: 16 (1950). [Chap. 11, Sec. 2]

M26   M. G. Mayer: *Phys. Rev.,* **78**: 22 (1950). [Chap. 11, Sec. 2]

M27   M. G. Mayer, S. A. Moszkowski, and L. W. Nordheim: *Revs. Mod. Phys.,* **23**: 315 (1951). [Chap. 6, Sec. 3; Chap. 17, Sec. 3]

M28   K. I. Mayne: *Repts. Progr. in Phys.,* **15**: 24 (1952). [Chap. 3, Sec. 3]

M29   W. V. Mayneord: *Brit. J. Radiol.,* **18**: 12 (1945). [Chap. 25, Sec. 4]

M30   W. V. Mayneord and J. E. Roberts: *Brit. J. Radiol.,* **10**: 365 (1937). [Chap. 25, Sec. 2]

M31   G. W. McClure: *Phys. Rev.,* **90**: 796 (1953). [Chap. 18, Sec. 4]

M32   B. D. McDaniel, G. von Dardel, and R. L. Walker: *Phys. Rev.,* **72**: 985L (1947). [Chap. 24, Sec. 2]

M33   F. K. McGowan: *Phys. Rev.,* **93**: 163 (1954). [Chap. 6, Sec. 5]

M34   H. A. C. McKay: *Progr. Nuclear Phys.*, **1**: 168 (1950). [Chap. **7**, Sec. 9]

M35   L. W. McKeehan: *Am. J. Phys.*, **16**: 187, 356 (1948). [Chap. 11, Sec. 3]

M36   W. A. McKinley, Jr., and H. Feshbach: *Phys. Rev.*, **74**: 1759 (1948). [Chap. 19, Sec. 1]

M37   E. M. McMillan: *Phys. Rev.*, **47**: 801A (1935). [Chap. 21, Sec. 2]

M38   J. R. McNally, Jr.: *Am. J. Phys.*, **20**: 152 (1952). [Chap. 5, Sec. 3]

M39   L. Meitner: *Z. Physik.*, **9**: 131, 145 (1922). [Chap. 6, Sec. 5]

M40   L. Meitner and W. Orthmann: *Z. Physik*, **60**: 143 (1930). [Chap. 17, Sec. 1]

M41   E. Melkonian: *Phys. Rev.*, **76**: 1744, 1750 (1949). [Chap. 10, Sec. 3]

M42   V. W. Mellor: "A Comprehensive Treatise on Inorganic and Theoretical Chemistry," vol. 1, p. 255, Longmans, Green & Co., Ltd., London, 1922. [Introd.]

M43   N. Metropolis and G. Reitwiesner: NP-1980, 1950. [Chap. 11, Sec. 3]

M44   F. Metzger and M. Deutsch: *Phys. Rev.*, **78**: 551 (1950). [Chap. 6, Sec. 8; Chap. 23, Sec. 2]

M44a Stefan Meyer and C. Ulrich: *Sitzber. Akad. Wiss. Wien, Math.-naturw. Kl.*, **132**(IIa): 279 (1923). [Chap. 16, Sec. 2]

M45   D. W. Miller, R. K. Adair, C. K. Bockelman, and S. E. Darden: *Phys. Rev.*, **88**: 83 (1952). [Chap. 14, Sec. 2]

M46   R. A. Millikan: *Phil. Mag.*, **19**: 209 (1910). [Introd.]

M47   S. Millman and M. Fox: *Phys. Rev.*, **50**: 220 (1936). [Chap. 5, Sec. 2]

M48   E. A. Milne: *Phys. Rev.*, **93**: 762 (1954). [Chap. 13, Sec. 4]

M49   E. C. Molina: "Poisson's Exponential Binomial Limit," D. Van Nostrand Company, Inc., New York, 1942. [Chap. 26, Sec. 1; Chap. 28, Sec. 2]

M50   C. Möller: *Ann. Physik*, **14**: 531 (1932). [Chap. 18, Sec. 2; Chap. 19, Sec. 2]

M51   G. W. Monk, J. D. Graves, and J. L. Horton: *Rev. Sci. Instr.*, **18**: 796L (1947). [Chap. 3, Sec. 3]

M52   J. H. Montague: *Phys. Rev.*, **81**: 1026 (1951). [Chap. 22, Sec. 1]

M53   C. G. Montgomery and D. D. Montgomery: *Phys. Rev.*, **44**: 779L (1933). [Chap. 27, Sec. 4]

M54   P. B. Moon: "Artificial Radioactivity," Cambridge University Press, London, 1949. [Chap. 6, Sec. 4]

M55   K. Z. Morgan: *J. Appl. Phys.*, **19**: 593 (1948). [Chap. 25, Sec. 3]

M56   A. Morrison: *Nucleonics*, **5**(6): 19 (1949), and personal communication. [Chap. 25, Sec. 3]

M57   P. Morrison in E. Segrè (ed.): "Experimental Nuclear Physics," vol. 2, John Wiley & Sons, Inc., New York, 1953. [Chap. 1, Sec. 3; Chap. 11, Secs. 3, 4; Chap. 12, Sec. 2]

M58   P. Morrison and L. I. Schiff: *Phys. Rev.*, **58**: 24 (1940). [Chap. 21, Sec. 2]

M59   P. M. Morse: "Vibration and Sound," p. 246, 1st ed., 1936, or p. 316, 2d ed., 1948, McGraw-Hill Book Company, Inc., New York. [Appendix C, Sec. 3]

M60   H. G. Moseley: *Phil. Mag.*, **26**: 1024 (1913); **27**: 703 (1914). [Introd.; Chap. 1, Sec. 4]

M61   S. A. Moszkowski: *Phys. Rev.*, **82**: 35 (1951). [Chap. 6, Sec. 3; Chap. 17, Sec. 3]

M62   S. A. Moszkowski and C. H. Townes: *Phys. Rev.*, **93**: 306 (1954). [Chap. 4, Sec. 5]

M63   N. F. Mott: *Proc. Roy. Soc. (London)*, **A118**: 542 (1928). [Chap. 1, Sec. 3]

M64   N. F. Mott: *Proc. Roy. Soc. (London)*, **A124**: 425 (1929). [Chap. 19, Sec. 1]

M65   N. F. Mott: *Proc. Roy. Soc. (London)*, **A126**: 259 (1930). [Chap. 10, Sec. 5; Chap. 19, Sec. 2]

M66   N. F. Mott: *Proc. Cambridge Phil. Soc.*, **27**: 255 (1931). [Chap. 20, Sec. 1]

M67   N. F. Mott: *Proc. Roy. Soc. (London)*, **A135**: 429 (1932). [Chap. 19, Sec. 1]

M68   N. F. Mott: "Elements of Wave Mechanics," Cambridge University Press, London, 1952. [Chap. 2, Sec. 5; Appendix C, Sec. 6]

M69   N. F. Mott and H. S. W. Massey: "The Theory of Atomic Collisions," Oxford University Press, London, 1949. [Chap. 2, Sec. 7; Chap. 10, Sec. 5; Chap. 14, Sec. 1; Chap. 18, Sec. 2; Chap. 19, Sec. 2; Appendix C, Secs. 3, 5, 6]

M70   W. E. Mott, R. B. Sutton, J. G. Fox, and J. A. Kane: *Phys. Rev.*, **90**: 712L (1953). [Chap. 10, Sec. 9]

M71   H. T. Motz and D. E. Alburger: *Phys. Rev.*, **86**: 165 (1952). [Chap. 3, Sec. 4]

M72   H. Motz and L. I. Schiff: *Am. J. Phys.*, **21**: 258 (1953). [Chap. 18, Sec. 6]

M73   N. Moulin: *Ann. chim. et phys.*, **21**: 550 (1910); **22**: 26 (1911). [Chap. 22, Sec. 4]

M74   C. O. Muelhause and H. Friedman: *Rev. Sci. Instr.*, **17**: 506 (1946). [Chap. 28, Sec. 1]

M75   K. Murakawa and S. Suwa: *Phys. Rev.*, **87**: 1048 (1952). [Chap. 4, Sec. 5; Chap. 5, Sec. 3]

M76   O. E. Myers: *Nucleonics*, **5**(5): 37 (1949). [Chap. 17, Sec. 1]

N1   H. Nagaoka: *Phil. Mag.*, **7**: 445 (1904). [Introd.]

N2   M. E. Nahmias: *Proc. Cambridge Phil. Soc.*, **31**: 99 (1935). [Chap. 17, Sec. 2]

N3   R. Naidu: *Ann. phys.*, **1**: 72 (1934). [Chap. 22, Sec. 5]

N4   National Bureau of Standards: Nuclear Data, *Cir.* 499, 1950, and supplements. [Chap. 16, Sec. 1]

N5   National Bureau of Standards: Tables for the Analysis of Beta Spectra, *Appl. Math. Ser.* 13, 1952. [Chap. 17, Sec. 3; Appendix D]

N6   National Bureau of Standards: Mass Spectroscopy in Physics Research, *Cir.* 522, 1953. [Chap. 7, Introd.; Chap. 8, Sec. 3]

N7   G. J. Neary: *Proc. Roy. Soc. (London)*, **A175**: 71 (1940). [Chap. 17, Sec. 1]

N8   A. T. Nelms: Graphs of the Compton Energy-Angle Relationship and the Klein-Nishina Formula from 10 kev to 500 Mev, *Natl. Bur. Standards (U.S.) Cir.* 542, 1953. [Chap. 23, Sec. 2]

N9   A. S. Newton: *Phys. Rev.*, **75**: 17 (1949). [Chap. 11, Sec. 3]

N10   E. P. Ney and A. K. Mann: *Phys. Rev.*, **69**: 239L (1946). [Chap. 3, Sec. 3]

N11   W. W. Nicholas: *Bur. Standards J. Research*, **2**: 837 (1929). [Chap. 20, Sec. 1]

N12   A. O. Nier: *J. Am. Chem. Soc.*, **60**: 1571 (1938). [Chap. 7, Sec. 1]

N13   A. O. Nier: *Phys. Rev.*, **53**: 922A (1938). [Chap. 7, Sec. 4]

N14   A. O. Nier: *Phys. Rev.*, **55**: 153 (1939); errata, **60**: 112 (1941). [Chap. 7, Introd.]

N15   A. O. Nier: *Phys. Rev.*, **57**: 30 (1940). [Chap. 7, Sec. 8]

N16   A. O. Nier: *Rev. Sci. Instr.*, **11**: 212 (1940). [Chap. 3, Sec. 3]

N17   A. O. Nier: *Rev. Sci. Instr.*, **18**: 398 (1947). [Chap. 3, Sec. 3]

N18   A. O. Nier: *Phys. Rev.*, **77**: 789 (1950). [Chap. 7, Sec. 5]

N19   A. O. Nier: *Phys. Rev.*, **81**: 624L (1951). [Chap. 3, Sec. 3]

N20   A. O. Nier and A. Gulbransen: *J. Am. Chem. Soc.*, **61**: 697 (1939). [Chap. 7, Introd.]

N21   A. O. Nier and T. R. Roberts: *Phys. Rev.*, **81**: 507 (1951). [Chap. 3, Sec. 3]

N22   L. W. Nordheim: *Phys. Rev.*, **75**: 1894 (1949). [Chap. 11, Sec. 2]

N23   L. W. Nordheim: *Phys. Rev.*, **78**: 294L (1950); *Revs. Mod. Phys.*, **23**: 322 (1951). [Chap. 4, Sec. 4; Chap. 6, Sec. 3; Chap. 17, Sec. 1]

N24   Nuclear Science Abstracts: vol. 7, no. 6B, supplement, p. 2, 1953. [Chap. 4, Sec. 3]

O1   W. E. Ogle and P. G. Kruger: *Phys. Rev.*, **67**: 282 (1945). [Chap. 24, Sec. 2]

O1a   A. Okazaki, S. E. Darden, and R. B. Walton: *Phys. Rev.*, **93**: 461 (1954). [Chap. 14, Sec. 2]

O2   F. Oppenheimer: *Proc. Cambridge Phil. Soc.*, **32**: 328 (1936). [Chap. 16, Sec. 1]

O3   J. R. Oppenheimer: *Phys. Rev.*, **60**: 164A (1941). [Chap. 6, Sec. 5]

O4   J. R. Oppenheimer and M. S. Plesset: *Phys. Rev.*, **44**: 53L (1933). [Chap. 24, Sec. 2]

O5   J. R. Oppenheimer and J. S. Schwinger: *Phys. Rev.*, **56**: 1066L (1939). [Chap. 6, Sec. 5]

O6   J. S. Osoba: *Phys. Rev.*, **76**: 345 (1949). [Chap. 6, Sec. 7]

O7   G. E. Owen and C. S. Cook: *Phys. Rev.*, **76**: 1726L (1949). [Chap. 17, Sec. 3]

O8   C. L. Oxley, W. F. Cartwright, and J. Rouvina: *Phys. Rev.*, **93**: 806 (1954). [Chap. 10, Sec. 9]

O9   C. L. Oxley and R. D. Schamberger: *Phys. Rev.*, **85**: 416 (1952). [Chap. 10, Sec. 9]

P1   G. E. Pake: *Am. J. Phys.*, **18**: 438, 473 (1950). [Chap. 4, Sec. 2; Chap. 5, Sec. 2]

P2   F. A. Paneth: "The Origin of Meteorites," Clarendon Press, Oxford, 1940. [Chap. 8, Sec. 2]

P3   F. A. Paneth: *Nature*, **166**: 931 (1950); *Nucleonics*, **8**(5): 38 (1951). [Chap. 15, Sec. 1; Chap. 25, Sec. 2]

P4   F. A. Paneth and G. Hevesy: *Sitzber. Akad. Wiss. Wien, Math.-naturw. Kl.*, **122**(IIa): 993 (1913). [Chap. 3, Sec. 1]

P5   W. K. H. Panofsky and F. L. Fillmore: *Phys. Rev.*, **79**: 57 (1950). [Chap. 10, Sec. 9]

P6   H. M. Parker: MDDC-1012, 1947. [Chap. 21, Sec. 2]

P7   S. Pasternack and H. S. Snyder: *Phys. Rev.*, **80**: 921L (1950). [Chap. 14, Sec. 2]

P8   W. Pauli: in "Rapports du Septième Conseil de Physique Solvay, Brussels, 1933," Gauthier-Villars & Cie, Paris, 1934. [Chap. 17, Sec. 2]

P9   W. Pauli: *Phys. Rev.*, **58**: 716 (1940); *Revs. Mod. Phys.*, **13**: 203 (1941). [Chap. 4, Sec. 7]

P10   K. Pearson: *Phil. Mag.*, **50**: 157 (1900). [Chap. 27, Sec. 2]

P11   R. L. Pease and H. Feshbach: *Phys. Rev.*, **88**: 945 (1952). [Chap. 10, Secs. 6, 8]

P12   G. H. Peebles and M. S. Plesset: *Phys. Rev.*, **81**: 430 (1951). [Chap. 25, Sec. 3]

P13   W. F. Peed, E. J. Spitzer, and L. E. Burkhart: *Phys. Rev.*, **76**: 143L (1949). [Chap. 1, Sec. 4]

P14   R. Peierls: *Proc. Roy. Soc. (London)*, **A149**: 467 (1935). [Chap. 28, Sec. 5]

P15   I. Perlman, A. Ghiorso, and G. T. Seaborg: *Phys. Rev.*, **77**: 26 (1950). [Chap. 6, Sec. 2; Chap. 11, Sec. 3; Chap. 16, Sec. 4]

P16   I. Perlman and T. J. Ypsilantis: *Phys. Rev.*, **79**: 30 (1950). [Chap. 2, Sec. 6; Chap. 16, Sec. 4]

P17   F. Perrin: *Compt. rend.*, **197**: 1100 (1933). [Chap. 24, Sec. 2]

P18   E. Persico and C. Geoffrion: *Rev. Sci. Instr.*, **21**: 945 (1950). [Chap. 3, Sec. 3; Chap. 17, Secs. 1, 3]

P19   H. B. Phillips: "Analytical Geometry and Calculus," John Wiley & Sons, Inc., New York, 1947. [Appendix B, Sec. 3]

P20   J. A. Phillips and P. G. Kruger: *Phys. Rev.*, **76**: 1471 (1949). [Chap. 24, Sec. 2]

P21   J. A. Phillips, J. S. Lawson, Jr., and P. G. Kruger: *Phys. Rev.*, **80**: 326 (1950). [Chap. 10, Sec. 4]

P22   R. W. Pidd, C. L. Hammer, and E. C. Raka: *Phys. Rev.*, **92**: 436 (1953). [Chap. 2, Sec. 3]

P23   M. S. Plesset and S. T. Cohen: *J. Appl. Phys.*, **22**: 350 (1951).   [Chap. 25, Sec. 3]

P24   Plutonium Project Report, *Revs. Mod. Phys.*, **18**: 513 (1946); *J. Am. Chem. Soc.*, **68**: 2411 (1946).   [Chap. 11, Sec. 3]

P25   E. C. Pollard: *Phys. Rev.*, **47**: 611 (1935).   [Chap. 2, Sec. 7]

P26   H. Pose: *Z. Physik*, **64**: 1 (1930).   [Chap. 13, Sec. 4]

P27   H. L. Poss: BNL-26, 1949.   [Chap. 4, Secs. 3, 5]

P28   R. V. Pound: *Progr. Nuclear Phys.*, **2**: 21 (1952).   [Chap. 5, Sec. 2]

P29   C. F. Powell: *Repts. Progr. in Phys.*, **13**: 350 (1950).   [Chap. 2, Sec. 3]

P30   R. D. Present: *Phys. Rev.*, **60**: 28 (1941).   [Chap. 2, Sec. 1]

P31   M. A. Preston: *Phys. Rev.*, **71**: 865 (1947).   [Chap. 2, Sec. 6; Appendix C, Sec. 5]

P32   M. A. Preston: LT-29, 1950.   [Chap. 17, Introd.]

P33   M. A. Preston: *Phys. Rev.*, **83**: 475L (1951).   [Appendix C, Sec. 5]

P34   H. Primakoff: *Phys. Rev.*, **85**: 888 (1952).   [Chap. 8, Sec. 3]

P35   W. G. Proctor: *Phys. Rev.*, **79**: 35 (1950).   [Chap. 5, Sec. 2]

P36   M. H. L. Pryce: *Proc. Roy. Soc. (London)*, **A63**: 692 (1950).   [Chap. 11, Sec. 3]

P37   E. M. Purcell, H. C. Torrey, and R. V. Pound: *Phys. Rev.*, **69**: 37L (1946). [Chap. 5, Sec. 2]

R1   I. I. Rabi, J. M. B. Kellogg, and J. R. Zacharias: *Phys. Rev.*, **46**: 157 (1934). [Chap. 5, Sec. 2]

R2   I. I. Rabi, J. R. Zacharias, S. Millman, and P. Kusch: *Phys. Rev.*, **53**: 318L (1938).   [Chap. 5, Sec. 2]

R3   N. F. Ramsey in E. Segrè (ed.): "Experimental Nuclear Physics," vol. 1, pt. III, John Wiley & Sons, Inc., New York, 1953.   [Chap. 4, Sec. 5; Chap. 5, Secs. 1, 2]

R4   N. F. Ramsey in E. Segrè (ed.): "Experimental Nuclear Physics," vol. 1, pt. IV, John Wiley & Sons, Inc., New York, 1953.   [Chap. 10, Secs. 4, 9]

R5   R. B. Randels, K. T. Chao, and H. R. Crane: *Phys. Rev.*, **68**: 64 (1945). [Chap. 19, Sec. 1]

R6   W. Rarita and J. Schwinger: *Phys. Rev.*, **59**: 436 (1941).   [Chap. 4, Sec. 5; Chap. 10, Sec. 8]

R7   J. O. Rasmussen, F. L. Reynolds, S. G. Thompson, and A. Ghiorso: *Phys. Rev.*, **80**: 475L (1950).   [Chap. 7, Sec. 2]

R8   J. O. Rasmussen, Jr., S. G. Thompson, and A. Ghiorso: *Phys. Rev.*, **89**: 33 (1953).   [Chap. 16, Secs. 1, 4]

R9   V. K. Rasmussen, W. F. Hornyak, C. C. Lauritsen, and T. Lauritsen: *Phys. Rev.*, **77**: 617 (1950).   [Chap. 6, Sec. 5]

R10   Lord Rayleigh: "Theory of Sound," Macmillan & Co., Ltd., London, 1894. [Appendix C, Sec. 3]

R11   G. W. Reed and A. Turkevich: *Phys. Rev.*, **92**: 1473 (1953).   [Chap. 11, Sec. 3]

R12   A. F. Reid: "Preparation and Measurement of Isotopic Tracers," J. W. Edwards, Publisher, Inc., Ann Arbor, Mich., 1946.   [Chap. 28, Sec. 1]

R13   F. Reines and C. L. Cowan, Jr.: *Phys. Rev.*, **92**: 830L (1953).   [Chap. 17, Sec. 2]

R14   J. R. Reitz: *Phys. Rev.*, **77**: 10 (1950).   [Chap. 17, Secs. 1, 3]

R15   F. L. Reynolds: *Rev. Sci. Instr.*, **22**: 749 (1951). [Chap. 16, Sec. 1]

R16   F. L. Ribe: *Phys. Rev.*, **83**: 1217 (1951). [Chap. 22, Sec. 1]

R17   P. I. Richards, E. E. Hays, and S. A. Goudsmit: *Phys. Rev.*, **85**: 630 (1952).
       [Chap. 3, Sec. 3; Chap. 11, Sec. 3]

R18   F. K. Richtmyer and E. H. Kennard: "Introduction to Modern Physics,"
       4th ed., McGraw-Hill Book Company, Inc., New York, 1947. [Chap. 2,
       Sec. 5; Chap. 4, Sec. 3; Chap. 9, Sec. 2; Appendix A, Sec. 1]

R19   W. Riss: *Sitzber. Akad. Wiss. Wien, Math.-naturw. Kl.*, **133**(IIa): 91 (1924).
       [Chap. 16, Sec. 2]

R20   A. Roberts: *Rev. Sci. Instr.*, **12**: 71 (1941). [Chap. 26, Sec. 1]

R21   A. Roberts, L. G. Elliott, J. R. Downing, W. C. Peacock, and M. Deutsch:
       Phys. Rev., **64**: 268 (1943). [Chap. 25, Sec. 2]

R22   J. M. Robson: *Phys. Rev.*, **81**: 297A (1951). [Chap. 3, Sec. 4]

R23   G. W. Rodeback and J. S. Allen: *Phys. Rev.*, **86**: 446 (1952). [Chap. 17,
       Sec. 2]

R24   H. Roderick and C. Wong: *Phys. Rev.*, **92**: 204L (1953). [Chap. 2, Sec. 2]

R25   E. Rodgers: *Phys. Rev.*, **57**: 735 (1940). [Chap. 26, Sec. 2]

R26   W. K. Roentgen: *Sitzber. Würzberger Phys.-Med. Ges.*, December, 1895.
       Condensed English translations are given by W. F. Magie, "Source
       Book in Physics," McGraw-Hill Book Company, Inc., New York, 1935.
       [Introd.]

R27   G. A. Ropp: *Nucleonics*, **10**(10): 22 (1952). [Chap. 7, Sec. 8]

R28   M. E. Rose: *Phys. Rev.*, **57**: 958 (1940). [Chap. 2, Sec. 7]

R29   M. E. Rose: *Nucleonics*, **2**(6): 57 (1948); **3**(1): 57 (1948). [Chap. 4, Sec. 5;
       Chap. 10, Sec. 8]

R30   M. E. Rose: *Phys. Rev.*, **76**: 678 (1949); erratum, **78**: 184L (1950). [Chap. 6,
       Sec. 5]

R31   M. E. Rose, G. H. Goertzel, and C. L. Perry: ORNL-1023, 1951. [Chap. 6,
       Sec. 5]

R32   M. E. Rose, G. H. Goertzel, B. I. Spinrad, J. Harr, and P. Strong: *Phys. Rev.*,
       83: 79 (1951). [Chap. 6, Sec. 5]

R33   M. E. Rose and J. L. Jackson: *Phys. Rev.*, **76**: 1540L (1949). [Chap. 17,
       Sec. 3]

R34   M. E. Rose and G. E. Uhlenbeck: *Phys. Rev.*, **48**: 211 (1935). [Chap. 6,
       Sec. 5]

R35   S. Rosenblum: *Compt. rend.*, **188**: 1401 (1929); *J. phys.*, **1**: 438 (1930) et seq.
       [Chap. 16, Sec. 1]

R36   L. Rosenfeld: "Nuclear Forces," Interscience Publishers, Inc., New York,
       vol. I, 1948, vol. II, 1949. [Chap. 3, Sec. 5; Chap. 11, Sec. 3]

R37   B. Rossi and K. Greisen: *Revs. Mod. Phys.*, **13**: 240 (1941). [Chap. 18, Sec.
       2]

R38   A. E. Ruark: *Phys. Rev.*, **44**: 654 (1933). [Chap. 15, Sec. 1]

R39   L. H. Rumbaugh and L. R. Hafstad: *Phys. Rev.*, **50**: 681 (1936). [Chap. 7,
       Sec. 7]

R40   H. N. Russell: *Science*, **94**: 375 (1941). [Chap. 8, Sec. 2]

R41   B. M. Rustad and S. L. Ruby: *Phys. Rev.*, **89**: 880L (1953); **90**: 370A (1953);
       97: 991 (1955). [Chap. 17, Sec. 2]

R42   E. Rutherford: *Phil. Mag.*, **11**: 166 (1906); **12**: 134 (1906). [Introd.]

R43   E. Rutherford: *Phil. Mag.*, **21**: 669 (1911). A facsimile is included in the
       anthology "Foundations of Nuclear Physics," compiled by R. T. Beyer,
       Dover Publications, New York, 1949. [Introd.; Chap. 1, Sec. 3]

R44   E. Rutherford: "Radioactive Substances and Their Radiations," Cambridge
       University Press, London, 1913. [Chap. 16, Sec. 2; Chap. 17, Sec. 1]

R45   E. Rutherford: *Phil. Mag.*, **37**: 537 (1919).   [Chap. 2, Secs. 1, 7]

R46   E. Rutherford: *Phil. Mag.*, **37**: 581 (1919).   [Introd.]

R47   E. Rutherford: *Proc. Roy. Soc. (London)*, **A97**: 374 (1920).   [Chap. 13, Sec. 2]

R48   E. Rutherford: *Phil. Mag.*, **47**: 277 (1924).   [Chap. 22, Sec. 1]

R49   E. Rutherford: *Phil. Mag.*, **4**: 580 (1927).   [Chap. 2, Secs. 1, 4]

R50   E. Rutherford, J. Chadwick, and C. D. Ellis: "Radiations from Radioactive Substances," Cambridge University Press, London, 1930. [Chap. 2, Sec. 7; Chap. 16, Sec. 4; Chap. 17, Sec. 1]

R51   E. Rutherford and T. Royds: *Phil. Mag.*, **17**: 281 (1909).   [Chap. 22, Sec. 1]

R52   E. Rutherford and F. Soddy: *Phil. Mag.*, **4**: 370 (1902); **4**: 569 (1902); **5**: 576 (1903).   [Chap. 15, Introd., Secs. 1, 5]

R53   E. Rutherford, E. C. Wynn-Williams, W. B. Lewis, and B. V. Bowden: *Proc. Roy. Soc. (London)*, **A139**: 617 (1933).   [Chap. 16, Sec. 1]

R54   A. Rytz: *J. recherches centre natl. recherche sci., Labs. Bellevue (Paris)*, **25**: 254 (1953).   [Chap. 16, Sec. 1]

S1   D. C. Sachs and J. R. Richardson: *Phys. Rev.*, **83**: 834 (1951).   For important corrections, see *Phys. Rev.*, **89**: 1163 (1953); **94**: 79 (1954).   [Chap. 22, Sec. 2]

S2   R. G. Sachs: *Phys. Rev.*, **72**: 91 (1947).   [Chap. 4, Sec. 5]

S3   E. E. Salpeter: *Phys. Rev.*, **82**: 60 (1951).   [Chap. 10, Secs. 3, 4]

S4   B. W. Sargent: *Proc. Roy. Soc. (London)*, **A139**: 659 (1933).   [Chap. 6, Sec. 3]

S5   B. W. Sargent: LP-16, 1947.   [Chap. 16, Sec. 2]

S6   F. Sauter: *Ann. Physik*, **11**: 454 (1931).   [Chap. 24, Sec. 1]

S7   A. L. Schawlow and C. H. Townes: *Science*, **115**: 284 (1952).   [Chap. 2, Sec. 3]

S8   L. I. Schiff: *Phys. Rev.*, **50**: 88 (1936).   [Chap. 28, Sec. 1]

S9   L. I. Schiff: *Phys. Rev.*, **50**: 394A (1936).   [Chap. 28, Sec. 6]

S10   L. I. Schiff: *Phys. Rev.*, **70**: 87L (1946).   [Chap. 20, Sec. 1]

S11   L. I. Schiff: "Quantum Mechanics," McGraw-Hill Book Company, Inc., New York, 1949.   [Chap. 2, Sec. 5; Chap. 6, Secs. 4, 8; Chap. 24, Sec. 2; Appendix C, Sec. 2]

S12   L. I. Schiff and R. D. Evans: *Rev. Sci. Instr.*, **7**: 456 (1936).   [Chap. 28, Sec. 3]

S13   H. W. Schmidt: *Physik. Z.*, **8**: 361 (1907).   [Chap. 17, Sec. 1]

S14   T. Schmidt: *Z. Physik*, **106**: 358 (1937).   [Chap. 4, Sec. 4]

S15   T. Schmidt: *Naturwiss.*, **28**: 565 (1940).   [Chap. 4, Sec. 5]

S16   B. F. J. Schonland: *Proc. Roy. Soc. (London)*, **A108**: 187 (1925).   [Chap. 21, Sec. 3]

S17   H. Schüler and T. Schmidt: *Z. Physik*, **92**: 148 (1934).   [Chap. 7, Sec. 2]

S18   H. Schüler and T. Schmidt: *Z. Physik*, **94**: 457 (1935).   [Chap. 4, Sec. 5; Chap. 5, Sec. 3]

S19   H. Schulze: *Physik. Z.*, **36**: 68 (1935); *Z. Physik*, **94**: 104 (1935).   [Chap. 22, Sec. 6]

S20   E. von Schweidler: Premier Congrès International de Radiologie, Liége, 1905.   [Chap. 15, Sec. 1]

S21   J. Schwinger: *Phys. Rev.*, **73**: 416L (1948); **76**: 790 (1949).   [Chap. 4, Sec. 3]

S22   J. Schwinger: *Phys. Rev.*, **78**: 135 (1950).   [Chap. 10, Sec. 5]

S23   J. Schwinger and E. Teller: *Phys. Rev.*, **52**: 286 (1937).   [Chap. 10, Sec. 3]

S24   G. T. Seaborg: *Phys. Rev.*, **85**: 157L (1952).   [Chap. 11, Sec. 3]

S25   E. Segrè: *Phys. Rev.*, **86**: 21 (1952).   [Chap. 11, Sec. 3]

S26   E. Segrè, R. S. Halford, and G. T. Seaborg: *Phys. Rev.*, **55**: 321L (1939).   [Chap. 7, Sec. 10]

S27   E. Segrè and C. Wiegand: *Phys. Rev.*, **70**: 808 (1946).   [Chap. 22, Sec. 6]

S28   F. Seitz and D. W. Mueller: *Phys. Rev.*, **78**: 605 (1950).   [Chap. 28, Sec. 4]

S29   H. Semat: "Atomic Physics," Rinehart & Company, Inc., New York, 1946.
      [Chap. 2, Sec. 5]

S30   M. M. Shapiro: *Phys. Rev.*, **90**: 171 (1953).   [Chap. 2, Sec. 8; Chap. 14, Sec.
      2]

S31   P. Shapiro: *Phys. Rev.*, **93**: 290 (1954).   [Chap. 6, Sec. 9]

S32   R. Sherr: *J. Chem. Phys.*, **6**: 251 (1938).   [Chap. 7, Sec. 8]

S33   R. Sherr and J. B. Gerhart: *Phys. Rev.*, **91**: 909 (1953).   [Chap. 6, Sec. 3]

S34   C. W. Sherwin: *Phys. Rev.*, **75**: 1799 (1949).   [Chap. 17, Sec. 2]

S35   F. C. Shoemaker, J. E. Faulkner, G. M. B. Bouricius, S. G. Kaufmann, and
      F. P. Mooring: *Phys. Rev.*, **83**: 1011 (1951).   [Chap. 14, Sec. 1]

S36   C. G. Shull, E. O. Wollan, G. A. Morton, and W. L. Davidson: *Phys. Rev.*,
      73: 842 (1948).   [Chap. 10, Sec. 3]

S37   F. B. Shull and E. Feenberg: *Phys. Rev.*, **75**: 1768L (1949).   [Chap. 17, Sec. 3]

S37a K. Siegbahn: "Beta- and Gamma-ray Spectroscopy," Interscience Pub-
      lishers, Inc., New York, 1955.   [Chap. 17, Introd.]

S38   A. J. F. Siegert: *Phys. Rev.*, **56**: 750 (1939).   [Chap. 14, Sec. 1]

S39   R. Sievert: *Acta Radiol.*, **21**: 189 (1940).   [Chap. 25, Sec. 2]

S40   D. H. Simmons: *Proc. Phys. Soc. (London)*, **A65**: 454 (1952).   [Chap. 22,
      Sec. 2]

S41   R. Simon: *Phys. Rev.*, **69**: 596 (1946).   [Chap. 7, Sec. 8]

S42   G. J. Sizoo, C. Eijkman, and P. Green: *Physica*, **6**: 1057 (1939).   [Chap. 21,
      Sec. 2]

S43   T. H. R. Skyrme: *Progr. Nuclear Phys.*, **1**: 115 (1950).   [Chap. 6, Sec. 3;
      Chap. 17, Introd.]

S44   J. C. Slater and N. H. Frank: "Electromagnetism," McGraw-Hill Book
      Company, Inc., New York, 1947.   [Appendix C, Sec. 3]

S45   J. C. Slater and N. H. Frank: "Mechanics," McGraw-Hill Book Company,
      Inc., New York, 1947.   [Chap. 2, Sec. 5; Appendix B, Sec. 3; Appendix C,
      Secs. 2, 6]

S46   H. Slätis and K. Siegbahn: *Arch. Fys.*, paper 32, **4**: 485 (1952).   [Chap. 6,
      Sec. 5]

S47   A. M. Smith: *Phys. Rev.*, **82**: 955L (1951).   [Chap. 17, Sec. 3]

S48   D. D. Smith and J. R. McNally, Jr.: *J. Opt. Soc. Amer.*, **40**: 878 (1950).
      [Chap. 7, Sec. 2]

S49   J. H. Smith: *Phys. Rev.*, **71**: 32 (1947).   [Chap. 22, Sec. 3]

S50   L. P. Smith, W. E. Parkins, and A. T. Forrester: *Phys. Rev.*, **72**: 989 (1947).
      [Chap. 7, Sec. 7]

S51   L. W. Smith and P. G. Kruger: *Phys. Rev.*, **72**: 357 (1947).   [Chap. 19, Sec. 1]

S52   H. D. Smyth: "Atomic Energy for Military Purposes," Princeton University
      Press, Princeton, N.J., 1945.   [Chap. 7, Secs. 7, 8]

S53   W. R. Smythe and A. Hemmendinger: *Phys. Rev.*, **51**: 178 (1937).   [Chap. 7,
      Sec. 7]

S54   A. H. Snell: *Nucleonics*, **8**(3): 3 (1951).   [Chap. 3, Sec. 4]

S55   E. Snitzer: *Phys. Rev.*, **89**: 1237 (1953).   [Chap. 22, Sec. 1]

S56   H. S. Snyder and W. T. Scott: *Phys. Rev.*, **76**: 220 (1949).   [Chap. 19, Sec. 1]

S57   F. Soddy: *Ann. Repts. on Progr. Chem. (Chem. Soc. London)*, **99**: 72 (1911).
      [Chap. 3, Sec. 1]

S58   F. Soddy: "Chemistry of the Radio-Elements," Part II, Longmans, Green &
      Co., Ltd., London, 1914.   [Introd.; Chap. 1, Sec. 5; Chap. 3, Sec. 1]

S59   F. Soddy: *Proc. Roy. Inst. Gt. Brit.*, **22**: 117 (1917); *J. Chem. Soc.*, **115**: 1
      (1919).   [Chap. 3, Sec. 1]

S60   H. Sommer, H. A. Thomas, and J. A. Hipple: *Phys. Rev.*, **80**: 487L (1950). [Chap. 4, Sec. 3]

S61   A. Sommerfeld: *Ann. Physik*, **11**: 257 (1931).   [Chap. 20, Sec. 1]

S62   R. W. Spence and G. P. Ford: *Ann. Rev. Nuclear Sci.*, **2**: 399 (1953).   [Chap. 11, Sec. 3]

S63   L. V. Spencer and U. Fano: *Phys. Rev.*, **81**: 464L (1951).   [Chap. 25, Sec. 3]

S64   G. L. Squires: *Progr. Nuclear Phys.*, **2**: 89 (1952).   [Chap. 10, Sec. 5]

S65   E. Stahel and J. Guillissen: *Phys. Rev.*, **57**: 341L (1940); *J. phys. radium*, **1**: 12 (1940).   [Chap. 21, Sec. 2]

S66   E. Stahel and P. Kipfer: *Helv. Phys. Acta*, **9**: 492 (1936).   [Chap. 21, Sec. 2]

S67   H. H. Staub in E. Segrè (ed.): "Experimental Nuclear Physics," vol. 1, John Wiley & Sons, Inc., New York, 1953.   [Chap. 25, Sec. 2]

S68   M. B. Stearns, S. De Benedetti, M. Stearns, and L. Leipuner: *Phys. Rev.*, **93**: 1123L (1954).   [Chap. 2, Sec. 3]

S69   A. F. Stehney and N. Sugarman: *Phys. Rev.*, **89**: 194 (1953).   [Chap. 17, Sec. 3]

S70   W. E. Stephens: *Phys. Rev.*, **45**: 513 (1934).   [Chap. 3, Sec. 3]

S71   M. O. Stern: *Revs. Mod. Phys.*, **21**: 316 (1949).   [Chap. 3, Sec. 4]

S72   O. Stern: *Phys. Rev.*, **51**: 1028A (1937).   [Chap. 7, Sec. 7]

S73   G. Stetter: *Z. Physik*, **120**: 639 (1943).   [Chap. 22, Sec. 4]

S74   G. Stetter and W. Jentschke: *Physik. Z.*, **36**: 441 (1935).   [Chap. 22, Sec. 4]

S75   A. T. Stewart and G. L. Squires: *Phys. Rev.*, **90**: 1125L (1953).   [Chap. 10, Sec. 3]

S76   J. A. Stratton: "Electromagnetic Theory," McGraw-Hill Book Company, Inc., New York, 1941.   [Chap. 2, Sec. 5; Chap. 4, Sec. 5]

S77   T. D. Strickler: *Phys. Rev.*, **92**: 923 (1953).   [Chap. 23, Introd.]

S78   J. W. Strutt: *Proc. London Math. Soc.*, **4**: 253 (1873).   [Appendix C, Sec. 4]

S79   M. H. Studier and E. K. Hyde: *Phys. Rev.*, **74**: 591 (1948).   [Chap. 16, Sec. 2]

S80   W. H. Sullivan: "Trilinear Chart of Nuclear Species," John Wiley & Sons, Inc., New York, 1949.   [Chap. 3, Secs. 2, 5; Chap. 8, Sec. 3; Chap. 16, Sec. 3]

S81   R. B. Sutton, T. Hall, E. E. Anderson, H. S. Bridge, J. W. DeWire, L. S. Lavatelli, E. A. Long, T. Snyder, and R. W. Williams: *Phys. Rev.*, **72**: 1147 (1947).   [Chap. 10, Sec. 3]

S82   R. Swinne: *Physik. Z.*, **13**: 14 (1912); **14**: 142 (1913).   [Chap. 16, Sec. 4]

S83   L. Szilard and T. A. Chalmers: *Nature*, **134**: 462 (1934).   [Chap. 7, Sec. 9]

T1   F. L. Talbott, A. Busala, and G. C. Weiffenbach: *Phys. Rev.*, **82**: 1 (1951). [Chap. 6, Sec. 9]

T2   F. L. Talbott and N. P. Heydenburg: *Phys. Rev.*, **90**: 186 (1953).   [Chap. 13, Sec. 4]

T3   I. Tamm: *Z. Physik*, **62**: 545 (1930).   [Chap. 23, Sec. 2]

T4   J. Tandberg: *Proc. Phys. Soc. (London)*, **50**: 87 (1938).   [Chap. 28, Sec. 5]

T5   G. T. P. Tarrant: *Proc. Roy. Soc. (London)*, **A128**: 345 (1930).   [Chap. 24, Sec. 2]

T6   G. T. P. Tarrant: *Proc. Roy. Soc. (London)*, **A135**: 223 (1932).   [Chap. 24, Sec. 2]

T7   R. F. Taschek, H. V. Argo, A. Hemmendinger, and G. A. Jarvis: *Phys. Rev.*, **76**: 325 (1949).   [Chap. 3, Sec. 4]

T8   H. Taub and P. Kusch: *Phys. Rev.*, **75**: 1481 (1949).   [Chap. 5, Sec. 1]

T9   A. E. Taylor: *Repts. Progr. in Phys.*, **15**: 49 (1952).   [Chap. 22, Sec. 3]

T10   H. M. Taylor and N. F. Mott: *Proc. Roy. Soc. (London)*, **A142**: 215 (1933). [Chap. 6, Sec. 5]

T11   T. B. Taylor: *Phys. Rev.*, **92**: 831L (1953).   [Chap. 14, Sec. 2]

T12   G. M. Temmer: *Phys. Rev.*, **76**: 424 (1949).   [Chap. 14, Sec. 2]

T13   H. G. Thode: *Research*, **2**: 154 (1949).   [Chap. 7, Introd., Sec. 5]

T14   H. G. Thode and R. L. Graham: *Can. J. Research*, **A25**: 1 (1947).   [Chap. **7**, Sec. 6]

T15   H. G. Thode, R. L. Graham, and J. A. Ziegler: *Can. J. Research*, **B23**: 40 (1945).   [Chap. 7, Sec. 8]

T16   H. G. Thode, J. Macnamara, and C. B. Collins: *Can. J. Research*, **B27**: 361 (1949).   [Chap. 7, Introd.]

T17   H. G. Thode and R. B. Shields: *Repts. Progr. in Phys.*, **12**: 1 (1949).   [Chap. 7, Sec. 1]

T18   R. G. Thomas: *Phys. Rev.*, **81**: 148L (1951).   [Chap. 14, Sec. 1]

T19   R. G. Thomas: *Phys. Rev.*, **88**: 1109 (1952).   [Chap. 10, Sec. 6]

T20   R. G. Thomas and T. Lauritsen: *Phys. Rev.*, **88**: 969 (1952).   [Chap. 13, Sec. 5]

T21   T. J. Thompson: UCRL-1910, 1952.   [Chap. 18, Sec. 5]

T22   J. J. Thomson: *Phil. Mag.*, **44**: 293 (1897).   [Introd.]

T23   J. J. Thomson: "The Corpuscular Theory of Matter," Constable & Co., Ltd., London, 1907.   [Introd.; Chap. 1, Sec. 2]

T24   J. J. Thomson: *Phil. Mag.*, **13**: 561 (1907); **20**: 752 (1910); **21**: 225 (1911); **24**: 209 (1912).   [Introd.]

T25   A. M. Thorndike: "Mesons: A Summary of Experimental Facts," McGraw-Hill Book Company, Inc., New York, 1952.   [Chap. 2, Sec. 3]

T26   C. H. Townes, H. M. Foley, and W. Low: *Phys. Rev.*, **76**: 1415L (1949). [Chap. 4, Sec. 5]

T27   C. H. Townes, A. N. Holden, and F. R. Merritt: *Phys. Rev.*, **74**: 1113 (1948). [Chap. 5, Sec. 3]

T28   J. W. Trischka: *Phys. Rev.*, **74**: 718 (1948).   [Chap. 5, Sec. 3]

T29   P. R. Tunnicliffe: *Phys. Rev.*, **89**: 1247 (1953).   [Chap. 10, Sec. 6]

T30   J. J. Turin and H. R. Crane: *Phys. Rev.*, **52**: 610 (1937).   [Chap. 21, Sec. 1]

T31   A. Turkevich and J. B. Niday: *Phys. Rev.*, **84**: 52 (1951).   [Chap. 11, Sec. 3]

T32   M. A. Tuve, N. P. Heydenburg, and L. R. Hafstad: *Phys. Rev.*, **49**: 402L (1936); **50**: 806 (1936).   [Chap. 10, Sec. 5]

T33   A. W. Tyler: *Phys. Rev.*, **56**: 125 (1939).   [Chap. 17, Sec. 3]

U1   C. T. Ulrey: *Phys. Rev.*, **11**: 401 (1918).   [Chap. 21, Sec. 2]

U2   H. C. Urey: *J. Appl. Phys.*, **12**: 270 (1941).   [Chap. 7, Sec. 8]

U3   H. C. Urey: *Science*, **108**: 489 (1948).   [Chap. 7, Introd.]

U4   H. C. Urey: *Phys. Rev.*, **88**: 248 (1952).   [Chap. 8, Sec. 2]

U5   H. C. Urey, F. G. Brickwedde, and G. N. Murphy: *Phys. Rev.*, **39**: 164L (1932); **40**: 1 (1932).   [Chap. 7, Secs. 2, 8]

U6   H. C. Urey and L. J. Greiff: *J. Am. Chem. Soc.*, **57**: 321 (1935).   [Chap. 7, Sec. 8]

U7   H. C. Urey and G. K. Teal: *Revs. Mod. Phys.*, **7**: 34 (1935).   [Chap. 7, Sec. 8]

V1   R. J. Van de Graaff, W. W. Buechner, and H. Feshbach: *Phys. Rev.*, **69**: 452 (1946).   [Chap. 19, Sec. 1]

V2   M. A. Van Dilla: The Dosimetry of X- and γ-rays with Liquid-filled Ion Chambers, Ph.D. thesis, Massachusetts Institute of Technology, Cambridge, Mass., 1951.   [Chap. 25, Sec. 3]

V3   M. A. Van Dilla and G. J. Hine: *Nucleonics*, **10**(7): 54 (1952).   [Chap. 25, Sec. 3]

V3*a*   D. M. Van Patter and W. Whaling: *Revs. Mod. Phys.*, **26**: 402 (1954). [Chap. 3, Sec. 5; Chap. 11, Sec. 3; Chap. 12, Sec. 2]

V4   R. W. Varder: *Phil. Mag.*, **29**: 725 (1915).   [Chap. 21, Sec. 3]

V5   J. A. Victoreen: *J. Appl. Phys.*, **14**: 95 (1943).   [Chap. 24, Sec. 1]

W1   M. A. Waggoner: *Phys. Rev.*, **82**: 906 (1951).   [Chap. 6, Sec. 7]

W2   E. Wagner and H. Kulenkampff: *Physik. Z.*, **23**: 503 (1922).   [Chap. 21, Sec. 2]

W2*a*   H. E. Walchli: A table of nuclear moment data, ORNL-1469, USAEC Technical Information Service, Oak Ridge, Tenn., June 1, 1953.   [Chap. 4, Sec. 4]

W3   E. C. Waldron, V. A. Schultz, and T. P. Kohman: *Phys. Rev.*, **93**: 254L (1954).   [Chap. 8, Sec. 3]

W4   R. L. Walker: *Phys. Rev.*, **76**: 527 (1949).   [Chap. 24, Sec. 2]

W5   M. C. Walske: Ph.D. thesis, Cornell University, Ithaca, N.Y., 1951.   [Chap. 22, Sec. 2]

W6   M. C. Walske: *Phys. Rev.*, **88**: 1283 (1952).   [Chap. 22, Sec. 2]

W6*a*   M. Walt, R. L. Becker, A. Okazaki, and R. E. Fields: *Phys. Rev.*, **89**: 1271 (1953).   [Chap. 14, Sec. 2]

W6*b*   M. Walt and H. H. Barschall: *Phys. Rev.*, **93**: 1062 (1954).   [Chap. 14, Sec. 2]

W7   T. J. Wang: *Nucleonics*, **7**(2): 55 (1950).   [Chap. 25, Sec. 2]

W8   R. E. Warren, J. L. Powell, and R. G. Herb: *Rev. Sci. Instr.*, **18**: 559 (1947). [Chap. 3, Sec. 3]

W9   S. D. Warshaw: *Phys. Rev.*, **76**: 1759 (1949).   [Chap. 22, Sec. 2]

W10   E. D. Warters, W. A. Fowler, and C. C. Lauritsen: *Phys. Rev.*, **91**: 917 (1953). [Chap. 6, Sec. 1]

W11   B. E. Watt: *Phys. Rev.*, **87**: 1037 (1952).   [Chap. 11, Sec. 3]

W12   K. Way and E. P. Wigner: *Phys. Rev.*, **73**: 1318 (1948).   [Chap. 11, Sec. 3]

W13   B. Weaver: *Phys. Rev.*, **80**: 301L (1950).   [Chap. 7, Sec. 2]

W14   J. H. Webb: *Phys. Rev.*, **74**: 511 (1948).   [Chap. 18, Sec. 4]

W15   D. L. Webster: *Phys. Rev.*, **9**: 220 (1917).   [Chap. 20, Sec. 1]

W16   H. C. Webster: *Proc. Roy. Soc. (London)*, **A136**: 428 (1932).   [Chap. 13, Sec. 2]

W17   I. G. Weinberg and J. M. Blatt: *Am. J. Phys.*, **21**: 124 (1953).   [Chap. 11, Sec. 3]

W18   R. Weinstock: *Phys. Rev.*, **61**: 584 (1942).   [Chap. 20, Sec. 1]

W19   M. T. Weiss, M. W. P. Strandberg, R. B. Lawrance, and C. C. Loomis: *Phys. Rev.*, **78**: 202 (1950).   [Chap. 5, Sec. 3]

W20   V. F. Weisskopf: *Phys. Rev.*, **52**: 295 (1937).   [Chap. 11, Sec. 4]

W21   V. F. Weisskopf: MDDC-1175, 1947.   [Chap. 2, Sec. 6; Chap. 11, Sec. 4; Chap. 14, Sec. 2]

W22   V. F. Weisskopf: *Helv. Phys. Acta*, **23**: 187 (1950).   [Chap. 11, Sec. 4]

W23   V. F. Weisskopf: *Phys. Rev.*, **83**: 1073L (1951).   [Chap. 6, Sec. 4]

W24   V. F. Weisskopf: *Science*, **113**: 101 (1951).   [Chap. 11, Sec. 2]

W25   V. F. Weisskopf and D. H. Ewing: *Phys. Rev.*, **57**: 472 (1940).   [Chap. 11, Sec. 4; Chap. 14, Sec. 2]

W26   C. F. von Weizsäcker: *Z. Physik*, **96**: 431 (1935).   [Chap. 11, Sec. 3]

W27   C. F. von Weizsäcker: *Naturwiss.*, **24**: 813 (1936).   [Chap. 6, Sec. 6]

W28   G. W. Wetherill: *Phys. Rev.*, **92**: 907 (1953).   [Chap. 11, Sec. 3]

W29   S. Wexler: *Phys. Rev.*, **93**: 182 (1954).   [Chap. 21, Sec. 2]

W30   P. K. Weyl: *Phys. Rev.*, **91**: 289 (1953).   [Chap. 22, Sec. 6]

W31   J. A. Wheeler: *Ann. N.Y. Acad. Sci.*, **48**: 219 (1946).   [Chap. 21, Sec. 4]

W32   J. A. Wheeler: *Revs. Mod. Phys.*, **21**: 133 (1949).   [Chap. 2, Sec. 3]

W33   J. A. Wheeler: *Phys. Rev.*, **92**: 812 (1953).   [Chap. 2, Sec. 3]

W34   J. A. Wheeler and R. Ladenburg: *Phys. Rev.*, **60**: 754 (1941). [Chap. 18, Sec. 2]

W35   J. A. Wheeler and W. E. Lamb: *Phys. Rev.*, **55**: 858 (1939). [Chap. 24, Sec. 2]

W36   R. Whiddington: *Proc. Roy. Soc. (London)*, **A86**: 360 (1911); **A89**: 554 (1913). [Chap. 21, Sec. 3]

W37   G. R. White: *Phys. Rev.*, **80**: 154 (1950). [Chap. 25, Sec. 3]

W38   G. R. White: X-ray Attenuation Coefficients from 10 kev to 100 Mev, *Natl. Bur. Standards (U.S.) Rept.* 1003, 1952. [Chap. 23, Introd.; Chap. 24, Sec. 1; Chap. 25, Sec. 1]

W39   H. E. White: "Introduction to Atomic Spectra," McGraw-Hill Book Company, Inc., New York, 1934. [Chap. 4, Introd., Secs. 1, 4; Chap. 5, Sec. 1]

W40   M. G. White: *Phys. Rev.*, **49**: 309 (1936). [Chap. 10, Sec. 5]

W41   P. White and G. Millington: *Proc. Roy. Soc. (London)*, **A120**: 701 (1928). [Chap. 21, Sec. 3]

W42   W. J. Whitehouse: *Progr. Nuclear Phys.*, **2**: 120 (1952). [Chap. 11, Sec. 3]

W43   W. J. Whitehouse and G. A. R. Graham: *Can. J. Research*, **A25**: 261 (1947). [Chap. 10, Sec. 4]

W44   G. N. Whyte: *Nucleonics*, **12**(2): 18 (1954). [Chap. 25, Sec. 2]

W45   G. C. Wick: *Nature*, **142**: 993 (1938). [Chap. 10, Sec. 7]

W46   G. C. Wick: *Ricerca sci.*, **11**: 273 (1940); **12**: 858 (1941); *Nuovo cimento*, vol. 9, no. 3, 1943. [Chap. 18, Sec. 5]

W47   E. P. Wigner: *Phys. Rev.*, **51**: 106 (1937); **56**: 519 (1939). [Chap. 4, Sec. 1; Chap. 6, Sec. 3; Chap. 11, Secs. 2, 3]

W48   E. P. Wigner: *Phys. Rev.*, **51**: 947 (1937). [Chap. 11, Sec. 3]

W49   E. P. Wigner: *Phys. Rev.*, **70**: 15 (1946). [Chap. 14, Sec. 1]

W50   E. P. Wigner: *Am. J. Phys.*, **17**: 99 (1949). [Chap. 11, Sec. 4]

W51   E. P. Wigner and L. Eisenbud: *Phys. Rev.*, **72**: 29 (1947). [Chap. 14, Sec. 1]

W52   D. R. Wiles: *Nucleonics*, **11**(11): 32 (1953). [Chap. 6, Sec. 3]

W53   E. J. Williams: *Proc. Roy. Soc. (London)*, **A125**: 470 (1929). [Chap. 21, Sec. 3]

W54   E. J. Williams: *Proc. Roy. Soc. (London)*, **A130**: 310 (1931). [Chap. 21, Secs. 1, 3]

W55   E. J. Williams: *Proc. Roy. Soc. (London)*, **A130**: 328 (1931). [Chap. 18, Sec. 3; Chap. 21, Sec. 1]

W56   E. J. Williams: *Proc. Roy. Soc. (London)*, **A135**: 108 (1932). [Chap. 18, Sec. 2; Chap. 21, Sec. 1; Chap. 22, Sec. 5]

W57   E. J. Williams: *Proc. Roy. Soc. (London)*, **A169**: 531 (1939). [Chap. 19, Sec. 1]

W58   E. J. Williams: *Phys. Rev.*, **58**: 292 (1940). [Chap. 19, Secs. 1, 2]

W59   E. J. Williams: *Revs. Mod. Phys.*, **17**: 217 (1945). [Chap. 18, Secs. 2, 3; Chap. 19, Sec. 1; Chap. 21, Sec. 1; Appendix C, Secs. 4, 6]

W60   E. J. Williams, J. M. Nuttall, and H. S. Barlow: *Proc. Roy. Soc. (London)*, **A121**: 611 (1928). [Chap. 24, Sec. 1]

W61   R. M. Williamson, C. P. Browne, D. S. Craig, and D. J. Donahue: *Phys. Rev.*, **84**: 731 (1951). [Chap. 12, Sec. 2]

W62   C. T. R. Wilson: *Proc. Roy. Soc. (London)*, **A104**: 1 (1923). [Chap. 21, Sec. 1]

W63   C. W. Wilson: "Radium Therapy, Its Physical Aspects," Chapman & Hall, Ltd., London, 1945. [Chap. 25, Sec. 2]

W64   H. A. Wilson: *Phil. Mag.*, **5**: 429 (1903). [Introd.]

W65   R. R. Wilson: *Phys. Rev.*, **60**: 749 (1941). [Chap. 22, Sec. 2]

W66   R. R. Wilson: *Phys. Rev.*, **71**: 385L (1947). [Chap. 22, Sec. 3]

W67   R. R. Wilson: *Phys. Rev.*, **90**: 720L (1953). [Chap. 23, Introd.]

W68   E. O. Wollan: *Phys. Rev.*, **72**: 445 (1947). [Chap. 17, Sec. 2]

W69   E. O. Wollan and C. G. Shull: *Phys. Rev.*, **73**: 830 (1948). [Appendix C, Sec. 6]

W70   W. M. Woodward and I. Halpern: *Phys. Rev.*, **76**: 107 (1949). [Chap. 6, Sec. 9]

W71   H. R. Worthington, J. N. McGruer, and D. E. Findley: *Phys. Rev.*, **90**: 899 (1953). [Chap. 10, Sec. 5]

W72   C. S. Wu: *Phys. Rev.*, **59**: 481 (1941). [Chap. 21, Sec. 2]

W73   C. S. Wu: *Revs. Mod. Phys.*, **22**: 386 (1950). [Chap. 17, Sec. 3]

W74   C. S. Wu: *Physica*, **18**: 989 (1952). [Chap. 17, Sec. 3]

W75   C. S. Wu and R. D. Albert: *Phys. Rev.*, **75**: 1107L (1949). [Chap. 17, Sec. 3]

W76   C. S. Wu and L. Feldman: *Phys. Rev.*, **76**: 696L (1949). [Chap. 17, Sec. 3]

W77   C. S. Wu and I. Shaknov: *Phys. Rev.*, **77**: 136L (1950). [Chap. 21, Sec. 4]

W78   S. J. Wyard: *Phys. Rev.*, **87**: 165L (1952). [Chap. 25, Sec. 3]

Y1   C. N. Yang: *Phys. Rev.*, **74**: 764 (1948). [Chap. 6, Secs. 8, 9]

Y2   C. N. Yang: *Phys. Rev.*, **84**: 599L (1951). [Chap. 21, Sec. 1]

Y3   C. N. Yang and J. Tiomno: *Phys. Rev.*, **79**: 495 (1950). [Chap. 6, Sec. 3]

Y4   F. L. Yost, J. A. Wheeler, and G. Breit: *Phys. Rev.*, **49**: 174 (1936). [Appendix C, Sec. 5]

Z1   C. T. Zahn and A. H. Spees: *Phys. Rev.*, **53**: 365, 511 (1938). [Chap. 3, Sec. 4]

Z2   I. Zlotowski: *Phys. Rev.*, **60**: 483 (1941). [Chap. 17, Sec. 1]

Z3   K. Zuber: *Nature*, **136**: 796 (1935). [Chap. 7, Sec. 7]

Z4   L. R. Zumwalt, C. V. Cannon, G. H. Jenks, W. C. Peacock, and L. M. Gunning: *Science*, **107**: 47 (1948). [Chap. 17, Sec. 1]

Glossary of Principal Symbols

The page numbers give the location of a more detailed definition or of the first use of a recurring symbol.

English Letters

A	Mass number	98
A	Atomic weight	653
$A_1, A_2, \ldots$	Wave amplitudes	62, 853
$A_0, A_2, A_4, \ldots$	Coefficients of Legendre polynomials in angular-correlation function	238
$A(E), B(E), \ldots$	Coefficients of $\cos^2 \vartheta$, $\cos^4 \vartheta$, $\ldots$ in experimental angular-correlation function	246
$A, B, C, \ldots M, N$	Number of atoms present for successive members of a radioactive decay series	470, 490
a	Width of a rectangular barrier	61
a	Interval factor of hyperfine structure	183
a	Vertex parameter of a hyperbola	836
a	True average rate of a random process	751
$a, b, c, \ldots$	Specific effectiveness of the random processes $x, y, z, \ldots$	766
$a, {}^1a, {}^3a$	Scattering length, or "Fermi intercept"	319, 324
$a_2, a_4, \ldots$	Coefficients of power series in $\cos \vartheta$ for angular-correlation functions	238
a_H	Radius of first Bohr orbit for hydrogen $(= \hbar^2/e^2 m_0)$	188, 898
a_H	Bound coherent scattering length for hydrogen $(= a_{para})$	327
a_r, a_ψ	Radial and angular acceleration	839
a_v, a_s, a_c, a_a	Energy coefficients in the semiempirical mass formula for volume	366
	surface	367
	coulomb	367
	asymmetry energy	369
	tabulation	383
B	Coulomb-barrier height	46, 874
B	Nuclear binding energy	132, 295
B	Magnetic field or induction	103
B	Atomic stopping number	638
B	Build-up factor for γ rays	732
$B, \bar{B}$	Dimensionless functions of Z and T in the bremsstrahlung cross section	603, 604

Greek Letters

Abbreviations

Conventional Symbols

Index

953